ANNUAL REVIEW OF PLANT PHYSIOLOGY

ANNUAL REVIEW OF PLANT PHYSIOLOGY

LEONARD MACHLIS, *Editor*
University of California, Berkeley

WINSLOW R. BRIGGS, *Associate Editor*
Harvard University

RODERIC B. PARK, *Associate Editor*
University of California, Berkeley

VOLUME 20

1969

PUBLISHED BY
ANNUAL REVIEWS, INC.
4139 EL CAMINO WAY
PALO ALTO, CALIFORNIA 94306, U.S.A.

ANNUAL REVIEWS, INC.
PALO ALTO, CALIFORNIA, U.S.A.

Standard Book Number 8243-0620-1
Library of Congress Catalog Card Number: A51-1660

FOREIGN AGENCY

Maruzen Company, Limited
6, Tori-Nichome Nihonbashi
Tokyo

PRINTED AND BOUND IN THE UNITED STATES OF AMERICA
BY GEORGE BANTA COMPANY, INC.

PREFACE

Our membership now includes Dr. Israel Zelitch, who was appointed to the Editorial Committee effective January 1, 1969. He replaces Dr. Aubrey Naylor, who completed five years of outstanding service. We also wish to acknowledge the participation of Dr. Peter Ray as a guest of the Committee in selecting titles and authors for Volume 20.

This volume, like all of its predecessors, is the handiwork of the authors. However, between the receipt of the manuscripts and the book you now have in hand, each review received constant care and attention from our Assistant Editor, Miss Jean Heavener, to whom we are most grateful. We acknowledge also the excellent services of the George Banta Company, Inc., our printers.

By the time Volume 20 is published, it is likely that Dr. J. Murray Luck, Editor-in-Chief of *Annual Reviews, Inc.,* will have retired. The Editors are personally grateful to Murray Luck for the opportunity of working with him over many years. The Committee wishes to express on behalf of all plant physiologists their thanks to him for making possible the *Annual Review of Plant Physiology.* We say goodbye with profound regret and wish him well in his retirement.

THE EDITORIAL COMMITTEE

CONTENTS

"... brevity can never ... do justice to all the facts of a complex situation. On such a theme one can be brief only by omission and simplification."
(A. Huxley—foreword to *Brave New World Revisited*)

Hans Gaffron

RESISTANCE TO KNOWLEDGE

By Hans Gaffron

*The Florida State University, Institute of Molecular
Biophysics (Fels Fund), Tallahassee, Florida*

"Everything reasonable has been thought of before.
We just have to try to think it once anew."

(Goethe)

"It is hardly possible to state any truth strongly
without apparent injustice to some other."

(Mach)

When the editors of the *Annual Review of Plant Physiology* honored me with an invitation to fill a few pages in a manner different from the usual specialized review, I decided that the best I could do was to tell the young scientist about the hopes or worries of an older colleague who has seen the proverbial better times.

At best, five per cent of the population are truly familiar with the cultural problems of our era. These are the five per cent who study, discuss, and write the articles and books of which I have appended a sample list. My aim is to emphasize that these five per cent ("we the intellectuals") are talking mainly to one another. Judging from what happens in the real world, very little of what is called common, or even obvious, knowledge among this small group seems to influence the behavior and judgment of the 95 per cent of the people and their chosen leaders who together constitute the living power of the species.

The following is therefore addressed to the biologists who were not yet born when two world wars had all but proved the cultural decline of the West. While they were growing up, the fabulous success of applied science apparently reversed the sinister trend. The living standards in the Western countries, as well as their destructive powers, are higher now than in the golden age before 1914. This so-called triumph of scientific progress has made it quite hard for young enthusiastic people to realize that the decline of the West continues, and that more of the same kind of technical progress offers no solution.

At the time of Erasmus it was considered wise, as well as ethically permissible, for the happy few to stay aloof from the affairs of the world and to contemplate with amused equanimity the rule of folly among men. The world and human nature were as God had made it and had to be taken whole. It would be part of that preordained folly to try to change it. Four hundred years later it has become clear that we ourselves are now remaking our world. Therefore it is not permissible to sit back and smile at the horrendous mistakes which are being committed out of sheer ignorance about man's nature and its possibilities. When those who have a couple of thou-

1

sand dollars may in a few hours fly to any region of the globe, when on this shrunken planet a billion people are constantly disturbed with news that during all previous history was none of their business, when so many are made to witness events they never cared to dream about, a biologist may wonder what this will do to the minds of people who were hitherto encapsulated in their particular cultural background and limited traditional knowledge, and who saw in any difference of opinion with their neighbors enough of an excuse to start understandably rapacious wars or completely irrational ones.

In this age of biology we ought to be able to do something rational about our cultural affairs. That means we have to begin in earnest with a science of human nature. Ordinarily, a younger biologist, when asked today what he would consider a worth-while problem, is likely to mention the origin of life, the problems of aging, the molecular basis of conscience, the genetic remodeling of future generations, and so on. Such problems are not only great but have also the advantage of being perfectly safe. They touch questions about the mind of man at great distance from the immediate present. But an enquiry as to whether the mental development of modern man, or the lack of it, justifies his acquiescence with social institutions as they presently exist, is risky. No scientist is to be blamed when he subconsciously avoids immersing himself seriously into such matters. Continually since the times of Bruno and Galileo there have been disagreeable encounters between independent philosophers, natural and otherwise, and the men of God who, since ancient times, insist that the minds of the people have been given into their hands to care for. Trespassers, therefore, will be prosecuted. Hence even modern scientists generally prefer to stick to investigations which are not likely to be called controversial.

The ultimate aim of the combined studies of human nature is, of course, a moral and a political one; and for this reason the latter will be discouraged. Those whose power depends on millions of unthinking followers realize that this kind of biology and the teaching of it is subversive. Why otherwise should a society which is so eager to exploit immediately any discovery in physics or medical biochemistry demur at making practical use of what sociologists or psychologists have discovered about the behavior and the motives of its members? But as fortunate citizens of this country, we know that in the Anglo-Saxon nations so far people have not been abducted in the early hours of the morning for having made statements deemed ideologically dangerous to those in power. The worst that can happen to a biologist who wants to investigate the causes of narrow-mindedness and stubbornly preserved ignorance in the minds of public leaders is that they probably will not pay him to do so. Such tolerant practice will last until his work shows a kind of success which calls for far-reaching social reforms so convincingly that not only the intellectuals but also the man in the street may be willing to go for them. Many, considering the way they have been trained, and particularly when they are already on the way "up," may not find this a problem they ought to bother with. Having joined what has become a lucrative profession and which in addition offers the traditional lure of free intellectual adventure, they see no reason why they as contented specialists should take time to read and ponder a few of the books and articles on the cultural dilemma of our times which their older colleagues have felt obligated to put before them. Is it not troublesome enough that there is scarcely time to cover the literature in one's own field? To this we must answer that pure self-interest—namely the desire to end one's life in a society not so tormented as ours by the baffling conflict between surviving superstitions and new biological insights—should dictate a young scientist's choice of work in a field where the problems reach from the chemistry of emotions to the ancient question of whether intellectuals are forever condemned to remain so powerless in public affairs.

I am, of course, aware of the incessant flow of dedicated expert articles and books which appear or are reviewed in the *Saturday Review*, the *Bulletin of the Atomic Scientists*, *Foreign Affairs*, *Science*, even *Time* and *Life*, etc., etc. In addition, we have the Pugwash conferences and other valiant efforts of the intellectual world in behalf of common sense when it is supported by indisputable facts available to anyone who wants to inform himself. Yet the ever-recurring waves of violence or authoritarian pronouncements of world leaders drown out the voices of reason. Quite obviously, the gap between the world of the intellectuals, defined as those who think because they cannot do otherwise, and those who wield the power while they also claim that they cannot do otherwise, has not been bridged. Thus the biologist who wishes to find out why he and his like are so ineffective in the affairs of men must turn to the slow method of scientific analysis.

Pre-1914 Prejudices and Indoctrination

In contrast to what a scientist is usually trying to establish by his writings, this article does not offer new insight nor results based on objective original research, only views on how socially important prejudices, including mine, have changed during the last half-century under the influence of what is usually called the scientific viewpoint. Though this viewpoint is shared at the present time only by a few, there is no reason why it could not be the start of a new kind of ethical indoctrination which, when properly imparted to the young, would hold as securely as those for which in former times the appeal to the authority of supernatural powers appeared indispensable.

The spiritual world I grew up in lasted practically unchanged till the middle 1920's. Part of my early indoctrination before 1914 was essentially based on a pious faith in progress. I learned that in principle the Christian Europeans had given up war long before I was born. The modern ways to exploit inexhaustible natural resources made such barbaric methods to enrich the various fatherlands obsolete. Now everybody could be a winner without someone else having to lose. By the same token, the lower class people would soon get enough money so that there would be no need to pity them. In addition, they were promised to be taken care of in heaven. Ar-

mies were needed only to maintain the national honor; as an example of
what that meant, I was told how it had been necessary that all honorable
European countries send soldiers to China to shoot the nasty Boxers. And
honor was again on everybody's lips in 1914.

The first political map I saw had three main colors: pink for British
rule, violet for French, and green for Russian. Pink was everywhere—over
a good part of the world. Under the pink and violet colors lived many hopelessly savage tribes, as in Africa, for instance. The wise Christian Europeans prevented them from torturing each other to death in the most grue-
some ways. Nevertheless, it was to be hoped that these savages would somehow fade away and become less of the white man's burden. Conspicuous on
the map were also China and the United States in yellow; white unexplored
patches were at the poles, inside Asia, and in Africa. They beckoned courageous explorers to become living or dead heroes who somehow let all their
compatriots, who did nothing, feel more important. We Germans had come
too late to receive our just share of the colonial world, but a good compensation was that we were ahead in the spiritual world because of our philosophers, poets, composers, and scientists. China was the most foreign of all
countries. Its art objects had to be collected by anybody who was somebody.
On the other hand, the incredible numbers of Chinese were a vague but distinctly disagreeable threat. Yet a rapid increase in the populations of Europe was a sign of well-being. To be slow in producing children was a sign
of decadence. America was an enormous, mainly unexplored country where
enterprising people went either because they wanted to make a million or
had already stolen one.

This was the kind of outer world I was made to believe in when I was
brought from Peru to Europe and Germany at the age of ten. I assume it
was, except for patriotic variations, the same indoctrination that all bour-
geois children received throughout Europe, and Alan Paton has recently
mentioned that the same attitude prevailed in remote South Africa. Actually, the political world was only dimly seen. It was unnecessary to worry
about it, for it was in the hands of leaders appointed by the grace of God.

My standard of justice was set for good by what I had heard and later
avidly read about the Dreyfus case. In a civilized country, official injustice
to one man was enough to rally all men of good will and integrity to set
things right. Compromises were impossible—either you were civilized or
you were not. Today justice is measured by degrees. It makes a difference
whether only a few or thousands of innocent people at once are mishandled
or murdered because of "reasons of state." Sometimes a modern Zola writes
disagreeable articles and then the case is officially deeply regretted. The
true cultural decline of the West is sensed only by those who remember
Dreyfus.

After the military had been defeated in 1919, the Weimar republic came
into being. Arts and sciences re-emerged and unfolded quickly to a prewar
level. In the Twenties all Europe enjoyed an incredible upsurge, seemingly
a complete cultural recovery. Research, literature, painting, music, and the-

ater flourished just in time for me, between the ages of 17 and 27, to believe that this was a great era in which to be alive. Inflation, poverty, and political murders followed by lopsided application of justice, I considered the distasteful but understandable aftermath of the war. The war had clearly been a terrible mistake, and we were sure that such idiotic, useless killings among civilized peoples would not occur again. The one truly new apparition on the cultural horizon was the Soviet Union: horror stories on the one hand, and great hopes on the other, for this was the first attempt at running a country in a rational and just manner on behalf of all the people.

The long misery of the first world war had helped me to get rid of the illusions of false patriotism and church religion in a logical, interesting, and rather enjoyable way. (To the subconscious influence on a child's mind of Catholicism in the Latin American style, I shall return later.) But the political trials under Stalin, the breakdown of the German republic, and the swift disappearance also in Italy of all but the trappings of civilization destroyed the last of my cherished illusions—the belief that the Europeans would instinctively repudiate criminals as their leaders.

Today the pink and the violet have disappeared from the political maps of the world, leaving a very impressive blotch of Russian green, with only the United States and China as large as before. No white unexplored spaces are left. Between 1914 and now, about 100 million people (50 million officially counted) were prematurely deprived of their lives for no other reason than the irrational brutal actions of their fellow men. Part of the horror is that nobody misses them any more. But the ideal of a stable, advancing, trustworthy Western civilization did vanish. Can it be revived? In the seventh year of our private American missionary war, young people have a hard time believing that this ideal was ever more than the Utopia of a few. I like to stress the point, therefore, that before 1914 this ideal was alive in nearly everybody's mind regardless of his immediate political aims or church affiliations.

Every society is faced with the problem of how to civilize its children to make them conform to customs and, if possible, to follow an ideal set on a somewhat higher level than that considered practical for the moment. Every year in the United States, 3.6 million little barbarians arrive, not to mention the million and a half every month in India and unknown millions in China. The comfort, if not the safety, of the parents requires from the first day the application of a technique to achieve obedience, preferably one which culminates in submission to rules by the subconscious consent of the ruled. The diversity of such techniques of necessary indoctrinations, as well as differences in ideals proclaimed as the ultimate good, have been one of the main causes for strife and fanatical bloodletting throughout the course of human history. In our age of scientific historical surveys, the time has arrived for a comparative analysis of the various indoctrination systems now being practised to see which of them are the most promising for the mental development of the next generations. This thought has been following me ever since I lived through three successive levels of religious and ethical instructions. During my preschool years, I spent more time in the company of servants than of my parents. Thus I learned to share their beliefs, which one would not hesitate to call dark and cruel superstitions of a bygone age were it not that they form a part of the Catholic faith as it is still being practised among the Indians and the very poor of Latin America. Looking backward, the essence seems to have been a constant fear of punishment for the sin of being a little more alive than required for mere survival. The affirmation that God is Love and that after some years of burning in purgatory all will be well in the next world made much less impression on me than the detailed stories of how the devil was going to torture us unless we had a particular patron saint (or better still, several of them) who would argue for mitigating circumstances. The power of the saints was evident from the way they lived in the splendors of their churches. The high vaults resonating with the voices of the murmuring and chanting monks, the gold glittering in the light of the many candles were an unforgettable fascinating reality. These impressive rituals somehow imparted credence to an unreal world whose existence had to be believed.

In addition, the lower class people populated my mind with ghosts of an unfriendly disposition, and though they seemed not to play an official role in church affairs, they had the frightful advantage of existing right here with us in our daily lives on earth. Because of the regular return to the upper world of my parents, where everything was serene, understandable, nonmystical and definitely free of ghosts, all this did no lasting harm, I assume, but it instilled in me a great emotional attraction to any kind of beautiful rites. Then came years of Protestant instruction with the emphasis on one's own ability to distinguish between right and wrong according to one's conscience. There was less emphasis on absolute obedience to an authoritarian church, but insistence on salvation through unwavering faith. I do not remember any particular criticisms of church religion by my father, who was a zoologist and physician. Simply by his knowledgeable answers to any questions I might raise, he easily remade me into a believer in evolution long before I was truly able to understand the validity of the arguments in favor of Darwinism. In the meantime, I had discovered those philosophers whose writings do not appear in the usual high school curricula. To my relief, I learned that in past centuries there had been quite a few thinkers who had agreed that an earnest contemplation of the wonders of this world compensated fully for a loss of a belief in the hereafter or the existence of a capricious supernatural power outside of nature.

When I began my university studies, I took two books with me which had just appeared—Karl Jasper's *Psychology of World Views* and Spengler's *Decline of the West*. I was fascinated by both, though I have never finished perusing either of them because of their verbosity. I hated and cursed the Spengler; it promised us a terrible future. But I liked Jasper's idea of establishing a science which might tell us exactly why we as individuals behave, and behave so differently, as we do. I never separated myself from these books; they have remained emotional poles of departure for daydreams of what to fear and what to hope for mankind. Probably I would have forgotten them were it not that—all his bombastic, apodictic, and often ridiculously nonsensical statements notwithstanding—Spengler's ghastly predictions have become true. As anyone can see, the end of the time of the tyrants is a long way from being over, and even a great republic continues with military missions to save Asian countries from communism, which, as our authorities do not tire of asserting, is for the natives a fate worse than the most thorough destruction of their country. My only antidote to despair is Jasper's idea of a natural science of the mind. Fifty years later nearly everywhere in our universities the intuitive approaches in this field—such as Freud's, for instance—are being patiently transformed into respectable biology. Thus my hope is that if the coming generation of biologists will be permitted to survive and to go ahead with their subversive studies, we shall find the means to break the curse of Spengler's and Toynbee's prophecies. Some biologists offer what is, to me, a meaningless sort of consolation. They point out that because of the customary bungling and inefficiency in the application also of destructive means, the species may survive somewhere even when our civilization ends. But who is really interested in the survival of the species, in contrast to that of his family, his own culture, and the few people who represent the latter most brilliantly? My title was chosen to emphasize that a scientifically planned change of human nature must appear subversive in the eyes of those who thrive on the ignorance and habitual thoughtlessness of the majority. Like every great problem in science, this situation has no overall sweeping a priori solution. The solution is not in sight—only some most astonishing and promising possibilities.

Personal Aspects of Science Before 1940

The year 1940 stands as the date when what took at least two decades to develop became obvious: the decline of the West, the ascendancy of technology as the main instrument of power, and the enslavement of Western man by his own machines. Those born after 1940 must experience as much difficulty in imagining the essentially simple and venerable aspect which science had during the four centuries before their time as to imagine now the beauty of their home towns in the years before the big trees were cut to make room for parking lots and four-lane traffic. The young who must live with the new ugliness may, therefore, try to take the opposite view and say that it took science four centuries to grow up until it suddenly matured and broke out into full bloom.

In order to get speedily away for good from the unprofitable discussion of pure versus applied science, let me repeat Heisenberg's formulation: "Science clears the fields on which technology can build." In turn, technology delivers to science bigger and better bulldozers to clear the fields ever faster.

Some 30 or more years ago the philosopher Cassirer began a discussion of science with these words:

> Science is the last step in man's mental development and it may be regarded as the highest and most characteristic attainment of human culture. It is a very late and refined product that could not develop except under special conditions. Even the conception of science in its specific sense did not exist before the times of the great Greek thinkers, it had to be re-discovered and re-established in the age of the Renaissance. There is no second power in our modern world which may be compared to that of scientific thought.

What used to—and in many cases still does—lure people into science one hardly can say better than Russell:

> Disinterested curiosity, which is the source of almost all intellectual efforts, finds with astonished delight that science can unveil secrets which might well have seemed forever undiscoverable. The desire for a larger life and wider interests, for an escape from private circumstances and even from the whole recurring human cycle of birth and death, is fulfilled by the impersonal cosmic outlook of science as by nothing else. A life devoted to science is therefore a happy life, and its happiness is derived from the very best sources that are open to dwellers on this troubled and passionate planet.

The next paragraph from an article by Gerald Holton further describes those points we must see clearly in order to appreciate the difference I shall come to below:

> Science, of course, is not an occupation, such as working in a store, or on an assembly line, that one may pursue or abandon at will. For a creative scientist it is not a matter of free choice what he shall do, indeed it is erroneous to think of him as advancing toward knowledge, it is rather knowledge which advances toward him, grasps him and overwhelms him. Even the most superficial glance at the life and work of a Kepler, a Dalton or a Pasteur would clarify these points.

All this may appear almost self-evident to the young scientist himself. But to the public, which is informed daily about the results of science, such thoughts are entirely alien.

And, as we know from the social history of science, those establishments whose power rests with the God-given ignorance and thoughtlessness of their subjects rightly recognize free science as an ever-present threat. The innocent game of making discoveries has led in the past to a new philosophy about the structure of the world and, lately, about the nature of man. It is an assiduously cultivated myth that in the twentieth century things have changed, that state and church have become totally reconciled to limitless enquiry and are now the supporters of free men. The refined modern way of minimizing the subversive power of research is to distract the minds of the scientists from certain problems by offering them unheard-of opportunities to run after those others which are likely to lead them away from thinking methodically about the plight of man as a spiritual being. In addition, the trite arguments about the inability of the scientific method to deal with transcendental questions are being recast in the jargon of our time and therefore sound erudite, scientific, and liberal. The meaning, however, remains always the same. The only valid spiritual guidelines mankind has ever received to fulfill its destiny according to revealed truth are likely to be undermined by claims that social values have evolved like any other manifestations of human intelligence and might as well be studied objectively. An effective line to counter any such claims goes like this. Are not thoughtful scientists always willing to admit that science is unable to provide or support spiritual values by means of its own philosophy because the latter rests on the collection of facts which are morally neutral? For a more detailed discussion see, for instance, the article by Gerald Holton: "Modern Science and the Intellectual Tradition." The danger to a science of the mind arises only indirectly from the ignorance of the 95 per cent, who are so important in a democracy. Their ignorance is carefully abetted and preserved by those men in leading positions who consider it a cardinal virtue to share with the masses some century-old prejudices. Such distinguished personages often enjoy an admirably high level of knowledge, education, and artfulness. They just suffered the mishap of never having been involved in a scientific enquiry. They keep repeating that science is incapable of setting values. I quote from the article I referred to above:

> There are other evidences of the wide-spread notion that science itself cannot contribute positively to culture. Toynbee, for example, gives a list of "creative individuals" from Xenophon to Hindenburg, from Dante to Lenin, but does not include a single scientist . . . one may even exhibit a touch of pride in professing ignorance of the structure of the universe or one's own body, of the behavior of matter or of one's own mind.

It is easy to predict that in the near future the science of human behavior will see a struggle not only for the freedom of research, which is considered less of a threat, but for free teaching, and, most important, for unhampered application of results. The biologist must therefore know where he stands and be sure of his answers. Accumulation of facts and their superficial classification are, of course, not science. Raw data tell us as much about the edifice of science as a heap of bricks would tell us about a house under construction.

> As a rule the framing of hypotheses is the most difficult part of scientific work, and the part where great ability is indispensable. So far, no method has been found which would make it possible to invent hypothesis by rule. Usually some hypothesis is a necessary preliminary to the collection of facts, since the selection of facts demands some way of determining relevance. Without something of this kind the mere multiplicity of facts is baffling.

If we quote, for instance, these sentences from Russell's *History of Philosophy* to our learned opponents, they will immediately say that they knew this all along. Well, if so, why do they repeat or permit others to repeat that the purpose of science is merely the collection of useful facts? And that this kind of occupation only leads to a demoralization of the people in general . . . ? The reason has been clearly stated by the Catholic philosopher Maritain: science as a force in society works for "the denial of [revealed] truths and eternal values." And to this accusation science must indeed plead guilty. In view of what has happened to Western civilization, we biologists would like to learn how to mold the minds of men so that any values, old or new, become more effective as a vaccine against bestiality.

Considering the power of business and politics, this is, of course, a big program. Our fully accepted standards of advertising, particularly on television, and the eye-opening United Nations sessions during the Near East crisis are impressive examples of the prevailing cult of nontruth. We biologists (or any scientist, if he cares) should strive to make it plain that certain of the oldest and most acclaimed ethical rules (of which smart people secretly believe that nobody keeps them truly) are indispensable in the pursuit of science and are obeyed routinely as a matter of course. Scientific progress is impossible without seeking the truth wherever the way may lead. The scientist must be willing to retrace his steps, eat his words, admit errors and defeat, change his mind under pressure of the better argument, even acknowledge the superiority of a rival scientist. To live up to these tenets is not always easy, and our saintliness is not untainted.

Errors and mental blocks occur with scientists as naturally as with anybody else. They are bound to come up like suckers from the understock of personal beliefs on which all science is rooted. Constant pruning is part of the art of transforming individual intuitions into generally acceptable statements (see Polanyi).

The great scientist is accustomed to check his errors so thoroughly that none may ever show up. A good example of the contrary is the following. I had formed the opinion that the photochemical anaerobic oxidation of sulfide to sulfur in purple bacteria had to be reversible and that the bacteria would release hydrogen sulfide in the dark. I found they did, and after some polemics the matter was settled as true some years later. But at the same time, I wanted to see also the sequel, the photochemical oxidation of sulfide to sulfate reversed in the dark, though van Niel had maintained that this never happened in his cultures. I proved to my satisfaction that the reaction did happen. Each time I tipped sulfate into a suspension of resting purple bacteria, they began to evolve sulfide as expected while nothing happened without sulfate. The truth, as van Niel later showed, was that nearly any other salt can also bring the bacteria into action. Under the circumstances, having just proved that the first step from sulfide to sulfur was indeed reversible, an unspecific response to sulfate was for me so unexpected that I failed to do the simple control. A good description of this kind of situation I found recently in Vauvenargues: "Those who cannot manage to look from many viewpoints sometimes attribute to one entire object what actually belongs only to the little they are aware of. The neatness of their ideas hinders them from being suspicious." I could give one or two more examples of my lack of due caution. But it may happen that a very great scientist, to the distress of his best informed admirers, becomes so infatuated with his own preconceived idea that he uses all his prestige and experimental skill to uphold an error even when there is overwhelming evidence to the contrary. If his prestige is so high that it has led to a "cult of the individual" within the scientific community, the damage to the work of lesser investigators in the same field may amount to a considerable retardation of scientific progress.

Another failing, particularly unfitted for a scientist, is to accept the master's view as dogma and develop a complete block against any other hypotheses. Again I take myself as an example. I had had the incredible good luck to come into Otto Warburg's laboratory at the age of 23. I promptly fell under the spell of the famous man who a couple of years later supported my first quasi-independent research efforts in the most generous manner. So my loyalty was absolute. Consequently, when I first met van Niel in 1931, and when he explained to me photosynthesis on the basis of the theory of Wieland as an oxido-reduction with water, it did not penetrate. I understood the message, but it went against the words of the master, and in my heart I did not believe it. Consequently, as late as 1936 Wohl and I were thinking about a hypothetical way to reduce a carbon dioxide compound directly à la Willstätter-Warburg. Only when Hill's chloroplast reaction and later my photoreduction experiments made any other than van Niel's view untenable was I ready to give in.

Upon such a complete surrender of one's critical faculty in a circumscribed area, while remaining otherwise fairly reasonable, rests the initial success of authoritarian governments. In our time it is the most sinister weakness in a human mind, and it behooves us biologists to find out what can be done about it. It happened to me when there was not the slightest ulterior motive to "arrange my thoughts" according to the views of somebody else.

With the change in the conditions of a scientific career since 1940, other troubles and temptations have come up for the scientist. Polanyi writes about that as follows:

. . . The scientist seeking guidance from scientific opinion must not be tempted to canvass primarily his fellow scientists' approval. Though his income, his independence, his influence, in fact his whole standing in the world will depend throughout his career on the amount of credit he can gain in the eyes of scientific opinion, he must not aim primarily at this credit, but only at satisfying the standards of science. For the shorter way of gaining credit with scientific opinion may lead far astray from good science. The quickest impression on the scientific world may be made not by publishing the whole truth and nothing but the truth, but rather by serving up an interesting and plausible story composed of parts of the truth with a little straight invention admixed to it. . . . A considerable reputation can be built up and a very comfortable university post be gained before this kind of swindle transpires—if it ever does. . . . The tradition of science, it would seem, must be upheld as an unconditional demand if it is to be upheld at all. It can be made use of by scientists only if they place themselves at its service. It is a spiritual reality which stands over them and compels their allegiance.

In the 1920's it was still expected that in every scholar the memories of a broad liberal education would linger vividly enough so that the "problem of the two cultures" brought up by Snow after 1940 would strike him as purely artificial. Forty years later we are constantly celebrating the triumphs of the natural sciences in changing man's environment while completely neglecting the question of how the hypnotized masses will like this new world when they awake from their trance and find that they do not understand a thing any more.

SCIENCE AFTER 1940, "MISSION-DIRECTED"

In the meantime, something has happened that has destroyed most of the aristocratic aspects of science. The state has taken over science and lured into the profession thousands who before 1940 would have had doubts whether it would pay to join. A characteristic difference between 50 years ago and today can be seen in the professor's standard answer to the student's question: "Shall I go into the academic profession?" It used to be "No." If a man of 22 was not sure that nothing else would do, the academic career was not for him. The answer in our time is: "With your good grades, by all means. If you become disillusioned there is always the way into industry or administration."

The student now, in 1969, finds it difficult to believe that, at least with many of us in the 1920's, there was never the thought of having to hurry, or of having to publish results prematurely and more than once lest they be overlooked or taken over in their entirety by somebody else. Even important discoveries were left for a year or two in the hands of the man with whom they originated so that he could develop them according to his means and abilities. We used to say: "An apple already bitten into is not very attractive." The man who had the first bite was expected to keep and eat his apple. But then more and more people appeared on the scene who felt no compunction to bite quickly into every apple within reach and then often drop it just as quickly. It was considered very bad manners; but they were the men of the future. And now in the age of the citation index our old forms sound absurd and rather suspicious, as if we expected to hold patents or property rights on matters that are so obviously in the public domain as a published paper. We were, in addition, under the delusion that those who cared too much about public opinion or applause were at a disadvantage. We believed with Goethe that he is badly off who does not get his full reward for his efforts while working, long before his results are published. (Compare Curt Stern's *The Road and Not the Goal* with Watson's *The Double Helix*.) From the point of view of modern technical society, the egocentric, epicurean attitude, which in its logical extrapolation leads to publishing nothing but the best, must be strongly discouraged as an abnormal deviation. Today's society is not interested in the private intellectual pleasures of the individual, only in his exploitable results, no matter how preliminary or unimportant they may appear to him.

The phenomenal increase in the number of people whose work brings them in contact with scientific investigations has changed not only the image of the average scientist but also his motives and relationship with his colleagues. The latter are not fellows working in neighboring fields—their fields—but all too often are direct competitors in simultaneous, absolutely identical, experiments. Not only has the ruthlessness of accomplished business techniques invaded the areas where industrial exploitation overlaps research, but this kind of behavior is no longer considered as alien to science. The quick result in well advertised, i.e., fashionable, areas, is what counts. Hence this duplication or quadruplication of research projects, with the concomitant cancerous growth of the printed literature.

With such a large number of intelligent and energetic people attracted into science, it has become more difficult to be original. If a scientist is responsible for a department or an expensive laboratory, he must keep it going with money he will not get unless he convinces the administration or some government agency that certain useful results are forthcoming. A six-year period without a publication, a not uncommon situation with great scientists in the past, looks suspiciously inefficient in an era where the "critical size" of a cooperative group is scrutinized and no worthwhile results are expected from the lonely experimentalist.

The biggest customer for scientific "facts" and lots of them—never mind whether it was fun or boring to obtain them—is the government. I am unable to retrieve the reference to the following quotation which expresses the situation admirably:

> Young, high-spirited practitioners of the scientific method deluge us with new inventions, discoveries, techniques and an endless sequence of new facts, mainly at the insistence and under the direction of such unscientific laymen who may be called the state, meaning government bureaucrats, industrial administrators, jobseekers and society in general. Sooner or later all these originally individual endeavors to enjoy scientific research tend to become mission-directed, because the means to continue in a more elegant or profound way with the research one has started requires that we get the understanding and sympathy of the one or the other granting agencies. We know, of course, that the review board consists of scientists who will value any kind of research for its own sake and will not look too sharply whether it will fit a pattern which happens to be the guiding one for this particular agency. But, nevertheless, in general, research in this country is mainly determined by what the people in power consider to be the best for the good of the country.

Today, in 1969, the call for mission-directed investigations "for the good of the country" reaches into the remotest corner of university campuses.

Science and technology have largely become national institutions, and a large fraction of our available talent is in bondage to a government bureaucracy. The young men of today believe, of course, that this is the way things ought to be. To them, if they think about that at all, the free science of the single individual was merely a primitive phase, as primitive as the community of early Christians in comparison with the Church of Rome. But anyone who has wandered through those endless corridors, gone up and down the elevators in the enormous Washington buildings that house those who work to channel scientific inventions in the direction which is best for the country, cannot help thinking that he is in the midst of an organization which has developed its own rules for existence. Simone Weil wrote once: "Every human group that exercises power does so not in such a way as to bring happiness to those who are subject to it, but in such a way as to increase that power." The government demands directed research, the agencies whose existence depends on the government will therefore follow suit. Gaylord Simpson reminds us that: "NASA—like the Defense Department —entirely mission-directed . . . neither had any interest or any mission to improve the conditions of man's life here on earth or to make the continuation of that life possible." And, I may add, neither had any church that makes the hereafter its primary focus. (See also Spinoza on law.)

> Oppressive regimentation begins inconspicuously with the imposition of restrictions almost everybody gladly recognizes as necessary and overdue. It proceeds with the imposition of a set of approved ideas and uniform standards of behaviour. Unless checked in time, it ends up by controlling everything (Barzini).

How much chance do the scientists have to retain that minimum of power (= money) which permits them to investigate problems the government is not interested in? With the demand for the obvious, the "crazy idea" has little chance to be supported. Who would propound a ten-year, full-fledged program well staffed and housed, financed on the level of a particle accelerator or minor moon rocket, to find access to a cure for a disease much more dangerous to society than cancer; a disease that afflicts all of us in various degrees, and insidious because it is rarely painful, certainly least painful to those who suffer most from it, in short: stupidity? Yet such a project is neither absurd nor far from hopeless. In part it is already being supported under various aliases such as human genetics, educational research, psychology, diseases of the mind, literary essays on human understanding, etc., etc. Bernal wrote recently:

> The important thing in this is not so much the attitude of individual scientists as the collective effort to block out at least ideal policies which would have the general direction of making science serve the preservation and not the destruction of humanity. The more scientific effort is directed to military ends, the more resistance it will create in the minds of scientists. The awareness of the proper use of science in society is not easy to reach, and it is harder still to get agreement on it even among scientists. . . . (The scientist) sees a world in which the use of science has become the dominating factor. Mankind cannot progress, can-

not even exist today without science. However, far from giving him a sense of power, it emphasizes his awareness of his present weakness and futility. The powers of ignorance and greed distort science and lead it astray for war and destructive ends.

Nothing illuminates the misunderstanding of the public about the role of scientific research as clearly as the recent notion of its representatives that for the benefit of the country (again!) the flow of funds in support of science can be restricted or turned off as if it were a road-building program. In an emergency, a temporary tourniquet to restrict blood flow can be put on at several parts of the body without causing permanent damage—except around the neck.

Intellectual adventurers and artists rarely produce something easily saleable that may sustain them if their usual general support fails. They must continue producing to maintain the flow of ideas that later determine the liveliness or dullness of a country's civilization.

Exploration of Space and the Man-Machine

Though industry had partly broken with the tradition of the one-man program in science, namely the master and his pupils, so typical for academic research, the event that initiated a new phase in the history of mankind and with it a new belief as to the way scientific problems ought to be solved, was the Manhattan project. It demanded the cooperation of many first-rate men trained in a great diversity of skills. It also required such large amounts of money that only the government could support it. But its colossal success initiated the new style in the approach to scientific problems. The eradication of infantile paralysis was a somewhat similar example in the field of biology. And now we have the project to put a man on the moon. That eventually the latter will succeed there is no doubt. Yet two kinds of questions are rarely asked by those who in the end have to pay for such enterprises. For example, as to space: is that trip to the moon necessary? As to the idea that money and manpower will solve practically any problems: why has cancer not been cured long ago? The public has not been properly told that crash programs on the grand scale can be expected to succeed in a foreseeable time only if some key principles in basic science have already been discovered and are ready for development. Only in such circumstances does it pay to seek for the final solution by the proverbial method of leaving no stone unturned. The obverse situation, to which I shall address myself later, obtains when we already possess fundamental scientific insights concerning profound problems which, however, the public or its leadership fear to see applied in real life, and therefore steadfastly ignore.

Without the decision of the two governments, the Russian and the American, to put a man on the moon, the exploration of space to the extent we have it now might have taken another 50 years filled with quiet yet exciting research for the selected few. Other choices for spending all these billions would have been to eliminate most pockets of poverty in this country and to redirect the fundamental misorientation of all that is called "education." A program for a balanced population could have been vigorously put forward, and the age of ruthless power politics and unimaginably stupid wars would thereby have been brought nearer its end for the benefit of all the people.

What has happened in reality has again been exclusively the concern of a minority—those who profit from this enterprise. The true benefit, the spiritual excitement, triumph, and wonder has accrued to the very few, the one per cent or less of the population who really understand the scientists, and to those whose imagination lets them grasp intuitively the new confrontation of man with his cosmic environment. The cooperation among scientists, engineers, and administrators has indeed produced the greatest technical triumph the world has so far seen. The nearer planets, Mars and Venus, are open for inspection. The research on the evolution of our planetary system, and, even much more important, that on the appearance of living things, enters an entirely new chapter. For the biologist this development is exciting beyond description. But mainly for one reason. We might receive a very serious lesson about man's place in the universe, namely that there is no speck of life anywhere within a distance of more than four light years. This would forcefully remind us that planet Earth has to be managed in its entirety as a life sanctuary.

Yet the others, the nonscientists and laymen, unless they are employees in some of these enormous government projects, will not have any tangible benefits from the conquest of the moon or exploration of Mars other than the satisfaction they obtain from hearing on the radio how their favorite team won in an international sport contest. Are the people of the small nations of Europe in any way worse off for not sharing in the patriotic prestige of being citizens of a moon-conquering country? When these questions first bothered the community of scientists, the United States had not yet embarked on waging a full-fledged preventive war against a badly analyzed future threat in Asia. Now the expenses for our space sport pale in comparison with those spent to convert Asians to democracy. Is anything more urgent than studies to understand why people en masse are so easily persuaded, yet singly so difficult to convince?

I urge the young scientist who has not yet made up his mind, to peruse carefully A. M. Weinberg's essay "Criteria for Scientific Choice." At one point this author asks: "How can one measure the merit of behavioral sciences and nuclear energy on the same scale of values?"

On the political and technical aspects of the space mission we have an excellent critical literature. What has been neglected is the effect of the space mission on man himself. The space mission has produced a new creature—the machine-man. While de Lamettrie tried to prove to his 18th century readers that man functions like a machine, we, 200 years later, are showing experimentally that man can serve very well at least as part of one. The coming dehumanization of man was seen long before 1940. On the last pages of his second volume of the *Decline* Spengler described, 45 years ago, how Western man has become the slave of his creation, the machine, which is going to unfold fully its secret devilish power in the years to come. Ortega y Gasset especially detested the rise of the specialist. Chapter 12 of his *Revolt of the Masses* is entitled "The Barbarism of Specialization."

Ortega speaks of the disproportion between the complexity of present-day problems and the capacity of present-day minds.

> The majority of the investigators themselves have today not the slightest suspicion of the very great and dangerous internal crisis through which their science is passing. . . . Now it turns out that the actual scientific man is a prototype of the mass man, because science itself, the root of our civilization, automatically converts him into mass man, makes of him a primitive and modern barbarian. The fact is well known. . . . That state of not listening, of not submitting to higher courts of appeal which I have repeatedly put forward as characteristic of the mass man, reaches its height precisely in these partially qualified men. They symbolize and to a great extent constitute, the actual dominion of the masses, and their barbarism is the most immediate cause of European demoralization. . . . The civilization of the last century, abandoned to its own devices, has brought about the rebirth of primitivism and barbarism. . . . But if the specialist is ignorant of the inner philosophy of the science he cultivates, he is much more radically ignorant of the historical conditions requisite for its continuation. That is to say how society and the heart of man are to be organized in order that they may continue to be investigators.

The following is a quotation from an article by Eric Fromm:

> The 19th century said 'God is dead.' The 20th century could say 'man is dead.' Means have been transformed into ends. The consumption of things has become the aim of life, to which living is subordinate. We produce things that act like men, and men that act like things. Man has transformed himself into a thing, and worships the products of his own hands. He is alienated from himself and has regressed to idolatry, even though he uses God's name. Emerson already saw that 'things are in the saddle and ride mankind.' Today many of us see that the achievement of well-being is possible under only one condition, if we put man back into the saddle.

One more quotation—Aldous Huxley writes: "Industrial man, a sentient, reciprocating engine, having a fluctuating output, coupled to an iron wheel revolving with uniform velocity, and then we wonder why this should be the golden age of revolution and mental derangement." Was it not Samuel Butler of "Erewhon" fame who said a hundred years ago that only machines progressed?

Scientists as a class of useful experts, like lawyers, doctors, and engineers, never had it so good. Few among them seem disturbed by the ominous tendency of any man, Western or Asian, if he is only given the opportunity, to advance from a person who loves to play with machines into one who likes to serve them. Enough has been said about the tyranny of the automobile; but truly frightening is a new branch of human biology, which aims at changing a man, to remodel and squeeze and integrate him until he functions as a reliable wheel in the system. Long before we, the citizens of this democracy, after intelligent debate, shall have agreed to finance an all-out program of human eugenics, to eliminate properly analyzed undesirable genetic traits and to conserve desirable ones, we may have succumbed irreversibly to our idolized machines without so much as one nation-wide debate. With an artificial kidney, a plastic heart and a sterilized soul (all already available) it will soon be possible to put a 10-year guarantee on a fully-brained machine. Unbelievable? Here is the official summary of a well-financed government program dated 1967:

> Human Factors Engineering focuses attention on the human component of equipment and systems, and considers man as an integral functional part of the man-machine combination. Because of his superior capacity for sensing, controlling, improvising, and decision-making, man, when properly employed, has great potential for improving system performance. On the other hand, he may contribute to system degradation, particularly if his capabilities and limitations are not recognized and taken into account adequately during system definition, design, fabrication, and operation.

Since the preceding paragraphs were written, we have had another milestone of progress. A minister at a funeral of one of our 50,000 yearly automobile victims may in the near future console the parents with words reminiscent of those said a million times over the graves of war casualties: "Your son did not die quite in vain. His good heart continues to beat in another man's breast." Recently a moribund person has been eviscerated to increase the survival chances of four others. What is right and good for an intact organ we can expect, of course, to be right for any unique and vital extract from such organs; in short, we are back to cannibalism on a scientific basis. But still the Hippocratic oath forces doctors to keep a completely paralyzed man in a semiliving state at the expense of the finances and, more important, the sanity of his relatives. Instead of age-old trivia such as quibbling about pornography, our lawgivers should get busy with these awesome new questions which nobody has so far thought through properly.

This is only a beginning. In order to serve society better, what else will be done to us while we are alive? This last line may stimulate the reader's imagination: "Split-brain monkeys can handle more visual information than normal animals" (from an article by M. S. Gazzaniga on "The Split Brain in Man").

On this planet the force called "Faustian" by Spengler drives Western man to continuous action even after his basic instinctive drives have been satisfied. This restless urge to mold a world according to his, unfortunately quite limited, imagination—this force has pushed man himself into a corner from which he must now try to liberate himself. At the moment it looks as if stupidity and meanness, combined with the forces of technology, are going to win the race towards cultural extermination before reason, in the form of biology and psychology, has had a good chance to discover the best way to reverse the trend.

THE SCIENCE OF HUMAN NATURE

The human psyche is fabulously complex, simultaneously terrifying and awe-inspiring; but so is the cosmos. To contemplate with deep emotion world and mind in all their transcendent glory and to reflect on this poetically and philosophically has been the core of a humanistic education. To develop a world view on this basis alone is, unfortunately, the way to extinguish all impetus to start working humbly and patiently on the exciting task of understanding the world more profoundly by the method of the "control experiment." The church was dead set against this insolent assault upon God's creation. Yet the success in changing our environment by a method which rests upon the pretense that we might understand what is lastly beyond all understanding has been overwhelming. The same will be true concerning studies of human nature. Surreptitiously scientists in many branches of biology are already at work. Since the public has no inkling what this is going to lead to, we biologists have not been burned yet. That some caution in the pursuit of such research is generally felt to be advisable may be guessed from Dobzhansky's remark: "It would not do for a student of human evolution to ignore the tragic human predicament, although scientists in general have prudently avoided coming to grips with such problems." The contrast to traditional teachings on the nature of man is sharply illuminated by the opinion of a psychotherapist, A. S. Maslow, who sums up some of the new insights by stating: "One conclusion . . . is a very revolutionary one, that no other large culture has ever arrived at, namely that our deepest needs are not in themselves dangerous or evil or bad." Scientists must take care, therefore, to emphasize that a study of human nature is in perfect harmony with certain humanistic and religious ideals concerning our society. Science supports by typically demonstrable results some of our cherished traditional values which, when left in trust of philosophers alone, would not be altogether safe from devastating attacks by purely logical analysis.

In old age, H. Spencer wrote (around 1904) about opinions he had earlier as follows: "Believing as I did that right guidance, individual and social, depends upon acceptance of evolutionary views of mind and of society, I was hopeful that its effects would presently be seen on educational methods, political opinions and men's ideas about human life. Obviously these hopes that beneficial results would presently be wrought, were too sanguine. My confidence in the rationality of mankind was much greater than it is now."

Whose fault is it that so little was done before 1914 and between the wars to educate the people in a manner that might have preserved what was good in that now remote era? The historians' verdict will perhaps be that we scientists were, and still are, to blame. We chose to investigate everything in sight—with one exception, ourselves. The reason: cowardice. The vast majority of nonscientists considered such inquiries as an intrusion, an imposition, and a threat to the tradition of both personal comfort and public conformism, the latter an important component of the art of government. It was much safer, therefore, for a natural philosopher just to dream of progress based on the power of education—an education which would help only the few who like himself would remain anyhow powerless in the real world of political events. One need only read with what derision Spengler treats the political aspirations of the thinkers as compared with those of the doers (see also "A Plea for More Thinker-Doer Administrators" by H. O. Brogan). I am aware that a prodigious amount of research is being done under such headings as social studies or child development or education or psychology. But these activities are supported so far by a tiny fraction of the taxpayers' money in comparison with what is given to particle physics, space politics, or the training of soldiers, the old art of inducing a man to kill without any personal reason whatever.

What will take great sums of money but is perhaps the most important task in the studies of human nature is to ascertain the true personality of "the masses." It may be just a superstition to assume that 90 per cent of mankind must exist naturally and forever on slightly subhuman levels of the mind, as the philosophers (Ortega), the historians (Spengler, Toynbee), certainly the priests, and many philanthropists seem to be certain of. Maybe the unteachable fraction is only 50 per cent. Who knows?

Even in countries with such high literacy as ours, people do not read books. Too few have the opportunity to grow up as I did, surrounded by a thousand books. Nor do they receive as a matter of course reasonable, testable answers to whatever question might come into their heads at the impressionable and, as some psychologists think, crucial years before school indoctrination starts. Qualitatively we all agree that part of the solution may be found right here. We know very well how to prevent malnutrition of the body, and sometimes get around to feeding some of our poor. But as to early malnutrition of the mind, we know precious little. It is quite possible that the traditional religious teaching might really do much more harm than we are aware of. He who does not trust the inherent reasonableness of people and their ability for deliberate judgment when properly informed denies among other things the rationality of our judicial system and should plead for the transfer of all proceedings at law to the computer (something I believe for other reasons such as speed to be a practical improvement). Recent changes in the definition of justice or the psychology of law enforcement, in the methods of education or the relationship between government and churches, etc., are attributable to a few courageous individuals who in their idealism persist in their endeavors. Most of us find our lives too short for the thankless task of pressing for such obvious reforms.

And so it has come about that more money is being spent to make humans fit into a particular machinery than into their own society—or to remodel society to serve human needs better. The engineer has a very precise idea where he can fit a man into his machine which he invented with that purpose in mind. The sociologist, after centuries of contemplating mankind as a whole, has only vague and timid ideas about what he ought to do to improve society. Furthermore, the ordinary man has no opinion whether he should approve or disapprove of the engineer's tricks which he finds thrilling, even if sometimes a little nauseating. But he has been indoctrinated with definite opinions about society and is opposed immediately to anything he has not heard a hundred times before. Sociologists know quite well where and why our society is ailing at so many places, but so far as I know it has not occurred to them to ask the biologists what the individual roots of these evils might be. To what extent does the average sociologist think as a matter of course in terms of evolution and genetics, or of imprinting during the first years of a child's life? It makes a difference whether one believes that what is worth knowing about human nature has been known for quite a while and is to be found for the greater part in the Bible, in poetry, the law books, and similar revered sources of knowledge, or whether one realizes that we have just begun to understand ourselves as a biological phenomenon. On the other hand, it would be foolish to reject certain forms of gaining insight merely because they have been practiced since thousands of years before our time without the benefit of scientific analysis. But just as in any other science, the reliability and limitations of the older methods to deal with human nature have to be reappraised. In this way, the old might be fitted to the new without leaving that crack Conant is so worried about. Obviously, the scientific outlook must encompass also the views obtained in nonscientific fields. The humanities belong in any science about the nature of man. If this appears to be too vast an undertaking, we ought to have a look at what the computer may be able to do for us. The results from feeding literature, history, criminal codes, and law cases into computers might lead to the first objective appraisal of how much to expect from a modernized program of child and adult education.

Since I wish to entreat all young biologists to think twice before devoting their lives to problems less urgent than this one, I must point out that the need was seen quite clearly 30 years ago by Hogben. In a chapter entitled "Politics and the Science of Human Nature," he said:

> The leaders of liberal and of socialist thought on social questions have shown . . . little interest in the standpoint of the many eminent biologists. . . . Since liberalism has its roots in a pre-scientific view of human nature, it has always been inimical to the objective study of human behavior. . . . The rational view is that scientific

study of the way in which patterns of human nature are conditioned is the matter of supreme importance if we wish to advance to a more rational organization of human welfare. There is good reason for believing that scientific ignorance has much to do with the crumbling away of our social tradition under the stress of economic disaster. . . . We shall not harmonize the public needs of a progressive society with the private needs of human nature until we have a science of human nature.

Everybody knows that one cannot join the 60-mile-an-hour rush of a four-lane highway at the supposedly safe speed of 25 miles an hour without causing turbulence, if not disaster. Yet we are expected to cope with the self-inflicted problem of an ever-accelerating technology with patterns of thought considered safe and proper by our forefathers.

Obviously, we must develop a new set of prejudices of a kind which remains workable and flexible, because they will be based on scientific insights instead of upon revelations of yesterday's eternal truths which, being too rigid, are likely to break down painfully under any real stress. We brag constantly about the progress made in the field of the exact sciences and remain dumb about those concerning political or emotional human interests. In the area of practical human relations there seems to exist even a superstition that truth and reasonableness must be carefully sidestepped if one's country is to prosper. (See the modern example in the Arab-Israeli debate of the Security Council mentioned above.)

Once the new tool, the analysis of human nature, is properly working, we shall know what we have done wrong during the last 2000 years and which is more at fault—the method of shaping children into responsible citizens, or the raw material, the species itself. If its present genetic makeup turns out to be beyond redemption, it will be recast either in the cruelest ways by nature itself, or on our own terms. The task which comes first and is more urgent than all others is to inform the people that these choices are theirs and that in a democracy it will take years of knowledgeable debate to come to an equitable solution of how to proceed.

The "wave of the future," the mechanization of our ways of life, is spreading around the globe. The dream is of a Western standard: a life expectancy of 70 years, soap and hot water, eventually books and the time to read them alone in a quiet room, preferably with a window looking out into a pretty garden. Very few know that this planet has only space enough to fulfill this dream for at best half the world population we already have. Anyone who can truly say that he is not much interested in the living standards which will prevail during his future years nor during the life of his children is, of course, excused and need not worry about this amazing problem. But should he choose to worry, he ought to admit that any remodeling of our value system better be thoughtful than thoughtless, guided by studies on human nature rather than by fitful responses to human crises. Some will say that if a rational approach were possible it would have been tried before. This does not make sense because we have known only for 100 years that human nature is subject to change by other and more permanent means that just social coercion; we have known only for 50 years that what has been achieved with cattle, dogs, corn, fruits, etc.—namely the selection of better varieties—is perfectly applicable to man, if we could only decide what selection to make. But a science of educational psychology which promises to be the least dangerous way to start tampering with some of man's undesirable traits, is just in the process of being born.

To the extent that science and technology are shaping man's future, a scientist should be interested in doing scientifically what so far historians and political soothsayers have often confidently attempted: predict a bit of the future. With such predictions I do not mean obvious extrapolations of the development of machines and drugs and what they will do for us (the usual content of science fiction), or predictions for the life of the individual which we must leave to the physician. A more important but attractive field for prophecy is to contemplate what may happen to society provided the newest of sciences, the study of human nature, is allowed to unfold with the aid of subsidies comparable to those now given to the development of particle accelerators or biological poisons, as well as active warfare. The seeds for a biology of the mind are sprouting everywhere and include intuitive psychology, brain surgery, biochemical drug experiments, and hypnotism.

No other science is likely to probe so near to the regions where traditional habits and superstitions, despite recent sociotechnological changes, have so far ruled unchallenged. Certain nerves in the body of Western culture have already been painfully touched, particularly those intended to transmit religious signals. Unchecked they have grown into domains clearly reserved in the modern world for the rule of demonstrable instead of revealed truth.

The great difficulty is that if anyone even tentatively suggests that our great institutions ought to be analyzed from the point of view of knowledge already existing of man as a social animal, he will find himself immediately opposed by millions who cry out that their eternal values are being threatened.

RESISTANCE TO KNOWLEDGE

Non-Catholics have no reason to feel particularly advanced, modern, or superior because their denomination has nothing to do with the recent scandal caused by the papal encyclical on birth control. Any fundamentalist belief, be it Christian or Islamic or secular, which demands absolute obedience to rules which have only mythical, historical, or metaphysical roots is likely to produce similar vicissitudes for the lives of the faithful. In centuries past, people tolerated the misery stemming from enforced conformism in thought and behavior in the same manner as their abject poverty, namely in "quiet desperation." There was no way to prove that certain religious demands were quite naturally and generally unenforceable and that for this reason they created insolvable conflicts. The churches took advantage of this situation by inventing the notion of "sin." In our time, it can be demonstrated that it makes sense to stop at a red traffic light without much loss of personal freedom. Or, with a little support by the police, we can see the reasonableness of the golden rule, which prevents most of us from commit- ting murder without feeling intolerably frustrated. But to be told to stop making love is another matter, and in the age of the pill it seems plain fool- ish. While this most personal of problems is at the bottom of the present commotion about the pill in this country, my concern here is the magnitude of the harm done to all of mankind in terms of the population problem by insisting that well-established scientific knowledge should be ignored for purely imagined, easily refutable reasons. Good friends, after reading an earlier version of my manuscript, concluded from such lines as the preced- ing ones that I am dogmatically against all aspects of religion. Therefore, though it has been said so often before, let me restate the following. All civilizations, some completely alien to ours, have developed religious rites for complex emotional reasons science does not yet understand. We scien- tists have no desire to usurp a task which the churches have fulfilled always tolerably and sometimes superbly, namely to offer consolation about injus- tice and the senselessness of early death or lifelong misery; to heighten and dignify with beautiful and solemn rites moments of joy as well as of grief common to us all. Fiction, poetry, art, and religion are outside the scientific domain. They presuppose individuality, the uniqueness of each person, which, interestingly enough, modern genetics has demonstrated to be scientifically correct. Science, on the other hand, is based on common knowledge and mutual critique. It follows that personal truth and scientific truth have noth- ing in common but the sound of the word. Personal truth is part of knowing oneself and cannot be falsified by logical argument, while scientific truth remains believable only until it is shown to be not believable any more, whereupon it has to be amended and widened in the seams like an outgrown child's dress.

For over a thousand years the theologians claimed to have all the answers about heaven and earth. And the greatest triumph of the Catholic church, to mention the most powerful institution, has been that Hume, Vol- taire, and all the rest of her sworn enemies up to Sartre and Russell, could not put a dent in her armor. But now experimental biology and technology, with perhaps only a fraction of the intelligence and wit of the great philos- ophers, have given us answers about man's nature on earth which are over- whelmingly convincing. It is clear that the churches must stop dictating in detail how a man should live his private life and retreat for good to the tasks which are truly their own. The worst trouble comes when the churches hope to maintain their power over the daily lives and common activities of modern man by suppressing or withholding new information from their faithful, just as the communist political hierarchy does.

Young biologists should never forget that between the times of Archimedes and Hipparchus and the age of Roger Bacon, there were 14 centuries of no science at all in the West. And when it finally resumed its growth, it truly flourished only in those parts of Europe that had been shaken up by the Reformation. The regions that were, and have remained, in the firm grip of a powerful state church, such as southern Italy, the Iberian peninsula, and the former Spanish and Portuguese colonies in South America, are precisely the countries which have contributed next to nothing to the development of modern science from 1500 up to the present day.

Geneticists will rightly protest any attempt to explain this psychologically interesting phenomenon on the basis of a different distribution of intellectual talents between north and south Europeans. We need only to remember the eminent explorers, warriors, writers, poets, philosophers, and artists who have come from the very same countries. It must be a matter of education and a continuation up to the present of the medieval form of thought control. Thus the perpetual resistance of the Catholic church has been to a great extent responsible for the fact that even in this predominantly Protestant country the necessary millions of dollars were not put into research for the pill and for its cheap distribution at a time when it would have greatly influenced what we have to contend with now. The famines we shall have to witness in the coming years will still be called "natural" catastrophes. Circumstances beyond our control, as we are apt to say, will make it impossible to help India and South America with either sufficient food or pills. From 1923 on, the literature on birth control has increased steadily, together with the objective evidence that a liberalization of the law was not only desirable for humane reasons, but would soon become absolutely necessary. Every properly informed scholar who saw an opportunity to do so within the context he was writing about, has admonished his readers that this was the greatest problem not only in India but anywhere—though in the United States not yet for calamitous economic pressures, but only for reasons of human decency. A recent article in BioScience tells us "it is estimated that there are one million induced abortions annually in the United States."

Only a century ago a famine in India was clearly one of those unforeseeable acts of God. In our time, the world, as represented by the delegations in the United Nations, or at least its FAO section, knows only too well that the occurrence and extent of famines not only can be predicted, but also that there are means by which, at least in principle, such misery can be alleviated, if not prevented in the future. To the extent that we live in a man-made environment and have usurped control, at least partially, over the forces of nature, mishaps are no longer pure Acts of God, inevitable and unforeseeable. The concepts of right and wrong, of justice and guilt, become applicable when we know perfectly well what is going to happen but fail to take precautions. (See *Food Supplies and Population Growth,* 1963; Greet: *Human Fertility and Population Problems,* 1963; Hardin: *Population, Evolution, Birth Control,* 1964; and Durand: *World Population,* 1967). If 40 years ago those who had no conformist blinders and no reasons to be afraid of uninformed and bigoted voters had been able to convince our government to further quietly the research that Gregory Pincus was soon to start privately—in the same way as the government now quietly works on means to control all of us by "humane" paralyzing gases —the story of this century would have ended on a happier note.

There is a simple way to bring natural philosophy and fundamentalist beliefs into a workable agreement. The churches admit that the laws of nature are those of the Lord and that it is hopeless to try to circumvent them; that the true definition of science, as Simone Weil said, is "a study of the beauty of the world." Science, on the other hand, admits that no way has as yet been found to explain man's capacity to discover or invent natural laws, to meditate upon himself and his place in nature, or his power to produce art, and that thousands of years of introspection and intuition have given us rules of thumb about the civilized ways to curb as well as to cultivate our emotions. These old rules ought to be followed reasonably until there is scientific evidence that in this or that traditional form they are unsound and must be readjusted. The prospect that we can soon transform conflict into cooperation may be, alas, as dim as that of escaping nuclear war.

While the rejection of scientific views on human nature arises as a principle in any fundamentalist religion (de Chardin was forbidden to publish until he died in 1950) the harmful result comes with the all-pervading success of such authoritarian indoctrinations. Even in this republic things have changed since H. L. Menken wrote around 1930: "Alone among the great nations of history we have got rid of religion as a serious scourge, and by the simple process of reducing it to a petty nuisance. For men become civilized, not in proportion to their willingness to believe, but in proportion to their readiness to doubt." The power of religious custom is still such, in 1969, that no one can hope to be elected to an important public office if he lets it be known that he is an atheist and has no need nor sees a reason to join any of the fashionable denominations.

Most great religions were founded when human lives were short in comparison to the rate of cultural changes. The world of the grandchild made sense from the point of view of the grandfather; they understood each other without taking courses in recent history. From the time the horse was domesticated until 150 years ago, man could not move faster over land than his mount. Now with 600 miles an hour possible for a man on the move, our lives have become very long in terms of environmental changes. For the first time in human history, we are clearly aware of being condemned to live in an age of furious and irreversible technological progress. And suddenly it has become apparent that the changes in law and theology, which in the past took centuries to mature, must be speeded up also to fulfill their social task of maintaining order while the flood of new knowledge and technical innovations is tearing many good old customs to pieces. For instance, consider the Vatican ecumenical council which raised so many hopes among the church intellectuals who are dismayed at what has happened since.

No doubt, well-established lawyers, judges, historians, and writers are people of highest intelligence and memory. Of course they know who Darwin, Mendel, Freud, even Gregory Pincus were, and when asked would still be able to pass a routine college examination. Yet in real life they act as if they had never heard of these men who made a 2000-year-old tradition of thinking about man, his nature, and his habits nearly obsolete. The great change is taking place not because what seemed well established suddenly was shown to be all wrong, but because the old view was incomplete and one-sided, and in many ways antiquated. The office holders and business leaders do not realize that the study of man has just begun, and it does not give them pause to think that their decisions may soon be shown to be based on false premises about the educability of man and on wrong concepts about what really moves him. Only when catastrophes come thick and fast do they tend to remember that their fellow intellectuals from the natural sciences have been lecturing, warning, cajoling, in short pestering them for years about the consequences to be expected because of their neglect of data which were all available in their own official files. Dismayed, the great leaders summon the scientists to give advice as "experts," as if the latter were conjurors with a bag of tricks from which the clever men of affairs were at liberty to choose just the one which would work a miracle according to their needs while leaving traditional views undisturbed. That these "experts" include the only group of men whom the future will remember as having lifted the spirit of humanity in our time above the level of century-old short-sightedness, does not disturb the minds of the politicians. They are not ashamed to tell their voters that the naïveté in political matters of well-meaning intellectuals such as the Bohrs, Einsteins, Russells, Sartres, and Szilards, is only too well known. They do not realize that an occasional half-hour remedial lecture on the facts of terrestrial biology by people like Gardner or Udall or Harrison Brown or Warren Weaver, do not really help. Quick stop-gap information can never replace constant awareness of the unique biological situation which now prevails for man on this planet. In addition, there is the disheartening experience of the apparent impossibility of convincing many writers and philosophers educated in the humanities of the error of looking down on science because, supposedly, it is the inventor of the hated machines, and to make them realize instead that science is really a new philosophy and not merely a technique. This is the reason why a good many of the intelligentsia side with those who are just plain ignorant when the question arises concerning reforms of the kind scientists are likely to propose.

The problems facing us are scientifically much simpler, sociologically much more difficult, than we usually imagine. Certain questions which have been prematurely discussed in popular magazines, such as experimental research about the meaning of race, or the inheritance and selection of particular traits, or how and when instinctive behavior erases civilized reponses, are not yet everybody's business to know and to vote about. What is everybody's business to think about is that unless something effective is done, the world in 1980 will be a "human antheap" swarming with 8×10^9 people. Here in the United States we are "looking forward" to the task of making at least 45 million more people happy, added to the over 200 million we already have. No congressman ventures to say that regulation of birth has to be incorporated into law.

I cannot praise highly enough the U.S. Department of the Interior Conservation Yearbook No. 2, entitled *The Population Challenge—What it Means to America, 1966*. The text is challenging, the pictures are beautiful, and the price of $1.25 is an outstanding bargain in the publishing world. The publication is adorned with the following citations. President Johnson: "I will seek new ways to use our knowledge to help deal with the explosion in world population and the growing scarcity in world resources." Secretary Udall: "I am suggesting that the United States set an example of how to plan the best relationship of human beings to their environment, the man to land ratio which would result in the highest development of the land and of free men." President Johnson again: "The concern is not with nature alone but with the total relation between man and the world around him. The object is not just man's welfare but the dignity of man's spirit." Quotation from President Johnson's speech at the United Nations: "Let us in all our lands, including this land, face forthrightly the problems of our multiplying populations and seek the answers to this most profound challenge to the future of all the world. Let us act on the fact that $5.00 invested in population control is worth $100.00 invested in economic growth." Is this not wonderful? And where is congressional action? Compare the articles by J. Murray Luck in *Science,* November 1, 1957, and by Kingsley Davis ten years later in *Science,* November 10, 1967. Secretary Udall's publication should be in the hands of every school teacher in the United States. The very beautiful illustrations and the good text make it first-rate teaching material. What would the rulers in the USSR do once they had made officially such pronouncements as those of our president; or printed a book as useful as that of our Department of the Interior? How can one say all the demonstrably true things and then quietly compromise with ignorance and superstition? Is that leadership? The proper and reasonable things have been pronounced like words of a magic formula in the dutiful hope that—against all expectation —the right action might somehow follow. *Dixi et animam salvavi.*

EDUCATION ON A SCIENTIFIC BASIS

Considered solely as an animal, man is just about the nastiest creature that has ever been evolved . . . not primarily through lack of good principles . . . but because he is increasing too fast and because of his ignorance and stupidity where he at least has the means to be far-seeking and sensible . . . (Thorpe)

Without respected parents and a reliable refuge in the home, children are likely to remain in their natural state—primates with a capacity for learning to speak and for imitating the tricks their elders use in order to survive. If the difference between one of those savages who exist by the thousands everywhere—not only on far-away continents—and one we call a civilized man is due mainly to environmental influences, we have obviously failed in our educational task. Should it turn out that such savage people can be made to imitate civilized behavior only under the threat of the police and never for any other reason, then rebreeding (which is far in the future) is the only solution. By contrast, the literature on revolutionary experiments in education is already voluminous. Such experiments are much less fearsome than genetical ones. An educational mistake will disappear with the individual and, before that, may be corrected by re-education or coercion during his lifetime. Mistakes in the course of some genetical experimentation that is sufficiently significant to be of lasting value can be caught only after the experimenters have died and the public has probably forgotten what it was all about. Compared with the latter, seemingly radical innovations in education are virtually harmless and, considering our increasing crime rate, long overdue. They are of undeniable ethical value and not Utopian at all. They only cost money—and for that reason those short-changed souls who unfortunately never had a modern education will vote against what is the most important spiritual task in any nation.

A national effort is under way to erase inequality in educational opportunities. Let us assume that this has been accomplished and that the children of poor whites and Negroes in Louisiana receive the same instruction as the children of the suburbanites in New England. What kind of a good education will that be? An education the parents approve of because it fulfills what they always thought of as the ideal education for themselves? Yet if so much is being said about the need for reforms and for a better understanding of science, it will not be good enough. The parents are the problem. They must be made to see that science and technology are ploughing up literally and figuratively the grounds in which their own ideals once were rooted, and out of which grew their present beliefs of what ought to be. Obviously we must prepare our children to face the world of tomorrow instead of making them conform to ours. If this is understood, the transition to the new basis for teaching our children is hardly a problem.

When we have accepted a teaching plan based on the evolution of man, a story which finally culminated in art, religion, philosophy, and science (see the books by von Weizsacker, Bronowski, Bohr, Tax, and many others), the results of several thousand years of metaphysical inventions can be put out of the way into the curiosity shop, where, of course, these beautiful fabrics must be preserved as part of the evidence of how the mind works. It is hard to get around the fact that in the last 50 years we have learned more about ourselves as a part of nature than in all preceding centuries together—and this at a time when the study of human nature has not quite reached its stride. Our schools ought to reflect this. Not to be misunderstood, I must say that today's fashion of teacher-sponsored science projects in high school competitions is little more than a corrupting abomination. It brings me letters like the following: "I am in the 9th grade. I heard that you have made life in the test tube. Please send me some and tell me all about it."

In the school system of tomorrow, all teachers, regardless of what they will teach as their specialty, must be conversant with the problems touched upon in the preceding pages. It is not a matter of curricula—that is for the experts to work out. It is a matter of obtaining the most intelligent, devoted, and courageous teachers that can be found in the nation. As Barzini expressed it in *The Italians* in behalf of Italy: "I would spend every available penny of state money for the education of the young." Teaching ought to be one of the best paid and most respected professions, comparable to that of law. When I first came to this country in 1931, I found in the Los Angeles *Times* on the front page, nicely framed as a special thought to ponder, "An education enables you to earn more than an educator." I have pondered that ever since and am sure that today, 36 years and another world war later, 95 out of 100 people find nothing wrong with that sagacious statement. In earlier centuries the aristocrats treated the teacher of their children as a kind of miserable slave. This aristocratic spirit has now descended on our middle class. The truth of the saying can easily be established by comparing the income of school teachers with that of lawyers, physicians, or research professors. One of the many duties of the five per cent is to insist that we ought to follow oriental thinking and consider the teacher as the revered guide toward what is worthwhile to wish for in our lives. Again—should the unthinkable happen and teachers become honored as they deserve—we may then insist that they be natural philosophers to start with.

The ordinary state of mind of a teacher, his orientation towards life, determines how he will answer without long preliminary ruminations those frequently embarrassing questions of younger children. A teacher who knows that it is possible and quite customary to violate moral laws and get away with it, while it is impossible to violate natural laws, let alone get away unpunished for the stupid attempt, is sure to answer in a way which the child will discover to be reliable and in agreement with his experience. At least, the teacher should know that it is immoral to invent answers where there are none. Being told that innumerable phenomena are not fully under-stood by anybody, or for which different answers have been given at differ-ent times, might put the pupil in a state of mind that transforms him faster into a thinking being from one that only parrots what he was supposed to learn. Our school system, even in some graduate colleges, gives grades for having a good memory and an ability with words, not for being sensibly worried at not having grasped the full depths of a problem.

If we cannot understand the nature of the electron fully, it is not sur-prising to find this to be true also for human nature. Children will not be mystified more when told that they are either all or nothing, according to their point of view about themselves, than by being told that God is three in one. Actually, from a cosmic viewpoint, mankind's possibilities and troubles are fairly easy to understand; and equally easy from the viewpoint of my own being, where nothing counts but I, while the rest is background. Every-body learns to shift these viewpoints unconsciously a hundred times a day according to outside pressure or his predilections. It belongs to the basic scientific training that a person be fully aware of this duality. The next point is one which no child has ever been told until the method of objective enquiry has made it evident: all that is, is natural, in both inner and outer worlds. What former ages called unnatural is either not understood, of in-frequent, or unaccustomed, or impractical for the smooth running of social traffic. Red lights and police are inescapable, but only where and as long as the need for them can be objectively justified. They should not be left where we have installed them in former times out of mere habit.

So far, education of children is based everywhere on the expressed or tacit assumption that man's relation to the world has always been the same and is not subject to change. If things are like that, it is quite logical that the child be confronted with commands as to its conduct in life which are absolute and not to be reasoned about.

Today the notion that we cannot step twice into the same river pervades everything, and, if we teach evolution (as we absolutely must, because it is the overriding fact of life) it is too illogical to persist with the demand that the child should believe in unchangeable eternal moral rules. There is no reason why one cannot teach that our present ethical systems, the golden rule, the ten commandments (perhaps in Szilard's extended modern ver-sion), the Christian demand for responsibility and charity, represent the highest moral development of mankind so far. Nothing has to be altered except the wrong notion that this is now the end and no more refinements are possible. To the contrary, in a world that extols change, development, and progress as we do, there is no greater moral obligation than to search for the causes of such mean and blind barbarisms as we witness all around us in our Western societies, while the loftiest moral principles we can think of have been preached incessantly since the beginning of the Christian era.

The trouble and misunderstanding which beset our teaching and our

ways of thinking about science and technical progress as opposed to the traditional role of the humanities, are on the whole as yet on such low intellectual levels (common sense levels, one might say) that it is not necessary to
take recourse to the highest standards of refined analysis (see Russell, Popper) in order to recognize the need for reforms.

Technology is conquering the world because it succeeds. Our future
methods of teaching might do the same. It would be a great step on the
road to peace to have the same teachings spread over the world for the
same reason, namely that it succeeds in making people civilized. We listen
incredulously when the Arabs explain their sacred hate against the tiny
Jewish state and wonder why they do not instead turn their income from oil
to emulate the Jews and make themselves comfortable. We shudder when we,
seldom enough, recapitulate the rebarbarization of Italy, Germany, and
Russia under their respective tyrants, yet we seem incapable of imagining
that this outcome might have been averted had our social science, together
with a science of human nature, been farther ahead and been accompanied
by a corresponding social technology, such as adding birth control to death
control. But who among our high school teachers and so-called educators (a
title often given thoughtlessly to the administrators of educational institutions), is aware that our new educational system has to be linked eventually
with equally advanced systems in Europe; and finally with those of all other
member states of the United Nations?

One of the earliest steps and simplest to comply with to further the understanding between peoples would be that all states require of their teachers
a knowledge of the principles and present efforts of the United Nations'
Educational, Scientific and Cultural Organization.

Unthinkable Thoughts

The definition of an unthinkable thought is the one rational solution to a
disagreeable problem which, though demonstrably feasible, remains un-
mentioned because it runs contrary to all cherished beliefs and values. The
public speaker thinks: "It will upset my voters—my congregation—the parents of my students. I shall lose my job without having done the least bit of
good by insisting that they face the truth." Unthinkable thoughts have
joined the sinful ones in the classification of thoughts that are better suppressed than developed. In contrast to sinful thoughts, the unthinkable ones
are not pleasurable. They merely disturb our moral equanimity and ethical
balance because they call for action, while we have no idea whether this
action will be successful.

Scholars, thinkers, and scientists, on the other hand, thrive on them.
Such men have trained themselves to think a matter through regardless of
the kind of a nightmare that may thereby come into view. After all, one is
never sure that there is only one solution to a problem. A much better one
may be found later on. And the idea that a problem should be left alone

because it will probably **disturb** his sleep is in turn unthinkable to the true intellectual.

Experimenting with social institutions.—Many of the troubles which assail us today may well be called eternal, for they are not too different from those that plagued our ancestors 3000 years ago. What is new are the solutions to such problems which have become available in our time through biology and psychology. Just as it took some effort to persuade people to abandon traditional quackery in favor of modern medicine, just as virtually every man now believes that the earth rotates once in a day, in clear contradiction to what he sees, so we must persuade the people that it is time to supplant some old prejudices by new ones. It is time that they learn to believe what they already know superficially about such matters as evolution, inheritance, psychology, or even physics.

The technical world has outpaced all norms of earlier ages. Now even religions have to adjust themselves to changes in human conditions anywhere in the world, and ours also are in for revision. When objective science has become so influential, the free discussion about the most suitable among religious ideologies and value systems is one of the conditions for civilized progress.

Because a few of the behavioral experiments performed in the laboratory with persons who volunteer as guinea pigs are harrowing and often somewhat painful, the thought persists that much greater and unforeseeable damage to society may result if we experiment deliberately with social institutions and populations in the open. People forget that unless protected by law, customs, fashions, and morals change all the time, not because of farsighted intention, but rather in the manner of contagious diseases. It stands to reason that the clumsiness of our judicial procedures, particularly in reversing decisions that do not work out right, are the source of much avoidable unhappiness.

One of the most talked-about among our social shortcomings is the phenomenal increase in costly divorces after acrimonious infighting. What great harm, may I ask, will result if in addition to the old form of a marriage for life, a marriage license is offered which expires after five years unless cause is shown why this marriage should continue? With the arrival of children, the temporary form automatically reverts to the traditional one.

What harm will be done if unwanted and unloved children, of which there are plenty, are collected into many small state orphanages which, in addition to the usual staff, accept volunteer girls whose duty consists in dispensing attention and kindness to the children? These institutions would not be only charitable but provide urgently needed information about the "nature and nurture" problem. Mothers who have given up a child would be instructed to use birth control under penalty. This would prevent careless abuse of these social institutions.

Under present laws, some criminals must be fed for life in prison or electrocuted, hanged, or poisoned, sometimes after years of barbarous on-again, off-again trials. What harm would be done if such a criminal were given a handful of sleeping pills to use at his convenience? Anyone can think of more of such harmless and possibly very beneficial social experiments.

Population policy.—The first ethical duty of the state must be to prevent the birth of children who are unwanted, not eagerly expected by loving parents, and for whom there will be no place in school and no good teacher. Such a demand was indeed Utopian 50 years ago. In our time it is merely the realizable extension of the privileges of the rich to all citizens—namely the right to be left unborn. For a small minority, this thought has become nearly trite, while the overwhelming majority have not heard it expressed even once. The current literature offers a large choice of paraphrases on the same theme. Here is one example from an article by A. B. Kinzel, president of the Salk Institute of San Diego. "Obviously important social decisions will be needed. The implication for society, if we lick the problem of aging, is staggering. It may be necessary to penalize someone for giving birth without a permit, as heavily as we now penalize an individual for murder."

Despite all "progress," the absolute number of the destitute on earth has quadrupled since 1800. There is no major social problem which would not become much easier to solve if instead of 4×10^9 we humans were only 2×10^9. The latter is still a very large figure, but reduction of the present number of people to one-half would give such a relief from all kinds of pressures that the world would perhaps be willing to listen to reason and truth instead of to fanatic or ridiculous lies. Yet people do not want to hear that if they are continually and hopelessly unhappy it would have been better for them not to have been born, and that even if they are happy, plenty of others consider them expendable. We hate both being crowded and being lonely. In its most primitive terms, the solution to this dilemma is simplicity itself. We humans who in our present numbers are the plague of the planet must be thinned out until we again begin to feel a need to cooperate with and to love one another. There are three prescriptions to achieve this: the bomb, the gas, and the pill.

And this brings up another point which illuminates our current hypocrisy from another side, namely the much vaunted "dignity of the individual." Great demagogues who want to incur favor with the masses assure them of their individual dignity, particularly each time they intend to treat them as rabble. As one among four billion (4×10^9), a man is absolutely nothing. Any commodity in such abundance is cheap, next to valueless, not commanding respect. Understandable, therefore, that the average man seems to care so little about how many of us are maimed and killed either in traffic accidents or political accidents called wars. To what extent inherent personal dignity has a chance to unfold depends, like evolution itself, on the capriciousness of fate which alone determines whether the individual differences in the genetic blueprints will find the opportunity to manifest themselves in real life.

The trend towards biochemical warfare.—World War III is in the process of being staged. The reason why it has not started already is that nuclear weapons destroy not only living things but also the precious machines, without which the surviving "developing nations" would find it difficult to develop any further. In other words, nuclear war is plainly too stupid an affair, even measured on the known high level of stupidity and meanness which were needed to bring about the preceding wars.

But there is a very rational solution to this dilemma: biochemical warfare. This, of course, has long been seen by the clever among those in power. It is absolutely ideal. It will wipe out quite specifically millions upon millions of *Homo sapiens,* while leaving the machines intact. In the age of automation, it is obvious that one-quarter of the usual crew will suffice to keep our beloved civilization going.

That the Russians say nothing about their progress in the methods of biochemical warfare is to be expected. But in our free society, the tremendous strides toward the mastery of biological and chemical mass killing should not be hidden from the public as if it were something to be ashamed of. Because a free distribution of birth control pills all over the world is considered expensive and immoral, it will not receive the necessary funds in Congress. This second method to save civilization while disposing of the surplus of mankind should therefore be duly praised. It is pretty certain that it has had already quite good financial support. The public is entitled to be sufficiently informed in order that it may look forward to this logical replacement for the bombs. On the other hand, the preparations have not reached the final stage yet. Thus we shall have a breathing spell to consider whether letting other people starve might not be the more natural, as well as cheaper, solution.

On breeding better men.—If the root of all evil is to be found in human nature, the advice of the scientist is as simple as it is fundamental: let us change it. This can be done easily under one condition: that people believe truly what they already know to be true. This sounds like a formula out of a fairy tale, obvious and mysterious at the same time. Schopenhauer put it this way: "It is the perversity of the heart which prevents people from solving a problem their intellect could easily cope with." These things can be done stupidly or intelligently. In themselves the practical decisions to be made are ethically neutral, either rational and correct or irrational and very likely false. Remember the English literature class? "There is nothing either good or bad but thinking makes it so."

Among biologists the recent writings on this question ought to have become well known because they are not only exciting but also exceedingly well written. A few references may suffice: Sonneborn's *The Control of*

Human Heredity and Evolution," 1965; Kingsley Davis' *Population Policy: Will Current Programs Succeed?,* 1967. I was, however, surprised to see that T. H. Morgan of 1932 has not been quoted with the very important point that nations made miserable by overpopulation might become mentally incapable of deciding on the right course of action.

Better leaders for the great society.—Communism-Marxism has the distinction of creating the idea of analyzing, planning, and experimenting with society as a whole. Few Americans realize how much Marxism has crept into their minds. The notion of system analysis for the benefit of business has become generally accepted.

In 1905, Santayana wrote: "We cannot, at this immense distance from a rational social order, judge what concessions individual genius would be called upon to make in a system of education and government in which all attainable goods should be pursued scientifically." After 64 years we may ask, has this distance diminished in any way? To the extent that the state has taken science into its own fold and shaped it into an indispensable tool for its purposes, including the servitude of men towards machines, one can say that it has. No science in itself can be irrational. On the other hand, an impact of scientific thought on the human elements within the structure of the state can hardly be detected. The administrators pay the scientists and not the other way round; thus they feel superior and remain as benighted as they please.

While everybody else must prove his competence to his peers by passing rigorous examinations if he wants to become an engineer, a judge, a physician, a druggist, or an appointed government expert, all a politician has to do is to appear good enough to the thoroughly incompetent voter. Can one imagine the Schlesingers, Galbraiths, Gavins, Morgenthaus, Rabinowitches, Restons, Cousins, and Kennans passing on the qualities and competences of one who desires to present himself to the people as a candidate for high office? An unthinkable thought—but what a gain for the nation if it became thinkable.

The threshold of ability which divides competence from failure goes up with the power of the office, i.e., with the potential damage a man may do by having less than the required education and imagination. If most human affairs expand exponentially, the effort to comprehend what is going on must follow in the same manner. Government by consent of the governed becomes an empty word if what is required of a statesman lies far above the heads of those who vote him into power.

Looking at the earth as a limited piece of real estate revolving under him as if he were an astronaut, the statesman cannot escape the duty of meditating on the ways to establish at least a minimum of world order, a world government. Considering the recent festival of lies at the Security Council, the idea of a world government, much discussed during the days of

Hutchins and Borgese at the University of Chicago, has since been removed among the unthinkable thoughts. Yet a very simple attitude can bring it to the fore again: respect for the great minds of our time. Let me quote a government expert, Rex Tugwell:

> It is not grossly inaccurate to describe the world's troubles at present as the inevitable adjustment of obsolete institutions, both political and economic, to technological imperatives. The more quickly the means for flexible adjustment and readjustment are devised and agreed to, the more quickly can peaceful progress be resumed.
>
> It is important that people of the West—that is, if we care especially about the West—should take the lead in shaping these adjustments rather than that they should persist in defending obsolete institutions for their own sake. Those institutions give every indication of being incapable of bearing the heavy load relentlessly being thrust upon them by the increase of the world's people and by the demands among them for equal and higher standards of life. If institutional obsolescence is not recognized in time the inevitable readjustments may be revolutionary; and modern revolutions have a frightening tendency to end in dictatorship of one sort or another.

Economics in a stationary or balanced society.—While finishing this manuscript, I came across the following newspaper notice (Guardian Weekly, September 19, 1968): "So the end of the world is at hand, after all. The news from Paris, which emerged from a Unesco symposium, was that within two decades our planet will be suffering from the effects of industrial pollution; that the atmosphere will become unbreathable, and life will cease in our rivers and lakes." In the past, laymen often have asked me whether studies of photosynthesis could not lead to a solution of the population problem. Therefore I wrote in 1946: "Since this globe offers a certain area of habitable and tillable ground, it is obvious that populations will have to be adjusted to an optimum density determined by the general standard of living that man is capable of attaining or willing to endure." Twenty-five years later this is still obvious only to the same five per cent of the population to whom it was obvious a generation ago. What disturbs me now is that this particular problem of how much we shall be willing to endure has apparently been neglected by the most prominent economists. From Burnham to Galbraith, authors have reaped fame by analyzing the structure of our present economy. Serious, carefully calculated, theoretical models of a non-expanding economy for a stationary population are missing. Here the only gains possible are free time (convertible into health and knowledge) and products of better quality. One reason that such studies have not emerged may be that they become plans—and a planned society is taboo. Yet hardly any of the problems raised in the preceding pages will find a rational—let alone optimal—solution unless society as a whole has become conversant with the ineluctable future economic exigencies and the possible ways to handle them.

READING LIST

"The reason why philosophers give us only limited pleasure is that they do not talk enough about things we already know."

(Vauvenargues)

The following list is partial and rather haphazard. It consists of books and articles which I either had on my shelf or which came to my attention during the last year. The *Bulletin of the Atomic Scientists,* the *Saturday Review, Foreign Affairs,* and *The Graduate Journal* (University of Texas) continue to bring articles on the points mentioned. Instead of subscribing now, it might be more interesting to pick up back issues of three or four years ago to see how much or how little influence the intellectuals have had on the course of events in the United States.

Bernal, J. D. After twenty-five years. In *The Science of Science* (Goldsmith, M., Mackay, A., Eds., Souvenir Press, London, 1964)

Barzini, L. *The Italians* (Atheneum Publ., New York, 1964)

Bertalanffy, L. von. Human values in a changing world. In *New Knowledge in Human Values* (Maslow, A. H., Ed., Harper Bros., New York, 1959)

Bohr, N. *Atomic Physics and Human Knowledge* (Science Editions, New York, 1961)

Bridgman, P. W. *The Way Things Are* (Viking Press, New York, 1961)

Brogan, H. O. A plea for more thinkerdoers as administrators. *A.A.U.P. Bulletin 53,* 322–24 (1967)

Bronowski, J. *The Identity of Man* (Doubleday, Garden City, 1966); *Science and Human Values* (Harper & Row, New York, 1965)

Brown, H. *The Next Hundred Years: Man's Natural and Technological Resources* (Viking, New York, 1957)

Bush, V. *Science is not Enough* (Essays, W. Morrow, New York, 1967)

Carter, L. J. Report on PSAC panel on world food supply. *Science,* **156,** 1578–79 (1967)

Cassirer, E. *An Essay on Man* (New Haven-Yale Press, 1944)

Chardin, T. de. *The Phenomenon of Man* (Harper, New York, 1959)

Conant, J. B. *Scientific Principles and Moral Conduct* (Cambridge Univ. Press, 1967)

Davis, K. Population policy: Will current programs succeed? *Science,* **158,** 730–39 (1967)

Denbigh, K. *Science, Industry and Social Policy* (Oliver & Boyd, Edinburgh, 1963)

Dobzhansky, T. *Mankind Evolving: The Evolution of the Human Species* (Yale Press, New Haven, 1962)

Durand, J. D., Ed. *World Population* (Ann. Amer. Soc. Pol. Soc. Sci., 369, Jan. 1967)

Eiseley, L. *The Firmament of Time,* Chap. 5, How human is man? (Atheneum Publ., New York, 1960)

Erasmus, D. (Rotterdam). *The Praise of Folly* (1509), transl. by J. Wilson, 1665 (Oxford Clarendon Press, 1925; Oxford Univ. Press, 1965)

Fromm, E. Value, psychology and human existence. In *New Knowledge in Human Values* (Maslow, A. H., Ed., Harpers, New York, 1959)

Gaffron, H. Photosynthesis and the production of organic matter on earth, in *Currents in Biochemical Research* (Green, D. E., Ed., Interscience, New York, 1946); Photosynthesis and solar energy projects, *Discourse: A Review of the Liberal Arts,* 3–14 (1960)

Gazzaniga, M. S. The split brain in man. *Sci. Am.,* **217,** 24–29 (1967)

Goldsmith, M., Mackay, A., Eds. *The Science of Science* (Souvenir Press, London, 1964)

Greet, R. O., Ed. *Human Fertility and Population Problems* (Proc. Seminar Am. Acad. Arts Sci., Schenckman Publ., New York, 1963)

Hardin, G., Ed. *Population, Evolution, Birth Control* (W. H. Freeman, San Francisco, 1964)

Haskins, C. P. Two faces of science. *Ventures,* **6,** 21–28 (Yale Univ. Press, 1966)

Hogben, L. T. *Retreat from Reason* (Random House, New York, 1937) ; *Science for the Citizen* (Alfred Knopf, New York, 1938)

Holton, G. Modern science and the intellectual tradition. *Science,* **131,** 1187–93 (1960)

Hutchings, Edward & Elizabeth, Eds. *Scientific Progress and Human Values* (American Elsevier Press, New York, 1967)

Huxley, A. *Time Must Have a Stop* (Epilogue) (Harpers, New York, 1944) ; *Brave New World Revisited* (Harpers, New York, 1958)

Huxley, Sir Julian. Education and the humanist revolution. *Nature,* **197,** 8–13 (1963)

Jaspers, K. *Psychologie der Weltanschauungen* (Springer, Berlin, 1922) ; English translation : *Philosophy of the World* (H. Regnery Co., Chicago, 1963)

Jaspers, K. *The Future of Mankind* (Phoenix Books, Univ. Chicago Press, 1961)

Jaspers, K., Bultmann, R. *Myth and Christianity* (Noonday Press, New York, 1958)

Kennan, G. F. *Democracy and the Student Left* (Bantam Books, Grosset & Dunlap, 1968)

Kinzel, A. B. Engineering, civilization and society. *Science,* **156,** 1343–45 (1967)

Lipmann, F. Disproportions created by the exponential growth of knowledge. *Perspectives Biol. Med.,* **5,** 324–26 (1962)

Lucas, F. L. *The Greatest Problem* (Macmillan, New York, 1961)

Luck, J. M. Man against his environment: The next hundred years. *Science,* **126,** 903–8 (1957)

Maritain, J. *Philosophy of Nature* (New York Phil. Library, 1951)

Maslow, A. H., Ed. *New Knowledge in Human Values* (Harpers, New York, 1959)

Miller, J. W., Malecki, G. S., Farr, M. J. ONR's role in human factors engineering. *Naval Research Reviews,* July 1967

Morgan, T. H. *The Scientific Basis of Evolution* (W. Norton, New York, 1932)

Ortega y Gasset, J. *Revolt of the Masses* (Translation : Norton, New York, 1932)

Paton, A. *S. R. L. Magazine* (1968)

Paul VI, Pope. Encyclical letter *"Humanae Vitae"* (Vatican Polyglot Press, 1968)

Polanyi, M. *Science, Faith and Society* (Oford Univ. Press, 1946, Univ. Chicago Press, 1964) ; *Tacit Dimension* (Doubleday, New York, 1966)

Popper, K. L. *Conjectures and Refutations. Growth of Scientific Knowledge* (Basic Books, 1962 ; Routledge & Kegan Paul, London, 1963)

Russell, B. *History of Western Philosophy* (Allen, London, 1955) ; *Authority and the Individual* (Beacon Press, Boston, 1963)

Santayana, G. *The Life of Reason. Reason in Science* (Scribners, 1906)

Simpson, G. G. Biology and the public good. *American Scientist,* **55,** 161–75 (1967)

Sonneborn, T. M., Ed. *The Control of Human Heredity and Evolution* (Macmillan, New York, 1965)

Spengler, O. *The Decline of the West* (C. H. Beck, Munich, 1920). Translation, Part I, *Form and Actuality* (New York, 1926) ; Part II, *Perspectives of World History* (New York, 1928) ; *Oswald Spengler, A Critical Estimate* (Hughes, H. S., 20th Century Library, Scribners, New York, 1952)

Spinoza, B. *Reflections and Maxims* (Phil. Library, 1965)

Stern, C. The journey, not the goal. *Scientific Monthly,* **58,** 96–100 (1944)

Stopes, M. C. *Contraception (Birth Control)* (John Bell & Sons and Danielson, Ltd., London, 1923)

Tax, S., Ed. *Evolution After Darwin,* Vol. II, *The Evolution of Man* (Univ. Chicago Press, 1960)

Thorpe, W. H. *Science, Man and Morals* (Cornell Univ. Press, Ithaca, 1966)

Tietze, C., Lewit, S. Abortion. *Scientific American,* **220,** 21–27 (1969)

Tugwell, G. Wonders may not cease. Preprint, *Proc. Agr. Econ. Soc.,* London, 1950

Tyndall, J. *Fragments of Science for Unscientific People* (Longman & Green, London, 1871)

U.S. Dept. Interior Conservation Yearbook No. 2. *The Population Challenge—What it Means to America* (1966)

Vauvenargues, Luc de C. *Oeuvres Choisies*

(Classiques Garniers, Éditions Garnier Frères, Paris, 1957)

Vogt, W. *Road to Survival* (Wm. Sloan Assoc., New York, 1948)

Wald, G. The origins of life. In *The Scientific Endeavor.* Centennial Celebration, *Natl. Acad. Sci.* (Rockefeller Inst. Press, 1965)

Watson, J. D. *The Double Helix* (Atheneum Press, New York, 1968)

Weil, S. *Seventy letters* (Translated by R. Rees, Oxford Univ. Press, 1965); *Simone Weil* by Rees, R. (Southern Illinois Univ. Press, Carbondale, 1966)

Weinberg, A. M. Criteria for scientific choice. *Minerva*, **1**, 159–71 (1963); *Reflections of Big Science* (M.I.T. Press, 1967)

Weizsacker, C. F. von. *The History of Nature* (Univ. Chicago Press, Phoenix Books, 1949)

BIOSYNTHESIS AND CONVERSION OF AROMATIC AMINO ACIDS IN PLANTS[1]

By Seiichi Yoshida[2]

Department of Biology
Tokyo Metropolitan University
Setagaya-ku, Tokyo, Japan

This review is concerned with the formation and conversion of aromatic amino acids in plants. Special attention will be focused on the metabolism of these compounds in higher plants, although detailed mechanism will also be discussed on work with microorganisms. Lack of space prohibits the inclusion of material on the control mechanism of aromatic biosynthesis recently revealed in microorganisms.

In recent years the biosynthesis of aromatic amino acids has received considerable attention, since these amino acids can be synthesized from carbohydrates by plants and many microorganisms, but not by animals. Now that the majority of the steps in protein amino acid biosynthesis are known, it can be stated reasonably that the path of aromatic biosynthesis, "the shikimate pathway," is one of the longest and most complicated pathways so far established. It requires at least ten enzymes to form these aromatic amino acids, and some of the intermediates also serve for the formation of biologically active substances essential for life such as *p*-aminobenzoic acid, ubiquinone, and vitamin K.

The biosynthetic pathway of aromatic amino acids is now completely elucidated for microorganisms, but it has been suggested that some alternative or modified pathway, not identical with the shikimate pathway, may be operative in higher plants. This will be discussed with special reference to the metabolism of alicyclic acids.

Higher plants not only synthesize the aromatic amino acids but also convert them into a wide variety of more complex aromatic compounds such as lignin, alkaloids, and flavonoids, now known to be derived partly, or wholly, from aromatic amino acids. Reviews on these compounds are to be found in recent volumes of this publication (15, 75, 108), so only the initial

[1] The following abbreviations are used: DAHP (3-deoxy-D-*arabino*-heptulosonate-7-phosphate) ; EPSP (3-enolpyruvylshikimate-5-phosphate) ; PR-transferase (anthranilate:5-phosphoribosyl-1-pyrophosphate phosphoribosyltransferase) ; DOPA (3,4-dihydroxyphenylalanine).

[2] The author wishes to thank Professor G. H. N. Towers of the University of British Columbia, Canada, for reviewing the English text.

metabolic events concerning the biogenesis of aromatic amino acids as well as their degradation, which so far has received little attention, will be considered.

Finally, the metabolism of nonprotein aromatic amino acids, recently found in several higher plants, will be discussed.

BIOSYNTHESIS OF AROMATIC AMINO ACIDS IN MICROORGANISMS

The pathway for the synthesis of aromatic amino acids in microorganisms is now well established as a result of the work of Davis and his collaborators with the use of auxotrophic mutants of *Escherichia coli*. This work has been previously reviewed by Sprinson (133), and only details of the recent discoveries of this pathway will be considered here.

Although the outline of this pathway had been nearly completely worked out by 1960, the formation of anthranilate and prephenate from phoshoshikimic acid was the least understood portion of the pathway. Efforts were concentrated on the identification of the branch-point substance leading to the three aromatic amino acids. With an auxotrophic mutant of *Aerobacter aerogenes* requiring anthranilate for growth, Gibson & Jackman (45) found a new intermediate, chorismate, which is formed from EPSP and can be converted enzymically to prephenate and anthranilate (46). These results by Australian workers established that chorismic acid is the real branch-point intermediate leading to the formation of anthranilate and prephenate, and the complete map of the shikimate pathway (Fig. 1) has now been established. Levin & Sprinson (80) have shown that *E. coli* preparations can catalyze the formation of EPSP from phosphoshikimic acid and phosphoenolpyruvate, and recently their group has demonstrated the conversion of EPSP to chorismate in extracts of *E. coli* (98). Chorismate synthase was inactive under aerobic conditions but could be activated by a reduced FAD-regenerating system in an atmosphere of H_2 or N_2. At the same time, chorismate was easily converted to prephenate by an enzyme from *E. coli* and *A. aerogenes*. Recently, Cotton & Gibson (22) have shown that *A. aerogenes* has two chorismate mutases, P and T. Chorismate mutase P has the activity of prephenate dehydratase and is inhibited by phenylalanine. Chorismate mutase T, on the other hand, is accompanied by prephenate dehydrogenase activity and is inhibited by tyrosine, although isozymes of *Saccharomyces cerevisiae* do not act on prephenate (81). There have been several investigations on anthranilate synthase in microorganisms. DeMoss (30) has obtained an enzyme from *Neurospora crassa* which converts chorismate to anthranilate in the presence of glutamine and thus showed that anthranilate synthase is a single enzyme. Attempts to obtain a transient intermediate have been unsuccessful, and postulated intermediates such as N-pyruvylanthranilate, N-glutamylanthranilate and 2,3-dihydro-3-hydroxyanthranilate have not been found to serve as precursors of anthranilate (82, 134). From these results it may be concluded that the postulated intermediates from chorismate to anthranilate are not free but are

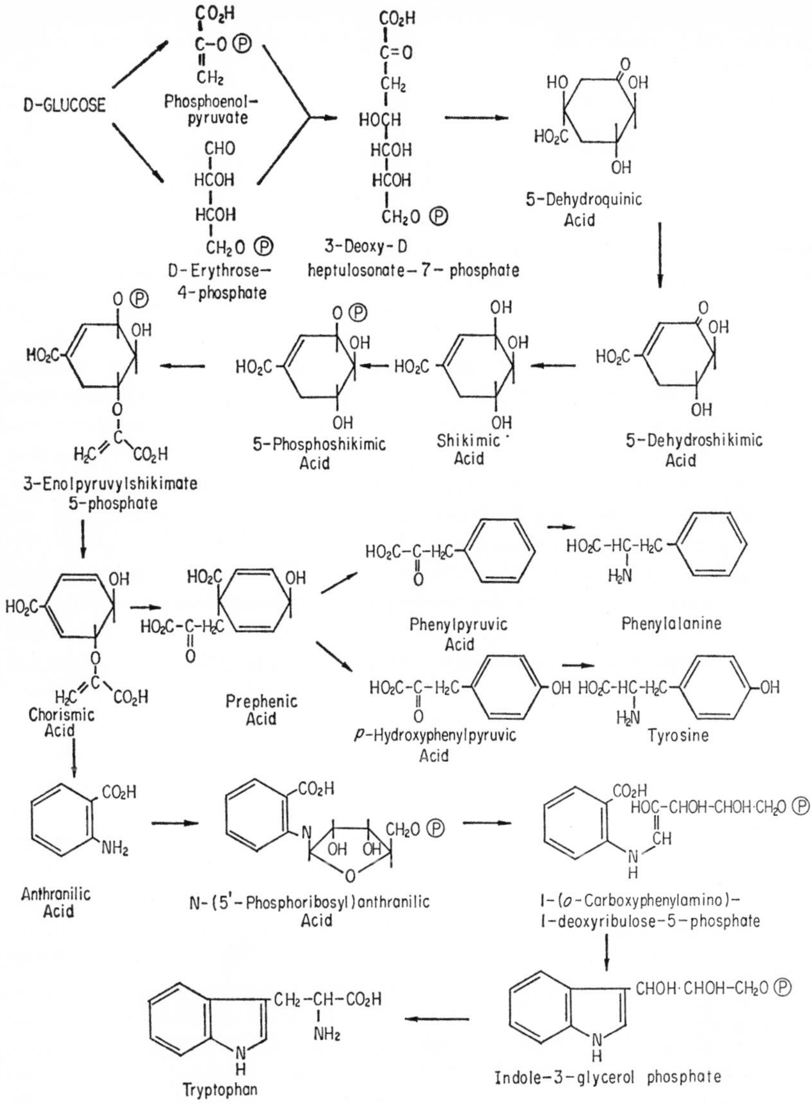

FIG. 1. The shikimate pathway for aromatic amino acid biosynthesis.

enzyme-bound intermediates and that anthranilate synthase is a single enzyme accompanied with PR-transferase (34), although there is evidence that this process involves at least two steps (131).

Much of the current information concerning the pathway of aromatic amino acid biosynthesis discussed above was obtained with aerobic and fa-

cultative anaerobic bacteria. Evidence is accumulating, however, that the
biosynthetic pathway in obligatory anaerobes is somewhat different from
that demonstrated for aerobic bacteria. With anaerobic bacteria from the
rumen, Allison (1) has obtained evidence that phenylacetate is used as a
precursor of phenylalanine, presumably by producing phenylpyruvate, which
in turn is transaminated to form phenylalanine. This does not preclude,
however, the function in the ruminal bacteria of the shikimate pathway
demonstrated in aerobic organisms. Further evidence of this alternative
pathway was presented by Allison & Robinson (3), who showed that *Chromatium* strain D and *Rhodospirillum rubrum* were able to synthesize phenylalanine from phenylacetate by carboxylation with atmospheric carbon
dioxide. They have shown also that *Ruminococcus albus* can synthesize
tryptophan from indole-3-acetate (2). The mechanism of the carboxylation
reaction is unknown, but a probable model for the reaction is the reduced
ferredoxin-dependent carboxylation of an acyl-CoA to produce the corresponding keto acid, which has recently been demonstrated to occur in several anaerobic microorganisms (4, 16). Since rumen liquor contains significant amounts of phenyl-substituted fatty acids, it may be more economical
for the ruminal bacteria to use phenylacetate in phenylalanine biosynthesis
than to synthesize the carbon skeleton from carbohydrates. In the case of
photosynthetic anaerobes, the situation is still obscure, since information
concerning the occurrence of phenylacetate in natural environments is lacking. The purple bacteria occur in nature as a secondary flora, depending for
their growth on the production of simple breakdown products by a primary
and varied microflora. *Chromatium* and other members of the Thiorhodaceae have been found in high numbers in anaerobic waste digestion lagoons,
and catabolism of phenylalanine to phenylacetate in these environments, as
has been found in the rumen, seems likely. So, synthesis of phenylalanine
from phenylacetate probably occurs in many anaerobic environments. The
ability to use phenylacetate as a phenylalanine precursor in these environments would reduce energy requirements as compared with the synthesis of
phenylalanine from less complex substances and may indicate a fitting of
organisms to an ecological niche.

Biosynthesis of Aromatic Amino Acids in Higher Plants

Since it is not feasible to work with auxotrophic mutants of higher
plants, tracer experiments followed by enzymic studies have been most successfully applied to the study of aromatic biosynthesis in higher plants.
From the feeding experiment of shikimic acid-^{14}C to *Salvia*, McCalla &
Neish (84) have concluded that shikimic acid is a good precursor of both
phenylalanine and tyrosine in this plant. Support of this finding was given
by Gamborg & Neish (43), who fed several ^{14}C-labeled compounds to
young plants of wheat and buckwheat. In this experiment they found that
shikimic acid is superior to glucose and acetate as a precursor of both phenylalanine and tyrosine. Phenylpyruvic and *p*-hydroxyphenylpyruvic acids

were preferentially converted to phenylalanine and tyrosine, respectively, indicating that phenylalanine and tyrosine are formed independently from corresponding keto acids by transamination. There was some conversion of phenylalanine to tyrosine, which may be due to the direct hydroxylation of phenylalanine. This reaction, analogous to that of animal systems (68), has recently been found in spinach leaves by Nair & Vining (105). Wightman, Chisholm & Neish (155) also obtained evidence that shikimic acid is a good precursor of tryptophan in young barley shoots, and recently Delmer & Mills (29) have shown that shikimic acid, anthranilic acid, indoleglycerol phosphate, and indole can serve as precursors of tryptophan in cell cultures of *Nicotiana tabacum.*

Formation of shikimic acid in higher plants was demonstrated satisfactorily by Yoshida & Towers (159). By feeding specifically labeled pyruvic acid to cut shoots of *Pinus resinosa,* and also by isotope competition experiments with unlabeled erythrose, they have obtained evidence that shikimic acid is synthesized from phosphoenolpyruvate and erythrose-4-phosphate through dehydroshikimic acid.

The above results obtained by tracer experiments indicate that a shikimate pathway, similar to that of microorganisms, does function in higher plants. Further support for the operation of the shikimate pathway in higher plants has been provided by studies on enzymes from plant sources. Balinsky & Davies (8) described an enzyme preparation from cauliflower buds which resembles the *E. coli* 5-dehydroquinate dehydratase. They also obtained shikimate dehydrogenase from etiolated pea epicotyls (6) and characterized the mode of enzyme action from observations based on the use of several competitive inhibitors (7). Shikimate dehydrogenase was also isolated from mung beans (107) and tea plants (126). Balinsky & Davies (9) have given further information concerning the subcellular distribution of shikimate dehydrogenase and dehydroquinate dehydratase activities in plant cells. In cauliflower buds, both enzymes were found to occur mainly in the supernatant fraction, while in extracts of pea epicotyls, 30 per cent of the shikimate dehydrogenase activity was associated with the mitochondria. So far, there is no definite information whether any of the enzymes of the shikimate pathway are located in special subcellular components. It would be of interest to know whether chloroplasts contain enzymes of the shikimate pathway, since they contain quinones and phenolic compounds believed to be derived by this route. Minamikawa, Oyama & Yoshida (90) observed the changes in the activities of shikimate dehydrogenase and dehydroquinate dehydratase during the development of *Phaseolus mungo.* They showed that in the shoot-root axes both enzymes showed a sharp increase over 7 days, while in the cotyledons there was a gradual decrease in the activities of both enzymes, thus suggesting that the activity is intimately correlated with protein synthesis through aromatic amino acid biosynthesis. The fact that there is no significant variation in the enzyme activities between dark- and light-grown seedlings may indicate that light has no particular effect on the shikimate pathway. Such effects of physiological conditions on enzyme activity have been investigated by several workers. Minamikawa, Kojima & Uritani (87, 88) found that both enzyme activities markedly increased in response to wounding of sweet potato roots, and this was followed by active synthesis of polyphenols. Higuchi & Shimada (60, 61) also reported that in bamboo shoots higher activities of both enzymes were found in the lignified tissues. These results corroborate the hypothesis that in those regions where active synthesis of protein or phenolics occurs there is also observed an activation of the shikimate pathway.

Synthesis of 5-dehydroshikimic acid by an extract of mung bean seedlings was demonstrated by Nandy & Ganguli (106), who showed that the crude enzyme preparation converting glucose-6-phosphate to dehydroshikimic acid required both microsomes and supernatant fractions, whereas the supernatant fraction alone was able to convert phosphoenolpyruvate and erythrose-4-phosphate to dehydroshikimic acid. More direct evidence has been presented by Minamikawa & Uritani (94) on the first enzyme branching off from elementary sugar metabolism. They obtained an enzyme preparation from sweet potato roots which catalyzed the formation of DAHP from erythrose-4-phosphate and phosphoenolpyruvate. DAHP synthase in this tissue was very similar in its properties to that of $E.$ $coli$ (135), except that the plant enzyme required Mg^{++} for maximal activity. Minamikawa (86) extended this study and found enzyme activity in several plant tissues including $Trifolium$ $repens,$ $Phaseolus$ $mungo,$ $Spinacia$ $oleracea,$ and $Helianthus$ $annuus.$

Among the enzymes leading from shikimate to aromatic amino acids, only a few have been investigated seriously. Pal & Burma (114) have obtained evidence that extracts from mung bean seedlings are able to convert shikimate to phenylalanine and tyrosine in the presence of ATP, Mg^{++}, glutamate, and phosphoenolpyruvate, although the nature of the enzyme system involved was not investigated. Attempts to detect shikimate kinase in higher plants have so far been unsuccessful. The possibility that shikimic acid is first converted to enolpyruvylshikimate and then transphosphorylated to produce EPSP cannot be excluded. This idea stems from the fact that a nongrowing cellular suspension of enolpyruvylshikimate-accumulating strain of $E.$ $coli,$ incubated with shikimic acid in a nitrogen-free medium, can be shown to convert this substance to enolpyruvylshikimate without the formation of phosphoshikimic acid (28). Recently, Cotton & Gibson (23) have found a chorismate mutase in pea seedlings which resembles that of $E.$ $coli$ and $A.$ $aerogenes$ (22) in its properties and mode of feedback inhibition. Gamborg & Keeley (42) have obtained a prephenate dehydrogenase from the cotyledons of $Phaseolus$ $vulgaris,$ which is similar to that of $E.$ $coli$ (129), except that the bean enzyme requires NADP instead of NAD. Gamborg (39) has studied the enzymes of the shikimate pathway in cell suspension cultures of several plant tissues. Extracts from the culture cells tested had shikimate dehydrogenase and dehydroquinate dehydratase activities, but prephenate dehydrogenase was detected only in cultures of *Phaseolus aureus, P. vulgaris,* and *Glycine max.* Of the enzymes specific to tryptophan biosynthesis, only tryptophan synthase has been successfully demonstrated in pea (50) and *Cicer arietinum* (104).

Intermediates of the shikimate pathway have often been found in higher plants. Thus, shikimic acid is now known to be widely distributed in many plants (12), and recently Boudet et al. (14) have isolated 5-dehydroquinic and 5-dehydroshikimic acids from the leaves of *Quercus pedunculata.*

In conclusion, it may be safely stated that biosynthesis of aromatic amino acids in higher plants proceeds by a route similar to, if not identical with, that established in microorganisms. However, it is possible that some variations of this scheme will be found, and this viewpoint is discussed in the next section.

METABOLISM OF ALICYCLIC ACIDS IN HIGHER PLANTS

Since the discovery of shikimic acid as an important intermediate in the biosynthesis of aromatic amino acids, special attention has been focused on the role of shikimic acid and related alicyclic acids such as quinic acid in higher plants. As already discussed above, tracer experiments followed by enzymic studies indicate that the shikimate pathway, or at least one very similar to it, functions in higher plants. As a result of the work on the metabolism of alicyclic acids, however, there has been some dissent regarding an alternative or extended pathway. In this section the metabolism of these alicyclic acids in higher plants will be discussed with special reference to aromatic biosynthesis.

Occurrence and variation.—Quinic acid is widely distributed in higher plants (67). It has received particular attention, since it is present in combination with caffeic acid in a number of depsides, the chlorogenic acids, which have been extensively reviewed by Sondheimer (132). Similarly, shikimic acid, which had been thought to be of restricted distribution in the plant kingdom, has been found to be widely distributed in higher plants, especially in gymnosperms (57). The fact that shikimic acid has been found in higher concentration in lower cormophytes such as mosses, ferns, gymnosperms, and primitive angiosperms led to the assumption that the accumulation of this acid may represent a primitive character (69). The accumulation of the acid in plants may reflect a primitive characteristic in some instances, but this is not always the case, since it is also present in considerably high concentration in some advanced plants. A more useful generalization is that woody plants usually contain higher concentrations of the acid, while herbaceous plants, especially annuals, have little or no shikimic acid.

In *Pinus densiflora* the concentration of shikimic acid is highest in the bark, followed by roots, where significant lignification takes place (53). In the work of Hasegawa & Tateoka (54) with *Ginkgo biloba,* a maximum concentration was observed in August in both inner bark and leaf tissues, while a peak in July was observed in outer sapwood. A general increase in concentration with age is apparent with inner bark and outer sapwood, but considerable variation was observed throughout both. The results with outer sapwood, where the concentration is essentially zero, agrees with the fact that spring wood and autumn wood are formed in this region. Changes in shikimic acid content with increase in age of plants have been observed by several investigators. Hillis (62) observed that in *Eucalyptus sieberiana* a linear relationship exists between the shikimic acid content and the weight of the leaf up to the point where the leaf has reached full size, after which the shikimic acid content decreases as the leaves become older. Similar results were obtained with the leaves of *Ginkgo biloba, Pinus thunbergii* (54), and *Tsuga heterophylla* (48). Diurnal changes in shikimic acid content were observed by Tateoka (139) with *Ginkgo* leaves. She found that a gradual decrease of the acid in the daytime followed a profound increase in the night, suggesting that an active synthesis of shikimic acid from photosynthates may occur at night.

Changes in quinic acid content during the development of etiolated mung bean seedlings were described by Minamikawa, Oyama & Yoshida (89), who found that the maximum concentration of the acid was observed after 4 days of germination, followed by a gradual decrease up to 7 days. Similar results were obtained with wheat (17, 138) and conifer shoots (119). A linear relationship between the quinic acid content and growth was also observed during the ripening of apple fruits (63) and the senescence of rose petals (149). From these results it may be concluded that quinic acid as well as shikimic acid is actively metabolized during the growth of the plants.

Metabolism.—The widespread occurrence of quinic acid together with shikimic acid in higher plants suggests that quinic acid may also play an important role in aromatic biosynthesis. Weinstein, Porter & Laurencot (149, 150) have shown that quinic acid-^{14}C is readily metabolized to form mainly aromatic amino acids or their precursors in several higher plants. This is true even in leaves of *Kalanchoë* and avocado in which endogenous quinic acid has not been detected. These results suggest the possibility that quinic acid may enter into the shikimate pathway to form aromatic amino acids through shikimic acid. First evidence for the interconversion of quinate and shikimate was obtained by Carr et al. (18), who found that a strain of *Lactobacillus pastorianus* can convert quinate or shikimate to dihydroshikimate. In this organism, interconversion of quinate and shikimate occurs. In this connection it is of interest to note that Hathway (56) has found dihydroshikimic acid in the fruits of *Terminalia chebula*. It appears likely that dihydroshikimic acid in the fruits may be formed from either shikimic or quinic acid, both of which are abundant in this fruit. The interconversion of quinate and shikimate in higher plants has been investigated with ^{14}C-labeled acids by several authors. Goldschmid & Quimby (48) showed this interconversion in the needles of *Tsuga heterophylla*. Similar results have been obtained with the primary leaves of wheat (125), although Weinstein, Porter & Laurencot (151) reported that only the conversion of quinate to shikimate occurs in the bean (*Phaseolus vulgaris*), the reverse reaction not being observed. Gamborg (41) has demonstrated the interconversion of these acids with enzymes from cell suspension cultures of *Phaseolus aureus*. If the reaction sequences of the shikimate pathway derived from work on microorganisms can generally serve as a model for this path in higher plants, quinate must be depicted as having access to this pathway via quinate dehydrogenase. The presence of quinate dehydrogenase has so far been recorded in *Aerobacter aerogenes* (95) and in cell suspension cultures of mung bean tissues (40). Attempts to detect this enzyme in cultures of other tissues (39), in wheat leaves (138), or in sweet potato roots (87) have been unsuccessful. The fact that quinate dehydrogenase has not been detected in most higher plants in spite of the active metabolism of quinic acid suggests that the biosynthesis of aromatic amino acids in higher plants is not restricted to the shikimate pathway. Weinstein, Porter & Laurencot (150) found that the specific activities of phenylalanine and tyrosine from quinate-^{14}C are different according to the plants used. In both bean and *Kalanchoë*, tyrosine was preferentially labeled rather than phenylalanine, while the reverse was true in tobacco, apple, and avocado. In the feeding experiment of quinate-^{14}C to rose blossoms, these authors (149) found the relatively lower specific activity of shikimate as compared with the aromatic amino acids. Similar results were obtained by Rohringer et al. (125), who found that the efficiency of shikimate and quinate was different as precursors of phenylalanine and tyrosine in the primary leaves of wheat. These results suggest that an alternative pathway from quinate rather than shikimate to phenylalanine and tyrosine may exist in some plants. However, more work needs to be done to establish this, and Neish (110) has pointed out that it is possible that quinic acid can be dehydrated directly to shikimic acid, or that quinic acid can be converted to phosphoshikimic acid via phosphoquinic acid. It is also possible that quinic acid is oxidized to dehydroquinic acid by quinate-cytochrome 555 oxidoreductase, recently found in the particulate fraction of *Acetomonas oxydans* (154). Additional evidence for the alternative pathway of aromatic biosynthesis was presented by Weinstein, Porter & Laurencot (151) in studies of the tryptophan biosynthesis of bean leaves. They found that neither shikimate-^{14}C nor quinate-^{14}C was converted to tryptophan, although both gave rise to labeled phenylalanine and tyrosine. Similar results were obtained by Rohringer et al. (125), who have shown that activity from shikimic and quinic acids-^{14}C was not incorporated into tryptophan in wheat leaves. It is premature to decide from these results whether the biosynthesis of tryptophan proceeds through the shikimate pathway or not. It is necessary to work with plants which are actively synthesizing tryptophan or its congeners such as indican.

Formation of Phenolics Derived from the Shikimate Pathway

Studies of the shikimate pathway have revealed that a number of aromatic compounds are formed from intermediates of this pathway, most of the results being established with aromatic auxotrophs of microorganisms (117, 118). These compounds are now known to be not only intermediates of degradative pathways but also intermediates in the synthesis of biologically active substances such as p-aminobenzoic acid, ubiquinone, and vitamin K, and much attention has been paid to formation of these aromatic compounds.

Protocatechuic acid.—First evidence for the formation of protocatechuic acid from dehydroshikimic acid was provided by Gross (51), who isolated an enzyme which catalyzed this conversion from a mutant of *Neurospora crassa*. Hattori, Yoshida & Hasegawa (58) and later Yoshida (157) found that a strain of *Pseudomonas ovalis* formed protocatechuic acid from both quinic and shikimic acids through dehydroshikimic acid. The latter author suggested that, in this organism, protocatechuic acid thus formed might be further degraded to CO_2 through the β-ketoadipate pathway. In higher plants, evidence has been accumulating for the formation of protocatechuic acid from shikimic acid. During his study of the interconversion of shikimic and quinic acids by cell-free extracts of cell suspension cultures of mung bean roots, Gamborg (41) found that shikimic acid-^{14}C is converted to protocatechuic acid in the presence of NADP. With slices of the hypocotyls of mung bean seedlings, Tateoka (140, 141) has obtained evidence that shikimic acid is converted to protocatechuic acid through dehydroshikimic acid and has demonstrated dehydroshikimate dehydratase activity in an extract of seedlings. Furthermore, she has shown that protocatechuic acid may be degraded through the β-ketoadipate pathway in this plant. Davis (27) stated that when dehydroshikimic acid accumulates in the cell, it inhibits later stages of aromatic biosynthesis, and Tatum et al. (142) considered that the formation of protocatechuic acid from dehydroshikimic acid is a detoxication process in *Neurospora crassa*. There is no reason, however, to believe that this process is only a detoxication process. Rather, it is reasonable to suppose that this side-reaction serves to provide respiratory substrates and is the regulatory sink of the carbon flow of the shikimate pathway. When the demand for aromatic amino acids has been satisfied through this pathway, intermediates such as shikimic acid may accumulate in the cell, and some of these intermediates might be degraded through this pathway to CO_2.

Gallic acid.—The biosynthesis of gallic acid was first demonstrated by Haslam, Haworth & Knowles (55) with *Phycomyces blakesleeanus*. They showed that gallic acid may possibly be formed directly from dehydroshikimic acid. Replacement studies showed that dehydroshikimic acid stimulated the formation of gallic acid, being superior in this respect to shikimic, quinic, or dehydroquinic acids. Protocatechuic acid is also produced by this fungus, but it was shown that protocatechuic acid-^{14}C was not converted to gallic acid, thus proving that hydroxylation of protocatechuic acid does not occur. With *Rhus typhina,* Cornthwaite & Haslam (21) obtained similar results to those obtained with the fungus. This view is supported by the work of Conn & Swain (20), who showed that shikimic acid-^{14}C was a more effective precursor of gallic acid than glucose or phenylalanine in *Geranium pyrenacium* leaves. Zaprometov (164) has also shown that shikimic acid is a good precursor of gallic acid esterified in the gallocatechins of the tea plant. Recently, Gamborg (41) demonstrated the formation of gallic acid in cell-free extracts of cell suspension cultures of mung bean when incubated with shikimic acid-^{14}C in the presence of NADP. He suggested that gallic acid might be derived from an intermediate of the reaction chemically, but it is difficult to imagine the chemical formation of gallic acid by the oxidation of dehydroquinic or dehydroshikimic acids under the conditions employed. There is a possibility that gallic acid is formed through dehydrogenation of dehydroshikimate with an NADP-linked dehydrogenase. Although other suggested pathways for gallic acid synthesis, in which trihydroxycinnamic acid and protocatechuic acid are involved as precursors (35, 165), cannot be excluded, it is likely that some, if not all, of gallic acid may be derived from dehydroshikimic acid.

p-*Aminobenzoic acid.*—It was suggested that p-aminobenzoic acid might be formed together with other compounds from chorismic acid (47). Evidence that the nitrogen of p-aminobenzoic acid arises from the amide nitrogen of glutamine has been presented by Srinivasan & Weiss (136), who have shown that an enzyme preparation from yeast converts phosphoshikimic acid to p-aminobenzoic acid. This observation was extended by Gibson, Gibson & Cox (44) with crude extracts of *Aerobacter aerogenes* which can convert chorismate to p-amino benzoate in the presence of glutamine. In their experiments it was uncertain whether one or more enzymes is required in this conversion, although the formation of anthranilate from chorismate and glutamine is catalyzed by a single enzyme (5, 30, 31, 82). Hendler & Srinivasan (59) have obtained evidence for the possible occurrence of a new intermediate between chorismate and p-aminobenzoate. They have found that crude extracts of baker's yeast can be separated into two enzyme fractions, both of which are needed for the conversion of chorismate to p-aminobenzoate. Further evidence that this reaction may involve at least two steps was obtained by cross-feeding experiments with *Neurospora* mutants which require only p-aminobenzoate for growth. These results corroborate the suggestion that the conversion of chorismate to p-aminobenzoate involves at least two steps, although the nature of the intermediate is not yet known.

Salicylic and 2,3-dihydroxybenzoic acids.—Salicylic acid is found less frequently in the plant kingdom. It occurs as gaultherin, a glycoside of methyl salicylate in species of *Gaultheria,* and Towers, Tse & Maass (144) have found it in 13 out of 22 species of this genus. On the other hand,

2,3-dihydroxybenzoic acid has been found more frequently in several plant species, and Ibrahim (64) has reported its occurrence in the Ericaceae, Asclepiadaceae, and Apocynaceae. It has been shown recently that 2,3-dihydroxybenzoic acid is a growth factor for certain multiple aromatic auxotrophs of *E. coli* and *A. aerogenes* and that it is formed from chorismate by cell-free extracts, the overall conversion requiring NAD and Mg^{++} (160). In the absence of these cofactors, chorismate gave rise to a substance which gave 2,3-dihydroxybenzoate on addition of the cofactors. The intermediate has been identified as 2,3-dihydro-2,3-dihydroxybenzoic acid (161). There are other possible routes to the biosynthesis of 2,3-dihydroxybenzoic acid. Ibrahim & Towers (65) have shown that this acid may arise from salicylic acid in leaf disks of several plants, and it has been demonstrated that it is an intermediate of tryptophan breakdown in *Aspergillus niger* (137). Although these pathways also account for the formation of this acid, some of it may be formed directly from chorismate in higher plants. As for the biosynthesis of salicylic acid, the situation is more obscure. Ratledge & Winder (123) have found that some species of *Mycobacterium* accumulate salicylic acid in the culture medium, and the production of this acid is particularly noticeable under conditions of iron-deficiency in *Mycobacterium smegmatis*. The lack of evidence for an aromatic precursor of salicylic acid led to the suggestion that it may be synthesized from an intermediate of the shikimate pathway by steps analogous to those involved in anthranilate formation but without the introduction of the amino group. The fact that growth of *M. smegmatis* on shikimic or quinic acids, or its incubation with these acids as a washed cell suspension, led to increased production of salicylic acid together with aromatic compounds (122, 124), suggests that it arises by the shikimate pathway, presumably via chorismic acid. The obvious structural relationship and the similarity in the manner of accumulation of salicylic acid and 2,3-dihydroxybenzoic acid are such as to suggest that both acids have a common precursor. The compound 2,3-dihydro-2,3-dihydroxybenzoic acid, recently identified by Young, Jackman & Gibson (161) as a proximate precursor of 2,3-dihydroxybenzoic acid, may be a common precursor of both salicylic and 2,3-dihydroxybenzoic acids. When this acid is dehydrated, salicylic acid may be formed, whereas 2,3-dihydroxybenzoic acid would be produced when it is dehydrogenated in the presence of NAD.

Quinones.—Evidence has been accumulating that shikimic acid is an efficient precursor of the aromatic nucleus of quinones including ubiquinone, vitamin K, and anthraquinone. Cox & Gibson (24, 25) have shown that in *E. coli* and *A. aerogenes* shikimate-^{14}C was incorporated into ubiquinone, the incorporation of the label being suppressed by the addition of *p*-hydroxybenzoic acid (115, 116), which in turn is formed from chorismate (46). This is also true for *Rhodospirillum rubrum* (38, 153) and maize shoots (152). On the other hand, there are some conflicting results on the biosynthesis of naphthoquinone. Leistner, Schmitt & Zenk (77) have found that in *Bacillus megaterium* α-naphthol as well as shikimic acid are efficient precursors of vitamin K_2. They obtained evidence that shikimic acid is incorporated *in toto* during vitamin K biosynthesis, the carboxyl group of the acid being transformed into one, or equally into both, of the keto groups of the quinone ring. This result is inconsistent with the finding of Chen & Bohm (19) and Bohm (13), who showed that shikimic acid is incorporated into the quinone ring during naphthoquinone biosynthesis in *Impatiens balsamina*. Zenk & Leistner (166) re-examined the biosynthesis of naphthoquinone in *I. balsamina* and obtained similar results with those of *B. megaterium*. (Dr. Bohm, in a personal communication, has stated that he has recently repeated these studies and obtained results in agreement with those of Zenk and co-workers.) Leistner, Schmitt & Zenk (77) have found, furthermore, that 3,4-dihydroxybenzaldehyde-^{3}H or protocatechuic acid-^{14}C is not incorporated into vitamin K_2 of *B. megaterium*, although Cox & Gibson (25) have postulated 3,4-dihydroxybenzaldehyde as a possible precursor. Since 3,4-dihydroxybenzaldehyde suppressed the incorporations of the ^{14}C of shikimic acid into vitamin K_2, the authors have claimed that the effect of this aldehyde on vitamin K biosynthesis must be an indirect one and cannot be explained as a precursor function of this compound. Leistner & Zenk (78, 79) have shown that shikimic acid is incorporated *in toto* during anthraquinone biosynthesis in *Rubia tinctorum*. From these results it is evident that the benzene ring of quinones arises from an intermediate of the shikimate pathway and not via aromatic amino acids.

Chloramphenicol.—In a study on the biosynthesis of chloramphenicol in *Streptomyces* sp., Vining & Westlake (148) found that shikimic acid is an efficient precursor of the *p*-nitrophenylserinol moiety of this compound. Since phenylalanine and tyrosine are poorly incorporated into chloramphenicol (49, 148), it is unlikely that the biosynthetic route to the phenylpropanoid portion of chloramphenicol goes through either of these amino acids but instead may branch off at an early step of the shikimate pathway. Siddiqueullah et al. (130) have recently found that *p*-aminophenylalanine is efficiently incorporated into the *p*-nitrophenylserinol moiety of chloramphenicol. From these results it appears that the branch point at which chloramphenicol biosynthesis diverges off from the route to the aromatic amino acids may be placed at or before prephenic acid. It can be imagined that *p*-aminophenylpyruvic acid might be a proximate precursor of this amino acid, and possibly the nitrogen of *p*-aminophenylpyruvic acid would arise from the amide nitrogen of gluatamine.

Nonprotein Aromatic Amino Acids in Higher Plants

Many new aromatic amino acids are presently recognized as plant constituents; normally they are not incorporated into protein but are encountered free or, less frequently, as γ-glutamyl dipeptides and malonyl derivatives. These nonprotein aromatic amino acids are of particular interest, since their biosynthesis is thought to be associated with special metabolic pathways which have not yet been elucidated. The occurrence and biosynthesis of DOPA, a familiar constituent of higher plants, have already been reviewed by Pridham (121), so that only the newly discovered amino acids will be discussed here.

m-*Carboxy-substituted aromatic amino acids.*—The four aromatic amino acids, i.e., m-carboxyphenylglycine, L-m-carboxyphenylalanine, D-(3-carboxy-4-hydroxyphenyl)glycine, and L-m-carboxytyrosine, possessing a carboxyl group *meta* to the side chain, have been isolated in recent years from nonprotein fractions of higher plants. So far, representatives of this group of amino acids have been found in four families: the monocotyledonous Iridaceae, the dicotyledonous Cucurbitaceae, and the closely related dicotyledonous families Cruciferae and Resedaceae. The biosynthesis of phenylglycine analogues has been investigated by Morris & Thompson (99) with *Iris* tissues, in which they administered m-carboxyphenylalanine-2-^{14}C. Their results showed that m-carboxyphenylglycine is derived from m-carboxyphenylalanine with loss of the aliphatic carboxyl carbon, although this transformation heretofore has not been demonstrated. These authors (100) and later Larsen (74) have obtained evidence that this is also true in the case of the formation of (3-carboxy-4-hydroxyphenyl)glycine from m-carboxytyrosine. From these results it might be concluded that m-carboxyphenylalanine analogues are converted to their next lower homologues with loss of the carboxyl carbon by a chain-shortening pathway. Although the biosynthesis of m-carboxyphenylalanine and m-carboxytyrosine from labeled phenylalanine or tyrosine has been demonstrated with *Iris* and *Reseda* (74, 100), the conversion was negligible, indicating that carboxylation of aromatic amino acids to form m-carboxy derivatives is not the major pathway for the biosynthesis of m-carboxyphenylalanine analogues. Recently, Larsen (73, 74) proposed an alternative biosynthetic pathway for the formation of these compounds. He administered labeled shikimic acid to *Reseda* leaves and found that shikimic acid is incorporated into m-carboxyphenylalanine and m-carboxytyrosine without prior degradation of the carbon skeleton, with the aromatic carboxyl group of the amino acids arising directly from the carboxyl group of shikimic acid. From these results it was suggested that an alternative concerted reaction converting chorismic acid to 3-(3-carboxy-6-hydroxycyclohexa-2,4-dienyl)pyruvic acid, an analogue of prephenic acid containing the C_3-side chain in a position *meta* to the carboxyl group on the ring and having the same carbon skeleton as m-carboxyphenylalanine analogues, would lead to the formation of these amino acids.

m-*Tyrosine.*—m-Tyrosine has been reported only in the latex of *Euphorbia myrsinites* by Mothes et al. (102). The biosynthesis of m-tyrosine has recently been demonstrated by Müller & Schütte (103), who have found that in *Euphorbia myrsinites* shikimic acid is a far better precursor of m-tyrosine than phenylalanine or acetate. This result suggests that this amino acid might arise directly from the shikimate pathway, not via phenylalanine, although it was suggested that it is formed from phenylalanine as a step in the biosynthesis of gliotoxin by *Trichoderma viride* (156). It is of interest to note that *m*-tyrosine is a good substrate for tyrosine ammonia-lyase (109).

L-β-*Phenylalanine*.—This amino acid has recently been isolated from the seeds of *Phaseolus angularis* as its γ-glutamyl peptide (71), and its structure was conclusively assigned by chemical synthesis (72). There is evidence that 3-dimethylamino-3-phenylpropionic acid (*N*-dimethyl-β-phenylalanine), an acid moiety of the ester alkaloid taxine, is derived from phenylalanine in *Taxus baccata* (76), so it is possible to suppose that this amino acid might be formed by transamination of benzoylacetic acid, which in turn is derived from cinnamic acid by β-oxidation, since there is ample evidence that β-oxidation of cinnamic acid derivatives does occur in higher plants (e.g., 35).

Orcylalanine.—Orcylalanine has only been found in the seeds of *Agrostemma githago* (127). The orcylalanine content is highest in mature seed, especially in the embryo (128), and becomes depleted as the seedling develops (52). A very active period of biosynthesis is initiated in the seeds approximately 30 days after flowering. Hadwiger et al. (52) have examined the biosynthesis of this amino acid in *A. githago* and found that serine provides the amino acid side chain while the aromatic ring and methyl group are derived from acetate. From this result they proposed a biosynthetic mechanism involving condensation of serine with orsellic acid with simultaneous decarboxylation of the latter. It is of interest that orsellic acid should be an intermediate, since so far it has been found as depsides in various lichens and more recently in the free state in the culture medium of some fungi (11, 101).

D-*Tryptophan*.—D-Amino acids are extremely rare in higher plants. Zenk & Scherf (167) isolated from apple fruits α-*N*-malonyl-D-tryptophan and found that this substance is widely distributed in higher plants. When D-tryptophan was fed to a variety of angiosperms, 134 out of 148 species were shown to form malonyl-tryptophan, whereas with L-tryptophan no conjugate was obtained. Further studies along this line by Zenk & Scherf (168) have revealed that a wide variety of Spermatophyta and Pteridophyta can malonylate D-tryptophan. Since they could not obtain evidence for the presence of a racemase in higher plants, it is unlikely that the formation of D-tryptophan is due to the action of such an enzyme. It appears that D-tryptophan might be formed by the transamination of the corresponding keto acid, since there is evidence for the occurrence of a transaminase specific to D-amino acids.

L-γ-*Phenylbutyrine*.—In the course of a study on the biosynthesis of mustard oil glucosides in *Reseda luteola* and *Nasturtium officinale*, Underhill (145, 146) found γ-phenylbutyrine (2-amino-4-phenylbutyric acid) to be an intermediate in the formation of gluconasturtiin and later showed the occurrence of this amino acid in the plant (147). A plausible biosynthetic mechanism of this amino acid from phenylalanine and acetate involving a chain-lengthening process, analogous to the formation of leucine from valine or of glutamate from aspartate, was suggested.

CONVERSION OF AROMATIC AMINO ACIDS IN PLANTS

Aromatic amino acids thus formed through the shikimate pathway are thought to be utilized essentially for protein synthesis, but in higher plants a considerable amount of these amino acids is converted to secondary metabolites such as lignin, flavonoids, and alkaloids. Initial reactions leading to these secondary metabolites involve decarboxylation and deamination of these amino acids. The decarboxylation of aromatic amino acids to form aromatic alkylamines has already been reviewed by Pridham (121), so only the deamination process will be discussed here. A great deal of information has been accumulated concerning the transformation of aromatic amino acids into secondary metabolites, but actually very little is known about the degradation of aromatic amino acids in plants. This process is also considered with special reference to deamination.

Early studies with radioactive compounds provided evidence that phenylalanine and tyrosine could be deaminated to the corresponding acrylic acid derivatives, which were then converted to a wide variety of aromatic plant constituents (85). An enzyme has been purified from barley that catalyzes the conversion of phenylalanine to *trans*-cinnamic acid and ammonia (70), and a similar enzyme that catalyzes the analogous deamination of tyrosine has been found in several plants (109). The deamination of DOPA by cell-free preparations of *Taraxacum* and *Hordeum* (83) has also been demonstrated, but this enzyme, DOPA ammonia-lyase, is of rather restricted occurrence and usually has low activity compared with other ammonia-lyases, suggesting that its activity may be due to the low specificity of other ammonia-lyases (162).

In recent years, a great deal of information has been presented on the role of these ammonia-lyases in the biosynthesis of secondary metabolites, since these enzymes are considered to be the regulatory enzymes which act immediately after a metabolic branching point. The role of phenylalanine ammonia-lyase in lignin formation has been presented by Yoshida & Shimokoriyama (158), who showed that the enzyme in *Fagopyrum esculentum* may be concerned with the regulation of lignin synthesis. The fact that this enzyme is predominant in vascular plants also supports this idea (163). Similar results on the role of phenylalanine ammonia-lyase were obtained in studies of chlorogenic acid biosynthesis in potato tubers (169) and in flavonoid synthesis of strawberry leaf disks (26). These results clearly indicate that phenylalanine ammonia-lyase is the key enzyme for the formation of phenolic compounds.

The mechanism of the marked increase in activity of this enzyme in response to light has been investigated by several workers. Zucker (169) has found that in potato tuber disks the development of this enzyme activity in light is preferentially inhibited by ethionine and analogues of purines and pyrimidines, thus proving the *de novo* synthesis of the enzyme in light. Nitsch & Nitsch (111) have found that the induction of this enzyme activity is stimulated by blue light in *Helianthus tuberosus,* while Durst & Mohr (32) have obtained evidence that induction is mediated by phytochrome in mustard seedlings (*Sinapis alba*). The latter authors have found that the activity of this enzyme is induced by far-red light and disappears rapidly when the light is turned off, the half-life of the activity being in the range of 6 hr (33). The effect of light of different wavelengths on the induction of this enzyme has been extensively investigated by Engelsma (36, 37). With gherkin seedlings (*Cucumis sativus*) he found that exposure of dark-grown gherkin seedlings to blue light causes temporary changes in the level of phenylalanine ammonia-lyase, showing an increase after a 90-min lag followed by decline after 180 min. Further study on the effect of red and far-red light has revealed the same result as blue light. From these results he concluded that light of different regions of the visible spectrum is initiated, the same sequence of dark reactions leading to enhanced production of phenylalanine ammonia-lyase, followed by a phase of inactivation of this enzyme and repression of its synthesis. The fact that a higher enzyme level can be obtained in blue light rather than in red or far-red light, and that only blue light is capable of inducing enzyme synthesis in excised hypocotyls, led to the idea that different pigment systems are involved.

The increase of phenylalanine ammonia-lyase activity in response to wounding has been reported by Minamikawa & Uritani (91, 92), with special reference to phenol synthesis in sweet potato roots. They have shown also that the increase in enzyme activity is due to the *de novo* synthesis of enzyme protein (93), and therefore it is assumed that enzyme synthesis may be triggered by factors that are produced or increased after wounding. Recently, Imaseki, Uchiyama & Uritani (66) have reported that ethylene may be one of the factors which stimulate the enzyme activity after wounding, since exogenously supplied ethylene causes a marked increase in the ammonia-lyase activity of the tissues.

Another role of phenylalanine ammonia-lyase has been proposed by Towers (143). Phenylalanine ammonia-lyase is of ubiquitous occurrence in higher plants (163), but recently this enzyme has also been found in fungi (10, 120). This enzyme is involved in the degradative pathway of the phenylalanine by these fungi. Ogata, Uchiyama & Yamada (112, 113) found that strains of *Rhodotorula* produce ammonia-lyase for phenylalanine when grown in a medium containing phenylalanine as sole carbon and nitrogen sources. Independent studies with *Schizophyllum commune* (97) have shown that the fungus not only converts phenylalanine to cinnamic acid but also produces $^{14}CO_2$ when administered ring-labelled phenylalanine-^{14}C, cinnamic acid-^{14}C, and benzoic acid-^{14}C. Similar results have been obtained with *Ustilago hordei* and *Spolobolomyces roseus* (96). Evidence obtained from enzyme studies followed by tracer experiments clearly indicates that phenylalanine is degraded to CO_2 through cinnamic, benzoic, p-hydroxybenzoic, and protocatechuic acids. From these results it may be concluded that in fungi ammonia-lyases catalyze the initial reaction of the degradative pathway of aromatic amino acids. In higher plants there has been no conclusive evidence on the degradation of aromatic amino acids, but it can be imagined that a similar pathway may account for the degradation of amino acids, since cinnamic acids are converted to benzoic acids (35), which in turn are degraded to CO_2 through β-ketoadipate pathway.

LITERATURE CITED

1. Allison, M. J., *Biochem. Biophys. Res. Commun.*, **18**, 30–35 (1965)
2. Allison, M. J., Robinson, I. M., *Biochem. J.*, **102**, 36p–37p (1967)
3. Allison, M. J., Robinson, I. M., *J. Bacteriol.*, **93**, 1269–75 (1967)
4. Andrew, I. G., Morris, J. G., *Biochim. Biophys. Acta*, **97**, 176–79 (1965)
5. Baker, T. I., Crawford, I. P., *J. Biol. Chem.*, **241**, 5577–84 (1966)
6. Balinsky, D., Davies, D. D., *Biochem. J.*, **80**, 292–96 (1961)
7. Balinsky, D., Davies, D. D., *ibid.*, **80**, 296–300 (1961)
8. Balinsky, D., Davies, D. D., *ibid.*, **80**, 300–4 (1961)
9. Balinsky, D., Davies, D. D., *J. Exp. Botany*, **13**, 414–21 (1962)
10. Bandoni, R. J., Moore, K., Subba Rao, P. V., Towers, G. H. N., *Phytochemistry*, **7**, 205–7 (1968)
11. Birkinshaw, J. H., Gowlland, A., *Biochem. J.*, **84**, 342–47 (1962)
12. Bohm, B. A., *Chem. Rev.*, **65**, 435–66 (1965)
13. Bohm, B. A., *Biochem. Biophys. Res. Commun.*, **26**, 621–24 (1967)
14. Boudet, A., Gadal, P., Alibert, G., Marigo, G., *Compt. Rend.*, **265**, 119–22 (1967)
15. Brown, S. A., *Ann. Rev. Plant Physiol.*, **17**, 223–44 (1966)
16. Buchanan, B. B., Bachofen, R., Arnon, D. I., *Proc. Natl. Acad. Sci. U.S.*, **52**, 839–47 (1964)
17. Carles, J., Lattes, F., *Compt. Rend.*, **249**, 447–49 (1959)
18. Carr, J. G., Pollard, A., Whiting, G. C., Williams, A. H., *Biochem. J.*, **66**, 283–85 (1957)
19. Chen, D., Bohm, B. A., *Can. J. Biochem.*, **44**, 1389–95 (1966)
20. Conn, E. E., Swain, T., *Chem. Ind. (London)*, 592–93 (1961)
21. Cornthwaite, D., Haslam, E., *J. Chem. Soc.*, 3008–11 (1965)
22. Cotton, R. G. H., Gibson, F., *Biochim. Biophys. Acta*, **100**, 76–88 (1965)
23. Cotton, R. G. H., Gibson, F., *ibid.*, **156**, 187–89 (1968)
24. Cox, G. B., Gibson, F., *Biochim. Biophys. Acta*, **93**, 204–6 (1964)
25. Cox, G. B., Gibson, F., *Biochem. J.*, **100**, 1–6 (1966)
26. Creasy, L. L., *Phytochemistry*, **7**, 441–46 (1968)
27. Davis, B. D., *J. Bacteriol.*, **64**, 749–63 (1952)
28. Davis, B. D., Mingioli, E. S., *J. Bacteriol.*, **66**, 129–36 (1953)
29. Delmer, D. P., Mills, S. E., *Plant Physiol.*, **43**, 81–87 (1968)
30. DeMoss, J. A., *J. Biol. Chem.*, **240**, 1231–35 (1965)
31. Doy, C. H., *Biochim. Biophys. Acta*, **118**, 173–88 (1966)
32. Durst, F., Mohr, H., *Naturwissenschaften*, **53**, 531–32 (1966)
33. Durst, F., Mohr, H., *ibid.*, **53**, 707 (1966)
34. Egan, A. F., Gibson, F., *Biochim. Biophys. Acta*, **130**, 276–77 (1966)
35. El-Basyouni, S. Z., Chen, D., Ibrahim, R. K., Neish, A. C., Towers, G. H. N., *Phytochemistry*, **3**, 485–92 (1964)
36. Engelsma, G., *Planta*, **75**, 207–19 (1967)
37. Engelsma, G., *ibid.*, **77**, 49–57 (1967)
38. Friis, P., Daves, G. D., Jr., Folkers, K., *J. Am. Chem. Soc.*, **88**, 4754–56 (1966)
39. Gamborg, O. L., *Can. J. Biochem.*, **44**, 791–99 (1966)
40. Gamborg, O. L., *Biochim. Biophys. Acta*, **128**, 483–91 (1966)
41. Gamborg, O. L., *Phytochemistry*, **6**, 1067–73 (1967)
42. Gamborg, O. L., Keeley, F. W., *Biochim. Biophys. Acta*, **115**, 65–72 (1966)
43. Gamborg, O. L., Neish, A. C., *Can. J. Biochem. Physiol.*, **37**, 1277–85 (1959)
44. Gibson, F., Gibson, M. I., Cox, G. B., *Biochim. Biophys. Acta*, **82**, 637–38 (1964)
45. Gibson, F., Jackman, L. M., *Nature*, **198**, 388–89 (1963)
46. Gibson, M. I., Gibson, F., *Biochem. J.*, **90**, 248–56 (1964)
47. Gibson, M. I., Gibson, F., Doy, C. H., Morgan, P., *Nature*, **195**, 1173–75 (1962)
48. Goldschmid, O., Quimby, G. R., *Tappi*, **47**, 528–33 (1964)
49. Gottlieb, D., Carter, H. E., Robbins, P. W., Burg, R. W., *J. Bacteriol.*, **84**, 888–95 (1962)
50. Greenberg, J. B., Galston, A. W., *Plant Physiol.*, **34**, 489–94 (1959)
51. Gross, S. R., *J. Biol. Chem.*, **233**, 1146–51 (1958)
52. Hadwiger, L. A., Floss, H. G., Stoker, J. R., Conn, E. E., *Phytochemistry*, **4**, 825–30 (1965)
53. Hasegawa, M., Nakagawa, T., Yo-

shida, S., *J. Japan. Forestry Soc.,*
39, 159–63 (1957)

54. Hasegawa, M., Tateoka, T., *J. Japan,
Forestry Soc.,* **42,** 224–25 (1960)

55. Haslam, E., Haworth, R. D.,
Knowles, P. F., *J. Chem. Soc.,*
1854–59 (1961)

56. Hathway, D. E., *Biochem. J.,* **63,**
380–87 (1956)

57. Hattori, S., Yoshida, S., Hasegawa,
M., *Physiol. Plantarum,* **7,** 283–89
(1954)

58. Hattori, S., Yoshida, S., Hasegawa,
M., *Arch. Biochem. Biophys.,* **74,**
480–82 (1958)

59. Hendler, S., Srinivasan, P. R., *Biochim. Biophys. Acta,* **141,** 656–58
(1967)

60. Higuchi, T., Shimada, M., *Plant Cell
Physiol.* (*Tokyo*), **8,** 61–69 (1967)

61. Higuchi, T., Shimada, M., *Japan J.
Agr. Biol. Chem.,* **31,** 1179–83
(1967)

62. Hillis, W. E., *J. Exp. Botany,* **10,**
87–89 (1959)

63. Hulme, A. C., Wooltorton, L. S. C.,
J. Sci. Food Agr., **8,** 117–22
(1957)

64. Ibrahim, R. K., *Naturwissenschaften,*
50, 734 (1963)

65. Ibrahim, R. K., Towers, G. H. N.,
Nature, **184,** 1803–4 (1959)

66. Imaseki, H., Uchiyama, M., Uritani,
I., *Japan J. Agr. Biol. Chem.,* **32,**
387–89 (1968)

67. Karrer, W., *Konstitution und Vorkommen der organischen Pflanzenstoffe,* 394 (Birkhäuser, Basel,
1207 pp., 1958)

68. Kaufman, S., *Trans. N.Y. Acad. Sci.,*
26, 977–83 (1964)

69. Kinzel, H., Walland, A., *Z. Pflanzenphysiol.,* **54,** 371–74 (1966)

70. Koukol, J., Conn, E. E., *J. Biol.
Chem.,* **236,** 2692–98 (1961)

71. Koyama, M., Obata, Y., *Japan. J.
Agr. Biol. Chem.,* **30,** 472–77
(1966)

72. Koyama, M., Obata, Y., *ibid.,* **31,**
738–42 (1967)

73. Larsen, P. O., *Biochim. Biophys.
Acta,* **115,** 529–31 (1966)

74. Larsen, P. O., *ibid.,* **141,** 27–46
(1967)

75. Leete, E., *Ann. Rev. Plant Physiol.,*
18, 179–96 (1967)

76. Leete, E., Bodem, G. B., *Tetrahedron
Letters,* 3925–27 (1966)

77. Leistner, E., Schmitt, J. H., Zenk,
M. H., *Biochem. Biophys. Res.
Commun.,* **28,** 845–50 (1967)

78. Leistner, E., Zenk, M. H., *Z. Naturforsch.,* **22b,** 865–68 (1967)

79. Leistner, E., Zenk, M. H., *Tetrahedron Letters,* 475–76 (1967)

80. Levin, J. G., Sprinson, D. B., *J.
Biol. Chem.,* **239,** 1142–50 (1964)

81. Lingens, F., Goebel, W., Uesseler,
H., *Biochem. Z.,* **346,** 357–67
(1966)

82. Lingens, F., Sproessler, B., Goebel,
W., *Biochim. Biophys. Acta,* **121,**
164–66 (1966)

83. Macleod, N. J., Pridham, J. B.,
Biochem. J., **88,** 45p (1963)

84. McCalla, D. R., Neish, A. C., *Can.
J. Biochem. Physiol.,* **37,** 531–36
(1959)

85. McCalla, D. R., Neish, A. C., *ibid.,*
37, 537–47 (1959)

86. Minamikawa, T., *Plant Cell Physiol.*
(*Tokyo*), **8,** 695–707 (1967)

87. Minamikawa, T., Kojima, M., Uritani, I., *Plant Cell Physiol.*
(*Tokyo*), **7,** 583–91 (1966)

88. Minamikawa, T., Kojima, M., Uritani, I., *Arch. Biochem. Biophys.,*
117, 194–95 (1966)

89. Minamikawa, T., Oyama, I., Yoshida,
S., *Botan. Mag. Tokyo,* **81,** 135–
40 (1968)

90. Minamikawa, T., Oyama, I., Yoshida,
S., *Plant Cell Physiol.* (*Tokyo*),
9, 451–60 (1968)

91. Minamikawa, T., Uritani, I., *Arch.
Biochem. Biophys.,* **108,** 573–74
(1964)

92. Minamikawa, T., Uritani, I., *J. Biochem.* (*Tokyo*), **57,** 678–88 (1965)

93. Minamikawa, T., Uritani, I., *Japan
J. Agr. Biol. Chem.,* **29,** 1021–26
(1965)

94. Minamikawa, T., Uritani, I., *J. Biochem.* (*Tokyo*), **61,** 367–72 (1967)

95. Mitsuhashi, S., Davis, B. D., *Biochim. Biophys. Acta,* **15,** 268–80
(1954)

96. Moore, K., Subba Rao, P. V.,
Towers, G. H. N., *Biochem. J.,*
106, 507–14 (1968)

97. Moore, K., Towers, G. H. N., *Can.
J. Biochem.,* **45,** 1659–65 (1967)

98. Morell, H., Clark, M. J., Knowles,
P. F., Sprinson, D. B., *J. Biol.
Chem.,* **242,** 82–90 (1967)

99. Morris, C. J., Thompson, J. F.,
Arch. Biochem. Biophys., **110,**
506–10 (1965)

100. Morris, C. J., Thompson, J. F., *ibid.,*
119, 269–71 (1967)

101. Mosbach, K., *Z. Naturforsch.,* **14b,**
69–70 (1959)

102. Mothes, K., Schütte, H. R., Müller, P., Ardenne, M. V., Tümmler, R., *Z. Naturforsch.*, **19b**, 1161–62 (1964)

103. Müller, P., Schütte, H. R., *Flora A*, **158**, 421–32 (1967)

104. Nair, P. M., Vaidyanathan, C. S., *Arch. Biochem. Biophys.*, **104**, 405–15 (1964)

105. Nair, P. M., Vining, L. C., *Phytochemistry*, **4**, 401–11 (1965)

106. Nandy, M., Ganguli, N. C., *Biochim. Biophys. Acta*, **48**, 608–10 (1961)

107. Nandy, M., Ganguli, N. C., *Arch. Biochem. Biophys.*, **92**, 399–408 (1961)

108. Neish, A. C., *Ann. Rev. Plant Physiol.*, **11**, 55–80 (1960)

109. Neish, A. C., *Phytochemistry*, **1**, 1–24 (1961)

110. Neish, A. C., in *Biochemistry of Phenolic Compounds*, 295–359 (Harborne, J. B., Ed., Academic Press, New York, 618 pp., 1964)

111. Nitsch, C., Nitsch, J. P., *Compt. Rend.*, **262**, 1102–5 (1966)

112. Ogata, K., Uchiyama, K., Yamada, H., *Japan. J. Agr. Biol. Chem.*, **30**, 311–12 (1966)

113. Ogata, K., Uchiyama, K., Yamada, H., *ibid.*, **31**, 200–6 (1967)

114. Pal, M., Burma, D. P., *Trans. Bose Res. Inst. (Calcutta)*, **27**, 27–32 (1964)

115. Parson, W. W., Rudney, H., *Proc. Natl. Acad. Sci. U.S.*, **51**, 444–50 (1964)

116. Parson, W. W., Rudney, H., *ibid.*, **53**, 599–606 (1965)

117. Pittard, A. J., Gibson, F., Doy, C. H., *Biochim. Biophys. Acta*, **49**, 485–94 (1961)

118. Pittard, A. J., Gibson, F., Doy, C. H., *ibid.*, **57**, 290–98 (1962)

119. Plouvier, V., *Compt. Rend.*, **249**, 1563–65 (1959)

120. Power, D. M., Towers, G. H. N., Neish, A. C., *Can. J. Biochem.*, **43**, 1397–1407 (1965)

121. Pridham, J. B., *Ann. Rev. Plant Physiol.*, **16**, 13–36 (1965)

122. Ratledge, C., *Nature*, **203**, 428–29 (1964)

123. Ratledge, C., Winder, F. G., *Biochem. J.*, **84**, 501–6 (1962)

124. Ratledge, C., Winder, F. G., *ibid.*, **101**, 274–83 (1966)

125. Rohringer, R., Fuchs, A., Lunderstädt, J., Samborski, D. J., *Can. J. Botany*, **45**, 863–89 (1967)

126. Sanderson, G. W., *Biochem. J.*, **98**, 248–52 (1966)

127. Schneider, G., *Naturwissenschaften*, **44**, 422 (1957)

128. Schneider, G., *Physiol. Plantarum*, **14**, 638–45 (1961)

129. Schwinck, I., Adams, E., *Biochim. Biophys. Acta*, **36**, 102–17 (1959)

130. Siddiqueullah, M., McGrath, R., Vining, L. C., Sala, F., Westlake, D. W. S., *Can. J. Biochem.*, **45**, 1881–89 (1967)

131. Somerville, R. L., Elford, R., *Biochem. Biophys. Res. Commun.*, **28**, 437–44 (1967)

132. Sondheimer, E., *Botan. Rev.*, **30**, 667–712 (1964)

133. Sprinson, D. B., *Advan. Carbohydrate Chem.*, **15**, 235–70 (1960)

134. Srinivasan, P. R., *Biochemistry*, **4**, 2860–65 (1965)

135. Srinivasan, P. R., Sprinson, D. B., *J. Biol. Chem.*, **234**, 716–22 (1959)

136. Srinivasan, P. R., Weiss, B., *Biochim. Biophys. Acta*, **51**, 597–99 (1961)

137. Subba Rao, P. V., Moore, K., Towers, G. H. N., *Biochem. Biophys. Res. Commun.*, **28**, 1008–12 (1967)

138. Szymanski, C. D., *An Attempt to Detect Quinic Dehydrogenase in Quinic Acid-Containing Plants* (Doctoral thesis, State Univ. Coll. Forestry, Syracuse Univ., Syracuse, 1962)

139. Tateoka, T. N., *Botan. Mag. Tokyo*, **76**, 391–94 (1963)

140. Tateoka, T. N., *ibid.*, **78**, 294–98 (1965)

141. Tateoka, T. N., *ibid.*, **81**, 103–4 (1968)

142. Tatum, E. L., Gross, S. R., Ehrensvärd, G., Garnjobst, L., *Proc. Natl. Acad. Sci. U.S.*, **40**, 271–76 (1954)

143. Towers, G. H. N., in *Symposium on Phytochemistry* (Harborne, J. B., Ed., Cambridge; in press, 1968)

144. Towers, G. H. N., Tse, A., Maass, W. S. G., *Phytochemistry*, **5**, 677–81 (1966)

145. Underhill, E. W., *Can. J. Biochem.*, **43**, 179–87 (1965)

146. Underhill, E. W., *ibid.*, **43**, 189–98 (1965)

147. Underhill, E. W., *ibid.*, **46**, 401–5 (1968)

148. Vining, L. C., Westlake, D. W. S., *Can. J. Microbiol.*, **10**, 705–16 (1964)

149. Weinstein, L. H., Porter, C. A., Laurencot, H. J., *Contrib. Boyce Thompson Inst.*, **20**, 121–34 (1959)
150. Weinstein, L. H., Porter, C. A., Laurencot, H. J., *ibid.*, **21**, 201–14 (1961)
151. Weinstein, L. H., Porter, C. A., Laurencot, H. J., *Nature*, **194**, 205–6 (1962)
152. Whistance, G. R., Threlfall, D. R., Goodwin, T. W., *Biochem. Biophys. Res. Commun.*, **23**, 849–53 (1966)
153. Whistance, G. R., Threlfall, D. R., Goodwin, T. W., *Biochem. J.*, **101**, 5p–6p (1966)
154. Whiting, G. C., Coggins, R. A., *Biochem. J.*, **102**, 283–93 (1967)
155. Wightman, F., Chisholm, M. D., Neish, A. C., *Phytochemistry*, **1**, 30–37 (1961)
156. Winstead, J. A., Suhadolnik, R. J., *J. Am. Chem. Soc.*, **82**, 1644–47 (1960)
157. Yoshida, S., *Botan. Mag. Tokyo*, **77**, 10–16 (1964)
158. Yoshida, S., Shimokoriyama, M., *Botan. Mag. Tokyo*, **78**, 14–19 (1965)
159. Yoshida, S., Towers, G. H. N., *Can. J. Biochem. Physiol.*, **41**, 579–86 (1963)
160. Young, I. G., Cox, G. B., Gibson, F., *Biochim. Biophys. Acta*, **141**, 319–31 (1967)
161. Young, I. G., Jackman, L. M., Gibson, F., *Biochim. Biophys. Acta*, **148**, 313–15 (1967)
162. Young, M. R., Neish, A. C., *Phytochemistry*, **5**, 1121–32 (1966)
163. Young, M. R., Towers, G. H. N., Neish, A. C., *Can. J. Botany*, **44**, 341–49 (1966)
164. Zaprometov, M. N., *Biokhimia*, **27**, 366–77 (1962)
165. Zenk, M. H., *Z. Naturforsch.*, **19b**, 83 (1964)
166. Zenk, M. H., Leistner, E., *Z. Naturforsch.*, **22b**, 460 (1967)
167. Zenk, M. H., Scherf, H., *Biochim. Biophys. Acta*, **71**, 737–38 (1963)
168. Zenk, M. H., Scherf, H., *Planta*, **62**, 350–54 (1964)
169. Zucker, M., *Plant Physiol.*, **40**, 779–84 (1966)

CONTROL OF ENZYME FORMATION AND INACTIVATION IN PLANTS

By K. T. GLASZIOU

David North Plant Research Centre
Brisbane, Australia

INTRODUCTION

Regulation of growth of higher plants appears to be dominated by three interacting systems. One is a sequential developmental program, apparently 'written' in the genome. The second is a closed-loop system with positive feedback, which may be partially described by equations based on the exponential growth law. The third is an array of closed-loop systems with a bewildering complexity of mainly negative feedback elements which operate to negate the noise level generated by unwanted inputs. This third category of systems may perform with such efficacy as to ensure the unfolding of the sequential developmental program almost unerringly, despite relatively large fluctuations in environmental variables. It is now clear that these feedback mechanisms include rapid, controlled changes in the rates of enzyme synthesis and irreversible degradation.

The substantial advances made in the understanding of control of enzyme synthesis in microorganisms have been largely due to the technique of genetic analysis coupled to biochemical measurements. The student of control systems in higher plants faces numerous and in some cases insuperable difficulties. Genetic analysis is not likely to become a very useful tool. The experimental materials in use are usually nonhomogeneous in respect to cell type, each type having an extremely intricate internal organization. An enzyme extracted from such tissue may have originated from several different cell types or different localities in the same cell type.

The difficulties may be minimized by use of relatively homogeneous tissues, but in simplifying the problems, we may forego the possibility of comprehending those aspects of control systems which permit the development and maintenance of heterogeneous functionality in neighboring cells of identical genotype.

METHODS FOR INVESTIGATING CONTROL OF ENZYME FORMATION AND INACTIVATION

The use of specific inhibitors of steps involved in enzyme synthesis is, at present, the most generally useful tool for analysing control over enzyme synthesis in higher plants. However, a sound methodology is still in the

63

primitive stages of evolution, and for this reason I will attempt to provide information on approaches being tested in various laboratories.

Some workers have found it profitable to study synthesis of several enzymes concurrently and to monitor other cellular activities such as respiration, leakiness of tissue, etc., to help distinguish between general or toxicity effects and the specific inhibition or control of a partial process of enzyme synthesis. The value of this approach is such that it should generally be adopted.

In most cases a thorough investigation of the properties of the isolated enzyme has been essential to show whether a single enzyme is being studied and whether low or high molecular weight substances affecting enzyme activity are present in the extracts. In some instances enzymes under study have been secreted or otherwise lost to the medium bathing the tissue (20, 88), and this possibility needs checking.

When the activity of an enzyme has been shown to increase rapidly in a plant tissue in response to some particular treatment, the introduction of a specific inhibitor of a particular step in protein synthesis has been used to adumbrate whether the changed activity is due to *de novo* synthesis or formation from pre-existing protein. It has been generally necessary to use several inhibitors of each class and to have information on the effects of these inhibitors on other enzymes undergoing synthesis in the same tissue. If no inhibition is observed, studies on activation and inactivation of the isolated enzyme may supply a sufficient explanation for the changes observed in intact cells. For enzymes of suitable stability, the density labeling technique (84) has also been used to establish that *de novo* synthesis has occurred (42, 54, 88).

Control systems dependent on metabolites are likely to involve induction of enzyme synthesis by substrates, or precursors of substrates, and repression of enzyme synthesis by immediate or eventual products. Tests using metabolites or tissue extracts for regulator activity are more fruitful if effects can be assayed on a group of enzymes, since buffer ions and common metabolites such as some amino and organic acids have been found to inhibit enzyme synthesis nonspecifically.

When investigating possible controllers of mRNA synthesis, knowledge is required of the time course of change of enzyme activity and at what intervals mRNA synthesis is limiting for synthesis of each enzyme being investigated. If the compound under test regulates synthesis or stabilization of a particular mRNA species, its effects will be detected only when the mRNA level limits the rate of enzyme production. Also, if mRNA synthesis limits production of one enzyme and not another, a nonspecific inhibitor of RNA synthesis will have an apparently specific effect on synthesis of one of the enzymes. Knowledge of when mRNA is limiting for production of a particular enzyme may be gained by addition of an inhibitor of RNA synthesis at different times during the incubation period. It is important to select enzymes, synthesis of which can be measured in short time intervals, to minimize secondary effects due to inhibition of rRNA or tRNA synthesis.

Inhibitors of RNA synthesis.—Actinomycin D and 6-methyl purine have come into general use as inhibitors of RNA synthesis. Secondary effects of both have been detected on processes such as respiration (52, 97). The amount of actinomycin D required to effectively inhibit DNA-dependent RNA polymerase isolated from maize was $1\mu g$ per $50\mu g$ DNA (163). As actinomycin-DNA complexes are normally stable [see (66) for review], the concentration of actinomycin D required to inhibit the RNA polymerase will be a function of the amount of DNA present. The concentrations usually required to inhibit enzyme synthesis in plant tissues appear to be excessive, and in some cases this may be due to poor penetration. In sugar cane tissue, cold treatments have been used to suspend temporarily metabolic processes while waiting for actinomycin D or other inhibitors to penetrate to an effective concentration. The cold treatment by itself did not affect the subsequent rate of enzyme synthesis (52).

Many other antibiotics and purine and pyrimidine analogues are considered to have specific effects on RNA synthesis, and there is need for information about their effectiveness and specificity when used on plant tissues. Chromomycin A, daunomycin, cinerubin, nogalomycin, mithramycin, olivomycin (66, 93), rifamycin (75), and 3'-deoxyadenosine (151), as well as others, are of potential use.

Inhibitors of DNA synthesis.—5-Fluorodeoxyuridine may be satisfactory as a specific inhibitor of DNA synthesis in plant tissues (39, 44, 91, 118). The antibiotics phleomycin, mitomycin, porfiromycin, streptonigrin, novobiocin, and edeine are reported to inhibit DNA synthesis preferentially [see (66) for review], but more knowledge is needed on their effects on plant tissues.

Inhibitors of protein synthesis.—Cycloheximide (actidione) has found extensive use as an inhibitor of enzyme synthesis in plant cells. It does not affect amino acid activation or synthesis of aminoacyl-tRNA (153), and is considered variously to inhibit the transfer reaction in peptide bond formation (69) and to affect initiation of polypeptide chains in a cell free system from wheat embryos (113). Work on rabbit reticulocytes indicates a differential effect of cycloheximide in initiation and extension of polypeptide chains, the latter process being more susceptible to inhibition at very low concentrations (63). Cycloheximide is reported to be toxic for plants, fungi, protozoa, and mammalian cells, but not for bacteria [see (66) for review]. It does not inhibit protein synthesis in cell-free extracts from *Escherichia coli* (37). Other glutarimide antibiotics such as acetoxycycloheximide, streptovitacin A, and streptimidone have found use in investigations of proteins synthesis in yeasts (153) and mammalian systems (37).

Chloramphenicol causes reversible inhibition of protein synthesis in intact bacterial cells in the concentration range 10^{-5} to 10^{-6}M. Only the D $(-)$ threo isomer is active, and other cell processes such as RNA synthesis and ATP formation are unaffected. In contrast, concentrations above 10^{-3}M are often required to inhibit effectively protein synthesis in intact cells of higher animals and plants, and both the D $(-)$ threo and the L $(-)$ threo isomers may be active (64). Concentrations of chloramphenicol in the range 10^{-3}M inhibited oxidative phosphorylation in isolated maize mitochondria (74) and NADH oxidation in isolated beef heart mitochondria (47). However, chloramphenicol effects on protein synthesis in higher organisms are not exclusively attributable to secondary effects since cell-free protein synthesis from sources such as reticulocytes (177) and rat spleen (165) was inhibited at bacteriostatic concentrations.

The process of protein synthesis in cell organelles such as mitochondria (22) and plastids (1, 102) appears to have characteristics akin to bacterial systems and is particularly susceptible to inhibition by chloramphenicol, tetracyclines, and macrolide antibiotics, and insensitive to cycloheximide. As protein synthesis occurring outside these organelles appears to have a contrasting spectum of relative sensitivity, these inhibitors may be used to study the intracellular localization of synthesis of a particular enzyme. However, chloramphenicol appears to be unreliable for use on higher plants, and more work is required to show whether the tetracyclines, the macrolide antibiotics such as erythromycin, carbomycin, speramycin, oleandomycin, lincomycin, etc. (22, 104), or aminoglycoside antibiotics such as spectinomycin (4) may be better specific inhibitors of protein synthesis in plant organelles.

Puromycin has been used to inhibit enzyme synthesis in many plant tissues and also in cell-free systems (126). It is considered to compete with the incoming aminoacyl-tRNA for the activated carboxyl group on the growing end of ribosome-bound peptidyl-tRNA (66, 167). Incorporation of puromycin into the growing peptide results in chain termination. Puromycin has been used extensively in the analysis of partial processes of protein synthesis in cell-free systems from bacteria. Requirements for chain initiation appear to be the formation of an activated complex consisting of the 30 S ribosomal subunit, GTP, and a mRNA molecule commencing with the sequence ApUpG . . . . . . , initiation factors, low Mg^{++}, and a species of formylmethionyl-tRNA. On the addition of the 50 S ribosomal subunit, amino acid polymerising factors, aminoacyl-tRNA, and GTP, the system becomes competent to carry out amino acid polymerization (3, 67, 82, 103, 120, 121, 160). Formylmethionyl puromycin can be formed if puromycin and 50 S ribosomal subunits are added to the chain initiation system (82).

Little is known about chain initiation in protein synthesising systems in plants. In particular, it is not certain whether N-formylmethionyl-tRNA or other N-substituted aminoacyl-tRNA species are required for *in vivo* chain initiation, whether there are different requirements for protein synthesising systems for organelles and cytoplasm (149), or whether initiation can commence at internal cistrons of a polycistronic mRNA (8).

Amino acid analogues.—Selenomethionine, thienyl alanine, 5-hydroxytryptophan, *p*-fluororphenylalanine, azatryptophan, etc., are potentially useful in that they may be incorporated into protein to produce inactive enzymes without seriously interfering with the general mechanism of protein synthesis. Other analogues such as 5-methyl tryptophan may inhibit amino acid activation. Little is known about their mechanism of action in plants.

A competitive substrate for L-proline activation by prolyl-tRNA synthetase of mung bean (132) is L-azetidine-2-carboxylic acid. It is not recognised by the proline activating system of liliaceous plants in which it is a natural product (131). It strongly inhibited growth of cucumber and pumpkin seedlings, but did not affect development of isocitritase activity in the cotyledons, indicating activation of precursors rather than de novo synthesis of this enzyme (133).

Use of inhibitors of protein synthesis to localize effects of exogenously applied regulators.—Once turnover or synthesis rather than activation-inactivation reactions has been established to explain changes in enzyme levels, the step at which a regulatory substance exerts its effect is sometimes demonstrable by systematic use of specific inhibitors. The following procedure has been applied (53) and may have some general utility. Peptide-bond formation was blocked with a suitable inhibitor and the effect of a regulatory substance tested on the rate of inactivation of preformed enzyme. If the regulator had no effect, a study was next made on the effects of inhibitors of RNA synthesis applied at intervals over a suitable time course. If over some intervals inhibitors of RNA synthesis had no effect on enzyme synthesis, the result was taken to indicate that RNA levels were nonlimiting. The ability of the regulator to modulate amino acid polymerization steps was then determined from its effect on enzyme synthesis during such an interval. If there was no effect, the combined results were taken to indicate that the regulator should operate when RNA levels were limiting, and this hypothesis was tested directly by applying the regulator during an interval when the time-course study had shown that inhibitors of RNA synthesis were highly effective.

If effects of the regulator were observed only when RNA levels were limiting, an analysis was made to indicate whether RNA synthesis or stability was affected. The regulator was added after blocking further RNA synthesis with a suitable inhibitor. The amount of enzyme formed over a fixed time interval was then measured. If an effect of the regulator was obtained after RNA synthesis had been blocked, the result was taken to indicate stabilization of preformed RNA. If the time interval used was short, it was concluded that mRNA synthesis or stability was involved. Confirmatory evidence on mRNA involvement may be obtained by concomitant studies on synthesis of other enzymes not limited by RNA levels during the same time interval, provided it is reasonable to suppose that synthesis of these enzymes is mediated by a common pool of ribosomes and tRNA molecules.

Procedures to ensure effective entry or removal of potential regulators or inhibitors need to be worked out for individual tissues. Lowering the temperature during such steps may suffice (52, 99). Although final answers are not possible as to whether the regulatory substance acts directly or indirectly, the field for further work may be indicated more definitively.

Anomalous results using inhibitors of enzyme synthesis.—The complexity of control systems plus intracellular compartmentation ensure the inevitability of surprising results, but this expectation does not necessarily predicate confusion. Thus, the cycloheximide promotion of synthesis of the chloroplast enzyme, ribulose diphosphate carboxylase (156), or the simultaneous effects of chloramphenicol in inhibiting synthesis of nitrite reductase located in chloroplasts and promoting synthesis of nitrate reductase located externally to the chloroplasts (147) may merely reflect interference with normal competition for intermediary metabolites. The induction in potato slices of phenylalanine ammonia-lyase, followed sequentially by induction of a system for inactivating the enzyme (185), is reminiscent of work on liver tryptophan pyrrolase (49) in which actinomycin D promotion of enzyme synthesis was considered to be brought about by blocking synthesis of RNA essential for formation of a repressor of hydrocortisone-induced tryptophane pyrrolase synthesis. It should be possible to obtain a similar actinomycin D effect, if not on potato phenylalanine ammonia-lyase, at least on some plant enzyme system. The adequate explanation of such anomalies may contribute more valuable information on control systems than predicted responses.

Radioisotope techniques purporting to measure rates of nucleic acid, protein, and enzyme synthesis or turnover.—A large number of publications have appeared which attempt to demonstrate various controls over nucleic acid or protein synthesis by the effects of supposed regulators on the incorporation of radioactive precursors. In some instances useful results are obtained, but many are difficult, if not impossible, to interpret for reasons covered by Reiner in 1953 (135). More modern double labeling techniques and elegant technology in fractionation and analytical procedures involve more work but do not necessarily shed more light.

The fundamental difficulties which render incorporation studies hazardous may be illustrated without recourse to differential equations. For the hypothetical reaction sequence,

$$A^* \rightleftharpoons A^* \rightarrow B \rightarrow C \rightarrow \text{Breakdown Products}$$

Medium | Tissue Precursor pools | Boundary

the labeled precursor A^* is added to the medium with and without regulatory substance and a difference in radioactivity in C is taken to indicate an effect on its synthesis or turnover. In fact, if the regulatory substance affected the rates of any of the reactions by any means, it would almost certainly change the amount of radioactivity appearing in C. For example, assuming it accelerated the formation of B from intracellular pools, it could conceivably double the pool size of B, decrease its specific activity to half or considerably less, and change the rate of synthesis of C not at all or up to double. The amount of radioactivity in C could easily register a decrease under circumstances in which synthesis of C increased.

SUBSTRATE INDUCTION OF ENZYME SYNTHESIS

Work on thymidine enhancement of thymidine kinase in wheat embryos and lily microspores has been reviewed previously in this series (162). Induction of nitrate reductase in higher plant tissues by nitrate or molybdenum is well established (81, 85). In short-term experiments on detached cotyledons from radish seedlings, induction of nitrate and nitrite reductase by nitrate was largely prevented by puromycin and actinomycin D, indicating de novo synthesis and a requirement for mRNA synthesis to precede enzyme synthesis (85). The operation of this sytem in higher plants is reviewed in more detail by Hageman & Beevers in this volume.

Of general interest are the findings of Pateman & Cove (127) on induction of nitrate reductase in Aspergillus nidulans. Results of genetic analysis appear to be best explained by a model involving interaction of nitrate with the product of a regulatory gene to form an active complex which binds to the operator site and permits initiation of operon transcription. In contrast, the product of the regulatory gene for the E. coli lac operon is prevented from binding to the operator site by inducer (55), and transcription is initiated in its absence. Nitrite reductase is also induced by nitrate, but the structural genes for the two enzymes map at different locations. Whether part of the control system in plants can be accounted for in similar terms remains to be seen.

Light-induced synthesis of phenylalanine ammonia-lyase.—Tissue slices from sweet potato (115) and potato (184) produce phenylalanine ammonia-lyase when incubated in water. Enzyme synthesis in potato was enhanced by light and prevented by purine and pyrimidine analogues, ethionine, and cycloheximide (184, 185). The relationship between the activity of phenylalanine ammonia-lyase and the amount of chlorogenic acid synthesised from endogenous substrate is indicative that regulation of synthesis of this enzyme is an important component in control of production of phenolic compounds (115, 184, 186).

The rapid increase of phenylalanine ammonia-lyase after light treatment of potato tuber slices (184), gherkin seedlings (34), and mustard seedlings (30, 137) may be followed by a decline. During the early stages of enzyme synthesis in potato tissue, cycloheximide prevented further increases, the enzyme level remaining constant. When about 60 per cent of the maximum enzyme level had been attained, treatment with cycloheximide was followed by enzyme loss. Higher levels of cycloheximide applied after this stage reduced loss of the enzyme (185). Similar observations were recorded on gherkin seedlings (35). These results were taken to indicate that induction of synthesis of phenylalanine ammonia-lyase is followed sequentially by induction of an inactivating system, which itself is dependent on protein synthesis (35, 185).

The effect of light quality on induction of phenylalanine ammonia-lyase has been examined in tuber tissue of artichoke (119), etiolated hypocotyls of gherkin seedlings (34), etiolated mustard seedlings (137), and strawberry leaf disks (26). In gherkin hypocotyls, a 10-min exposure to red light led to an accumulation of hydroxycinnamic acid which could be abolished with far-red light, thus implicating the phytochrome system. However, no induction of phenylalanine ammonia-lyase or cinnamic acid hydroxylase could be demonstrated under these conditions (34, 36). The induction of phenylalanine ammonia-lyase was considered to be a response to high energy light reactions of photomorphogenesis, mediated by two distinct pigments absorbing maximally in the blue and red regions of the spectrum (34).

Leaves from wild strawberry plants grown in a greenhouse had low phenylalanine ammonia-lyase activity and only trace amounts of flavonoids (27). Leaf disks from these plants accumulated large amounts of flavonoids and had correspondingly high levels of phenylalanine ammonia-lyase when floated on solutions in the light. Thus, the increase of this enzyme is not necessarily an event accompanying the light-induced development of plastids in an etiolated tissue (26). When the leaf disks were given 5 min of red or far-red light prior to incubation in the dark, the far-red light treatment resulted in a marked inhibition or leucoanthocyanin production but no diminution of phenylalanine ammonia-lyase level. Maximum stimulation of enzyme production occurred in blue light, so that there was no evidence for phytochrome involvement as a control mechanism on enzyme level (26).

In contrast, the light-induced synthesis of phenylalanine ammonia-lyase in mustard seedlings is attributed to phytochrome in the P730 form (30, 137). Far-red light was used on the grounds that long term irradiation with far-red will maintain a constant but low level of P730, the action of which will cease at the moment the light is turned off (76, 116). Phenylalanine ammonia-lyase activity was lost with a half-life of about 6 hr if mustard seedlings were transferred from far-red light to darkness when the enzyme level had reached a plateau (30). If the dark treatment commenced when the enzyme level was still increasing rapidly, the increase ceased but there was no loss of formed enzyme. On transfer back to far-red light, rapid enzyme synthesis resumed virtually immediately and could be completely repressed with cycloheximide or puromycin, but much less so with actinomycin D (137). This result may indicate that the light effect is fairly directly on peptide bond formation in this system. It also appears that there is a sequential induction of a system for inactivating the enzyme, similar to that reported in potato.

PRODUCT REPRESSION OF ENZYME SYNTHESIS

The existence of a vacuolar (inner space) invertase in sugar cane stalk parenchyma cells was indicated by tracer studies on sugar storage in rapidly expanding immature internodal tissue (56). The vacuolar enzyme was not present in mature storage tissue which contained large amounts of sucrose and very little reducing sugar, indicating that the enzyme was inactivated during the maturation process by some long term control system (57). The total invertase content of immature internodes varied seasonally (80), and the growth rate of these internodes was proportional to the invertase activity (58, 78).

The auxin-mediated short term control system on vacuolar invertase was discovered by Sacher (142). Discrepancies in the vacuolar levels of glucose and fructose between water-treated and α-naphthalene acetic acid (NAA)-treated tissues led to investigations of auxin effects on vacuolar invertase levels and the finding that NAA at 10^{-5} M gave increased activity after an 18-hr incubation period, compared with water controls similarly treated. In later experiments, this time interval was reduced to 2 to 3 hr (61). Since the invertase content of water-treated tissue also increased substantially, it appeared that incubation in water may have caused loss of an endogenous inhibitor. Product inhibition was an obvious possibility, and glucose was found to prevent any increase in invertase content. The *in vitro* activity of the enzyme was not affected by NAA, and from these observations it was speculated that synthesis of invertase was regulated by auxin and a negative feedback control system dependent upon reaction products of invertase activity (142).

Concurrent work showed that sucrose had to undergo breakdown prior to being stored in the vacuole, breakdown being catalysed by the cell wall (outer space) invertase (143). Both in intact plants (155) and in tissue slice experiments (144) the cell wall invertase was found to be relatively stable, the large increase in total invertase which could be repressed with glucose being due to changes in vacuolar invertase (144).

Obviously, glucose effects on the level of vacuolar invertase need not have been direct effects of the glucose molecule. A large number of sugars were found to have similar effects, while some polyhydric alcohols increased the invertase level (60, 62). Neither glucose nor mannitol affected the stability of the isolated enzyme. Partially purified invertase was found to be stable at pH 5.2, but unstable at pH 4.4. However, no effect of glucose could be demonstrated on tissue pH (60). The possibility that reductions in enzyme levels were due to low or high molecular weight inhibitors present in extracts was investigated with negative results (61, 62). Inhibitors of RNA synthesis such as actinomycin D and 6-methyl purine prevented increases in invertase activity (52, 61), as did inhibitors of protein synthesis including puromycin, fluoride (61), cycloheximide (53), and p-fluorophenyl alanine (Gayler, unpublished data). Under appropriate conditions all of these inhibitors will cause rapid loss of invertase activity. Glucose gave the same maximum loss rate (61), and the enzyme disappearing from the tissue did not appear in the medium (Glasziou & Waldron, unpublished data). There can be little doubt that fluctuations in vacuolar invertase levels represent changes in the balance of synthesis and destruction of the enzyme.

D-Glucosamine affected invertase synthesis in an almost identical manner to D-glucose. D-glucosamine labeled with ^{14}C accumulated in the tissue, together with the phosphorylated glucosamine and N-acetyl glucosamine. The carbon chain was not fragmented or converted to glucose or fructose. Glucosamine and its metabolic derivatives were not detected in tissues treated with ^{14}C-glucose (60). Taken together with studies on many other sugars and derivatives, it was concluded that the glucose molecule was active as its β-anomer in the D-pyranose form (62). Sugars and related compounds which promoted invertase synthesis were considered to compete with endogenous glucose for the active site of a macromolecular regulator. Only sucrose, glucose, and fructose occur at sufficiently high concentrations in the cane stalk to qualify as potential *in vivo* regulators.

Studies on molecular structure and activity also led to the conclusion that glucose and fructose acted in different ways in inhibiting invertase synthesis. Confirmatory evidence was obtained when invertase synthesis in more mature tissue was sometimes found to be sensitive to fructose and not glucose, and by the demonstration that in immature tissue glucose inhibited invertase and not peroxidase synthesis, but that fructose inhibited synthesis of both enzymes (62).

Localisation of the glucose effect to a particular partial process in invertase synthesis was assigned from the following considerations. The maximum loss rate for invertase was the same whether glucose or general inhibitors of protein synthesis were the causative agents. Therefore, it is unlikely that glucose activates an enzyme causing invertase destruction (61). Peroxidase synthesis was unaffected under conditions in which glucose blocked invertase synthesis, indicating that glucose does not alter levels or effectiveness of substrates, ribosomes, or enzymes which are common requirements for synthesis of the two enzymes (62). Conditions could be arranged in which the inhibitors of RNA synthesis, actinomycin D (61) or 6-methyl purine (52), would either virtually completely prevent invertase synthesis or have little effect, indicating whether RNA levels were limiting or nonlimiting for invertase formation. Following treatment in glucose solutions, invertase was rapidly synthesised on transfer of tissues to water, but not if transferred to actinomycin D (61). It appears that mRNA specifically required for invertase synthesis became rate-limiting during the glucose pretreatment. Apparently glucose cannot act solely by blocking synthesis of invertase mRNA, as it also inhibited invertase synthesis when the absence of an actinomycin D effect indicated that the mRNA level was nonlimiting (61). These observations lead to the conclusion that glucose is a specific inhibitor of the amino acid polymerization step for invertase synthesis, that such inhibition leads to destruction of existing invertase mRNA molecules, and possibly that glucose repression also is manifested as a blockage of further synthesis of invertase mRNA.

Effects of hormones on synthesis of invertase and other enzymes in this tissue are considered in later sections.

CHANGES IN ENZYME ACTIVITY IN AGEING TUBER TISSUE SLICES

Ageing storage tissues from artichoke, beet, carrot, potato, turnip, etc., have long been favoured experimental material for study in the development of salt accumulating capacity which is coincident with changes in respiratory metabolism and oxidative phosphorylation (96, 139). Shortly after cutting beetroot or swede tissues, the mitochondria disintegrated, and the endoplasmic reticulum was reduced to small cytoplasmic vesicles. This was followed by reorganization of cell substructures which was coincident with the onset of ion accumulation (86, 168). Inhibitors of protein synthesis inhibited development of enhanced salt uptake (107, 164) and respiratory activity (23, 96, 128). In carrot tissue, the proportion of ribosomes present as polysomes increased from about 10 to 65 per cent after 6-hr ageing, and this increase was accompanied by an increase in activity of a number of enzymes, apparently as part of a general increase in protein synthesis (98).

During the ageing process, some enzymes such as invertases (5, 6, 18, 32, 45, 171-173), ascorbic acid oxidase (32), and fatty acid synthetase (178) increase to abnormally high levels, the increases being largely prevented by inhibitors of protein and nucleic acid synthesis.

The nature of the stimulus accompanying cutting which results in synthesis of these enzymes has proved elusive. Invertase in sugar beet tissue increased to about the same extent whether the tissue was incubated in water or placed on agar (18). Edelman found that if tissue was suspended on a thread and incubated in a humidity chamber, invertase increased in the same way as for tissue in water (quoted in 18). Hence the stimulus is not readily explicable in terms of endogenous repressor substances being washed from the tissue, or products of ruptured cells moving into intact cells. Respiration in potato disks more than 1 mm thick is rate-limited by oxygen availability (105, 106), and this may explain restriction of invertase development in the internal cells (172). However, the measured oxygen concentration at the centre of intact potato tubers is near atmospheric (16), and invertase developed, though at a reduced rate, in artichoke tissue under a N_2 atmosphere (32). Repression of synthesis of these enzymes in intact organs by high internal CO_2 concentrations is also unlikely since 5 per cent (v/v) CO_2 in air did not affect induction of invertase synthesis (32).

The rate of invertase synthesis over a 24-hr period in artichoke tissue slices was markedly inhibited by IAA at concentrations higher than 5×10^{-5} M, whereas gibberellic acid stimulated synthesis by as much as 80 per cent (31). Similar effects of IAA were observed on invertase synthesis in sugar beet slices, as well as slight stimulatory effects of gibberellic acid and abscisic acid (18). Loss of endogenous auxin from the tissue does not provide a satisfactory explanation for derepression of synthesis of invertase and other enzymes in storage tissue slices. Some other possible causes are loss of volatile metabolites, changes in tissue tensions, osmotic shock, loss of sources of endogenous repressors which undergo very rapid turnover, or perhaps exposure to light.

Control of Enzyme Formation in Photosynthetic Tissues

Chloroplasts appear to have some degree of genetic autonomy. They contain both DNA and RNA. Isolated, purified chloroplasts are capable of synthesising DNA, RNA, and protein, and chloroplast ribosomes support amino acid incorporation in cell-free systems (9, 33, 65, 158; for reviews see 12, 92). Chloroplast DNA formed hybrid molecules with chloroplast but no other ribosomal RNA, indicating that one of the functions of chloroplast DNA is to code for the RNA of chloroplast ribosomes (150, 157, 166). Nuclear DNA also appears to have many cistrons coding for chloroplast ribosomal RNA (166).

Enzyme formation accompanying chloroplast development.—Enzyme formation attendant upon chloroplast development in response to light treatments of dark-grown cells or leaves has been studied in a variety of algae and plants (10, 17, 41, 50, 51, 68, 71, 90, 112, 114, 156).

Hageman & Arnon (71) showed that NADP-glyceraldehyde phosphate dehydrogenase appeared only in leaves of seedlings that had been exposed to light. Using red kidney beans, Marcus found that this enzyme increased in response to brief exposures of 5 min to low intensity red light. If the red light treatment was followed by far-red, the effect was nullified. Chlorophyll formation was negligible in either red or a red followed by far-red treatment (112). In dark-grown pea seedlings, similar increases in response to brief red light treatments have been observed for Fraction I protein and its associated ribulose diphosphate carboxylase activity, membrane-bound ferredoxin-NADP reductase, NADP-glyceraldehyde phosphate dehydrogenase and alkaline fructose-1,6-diphosphatase (68). The magnitude of the increases and the reversibility of the response when red light was followed by far-red are taken to indicate that the phytochrome system is the primary photoregulator of synthesis of these enzymes (68). Similar results are recorded for etiolated rye seedlings (41). Cell-free ribosomal systems from dark grown maize or bean seedlings showed enhanced amino acid incorporating ability and a higher percentage of polyribosomes if the intact leaves were exposed to light shortly prior to harvest. Red light was most effective (179).

A second photosystem requiring higher light intensity is implicated in chlorophyll formation and other aspects of chloroplast development. The photoacceptor for this system appears to be protochlorophyllide (94, 136, 175).

Attempts have been made to localize sites of synthesis of various enzymes in photosynthetic tissues based on the sensitivity of enzyme synthesis to antibiotics reputedly specific for inhibiting protein synthesis occurring in cell organelles or cytoplasm. The 70S ribosomal system of chloroplasts is particularly sensitive to chloramphenicol (1, 22, 102) as compared with the

80S ribosomal system of the cytoplasm which is sensitive to cycloheximide (37, 113, 153).

Chloramphenicol inhibited synthesis of ribulose diphosphate carboxylase, Fraction 1 protein, and NADP-glyceraldehyde phosphate dehydrogenase following exposure to light of dark-adapted *Euglena gracilis* cells. At the concentration used, chloramphenicol did not affect cell division. Cyclohexi-mide stimulated synthesis of both enzymes. The synthesis of cytochrome-552, ferredoxin-NADP-reductase, and cytochrome-561, which are proteins of the photosynthetic electron transport chain, was inhibited by both chlor-amphenicol and cycloheximide. The results indicated that the enzymes cata-lysing the cyclic reduction of CO_2 in photosynthesis are synthesised on chlo-roplast ribosomes. It was suggested that proteins of the photosynthetic elec-tron transport chain are also synthesised on chloroplast ribosomes, and that the cycloheximide inhibition of synthesis of these proteins may be indirect and related to cytoplasmic synthesis of structural elements necessary for chloroplast development (156, 157).

In corn seedlings, chloramphenicol inhibited nitrate-induced synthesis of nitrite reductase (147), an enzyme localised in chloroplasts (85). Nitrate reductase occurs outside the chloroplast (138), and chloramphenicol did not inhibit its synthesis which was also induced by nitrate (147). Nitrate reduc-tase synthesis was inhibited by cycloheximide (85). These observations are indicative that nitrite reductase is synthesised on chloroplast ribosomes and nitrate reductase on cytoplasmic ribosomes.

EFFECTS OF PLANT GROWTH REGULATORS

Cytokinins.—This group of growth regulators inhibited RNase synthesis in injured tobacco leaves (7) and bean pulvinal tissue (2), RNase and DNase increases in excised barley leaves (159), and invertase and peroxi-dase synthesis in expanding internodal tissue of sugar cane (53). Cytoki-nins enhanced synthesis of amylase in bean hypocotyl (24), S-adenosyl-me-thionine: tyramine methyltransferase in barley root tips (161), proteinase and isocitric lyase in squash cotyledons (129, 130), and two peroxidase iso-enzymes in tobacco pith cells (48).

The cytokinins isopentenyl-adenosine and its hydroxylated derivative *cis*-hydroxy isopentenyl adenosine are found in the tRNA of higher plants and animals as well as in yeast and bacteria (73). Extracts of tRNA from higher animals and microorganisms had cytokinin activity in the tobacco callus assay (154). Cytokinins labeled with ^{14}C were recovered from tRNA fractions following administration to plant tissues (46).

Isopentenyl-adenosine occurs in yeast tRNA[ser] and tRNA[tyr] adjacent to the anticodon of each molecule. When tRNA[ser] was treated with iodine, the isopentenyl-adenosine was modified without other alteration to the molecule (140). The modified tRNA[ser] accepted serine in the presence of ATP and activating enzyme as well as did the untreated sample, but did not bind effectively with mRNA-ribosome complexes (43), indicating that transfer function of aminoacyl-tRNA may be modified by alterations to the nucleoside adjacent to the anticodon. Eight cytokinins have been isolated from sweet corn (100) so that a high degree of flexibility could be achieved in regulating rates of enzyme synthesis by modulating the activity of tRNA.

Cytokinins could conceivably enter into preformed tRNA by a transfer reaction of the group attached at the 6 position of the purine ring. If so, rapid modulation of the rate of protein synthesis could be expected following treatment of a tissue with a cytokinin. Alternatively, cytokinins may enter tRNA only during its synthesis, in which case a considerable lag could be expected before significant modulation of enzyme synthesis would be evident. The effect should be observed on the amino acid polymerization step of protein synthesis.

Benzyl-adenine and furfuryl-adenine inhibited invertase and peroxidase synthesis in immature internode tissue slices of sugar cane. When either RNA synthesis or subsequent steps were made rate limiting for synthesis of these enzymes, effects of other regulators on either step could be detected within 1 to 2 hr after addition. No similar short term effect of cytokinins was observed. The minimum time to obtain a significant effect on either enzyme was about 6 hr. Entry of cytokinins into the tissue is not likely to be a problem since 6-methyl purine and adenine entered readily. Cell division in this tissue is already completed. The cytokinin-mediated inhibition of synthesis of these two enzymes is thus inconsistent with effects on DNA replication, short-term control of synthesis of mRNA specifying either enzyme, or any rapid control of peptide-bond formation such as might be expected by group transfer from cytokinins into preformed tRNA. The observations are consistent with modulation of enzyme synthesis following incorporation of cytokinins into newly synthesised tRNA (53).

Gibberellins.—Secretion of starch liquefying enzymes from the aleurone layers of cereal seeds was observed in the 1890's (15, 70), and was shown to be a response to a factor originating from the embryo. Later work demonstrated that the embryo factor was gibberellin-like (134, 180), and gibberellic acid was shown to stimulate the malting process (95, 101, 145), the release of reducing sugars from the endosperm (122, 123, 181), and the dissolution of the endosperm contents in the complete absence of the embryo (125).

Enzymes thought to arise in the aleurone layer in response to gibberellic acid treatment include endo-β-glucanase and endopentanase (109, 110), proteases (13, 88, 141, 182, 183), α-amylase (14, 109, 111, 124, 169, 183), ribonuclease (12), and peroxidase (29). Enzyme activation also occurs in the endosperm (29, 176). Only control of enzyme formation in the isolated aleurone layer will be considered in detail.

Production of α-amylase, ribonuclease (20), and protease (88) in aleurone tissue was quantitatively comparable with production of these enzymes in embryo-less half seeds. To obtain this result for α-amylase, it was necessary to include about 20 mM Ca^{++} in the buffered medium to prevent apparent irreversible inactivation of the enzyme (20). These enzymes undergo *de novo* synthesis as demonstrated by the density labeling technique (42, 88, 170).

Synthesis and secretion of amylase (20) and protease (88) occurred simultaneously in aleurone tissue from barley var. Himalaya, but ribonuclease was first accumulated in the tissue and released subsequently (20). For isolated aleurone strips from barley var. Proctor, gibberellic acid promoted production but not secretion of α-amylase and protease (109).

The dependence of synthesis and secretion of α-amylase on an exogenous supply of gibberellic acid appears to vary with the source of the seed. Briggs, using barley var. Proctor, (14) recorded no release of α-amylase into the medium in 5 days in the absence of gibberellic acid. Chrispeels & Varner (20) found that small amounts of α-amylase were synthesised by aleurone from barley var. Himalaya in the absence of gibberellic acid. Naylor (117) recorded no release of α-amylase by aleurone from *Avena fatua* var. Montana during 7 days without exogenous gibberellic acid, but aleurone from *Avena sativa* var. Torch commenced releasing the enzyme after 3 days in the absence of the hormone. Both varieties released α-amylase in the presence of a complete amino acid mixture without exogenous gibberellic acid. For var. Montana, enzyme release commenced at about 50 hr on a medium containing a complete mixture of amino acids, at about 40 hr on gibberellic acid alone, and at about 20 hr on gibberellic acid plus amino acids. An incomplete mixture of 7 amino acids did not stimulate enzyme release. Chrispeels & Varner (20) recorded a small stimulation of α-amylase production when a mixture of 16 amino acids was added to the incubation medium for var. Himalaya. MacLeod et al. (109) found that initiation of α-amylase production preceded protease production by about 8 hr in aleurone tissue from barley var. Proctor, whereas these two enzymes were produced simultaneously in barley var. Himalaya (88). It seems that α-amylase production is not necessarily a consequence of protease-mediated amino acid release.

Inhibitors of protein synthesis prevented the increases in enzyme level (14, 20, 117, 124). In the test system used by Chrispeels & Varner (20), ribonuclease release commenced 20 to 24 hr after addition of gibberellic acid. Cycloheximide added at 20 hr prevented further enzyme synthesis and inhibited release of formed enzyme. If added 28 hr after gibberellic acid, preformed enzyme was released, indicating that continued protein synthesis was required for the completion of the secretory apparatus.

Results obtained with inhibitors of nucleic acid synthesis are anomalous. Paleg (124) observed little effect of actinomycin D at concentrations up to 500μg/ml on gibberellic acid promotion of amylase production by embryoless half seeds of barley var. Naked Blanco Mariout, and concluded that RNA synthesis was not essential for expression of the hormone effect. Naylor (117) obtained complete inhibition of α-amylase synthesis when half seeds of *Avena fatua* were soaked for 30 min, the aleurone removed and incubated on gibberellic acid and actinomycin D. Chrispeels & Varner (20) incubated half seeds of barley var. Himalaya on moist sand for 3 days to permit imbibition to occur, then removed the aleurone to buffered media. If gibberellic acid was included, α-amylase production commenced in about 7 hr. Actinomycin D at $100\mu g/ml$ inhibited α-amylase production by 58 to 80 per cent (20, 88) when added at the same time as gibberellic acid. Protease production was inhibited by 79 per cent under the same conditions (29). Lower concentrations of actinomycin D inhibited α-amylase synthesis poorly but had profound effects on its secretion (20). If the antibiotic was added 8 hr after gibberellic acid, it had little effect on α-amylase synthesis but strongly inhibited ^{14}C-uridine incorporation into nucleic acid (21).

Taken at face value, these results would indicate that under some conditions RNA synthesis may become limiting for enzyme production or secretion, but that it is not essential for expression of the gibberellic acid effect. Alternatively, it may be assumed that under some conditions actinomycin D is a very poor inhibitor of synthesis of RNA required for α-amylase production. This hypothesis (21) is based on comparative studies of the effects of actinomycin D, 6-methyl purine, and 8-azaguanine, which indicated that on withdrawal of gibberellic acid a specific RNA fraction became rate limiting for α-amylase synthesis. Synthesis of this fraction was thought to be strongly inhibited by 8-azaguanine and 6-methyl purine, but very poorly by actinomycin D. The interpretation would appear to be justified if 8-azaguanine and 6-methyl purine are specific inhibitors of RNA synthesis, having no side effects. However, for 6-methyl purine acting on sugar cane tissue, respiration is strongly inhibited in a very short time by concentrations above $0.5mM$ (52), and this is the low end of the range used on the aleurone tissue.

The minimum time required to observe promotion of α-amylase synthesis in response to the initial application of gibberellic acid was about 6 to 7 hr (20, 124). Once the gibberellic acid effect had been elicited, there was a fairly rapid response to subsequent shifts in gibberellic acid concentration, regardless of whether the concentration was increased or decreased (21). This observation is indicative of a continuous, closely coupled, control system responding quantitatively to gibberellic acid.

A specific effect of gibberellic acid on a small number of enzymes and proteins is conceivable in many ways. A simple hypothesis arises by invoking one of the models of operator functioning (87), in which the operator site is transcribed and induction by gibberellic acid occurs by removal of repressor(s) from both the DNA operator site and the transcribed operator site occurring at the commencement of the mRNA molecule. If this latter site was translated into the peptide chain, it could provide a convenient tag for the cell to recognise enzymes destined for secretion. For this model, gibberellic acid control would occur both when mRNA synthesis was limiting or nonlimiting.

Apparent specific, quantitative effects of the hormone on enzyme synthesis could also occur if it controlled the concentration of a metabolite which had become limiting for synthesis of a group of enzymes in a particular cell compartment, or if it controlled development and functioning of a secretory apparatus from which there was feedback control on enzyme synthesis.

Besides effects on hydrolases of cereal seed aleurone layers, gibberellins are reported to enhance enzyme synthesis in other tissues, including a 3'-nucleotidase of wheat embryos (152) and various invertases from sugar cane (53, 59), *Avena* internodes (89), and artichoke tuber tissue (31). Inhibition at very high gibberellin concentrations has been reported for invertase and peroxidase in sugar cane (59) but is ascribed to components other than gibberellic acid (GA_3) present in some commercial batches of gibberellins (53).

Gibberellic acid enhanced invertase synthesis in tissue slices from expanding sugar cane internodes when mRNA was made limiting for invertase formation by pretreatment of tissue with glucose (59). During treatments in which steps subsequent to RNA synthesis limited invertase synthesis for a considerable portion of the incubation periods, gibberellic acid effects were small. Hence any direct effect of gibberellic acid on the amino acid polymerization process for this enzyme is unlikely. Supplied at a stage when mRNA levels were limiting for synthesis of both invertase and peroxidase, a substantial increase in invertase level was still obtained in response to gibberellic acid if 6-methyl purine was added to prevent further RNA synthesis. The effectiveness of 6-methyl purine in blocking RNA synthesis was shown by its concomitant effect on peroxidase synthesis, and there was no gibberellic acid enhancement of synthesis of this enzyme. It appears that the gibberellic acid effect was enzyme specific, that it did not directly affect amino acid polymerization, and since RNA synthesis was unnecessary for its expression, it did not directly control production of the mRNA specifying invertase synthesis. The most probable mode of action appears to be specific stabilization of preformed mRNA (53).

In intact cane, gibberellic acid effects on internode elongation were spectacular, and dry weight increases were highly correlated with total acid invertase levels (58). The invertase consists of two components, cell wall and vacuolar invertase. In the intact plant, cell wall invertase was relatively stable, but vacuolar invertase fluctuated diurnally (155).

The relationship between sugar utilization, invertase levels and growth is illustrated in Figure 1, and has been discussed previously (58), but the role of irreversible extension growth operating as a negative feedback control and limiting any tendency for the vacuolar osmotic concentration to rise was overlooked. If the data are now correctly interpreted, the correlation between total invertase and dry matter production is secondary, but points to a primary obligatory correlation between cell wall invertase and carbohydrate input into the cell, carbohydrate being translocated as sucrose (77, 79) and hydrolysed by cell wall invertase prior to entry into metabolic

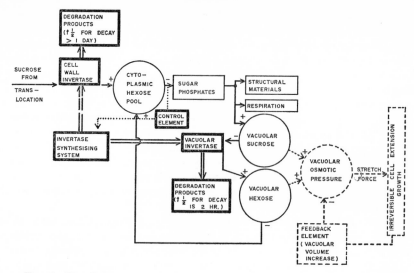

Fɪɢ. 1. Regulation of sugar flow into rapidly elongating sugar cane stalk parenchyma cells. Control on sugar input is by cell wall invertase, secretion of which ceases during early stages of elongation. The enzyme decays slowly and is replaced by a different invertase in mature, fully elongated cells. The cytoplasmic hexose pool is partitioned into formation of structural materials and accumulation of sucrose in the vacuole. The osmotic pressure generated in the vacuole supplies the stretching force for irreversible cell elongation. The concomitant increase in vacuolar volume negates any tendency for the vacuolar osmotic concentration to rise. The rate of synthesis of vacuolar invertase is in inverse relation to the level of the cytoplasmic hexose pool, while its decay rate is rapid and constant. A fall in sugar supply from translocation results in an increase in vacuolar invertase. In hydrolysing sucrose, vacuolar invertase helps maintain the osmotic pressure and provides hexoses which move back to the cytoplasm to maintain the growth rate. Vacuolar invertase is absent from mature cells, thus permitting sugar storage. (Composed from data in 58, 61, 62, 155).

or sugar storage pathways (143). It follows that the *in vivo* effect of gibberellic acid in promoting growth rate in sugar cane is almost certainly because of an increased level of cell wall invertase.

If tissue slice experiments reflect that *in vivo* situation for sugar cane, the stabilization of invertase mRNA by gibberellic acid (53) must be associated with an effect on secretion of cell wall invertase. The hypothesis appears to be verifiable by direct experiment.

Auxins.—Enhancement of enzyme synthesis by IAA or synthetic auxins has been reported for a benzoyl-aspartate conjugation system in pea epicotyl segments (174), cellulase in pea and bean epicotyls and maize shoots (38-40, 108), cellulose synthetase in *Avena* coleoptile sections (72), a peroxidase isoenzyme in tobacco pith (48), pectinase, β-1, 3-glucanase and pectinesterase in pea epicotyls (28), and invertase in sugar cane (61). Inhibition of enzyme synthesis was reported for enzymes such as 3'-nucleotidase in wheat embryos (152), an insoluble invertase in artichoke tuber tissue (31), two peroxidase isoenzymes in tobacco pith (48), and peroxidase in sugar cane (59). In each case cited, some evidence has been given that *de novo* enzyme synthesis is involved.

Indole acetic acid applied to the decapitated apex of pea epicotyls induced cell division, swelling of parenchyma cells, and 1.5 to 2.5-fold increases in DNA, RNA, and protein content, and a ninefold increase in cellulase after 2 days. These changes were prevented by actinomycin D and puromycin; but 5-fluorodeoxyuridine, which prevented cell division and the DNA increase, did not prevent the initial IAA-induced rise in RNA, protein and cellulase levels (38, 39). Detached pea epicotyls incubated in IAA gave substantial increases in cellulase activity in 6 to 12 hours (40).

Cycloheximide completely inhibited the IAA-induced increment in cellulase activity in decapitated pea epicotyls. Ribosomes isolated from epicotyl segments contained cellulase activity which was removable by brief treatment with RNase, proteinase or Mg^{++}-free medium. Whether expressed on a per segment or a RNA basis, the amount of cellulase activity associated with isolated ribosomes was increased manyfold by pretreating tissue with IAA. The isolated ribosomes sustained amino acid incorporation into protein in the presence of ATP and GTP. If the ribosome fraction was obtained from tissue pretreated with IAA, there was a measurable increase in cellulase activity during 15-min incubation with ATP and GTP (108). The results for cellulase are consistent with an IAA-induced increase in synthesis or stability of mRNA required for synthesis of the enzyme. Other possibilities would be an IAA-induced stabilization of the enzyme either directly or by binding to ribosomes.

Auxin (IAA or NAA) enhancement of invertase synthesis in elongating internode tissue from sugar cane was measurable within 2 to 3 hr from commencement of treatment. If protein synthesis was blocked, auxin did not change the rate of loss of invertase. When actinomycin D had no effect on invertase synthesis, thereby indicating that mRNA was nonlimiting, auxin had no effect. However, when invertase synthesis could be inhibited by actinomycin D or 6-methyl purine, auxin effects were also observed (53, 59, 61), the optimum concentration being in the range 10^{-6} to $10^{-7}M$. Hence, the auxin effect was localized to either synthesis or stabilization of mRNA. Differentiation between these alternatives was obtained by treating with auxin when mRNA synthesis was limiting for invertase formation, and after having blocked further mRNA synthesis with actinomycin D or 6-methyl purine (53). Auxin stimulation of invertase synthesis was still obtained, forcing the conclusion that like gibberellic acid, the mode of action of auxin in increasing invertase synthesis must be via mRNA stabilization.

Unlike gibberellic acid, little or no internode elongation was obtained by spraying intact cane plants with auxin solutions or by treating plants with the apical meristem removed with auxin in lanolin (Bull & Robinson, personal communication). Using the same arguments discussed previously which led to the conclusion that gibberellic acid promotes secretion of invertase into the cell wall, it would appear that auxin does not act likewise, and its effect is more probably on stabilization of that mRNA fraction producing invertase destined for the vacuole. This should show little or no *in vivo* response in sugar cane, as product repression would negate any tendency for vacuolar invertase to increase beyond that needed to maintain the cytoplasmic hexose pool. A fairly direct mechanism of auxin action is possible by means of increasing the rate of attachment of mRNA to ribosomes, or decreasing the activity of nucleolytic enzymes, etc., but alternatively auxin may promote sequestration of invertase mRNA into a cell compartment where its stability is higher. Both sets of alternatives appear to fit the findings on cellulase of Maclachlan and co-workers, who also drew attention to the possibility that auxin may be concerned with control of enzyme secretion (28).

Abscisic acid.—Enhancement of invertase synthesis was reported in sugar beet tissue (18), and invertase and ribonuclease in sugar cane tissue [(53) and Waldron, personal communication]. Inhibition of enzyme synthesis was reported for amylase in barley endosperm (25) and aleurone (19, 21). Both inhibition and promotion of development of invertase activity were observed in carrot slices dependent on the abscisic acid concentration (146). Abscisic acid and gibberellic acid apparently have effects on isolated yeast invertase (146), but no similar effects were observed for sugar cane invertase (53).

Abscisic acid inhibition of gibberellic acid-promoted amylase synthesis in barley aleurone was virtually complete within 3 hr of application (21). Abscisic acid promotion of invertase and ribonuclease synthesis in expanding internode tissue from sugar cane was also demonstrable within 2 to 3 hr from application. The abscisic acid effect on invertase was not on enzyme breakdown and took place at a step subsequent to mRNA synthesis (53).

Enzyme and mRNA Stability in Higher Plants

The half-time for loss of a number of enzymes has been measured after blocking further protein synthesis with an inhibitor. These estimates include figures of 24 to 30 hr for cellulase from pea epicotyl (40); 2 to 3 days for isocitric lyase and malate synthetase from watermelon seedlings (83); 4.2 hr for both NADH: and FMNH2: nitrate reductase from corn seedlings (148); and for sugar cane enzymes, 2 hr for vacuolar invertase (61), 2 to 4 hr for soluble RNase (Waldron, personal communication), and no observable breadown of newly synthesised peroxidase (62). In the absence of light, which stimulates its synthesis, phenylalanine ammonia-lyase of mustard seedlings may decay with a half-life of 6 hr (30).

Maclachlan and co-workers (40) comment that below pH 5.0, the *in vitro* rate of denaturation of cellulase from pea epicotyl was comparable to that in intact cells. Hatch & Cillikens (personal communication) showed that isolated sugar cane invertase became progressively less stable as the pH was shifted away from the optimum for activity. Protection against denaturation was conferred by sucrose. The reaction order varied with conditions, but none was found to give the first order loss obtained in intact cells (61). Also in intact cells, maximum loss rates were attained in the presence of glucose which blocked invertase synthesis but maintained protective levels of sucrose in the vacuole and did not cause any change of pH of expressed juice. The mechanism of inactivation in the intact cell remains unknown, except that it is apparently irreversible since the rise in invertase level which occurs on removal of glucose may be completely blocked by actinomycin D or inhibitors of peptide bond formation (61).

The rate of amino acid incorporation into protein in the presence of actinomycin D has been used to obtain a rough estimate of an average half-life for mRNA species in potato tuber slices of from 1.5 to 2 hr (23). Measurement of enzyme-forming capacity after blocking RNA synthesis with actinomycin D or 6-methyl purine gave values of 1.5 to 2 hr for the half-life of peroxidase mRNA in sugar cane (52).

Perspective

It seems probable that in cells of eucaryotic organisms, the readout of information specifying the amino acid sequence of polypeptide chains of all enzymes is under continuous control and at many levels, although not necessarily at all levels simultaneously.

One control level is on template availability for transcription, operating as a selective opening or closing of gene groups by unblocking or blocking of chromosomal regions (11, 162). A second level is predicated to be similar to the bacterial regulator-operator system both by popular vote and by the demonstration of rapid substrate induction in several plant systems of synthesis of enzymes such as nitrate reductase, which is apparently dependent on prior induction of mRNA synthesis (85). However, the applicability of the Jacob-Monod operon concept to higher plants is not proven. A third level of control is probable on mRNA stability (53). A fourth level appears to modulate translation such as in glucose repression of sugar cane invertase synthesis (61). A fifth level of control exists on enzyme activity and stability and may be coupled to levels of various regulators including metabolites.

Assuming that it is within the bounds of possibility, the attainment of a complete knowledge of all control systems operating for even a single enzyme in one cell type from one genotype of a higher plant species would be a task of enormous complexity and magnitude. There is positive feedback in this type of investigation. Complexity increases as knowledge increases. The hexose control system on vacuolar invertase level (Fig. 1) has the properties of a bio-oscillator. For a complete description we would need knowledge of its coupling to other oscillators and synchronizers. Obviously, only very limited objectives are attainable. Two that may commend themselves to plant biologists are a fuller description at the molecular level of mechanisms by which plant growth regulators exert effects on synthesis of enzymes and, perhaps more importantly, mechanisms of control on synthesis and activity of enzymes directly concerned with regulation of gas exchange, and product formation and dispersion during photosynthesis.

LITERATURE CITED

1. Aaronson, S., Ellenbogen, B. B., Yellen, L. K., Hutner, S. H., *Biochem. Biophys. Res. Commun.,* **27,** 535–38 (1967)
2. Abeles, F. B., Holm, R. E., Gahagan, H. E., in *Proc. Intern. Conf. Plant Growth Substances, 6th,* Ottawa, 1967 (Wightman, F., Setterfield, G., Eds., Runge Press, Ottawa, 1968)
3. Allende, J. E., Seeds, N. W., Conway, T. W., Weissbach, H., *Proc. Natl. Acad. Sci. U.S.,* **58,** 1566–73 (1967)
4. Anderson, P., Davies, J., Davis, B. D., *J. Mol. Biol.,* **29,** 203–15 (1967)
5. Bacon, J. S. D., *Biochem. J.,* **79,** 20P (1961)
6. Bacon, J. S. D., MacDonald, I. R., Knight, A. H., *Biochem. J.,* **94,** 175–82 (1965)
7. Bagi, G., Farkas, G. L., *Phytochemistry,* **6,** 161–69 (1967)
8. Berberich, M. A., Kovach, J. S., Goldberger, R. F., *Proc. Natl. Acad. Sci. U.S.,* **57,** 1857–64 (1967)
9. Boardman, N. K., Francki, R. I. B., Wildman, S. G., *J. Mol. Biol.,* **17,** 470–89 (1966)
10. Bogorad, L., in *Organizational Biosynthesis,* 395–418 (Vogel, H. J., Lampen, J. O., Bryson, V., Eds., Academic Press, New York, 1967)
11. Bonner, J., Dahmus, M. E., Fambrough, D., Huang, R. C., Marushige, K., Tuan, D. Y. H., *Science,* **159,** 47–56 (1968)
12. Brawerman, G., in *Biochemistry of Chloroplasts,* **1,** 301–17 (Goodwin, T. W., Ed., Academic Press, London, 1966)
13. Briggs, D. E., *J. Inst. Brewing,* **69,** 13–19 (1963)
14. Briggs, D. E., *ibid.,* **70,** 14–24 (1964)
15. Brown, H. T., Escombe, F., *Proc. Roy. Soc. (London),* **63,** 3–25 (1898)
16. Burton, W. G., *New Phytologist,* **49,** 121–34 (1950)
17. Chen, S., McMahon, D., Bogorad, L., *Plant Physiol.,* **42,** 1–5 (1967)
18. Cherry, J. H., in *Proc. Intern. Conf. Plant Growth Substances, 6th,* Ottawa, 1967 (See Ref. 2)
19. Chrispeels, M. J., Varner, J. E., *Nature,* **212,** 1066–67 (1966)
20. Chrispeels, M. J., Varner, J. E., *Plant Physiol.,* **42,** 398–406 (1967)
21. Chrispeels, M. J., Varner, J. E., *ibid.,* 1008–16
22. Clark-Walker, G. D., Linnane, A. W., *Biochem. Biophys. Res. Commun.,* **25,** 8–13 (1966)
23. Click, R. E., Hackett, D. P., *Proc. Natl. Acad. Sci. U.S.,* **50,** 243–50 (1963)
24. Clum, H. H., *Plant Physiol.,* **42,** 568–72 (1967)
25. Cornforth, J. W., Milborrow, B. V., Ryback, G., Wareing, P. F., *Nature,* **205,** 1269–70 (1965)
26. Creasy, L. L., *Phytochemistry,* **7,** 441–46 (1968)
27. Creasy, L. L., Swain, T., *Phytochemistry,* **5,** 501–9 (1966)
28. Datko, A. H., Maclachlan, G. A., *Plant Physiol.,* **43,** 735–42 (1968)
29. Duffus, J. H., *J. Inst. Brewing,* **72,** 569–73 (1966)
30. Durst, F., Mohr, H., *Naturwissenschaften,* **53,** 707 (1966)
31. Edelman, J., Hall, M. A., *Nature,* **201,** 296–97 (1964)
32. Edelman, J., Hall, M. A., *Biochem. J.,* **95,** 403–16 (1965)
33. Eisenstadt, J. M., Brawerman, G., *J. Mol. Biol.,* **10,** 392–402 (1964)
34. Engelsma, G., *Planta,* **77,** 49–57 (1967)
35. Engelsma, G., *Naturwissenschaften,* **54,** 319–20 (1967)
36. Engelsma, G., Meijer, G., *Acta Botan. Neerl.,* **14,** 54–72 (1965)
37. Ennis, H. L., Lubin, M., *Science,* **146,** 1474–76 (1964)

38. Fan, D. F., Maclachlan, G. A., *Can. J. Botany*, **44**, 1025–34 (1966)
39. Fan, D. F., Maclachlan, G. A., *Plant Physiol.*, **42**, 1114–22 (1967)
40. Fan, D. F., Maclachlan, G. A., *Can. J. Botany*, **45**, 1837–44 (1967)
41. Feierabend, J., Pirson, A., *Z. Pflanzenphysiol.*, **55**, 235–45 (1966)
42. Filner, P. F., Varner, J. E., *Proc. Natl. Acad. Sci. U.S.*, **58**, 1520–26 (1967)
43. Fittler, F., Hall, R. H., *Biochem. Biophys. Res. Commun.*, **25**, 441–46 (1966)
44. Flamm, W. G., Birnsteil, M. C., in *The Nucleohistones* (Bonner, J., Tso, P., Eds., Holden-Day, San Francisco, Calif., 1964)
45. Flood, A. E., Rutherford, P. P., Weston, E. W., *Nature*, **214**, 1049–50 (1967)
46. Fox, J. E., Chen, C.-M., *J. Biol. Chem.*, **242**, 4490–94 (1967)
47. Freeman, K. B., Haldar, D., *Biochem. Biophys. Res. Commun.*, **28**, 8–12 (1967)
48. Galston, A. W., Lavee, S., Siegel, B. Z., in *Proc. Intern. Conf. Plant Growth Substances, 6th,* Ottawa, 1967 (See Ref. 2)
49. Garren, L. D., Howell, R. R., Tomkins, G. M., Crocco, R. M., *Proc. Natl. Acad. Sci. U.S.*, **52**, 1121–29 (1964)
50. Gassman, M., Bogorad, L., *Plant Physiol.*, **42**, 774–80 (1967)
51. Gassman, M., Bogorad, L., *ibid.*, 781–84
52. Gayler, K. R., Glasziou, K. T., *Phytochemistry*, **7**, 1247 (1968)
53. Gayler, K. R., Glasziou, K. T., *Planta*, **83**, 185–94 (1969)
54. Gientka-Rychter, A., Cherry, J. H., *Plant Physiol.*, **43**, 653–64 (1968)
55. Gilbert, W., Müller-Hill, B., *Proc. Natl. Acad. Sci. U.S.*, **58**, 2415–21 (1967)
56. Glasziou, K. T., *Plant Physiol.*, **36**, 175–79 (1961)
57. Glasziou, K. T., *Nature*, **193**, 1100 (1962)
58. Glasziou, K. T., Bull, T. A., in *Proc. Congr. Intern. Soc. Sugarcane Technol., 12th,* Puerto Rico, 1965, 575–81 (Bague, J., Ed., Elsevier, Amsterdam, 1967)
59. Glasziou, K. T., Gayler, K. R., Waldron, J. C., in *Proc. Intern. Conf. Plant Growth Substances, 6th,* Ottawa, 1967 (See Ref. 2)
60. Glasziou, K. T., Waldron, J. C., *Australian J. Biol. Sci.*, **17**, 609–18 (1964)
61. Glasziou, K. T., Waldron, J. C., Bull, T. A., *Plant Physiol.*, **41**, 282–88 (1966)
62. Glasziou, K. T., Waldron, J. C., Most, B. H., *Phytochemistry*, **6**, 769–75 (1967)
63. Godchaux, W., III, Adamson, S. D., Herbert, E., *J. Mol. Biol.*, **27**, 57–72(1967)
64. Godchaux, W., III, Herbert, E., *J. Mol. Biol.*, **21**, 537–53 (1966)
65. Goffeau, A., Brachet, J., *Biochim. Biophys. Acta*, **95**, 302–13 (1965)
66. Goldberger, I. H., *Am. J. Med.*, 39, 722–52 (1965)
67. Gordon, J., *Proc. Natl. Acad. Sci. U.S.*, **58**, 1574–78 (1967)
68. Graham, D., Grieve, A. M., Smillie, R. M., *Nature*, **218**, 89–90 (1968)
69. Grollman, A. P., *Proc. Natl. Acad. Sci. U.S.*, **56**, 1867–74 (1966)
70. Haberlandt, G., *Ber. Deut. Botan. Ges.*, **8**, 40–48 (1890)
71. Hageman, R. H., Arnon, D. I., *Arch. Biochem. Biophys.*, **57**, 421–36 (1955)
72. Hall, M. A., Ordin, L., in *Proc. Intern. Conf. Plant Growth Substances, 6th,* Ottawa, 1967 (See Ref. 2)
73. Hall, R. H., Csonka, L., David, H., McLennan, B., *Science*, **156**, 69–71 (1967)
74. Hanson, J. B., Hodges, T. K., *Nature*, **200**, 1009 (1963)
75. Hartmann, G., Honikel, K. O., Knüsel, F., Nüesch, J., *Biochim. Biophys. Acta*, **145**, 843–44 (1967)
76. Hartmann, K. M., *Photochem. Photobiol.*, **5**, 349–66 (1966)
77. Hartt, C. E., Kortschak, H. P., Forbes, A. J., Burr, G. P., *Plant Physiol.*, **38**, 305–18 (1963)
78. Hatch, M. D., Glasziou, K. T., *Plant Physiol.*, **38**, 344–48 (1963)
79. Hatch, M. D., Glasziou, K. T., *ibid.*, **39**, 180–84 (1964)
80. Hatch, M. D., Sacher, J. A., Glasziou, K. T., *Plant Physiol.*, **38**, 338–43 (1963)
81. Hewitt, E. J., Notton, B. A., Afridi, M. M. R. K., *Plant Cell Physiol.*, **8**, 385–97 (1967)
82. Hille, M. D., Miller, M. J., Iwasaki, K., Wahba, A. J., *Proc. Natl. Acad. Sci. U.S.*, **58**, 1652–54 (1967)
83. Hock, B., Beevers, H., *Z. Pflanzenphysiol.*, **55**, 405–14 (1966)

GLASZIOU

84. Hu, A. L., Bock, R. M., Halvorson, H. O., *Anal. Biochem.*, **4**, 489 (1962)
85. Ingle, J., Joy, K. W., Hageman, R. H., *Biochem. J.*, **100**, 577–88 (1966)
86. Jackman, M. E., Van Steveninck, R. F. M., *Australian J. Biol. Sci.*, **20**, 1063–68 (1967)
87. Jacob, F., *Science*, **152**, 1470–78 (1966)
88. Jacobsen, J. N., Varner, J. E., *Plant Physiol.*, **42**, 1596–1600 (1967)
89. Kaufman, P. B., Ghosheh, N., Ikuma, H., *Plant Physiol.*, **43**, 29–34 (1968)
90. Keller, C. J., Huffaker, R. C., *Plant Physiol.*, **42**, 1277–83 (1967)
91. Kihlman, B. A., *Actions of Chemicals in Dividing Cells* (Prentice-Hall, Englewood Cliffs, New Jersey, 1966)
92. Kirk, J. T. O., in *Biochemistry of Chloroplasts*, **1**, 319–40 (Goodwin, T. W., Ed., Academic Press, London, 1966)
93. Kersten, W., Kersten, H., Szybalski, W., *Biochemistry*, **5**, 236–44 (1966)
94. Klein, S., Bryan, G., Bogorad, L., *J. Cell Biol.*, **22**, 433–42 (1964)
95. Kringstad, H., Busengdal, H., Rasch, S., *J. Inst. Brewing*, **66**, 477–80 (1960)
96. Laties, G. G., *Australian J. Sci.*, **30**, 193–203 (1967)
97. Laszlo, J., Miller, D. S., McCarty, K. S., Hochstein, P., *Science*, **151**, 1007–9 (1966)
98. Leaver, C. J., Key, J. L., *Proc. Natl. Acad. Sci. U.S.*, **57**, 1338–44 (1967)
99. Leive, L., Kollin, V., *Biochem. Biophys. Res. Commun.*, **28**, 229–36 (1967)
100. Letham, D. S., in *Proc. Intern. Conf. Plant Growth Substances*, *6th*, Ottawa, 1967 (See Ref. 2)
101. Linko, M., Enari, T., *J. Inst. Brewing*, **66**, 480–86 (1960)
102. Linnane, A. W., Stewart, P. R., *Biochem. Biophys. Res. Commun.*, **27**, 511–16 (1967)
103. Lucas-Lenard, J., Lipmann, F., *Proc. Natl. Acad. Sci. U.S.*, **55**, 1562–66 (1966)
104. Mao, J. C. H., Wiegand, R. G., *Biochim. Biophys. Acta*, **157**, 404–13 (1968)
105. MacDonald, I. R., *Plant Physiol.*, **42**, 227–32 (1967)
106. MacDonald, I. R., *ibid.*, **43**, 274–80 (1968)
107. MacDonald, I. R., Bacon, J. S. D., Vaughan, D., Ellis, R. J., *J. Exptl. Botany*, **17**, 822–37 (1966)
108. Maclachlan, G. A., Davis, E., Fan, D. F., in *Proc. Intern. Conf. Plant Growth Substances*, *6th*, Ottawa, 1967 (See Ref. 2)
109. MacLeod, A. M., Duffus, J. H., Johnston, C. S., *J. Inst. Brewing*, **70**, 521–28 (1964)
110. MacLeod, A. M., Millar, A. S., *J. Inst. Brewing*, **68**, 322–32 (1962)
111. MacLeod, A. M., Palmer, G. H., *J. Inst. Brewing*, **72**, 580–89 (1966)
112. Marcus, A., *Plant Physiol.*, **35**, 126–28 (1960)
113. Marcus, A., Feeley, J., *Proc. Natl. Acad. Sci. U.S.*, **56**, 1770–77 (1966)
114. Margulies, M. M., *Plant Physiol.*, **42**, 218–20 (1967)
115. Minamikawa, T., Uritani, I., *Arch. Biochem. Biophys.*, **108**, 573–74 (1964)
116. Mohr, H., *Z. Pflanzenphysiol.*, **54**, 63–83 (1966)
117. Naylor, J. M., *Can. J. Botany*, **44**, 19–32 (1966)
118. Nitsan, J., Lang, A., *Develop. Biol.*, **12**, 358–76 (1965)
119. Nitsch, C., Nitsch, J. P., *Compt. Rend.*, **262**, 1102–5 (1966)
120. Nomura, M., Lowry, C. V., *Proc. Natl. Acad. Sci. U.S.*, **58**, 946–53 (1967)
121. Ohta, T., Sarkar, S., Thach, R. E., *Proc. Natl. Acad. Sci. U.S.*, **58**, 1638–44 (1967)
122. Paleg, L. G., *Plant Physiol.*, **35**, 293–99 (1960)
123. Paleg, L. G., *ibid.*, 902–6
124. Paleg, L. G., in *Proc. Intern. Conf. Plant Growth Substances*, *5th*, Gif S/Yvette, 1963, 303–17 (Ed. Centre Natl. Rech. Sci., Paris, 1964)
125. Paleg, L. G., Sparrow, D. H. B., *Nature*, **193**, 1102–3 (1962)
126. Parisi, B., Ciferri, O., *Biochemistry*, **5**, 1638–45 (1966)
127. Pateman, J. A., Cove, D. J., *Nature*, **215**, 1234–37 (1967)
128. Payes, B. (Doctoral thesis, Univ. Calif., Los Angeles, 1966)
129. Penner, D., Ashton, F. M., *Plant Physiol.*, **42**, 791–96 (1967)
130. Penner, D., Ashton, F. M., *Biochim. Biophys. Acta*, **148**, 481–85 (1967)

131. Peterson, P. J., Fowden, L., *Nature,* **200,** 148–51 (1963)

132. Peterson, P. J., Fowden, L., *Biochem. J.,* **97,** 112–24 (1965)

133. Presley, H. J., Fowden, L., *Phytochemistry,* **4,** 169–76 (1965)

134. Radley, M., *Chem. Ind. (London),* 877 (1959)

135. Reiner, J. M., *Arch. Biochem. Biophys.,* **46,** 53–79 (1953)

136. Rhodes, M. J. C., Yemm, E. W., *New Phytologist,* **65,** 331–42 (1966)

137. Rissland, I., Mohr, H., *Planta,* **77,** 239–49 (1967)

138. Ritenour, G. L., Joy, K. W., Bunning, J., Hageman, R. H., *Plant Physiol.,* **42,** 233–37 (1967)

139. Robertson, R. N., *Biol. Rev.,* **35,** 231–60 (1960)

140. Robins, M. J., Hall, R. H., Thedford, R., *Biochemistry,* **6,** 1837–48 (1967)

141. Rowsell, E. V., Goad, L. J., *Biochem. J.,* **90,** 12P (1964)

142. Sacher, J. A., Glasziou, K. T., *Biochem. Biophys. Res. Commun.,* **8,** 280–82 (1962)

143. Sacher, J. A., Hatch, M. D., Glasziou, K. T., *Plant Physiol.,* **38,** 348–54 (1963)

144. Sacher, J. A., Hatch, M. D., Glasziou, K. T., *Physiol. Plantarum,* **16,** 836–42 (1963)

145. Sandgren, E., Beling, H., *Die Brauerie,* **11,** 231 (1958)

146. Saunders, P. F., Poulson, R. H., in *Proc. Intern. Conf. Plant Growth Substances, 6th,* Ottawa, 1967 (See Ref. 2)

147. Schrader, L. E., Beevers, L., Hageman, R. H., *Biochem. Biophys. Res. Commun.,* **26,** 14–17 (1967)

148. Schrader, L. E., Ritenour, G. L., Eilrich, G. L., Hageman, R. H., *Plant Physiol.,* **43,** 930–40 (1968)

149. Schwartz, J. H., *J. Mol. Biol.,* **30,** 309–22 (1967)

150. Scott, N. S., Smillie, R. M., *Biochem. Biophys. Res. Commun.,* **28,** 598–603 (1967)

151. Shigeura, H. T., Boxer, G. E., Meloni, M. L., Sampson, S. D., *Biochemistry,* **5,** 994–1004 (1966)

152. Shuster, L., Gifford, R. H., *Arch. Biochem. Biophys.,* **96,** 534–40 (1962)

153. Siegel, M. R., Sisler, H. D., *Biochim. Biophys. Acta,* **87,** 83–89 (1964)

154. Skoog, F., Armstrong, D. J., Cherayil, J. D., Hampel, A. E., Bock, R. M., *Science,* **154,** 1354–56 (1966)

155. Slack, C. R., *Australian J. Biol. Sci.,* **18,** 781–88 (1965)

156. Smillie, R. M., Graham, D., Dwyer, M. R., Grieve, A., Tobin, N. F., *Biochem. Biophys. Res. Commun.,* **28,** 604–10 (1967)

157. Smillie, R. M., Scott, N. S., Graham, D., in *Comparative Biochemistry and Biophysics of Photosynthesis,* 332–53 (Shibata, K., Takamiya, A., Jagendorf, A. T., Fuller, R. D., Eds., University Park Press, Pennsylvania/Univ. Tokyo Press, Tokyo, 1968)

158. Spencer, D., Whitfield, P. R., *Biochem. Biophys. Res. Commun.,* **28,** 538–42 (1967)

159. Srivastava, B. I. S., Ware, G., *Plant Physiol.,* **40,** 62–64 (1965)

160. Stanley, W. M., Jr., Salas, M., Wahba, A. J., Ochoa, S., *Proc. Natl. Acad. Sci. U.S.,* **56,** 290–95 (1966)

161. Steinhart, C. E., Mann, J. D., Mudd, S. H., *Plant Physiol.,* **39,** 1030–38 (1964)

162. Stern, H., *Ann. Rev. Plant Physiol.,* **17,** 345–78 (1966)

163. Stout, E. R., Mans, R. J., *Biochim. Biophys. Acta,* **134,** 327–36 (1967)

164. Sutcliffe, J. F., *Nature,* **188,** 294–97 (1960)

165. Talal, N., Exum, E. D., *Proc. Natl. Acad. Sci. U.S.,* **55,** 1288–95 (1966)

166. Tewari, K. K., Wildman, S. G., *Proc. Natl. Acad. Sci. U.S.,* **59,** 569–76 (1968)

167. Traut, R. R., Monro, R. E., *J. Mol. Biol.,* **10,** 63–72 (1964)

168. Van Steveninck, R. F. M., Jackman, M. E., *Australian J. Biol. Sci.,* **20,** 749–60 (1967)

169. Varner, J. E., *Plant Physiol.,* **39,** 413–15 (1964)

170. Varner, J. E., Johri, M. M., in *Proc. Intern. Conf. Plant Growth Substances, 6th,* Ottawa, 1967 (See Ref. 2)

171. Vaughan, D., MacDonald, I. R., *J. Exptl. Botany,* **18,** 578–86 (1967)

172. Vaughan, D., MacDonald, I. R., *ibid.,* 587–93

173. Vaughan, D., MacDonald, I. R., *Plant Physiol.,* **42,** 456–58 (1967)

174. Venis, M. A., *Nature,* **210,** 534–35 (1966)

175. Virgin, H. I., Kahn, A., von Wett-
    stein, D., *Photochem. Photobiol.*,
    2, 83–91 (1963)
176. Wallerstein, J. S., Hale, M. G., Alba,
    R. J., *Wallerstein Lab. Commun.*,
    11, 17 (1948)
177. Weisberger, A. S., Wolfe, S., *Federa-
    tion Proc.*, **23**, 976–83 (1964)
178. Willemot, C., Stumpf, P. K., *Plant
    Physiol.*, **42**, 391–97 (1967)
179. Williams, G. R., Novelli, G. D., *Bio-
    chim. Biophys. Acta*, **155**, 183–92
    (1968)

180. Yomo, H., *Hakko Kyokai Shi*, **16**,
    444–48 (1958)
181. Yomo, H., *ibid.*, **18**, 600–2 (1960)
182. Yomo, H., *ibid.*, **19**, 284–85 (1961)
183. Yomo, H., Iinuma, H., *Am. Soc.
    Brewing Chemists Proc.*, 97–102
    (1964)
184. Zucker, M., *Plant Physiol.*, **40**, 779–
    84 (1965)
185. Zucker, M., *ibid.*, **43**, 365–74 (1968)
186. Zucker, M., Nitsch, C., Nitsch, J.
    P., *Am. J. Botany*, **52**, 271–77
    (1965)

DUAL MECHANISMS OF SALT UPTAKE IN RELATION TO COMPARTMENTATION AND LONG-DISTANCE TRANSPORT

By George G. Laties

*Department of Botanical Sciences and Molecular Biology Institute
University of California, Los Angeles*

While investigations of salt transport continue to resemble the parable of the blind men and the elephant, many more hands have been laid on of late—in an increasingly sensitive manner—and in consequence a more cohesive and rigorous view of at least the phenomenology of salt transport in higher plants and algae is gradually emerging. The subject in general has been meticulously reviewed at frequent intervals (11, 15, 51, 56). The recency of the latest published reviews and proceedings of symposia (67, 87) assures that few revelations are to be expected in these pages. Rather it will be my intention to examine a body of material in a personal, and hence a polarized, way, with the hope that such a presentation will elicit the appearance of alternative views, and will help to crystallize, and perhaps in time resolve, many unsettled aspects of the problem. Thus the treatment will be more heuristic than complete, and many noteworthy contributions will be neglected. Where my views are contrary to those of others, and particularly where I invoke interpretations of their work not shared by the authors themselves, I would hope that our differences will lead to an ultimate understanding which will prove generally satisfying.

It was intended originally to present a broad review encompassing several areas in the field of salt uptake which have received major attention in the last years. However, to do so would unavoidably have led to superficial coverage, and the choice was made in favor of a more extensive treatment of a limited area, with the expectation that other aspects of the problem will be treated in depth in the future by other authors. Consequently, little will be said directly about recent excellent work pertaining to cell electropotentials and ion transport in higher plant cells (16, 26, 34, 42, 62), nor about investigations dealing with compartmentation, specific ion fluxes, and membrane potentials in algal cells (for example, 15, 18, 28–30, 63, 64, 84, 85) and higher plant cells (13, 32, 60, 72, 96). Provocative work on the coupling of photosynthesis to ion transport both in algae (64, 85, 86) and in higher plants (43, 44) will unhappily be slighted, as will the gravid relationship between ion uptake and organic acid synthesis (33, 70). Further, attention can only be directed to the great progress which has been made in the use of autoradiography and electron probe X-ray microanalysis in the supplementation of kinetic studies relating to cellular absorption and long distance transport (49, 50).

Dual Mechanisms of Salt Absorption

In recent years our views of the salt absorption process have been profoundly affected by the discovery that ion uptake in higher plant cells is mediated by dual or multiple mechanisms. The meaning of this generalization will be elaborated and examined below. However, it is useful to stress at once that two important elements pertaining to both the conception and interpretation of absorption experiments have followed from the discovery in question. First, the level of external salt concentration of interest in absorption studies has been reduced some 500 to 1,000 times below historically prevalent experimental concentrations. Secondly, the experimental time scale has also been sharply reduced—with the recognition that absorption kinetics change significantly with time even within experimental periods of but several hours' duration (see below). In the past, absorption studies have been carried out at salt concentrations akin to, or in excess of, concentrations typical of the common nutrient solutions—that is, at levels from 1 to 50 mM. However, in 1952 Epstein & Hagen (23) made two significant discoveries which had a marked impact on work that followed. They noted first that in barley roots, certain of the alkali cations, e.g., K, Rb, and Cs, interfered competitively with the absorption of one another. Secondly, they perceived that while Na exerted no influence on Rb uptake at low Rb concentrations (1.0 mM), Na proved a competitive inhibitor of Rb absorption at high concentrations of the latter ($>$ 10 mM). Thus, it was recognized that two sites were involved in K, Rb and Cs absorption. A site operating at low concentrations was deemed quite specific, in terms of its indifference to Na—while a site operating at high concentrations was considered less specific—mediating Na uptake, as well as K, Rb and Cs transport. In subsequent years, Hagen & Hopkins (31) defined two systems for phosphate absorption by barley roots which differed broadly in their affinity for phosphate, and Fried & Noggle (27) further elucidated the multiple nature of the sites involved in cation absorption.

In 1963, Epstein and his colleagues (25) comprehensively delineated the characteristics attributable to each of the dual mechanisms involved in potassium absorption, and it is worth specifying the salient features of each system here, since much that follows will depend upon these details. The data pertain to K (Rb) and Na absorption by excised young barley roots in 10-min experimental periods. System 1, the high-affinity system or mechanism, has a K_s for potassium of approximately 0.025 mM, and a V_{max} of about 12 μmole/g fresh weight/hr. The K_I for Na (i.e., the reciprocal "affinity constant" for Na derived from its competitive interference with K uptake) for system 1 is 1.25 mM, and the V_{max} for K uptake in the presence of Na is essentially 12, which is to say that Na is a very poor, but nevertheless competitive, inhibitor of K uptake by system 1. By contrast, the K_S for potassium for system 2 is about 17 mM, and the K_I for Na is 0.84 mM, which is to say that mechanism 2 strongly favors Na absorption, albeit K and Na absorption are again competitive. In barley roots in short term experiments at high concentration, the contributions of systems 1 and 2 to the total uptake are essentially equal. That is, the V_{max} of systems 1 and 2, considered separately, are roughly similar. Total uptake in 10-min experiments is approximately 24 μmole/g/hr. In brief, the affinity of system 1 for K is roughly 700 times that of system 2. While system 1 favors K over Na by a factor of 50, system 2 favors Na over K by a factor of 20. Further, the counter-anion exerts little influence on K (Rb) uptake by system 1, but has a considerable effect on K uptake by system 2. That is, for system 2, K uptake is very much greater from a solution of KCl than from K_2SO_4. In recent years, the isotherm for system 2 has turned out to be multiple in itself (20, 22), but attention in what follows centers on the distinction between the low and high affinity mechanisms. [For a full discussion of dual mechanisms see Epstein (22).]

Are dual mechanisms in parallel or in series?—With recognition of the widespread, if not universal, prevalence of dual mechanisms of both cation and anion (21, 22) uptake, the significance of duality has naturally become a question of overriding interest. As a first step in assessing the physiological significance of dual mechanisms, it is urgent to know whether the two systems are operating in parallel or in series. Insofar as total uptake has been taken to be the sum of absorption by systems 1 and 2, and insofar as the upper limit of system 1, i.e., V_{max} for system 1, is normally subtracted from the total uptake in order to effectively characterize system 2 kinetically, systems 1 and 2 have tacitly been considered to operate in parallel[1], albeit it has been left open whether or not they deliver ions into the same compartment (25). On the basis of a comparison between essentially nonvacuolate maize root tips and vacuolate proximal root sections, Torii & Laties (92) came to the view that system 1 operates at the plasma membrane, while system 2 functions at the tonoplast. How the two systems may be thought to be in series, and yet be kinetically distinguishable and discernible, is further discussed below. But first a qualitative summary of the reasons for favoring the serial view is offered as a framework for later more rigorous discussion. (*a*) Salt levels in fertile soils are in the range of system 1 (8, cf. 25), and roots exhibit maximal ion uptake at concentrations well below 0.1 mM, so long as the soil or nutrient solution is adequately replenished at the root surface (93). That is, the plasma membrane is faced with concentrations in the range of system 1, and it is difficult to conceive

---

[1] Now explicitly deemed in parallel. For full development of this view, see Welch, R. M., Epstein, E., *Proc. Natl. Acad. Sci.*, **61**, 4417–53 (1968), a paper which appeared too late for inclusion in this review.

the evolutionary pressure for the development of a parallel absorption system with an ion affinity almost three orders of magnitude less than that for system 1. (*b*) Nonvacuolate root tips evince a simple system-1 absorption isotherm, while vacuolate root sections display a multiple isotherm reflecting the operation of systems 1 and 2 (92). (*c*) Transport to the stele is characterized by kinetics and inhibitor sensitivity typical of system 1, while total root absorption shows the kinetic behavior and inhibitor sensitivity of both systems (58). Since the symplastic theory of long-distance transport invokes the plasma membrane as the single permeability barrier (3, 12, 55), long-distance transport may be expected to reflect the characteristics of system 1. (*d*) In those cases where permeability and transport characteristics of a tissue change with time—such as during the ageing of freshly prepared storage organ slices or decorticated maize roots—it is the plasma membrane which suffers the change (47, 59, 69), and it is the isotherm for system 1 which is seen to change accordingly. (*e*) When the permeability of the plasma membrane is markedly increased by treatment of beet slices with polylysine (88), system 1 disappears, as measured by afflux analysis (71).

In addition to the qualitative considerations set out above, let us consider the quantitative kinetic consequences of considering systems 1 and 2 in parallel. The formalism which treats the kinetics of the salt transport process much as the kinetics of an enzyme reaction under simple limiting conditions offers an immensely useful operational description of the transport process, which Epstein and his colleagues have used to very great effect (23, 25). For two systems operating in parallel we have:

$$v_t = \frac{V_1(S)}{K_1 + (S)} + \frac{V_2(S)}{K_2 + (S)} \qquad\qquad 1.$$

where v equals the total uptake during the experimental period, S designates the external concentration of the ion being absorbed, V represents the maximal uptake rate mediated by system 1 (V_1) and system 2 (V_2) respectively, and K_1 and K_2 denote the ostensible "dissociation constants" or reciprocal "affinity constants" of the system 1 and 2 carrier-ion complexes. Oertli (68) has recently formulated the absorption process in terms of the parallel operation of a pump and leak system—the pump being an inwardly directed active transport mechanism, and the leak representing a carrier-mediated bidirectional passive transport. The pump-leak formulation also yields biphasic absorption curves with concentration, and with certain reasonable simplifying assumptions leads to a rate expression analogous to Equation 1. The pump-leak concept unequivocally places both systems at the plasma membrane. If the two terms of Equation 1 are summed, and the full expression thrown into the reciprocal form we have:

$$\frac{1}{v_t} = \frac{1 + \dfrac{K_1 + K_2}{(S)} + \dfrac{K_1 K_2}{(S)^2}}{V_1 + V_2 + \dfrac{V_1 K_2 + V^2 K_1}{(S)}}$$

2.

The summing is formally equivalent to the expression for two enzymes operating on one substrate (17), and the shape of the curve when $1/v$ is plotted against $1/S$ will depend on the relative values of K_1, K_2, V_1 and V_2. If in approximation of the known parameters of systems 1 and 2, K_1 is set

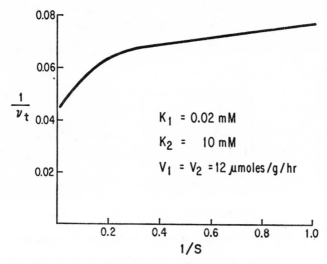

FIG. 1. Double reciprocal plot of Eq. 2. Parameters indicated in the figure.

at 0.02 mM, and K_2 at 10 mM, while both V_1 and V_2 are set at 12 μmole/g/hr [cf. (25)], the reciprocal formulation of $1/v$ against $1/S$ will in no sense be a straight line, but rather will take the form of the curve in Fig. 1. By constrast, if absorption by system 1, or by system 2 per se is individually plotted reciprocally, the anticipated linearity is beautifully fulfilled (25). We may further note that when absorption in the range of system 2 proceeds for hours rather than minutes, a plot of $1/v$ against $1/S$ is perfectly linear without any correction for the contribution of system 1 (23). What can be said about this apparent contradiction?

The disappearance of system 1: a model.—In this connection, I wish to look again at the serial model, and to impose certain specifications thereupon which seem to be borne out by experiment. The following assumptions are inherent in the model: (*a*) System 1 operates at the plasma membrane and delivers ions to the cytoplasm. (*b*) System 2 functions at the tonoplast and transports ions to the vacuole. (*c*) Roots grown for some time in water or dilute $CaSO_4$ have a relatively empty cytoplasm, i.e., in the absence of ions from without, the tonoplast pumps deplete the cytoplasm by moving ions into the vacuole. (d) When salt is provided externally in the range of system 1, system 1 transport tends to fill the cytoplasm, i.e., with a relatively empty cytoplasm, the rate of movement of ions into the cytoplasm initially exceeds the rate of transport of ions from cytoplasm to vacuole. The cytoplasm "fills" in the sense that it ultimately achieves a pseudo steady-state concentration where influx and efflux are equal (63, 72). (e) Ion transport to the vacuole increases with cytoplasmic concentration, and when the cytoplasm is "full," ion transport to the vacuole is maximal (i.e., for the range of system 1). The cytoplasm is now a filled conduit between the external solution and the vacuole, with the tonoplast the rate-limiting barrier.

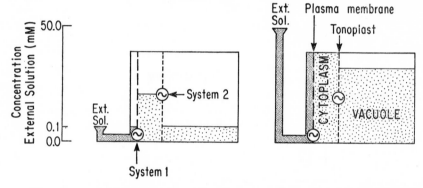

FIG. 2. Analogue model of dual transport mechanisms in series. See text.

Figure 2 presents a grossly simplified and manifestly inadequate hydrodynamic analogy which carries the model somewhat farther. The cytoplasm and vacuole are, of course, in series, and the plasma membrane is depicted as having a greater traversibility than the tonoplast. Traversibility in this context is an operational term which is used to describe the readiness with which ions pass the membrane, without regard to whether the fluxes are active or passive. In the model, pressures, or heads, are solely hydrodynamic, there being no barriers to gas movement. At low external concentrations—that is, in the range of system 1—the plasma membrane pump raises ethe level in the cytoplasm well above that of the external solution. At the same time, there is a clow movement of material into the vacuole, passive and active components of which increase with the cytoplasmic head. When the cytoplasm is "full," flux into the vacuole is equivalent to flux into the cell.

If now the external head is raised markedly, the cytoplasm may be filled more rapidly and to a greater extent than by the action of the plasma membrane pump—the cytoplasm being under pressure, so to speak. While entry under conditions of a high external head is thought to be passive to a considerable degree, diffusive penetration is by no means unrestrained. That is, the plasma membrane remains a considerable kinetic barrier if not the rate-limiting one. Further, the plasma membrane pump continues to operate. The enhanced cytoplasmic head leads to an effective engagement of the tonoplast pump—and we thereupon witness the operation of system 2. Thus, to return specifically to salt transport, there are two consequences of presenting a tissue with a high external salt concentration. First, the cytoplasm is rapidly filled—with the result that the tissue suffers an initial salt increment upon which a subsequent steady rate of uptake is superimposed. Secondly, subsequent to the initial act of cytoplasmic filling, "steady-state" uptake reflects the delivery of ions to the vacuole and kinetically it is now as if one transport system were operating, namely, system 2.

We see that the kinetic visualization of dual mechanisms depends upon both the relatively high affinity of system 1 compared with system 2 for the transport of a given ion, and on the relatively greater traversibility of the plasma membrane at low concentrations, compared with the tonoplast. The flux values for plasma membrane and tonoplast respectively in higher plant cells either fit the latter requirement, or may be deemed consistent with that requirement under appropriate conditions (72, cf. 59, 60, 69). By contrast, in a variety of large-celled algae the traversibility of the tonoplast seems to be much greater than that of the plasma membrane [*Nitella* (63, 65); *Chaetomorpha* (18); *Hydrodictyon* (84)]. Under the circumstances, it will be of great interest to determine whether the latter algae manifest a dual or multiple isotherm (they should not), and to compare their behavior in this respect with *Valonia*, which may be thought anomalous with respect to the disposition of membrane potentials and pumps (28, 29).

While the most straightforward explanation for the dual isotherm is that offered above, and encompassed in the model, there are two phenomena that have been described in algae which, if found to apply to higher plant cells, may assume marked importance in our views of absorption kinetics. Specifically, in *Nitella* the influx of potassium suddenly jumps fivefold as the external concentration is increased from 1.0 to 2.0 mM. At the same time, membrane resistance drops six to sevenfold (Spanswick, personal communication). In *Valonia* a relatively small change in turgor pressure decreases potassium influx at least threefold and increases efflux (30). Both phenomena, if applicable, can be expected to have a marked effect on absorption isotherms.

To return to root absorption, in short experimental periods when the cytoplasm is initially relatively empty, its filling at low external concentrations will be witnessed as the contribution of system 1. At higher external concentrations, the relatively rapid filling of the cytoplasm will provide the base line for system 2. It is as if, in the summing of the two terms of Equation 1, the first is considered a constant. In this view, in experiments of longer duration, the first term will soon be overwhelmed, and analysis of absorption as a function of concentration will nicely fit expectations based on the operation of a single carrier system. What evidence supports this view?

At external concentrations of 10 mM or greater, net uptake rates over a period of several hours for a great variety of plant tissues—roots and storage organ slices alike—cluster about values of 4 to 6 μmole/g/hr. By contrast, barley root absorption in an initial 10-min period evinces a total V_{max} of some 24 μmole/g/hr, and a rate of some 18 μmole/g/hr at an external KCl concentration of 10 mM (25). As pointed out, correction for V_{max} of system 1 must be made in 10-min experiments if the characteristics of system 2 are to be adequately described. However, in 3-hr experiments, again with barley roots, $1/v$ is a linear function of $1/S$ in the range of system 2, without any correction for system 1 (23). It is significant that in the latter instance, uptake at an external concentration of 10 mM is approximately 7 μmole/g/hr, rather than 18 μmole/g/hr—i.e., equivalent to the expected uptake of one system alone and not to the sum of two systems operating at the same time. With more prolonged absorption periods, or with roots raised under full nutrient conditions, it is to be expected that the total net absorption rate would approach 4 to 6 μmole/g/hr. The foregoing comparison emphasizes the special features of short-term experiments originally stressed by Epstein and his colleagues (24). Particularly, details of the absorption process which are lost in longer periods can be illuminated in short-term experiments.

The general aspects of cytoplasmic filling have been examined by Osmond & Laties in red beet discs (69). In the experiments in question, the exchange-time was first determined for wash-exchanging the contents of the cytoplasm [$t_{1/2}$ at 25° for Cl is approximately 30 to 40 min in beet discs; in barley roots it is a mere 5 to 6 min (Pitman, personal communication)]. Following a period of absorption (of ^{42}K, or ^{36}Cl), discs were bathed in unlabeled salt solution so as to wash-exchange the bulk of the cytoplasmic label. Hence the label remaining in the tissue was predominantly in the vacuole. At very low external concentrations, 0.01 mM, the time-course of uptake to the vacuole was described by a curve concave upward to begin with and finally linear. With increasing external concentration, absorption became linear with time following increasingly shorter periods. At concentrations above the range of system 1, absorption proved linear from the start. The interpretation made of the rising rate of uptake to the vacuole with time at low external concentration is that transport to the vacuole increases with increasing concentration in the cytoplasm [cf. (79)]. An isotherm for transport to the vacuole can be constructed in the low concentration range, albeit system 1 is postulated to operate at the plasma membrane. It is axiomatic that at low external concentrations, transport across the tonoplast is dependent upon ions delivered across the plasma membrane by system 1. If the initial rates of vacuolar chloride up-take at low external concentrations are utilized, a conventional hyperbolic isotherm may be plotted. However, if the steady rates at each concentration are plotted—i.e., slopes of the linear portions of the time-course curves at each concentration—the chloride isotherm is almost a horizontal line. That is, once the cytoplasm is filled, transport to the vacuole is virtually independent of the external concentration in the range of system 1. Filling time, however, is inversely related to the external concentration. The foregoing is to be expected only when the plasma membrane influx is greater than the tonoplast influx to the vacuole prior to cytoplasmic filling. The foregoing observations emphasize the need for an extensive comparison of the duality of the absorption isotherm in low salt and high salt roots respectively.

If the cytoplasm is first prefilled with nonradioactive chloride, subsequent movement of radioactive chloride to the vacuole is sharply diminished. The time required for the maximal prefilling effect coincides with the filling time as measured directly. Further, if prefilled tissue is incubated for some time in the absence of KCl, the prefilling effect is dissipated by dint of the transfer of cytoplasmic salt to the vacuole, and subsequently administered ^{36}Cl is then transported to the vacuole at the rate typical of untreated tissue. The recovery rate of prefilled tissue has much the same time-constant as the filling process. With respect to radioisotope absorption, the cytoplasm acts as a mixing chamber. When it is empty—as appears to be the case in discs aged in dilute $CaSO_4$—radioisotope passes undiluted to the vacuole. When it is prefilled, radioisotope is diluted in the cytoplasm, and the movement of label to the vacuole is thus diminished. At high external concentrations, the effect of prefilling is markedly reduced. Under the latter conditions, the specific activity of the cytoplasm presumably rapidly attains that of the external solution, in accordance with the postulated diffusive penetration of the plasma membrane at high external concentrations. In summary, systems 1 and 2 are independently perceptible in short absorption periods when the cytoplasm is initially depleted. In long periods, when the cytoplasm has been filled to a pseudo steady-state concentration (63, 72), net uptake will be to the vacuole. At high concentrations, especially following an initial period of cytoplasmic filling, there will be ostensibly but one system operating, system 2. System 1 will be functional but masked.

Long-Distance Transport in Relation to Dual Mechanisms

Theories of long-distance transport.—The major theories regarding the means whereby salts are delivered to the xylem, ultimately to be moved to the shoot, are clearly distinguishable in their formulation, if not experimentally. The theory of Crafts & Broyer (12) postulates that ions are accumulated in the cytoplasm of the cortex cells, which in concert deliver ions to the stele through the cytoplasmic continuum, the symplasm (3, 12, 55). In this view, the active or metabolically implemented event is limited to ion

transport across the plasma membrane, and subsequent aspects of ion movement to the xylem are deemed passive. Further, the cortex is considered a
gathering agency, the vacuoles of the cortex are looked upon as diversion-
ary sumps, and the endodermis is considered a barrier to passive movement
between cortex and stele by way of the wall free-space. In the alternative
view, ions destined for the xylem move freely through the cortical free
space, to be actively transported for the first time either by the endodermis
(91) or by cells within the stele (1, 2, 38, 73, 75, 76). In this view in its
purest form, the cortex is an incidental component in radial salt transport,
and an active process apart from transport across the plasma membrane of
the cortex cells is considered responsible for accumulation in the xylem.
The latter theory has lately been modified to assign the active role to the
stelar parenchyma (73, 75, 76) or to the xylem elements themselves (1, 2,
16, cf. 38) while imputing a preliminary selective function to the cortex.
For two reasons, emphasis has recently been placed on the involvement of a
unique active process—apart from root absorption per se—in ion transport
to the conducting elements. First, the total transport of K plus Na to the
shoots of barley seedlings from solutions of relatively high concentration
has been found to be virtually independent of concentration and the ratio of
K to Na. Pitman has taken this to suggest a saturated anion pump as the
prime-mover of cation transfer to the xylem (73, 76). Secondly, the enhanced preference for K in movement to the shoot, over that exhibited by
the absorption process per se, has further suggested an additional active
process in long-distance transport (5, 6, 75, 79). Both these matters will be
taken up below.

I wish first to examine some general considerations which strongly pre-
dispose me to the symplasm theory, and then to proceed to more specific
details. Attention has been drawn in earlier pages to what appears to be a
maximal or near maximal rate for steady salt absorption by a variety of
fibrous roots, tissue slices, and even algae—namely 4 to 6 μmole/g fr wt/hr.
It is further to be noted that this maximal value characterizes both root
absorption per se and radial transport to the xylem. In low salt roots, the
bulk of salt taken up initially finds its way to the cortex vacuoles (36, 37,
80, 90). When the cortex cells approach saturation, absorption continues
unabated, but salts are now delivered to the xylem—as can be measured by
their appearance in the xylary exudate (36, 37). That is, transport to cortex vacuoles, and to the stele, are competing processes in parallel, the rate-
limiting event in both cases being passage across the plasma membrane of
the cortex cells. When salt is withdrawn from the milieu, transport to the
xylem (37, 39, 95) or to the shoot (6, 90) occurs at the expense of cortex
vacuolar salt. Interestingly, redistribution from cortex vacuoles to stelar
vascular tissue frequently displays an endogenous rhythm (95). Barring the
unlikely prospect, at moderate external concentrations, that accumulation
into cortex cells is sufficiently rapid to markedly reduce the concentration in
the free space at the endodermis boundary, compared with the concentra-

tion in the external solution, it is only the symplasm concept which anticipates that vacuolar and radial transport should be in competition.

More to the point perhaps is the rate of accumulation or secretion which must be assigned to a selected group of stelar cells if stelar absorption is to be imputed to them. Thus, simply comparing the area of the tan- . gential face of the endodermal cylinder with the area of the combined surface of the cortex cells in maize or barley roots, it follows that, at the very least, the transport activity per unit surface of the external tangentially oriented endodermal plasma membrane must be roughly 40 times that of cortex cell plasma membranes if the endodermis is to account for observed rates of salt uptake. Where the endodermis is well developed and differentiated, and where absorption by the endodermis and delivery to the stele would perforce be limited to the passage cells, the rate of uptake by the latter would have to be from 150 to 200 times that of the average specific absorption rate of root tissue.

Recently Anderson & House (1) have re-examined the meaning of the gradient of absorptive capacity of maize roots from the apex to *circa* 10 cm behind the tip. They established that the hydraulic conductivity—a parameter essentially equivalent, in relation to transverse water movement, to the osmotic permeability of the roots to water—varies but little along the full length of the root. Thus the basis for the inverse relation between distance from the root tip and radial salt transport capacity was properly considered to pertain to salt absorption per se. Anderson & House established that xylem elements with visible cytoplasm may be seen as far as 10 cm from the root tip [cf. Davis (16)], and that the number of xylem vessels with visible cytoplasm decreases with distance from the tip much as does absorptive capacity. On this basis, they wish to assign the active process for ion transport into the xylem to the living xylem cells themselves, a tenous deduction which faces some formidable obstacles. For one thing, if the endodermis must display an inordinately high absorption rate to qualify as the site of the stelar pump (see above), the problem is compounded with the less prevalent xylem tissue. Anderson & House speak of accumulation of ions into the exudate "across the plasmalemma or tonoplast membranes of the xylem vessels." The foregoing concept stems from an early formulation by Hylmo (38) wherein single xylem cells were deemed responsible for exudation. Specifically, Hylmo considered that as each developing xylem cell matured to the point where its proximal cross wall ruptured, the peripherally disposed plasma membrane and tonoplast continued to pump salt into the vacuole—and hence into the xylary conduit—until the contiguous distal xylem cell matured and ruptured. In this view, the so-called "test-tube" xylem vessels were deemed solely responsible for salt accumulation in the exudation fluid. The disintegration envisaged by Hylmo has always seemed quantitatively inadequate, and continues to seem so in the light of Anderson & House's data that a quantity of exudate is secreted each hour equivalent to the full xylem volume of the total 10 cm excised root—namely, 4 μl. It goes without saying that a number of xylem cells having a total volume of 4 μl is not created and destroyed in a single excised root in an hour. At the very least, one would wish to know whether the membranes bounding the cytoplasm of xylem cells several centimeters from the tip are differentially permeable. That is, are the cells plasmolyzable? Are the manifestations of cytoplasm as seen in the electron microscope enough to warrant the assumption that the cells *in situ* are physiologically intact? If live xylem cells are considered the locus of stelar pumps without assuming that the cells must disintegrate to release their contents to the xylem stream, are we to assume a longitudinal xylary symplasm leaking into the nonliving mature xylem elements? It is entirely likely that a convincing inverse correlation could be made between absorption capacity and distance from the root tip on the basis of some other feature. While hydraulic conductivity does not change markedly with proximal distance, it has been recognized since the earliest studies that root absorption per se decreases with distance from the tip (80, 90). That is, the cortex gathering function (55, 80) bears the same relation to proximal distance as does the prevalence of cytoplasm-containing xylem cells. Considering the substantiation by Lundegardh (55) that exudation rate of wheat roots is proportional to the extent of contact between cortex and stele, and recalling his elegant demonstration that excised, detipped roots exude equally well from both ends when an arch of root is placed in solution, the model which continues to best fit the descriptive facts is that of the cortex accumulating and collecting ions and delivering them to an inert xylem.

In spite of what has been said above, Davis (16) has made a most provocative observation which must either be explained or explained away. He noted that the potential between the exudate of an excised maize root and the external solution is not dissipated as successive segments are cut basipetally from the tip, with the root, except for the exuding end, remaining in solution. If the xylem were a continuous open conduit, the potential should drop to zero. In fact, the potential does not drop until all but 1 to 2 cm of an 11-cm root is cut away—and then the potential drops to about half (15 mV) the normal potential. The explanation offered by Davis is that the xylem comprises living cells with differentially permeable cross walls through some 10 cm of the root length. Since individual xylem cells are considerably less than 1 cm long, one must know why the potential drops on cutting when the cut ends are 1 to 2 cm apart. Since the xylem contains cytoplasm through 10 cm of maize roots, is it possible that vessel end walls are plugged on cutting much as are sieve tubes? It would be informative to make resistance measurements over the length of a root excised and exuding at both ends [see Lundegardh (55)]. Knowing the total vessel length and cross section, and knowing the concentration of the xylary fluid, one could determine whether the resistance is or is not compatible with the presumption of an open conduit.

Sodium discrimination in long-distance transport.—What then of the enhanced selectivity for K over Na which characterizes transport to the shoot when compared with root absorption? It must be pointed out at once that the discussion of radial transport has taken no note so far of the relative contributions of systems 1 and 2 to the process. It may prove useful at this point to dwell on the dual nature of ion absorption in relation to long-distance transport, both to illuminate the latter and to re-enforce some judgments about the former. On the basis of the hypothesis offered at the outset regarding the localization of systems 1 and 2, it might be expected that at moderate concentrations in the range of system 2, radial transport should appear passive. While in submerged excised roots, which may be called a closed system, system 1 disappears kinetically after a short time when the cytoplasm is filled, in an open system (i.e., in seedlings) where the cytoplasmic salt of the root may be moved to the shoot as rapidly as absorption from the milieu takes place, absorption to the cytoplasm continues unabated (7). Thus, so long as the cytoplasm is being constantly depleted by salt movement to the vessels, system 1 continues to contribute significantly to total uptake. At an external concentration of 10 mM, transport by system 1 in an open system may be expected to be about equal to the diffusive flux through the plasma membrane [total uptake at 10 mM is less than twice the $V_{\max}$ for system 1 (25)]. For this reason, the isotherm for long-distance transport in the high range will not reflect unambiguous diffusion kinetics (see below). Since both system 1 pumping and diffusion contribute significantly to the radial transport process, the concentration of salt in the xylem vessels will exceed that in the solution and exudation will persist.

It must now be recalled that while system 1 favors K, system 2 markedly favors Na (4, 6, 25, 82, 83). Thus, so long as roots are not salt-saturated, transport across the plasma membrane will result in a sharp enrichment of K in the cytoplasm owing to the preference of system 1 for K (and to the activity of a Na extrusion pump, as will be seen below), and subsequent transport into the vacuole will further enrich the cytoplasm with K owing to the preference of system 2 for Na. Thus the cytoplasm will have a distinctly higher K/Na ratio than the vacuole—and on the assumption that it is the cytoplasmic salt which is delivered to the xylem through the symplasm, it follows that the shoot will have a higher K/Na ratio than will the total root. In this connection, it is pertinent that the ratio of K/Na in the shoot bears a constant relationship to the K/Na ratio in the root, albeit the former is always higher (73, 75, 76). It is of further significance that in barley seedlings prolonged continued delivery of K- enriched salt to the shoot corresponds closely to the relative growth rate of the seedlings (73, 76); that is, continuous growth provides the opportunity for the continuous withdrawal of Na from root cytoplasm to root vacuole, with resultant enrichment of K in the shoot.

Attention has been focussed from the outset on the importance of time as a factor in describing the kinetics of absorption and long distance transport. Pitman et al. (79, cf. 77) have recently offered additional insight into the selectivity of K over Na both in root vacuolar absorption and in transport to the shoot in studies which demonstrate the build-up of selectivity with time in low-salt barley roots exposed to a mixture of 2.5 mM KCl and 7.5 mM NaCl (10 mM K + Na, Cl). Barley roots reared in dilute CaSO$_4$, excised, and submerged in 10 mM K + Na, Cl show little selectivity for some 5 hr. Thereafter K absorption is markedly favored, Na uptake virtually coming to a stand-still. K absorption proceeds for some 15 hr in all, at which point the roots are salt saturated, and there is no further net uptake of either Na, K, or Cl. However, while an unabated influx of labeled K or Cl is readily demonstrable in high-salt roots, the influx of labeled Na has been reduced to an insignificant level. Experimental conditions are such that the noted absorption is primarily to the vacuole. Absorption periods extend through 30 hr, and in experiments involving radioisotope uptake, roots are exchange-washed in unlabeled salt solution for 10 min at the end of the experimental period. The half-time for cytoplasmic exchange in barley roots at 25° is about 6 min for Cl (Pitman, personal communication), 12 min for Na, and 50 min for K (78). Influx to the cytoplasm of barley root cells from the external solution has been shown by Pitman & Saddler (78) to be much the same for K and Na at high-salt concentration, i.e., 10 mM K + Na, Cl. Nevertheless, the ratio of K/Na in the cytoplasm is roughly 11/1, whereas the ratio in the vacuole is less than 3/1 (79). The flux from cytoplasm to vacuole is much greater for K than for Na. The above facts, taken together, have led Pitman and his co-workers to the view that there is an active Na extrusion pump at the plasma membrane [much as in *Nitella* (63), *Chaetomorpha* (18), and carrot (13)], as well as an inwardly directed K pump—the two together leading to a high K/Na ratio in the cytoplasm.[2] Jennings (41) further supports the existence of a K pump at the plasma membrane. At low external concentrations (less than 1.0 mM), the selectivity of the plasma membrane K pump (4, 25) adequately accounts for K enrichment in the cytoplasm. At high external concentrations (10 mM), the cytoplasmic Na extrusion pump ostensibly exerts considerable influence, although selective plasma membrane transport by system 1 remains a significant factor, since system 1 continues to account for at least half the total uptake (see above). The question remains, why is K selectivity at high external concentrations enhanced with time? The explanation may have to do partly with cytoplasmic filling—the Na extrusion pump being of little consequence when there is little Na in the cytoplasm. However, the Na exchange time being as short as it is, ($t_{1/2} = 12$ min at 25°), there would appear to be more to the explanation, including perhaps the development of the pump in response to the presence of salt (79).

With symplastic transport to the stele acknowledged, K enrichment in

---

[2] The operation of a Na extrusion pump in bean root cortical cells has been deduced by Scott, B. I. H., Gulline, H., Pallaghy, C. K. (*Australian J. Biol. Sci.,* **21,** 185–200, 1968) from measured values of fluxes, concentrations, and potential differences in relation to the Ussing-Teorell criterion for passive ion movement. See Pallaghy, C. K., Scott, B. I. H., as well (*Australian J. Biol. Sci.,* in press) for an extensive analysis of the electrochemical state of bean root cells.

the cytoplasm accounts for K enrichment in the shoot. However, the K/Na ratio in the cortex vacuoles is well below that in the cytoplasm, and it follows that additional discrimination must take place at the tonoplast. It is here that the preference of system 2 for Na must exert its effect (see 40). While the vacuolar Na concentration is three to four times that in the cytoplasm, the K concentration is roughly the same in both compartments (78).

The ostensible disparity between Pitman's observations and those of Epstein and his colleagues (25, 82, 83) regarding K selectivity in the range of system 2 poignantly emphasizes the importance of time—and hence of salt status (77)—in the kinetic characterization of the absorption process. While Epstein limited the absorption period to 10 to 20 min, and used roots freshly excised from seedlings grown in dilute $CaSO_4$, Pitman studied Na absorption by roots held in 10 mM K + Na, Cl over a period of several hours (79). The short term experiments with low-salt roots permitted an examination of system 2—located at the tonoplast as herein postulated—relatively unobscured by the salt status of the cytoplasm. By contrast, in roots held in Na for some time, the development of a Na exclusion mechanism—presumably a Na extrusion pump situated at the plasma membrane—so influenced the cytoplasmic K/Na ratio that the characteristics of system 2 were masked by the pre-empting control of the cytoplasmic milieu. Uptake into the vacuoles of the root will perforce reflect events at both the plasma membrane and tonoplast. Which events exert the greater control will depend on external salt concentration, salt status of the roots, and time.

It is not surprising that the total cation delivered to the vacuole is equivalent to the quantity of absorbed chloride—the latter being the most prevalently transported anion. However, where long distance transport is concerned, the upper limit of K plus Na absorption need not be set by an anion pump at the plasma membrane of either root cortex, stelar parenchyma, or xylem (witness K and Na absorption and transport from dilute sulfate solutions). The apparent limit of K plus Na uptake to the shoots—ascribed to a constraint imposed by an anion pump implementing salt movement into the stele (73, 76)—may be ascribed to salt saturation of the cells of the shoot (see below).

Bange (4, 5) and Bange & Vliet (6) have examined the basis for the selective movement of K to the shoots of maize seedlings. They came to the conclusion that two carriers are involved in K and Na absorption, the first of which has a very great, and selective, affinity for K, and the second of which is essentially unselective, and has an affinity for K 100 times less than the first system. Furthermore, it is the first system which is deemed primarily responsible for K movement to the shoot. Thus, while Bange's two systems are not couched in terms of Epstein's mechanisms 1 and 2, they very much seem to fit the bill, and by the same token, to fit the hypothesis being proposed herein. Subsequently, Bange & Hooymans (7) extended their views to suggest that separate carriers mediate K and Na transport, and that the competition for absorption between the two ions has to do with competition between the separate ion carrier complexes for some common requisite rather than with competition between the ions themselves for a single carrier (cf. 73). The judgment was made because neither ion appeared to totally suppress the absorption of the other as its relative concentration was increased, nor did the absorption of a given ion, when its concentration was raised in the presence of the other, attain the maximal rate achieved in the absence of the other. However, the analysis was made by direct plotting through a limited concentration range, and an indication of competitiveness of the ions per se for a common carrier, so unequivocally demonstrated in Epstein's analysis (23, 25), could well have been missed. Visual inspection of the graphs suggests that the K_s for a given ion (Na) is noticeably lower in the presence of the other (K)—an indication of competitiveness. Further, concentrations at which the K/Na interrelationships were explored lay above that for the maximal activity of the high affinity system described by Bange (4) in maize, and just in the midst of the low affinity system. In view of the relatively different affinities for K and Na displayed by these two systems, the range chosen to examine their interaction may well have led to ambiguity. Further, the analysis was made in the absence of Ca^{++}, a condition which precludes an accurate estimation of ion affinity and of competitiveness (81, 94).

Bange & Hooymans speak of absorption, which is thought to involve carrier-mediated transport from the solution directly to the vacuole, and of binding, which is considered to represent the association of ions with elements in the cytoplasm. In the latter instance, ions are thought to pass the plasma membrane passively, i.e., by diffusion. "Bound" ions are available for further transport to the vacuole, and insofar as binding sites and carriers are considered to display similar specificity regarding K and Na respectively, it is considered that carriers and binding sites bear a generic chemical resemblance to each other. However, binding sites are estimated to exist at a concentration of 0.1 M in the cytoplasm—which implicates most of the cytoplasm.

Binding sites are a purely operational concept. Their postulated existence stems from the observation that at low concentrations the time-course of Rb or Na absorption is nonlinear, i.e., there is an absorption shoulder of relatively rapid uptake, followed by a prolonged period in which absorption is linear with time. The initial period of rapid uptake, approximately 2 hr, is taken to represent cytoplasmic binding. At very low concentrations (0.005 mM Rb_2SO_4), 5 mM Ca^{++} abolishes the shoulder. At higher concentrations (0.1 mM RbCl), the shoulder persists in the presence of Ca^{++}. Where Na absorption is at issue, Ca^{++} abolishes the shoulder at 0.1 mM Na_2SO_4, and fails to do so at 2.5 mM Na_2SO_4. The regression of the linear element of the absorption time-course to the ordinate gives an estimate of the quantity of Rb, or Na "bound." Whatever the means whereby monovalent cations enter the cytoplasm, entry is markedly controlled by Ca^{++} (cf. 94).

Perhaps the effect of Ca^{++} may offer a clue to the interpretation of phenomena described above. Rains, Schmid & Epstein have emphasized the essentiality of Ca^{++} in maintaining the specificities of the dual absorption mechanisms (81), and in maintaining the integrity of the absorption mechanism in general. Thus, at low concentrations in the presence of Ca^{++}, Na interferes but slightly with K absorption, whereas in the absence of Ca^{++}, Na and K interfere with each other through a wide range of ratios. More to the point, perhaps, Ca^{++} severely inhibits Na uptake by system 1—so much so that in the presence of low levels of K the competitive interference by K, together with the inhibition by Ca^{++}, virtually abolishes Na absorption in the low range (82).

In the framework of the hypothesis set out earlier regarding the locus of systems 1 and 2, I would propose the following interpretation of Bange & Hooymans' observations in relation to Epstein's discoveries. The alkali cations traverse the plasma membrane both by the intermediation of system 1 and by diffusion, the former being of greatest consequence at low concentrations. Ca^{++} serves to knit the plasma membrane, minimizing diffusive penetration and emphasizing the role of system 1. Since system 1 markedly favors K over Na, Na uptake is reduced to vanishingly low rates at low concentrations in the presence of Ca^{++} and K (82). In the absence of Ca^{++}, diffusive penetration of Na (and of the other alkali cations as well) into the cytoplasm is considerable, leading first to the shoulder described by Bange & Hooymans, and secondly to the diminished specificity vis-à-vis K and Na, which reflects the characteristics of tonoplast transport rather than plasma membrane transport. In this view, the shoulder represents a relatively rapid filling of the cytoplasm—which is followed by slower transport across the tonoplast. When Ca^{++} is present, transport across the plasma membrane becomes the rate-limiting event, and hence absorption is linear with time. When the external concentration is raised sufficiently, Ca^{++} notwithstanding, the time-course becomes biphasic again, as the cytoplasm is filled more rapidly than salt is initially transferred to the vacuole.

Bange & Hooymans' observations recall an earlier instance of biphasic absorption kinetics which may bear on current views of absorption in relation to compartmentation. When potato slices are transferred from room temperature to the cold, chloride absorption, normally linear with time, becomes biphasic (45, 61). While a new shoulder is produced each time the tissue is warmed and returned to the cold, the development of a shoulder can be prevented by the administration of dinitrophenol during the warm experience. In the past, the shoulder was attributed to "latent ion transport capacity"—developed at room temperature and manifested for the first hour in the cold—but in view of our increasing comprehension of compartmentation and the kinetics pertaining thereto, it seems more likely that the shoulder is related to filling an empty cytoplasm, the cytoplasm being emptied, relatively speaking, in favor of the vacuole each time the tissue is returned to room temperature in the absence of salt.

When Na "binding" is prevented in barley roots by the impairment of Na access with Ca^{++}, additional "binding" sites are not made available to K (7). This is entirely in accord with the concept of filling the cytoplasm. Further, the K_s for "binding" of Rb (7) is much like the K_s for absorption of Rb by system 1 (25). Finally, while the time-course for uptake is biphasic with excised roots (0.1 mM Rb), it is linear with intact seedlings (7). In the interpretation being offered, the cytoplasm is simply not "filled" when cytoplasmic salt is constantly transferred to the shoot.

The symplasm in radial transport.—Whether or not cells within the stele perform an active function of xylary secretion in addition to the active transport across the plasma membrane of the cortex cells, Pitman has calculated that diffusion through the free space does not deliver ions to the stele rapidly enough to supply the quantity of salt appearing in barley root exudates (73). The disparity is very great. Consequently, the symplasm is a major pathway of radial ion movement in all cases. If it be accepted that ions may permeate the plasma membrane passively at high external concentrations, it follows that there is no need to invoke passage through the free-space to explain the diminishing selectivity which attends radial transport as concentration is increased. In fact, Pitman (73, 75) has shown that the K/Na ratio in barley shoots drops markedly as the external concentration of both ions is increased, while their ratio in solution is kept constant. Anderson & Reilly (2), in turn, have demonstrated that removal of the outer cortical layers diminishes salt exuded by excised maize roots at concentrations of 1.0 mM or less, but not at concentrations in excess of 10 mM. That is, the system 1 mediated cortex gathering-function matters at low external concentrations, whereas it is of relatively little consequence when entry into and through the symplast is diffusive.

Isotherms of long-distance transport.—Lüttge & Laties (57–59) have specifically examined the question of long-distance transport in relation to the roles of systems 1 and 2 in the process. Isotherms for transport to the xylem in maize roots were obtained from exudation studies of single roots, as well as from "two-plate" experiments—wherein transport was effected from root tips immersed in experimental solution in a small donor petri dish or plate to an unlabeled solution bathing the excised basal root end immersed in a receptor dish. In addition, isotherms were constructed for transport to the shoots of intact seedlings. In each case, root absorption per se was characterized by the standard multiple isotherm denoting the involvement of systems 1 and 2. Long-distance transport, on the other hand, evinced a conventional isotherm in the range of system 1, while displaying a linear or exponentially rising isotherm in the range of system 2 (57). Long-distance transport manifested precisely the same isotherm through a wide concentration range typical of nonvacuolate root tips (92). Consequently, the interpretation put on the isotherm for transport to the xylem or shoot is that at low concentrations, system 1 at the plasma membrane mediates salt absorption to the symplasm, and the kinetics of this process are reflected in the hyperbolic isotherm for ion movement to the xylem. At high concentrations, considerable diffusive movement through the plasma membrane is superimposed on the activity of system 1, and the isotherm for long distance movement tends towards the linear. Absorption per se, on the other hand, involving as it does transport to the vacuole, evinces the intermediation of system 2 at the tonoplast at high concentration, and the overall isotherm is thus double or multiple. The isotherm for long-distance transport is reminiscent of those constructed by Oertli (68) on the basis of a model where an active pumping system and a passive leak system operate side by side.

Two-plate experiments allow separate evaluation of long-distance transport through the stele and through the cortex cylinder, respectively, of decorticated maize roots (57). Absorption by the cortex is almost equivalent to absorption by the intact root—the freshly excised stele contributing little to total uptake (cf. 47). Long-distance transport, on the other hand, is accomplished only by the intact root, neither cortex nor stele implementing the process individually. The foregoing observations speak for the gathering function of the cortex and the passive function of the xylary conduits in the stele. The decortication process does not appear to impair the absorptive capacity of cortex cells abutting the sheared endodermis, and therefore there is no reason to presume that the behavior of live xylem cells will be impaired by decortication [cf. Anderson & Reilly (2)]. The failure of excised steles to exude is consequently of considerable significance. Absorption by the cortical cylinder has all the characteristics of absorption by the intact root. When decorticated roots are left attached to the seedling, salt transport to the shoots is first enhanced compared with transport in seedlings with intact roots, and after a day, diminished (59). The noted behavior is very much in accord with the known characteristics of excised steles, which show little differential permeability of the plasma membrane, and little capacity for salt absorption, immediately on excision—and manifest marked differential permeability (and active transport) after a day's incubation (see below). In newly excised steles attached to the shoot, the symplast is leaky and serves as an effective diffusion path to the xylem. A leaky stelar parenchyma is the linchpin of the symplasm theory of radial transport. Following ageing, excised stele comes to resemble cortex, insofar as stelar cells become capable of active transport and the plasma membrane becomes differentially permeable (47, 59). In this condition, contrary to the presumed situation *in vivo*, stelar cells are not leaky, and the cells surrounding the xylem consequently retain the salt they absorb and less readily pass salt to the xylem. The observed behavior is totally at variance with the model wherein stelar parenchyma or living xylem cells per se are considered to be the seat of active transport into the xylem (1, 16, 38, 73).

This brings us to the contention of Yu & Kramer (97), that stele and cortex of maize roots absorb ions equally well. Except for one experiment, Yu & Kramer invariably separated stele and cortex after an absorption period by intact roots. Where uptake is by intact roots, stele and cortex do indeed absorb ions—phosphate in this case—to the same extent. Both Laties & Budd (47) and Lüttge & Laties (59) have emphasized that it is the plasma membrane which is leaky in freshly excised stele, and presumably *in vivo* as well. With ions delivered to the cytoplasm of stelar parenchyma by way of the symplast, there is every reason to expect system 2 of the tonoplast to effectively absorb salt into the vacuole. However, with freshly excised stele, passive flux across the "leaky" plasma membrane is still very much less than that ultimately across the plasma membrane of excised steles following the development of system 1 with ageing (see below)—and by implication, very much less than is delivered to the cytoplasm of stelar parenchyma *in vivo* by way of the symplasm. In the one instance where stele and cortex were separated before absorption by Yu & Kramer, the absorption rate was of the magnitude noted for newly decorticated steles by Laties & Budd. Further, Yu & Kramer studied absorption of ^{32}P-labeled phosphate, and the retention of labeled phosphate as organic phosphate in the cytoplasm in cells where the plasma membrane might be quite permeable to inorganic phosphate is entirely possible. For this reason, Yu has subsequently examined the distribution of Rb and of Cl between stele and cortex (98). While both ions were absorbed by stele and cortex alike, the two tissues were separated, as before, only after the absorption period.

In addition to the fact that transport to the shoot appears to involve discrimination between K and Na beyond that effected by transport across the plasma membrane of the cortex cells, a separate active act for secretion into the xylem has been postulated on the basis that total cation uptake (K + Na) to the shoot is very little influenced by external concentration through a very wide range (73, 75, 76). In this view, an anion pump in living xylem, or in stelar parenchyma, is the prime mover for cation accumulation in the xylem and ostensibly sets the upper limit of transport. Cations are thought to follow passively. The discrimination between K and Na is conceived to take place during delivery of salt to the periphery of whatever cells in the stele are considered to pump salt into the xylem. At relatively low concentrations there is agreement (41, 73, cf. 80) that radial transport is predominantly through the symplasm, and that selective plasma membrane absorption and Na extrusion (78, 79) primarily account for the ultimate K enrichment in the shoot. At high external concentrations, and under conditions of vigorous transpiration, passive diffusion through the water free space in the cortex wall gains significance (75)[3], and since the latter process is relatively nondiscriminatory, there is considerably less enrichment of K in the solution which bathes the stele. It must be emphasized that the latter interpretation does not conceive passive movement directly into the vascular elements, but rather limits passive movement to the radial path between the solution and the putative secretory cells of the stele. The foregoing is considered to be so even when transpiration lessens K selectivity in transport to the shoot (75), and the entire conception is based on the premise that the endodermis is not a barrier to free space diffusion (41, 74).

The view that stelar cells per se are responsible for xylary accumulation raises some poignant unanswered questions. Pitman envisages a symplast within the stelar parenchyma which may be supplied either by way of

---

[3] See Bowling, D. J. F., *Planta,* **83,** 53–59 (1968).

the cortex symplasm (low external concentration; low transpiration) or by way of the water free space in the cortex (high external concentration; high transpiration). In the first instance, is it considered that salt, enriched in K, leaks from the inner cortical cells only to be reabsorbed by stelar parenchyma in a second selective process? If the cortex symplast is considered to be one with the stele parenchyma symplast, at what barrier is the second selective act thought to take place? Assuming stelar parenchyma cells pump K (and perhaps to a lesser extent, Na) inwardly, how is this salt delivered to the xylem? Is the stelar parenchyma thought to secrete salt into the nonliving xylem in a process akin to the action of salt glands—i.e., is the function of the stelar parenchyma plasma membrane reversed compared with that of the cortex plasma membrane? Whether stelar parenchyma loses salt by secretion or by leakage, how may one view the directionality of this process? If the water free space is thought to extend within the stele, how is salt which is deposited in the nonliving xylem retained within the stele? These questions are put without regard to the earlier developed quantitative difficulties inherent in imputing xylary salt uptake entirely to stelar tissue. Nor has it been taken into account that there are reportedly no observed plasmodesmata among stelar parenchyma beyond 1.5 cm from the tip of maize roots (1), nor that the stelar fluid is equilibrated much more slowly than the cortex with tritiated water (2, 36). Pitman indicates that about half the exchangeable Na in the walls of barley roots bathed in NaI is in the stele—the implication being that the endodermis is no barrier to Na diffusion in the wall free space (74, cf. 41). The latter is an unsettling deduction to reconcile with both the lore and some of the disparate facts (55, 80, 90) relating to passive radial salt movement in the root. In Pitman's experiments, the isotope in the free space was estimated by extrapolating the isotope content of the roots to zero time following absorption measurements at intervals over a 1-hr period. Presumably, roots were decorticated after an hour for the determination of the distribution of Na exchange sites. The half-time for cytoplasmic exchange of Na at 2° is about an hour in barley roots (78), and it is entirely reasonable that Na which has moved through the symplasm into the stele will exchange with cell wall cations in the stele after leaking from stele parenchyma. Without further evidence it may still be assumed that the endodermis represents a barrier to free diffusion between the external solution and the stele through the free space. It is not out of the question, nevertheless, that there is cation exchange through the endodermis cell wall without net salt movement. In this connection, divalent cations seem to enter the stele passively (9; however, cf. 66[3].

As previously mentioned, the enhanced K selectivity of the shoot can be readily explained without postulating a separate active process within the stele. So long as the vacuoles of the cortex remain unfilled, the Na-selective action of system 2 at the tonoplast will sequester Na and cause a K-enriched cytoplasmic solution to be delivered to the stele by way of the symplasm. The only remaining unexplained feature within the framework

of the symplasm theory is the apparently zero order relation of shoot uptake to external concentration (73, 76). The anomaly is more apparent than
real.

The absorption periods in Pitman's experiments with barley seedlings
were of several days' duration. Absorption was directly dependent on
growth; in fact, uptake was expressed in terms of the increment of salt absorbed in a given interval per increment of dry weight in the same interval.
At high concentrations (10 to 100 mM) and prolonged experimental periods, the mature tissue of seedlings is fully salt saturated (73). In effect,
what is being observed is the net uptake by the new growth of shoot. It is
to be expected that this new growth, too, will be fully saturated in 3 days,
and consequently what one is measuring is the salt capacity of saturated
tissue. Since 10 mM salt is more than enough to saturate root tissue in a
relatively short time and to cause salt to move to the shoot (79, 90), it follows that tissue will be salt-saturated through the range 10 to 100 mM.
There is only 4 μl of xylem contents in a 10 cm barley root (1). An additional very small xylem volume is to be expected in the shoot. Thus, even if
the xylem contents were to come to equilibrium with the external solution,
the linear relationship of xylary fluid concentration with external concentration would not be perceived in the shoot at large. Shoot content would
reflect tissue saturation values and hence be indifferent to external concentration in this inordinately high range.

In fact, the exudate faithfully reflects the milieu through a wide range
of high concentrations at the same time that the exudation rate remains
constant. Only at the highest external concentration (50 mM) does the exudation rate drop noticeably (2). If a pump saturated well below 10 mM
(73) were limiting uptake to the xylem, the exudation rate would be expected to drop inversely with external concentration in the high range,
while the accumulation ratio remained 1.0. One might even anticipate an accumulation ratio less than 1.0. Neither expectation is met. When transport
to the shoot is studied in the range of system 2 in short-term experiments,
i.e., when shoot tissue is not saturated, the isotherm for shoot transport is
linear with a pronounced positive slope. By contrast, root absorption per se
in the same range is hyperbolic with concentration (57). Thus system 2 is
not implicated in shoot transfer and is consequently relegated to the tonoplast.

For the same reason that saturated barley roots show a maximal capacity for total alkali cation in whatever proportion, total uptake by the shoot
appears to be independent of the K/Na ratio in the external solution. Leaf
cells show the same absorption characteristics evinced by roots (89),
wherein it has been demonstrated that K and Na are competitive for system 2,
the preference for Na being 20 times that for K (25, 82, 83, cf. 40). So
long as the cytoplasmic concentration is sufficiently high, a condition to be
expected with high external concentration, system 2, presumed herein to be
at the tonoplast, will deliver ions to the vacuole at its maximal rate, the
inward flow comprising K and Na in accordance with their relative cyto-

plasmic concentration, and with the system 2 K_s, for K and Na respectively. It is thus to be expected that total absorption and final content in the leaf will be essentially constant in spite of the K/Na ratio and total concentration in the external solution, so long as system 2 is saturated. Total cation uptake to the vacuole has been linked with anion absorption, particularly Cl. The rigorous equivalence has been ascribed both to a chloride pump as the prime-mover in vacuolar transport (72) and to the transport of neutral salt per se across the tonoplast (cf. 63).

Transpiration and long-distance transport.—Transpiration in barley seedlings is considerable even under ordinary conditions (75). The enhancement of Na selectivity in shoot transport by increased transpiration is comprehensible in terms of passive entry and movement through the symplasm. With hydrodynamic flow through the symplasm, the selective withdrawal of Na to the vacuoles in a given time would be lessened. Na efflux from the root to the external solution may be lessened as well (41). With respect to the additional salt delivered to the tops under conditions of increased transpiration, the prospect of recirculation of salt by way of the phloem is opened (52, 53). In newly stripped steles, sulfate transport to the leaves of maize seedlings is proportional to transpiration. In seedlings with intact roots, long-distance transport is independent of transpiration at the same transpiration intensity (59). In summary, there is every reason to believe that at external concentrations bearing a resemblance to that of soil solutions, long-distance transport is initiated by a K-selective active uptake of ions into the symplasm of the cortex. At high concentrations, a passive nonselective component contributes to salt movement across the plasma membrane. In both cases, subsequent movement delivers ions to the stele, with additional K enrichment as Na is withdrawn to cortex vacuoles (40) and extruded to the environment (78, 79). Within the stele, ions leak into the xylem to be moved to the shoot in the transpiration stream. At low external concentrations, system 1 of the plasma membrane will be in kinetic control, and long distance transport will display the characteristics of an active process. At high external concentrations, a diffusive component into and through the symplasm will be superimposed on the active absorptive component, and long-distance transport will to some degree appear passive.[3] High transpiration rates will exaggerate the passive contribution. Further, at high transpiration rates there may be a limited direct flow of salt to the stele by way of the wall water free-space through an imperfect endodermal barrier (passage cells, incomplete Casparian strips, etc.).

PASSIVE PERMEATION: CRITERIA AND SIGNIFICANCE

The foregoing arguments have in large measure been based on the presumption that under certain circumstances there may be an appreciable passive flux through plant cell membranes—the plasma membrane in particular. While tacit acknowledgment of membrane permeability to ions is inherent in the recognition of membrane potentials as diffusion potentials, and in the understanding that equilibrium in plant cells vis-à-vis salt content involves an equality of active influx and a predominantly passive efflux (68), there is at the same time a tendency to consider plant cell membranes largely impermeable to ions on the basis of the reluctance with which salt may be washed from tissue in water. An outstanding critical discussion of the factors which relate ion permeation to membrane structure has recently been presented by Eisenman, Sandblom & Walker (19).

Theoretical considerations.—A very sensitive indication of diffusive permeation of a plant cell membrane can be garnered from the absorption isotherm. As has been abundantly demonstrated by Epstein (23, 25), the kinetics of carrier-mediated transport are effectively described by a relationship formally identical to the Michaelis-Menten formulation for the velocity of an enzymatic reaction. That is, the absorption rate is a hyperbolic function of concentration—whether carrier transport is active, i.e., involves a pump, or passive, i.e., involves diffusion exchange (68). The hyperbolic relationship may obtain as well when a given ion moves passively in response to the active transport of its counter ion (10, 41).

However, when ion passage through a membrane is truly diffusive, the flux of a given ion, for example, Cl, is described by the Goldman equation as follows (14, 34, 48):

$$J_{Cl} = \frac{+ P_{Cl}\, FE/RT}{1 - \exp\left(- FE/RT\right)} \cdot \left[(Cl_o) - (Cl_i)\, \exp\left(- \frac{FE}{RT} \right) \right] \qquad 3.$$

where Cl_o and Cl_i are the external and internal concentrations, respectively, E is the electrical potential difference, P is the permeability coefficient for chloride, and F, R, and T have the usual meaning. Where diffusion of the neutral solute is concerned, the driving force is simply a function of the concentration difference (more properly, chemical potential difference) across the membrane. However, where ion movement is at issue, it is the electrochemical potential difference which determines flux direction and magnitude. The electrical potential across plant cell membranes is most often a diffusion potential (14, 34, 35), and its value can be calculated from a knowledge of the permeability coefficients and concentrations of the cations and anions involved in a given situation. With reasonable assumptions for the relative values of P_K and P_{Cl} in a given tissue, and for internal ion concentrations, theoretical isotherms can be constructed for the influx of a given ion. Such has been done for diffusion of Cl into potato slices from KCl solution at 0°. The theoretical diffusion isotherm is a curve which is concave-upward, and the experimental curve fits the theoretical curve very closely (48). The reason for the exponentially rising isotherm is simply that with increasing external KCl concentration, and the assumption that P_K is somewhat greater than P_{Cl}, the membrane potential across the plasma membrane decreases, and the decrease in electrical potential with increasing chemical potential means that the driving force on chloride increases more rapidly than the external concentration. A verification of the validity of the pertinent assumptions was obtained by predicting and experimentally affirming the shape of the isotherm for Cl absorption from $CaCl_2$ solutions, and from solutions of KCl in which the K concentration was kept constant (40 mM) while the Cl concentration was varied (48, cf. 42).

Permeability changes in relation to physiological state.—With a theoretical framework in hand, observations relating to the change in shape of absorption isotherms concomitant with changes in physiological characteristics of a variety of plant tissues assume considerable significance. Freshly cut potato slices, for example, display an anomalous, exponentially rising isotherm for Cl absorption at room temperature. By contrast, aged potato discs show what may be termed a conventional hyperbolic isotherm (48). At low temperatures the isotherm even of aged tissue is linear to concave-upward. Freshly decorticated steles of maize roots show a marked concave-upward isotherm, while aged decorticated steles are characterized by a hyperbolic isotherm for chloride uptake (47, 59). Together with the alteration of isotherm shape, both potato slices and decorticated steles evince a profound increase in salt absorption capacity. The almost qualitative change in absorption capacity is but one manifestation of a basic metabolic transformation which occurs during the ageing of fresh slices and excised steles (46). The isotherm is a much more sensitive and revealing measure of a fundamental change in tissue characteristics than is the rate of absorption.

Some years ago Laties & Budd (47), and more recently Lüttge & Laties (59) and Osmond & Laties (69) explored the question of which membrane —plasma membrane, tonoplast, or both—is the seat of the permeability and absorption changes which take place. In the earlier work, isotherms of fresh and aged steles were examined in but one concentration range—that of system 2—the prevalence and implication of dual absorption mechanisms not yet being understood. Thus, while indirect considerations led to the view that it is primarily the plasma membrane which is altered with time, we were faced with the apparent anomaly, in retrospect, that the altered isotherm described uptake in a concentration range now imputed to system 2, or to tonoplast absorption. Subsequently, the consequences of ageing excised steles were examined with specific regard for the dual absorption mechanisms (59, 69). Chloride (and K) absorption in the range of system 1 was found to increase more than tenfold with overnight ageing of steles. Further, while the isotherm in the range of system 1 was barely discernible in fresh stele, it was well developed and hyperbolic in aged stele. Contrary to the condition in cortical tissue, the plasma membrane appears to be in kinetic control of uptake even in the 1 to 10 mM range of system 2. Thus, uptake is almost nil in this range in fresh tissue, and is essentially at the system 1 maximum in aged. At still higher concentrations, the fresh stele isotherm rises sharply concave-upward as expected from diffusive penetration, and uptake markedly exceeds that in aged steles. Cortex, on the other hand, shows a dual isotherm in both fresh and aged tissue, absorption being about twice as great in the aged. The foregoing observations emphasize that the plasma membrane may be in kinetic control whether transport is carrier-mediated or diffusive, depending on the tissue, and that at low concentrations transport by system 1 will exceed diffusion through the plasma membrane. It is indisputably system 1 which changes with time. Because of the foregoing anomaly the change suffered by system 1 in excised maize steles is sensed in the low range of system 2 (47).

System 1 in fresh red beet discs is virtually inoperative, while after two days or more of ageing it is well developed and characterized by a hyperbolic isotherm (69). System 2 is present at all times. Independent measurements of the specific fluxes at the plasma membrane and tonoplast serve to further implicate the plasma membrane as the seat of change (59, 69, cf. 94). It is primarily the plasma membrane influx which rises sharply with ageing both in red beet slices (69 cf. 94) and in maize steles (59). Thus, ageing is attended not just by a diminution in passive permeability but also by the development of an active transport system at the plasma membrane.[4] It is gratifying that isotherms constructed from plasma membrane and tonoplast influx data respectively match absorption isotherms for systems 1 and 2 (60). With unsaturated tissue, absorption isotherms can be taken to describe influx with some assurance. When aged beet discs are treated with polylysine in a manner designed to make the plasma membrane permeable, evidence of system 1 disappears, while system 2 remains intact (71). The latter observation further bolsters the tentative assignment of systems 1 and 2 to the plasma membrane and tonoplast respectively.

In conclusion, I wish to allude to a previously perplexing observation which now seems to fall into place. In connection with a study of the metabolic changes which occur in potato slices with ageing, Loughman (54) noted that while aged potato slices absorb phosphate 100 times more rapidly than fresh slices in 0.01 mM phosphate solution, the ratio of absorption rates in 10 mM solution drops to 2. When note is taken of the change in absorption isotherm characteristics in ageing potato slices (48), the various observations can be reconciled. Thus, as a concomitant to the profound metabolic changes which take place in thin storage organ slices (46), there is a marked enhancement of salt absorption capacity. Specifically, the change centers on the development of system 1 at the plasma membrane (59, 69). Consequently, in fresh slices, where phosphate uptake to the cytoplasm is primarily diffusion mediated, absorption is very much greater at high external concentrations. In aged discs, on the other hand, the high-affinity phosphate transport mechanism is well developed, and phosphate absorption is no more than doubled by moving into the system 2 range.

[4] See Polya, G. M., Atkinson, M. R., *Australian J. Biol. Sci.*, in press, for a trenchant study of the direct involvement of electron transport in the system 1, or high affinity, ion accumulation mechanism in beet slices.

LITERATURE CITED

1. Anderson, W. P., House, C. R., *J. Exptl. Botany,* **18,** 544–55 (1967)
2. Anderson, W. P., Reilly, E. J., *J. Exptl. Botany,* **19,** 19–30 (1968)
3. Arisz, W. H., *Protoplasma,* **46,** 5–62 (1956)
4. Bange, G. G. J., *Plant Soil,* **11,** 17–29 (1959)
5. Bange, G. G. J., *ibid.,* **22,** 280–306 (1965)
6. Bange, G. G. J., Vliet, E. van, *Plant Soil,* **15,** 312–28 (1961)
7. Bange, G. G. J., Hooymans, J. J. M., *Isotopes in Plant Nutrition,* 249–63 (Intern. At. Energy Agency, Vienna, 1967)
8. Barber, S. A., Walker, J. M., Vasey, E. H., *Agr. Food Chem.,* **11,** 204–7 (1963)
9. Biddulph, S. F., *Planta,* **74,** 350–67 (1967)
10. Briggs, G. E., *J. Exptl. Botany,* **14,** 191–97 (1963)
11. Brouwer, R., *Ann. Rev. Plant Physiol.,* **16,** 241–66 (1965)
12. Crafts, A. S., Broyer, T. C., *Am. J. Botany,* **25,** 529–35 (1938)
13. Cram, J., *Compartmentation and Control of Inorganic Ions in Higher Plant Cells* (Doctoral thesis, Cambridge Univ., England, 1967); *Biochim. Biophys. Acta,* **163,** 339–53 (1968) (a published paper containing Cram's thesis material)
14. Dainty, J., *Ann. Rev. Plant Physiol.,* **13,** 379–402 (1962)
15. Dainty, J., Gutknecht, J., *Oceanography and Marine Biology,* **6,** 163–200 (1968)
16. Davis, R. F., Jr., *Electropotentials and Ion Transport Across Excised Corn Roots* (Doctoral thesis, Wash. State Univ., Pullman, Wash., 86 pp., 1968)
17. Dixon, M., Webb, E., *Enzymes,* 2d ed. (Longmans, London, 1964)
18. Dodd, W. A., Pitman, M. G., West, K. R., *Australian J. Biol. Sci.,* **19,** 341–54 (1966)
19. Eisenman, G., Sandblom, J. P., Walker, J. L., Jr., *Science,* **155,** 965–74 (1967)
20. Elzam, O. E., Rains, D. W., Epstein, E., *Biochem. Biophys. Res. Commun.,* **15,** 273–76 (1964)
21. Epstein, E., In *Ecological Aspects of the Mineral Nutrition of Plants* (Rorison, I. H., Ed., Blackwell, Oxford, 1969)

22. Epstein, E., *Nature,* **212,** 1324–27 (1966)
23. Epstein, E., Hagen, C. E., *Plant Physiol.,* **27,** 457–74 (1952)
24. Epstein, E., Schmid, W. E., Rains, D. W., *Plant Cell Physiol. (Tokyo),* **4,** 79–84 (1963)
25. Epstein, E., Rains, D. W., Elzam, O. E., *Proc. Natl. Acad. Sci. U.S.,* **49,** 684–92 (1963)
26. Etherton, B., *Plant Physiol.,* **34,** 838–40 (1968)
27. Fried, M., Noggle, J. C., *Plant Physiol.,* **33,** 139–44 (1958)
28. Gutknecht, J., *Biol. Bull.,* **130,** 331–44 (1966)
29. Gutknecht, J., *J. Gen. Physiol.,* **50,** 1821–34 (1967)
30. Gutknecht, J., *Science,* **160,** 68–70 (1968)
31. Hagen, C. E., Hopkins, H. T., *Plant Physiol.,* **30,** 193–99 (1955)
32. Hiatt, A. J., *Plant Physiol.,* **43,** 893–901 (1968)
33. Hiatt, A. J., Hendricks, S. B., *Z. Pflanzenphysiol.,* **56,** 220–32 (1967)
34. Higinbotham, N., Intern. Symp., *Transport of Matter in Cells of Higher Plants. Abhandl. Deut. Akad. Wiss. Berlin, Kl. Med.* (1968)
35. Higinbotham, N., Etherton, B., Foster, R. J., *Plant Physiol.,* **42,** 37–46 (1967)
36. Hodges, T. K., Vaadia, Y., *Plant Physiol.,* **39,** 104–8 (1964)
37. Hodges, T. K., Vaadia, Y., *ibid.,* 109–14
38. Hylmo, B., *Physiol. Plantarum,* **6,** 333–405 (1953)
39. Jackson, J. E., Weatherley, P. E., *J. Exptl. Botany,* **13,** 128–43 (1962)
40. Jacoby, B., *Plant Physiol.,* **39,** 445–49 (1964)
41. Jennings, D. H., *New Phytologist,* **66,** 357–69 (1967)
42. Jennings, D. H., *J. Exptl. Botany,* **19,** 13–18 (1968)
43. Jeschke, W. D., *Planta,* **73,** 161–74 (1967)
44. Jeschke, W. D., Simonis, W., *Z. Naturforsch.,* **22,** 843–76 (1967)
45. Laties, G. G., *Proc. Natl. Acad. Sci. U.S.,* **45,** 163–72 (1959)
46. Laties, G. G., *Plant Physiol.,* **39,** 654–63 (1964)
47. Laties, G. G., Budd, K., *Proc. Natl. Acad. Sci. U.S.,* **52,** 462–69 (1964)
48. **Laties, G. G., MacDonald, I. R.,**

Dainty, J., *Plant Physiol.*, **39**, 254–62 (1964)

49. Läuchli, A., In *Vorträge aus dem Gesamtgebiet der Botanik*, 2 (In press)

50. Läuchli, A., Lüttge, U., *Planta*, **83**, 80–98 (1968)

51. Leggett, J. E., *Ann. Rev. Plant Physiol.*, **19**, 333–46 (1968)

52. Levi, E., *Physiol. Plantarum*, **21**, 213–26 (1968)

53. Levi, E., *Naturwissenschaften*, **55**, 42 (1968)

54. Loughman, B. C., *Plant Physiol.*, **35**, 418–24 (1960))

55. Lundegårdh, H., *Physiol. Plantarum*, **3**, 103–51 (1950)

56. Lüttge, U., in *Protoplasmatologia. Handbuch der Protoplasmaforschung*, **8** (In press)

57. Lüttge, U., Laties, G. G., *Plant Physiol.*, **41**, 1531–39 (1966)

58. Lüttge, U., Laties, G. G., *ibid.*, **42**, 181–85 (1967)

59. Lüttge, U., Laties, G. G., *Planta*, **74**, 123–87 (1967)

60. Lüttge, U., Bauer, K., *Planta*, **80**, 52–64 (1968)

61. MacDonald, I. R., Laties, G. G., *Plant Physiol.*, **38**, 38–44 (1963)

62. Macklon, A. E. S., Higinbotham, N., *Plant Physiol.*, **43**, 888–92 (1968)

63. MacRobbie, E. A. C., *J. Gen. Physiol.*, **47**, 859–77 (1964)

64. MacRobbie, E. A. C., *Australian J. Biol. Sci.*, **19**, 363–70 (1966)

65. MacRobbie, E. A. C., *ibid.*, 371–83

66. Moore, D. P., Mason, B. J., Maas, E. V., *Plant Physiol.*, **40**, 641–44 (1965)

67. Mothes, K., Müller, E., Nelles, A., Neumann, D., Eds., *Intern. Symp., Transport of Matter in Cells of Higher Plants. Abhandl. Deut. Akad. Wiss. Berlin, Kl. Med.*, No. 4 (1968)

68. Oertli, J. J., *Physiol. Plantarum*, **20**, 1014–26 (1967)

69. Osmond, C. B., Laties, G. G., *Plant Physiol.*, **43**, 747–55 (1968)

70. Osmond, C. B., Laties, G. G., *Plant Physiol.* (In press)

71. Osmond, C. B., Laties, G. G., *Biochim. Biophys. Acta* (In press)

72. Pitman, M. G., *Australian J. Biol. Sci.*, **16**, 647–68 (1963)

73. Pitman, M. G., *ibid.*, **18**, 10–24 (1965)

74. Pitman, M. G., *ibid.*, 541–46

75. Pitman, M. G., *ibid.*, 987–98

76. Pitman, M. G., *ibid.*, **19**, 257–69 (1966)

77. Pitman, M. G., *Nature*, **216**, 1343–44 (1967)

78. Pitman, M. G., Saddler, H. D. W., *Proc. Natl. Acad. Sci. U.S.*, **57**, 44 (1967)

79. Pitman, M. G., Courtice, A. C., Lee, B., *Australian J. Biol. Res.*, **21**, 871–81 (1968)

80. Prevot, P., Steward, F. C., *Plant Physiol.*, **11**, 509–34 (1936)

81. Rains, D. W., Schmid, W. E., Epstein, E., *Plant Physiol.*, **39**, 274–78 (1964)

82. Rains, D. W., Epstein, E., *Plant Physiol.*, **42**, 314–18 (1967)

83. Rains, D. W., Epstein, E., *ibid.*, 319–23

84. Raven, J. A., *J. Gen. Physiol.*, **50**, 1607–25 (1967)

85. Raven, J. A., *ibid.*, 1627–40

86. Raven, J. A., *J. Exptl. Botany*, **19**, 233–53 (1968)

87. Rorison, I. H., Ed., *Ecological Aspects of the Mineral Nutrition of Plants* (Blackwell, Oxford, 1969)

88. Siegel, S. M., Daly, O., *Plant Physiol.*, **41**, 1429–38 (1966)

89. Smith, R. C., Epstein, E., *Plant Physiol.*, **39**, 992–96 (1964)

90. Steward, F. C., Prevot, P., Harrison, J. A., *Plant Physiol.*, **17**, 411–21 (1942)

91. Steward, F. C., Sutcliffe, J. F., *Plant Physiology*, **2**, 253–465 (Steward. F. C., Ed., Academic Press, N.Y., 1959)

92. Torii, K., Laties, G. G., *Plant Physiol.*, **41**, 863–70 (1966)

93. Van den Honert, T. H., Hooymans, J. J. M., Volkers, W. S., *Acta Botan. Neerl.*, **4**, 139–55 (1955)

94. Van Steveninck, R. F. M., *Australian J. Biol. Sci.*, **18**, 227–33 (1965)

95. Wallace, A., Ashcroft, R. T., Lunt, O. R., *Plant Physiol.*, **42**, 238–42 (1967)

96. Weigl, J., *Planta*, **79**, 197–207 (1968)

97. Yu, G. H., Kramer, P. J., *Plant Physiol.*, **42**, 985–90 (1967)

98. Yu, G., Radial transport of ions in roots. *Progr. West. Sect. Am. Soc. Plant Physiol., Logan, Utah*, 1968, p. 2

VASCULAR TRANSPORT AND ITS SIGNIFICANCE IN PLANT GROWTH

By F. L. Milthorpe and J. Moorby

Macquarie University, North Ryde, N.S.W., Australia

Transport of water, mineral salts, organic materials, and growth substances within the plant have long been recognized as indispensable integral processes in the continued orderly growth of a plant. At least, the flow of mineral and organic substrates from sites of absorption or formation to regions of utilization is clearly essential; the flow of water is more a consequence of the need to replace the inevitable incessant losses and so maintain a suitable milieu for metabolism; whereas the nature, degree, and significance of the long-distance transport of growth substances remain to be ascertained.

At present, while the qualitative chrysalis of plant physiology is still struggling to emerge to its first quantitative instar, any treatment must be tentative at best—a provisional probing towards the unified numerical representation required for adequate appreciation and assessment. For many reasons, we have to be content here with a very cursory groping towards this goal and with a degree of quantification well below that which now could be achieved. We are aware of procedures and of model systems which could amply repay exploration, and we apologize to the reader for not having had opportunity to do so; we are also conscious of the pitfalls of glib application of such procedures to imperfectly understood systems. This treatment will also be cursory in the sense that we have not been able to consider all recent relevant contributions.

In general, the quantity q of a substance in solution which moves in time t through an area A normal to the direction of flow is given by

$$dq/dt = -DA \, dc/dz + fc \qquad 1.$$

where D is a diffusion coefficient, c the concentration, z the distance along the direction of flow, and f the rate of flow of solution in the z direction. Two components of flow are distinguished: a diffusion of the substance in proportion to its own concentration gradient, and a convection (or mass flow) of the substance due to the flow of the solution as a whole. The rate of flow of solution may be described by

$$f = -kA \, (\Delta P + \Delta \, (\rho gh))/l \qquad 2.$$

117

where k is a conductivity and ΔP and $\Delta(\rho g h)$ the differences in pressure and gravitational potentials of the solvent over distance l in the z direction (30). Except in tall trees, the gravitational term is usually negligible. [Where a differentially permeable membrane is interposed, the flow rate is related to the difference in water potential as defined by Slayter & Taylor (180) rather than to the difference in pressure potential.]

We must also recognize the possible effects of the movement of other entities—solutes, heat, and electricity—on the transport of the substance being considered. If these effects are substantial, the diffusion term D in Equation 1 should be replaced by

$$D_{11} \ dc_1/dz + D_{12} \ dc_2/dz + D_{13} \ dc_3/dz \qquad\qquad 3.$$

where the subscript 1 refers to the substance being considered and the subsequent subscripts to other entities which influence the transport of the first, the coefficients D_{12}, D_{13} . . . representing the effect of the gradient of the second, third, . . . substances on the movement of the first. Active transport may be defined as that which occurs when D_{12} or D_{13} are large compared with D_{11} (183); in effect, where the equilibrium or steady state of one component depends on the lack of equilibrium of one or more other components.[1] Metabolic energy may be expended directly or indirectly in such a system as, for example, in maintaining a flux of ions and thereby influencing the flux of water. In this definition, which is wider than that used by many biologists, expenditure of metabolic energy is not the sole means by which an "active" process is defined; thermo-osmosis, electro-osmosis, and other devices by which flow against an electro-chemical gradient can be maintained should also be included. Moreover, association with metabolism as, for example, a decrease in the flux following inhibition of respiration, does not necessarily imply an "active" process; it may reflect association with the movement of another entity or even a change in structure of the system.

The classical channels of transport are the xylem and phloem. Most investigations and discussions on transport within the plant have been confined to the movement within these tissues; many aspects have been reviewed in earlier volumes in this series and elsewhere (5, 31, 112, 113, 145, 189). The concentration of inorganic ions in the xylem sap (ca 400 to 2500 μg/ml) is often greater than that of the external medium (17) and contains a greater number of ionic species than phloem sap (5, 11, 93, 189, 191, 215); nevertheless, the concentrations of NO_3^-, K^+, and phosphate ions are comparable in both. Xylem sap also contains amino acids and amides, mainly of the glutamate and aspartate groups (208)—at concentrations 10^{-3} to 10^{-1} that of the phloem (5 to 10 mg/ml)—together with alkaloids,

---

[1] The coordinate system in which the flow is defined is, of course, allowed to move with the bulk flow of the solution; i.e., transport due to the term fc in Eq. 1 is "passive."

ureides, other nitrogenous compounds, sugars—in trace amounts compared with concentrations of 50 to 200 mg/ml in the phloem—organic acids, and growth substances such as gibberellins (25, 160, 176, 177) and kinins (98). Abscisic acid has been detected in phloem sap (86).

FLOW OF WATER

The flow of water has been considered in detail in five recent treatises (15, 54, 111, 159, 179), and it is superfluous to give more than the barest of general summaries here. Movement of water in the plant is much better understood than that of other substances—much progress in quantitative analysis has been achieved by accepting only the most essential geometry of the system, making some approximations and regarding the flow as a series of successive steady states of the relations given in Equations 1 and 2. Reasonable estimates of the conductances of the different components in the intricate series/parallel network are available (30). In general, the rate of flow of water through the plant is determined by the current rate of transpiration, but is modified by the hydraulic properties of the soil, the soil-water content (or water potential), the depth of penetration and concentration of roots, and the internal conductances of root, stem, and leaves. (Of the latter, that of the root appears to be about equal to that of the leaf and possibly half that of the stem.) In soils at field capacity (water potentials ∼−0.1 to −0.2 atm), most crop plants can maintain the supply of water to the leaves with potential transpiration rates up to about 7 mm day^{-1}. The major part of the difference in water potential between bulk soil and the leaves is then located in the plant. As the soil dries, adequate supplies of water can only be maintained at lower and lower transpiration rates, the major part of the difference in water potential then being in the soil. Increasing water deficits in the leaf are coupled with partial stomatal closure and a decrease in the actual rate of transpiration below the potential.

The rate of growth of the plant is reduced below its potential rate when the water content of the upper leaves falls to about, say, 90 per cent of that held at full turgor (about −8 atm water potential), and death occurs in many plants when the relative water content falls to 40 to 50 per cent (say, ∼−30 to −60 atm water potential). Many physiological processes are affected both directly and indirectly (111, 179), but it is most uncertain which are the first and key processes involved. Some recent evidence (69, 85, 163, 210) indicates that one of the first effects of a water deficit is a reduction of the transport of mineral ions, sucrose, and other metabolites. The effect seems to be exerted on the transfer from conducting tissue to leaf cells and not on movement within the sieve tubes themselves (210). Evidence interpreted to the contrary (163) may possibly have been due to retardation of "unloading" at sink sites and other factors. Water deficits lead to enhanced synthesis of sucrose at the expense of polysaccharides (85, 162) and, if large, to the disruption of membranes and irreversible damage to cells (84).

The unidirectional flow of water provides a means of transport for substances absorbed by and manufactured in the roots to the leaves, fruits, and stem. The extent to which this channel is used, and the influence of other components on transport therein, is considered in relation to particular substances.

Transport of Inorganic Ions

Current evidence (18, 30, 91, 224) indicates that the conductances of the endodermis and stele for the flow of water are not much different from that of the cortex. Moreover, the conductivities of the cell walls and of the symplast are probably not very different, but, associated with its much greater cross-sectional area, possibly about three times as much water moves through the cytoplasm as through the walls. In general, the conductance for water flow across the root would appear to be determined by the conductance of the cell membranes for the entry of water (91, 100); it may vary as much as tenfold with temperature, ionic composition, and inhibitors (17), these differences almost certainly arising from variations in structure.

As with water, two pathways of ion transport are normally recognized —the extracellular free-space regions of the cell wall and the symplasm— with transfer surely possible between both at all positions across the root (16, 186). The measured free space appears to be quite inadequate to allow transport at the rates observed (161); most of the ions move through the symplast. It is likely that the differential permeability to different ionic species is located mainly in the plasmalemma and that entry, at least of anions, into the cytoplasm involves a carrier-mediated system. Of the two alternative fates for ions within the symplast, accumulation in the vacuole certainly involves "active" uptake systems (167). Those ions moving directly to the xylem are possibly passively carried, with some local diffusion, by the streaming protoplasm, but movement out of the symplasm into the xylem vessels probably also involves a carrier-mediated system.

The frequently greater concentration of ions in the xylem sap than in the external solution may reflect differing affinities of the carrier-mediated systems for anions and cations. For example, in *Ricinus* (11), NO_3^-, Cl^-, SO_4^{-2}, $H_2PO_4^-$, and HPO_4^{-2} entered the xylem against their electrochemical potential gradients, K^+ was in equilibrium, and Na^+, Ca^{+2} and Mg^{+2} entered along their gradients. The suggestion (11) that transport of cations requires no expenditure of energy has been challenged (101), even though many investigators find that much of the transport is not directly associated with metabolism.

Uptake both by excised roots (1, 46, 206) and by intact plants (53, 115, 123–125) indicate a changing degree of importance of different parts of these pathways according to the external ionic concentration. With low concentrations ($<1 - 10$ mM), the symplasm pathway appears to provide the faster route, possibly because of the high affinity of the transfer mechanism across the plasmalemma and a limitation of the cell-wall pathway by a Donnan exclusion mechanism (1). With increasing concentration, the latter decreases and finally becomes negligible and the former becomes increasingly saturated. At high concentrations, the rate of transport is linearly related to external concentration: opinions differ concerning the site of the rate-limiting steps under these conditions, some (115, 123–125) favouring uptake through the plasmalemma and others (1, 90) the sites of transfer to the xylem vessels. We also doubt whether there is yet sufficient evidence to preclude transfer within the symplasm as a rate-controlling component. There is little evidence for the view that ions move through some areas of the plasmalemma by a metabolically mediated mechanism and through others by diffusion, the latter dominating at high external concentrations.

Entry into the vacuoles appears to be rapid and the loss therefrom slow: hence, most of the ions transported to the shoot probably proceed directly, mixing little with the ions already in the roots (34). Half-times of exchange rates of "symplasm" and "vacuolar" phosphorus in the tomato were found to be about 40 min and 90 hr, respectively (72). About 30 to 40 per cent of the phosphate ions were transported to the shoot within 1 to 4 hours of entering the root; about three-quarters of these appeared to be transported directly through the symplasm and cell walls. Of the phosphate absorbed by the root, about one-tenth was in the symplasm and nine-tenths in the vacuoles. Consequently, the rate of entry of ions into the xylem may be less than half the concurrent rate of entry into the roots. Similar results have been found with uptake of phosphorus by maize (123) and barley (34, 35).

Recent contributions to the extensively studied relationship between transport of ions to the shoot and the rate of water flow (168) indicate that the effects are confined to the transport pathway across the symplasm and along the xylem; uptake and movement through the vacuoles is not greatly affected unless the water potential of the root cells is quite low. When the water potential of the solution surrounding the roots is reduced to about −5 atm (that of a normal culture solution being about −0.4 atm), phosphate transport to the shoots (and presumably flow through the symplasm) is reduced, but uptake and concentration in the root tissues is not affected (70, 71, 72). Transport of SO_4^{-2} ions to the shoots of wheat appears to be increased by lowering the water potential, possibly as a result of increased permeability (97). Further reduction to about −7 to −8 atm (about incipient plasmolysis) does lead to substantial reduction in the amount absorbed by the root as well as that transported to the shoot (70, 109). At water potentials even as low as −20 atm, the mechanisms of ion uptake and integrity of the tonoplast appear to be maintained, but permeability of the plasmalemma and leakage from cells are greatly increased (73).

The differential transport of ions to the shoot—for example, the relatively greater amounts of K^+ than of Na^+—may well reside in the differential permeability of the plasmalemmas of the cortical or stelar cells or both. [The suggestion (101) that the tonoplast is involved seems unlikely, as it appears to exert little control over transport to the shoot.] Pitman (161) showed that selectivity between the transfers of Na$^+$ and K$^+$ to barley shoots was decreased when transpiration was increased and suggested that this effect was exerted on ion movement through the cell walls and symplasm. Much of the exclusion of Na$^+$ is located at the root surfaces and in the pathways to the xylem (66); some evidence (99) suggests that the retention is due to competition from Na-binding sites outside the transport path and that at low rates of flow, these have to be saturated before it can move to the xylem. There can also be discrimination between Rb$^+$ and K$^+$ (29, 146), but whereas the Na-binding sites seem to be Na-specific, Rb$^+$ and K$^+$ appear to compete for the same sites. The transport of Sr^{+2} from roots to shoots is relatively less than that of Ca^{+2} (168, 169). This discrimination probably arises from a mode of transport unique to the alkaline earths; it involves a series of exchange reactions (4, 6). The nature of the exchange sites is unknown, although the pectins in the xylem cell walls may be involved (6). Previously absorbed ^{45}Ca^{+2} could be "flushed out" of stems by transferring plants to solutions containing ^{40}Ca^{+2}, Sr^{+2}, or Mg^{+2}; transfer to KCl solutions and changes in the rate of transpiration, however, did not lead to any significant movement (6, 110).

Of the ions reaching a leaf, appreciable amounts are retranslocated via the phloem, the differing degrees of mobility probably being determined by the rate of movement into and out of the phloem. Phosphorus (5, 67) is particularly mobile. Most of that reaching very young leaves comes from older leaves, but most of that imported by rapidly expanding and mature leaves comes directly from the roots. Retranslocation appears to be controlled by the source leaves (67). Retranslocation of potassium, which has a mobility similar to that of phosphorus, is illustrated in Table I, which refers to barley seedlings grown in a solution of 2.5 meq litre^{-1}. The circulation of Na$^+$ and Cl$^-$ is much slower, at least at high internal concentration (66, 68, 75). Ions of the alkaline earths are not retranslocated. Analyses of exudate from aphid stylets and honeydew showed no detectable Ca, even when the xylem of *Salix* stem segments was perfused with a 100 ppm solution of Ca (87). Apparently, calcium ions cannot enter sieve tubes because they are preferentially absorbed on sites outside the phloem, such as in the bundle-sheath cells (166). Some movement could be detected with high Ca concentrations, when presumably these sites were saturated (129, 166), or with the addition of hydrogen ions or chelating agents (129). The evidence

TABLE I

RATES (μEQ DAY^{-1}) OF INTAKE OF K$^+$ BY LEAVES OF BARLEY (74)

	Young leaf	Intermediate leaf	Oldest leaf
Intake via xylem	2.0	2.7	1.9
Intake via phloem	1.3	0.7	−1.6
Net uptake	3.3	3.4	0.3

of 14 μg Ca per ml of sap supposedly from the phloem of *Yucca* (191) is equivocal because of likely contamination.

Although considerable space has been devoted above to discussing details of ion transport within the plant, in almost all ecological (including agricultural) situations the supply of ions to the shoots is primarily determined by the concentration in the soil solution and the ability of the roots to grow in order to reach these ions (2, 18, 114, 213). Of the three ways in which ions may reach the root surfaces—mass flow of the soil solution, diffusion through the soil solution, the growth of roots into regions not depleted of ions—the first two can only be effective with ions such as NO_3^-, which readily exchange between soil colloids and the soil solution. Some evidence suggests that Ca^{+2} and Mg^{+2} can be supplied by mass flow in sufficient amounts to meet the needs of the plant (3). Ions such as $H_2PO_4^-$, K^+, Mn^{+2}, Fe^{+3}, and Zn^{+2} move only very short distances, and sustained growth of the roots is necessary to absorb these (3, 151, 152); for example, ^{32}P is absorbed only from the root hair zone (116–119). In almost all field situations, root extension does not keep pace with the increasing demand from new shoot meristems; it is also possible that new roots formed late in life are less efficient absorbing units than those formed earlier. Consequently, the plant drifts during ontogeny towards a state of increasing internal starvation and with an increasingly greater proportion of the mineral supply to a new growing organ coming from older leaves rather than the external solution (219).

Both root extension and ion uptake per unit of root length is closely correlated with carbohydrate supply from the leaves, and hence with the intensity of photosynthesis and the size of the photosynthetic surface. For example, defoliation by cutting or grazing transiently reduces root extension and uptake per unit root surface (37), and ion uptake is intimately associated with the light supply to the leaves (39). A deficit of water in the upper soil layers where the minerals are in highest concentrations may lead to reduced growth as a consequence of reduced supply of minerals, although ample water is being absorbed from lower layers (57, 58). The effect of water supply on mineral uptake and distribution has been discussed by Gates (59) and on p. 119.

FLOW OF ORGANIC MATERIALS

Features of the transport system.—All workers agree that the sieve tubes are the principal channels for long-distance transport of organic substances from the leaves and that in most plants carbohydrate moves mainly as sucrose. There agreement usually ends; some workers still favour a simplified mass-flow hypothesis of the Münch type involving water as the transporting medium with (182, 184) or without (31, 41–43, 214, 215) "pumping stations" across the sieve plates, while others envisage a mass transport involving cytoplasm as the transporting medium (23, 195). A substantial measure of this disagreement stems from the difficulty of establishing the struc-

ture of functioning sieve tubes as they exist *in situ*. The existence of transcellular strands, described by Thaine (194, 195, 199) and at first hotly disputed (47, 199), has received strong but qualified support (44, 45, 51, 52,
196, 197, 200). (See also 21, 32, 33, 41–43, 51, 52, 143, 148 for various aspects of structure.) There is now reasonable evidence supporting the view
that longitudinal transcellular "cytoplasmic" strands extend from sieve tube
to sieve tube through the pores, and that the parietal layer of protoplasm
found along the vertical walls does not extend across the sieve plates. In
many respects this protoplasm differs from that of normal cells, having, in
mature sieve tubes, few mitochondria and a degenerate nucleus. (These are
probably necessary features of channels in which substances are to be
transported appreciable distances without being transformed, provided the
structure and functioning of such channels can be maintained.) The existence of membranes around these strands, the degree of their permeability
to different substances, the significance of the companion cells, and other
features are still much in doubt. Nevertheless, it seems likely that there is
no mass flow of solutions. Discussion and evaluation of the many uncertain
details involved are beyond our present terms of reference.

However, as pointed out in a timely and elegant paper by Canny &
Askham (22), much evidence still supports the original contention of
Mason and Maskell that the translocation system behaves as a diffusion analogue with an apparent diffusion coefficient 3×10^4 times greater than that
of sucrose in water. It is difficult to find admissable information on concentration gradients, since those usually measured are of bulk tissues, including
much that is irrelevant. It is still necessary to establish by acceptable techniques, such as aphid stylets, whether flow along the sieve tubes is proportional to the concentration gradient (diffusion), proportional to the concentration in and linear velocity of the transporting medium (mass flow), or
against a concentration gradient as indicated by bulk analyses of sugar beet
petioles (113).

Most of the mathematical models suggested (23, 27, 50, 61, 62, 184)
necessarily greatly simplify the system, often ignoring the pathways from
the chloroplast surfaces to the sieve tubes and those from the sieve tubes to
regions of utilization or storage; they also fail to take into account the interrelationships between the numerous sources and sinks. They often allow
for lateral transport from the sieve tubes but usually assume mass flow of a
solution and attempt to assess the velocity of transport assuming a constant
velocity, concentration of solution, and unidirectional flow. Possibly these
assumptions do not matter in respect to the conclusion that sucrose molecules move along the sieve tubes with velocities of 50 to 100 cm hr^{-1}, but
they are unacceptable for a general model of phloem transport in the whole
plant.

There is general agreement that the movement of sucrose into the
phloem requires a supply of metabolic energy (112, 113). If a leaf is supplied with ATP, the export of sucrose from the leaf is increased and the

uptake of sucrose by a vein immersed in sucrose solution is also increased (113). There is some doubt with such experiments if the ATP supplied ever enters the cells; however, it may act on membrane systems. Other indirect evidence indicates that "loading" of sucrose in the phloem involves phosphorylation and chemical transformation of the sucrose, is influenced by respiration inhibitors, and occurs against a concentration gradient — ~ 10 to 15 per cent in veins compared with ~0.4 per cent in mesophyll (7, 8, 55, 78, 87, 112, 113, 164, 175). There also appears to be an energy requirement for the movement of ions (7, 8, 94, 133), herbicides and viruses into the phloem.

Estimates of lateral transport ("leakage") from the sieve tubes range from 0.8 per cent of the instantaneous sieve-tube content of ^{11}C-labelled assimilates per centimetre moved (50, 137) to 2 to 11 per cent when ^{137}Cs was used (184). Part of this laterally transported material moves into the bark and part into the xylem, about 70 per cent of the carbon compounds reaching the xylem being sucrose and the remainder glucose and fructose (156–158). There is also some lateral transport from xylem to phloem (155).

In sugar cane, Glasziou et al. (64, 79, 80, 82, 170) explored some biochemical aspects of sucrose uptake from vascular tissue by stem parenchyma. They found that translocated sucrose moves from the vascular tissue into an outer "free space" which probably includes the cell walls. Here the sucrose is hydrolysed and the glucose and fructose formed move into a "metabolic" compartment, probably the cytoplasm, where they are phosphorylated and then combined to form a sucrose phosphate. This compound then passes into the storage compartment where it is dephosphorylated. The process can be reversed, especially in immature tissue, and the sucrose moved to other regions of the plant.

The movement of amino acids and amines in the phloem may be presumed to show features similar to those relating to sucrose. Few investigations have been made, and it is not known what chemical transformations are involved during the movement into and out of sieve tubes. Some evidence (205) suggests that there is free entry of amino acids with little selectivity into young leaves; with mature leaves there is little import and only small amounts of highly selected amino acids are exported; and during senescence there is extensive export of a wide range of amino acids. Although the phloem is the main pathway for export of amino acids manufactured in the leaf (24, 154), in many plants there is extensive manufacture of amino acids and amines in the root and translocation to the growing and storage regions of the shoot. Generally, this appears to be via the xylem (14, 24, 208), although such export via the phloem in sugar beet has been reported (105).

Flow in the plant.—While it is difficult to incorporate into a satisfactory quantitative model the influences of the numerous sources and sinks of varying intensities found in a normal intact plant, there is a growing body

of data relating to these. The potential sources, the leaves, are net impor-
ters of sucrose until they are about one-quarter to one-half of their final
size (88, 203) and may still continue to import after they have become net
exporters. In many plants, the proportion of photosynthate exported from a
leaf increases from zero when it is one-quarter to one-third its final size to
about 50 per cent by the time it reaches its maximum size. The photosynthetic production of the leaf then commences to decline and the proportion
of that production which is exported also declines (40, 102, 145, 175, 203,
205). During this time, the export of inorganic ions and amino acids usually
increases; it seems unlikely that there is any impairment of transport in the
sieve tubes themselves, although the processes "loading" sucrose into them
may be affected. [The decline in photosynthetic capacity of the leaf is associated mainly with a reduced intensity of the carboxylation reactions (153)
and with reduced activity of some of the enzymes involved (181).]

In maize and sugar cane, as much as 70 to 90 per cent of current photosynthate may be exported from leaves which also appear to maintain over
long periods their maximum capacities for photosynthesis. It is possible that
large amounts of export may also be found in other tropical grasses, Amar-
anthaceae, and other plants in which phosphoenolpyruvate (80, 81, 178)
rather than ribulose diphosphate is utilized as substrate for the primary carboxylation; these plants have a highly efficient photosynthetic system, and
much indirect evidence suggests that the rates of photosynthesis and of
translocation are closely correlated.

The reduction with increasing age in carbon assimilation by a leaf may
proceed until the compensation point is reached, there being no significant
resumption of sucrose import (89, 122). However, flow of some sucrose
molecules into mature leaves of wheat (108, 165) and tomato (107) has
been reported, and it seems possible for mature leaves to obtain materials
moving from the root (14). The leaf cells of senescing leaves appear to
lose the ability to accumulate sugars (102, 198, 216), although labelled sucrose exported from other leaves is accumulated by active absorbing systems such as aphids feeding on such leaves (22). The sieve tubes still seem
to be functional. There are other systems, however, such as old mother tubers of growing potato plants which, as net exporting organs in an advanced state of senescence, are still able to import and metabolize sucrose
exported from leaves (135).

The regions between which translocation occurs are influenced, not surprisingly, by the location of the sieve tubes and the number of interconnections between them. Much of the flow occurs between leaves on the same
orthostichy and adjoining roots (102, 145, 164, 175); nevertheless, conductances between orthostichies appear to be relatively large, the proportion of
translocated photosynthate moving to differing regions depending largely on
the relative activities of the sinks present. For example, photosynthate exported by the third leaf of wheat was found in each successively younger
leaf up to the seventh (40). All leaves of young tomato plants could supply

all of the fruit trusses, but as the plants aged, particular groups of leaves tended to supply particular trusses (107). Vascular connections appear to be more extensive and not to influence translocation as much as previously thought.

FLOW OF GROWTH SUBSTANCES

Evidence relating to the transport of growth substances was fully discussed recently in this journal (128). Here we are concerned with two features only: (a) the role of growth substances in the transport of other materials, and (b) the significance of the transport of specific growth substances in determining growth.

Effect of growth substances on transport of other substances.—The older experiments showing that the application of IAA increased the movement of soluble carbohydrates, nitrogenous substances, and ions into the treated regions extended over several days and did not distinguish between direct effects of IAA on transport mechanisms and those arising from enhanced growth. In more recent experiments, accelerated movement of ^{32}P and ^{14}C-labelled sucrose and photosynthate into internodes of decapitated bean plants on which IAA had been applied was shown within 6 hr of treatment (10, 38, 173). Further, the accumulation of ^{32}P in an IAA-treated region was reduced by triiodobenzoic acid (TIBA) applied either with the IAA or between the sites of application of IAA and ^{32}P (38). TIBA is claimed to block the movement of IAA (28)—although it undoubtedly also has other effects, such as inhibiting cell extension—and these authors concluded that movement of ^{32}P was stimulated by the basipetal transport of IAA. Hew et al. (83) showed that when IAA was applied to decapitated soybean plants, the export of photosynthate from the primary leaves was increased. The applied IAA could be recovered only from the stems, and it was concluded that it influenced translocation in the stem, having little effect on processes loading photosynthate into the sieve tubes.

As with IAA, of the few studies on the effect of gibberellins and kinetin on the transport of sucrose and other substances, most fail to distinguish between direct and indirect effects (e.g., 77, 225). In experiments ranging from 12 to 36 hr after application, GA_3 and kinetin alone had little effect on transport of ^{32}P to defruited peduncles and decapitated internodes, but they did show a large synergism when applied with IAA (172, 173). It seemed that a deficiency of IAA had to be remedied before effects of other substances could be demonstrated. In the grape, however, translocation of ^{14}C-labelled photosynthate over a 6-hr period was markedly increased in plants treated 3 days previously with either GA_3 or benzylaminopurine (174). Transport was reduced when 2-chloroethyltrimethylammonium chloride, which probably prevents gibberellin synthesis, was similarly used.

The above effects may well be similar to the movement of amino acids, sugars, and ions into kinetin-treated regions of detached leaves (76, 139–142). Mothes and his co-workers believe that kinetin directly influences the movement and accumulation of ^{14}C-labelled amino acids independently of any effect arising from the stimulation of protein synthesis; for example, the movement of α-aminoisobutyric acid, which is not incorporated into proteins, was also increased by kinetin. Müller & Leopold (141, 142), however, consider that the transport of non-metabolites is by mass-flow of solution to the kinetin-treated region, this being generated by the "active transport (of metabolites) through cell membranes at the phloem boundaries." They showed that kinetin stimulated the basipetal (and acropetal) transport of both ^{32}P and ^{22}Na in detached maize leaves, but only the former accumulated in the treated regions.

While the above experiments all substantiate the finding that metabolites move towards regions of high growth-substance concentration, it is not clear whether the recorded stimulation of movement is due to effects on movement within the sieve tubes, entry or exit therefrom, or entry into associated parenchyma. Almost all the effects noted could arise from the stimulation of "metabolic sinks" near or at the point of application; indeed, the synergistic effect of IAA, GA, and kinetin noted above supports this contention. It seems reasonable to conclude from available evidence that the application of these substances to plant tissues initiates or stimulates many enzymic activities, including the syntheses of protein and nucleic acids, within a few hours.

Long-distance transport of growth substances.—Fragmentary evidence shows that growth substances move considerable distances in both the phloem and the xylem. IAA and synthetic auxins such as 2, 4-D have been shown to move throughout the plant (cf. 120) and, indeed, the use of many herbicides depends on this. GA_3 appears to behave similarly (127). There is growing evidence that physiologically active quantities of gibberellins (25, 160, 177) and kinetins (98, 106) are produced in roots and translocated in the xylem. Hoad (86) has shown that abscisic acid (and also IAA and gibberellins) is present in the honeydew from aphids.

Although it is reasonable to conclude from this evidence that there is transport over long distances of auxins in the phloem, upward movement of kinins in the xylem, and possibly both acropetal and basipetal movement of gibberellins, abscisic acid, and the complex involved in the flowering stimulus (48, 49), evidence concerning the effective participation of these transported growth substances in regulating growth is still scanty. A great deal of indirect evidence suggests that the transport of auxins and other growth substances is concerned in the transient inhibition of axillary bud growth (cf. 65). However, there is little evidence that the rate of growth is influenced by growth substances transported over distances greater than a few centimetres (cf. 36, 217), and much of the diffuse and indirect evidence scattered through the literature suggests that those molecules of growth substances which do influence the rate of growth are produced *in situ* or in close proximity to the growing tissue.

THE SIGNIFICANCE OF TRANSPORT IN GROWTH

The significance of transport in growth is summarized by considering four particular systems, viz. leaves, ears of cereals, potato tubers, and storage roots of sugar beet. Further, information concerning the interrelationships of root and shoot growth mediated through transport is given in a current volume (218).

Transport in leaf growth.—From knowledge of the quantitative development of the leaf (92, 126, 130, 132, 187, 220, 221) it may be inferred that the primordial leaf completely depends on the import of all basic materials. During much of the time between initiation and unfolding from the terminal bud, its growth appears to be limited by the rate of supply of one or more metabolites. Sucrose, required to provide carbon skeletons for amino acids and many other compounds, seems to be the most likely. We reach this conclusion on the following grounds. The rates of increase in cell number and dry weight during this phase are related to total daily radiation by curves closely resembling the photosynthesis-light response curve (56, 132, 147). Removal of parts of the photosynthetic surface appreciably reduces these rates, and removal of younger competing leaf primordia increases them (89, 95, 96, 204). On the other hand, changes in concentration of mineral elements in the external solution around roots of plants of the same size has little short-term effect. Indirect evidence of this nature suggests that the rate of growth is related to the concentration of assimilates in the sieve tubes—although this has not been explored by direct observation. Further, the relative rate of growth during this phase reaches a maximum at a time when effective vascular connections between the leaf and the stem are established (220). The rate of protein synthesis per unit RNA also increases at this time (221), suggesting that amino acids were previously in short supply. The concentration of soluble sugars and the ratio of amino acids to proteins (188) are always very low, indicating that transported substrates are transformed as rapidly as they arrive.

By the time the leaf has reached about one-third of its final size, it becomes a net exporter of sucrose (cf. p. 126). Net import of nitrogen as nitrate or amino acids, depending on the species (24, 154), continues until about the time when the leaf attains its maximum area; in later stages, appreciable export of amino acids (from breakdown of its constituent proteins) continues. The capacity of the translocation system for export may decrease slightly, but it does not seem to become impaired until the leaf has reached a very advanced stage of senescence (205).

There is much indirect evidence to show that the supply of mineral elements plays an important role after the leaf has unfolded. The limitations here appear to reside in aspects of supply and demand rather than in any features of the vascular system (67, 74). Part may be attributed to the low conductance for ions across the root; certainly, even with high external concentrations the plant seems increasingly unable to meet the demands of the increasing number of sinks as it progresses through its ontogeny (92, 147). Removal of some of the sinks—the expanding leaves—leads immediately to increased growth of those remaining (95, 96, 222); increased supply of nitrogen and phosphorus increases the growth of expanding leaves and delays senescence. The changes in photosynthetic activity are closely correlated with the contents of nitrogen and phosphorus.

There is good indirect evidence of the involvement of growth substances in leaf growth (cf. 56, 92) but these seem generally to be formed *in situ* rather than imported from elsewhere. However, as pointed out earlier, lack of evidence of significant roles of translocated growth substances in this system reflects mainly the absence of adequate experimentation. At least, one system—the export from leaves to the apex of that complex involved in flower initiation—now seems to be adequately established (48, 49).

Transport and the growth of the cereal ear.—Very little attention has been given to the sources, nature, and amounts of material translocated to the growing inflorescence prior to anthesis, although appreciable quantities must be involved, not only to supply the growing inflorescence but also the elongating internodes. Growth following anthesis has received much attention (cf. 185, 201). There are sufficient fragments to allow a reasonable picture to be synthesized, although, surprisingly, there does not seem to be a complete documentation of any one crop in the same season. Summarizing, all evidence suggests that at least 90 to 95 per cent of the dry matter of the grains comes from photosynthesis after anthesis (201). Loss of stored carbohydrate in the stem is greater than can be accounted for by respiration, but, except in varieties with a short leaf persistence (185), less than 5 to 10 per cent moves into the grain (212). Expressed as a percentage of the final grain weight of barley, gross photosynthesis of the ear and the flag leaf plus peduncle each contribute about 75 per cent. Respiration of the ear is about 30 per cent and of the flag leaf about 20 per cent; i.e., about 45 per cent of the net income arises from the ear and 55 per cent is translocated from the flag leaf. In awnless wheat, ear photosynthesis is much less than in barley and some awned varieties of wheat (26) and is sufficient to balance ear respiration only; the rate of photosynthesis in the flag leaf region of wheat is about three times that of barley, and transport therefrom appears to account for all of the net increase in grain weight. Rice appears to behave as wheat. In maize, ear photosynthesis can account for only 1 to 2 per cent of the final weight; about half of the carbohydrate comes from the top 6 leaves, a third from the middle 4 to 5 leaves, and a sixth from the bottom 4 to 5 leaves.

The proportions stated above should be regarded as approximate only; they vary with environment, experimental manipulations, strengths of the receiving "sinks," and photosynthetic capacities of the "sources." During the week following anthesis, for example, the expanding top internode of wheat received as much assimilate, from both flag leaf and ear, as did the grain (26). Removal of grains and leaves leads to compensation and readjustment of the whole flow system. Although insignificant amounts of carbohydrate move to the grain from leaves below the flag leaf in intact plants, removal of the flag leaf augments the flow from the next lowest leaf (211). Reduction of floret number and shading of barley ears influenced the amount of translocation into the ears but did not affect rates of photosynthesis in leaves (150). Similarly, removal of two-thirds of the florets from wheat spikes did not affect the total export of ^{14}C-assimilate from the flag leaf, but more moved towards the roots and less to the ears (209). However, in other experiments (108), the net photosynthesis of the flag leaf was reduced by half within 3 to 15 hours of removing the ear; this was associated with increased concentration of assimilates in the flag leaf. Inhibition of ear photosynthesis by spraying with dichlorophenyldimethylurea caused a rapid increase in the rates of photosynthesis of the flag leaf and movement of assimilates into the ears but did not influence the concentration of sugars in the leaf.

These considerations suggest that the amount and pattern of movement is dictated by events in the sources and sinks; there do not appear to be any major impedances in the translocation pathways. There is usually ample photosynthetic capacity and only small amounts of the readily mobilizable carbohydrate stored in the stem are moved to the grain. We are not aware of any detailed quantitative investigations on the movement of nitrogenous and other substances in this system; parts of the nitrogen (144, 211) and phosphorus (219) come from the leaves, but the amounts involved are uncertain.

Transport and growth of potato tubers.—All the tubers on a potato plant which eventually grow to marketable size are initiated over a period of about 2 weeks and thereafter grow by both cell division and expansion. Available evidence (134, 171) indicates that the individual tubers on the plant grow at different rates at different times, the largest at any time not necessarily being the first to commence expansion or to maintain the fastest growth rate. Nevertheless, the tubers appear to compete between themselves for photosynthate, the mean size of tubers at maturity being an inverse function of the number of stems per unit area (9, 134) and hence of amount of foliage and root volume. In most plant competition systems, any competitor gaining an advantage usually continues increasingly to suppress the less successful. That this does not happen among tubers on the same stem is unexplained. The amounts of ^{14}C moved to any one tuber appear to be correlated with the current rate of growth of the tuber and its ability to transform sucrose to starch; there is little correlation with absolute size of tuber and no obvious relation between source leaf and position of the receiving tuber (121, 135). "Sink strengths" here appear to be predominant and vascular geometry to play little part.

Despite these variations between individuals, the rate of growth of the whole population of tubers on a plant is remarkably constant with time over a reasonably wide range of temperature and light conditions and of photosynthetic surface (131, 135). Previously assimilated material stored in the stems and leaves may contribute as much as 25 per cent of the current increase in weight of tubers and represents about 10 per cent of the material transferred to the tuber over its entire life (136). In addition, transfer from the haulm maintains a constant concentration of mobile ions in the tuber (135). The low concentration of Ca in tubers may be related to the immobility of this ion in the phloem.

The net assimilation rate of the whole plant appears to be closely associated with the rate of tuber growth. It increases soon after tuber initiation (12, 13, 63) and again late in the season when the total leaf area of the plant and the photosynthetic capacities of the leaves are decreasing (131). It is decreased if tubers are removed from the plant (19, 149) or if the rate of tuber growth is slowed down by exposure to low temperature (20). This evidence indicates that the rate of photosynthesis is controlled to an appreciable extent by the rate of tuber growth, but the factors which control the rate of tuber growth remain unknown.

Transport and growth of storage roots of sugar beet.—The distribution of assimilates between the storage root and leaves of sugar beet varies as the plant progresses through its ontogeny, the root receiving an increasingly larger proportion. Although the rate of growth is markedly influenced by light intensity, there is no effect on the developmental pattern, the proportion of assimilates going to the root always being that appropriate to the size of the plant (192).

The detailed distribution patterns of assimilates are similar to those found in many other species, young expanding leaves exporting little or no assimilate and that exported by older leaves being partitioned between the root and young leaves (103, 193). Much of that moving into young leaves is converted into amino acids (104), while much of that entering the root is stored as sucrose. Sucrose appears to move against the concentration gradient from sieve tubes to storage cells (but see p. 124) without transformation, despite the presence of all the necessary enzymes (113). It therefore contrasts with sugar cane (p. 125).

The normal restriction of movement of sucrose to the young leaves vertically above and the root segment vertically below the exporting leaf (103, 112, 138) appears to reflect simply differences in lengths of pathways rather than high resistances to lateral movement; for example, the removal of all mature leaves from one side of the plant, followed by exposure of one of the remaining leaves to $^{14}CO_2$, resulted in movement of ^{14}C into all the immature leaves (103).

Events in the petiole appear to play little part in controlling translocation (138, 190), but competition between developing leaves and the storage root is of greater significance (192, 193). Experiments with decapitated and partially defoliated plants of which different parts were kept at different temperatures or modified by varying the nutrient supply (36, 60–62, 193, 223) indicate generally that photosynthetic rates and amounts translocated to particular regions are determined to a considerable extent by the relative activities of the various sinks. Removal of one part, or reducing its growth by lowering its temperature, leads to enhanced growth of the other regions. Cooling the entire storage root results in increases in sucrose concentration back along the petioles and finally in the source leaves (193); although the net assimilation rate is reduced, some evidence suggests that photosynthetic rates are not, the increased rates of respiration in the source leaves compensating for the reduced translocation (36). Cooling segments of the petiole (190) leads only to transient reductions in translocation. Removal of up to half of the source leaves did not affect the rate of growth of storage roots, the net assimilation rate increasing accordingly (36). Reciprocal grafts between the roots and leaves of sugar beet and spinach beet showed that sugar beet roots with either sugar beet or spinach beet leaves always had a much higher net assimilation rate than spinach beet roots with either spinach beet or sugar beet leaves (202).

Conclusions

Although growth depends on the movement of massive amounts of various substances within the plant, the transport systems appear to be more than adequate to meet this demand. Of two exceptions, one—the supply of sucrose to apical meristems and young primordia—may be reasonably ascribed to the absence of vascular tissue and the low conductances of parenchymatous cells. The other—the lack of movement of alkaline earths and possibly some other elements in the phloem—may well arise from the systems controlling entry into the sieve tubes.

Restrictions of growth attributable to minerals are usually matters of supply to and size of absorbing regions, the circulation within the plant being very efficient. The flow of carbohydrates often appears to be determined by sink activity unless conditions for photosynthesis are particularly unfavourable. Indeed, there are numerous examples of photosynthetic activity being linked to the availability of sinks. [End-product repression of photosynthesis by high concentrations rarely seems to operate (207), although high rates of photosynthesis with low sink activity are often partially compensated by high respiration rates.] The regulation of the rate of sink activity is not understood.

These considerations lead to the aggravating conclusion that elucidation of the mechanism of phloem transport, which has long intrigued plant physiologists, is unlikely to lead to the eventual production of more efficient plants. The plant appears to have evolved a transport system which is always adequate for its needs and rarely restricts its functioning. Nevertheless, it would be most gratifying to understand the real nature of these expressways—not only the rapid flow along the highway proper but also the features of the inlets and outlets which control this flow.

Acknowledgements.—We are indebted to Dr. H. Greenway and others for many discussions, often disputed but rarely resolved. One of us (J.M.) was a member of the University of Nottingham during the preparation of this review.

LITERATURE CITED

1. Anderson, W. P., Reilly, E. J., *J. Exptl. Botany*, **19**, 19–30 (1968)
2. Barber, S. A., *Soil Sci.*, **93**, 39–49 (1962)
3. Barber, S. A., Walker, J. M., Vasey, E. H., *Proc. Intern. Soil Conf., New Zealand*, **3**, 121–24 (1962)
4. Bell, C. W., Biddulph, O., *Plant Physiol.*, **38**, 610–14 (1963)
5. Biddulph, O., in *Plant Physiology*, Vol. II, 553–603 (Steward, F. C., Ed., Academic Press, New York, 758 pp., 1959)
6. Biddulph, O., Nakayama, F. S., Cory, R., *Plant Physiol.*, **36**, 429–36 (1961)
7. Bieleski, R. L., *Plant Physiol.*, **41**, 447–54 (1966)
8. Bieleski, R. L., *ibid.*, 455–66
9. Bleasdale, J. K. A., *J. Agr. Sci.*, **64**, 361–66 (1965)
10. Booth, A., Moorby, J., Davies, C. R., Jones, H., Wareing, P. F., *Nature*, **194**, 204–5 (1962)
11. Bowling, D. J. F., Macklon, A. E. S., Spanswick, R. M., *J. Exptl. Botany*, **17**, 410–16 (1966)
12. Bremner, P. M., Radley, R. W., *J. Agr. Sci.*, **66**, 253–62 (1966)
13. Bremner, P. M., Taha, M. A., *ibid.*, 241–52
14. Brennan, H., Pate, J. S., Wallace, W., *Ann. Botany (London)*, **28**, 527–40 (1964)
15. Briggs, G. E., *Movement of Water in Plants* (Blackwell, Oxford, 142 pp., 1967)
16. Briggs, G. E., Hope, A. B., Robertson, R. N., *Electrolytes and Plant Cells* (Blackwell, Oxford, 217 pp., 1961)
17. Brouwer, R., *Symp. Soc. Exptl. Biol.*, **19**, 131–55 (1965)
18. Brouwer, R., *Ann. Rev. Plant Physiol.*, **16**, 241–66 (1965)
19. Burt, R. L., *Australian J. Biol. Sci.*, **17**, 867–77 (1964)
20. Burt, R. L., *ibid.*, **19**, 711–14 (1966)
21. Buvat, R., *Compt. Rend. Acad. Sci.*, **257**, 733–35 (1963)
22. Canny, M. J., Askham, M. J., *Ann. Botany (London)*, **31**, 409–16 (1967)
23. Canny, M. J., Phillips, O. M., *Ann. Botany (London)*, **27**, 379–402 (1963)
24. Carr, D. J., Pate, J. S., *Symp. Soc. Exptl. Biol.*, **21**, 559–99 (1967)
25. Carr, D. J., Reid, D. M., Skene, K. G. M., *Planta*, **63**, 382–92 (1964)
26. Carr, D. J., Wardlaw, I. F., *Australian J. Biol. Sci.*, **18**, 711–19 (1965)
27. Choi, I. C., Aronoff, S., *Plant Physiol.*, **41**, 1119–29 (1966)
28. Christie, A. E., Leopold, A. C., *Plant Cell Physiol. (Tokyo)*, **6**, 337–45 (1965)
29. Cline, J. F., Hungate, F. P., *Plant Physiol.*, **35**, 826–29 (1960)
30. Cowan, I. R., Milthorpe, F. L., in *Water Deficits and Plant Growth*, Vol. I, Chap. 6, 137–93 (Kozlowski, T. T., Ed., Academic Press, New York, 1968)
31. Crafts, A. S., *Translocation in Plants* (Holt, Rinehart & Winston, New York, 182 pp., 1961)
32. Crafts, A. S., *Science*, **160**, 325–27 (1968)
33. Cronshaw, J., Esau, K., *J. Cell Biol.*, **34**, 301–15 (1967)
34. Crossett, R. N., *Australian J. Biol. Sci.*, **21**, 225–33 (1968)
35. Crossett, R. N., Loughman, B. C., *New Phytologist*, **65**, 459–68 (1966)
36. Das Gupta, D. K., *Physiological Studies on the Root-Shoot Relationships in Sugar Beet* (Doctoral thesis, Univ. Nottingham, England, 1968)
37. Davidson, J. L., Milthorpe, F. L., *Ann. Botany (London)*, **30**, 185–98 (1966)
38. Davies, C. R., Wareing, P. F., *Planta*, **65**, 139–56 (1965)
39. Donald, C. M., *Advan. Agron.*, **15**, 1–118 (1963)
40. Doodson, J. K., Manners, J. G., Myers, A., *J. Exptl. Botany*, **15**, 96–103 (1964)
41. Duloy, M. D., Mercer, F. V., *Australian J. Biol. Sci.*, **14**, 391–401 (1961)

42. Duloy, M., Mercer, F. V., Rath-geber, N., *Australian J. Biol. Sci.*, **14**, 506–18 (1961)

43. Duloy, M., Mercer, F. V., Rathgeber, N., *ibid.*, **15**, 459–67 (1962)

44. Engleman, E. M., *Ann. Botany (London)*, **29**, 83–101 (1965)

45. Engleman, E. M., *ibid.*, 103–18

46. Epstein, E., *Nature*, **212**, 1324 (1966)

47. Esau, K., Engleman, E. M., Bisalputra, T., *Planta*, **59**, 617–23 (1963)

48. Evans, L. T., Wardlaw, I. F., *Australian J. Biol. Sci.*, **17**, 1–9 (1964)

49. Evans, L. T., Wardlaw, I. F., *Planta*, **68**, 310–26 (1966)

50. Evans, N. T. S., Ebert, M., Moorby, J., *J. Exptl. Botany*, **14**, 221–31 (1963)

51. Evert, R. F., Derr, W. F., *Am. J. Botany*, **51**, 875–80 (1964)

52. Evert, R. F., Murmanis, L., *Am. J. Botany*, **52**, 95–106 (1965)

53. Falk, S. O., *Physiol. Plantarum*, **19**, 602–17 (1966)

54. Fogg, G., Ed., *The State and Movement of Water in Living Organisms*, Symp. Soc. Exptl. Biol., No. 19 (University Press, Cambridge, 432 pp., 1965)

55. Ford, J., Peel, A. J., *J. Exptl. Botany*, **18**, 607–19 (1967)

56. Friend, D. J. C., *Proc. 12th Easter Sch. Agr. Sci. Univ. Nottingham*, 181–99 (1966)

57. Garwood, E. A., Williams, T. E., *J. Agr. Sci.*, **68**, 281–92 (1967)

58. Garwood, E. A., Williams, T. E., *ibid.*, **69**, 125–30 (1967)

59. Gates, C. T., *J. Australian Inst. Agric. Sci.*, **30**, 3–22 (1964)

60. Geiger, D. R., *Plant Physiol.*, **41**, 1667–72 (1966)

61. Geiger, D. R., Swanson, C. A., *Plant Physiol.*, **40**, 685–90 (1965)

62. Geiger, D. R., Swanson, C. A., *ibid.*, 942–47

63. Gifford, R. M., Moorby, J., *European Potato J.*, **10**, 235–38 (1967)

64. Glasziou, K. T., *Plant Physiol.*, **36**, 175–79 (1961)

65. Goodwin, P. B., *Proc. 10th Easter Sch. Agr. Sci. Univ. Nottingham*, 63–71 (1963)

66. Greenway, H., *Australian J. Biol. Sci.*, **18**, 249–68 (1965)

67. Greenway, H., Gunn, A., *Planta*, **71**, 43–67 (1966)

68. Greenway, H., Gunn, A., Pitman, M. G., Thomas, D., *Australian J. Biol. Sci.*, **18**, 525–40 (1965)

69. Greenway, H., Hiller, R. G., *Planta*, **75**, 253–74 (1967)

70. Greenway, H., Hughes, P. G., Klepper, B., *Physiol. Plantarum*, **22** (In press, 1969)

71. Greenway, H., Klepper, B., *ibid.*

72. Greenway, H., Klepper, B., *Planta*, **83**, 119–36 (1968)

73. Greenway, H., Klepper, B., Hughes, P. G., *Planta*, **80**, 129–41 (1968)

74. Greenway, H., Pitman, M. G., *Australian J. Biol. Sci.*, **18**, 235–47 (1965)

75. Greenway, H., Thomas, D., *Australian J. Biol. Sci.*, **18**, 505–24 (1965)

76. Gunning, B. E. S., Barkley, W. K., *Nature*, **199**, 262–65 (1963)

77. Halevy, A. H., Monselise, S. P., Plaut, Z., *Physiol. Plantarum*, **17**, 49–62 (1964)

78. Hartt, C. E., *Plant Physiol.*, **40**, 718–24 (1965)

79. Hatch, M. D., *Biochem. J.*, **93**, 521–26 (1964)

80. Hatch, M. D., Slack, C. R., *Biochem. J.*, **101**, 103–11 (1966)

81. Hatch, M. D., Slack, C. R., Johnson, H. S., *Biochem. J.*, **102**, 417–22 (1967)

82. Hawker, J. S., Hatch, M. D., *Physiol. Plantarum*, **18**, 444–53 (1965)

83. Hew, C. S., Nelson, C. D., Krotkov, G., *Am. J. Botany*, **54**, 252–56 (1967)

84. Hiller, R. G., Flowers, T. J., *Ann. Rept. Univ. Nottingham Sch. Agr. for 1966–67*, 104–6 (1967)

85. Hiller, R. G., Greenway, H., *Planta*, **78**, 49–59 (1968)

86. Hoad, G. V., *Life Sci.*, **6**, 1113–18 (1967)

87. Hoad, G. V., Peel, A. J., *J. Exptl. Botany*, **16**, 433–51 (1965)

88. Hopkinson, J. M., *J. Exptl. Botany*, **15**, 125–37 (1964)

89. Hopkinson, J. M., *ibid.*, **17**, 762–70 (1966)

90. House, C. R., Findlay, W., *J. Exptl. Botany*, **17**, 627–40 (1966)

91. House, C. R., Jarvis, P., *ibid.*, **19**, 31–40 (1968)

92. Humphries, E. C., Wheeler, A. W., *Ann. Rev. Plant Physiol.*, **14**, 385–409 (1963)

93. Husa, J. G., McIlrath, W. J., *Botan. Gaz.*, **126**, 186–94 (1965)

94. Husain, A., Spanner, D. C., *Ann.*

Botany (London), **30**, 549–61 (1966)

95. Hussey, G., *J. Exptl. Botany*, **14**, 316–25 (1963)
96. Hussey, G., *ibid.*, 326–35
97. Ingelsten, B., *Physiol. Plantarum*, **19**, 563–79 (1966)
98. Itai, C., Vaadia, Y., *Physiol. Plantarum*, **18**, 941–44 (1965)
99. Jacoby, B., *Plant Physiol.*, **39**, 445–49 (1964)
100. Jarvis, P., House, C. R., *J. Exptl. Botany*, **18**, 695–706 (1967)
101. Jennings, D. H., *New Phytologist*, **66**, 357–69 (1967)
102. Jones, H., Martin, R. V., Porter, H. K., *Ann. Botany (London)*, **23**, 493–508 (1959)
103. Joy, K. W., *J. Exptl. Botany*, **15**, 485–94 (1964)
104. Joy, K. W., *ibid.*, **18**, 140–50 (1967)
105. Joy, K. W., Antcliff, A. J., *Nature*, **211**, 210 (1966)
106. Kende, H., *Proc. Natl. Acad. Sci. U.S.*, **53**, 1302–7 (1965)
107. Khan, A. A., Sagar, G. R., *Ann. Botany (London)*, **30**, 727–43 (1966)
108. King, R. W., Wardlaw, I. F., Evans, L. T., *Planta*, **77**, 261–76 (1967)
109. Klepper, B., Greenway, H., *Planta*, **80**, 142–46 (1968)
110. Koontz, H. V., Foote, R. E., *Physiol. Plantarum*, **19**, 313–21 (1966)
111. Kozlowski, T. T., Ed., *Water Deficits and Plant Growth* (Academic Press, New York, 2 vols., 390 pp., 325 pp., 1968)
112. Kursanov, A. L., *Advan. Botan. Res.*, **1**, 209–78 (1963)
113. Kursanov, A. L., *J. Intern. Inst. Sugar Beet Res.*, **2**, 162–83 (1967)
114. Langer, R. H. M., *Proc. 12th Easter Sch. Agr. Sci., Univ. Nottingham*, 213–26 (1966)
115. Laties, G. G., *Australian J. Sci.*, **30**, 193–203 (1967)
116. Lewis, D. G., Quirk, J. P., *Plant Soil*, **26**, 99–118 (1967)
117. Lewis, D. G., Quirk, J. P., *ibid.*, 119–28
118. Lewis, D. G., Quirk, J. P., *ibid.*, 445–53
119. Lewis, D. G., Quirk, J. P., *ibid.*, 454–68
120. Little, E. C. S., Blackman, G. E., *New Phytologist*, **62**, 173–97 (1963)
121. Lovell, P. H., Booth, A., *New Phytologist*, **66**, 525–37 (1967)
122. Ludwig, L. J., Saeki, T., Evans, L.

T., *Australian J. Biol. Sci.*, **18**, 1103–18 (1965)
123. Luttge, U., Laties, G. G., *Plant Physiol.*, **41**, 1531–39 (1966)
124. Luttge, U., Laties, G. G., *ibid.*, **42**, 181–85 (1967)
125. Luttge, U., Laties, G. G., *Planta*, **74**, 173–87 (1967)
126. Maksymowych, R., *Am. J. Botany*, **50**, 891–901 (1963)
127. McComb, A. J., *Ann. Botany (London)*, **28**, 669–87 (1965)
128. McCready, C. C., *Ann. Rev. Plant Physiol.*, **17**, 283–94 (1966)
129. Millikan, C. R., Hanger, B. C., *Australian J. Biol. Sci.*, **18**, 211–26 (1965)
130. Milthorpe, F. L., *J. Exptl. Botany*, **10**, 233–49 (1959)
131. Milthorpe, F. L., *Proc. 10th Easter Sch. Agr. Sci., Univ. Nottingham*, 3–16 (1963)
132. Milthorpe, F. L., Newton, P., *J. Exptl. Botany*, **14**, 483–95 (1963)
133. Moorby, J., *J. Exptl. Botany*, **15**, 457–69 (1964)
134. Moorby, J., *European Potato J.*, **10**, 189–205 (1967)
135. Moorby, J., *Ann. Botany (London)*, **32**, 57–68 (1968)
136. Moorby, J., *European Potato J.*, **11** (In press, 1968)
137. Moorby, J., Ebert, M., Evans, N. T. S., *J. Exptl. Botany*, **14**, 210–20 (1963)
138. Mortimer, D. C., *Can. J. Botany*, **43**, 269–80 (1965)
139. Mothes, K., Engelbrecht, L., *Phytochemistry*, **1**, 58–62 (1961)
140. Mothes, K., Engelbrecht, L., Schütte, H. R., *Physiol. Plantarum*, **14**, 72–75 (1961)
141. Müller, K., Leopold, A. C., *Planta*, **68**, 167–85 (1966)
142. Müller, K., Leopold, A. C., *ibid.*, 186–205
143. Murmanis, L., Evert, R. F., *Am. J. Botany*, **53**, 1065–78 (1966)
144. Neales, T. F., Anderson, M. J., Wardlaw, I. F., *Australian J. Agr. Res.*, **14**, 725–36 (1963)
145. Nelson, C. D., in *Environmental Control of Plant Growth*, 149–74 (Evans, L. T., Ed., Academic Press, New York, 449 pp. (1963)
146. Newbould, P., Sanderson, J., Shone, M. G. T., Sidrak, G. H., *Agr. Res. Council Radiobiological Lab.*, Rept. ARCRL 12, 56–58 (H. M. Stationary Office, London, 1964)

147. Newton, P., *J. Exptl. Botany*, **14**, 458–82 (1963)
148. Northcote, D. H., Wooding, F. B. P., *Proc. Roy. Soc. (London) Ser. B*, **163**, 524–37 (1966)
149. Nösberger, J., Humphries, E. C., *Ann. Botany (London)*, **29**, 579–88 (1965)
150. Nösberger, J., Thorne, G. N., *Ann. Botany (London)*, **29**, 635–44 (1965)
151. Oliver, S., Barber, S. A., *Soil Sci. Soc. Am. Proc.*, **30**, 82–86 (1966)
152. Oliver, S., Barber, S. A., *ibid.*, 468–70
153. Osman, A. M., *The Influence of Internal Factors of Leaves in the Photosynthesis of a Wheat Crop* (Doctoral thesis, Univ. Nottingham, 1968)
154. Pate, J. S., *Ann. Botany (London)*, **30**, 93–109 (1966)
155. Peel, A. J., *J. Exptl. Botany*, **14**, 438–47 (1963)
156. Peel, A. J., *ibid.*, **15**, 104–13 (1964)
157. Peel, A. J., *ibid.*, **17**, 156–64 (1966)
158. Peel, A. J., *ibid.*, **18**, 600–6 (1967)
159. Philip, J. R., *Ann. Rev. Plant Physiol.*, **17**, 245–68 (1966)
160. Phillips, I. D. J., Jones, R. L., *Planta*, **63**, 269–78 (1964)
161. Pitman, M. G., *Australian J. Biol. Sci.*, **18**, 987–98 (1965)
162. Plaut, Z., Ordin, L., *Physiol. Plantarum*, **17**, 279–86 (1964)
163. Plaut, Z., Reinhold, L., *Australian J. Biol. Sci.*, **18**, 1143–55 (1965)
164. Porter, H. K., *Australian J. Sci.*, **29**, 31–40 (1966-67)
165. Quinlan, J. D., Sagar, G. R., *Weed Res.*, **2**, 264–73 (1962)
166. Ringoet, A., Sauer, G., Gielink, A. G., *Planta*, **80**, 15–20 (1968)
167. Robertson, R. N., *Biol. Rev. Cambridge Phil. Soc.*, **35**, 231–64 (1960)
168. Russell, R. S., *Ann. Rev. Plant Physiol.*, **14**, 271–94 (1963)
169. Russell, R. S., Newbould, P., in *Radioactivity and Human Diet*, 213–45 (Russell, R. S., Ed., Pergamon, Oxford, 552 pp., 1966)
170. Sacher, J. A., Hatch, M. D., Glasziou, K. T., *Plant Physiol.*, **38**, 348–54 (1963)
171. Sadler, E., *Factors Influencing the Development of Sprouts of the Potato* (Doctoral thesis, Univ. Nottingham, 1961)
172. Seth, A., Wareing, P. F., *Life Sci.*, **3**, 1483–86 (1964)
173. Seth, A., Wareing, P. F., *J. Exptl. Botany*, **18**, 67–77 (1967)
174. Shindy, W., Weaver, R. J., *Nature*, **214**, 1024–25 (1967)
175. Shiroya, M., Lister, G. R., Nelson, C. D., Krotkov, G., *Can. J. Botany*, **39**, 855–64 (1961)
176. Sitton, D., Richmond, A., Vaadia, Y., *Phytochemistry*, **6**, 1101–5 (1967)
177. Skene, K. G. M., *Planta*, **74**, 250–62 (1967)
178. Slack, C. R., Hatch, M. D., *Biochem. J.*, **103**, 660–65 (1967)
179. Slayter, R. O., *Plant-Water Relationships* (Academic Press, London, 366 pp., 1967)
180. Slayter, R. O., Taylor, S. A., *Nature*, **187**, 922–24 (1960)
181. Smillie, R. M., *Plant Physiol.*, **37**, 716–21 (1962)
182. Spanner, D. C., *J. Exptl. Botany*, **9**, 332–42 (1958)
183. Spanner, D. C., *Introduction to Thermodynamics* (Academic Press, London, 278 pp., 1964)
184. Spanner, D. C., Prebble, J. N., *J. Exptl. Botany*, **13**, 294–306 (1962)
185. Stoy, V., *Physiol. Plantarum Suppl.*, **4**, 1–125 (1965)
186. Sutcliffe, J. F., *Mineral Salts Absorption by Plants* (Pergamon, Oxford, 194 pp., 1962)
187. Sunderland, N., *J. Exptl. Botany*, **11**, 68–80 (1960)
188. Sunderland, N., Heyes, J. K., Brown, R., *Proc. 3rd Easter Sch. Agr. Sci., Univ. Nottingham*, 77–90 (1956)
189. Swanson, C. A., in *Plant Physiology*, Vol. II, 481–551 (Steward, F. C., Ed., Academic Press, New York, 758 pp., 1959)
190. Swanson, C. A., Geiger, D. R., *Plant Physiol.*, **42**, 751–56 (1967)
191. Tammes, P. M. C., Van Die, J., *Acta Botan. Neerl.*, **13**, 76–83 (1964)
192. Terry, N., *The Effect of Light and Temperature on the Growth of Sugar Beet* (Master's thesis, Univ. Nottingham, 1963)
193. Terry, N., *Physiology of Sugar Beet in Relation to Temperature* (Doctoral thesis, Univ. Nottingham, 1966)
194. Thaine, R., *Nature*, **192**, 772–73 (1961)
195. Thaine, R., *J. Exptl. Botany*, **13**, 152–60 (1962)

196. Thaine, R., *ibid.*, **15**, 470–84 (1964)
197. Thaine, R., *New Phytologist*, **64**, 118–30 (1965)
198. Thaine, R., Ovendon, S. L., Turner, J. S., *Australian J. Biol. Sci.*, **12**, 349–72 (1959)
199. Thaine, R., Preston, R. D., in *Formation of Wood in Forest Trees*, 259–72 (Zimmermann, M. H., Ed., Academic Press, New York, 562 pp., 1964)
200. Thaine, R., Probine, M. C., Dyer, P. Y., *J. Exptl. Botany*, **18**, 110–27 (1967)
201. Thorne, G. N., *Proc. 12th Easter Sch. Agr. Sci., Univ. Nottingham*, 88–105 (1966)
202. Thorne, G. N., Evans, A. F., *Ann. Botany (London)*, **28**, 499–508 (1964)
203. Thrower, S. L., *Australian J. Biol. Sci.*, **15**, 629–49 (1962)
204. Thrower, S. L., *ibid.*, **17**, 412–26 (1964)
205. Thrower, S. L., *Symp. Soc. Exptl. Biol.*, **21**, 483–506 (1967)
206. Torii, K., Laties, G. G., *Plant Physiol.*, **41**, 863–70 (1966)
207. Waldron, J. C., Glasziou, K. T., Bull, T. A., *Australian J. Biol. Sci.*, **20**, 1043–52 (1967)
208. Wallace, W., Pate, J. S., *Ann. Botany (London)*, **31**, 213–28 (1967)
209. Wardlaw, I. F., *Australian J. Biol. Sci.*, **18**, 269–81 (1965)
210. Wardlaw, I. F., *ibid.*, **20**, 25–39 (1967)
211. Wardlaw, I. F., Carr, D. J., Anderson, M. J., *Australian J. Agr. Res.*, **16**, 893–901 (1965)
212. Wardlaw, I. F., Porter, H. K., *Australian J. Biol. Sci.*, **20**, 309–18 (1967)
213. Watson, D. J., *Proc. 10th Easter Sch. Agr. Sci., Univ. Nottingham*, 233–47 (1963)
214. Weatherley, P. E., *Progr. Biophys. Chem.*, **13**, 251–55 (1963)
215. Weatherley, P. E., Peel, A. J., Hill, G. P., *J. Exptl. Botany*, **10**, 1–16 (1959)
216. Webb, J. A., Gorham, P. R., *Plant Physiol.*, **39**, 663–72 (1964)
217. Wheeler, A. W., *J. Exptl. Botany*, **17**, 621–26 (1966)
218. Whittington, W. J., Ed., *The Growth of Roots* (Proc. 15th Easter Sch. Agr. Sci., Univ. Nottingham, Butterworths, London, in press)
219. Williams, R. F., *Ann. Rev. Plant Physiol.*, **6**, 25–42 (1955)
220. Williams, R. F., *Australian J. Biol. Sci.*, **13**, 401–28 (1960)
221. Williams, R. F., Rijven, A. H. G. C., *Australian J. Biol. Sci.*, **18**, 721–43 (1965)
222. Wilson, G. L., *J. Exptl. Botany*, **17**, 440–51 (1966)
223. Winter, H., Mortimer, D. C., *Can. J. Botany*, **45**, 1811–22 (1967)
224. Woolley, J. T., *Plant Physiol.*, **40**, 711–17 (1965)
225. Zweig, G., Yamaguchi, S., Mason, G. W., *Advan. Chem. Ser.*, **28**, 122–34 (1961)

PHYSIOLOGY OF ABSCISIC ACID AND RELATED SUBSTANCES[1]

By Fredrick T. Addicott and Jessye Lorene Lyon

University of California, Davis, California

Introduction

Abscisic acid (ABA) is a plant hormone which now ranks in importance with the auxins, gibberellins, and cytokinins as a controlling factor in physiological processes. Interest in the physiology and chemistry of ABA has expanded almost explosively since 1965 when the structure was determined. Several hundred investigators are currently involved in ABA research, but many of the results have not yet been published. The results which are available can give only an incomplete picture of the physiology of ABA. This review, therefore, will be concerned primarily with describing the trends of the present lines of investigation, indicating as much as is possible of the physiological significance of abscisic acid.

During the 1950's, in several laboratories widely scattered around the world, investigation of growth-inhibiting substances in relation to processes such as abscission, dormancy, and germination was being given increasing attention. In these investigations particular diffusates or extracts had been found to both promote abscission, dormancy, etc., and inhibit growth in selected biological systems (see 23, 135, 159). As the investigations progressed, they expanded to include research on the chemical nature of the active substances. In most cases progress was slow. The active substances were present in very small amounts, and the extracts contained a surprising number of interfering substances. Also, the available methods of purification were relatively ineffective. Eventually, several of these research groups sought the collaboration of organic chemists and were able to achieve the isolation or identification of an active substance.

Three research programs appear, in retrospect, to have been directly concerned with ABA: (*a*) The program on the hormonal substances in cotton was led by Carns and Addicott. With the active collaboration of Ohkuma, this group achieved the first isolation of ABA (106) and published the structure in 1965 (105). (*b*) Several programs were concerned with dormancy-inducing substances in deciduous trees (see 46, 100, 123, 154, 158,

[1] We thank Dr. Kazuhiko Ohkuma for several very helpful discussions and Mrs. Alice B. Addicott for preparing the figures and reading the manuscript. We also thank the many colleagues who generously communicated results of their research in advance of publication.

161). A group led by Wareing and Cornforth isolated the active substance from *Acer* and determined that it was ABA (40, 122). (*c*) A program initiated by Van Steveninck (153) and continued by Rothwell & Wain (124) investigated a fruit abscission substance in lupins. In 1966 this substance was identified almost simultaneously in three independent laboratories. Koshimizu et al. (82) isolated crystals and based their identification on the known physical properties of ABA; Cornforth et al. (39) used optical rotatory dispersion to identify ABA in a highly active, partly crystalline concentrate; and Porter & Van Steveninck (118) based their identification on bioassay and co-chromatography in several solvent systems.

Many other investigations have been concerned with acidic growth-inhibiting substances, particularly with the fraction designated 'inhibitor β' (12, 14, 45–47, 68, 100). Milborrow (96) has shown that ABA appears to be the most active component of inhibitor β. Other investigations of natural inhibitors of growth and flowering, and of natural promotors of senescence, may quite possibly have been involved with ABA or related substances (54, 67, 109, 110).

NOMENCLATURE

Abscisic acid is the 'trivial' name for 3-methyl-5-(1'-hydroxy-4'-oxo-2',6',6'-trimethyl-2'-cyclohexen-1'-yl)-*cis, trans*-2,4-pentadienoic acid (Fig. 1). The compound was first named 'abscisin II' by the research group which

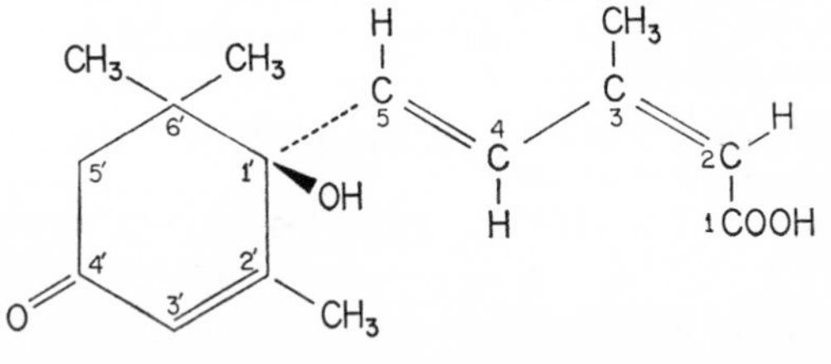

(*S*)-ABSCISIC ACID

FIG. 1. Structure of (*S*)-abscisic acid.

isolated it and determined its structure (6, 104–106). In keeping with long established custom, the original name as designated by the discoverers was, in general, accepted and used. However, there were some expressions that other names might be more useful or valuable. Consequently, in 1966 and 1967 the groups then most active in abscisic acid research reviewed the matter of nomenclature in some detail; after considerable deliberation they agreed upon the new name, abscisic acid, as the most reasonable and suitable of many alternatives. The deliberations, with a recommendation for the adoption of the new name, were reported to a special session of the Sixth International Conference on Plant Growth Substances (Ottawa, 24–28 July 1967), and the new name was approved (5, 8). Abscisic acid gives an indication of the compound's chemical nature and facilitates the naming of chemical derivatives; the etymological relation to the original name minimizes the possibility of confusion arising from the change. Consequently, the old name, abscisin II, and other names such as dormin, should no longer be used for this compound. This agreement on abscisic acid as the trivial chemical name of a specific substance does not preclude the continued use of the term 'dormin' in the special, collective physiological sense in which it was originally suggested by Wareing, Eagles & Robinson (161) "for substances which appear to function as endogenous dormancy-inducers." It may well be that other endogenous dormancy-inducing substances will be discovered, in which case 'dormin' would be a convenient term with which to designate that physiological group of substances.

The terms abscisin, abscisin I, and abscisin II have from the beginning been used as the names of specific chemical compounds isolated in crystalline form. The name 'abscisin' was given by Liu & Carns (89) to the compound which they isolated from the burs of mature cotton fruit; the name was later changed to 'abscisin I' (6).

The naturally occurring enantiomer of abscisic acid has been shown to be (S)-$(+)$-abscisic acid (35, 38). The synthetic, racemic substance is therefore (RS)-$(\pm)$-abscisic acid. For convenience in this review, the abbreviation ABA will be used to indicate (a) naturally occurring (S)-ABA, (b) racemic preparations of (RS)-ABA, and (c) extracts in which it is reasonably certain that (S)-ABA was the active substance. The isomer of abscisic acid which has a *trans* configuration around the 2-double bond is designated '2-*trans*-abscisic acid' (t-ABA).

CHEMISTRY

Isolation.—Abscisic acid was first isolated from young cotton fruit (*Gossypium hirsutum*) by Ohkuma et al. (106), who found that the substance was a $C_{15}H_{20}O_4$ acid, soluble in many organic solvents; it melted at 160 to 161° C, sublimed at 120° C, and had an absorption maximum in methanol at 252 mμ. Further research involving elemental analysis, mass and infrared spectroscopy, and nuclear magnetic resonance revealed the structure shown in Figure 1 [Ohkuma et al. (105)]. Cornforth, Milborrow & Ryback (37) confirmed the structure by synthesis and further showed that ABA is dextrorotatory (38) and has a *sinister* (S) configuration around the asymmetric carbon atom (35).

As with the other plant hormones, abscisic acid occurs in very low concentrations, so that large amounts of plant material and large volumes of solvents must be employed in its isolation. Also, the numerous interfering substances present in the crude extracts make the work of purification very difficult. In the isolation of ABA most investigators have employed some variation of the following steps: (a) extraction with an aqueous organic solvent; (b) acid-base fractionation to yield organic acids; (c) gradient elution of carbon and/or silicic acid column chromatograms; (d) paper

TABLE I

YIELDS OF ABSCISIC ACID FROM PLANT MATERIALS

Source		Yield		Reference
Material	Weight (kg)	mg	µg/kg	
Gossypium fruit	225 (dry)	9.0	40	106
Acer leaves	28 (dry)	0.26	9	40
Lupinus fruit	206 (fresh)	5.2	25	82
Dioscorea tubers	337 (fresh)	5.5	16	64
Pisum fruit	1,300 (fresh)	9.0	7	73

and/or thin-layer chromatography followed by crystallization from the eluate. The process of purification has been guided by bioassays, usually measuring growth inhibition or abscission acceleration. Because of the losses which can occur with any of the many manipulations involved, the yields from these isolations (Table I) are certainly much lower than the amounts actually in the plant.

Chemical assays.—Two methods for identifying ABA in purified extracts are now available: a spectropolarimetric method [Cornforth, Milborrow & Ryback (38)] and a gas chromatographic method [Davis, Heinz & Addicott (43); Lenton, Bowen & Saunders (85)].

The first method utilizes the unique optical rotatory dispersion (ORD) of ABA, which has a very intense, positive 'Cotton effect' with extrema at 287 mµ and 245 mµ (38). The 'Cotton effect' is so large that in a well-purified extract, interference from other substances is negligible, and thus ORD can be used to give a quantitative estimate, as well as a qualitative determination of the ABA present. The ORD method can detect 0.2 µg of ABA in 0.7 ml of solvent (96). Using the ORD and UV absorption characteristics of ABA, Milborrow (96) developed a 'racemate dilution method' to determine the losses of ABA in the steps between initial extraction and the final measurement by ORD. The method is similar to the well-known isotope dilution methods for the determination of levels of naturally occurring substances in living organisms. In Milborrow's method a known amount of racemic (*RS*)-ABA is added to the crude extract. The total amount of ABA remaining after purification is determined from the UV absorption, and the (*S*)-ABA remaining after purification is determined by ORD. From these determinations, the amount of (*S*)-ABA originally present can be calculated. Milborrow found that losses of 60 to 80 per cent of the ABA had been occurring during purification of extracts. Aside from the cost of a spectropolarimeter, a serious limitation of ORD methods would appear to be the high degree of purification which is sometimes necessary to remove the numerous substances which can interfere with either the ORD or UV measurements. In particular, ABA and its 2-*trans* isomer have virtually identical ORD and UV spectra; however, they are separable by thin-layer chromatography (97).

The second chemical assay utilizes the volatile derivatives which can be prepared from ABA and estimated by means of gas-liquid chromatography (GLC). The method developed by Davis, Heinz & Addicott (43) includes adsorption of the acid fraction of the crude extract on a carbon-celite column, and elution with 60 per cent aqueous acetone; the more serious interfering substances remain adsorbed on the carbon. The sample is reacted with bis-(trimethylsilyl)acetamide and the trimethylsilyl derivatives are measured by GLC. By comparison with an authentic ABA sample, the ABA peak can be located and its area calibrated for quantitative determinations. The method has a sensitivity of 0.025 μg ABA. A similar method has been developed by Lenton, Bowen & Saunders (85) for the GLC of ABA after methylation with diazomethane. However, preparation of the trimethylsilyl derivatives is more rapid, and the reagents are considerably less hazardous. The GLC method requires less preliminary purification of samples than does ORD, and it will separate substances having closely similar characteristics to ABA such as *t*-ABA. However, its effectiveness is dependent on frequent calibrations and careful attention to the condition of the columns and instruments.

In addition to the above two methods, the strong UV absorption of ABA can sometimes be used to detect and measure ABA, but only if the sample is sufficiently pure. UV absorption can be useful as an adjunct to the ORD and GLC methods (see 43, 96).

Bioassays.—For the isolation of biologically active substances of unknown chemical properties, it is essential to have an appropriate bioassay. The choice of bioassay is dictated by the type of process believed to be influenced by the substance. Because of the 'polyphyletic' origins of abscisic acid, a large variety of bioassays were used in the early investigations of the substance. The bioassays which have been most extensively used in connection with ABA include: (*a*) acceleration of abscission in excised abscission zones (explants) (7, 153); (*b*) inhibition of coleoptile curvature or straight growth (6, 124); (*c*) inhibition of seed germination, including growth of excised embryos (41, 57); and (*d*) inhibition of growth of rice seedlings (64, 82). The list of potentially useful bioassays is not limited to the above; for example, the inhibition of synthesis of α-amylase in aleurone layers could be readily utilized (28).

The results from bioassays must be interpreted carefully, as none of the assays is really specific for ABA, and a great variety of factors influence biological responses to hormones (see 4). If the investigator is forced to rely on bioassays, he should use several in order to fully characterize his unknown material (see 12, 120). For example, a substance which had the combined abilities to inhibit coleoptile growth, inhibit α-amylase synthesis,

STRUCTURE	PHYSIOLOGICAL ACTIVITY
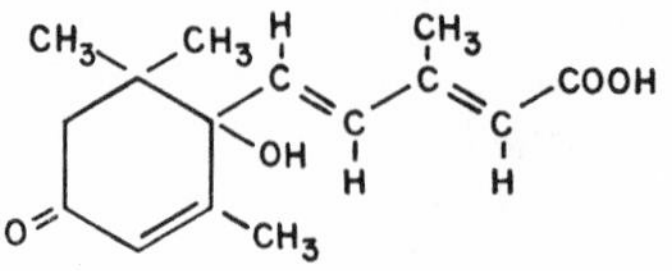 2-*trans*-abscisic acid	(−) Growth (37, 95) (−) Germination (139) (+) Flowering (99) (0) PA lyase (156)
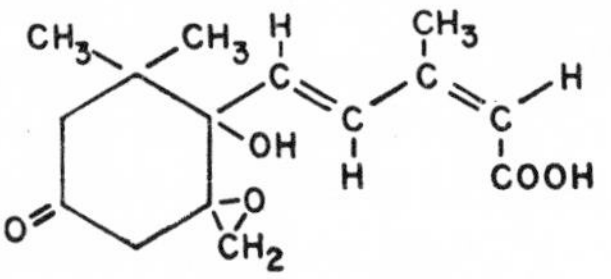 phaseic acid	(+) Abscission (42, 91)
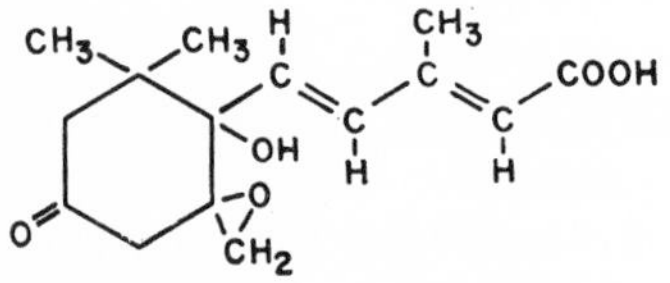 2-*trans*-phaseic acid	Untested
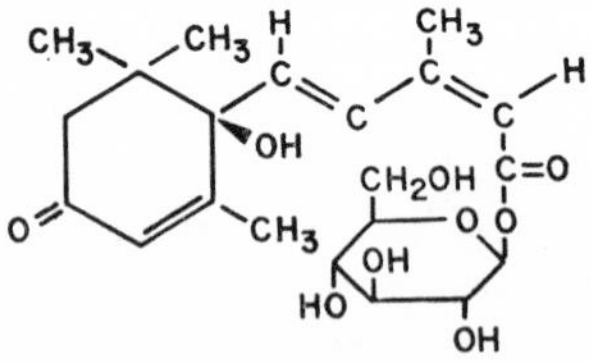 (+)-abscisyl-β-D-glucopyranoside	(−) Growth (83)
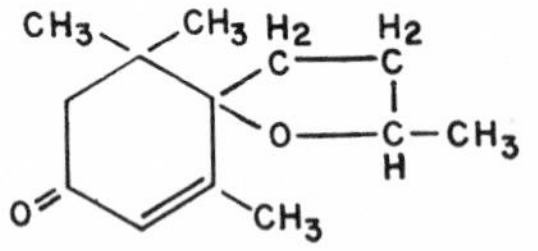 theaspirone	Untested

Fig. 2. Naturally occurring substances related to abscisic acid: structures and physiological activities. Symbols: (+) = acceleration or promotion; (−) = retardation or inhibition; (0) = no activity.

promote senescence, and accelerate abscission could be suspected of being physiologically related to abscisic acid.

Naturally occurring related substances.—The structures of substances related to abscisic acid which have now been found to occur naturally are shown in Figure 2. Phaseic acid, the abscisyl glucoside, and theaspirone have been crystallized and identified. Phaseic acid occurs in the seeds of *Phaseolus multiflorus* [MacMillan & Pryce (91)]. The abscisyl glucoside was isolated from the fruit of *Lupinus luteus* by Koshimizu et al. (83). Theaspirone was isolated from tea leaves where it is an important flavor constituent [Ina & Sakato (70)]. The 2-*trans*-isomer of abscisic acid was synthesized in the course of chemical investigations (37, 98, 121, 139) and was detected in cotton by GLC [Davis (42)] and in strawberries by TLC [Rudnicki & Pieniazek (127)]. Similarly, 2-*trans*-phaseic acid was detected in cotton by GLC [Davis (42)]. Little is yet known of the physiological activity of these substances. So far 2-*trans*-abscisic acid appears to have physiological properties similar to those of ABA. It is equally active in enhancing the flowering of *Plumbago* (as the methyl ester) (99), but it is considerably less active than ABA as a growth and germination inhibitor (37, 95, 139). Apparently, *t*-ABA does not affect the activity of phenylalanine ammonia lyase (156). The only physiological effect of phaseic acid yet known is its acceleration of abscission (42, 91). The abscisyl glucoside inhibits the growth of rice seedlings (83). Samples of 2-*trans*-phaseic acid and of theaspirone have not yet been available for physiological investigation. It appears likely that the substances described above are only the first of a large group of chemically and physiologically interrelated substances.

Synthetic related substances.—In the course of chemical investigations, a number of isomers of abscisic acid have been synthesized and isolated. Several substances intermediate in the synthesis or resulting from side reactions have also been reported. Some of the substances which have been described are shown in Figure 3, together with their known physiological activities.

The two stereoisomers in synthetic, racemic abscisic acid have recently been resolved by Cornforth et al. (35). The (*R*)-abscisic acid has been found by Milborrow (97) to be equally active with the naturally occurring (*S*)-enantiomer in the inhibition of growth. This is in contrast to earlier investigations (38, 137) which found the racemic preparation to be considerably less active than the naturally occurring isomer. The earlier results had been interpreted as indicating that the (*R*)-enantiomer was physiologically inactive. In the light of Milborrow's (97) work, a more probable interpretation is that the earlier samples contained sufficient impurities to reduce their physiological activity. In the limited physiological tests which have so far been conducted, the other substances shown in Figure 3 have been found to either accelerate abscission or to inhibit growth. It can be anticipated that many more synthetic substances related to abscisic acid will be reported in the near future.

FIG. 3. Synthetic substances related to abscisic acid: structures and physiological activities. Symbols: (+) = acceleration or promotion; (−) = retardation or inhibition; (O) = no activity.

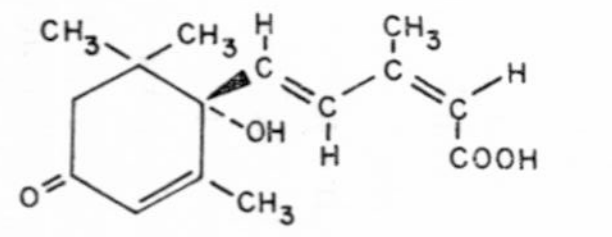

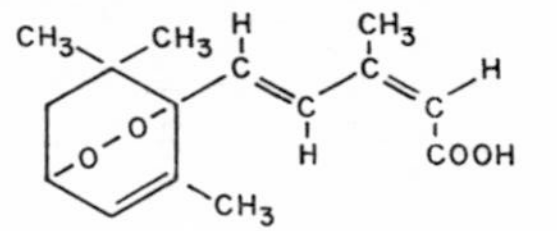

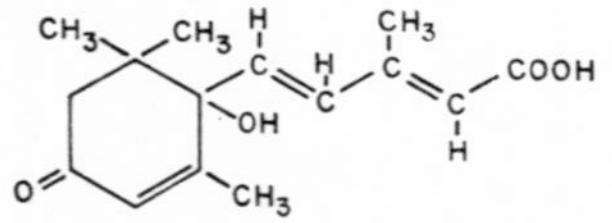

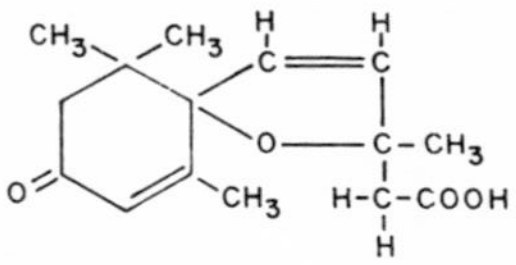

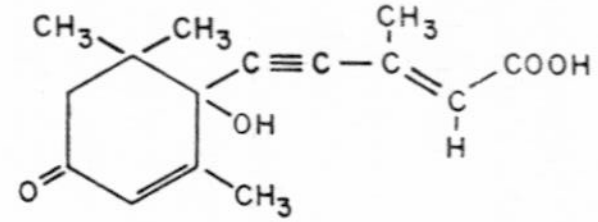

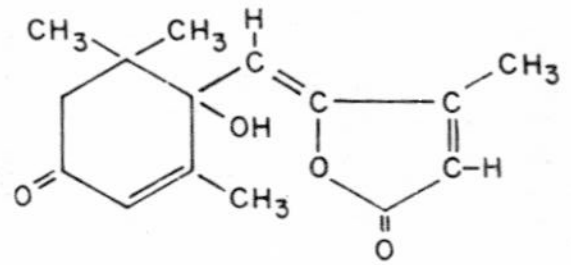

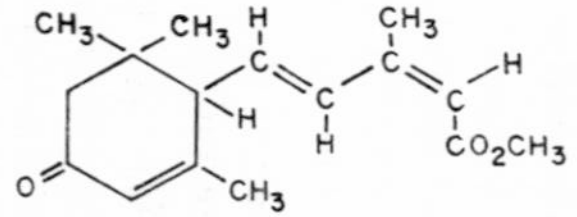

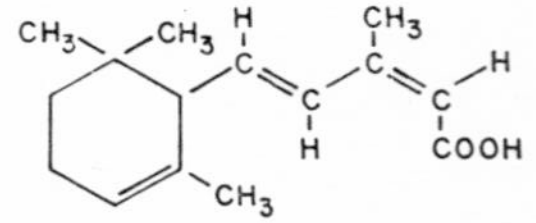

Occurrence

Chemical isolation.—A rigorous chemical proof of the occurrence of a substance requires first that the substance be isolated in pure form and crystallized, if possible. Then if the properties of the isolated substance are found to be the same as the properties of an already characterized substance, the two are considered identical. For abscisic acid, such isolations have been accomplished from *Acer* (40), *Lupinus* (82), *Dioscorea* (64), and *Pisum* (73) since the original isolation from *Gossypium* (106) (Table I). The identity of the isolated substance in each case was proved by the finding that its physical properties were the same as those already described for ABA.

Identification by ORD or GLC.—Positive identification of a substance by use of a single property such as its ORD or the position of its peak in GLC is considered much less sure than identification by means of isolation of the pure substance. Still, such identifications are strong and positive evidence of the occurrence of the substance.

Abscisic acid has now been detected by ORD or GLC in more than 30 species. The most extensive investigations have been conducted by Cornforth, Milborrow & Ryback (38) and Milborrow (96), but others have also contributed to this body of information (e.g., 48, 57, 85, 119). The species in which ABA has been detected are widely distributed among plants and include a fern, grasses, coconut palm, bean, potato, avocado, apple, peach, rose, linden, and willow. The parts of the plant in which ABA has been detected include leaves, stems, buds, tubers, rhizomes, fruits of all ages, pollen, seed coats, endosperm, and embryos. While the occurrence of ABA in mature and senescing tissues at first suggested that it was a senescence substance, its widespread occurrence in young fruits and leaves makes it clear that ABA cannot be considered exclusively such a substance.

Evidence from co-chromatography and bioassay.—In many investigations it has not been feasible to carry the experiments on the nature of the active substance to the point of identification by ORD or GLC. Often such investigations have used co-chromatography or combinations of bioassays to provide some evidence as to whether the active substance might be ABA. While not conclusive, co-chromatography in several solvent systems, especially when combined with two or more bioassays, provides strong evidence for the presence of ABA. Such investigations have detected ABA in peach seed coats (88), walnuts (94), *Citrus* shoots (59), grape seeds (90), and leaves and fruits of *Rosa* and *Crataegus* (148).

Evidence of related substances.—In addition to the above, there is considerable evidence for the occurrence in nature of substances having one or more of the physiological properties of abscisic acid. Most noteworthy among these substances are those investigated by Osborne (77, 109, 110) in senescent leaves of *Phaseolus, Coleus,* and several other species. Savich (133) has obtained a fraction from seedlings of *Phaseolus* having the chro-

matographic, and several of the physiological, properties of ABA. The abscission accelerating substance from mature apple fruit first reported by
Biggs (16) and further investigated by Scott (134) could well be ABA or
a similar substance, as ABA has already been identified in apple fruit and
leaves (96, 116). Also, the abscission accelerating substance from senescent
cotton leaves reported by Hall, Herrero & Katterman (62), and the acidic
inhibitor found by Olney (108) in *Veratrum,* could be ABA. References to
other growth inhibitory substances that may quite possibly include ABA are
widely scattered through the hormone literature (see 67). A few substances
such as the abscission accelerant reported by Hacskaylo & Moke (61), and
the growth inhibitor of Corcoran & West (34), seem unlikely to be abscisic
acid on the basis of their rather different solubility properties.

Abscisin I was isolated and crystallized from the mature fruit wall of
cotton (89). Its melting point, elemental analysis, and infrared absorption
spectrum indicate that it is chemically distinct from ABA, phaseic acid, and
their isomers. It is physiologically similar to ABA in its ability to inhibit
coleoptile growth and to accelerate abscission; however, it appears to have
only one-tenth the activity of ABA as an abscission accelerant (6, 89).

Correlative occurrence.—A large number of the investigations involving abscisic acid were undertaken to ascertain if its occurrence might in
some way be correlated with an important physiological event or process.
The correlation between net ABA activity and young fruit abscission in
cotton (6) suggested that determination of the actual levels of ABA during
fruit development could be valuable. The results of these determinations by
GLC are summarized in Figure 4 [Davis (42)]. There was a measurable
amount of ABA in the ovary at anthesis; after the second day there was a
rapid rise in the amount of ABA correlated with the period of young fruit
abscission at 5 to 10 days. Then the amounts decreased rapidly and reached
a very low level in fruit 20 to 30 days old. This low level is correlated with
the age at which immature seed removed from the fruit will germinate
readily. Before and after that period, germination of immature seed is poor
(1). The amounts of ABA in the maturing cotton fruit increased to a very
high level at 40 and still higher at 50 days. This is correlated with the period of fruit wall senescence; dehiscence commenced when the fruits were
45 days old. It was of further interest to determine whether there was a
difference in amounts of ABA in abscising and nonabscising young fruit.
The results of those determinations are shown in Figure 5. The amounts of
ABA in the young fruit which were senescent and abscising were from 2 to
4 times higher than in the normally developing fruit (42).

The available evidence suggests a similar correlation of the level of
ABA in flesh of rose fruit (74) and juice of apples (78) with inhibition of
seed germination in those species (see also 96, 115, 116). Indeed, the common occurrence of ABA in the flesh or juice of fruits (96) suggests that
ABA may well be one of the factors preventing the germination of many
seeds while they are still in the fruit (see 157).

Olmstead's (107) observations which established that short photope-

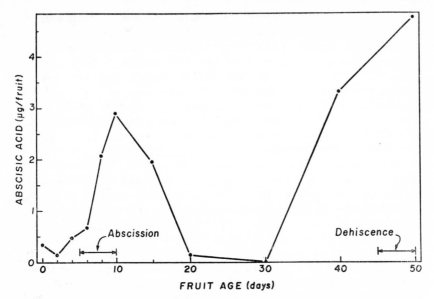

FIG. 4. Changes in abscisic acid during cotton fruit development as determined by gas-liquid chromatography. Note the rise in abscisic acid correlated with young fruit abscission and with the senescence and dehiscence of the mature fruit. [After Davis (42).]

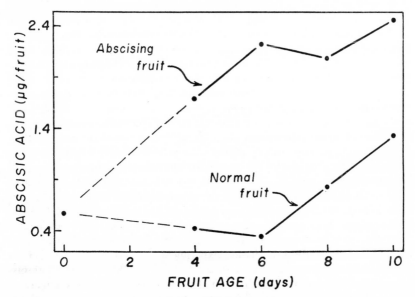

FIG. 5. Abscisic acid in abscising and in normal, developing young cotton fruit. The abscising fruit were loose and about to fall; the normal fruit were firmly attached. [After Davis (42).]

riods led to senescence and abscission in leaves of deciduous trees were followed by investigations showing that growth inhibitory substances increase in leaves with the advent of short days (100, 114). Abscisic acid has been shown to be the principal growth inhibitor involved (40, 96, 127).

Some seeds require stratification (cold treatment) before they can germinate. Sondheimer, Tzou & Galson (140) found that the level of ABA in the embryo of *Fraxinus* falls during stratification. Similar changes have also been reported for walnuts (94). With peaches (88) and *Acer negundo* (71) the source of seed dormancy is the seed coats, and in these, too, ABA decreases with stratification.

In pears, the level of ABA increases as the fruit ripens and also increases during storage even if the fruit does not ripen appreciably. When the fruit is stored under nitrogen, ABA decreases to a very low level (126). In pecans, the level of ABA increases during the relatively long period of fruit development (87).

If it is assumed that the effects of inhibitor β are due mainly to ABA (96), then it can be suggested that ABA is a major factor prolonging the rest of potatoes (see 68). Van Steveninck's (153) results can be similarly interpreted. He showed that the mature pods of lupin plants infected with pea-mosaic virus contained 2.5 times the amount of inhibitor β as the pods of healthy plants. Probably other increases of ABA correlated with disease will be found, particularly in plants which respond to infection by organ senescence and abscission.

RESPONSES TO ABSCISIC ACID

The number and variety of plant responses to abscisic acid is already so large and complex that even categorizing them is difficult. Broadly they fall into two major groupings: responses of promotion, and responses of inhibition. For convenience, the discussion will be organized under: (*a*) senescence and abscission; (*b*) growth retardation and inhibition; (*c*) miscellaneous responses; (*d*) interactions with other hormones; (*e*) biochemical responses; (*f*) morphological responses; and (*g*) agricultural uses.

Senescence and abscission.—Abscisic acid accelerated the loss of chlorophyll and the loss of turgor in abscising petiole stumps of explants (21). Senescent color changes in leaves are a common response to foliage applications of ABA (e.g., 26, 137). In isolated leaf discs ABA has accelerated the loss of chlorophyll in all species examined (11, 52, 128). Potato tubers treated with ABA became soft and senescent (52). When applied to Murcott oranges, ABA not only accelerated the loss of chlorophyll but heightened the color by increasing the levels of carotenoids in the flavedo (32).

Some of the earliest abscission experiments were with the young fruit of cotton where applications of extracts containing ABA accelerated abscission of both intact fruit and defruited pedicels (6). These investigations were soon extended to abscission acceleration of petiole stumps of explants of cotton and several other species (137). In such experiments ABA regularly leads to earlier onset, increased rates, and a higher final percentage of abscission (6, 49, 147). It is also of interest that with cotton explants which include the stem stump as well as the stumps of the two cotyledonary petioles, applications of ABA to the stem stump are almost as effective in promoting abscission as are applications to the petiole stumps. Further, applications to a single petiole stump are very effective in promoting abscission of the opposite untreated petiole (137).

When ABA is applied to intact leaves or foliage, abscission is commonly promoted (51, 137). Occasionally a single application has resulted in complete defoliation (30, 63); but usually several applications or prolonged exposure are required to induce leaf abscission (51, 137). Also, applications to plants which are young or still vigorously growing have sometimes failed to induce leaf abscission (26, 137). In *Citrus* the leaf abscission responses have been found to be dependent on the season; leaves sprayed in summer abscised, but those sprayed during the winter did not (31). Olives have responded in a similar manner (63). Such variations in response are not surprising, since the levels of the hormones with which ABA is presumably interacting vary greatly with variations in environmental factors, particularly with such factors as nitrogen and light (see 4). Some of the variations in response may also have been due to poor absorption or to rapid inactivation of ABA by the tissues of the leaf blade.

Growth retardation and inhibition.—In many of the early investigations with extracts containing ABA, bioassays which measured the growth inhibition by ABA were used. These included growth inhibition of coleoptiles (6, 12, 14), *Avena* mesocotyls (95), isolated cereal embryos (41), and rice seedlings (82). Growth inhibition responses of many other plant parts have been investigated, including leaf discs and sections (51, 146), hypocotyls (11, 51, 122), radicles (11, 12, 14), and root sections (51, 117). Abscisic acid inhibits or retards the growth of cultures of plant tissues (129, 141, 146) and of cultures of small aquatic plants such as *Lemna* and *Wolffia* (93, 149).

Inhibition of stem growth has been observed on many plants. The extent to which growth of the entire leafy shoot is retarded varies with many factors, as could be expected. Commonly, a shortening of internodes may be the only effect, but leaf growth retardation has also been observed (e.g., 88, 93). However, to effectively retard shoot growth, repeated or prolonged exposure to ABA may be required. This is in contrast to responses to the synthetic retardants; for example, the effect of a single dose of CCC will often persist for several weeks (26). On woody plants, especially on the deciduous trees, ABA can induce the typical dormant resting condition (51). With whole potatoes (52) and with isolated potato buds (92) abscisic acid is extremely effective in prolonging dormancy. A more limited prolongation of bud dormancy has also been observed in *Citrus* (33) and in the aerial tubers of *Begonia* (65).

The dormancy (rest) of many seeds can be greatly prolonged by ABA; some seeds will not germinate at all in its presence. Abscisic acid is particularly inhibitory to the germination of seed of lettuce (11, 79, 101, 131, 164), grasses (88, 142), *Lepidium* (cress) (57, 144), and several other species (130). With many of the species whose seeds require stratification before they can germinate, the levels of ABA are lowered during stratification (as discussed in a previous section); after stratification, application of ABA to the seeds has prevented germination (88, 115, 139). It is noteworthy that the effects of ABA in inhibiting seed germination (as well as many other processes) are relatively transient and that after rinsing away the inhibiting solution of ABA, germination has promptly resumed (e.g., 142).

Interest in the effects of ABA on flowering was heightened by the early observation that ABA appeared to increase in leaves under short days. Evidence had been presented earlier that the inhibition of flowering of long-day plants when held under short days could be due to a transmissible inhibiting substance formed in the leaves under short days (55). With the long-day plant, *Lolium temulentum,* Evans (54) found that 0.1 μg ABA injected into the cavity about the stem apex would strongly inhibit the flowering response. The treatment was most effective when applied 11 to 24 hr after the initiation of long days, near the time at which the flowering stimulus reaches the stem apex. Earlier or later injections were relatively ineffective. Inhibition of flowering of several long-day plants following sprays of ABA has been reported (26, 52, 165). Thus it is possible that abscisic acid is the postulated flowering inhibitor produced in the leaves of long-day plants which are held under short days.

The responses of short-day plants to abscisic acid have been quite varied. With short-day plants held under noninductive long days, ABA promoted flowering of *Chenopodium rubrum, Pharbitis nil,* black currant, and strawberry (52, 162, 167). However, under these conditions there was no effect of ABA on flowering of other short-day species (26, 52, 99), and interestingly, *Chenopodium rubrum* plants which were older (52) or of a different variety (44) did not respond either. With short-day plants placed under inductive short days, *Wolffia* and *Lemna* were affected so strongly that both growth and flowering were inhibited (93); flowering of *Pharbitis* was suppressed (167); and flowering of *Chenopodium* was delayed (44). In contrast, ABA enhanced the flowering of *Plumbago* under inductive short days (99).

Many of the effects of ABA on the flowering of short-day plants may be explainable as growth retardation responses. Numerous species display a competition between vegetative and reproductive growth. In such species, one would expect a promotion of flowering if vegetative growth is retarded or inhibited. This may be the case with the short-day plants. A similar view has been advanced by Carr (25). Further, consideration of the details of the experiments with short-day plants indicates that such factors as plant age (52, 167), variety (44), and cultural conditions (99) can greatly influence flowering. Such factors probably account for many of the observed differences.

It is significant that in all of the experiments in which abscisic acid has been used, it has been conspicuously nontoxic. Further, it has reduced the toxic effects of supra-optimal concentrations of other hormones (95). In many situations the effects of ABA were quite transient, and repeated applications were necessary to elicit a response. These observations indicate that plant tissues are well adapted to ABA and that the normal metabolic processes can respond readily to the substance either with some observable activity or, in some circumstances, by rapid inactivation of the applied abscisic acid.

Miscellaneous responses.—A variety of other types of responses to abscisic acid have now been reported. Application of ABA increased the cold hardiness of *Acer negundo* (72). Chlorophyll synthesis of seedlings of *Fraxinus* was inhibited by ABA (139). An increased yield of tubers followed treatment of potato plants with ABA; the result was interpreted as being due to retardation of vegetative growth (52). Adventitious bud formation was stimulated by ABA in detached *Begonia* leaves (66).

Contrary to its usual effects, in a few situations ABA has promoted growth or prevented abscission. Applied to emasculated flower buds of *Rosa sherardii,* ABA stimulated considerable parthenocarpic development and prevented abscission of 35 per cent of the treated fruit. In the same experiment, normal seeded controls set 40 per cent (75). An interesting synergistic promotion of growth of cucumber hypocotyls by ABA and $GA_4 + GA_7$ has been reported (11). The small promotion of growth shown by the mixture of gibberellins, and by ABA alone, was synergistically increased when ABA and the gibberellins were combined. Abscisic acid has promoted the germination of spores of the pathogenic fungi, *Gleosporum* and *Botrytis* (19).

No response to abscisic acid was found in preliminary experiments with vernalization of barley (11), or in pollen germination and tube growth of *Pinus mugo* (102). Abscisic acid had no effect on the germination of apple pollen, but reduced tube growth by about 50 per cent (12). It had no effect on the growth of several bacteria and fungi (12, 138).

Interactions with other plant hormones.—In the investigation of the action of plant hormones, a great variety of plant materials are employed; these include cultures of groups of plants, intact plants, parts of plants, plant organs, and isolated tissues. When abscisic acid became available, it was inevitable for it to be applied to this variety of plant materials in the hormonal investigations already in progress. The result has been a large number of reports to the effect that ABA can "decrease," "overcome," "reverse," "counteract," "inhibit," etc., the responses of plant materials to each of the growth-promoting hormones.

With gibberellins, ABA has commonly shown counteraction or inhibition of GA-induced responses, especially in the responses of growth, germination, and senescence (11, 28, 80, 146, 166). Among these the most striking inhibition is of the GA-induced synthesis of hydrolases in aleurone layers (28, 29). Some of the investigations have included kinetic analysis. These have, for the most part, shown a noncompetitive interaction between ABA and GA (11, 29, 164). However, in the growth of wheat coleoptiles, a "partial competitive" interaction was observed (166). In the growth of *Lemna,* GA cannot overcome the growth inhibition of ABA (149). In the abscission of cotton explants, GA (which is itself moderately promotive) does not modify the strong promotion by ABA (137). At the other end of the response spectrum is the synergism of ABA and $GA_4 + GA_7$ in the promotion of cucumber hypocotyl growth (11).

In combination with IAA, ABA has usually counteracted the IAA promotion of growth (6, 95, 124). It can partially overcome the IAA-induced retardation of abscission (15, 137, 147). The ABA inhibition of lettuce seed germination (131) and inhibition of growth of *Lemna* (149) could not be reversed by IAA, but ABA's inhibition of cell division in tissue cultures was partially reversed by IAA (146). The kinetic analyses of the interaction of ABA and IAA in both growth and abscission have shown the two substances to be noncompetitive (137, 164, 166).

Some promotive actions of the cytokinins are also counteracted by ABA. In cultures of *Lemna,* growth can be repeatedly inhibited or promoted by interchanging culture media containing either ABA or benzyladenine (151), and the counteraction is noncompetitive (150). The response to the change in medium is detectable within a few hours. The benzyladenine-induced swelling of immature *Begonia* tubers was inhibited by ABA (53). In barley seedlings the inhibition of coleoptile growth by ABA was overcome by kinetin and by benzyladenine (81). In the growth of wheat coleoptiles a "partial competitive" interaction between ABA and zeatin was found (166). On the other hand, the inhibition of mesocotyl growth by ABA could not be reversed by kinetin (95).

The interactions of abscisic acid and ethylene are still incompletely known. Each substance accelerates senescence, and in explant abscission they have closely similar effects both on the rate and morphology of abscission (see 3, 6). However, the individual effects of the two substances on other processes seldom resemble each other. The evolution of ethylene by bean explants (2) and *Citrus* leaves (31) is enhanced by treatment with ABA. In contrast, ethylene could not be detected after ABA treatment of *Citrus* fruit (31) and olive leaves (63). In *Citrus* explants the increased ethylene production followed rather than preceded separation (113). The possibility that ethylene might induce the development of ABA has not yet been investigated. A part of ethylene's promotive effect on senescence and abscission could be via the stimulation of the development of ABA, or via some other alteration of the hormone balance. For example, a well known effect of ethylene is its ability to lower the level of auxin.

From the above it is apparent that there is no single, clear pattern of interaction for ABA with the other hormones. Further, the finding of a competitive interaction in only a few plant materials and the failure to find it in many others emphasizes the questionable value and significance of such kinetic investigations with complex plant materials.

Biochemical responses.—The profound effects of abscisic acid on growth, abscission, and other processes in plants stimulated investigation of its possible biochemical role. Abscisic acid was found to prevent the hydrolysis of starch by barley seeds during germination, a process stimulated by GA [Paleg (112)]. Further, the strong stimulation of synthesis of α-amylase by GA in isolated aleurone layers of cereal seeds is counteracted by very small amounts of ABA (29). Abscisic acid appears also to inhibit the synthesis of proteases, ribonucleases, and probably all the hydrolytic enzymes whose syntheses in aleurone layers are promoted by GA [Chrispeels & Varner (29)].

In commercial enzyme preparations, ABA increased the activity of α-amylase but not the activity of β-amylase (69). Several other types of enzymes also are influenced by ABA. Abscisic acid promotes the development and retention of activity of phenylalanine ammonia lyase in *Phaseolus* (156). The development of invertase in slices of sugar beet tissue was promoted by ABA (27). In contrast, invertase development in slices of carrot root was inhibited by ABA, as was the activity of commercial yeast invertase (132). While the inhibition of synthesis of hydrolases in aleurone by ABA is a very strong one, its action on the development of nitrate reductase activity in aleurone was only slightly inhibitory (56). In germinating castor beans ABA strongly inhibited the development of fatty acid synthetase and appeared to act by blocking the *de novo* synthesis of proteins essential to the activity of the enzyme (58).

Thus, the physiological activities of ABA may be considered to be due, at least in part, to the ability to strongly influence development of certain enzymes without appreciably affecting other enzymes. Hence, investigators have attempted to ascertain the point at which ABA has its direct influence on biochemical events. Abscisic acid has been reported to block the synthesis of specific DNA's (149). While that report has not yet been confirmed, several investigations showing inhibition of RNA synthesis have been reported. Treatment of leaf discs with ABA led to a marked reduction of RNA; the reduction of the polyribosome fractions was particularly rapid (163). In leaf discs of *Xanthium*, ABA reduced the incorporation of [14C]-leucine into protein (111). In embryos of *Fraxinus*, ABA inhibited the incorporation of H^3 uridine and H^3 thymidine but not the incorporation of H^3 leucine. It was concluded that ABA maintains dormancy by inhibiting the production of specific types of mRNA and, therefore, the formation of specific proteins (155). Chrispeels & Varner (29) have interpreted their results as indicating that ABA might act by inhibiting the synthesis of enzyme-specific RNA molecules, or by preventing incorporation of RNA into an active enzyme-synthesizing unit.

The above results are of great interest and indicate that abscisic acid influences some of the fundamental, regulatory biochemical mechanisms of plants. However, the evidence does not demonstrate that the primary and direct effect of abscisic acid is on DNA or RNA. In much of the work so far reported, the time lapse between exposure to ABA and the measurement of responses has been sufficient to permit a great deal of biochemical activity before the first measurements. Thus, it is entirely possible that the changes in DNA or RNA are but a reflection of a much earlier key effect of the regulators. This cautionary interpretation applies to similar investigations with the other plant hormones and has been voiced strongly by Lang (84).

Morphological responses.—Many of the responses to ABA include visible modifications of the form of the treated plants. In the acceleration of abscission, ABA stimulates rapid cell divisions and the lysis of middle lamella and cell wall constituents (20, 21); the evidence suggests the rapid development of pectinases, cellulases, and proteases. In the induction of leaf senescence, ABA must certainly have some degenerative effects on the ultrastructure of the leaf, but these have not yet been investigated.

Applications of ABA to the emasculated flower buds of *Rosa sherardii* induced the development of parthenocarpic fruit which enlarged to about 65 per cent of the diameter of the normal controls. The treated fruit contained a considerable, but variable, number of pseudo-achenes which lacked embryos. Other species of *Rosa* responded to a much lesser extent (75). Possibly the physiological conditions in the emasculated fruit of *R. sherardii* permit a generalized growth response to ABA that is roughly analogous to the localized cell division and growth responses which regularly follow the application of ABA to abscission zones.

When applied to the leaves of actively growing young *Betula* plants, ABA arrested growth and the apical buds developed the morphology typical of resting buds, with the stipular scales closed around the apex (51). On young peach seedlings ABA induced a rosetted growth with short, thick internodes similar in appearance to those which emerge from inadequately stratified seeds (88). Application of ABA to the tip of the main stem of *Silene* reduced the growth of the main stem by 50 per cent and induced the development of four times the number of lateral branches as the controls (165). As already noted, ABA completely arrested vegetative growth in several species and the seed germination of many more species. In these instances it essentially blocked all morphological development. As discussed above, the promotion of flowering in certain short-day plants by ABA appears to be more a consequence of the restriction of vegetative growth than it is a specific stimulation of flowering.

Agricultural uses.—The responses described in the preceding section have suggested that abscisic acid might have a number of important agricultural applications. Actually, many of the investigations mentioned above were undertaken with the primary objective of appraising the value of ABA for the solution of a particular agricultural problem. At least three patents have been granted (13, 136, 160) covering the following agricultural uses: (*a*) induction of leaf senescence; (*b*) inhibition of shoot growth; (*c*) increased yield of plant tissue; (*d*) increased yield of tubers; (*e*) induction of flowering in short-day plants; (*f*) delay of flower opening; (*g*) stimulation of flower drop; (*h*) delay of sprouting of storage organs; (*i*) stimulation of fruit ripening; and (*j*) delay of germination.

While this list is very impressive, the agricultural value of abscisic acid itself appears uncertain. The obvious ability of plants to rapidly metabolize

ABA seriously limits its potential as an agricultural chemical. Further, there is little prospect that the cost of synthesis of ABA will soon be reduced to the point where large scale agricultural use would be feasible. However, there would appear to be excellent possibilities that other substances having the physiological properties of abscisic acid can be synthesized and produced commercially at a reasonable cost. Thus, continued exploration of the agricultural applications of ABA would appear to be well justified.

GENERAL PHYSIOLOGY

Biosynthesis.—The unusual chemical structure of abscisic acid stimulated a number of speculations as to its biosynthesis. An early paper [Addicott et al. (9)] suggested two possible modes of biosynthesis: (*a*) via an isoprenoid pathway [also suggested by Graebe (60) and Wright (166)]; (*b*) via a precursor such as violaxanthin, a carotenoid of widespread occurrence whose structure might give rise to ABA. The latter view has received some support from the experiments of Taylor & Smith (144). They showed that the radiation of xanthophylls, especially violaxanthin (143), gave rise to a neutral product which strongly inhibited the germination of *Lepidium*. On the other hand, the occurrence of ABA in young tissues of plants, as well as in old tissues, argues against the possibility that ABA is exclusively a degradation product. Further, synthesis of ABA occurs in young strawberry fruit long before the mature fruit pigments have developed (125). An alternative suggestion, that ABA and GA may arise from a common precursor such as mevalonic acid, has been offered by Wright (166). This suggestion is supported by the observations that ABA appears to increase at times when GA decreases and vice versa (72, 100, 162, 166), and by the possibility that ABA can inhibit the synthesis of GA (163). Also, there is some possibility that ABA interferes with the biosynthesis of IAA (166). Since auxins, gibberellins, cytokinins, and ABA occur and interact in many tissues, the prospect of rapid progress in understanding their biosynthetic interrelations appears excellent.

Transport.—The occurrence of ABA in diffusates from fruits suggested that it is readily transported in plants (6). Further, experiments such as those of Eagles & Wareing (51) and the later experiments of Evans with pure ABA (54) can be most reasonably interpreted as indicating that ABA is readily transported from the leaves to the stem apex. Similarly, abscission acceleration by ABA when applied to the petiole stumps of explants indicates a physiological response some distance from the site of application. Other evidence of the transport of ABA came from the detection of ABA in both phloem sap and xylem sap (22, 85, 116).

The transport of ABA in petiole and internode segments of *Coleus* has now been measured by Dörffling & Böttger (50). In younger segments, transport was strongly basipetal; in older segments, transport could take place in either basipetal or acropetal direction. Using the [2-^{14}C]ABA synthesized by Cornforth, Mallaby & Ryback (36), Milborrow found that basipetal transport in petioles was three times that of acropetal transport (97).

Inactivation.—When ABA was injected near the stem apex of *Lolium* at about the time the flowering stimulus reached the apex, flowering was strongly inhibited (54). Earlier injections were relatively ineffective. These observations are interpreted as indicating that the injected ABA was inactivated (or possibly dissipated) before it had an opportunity to interact in the flowering response. Later investigations have shown repeatedly that the effects of ABA are relatively transient and that for many types of plant processes ABA must be in continuous supply in order to have an effect (e.g., 151). The probable explanation of these observations is that plant tissues generally possess the biochemical means to inactivate ABA.

Milborrow (97) has found three labeled substances (presumably metabolites) in diffusates from petioles treated with [2-^{14}C]ABA. The chemical nature and biological activity of these products is still unknown. However, since the identification of the less active 2-*trans*-abscisic acid, phaseic acid, and the abscisyl glucoside in plants, it is a reasonable speculation that the conversion of ABA to these substances accounts, in part, for the observed inactivations. There could well be considerable interconversion within the plant among these substances, and undoubtedly there are other such substances yet to be discovered. Whether theaspirone has any place among these physiologically active substances also remains to be discovered.

Abscisic acid as a plant hormone.—Hormones are chemical regulatory agents in the correlative behavior of plants. To qualify as a hormone a substance must (*a*) be endogenous, (*b*) be transported, and (*c*) have a regulatory function at low concentrations. [See "Nomenclature of Chemical Plant Regulators," a Report by a Committee of the American Society of Plant Physiologists (152).] This discussion will next consider the several instances in which ABA appears to function in a hormonal capacity.[2]

After the discovery of a growth inhibitory substance in the young fruit of cotton and the observation that its activity was correlated with the period of abscission of young fruit, it became of interest to learn if the substance functioned as a plant hormone. The investigations with extracts from the young fruit showed that this was indeed the case. The purified extracts when reapplied in low amounts to either the young fruit or to the defruited pedicel accelerated onset and rate and increased the total amount of abscission. Since fruit abscission in cotton takes place at the base of the pedicel, transport was clearly involved (24; see also 137).

In the abscission of young fruit of lupin, Van Steveninck's early exper-

[2] This review will not consider the functions of ABA in relation to the "PESIGS" rules (76). The rules were designed as a test of whether one substance and only one substance controls the development of a morphological structure or limits the rate of a physiological process. It is now apparent that any of several naturally occurring regulatory substances can influence the rate and other attributes of the better known physiological processes (e.g., abscission, growth, flowering, senescence, dormancy).

iments (153), together with the later evidence that his substance was ABA, indicate that ABA is an abscission-accelerating hormone of lupin fruit.

For leaf abscission, there is now ample evidence of the occurrence of ABA in leaves (96, 127, 148) and the induction of abscission by ABA applied to leaves and debladed petioles (51, 137). The latter experiments indicate transport through the petiole. Together, these results suggest that ABA is also an abscission-accelerating hormone of leaves.

In deciduous trees, the ability of abscisic acid moving from the leaves to induce the dormancy of apical buds is well established (159). It is not yet clear how much ABA must reach the apical bud to induce dormancy, but the amounts will probably be quite low. This evidence indicates that ABA functions as a bud dormancy hormone (see also 159). In the potato tuber, the level of inhibitor β, of which the most active component appears to be ABA, falls during the rest period. Further, ABA in extremely low amounts prolongs the dormancy of excised potato buds (92). Thus ABA appears to be a hormonal factor inhibiting the development of the buds of the tuber.

As an inhibitor of seed germination, ABA is active on a great many species. It is not yet clear in most cases whether a strict hormonal relationship exists *in vivo*. However, the evidence from rose (74), peach (88), apple (115), box elder (71), and birch (17) have shown correlations between the levels of ABA in tissues external to the embryos (e.g., seed coats, fruit) and the inhibition of germination. Almost certainly a hormonal relationship exists in these cases.

In the flowering of long-day plants, the great sensitivity of flower induction in *Lolium* to inhibition by ABA, coupled with the knowledge that the stem apex is the responsive site and that leaves under short days can produce abscisic acid, gives very strong support to the possibility that ABA functions hormonally to inhibit the flowering of long-day plants that are held under short days.

While the evidence is still rather fragmentary, it is entirely possible that ABA is an important hormonal intermediary between the receptor of the signal of short photoperiods and the responsive biochemical mechanisms.

PHYSIOLOGICAL ROLES

From the preceding discussion it is apparent that abscisic acid is widely distributed, if not ubiquitous in plants. It appears that tissues of all ages are able to synthesize and inactivate or metabolize ABA. Considering its numerous physiological effects, many of which are in opposition to the growth-promoting hormones, auxin, gibberellin, and cytokinin, ABA appears to have an important role in the homeostasis of the plant. Several authors have already commented on the apparent balance between the hormones which tend to promote growth and those, such as ABA, which tend to retard and inhibit growth [Libbert (86), Thimann (145), Wright (166)]. The stability of the balance appears to depend on how well 'buffered' the level of each hormone is at any given stage of development. Thus,

only when an imbalance of hormones developed would the hormonal role of
one or another of the hormones become evident. For example, in leaves,
with the decline in auxin and gibberellin as the leaf ages, the influence of
ABA in promoting senescence and abscission becomes very apparent (see
4).

Hormonal roles.—For abscisic acid the following hormonal roles now
appear to be established or to be almost certain on the basis of the available
evidence: (*a*) acceleration of abscission in fruits and leaves; (*b*) induction
and prolongation of dormancy (rest) in the shoots of deciduous trees and
in tubers; (*c*) inhibition of germination by prolonging the dormancy (rest)
of seeds; and (*d*) inhibition of flowering of long-day plants when held
under short days.

In addition to the above, there are other important regulatory influences
of ABA which apparently will not meet all three criteria for hormonal action. We might refer to such influences as 'hormonoid.' In the following
cases a regulatory influence is clear, but the factor of transport appears to
be lacking: (*a*) the abortion of young fruit, and presumably buds also, is in
part a response to an increase in levels of ABA; (*b*) the senescence of
leaves is promoted by ABA via either an increase in absolute amounts of
ABA or a relative increase due to a decrease in auxin or other hormones;
(*c*) the dormancy of some embryos (e.g., *Fraxinus*) is due to inhibiting
amounts of ABA present in the embryo itself and these must fall before
germination can take place.

Biochemical roles.—Knowledge of the influence of ABA on the synthesis and activity of enzymes in the plant is still quite incomplete. However, two broad roles are suggested by the evidence now available.

The first role involves ABA's ability to inhibit the GA-induced synthesis of hydrolytic enzymes. This ability has been clearly defined in the investigations of enzyme synthesis in relation to germination of cereal seeds.
Here ABA is able to inhibit strongly the synthesis and development of amy-
lases, proteases, and the other hydrolytic enzymes which are essential to
germination. Possibly ABA's inhibitory effect on growth can also be ascribed to inhibition of hydrolytic enzymes. Such enzymes are an essential
part of the metabolic machinery of the plant.

A second biochemical role, whose relation to the first is as yet unclear,
is indicated by the ability of ABA to promote the biochemical changes of
senescence and abscission. In the shift from a more mature, relatively stable
physiology to the degenerative changes of senescence and abscission, there
is a shift in the patterns and levels of enzymatic activities. This shift requires energy and almost certainly some synthesis of enzymes. However,
the site at which ABA acts in order to bring about these biochemical effects
remains to be discovered, as does the site of action for the other major hormones.

It seems appropriate to close this review with a brief paraphrase of
James Bonner's remarks on "The probable future of auxinology" (18),
since the development of research on abscisic acid is progressing in much

the same manner as did research on auxin. The pace of ABA research has been extremely rapid; investigators have been able to utilize immediately the experience accumulated since modern hormone research was ushered in by Went in 1928. In the immediate future, innumerable investigations of the responses of plants to ABA can be anticipated. Many of these will be designed to solve agricultural problems. There will be experiments to further clarify the roles of abscisic acid as a hormone in the correlative processes of plants. Finally, there will be many investigations attempting to discover the basic biochemical function of ABA.

LITERATURE CITED

1. Abdel-Al, M. S. M., *Some Aspects of Seed and Boll Maturation in Cotton* (Master's thesis, Mississippi State Univ., State College, Miss., 1964)
2. Abeles, F. B., *Physiol. Plantarum,* **20**, 442–54 (1967)
3. Addicott, F. T., *Encycl. Plant Physiol.,* **15/2**, 1094–1126 (1965)
4. Addicott, F. T., *Plant Physiol.,* **43**, 1471–79 (1968)
5. Addicott, F. T., Carns, H. R., Cornforth, J. W., Lyon, J. L., Milborrow, B. V., Ohkuma, K., Ryback, G., Smith, O. E., Thiessen, W. E., Wareing, P. F., in *Biochemistry and Physiology of Plant Growth Substances* (Runge Press, Ottawa, 1969)
6. Addicott, F. T., Carns, H. R., Lyon, J. L., Smith, O. E., McMeans, J. L., in *Régulateurs Naturels de la Croissance Végétale,* 687–703 (C. N. R. S., Paris, 748 pp., 1964)
7. Addicott, F. T., Lynch, R. S., Livingston, G. A., Hunter, J. K., *Plant Physiol.,* **24**, 537–39 (1949)
8. Addicott, F. T., Lyon, J. L., Ohkuma, K., Thiessen, W. E., Carns, H. R., Smith, O. E., Cornforth, J. W., Milborrow, B. V., Ryback, G., Wareing, P. F., *Science,* **159**, 1493 (1968)
9. Addicott, F. T., Ohkuma, K., Smith, O. E., Thiessen, W. E., *Advan. Chem.,* **53**, 97–105 (1966)
10. Asmundson, C. N., Ingersoll, R., Smith, O. E., Kumamoto, J., *Abstr. Am. Chem. Soc. Meeting, San Francisco, April 1968*
11. Aspinall, D., Paleg, L. G., Addicott, F. T., *Australian J. Biol. Sci.,* **20**, 869–82 (1967)
12. Barlow, H. W. B., Hancock, C. R., Lacey, H. J., in *Plant Growth Regulation,* 127–40 (Iowa State Univ. Press, Ames, Iowa, 850 pp., 1961)
13. Barnsley, G. E., Gabbott, P. A., Milborrow, B. V., British Pat. No. 1,101,844 (31 Jan. 1968)
14. Bennet-Clark, T. A., Kefford, N. P., *Nature,* **171**, 645–47 (1953)
15. Bhardwaj, S. N., Abrol, Y. P., *Indian J. Exptl. Biol.,* **5**, 264–65 (1967)
16. Biggs, R. H., *Physiological Basis of Abscission in Plants* (Doctoral Thesis, Purdue Univ., Lafayette, Ind., 1957)
17. Black, M., Wareing, P. F., *J. Exptl. Botany,* **10**, 134–45 (1959)
18. Bonner, J., in *Plant Growth Regulation,* 819–27 (See Ref. 12)
19. Borecka, H., Pieniazek, J., *Bull. Acad. Polon. Sci., Ser. V,* **16**, 655–59 (1968)
20. Bornman, C. H., *S. Afr. J. Sci.,* **63**, 325–31 (1967)
21. Bornman, C. H., Spurr, A. R., Addicott, F. T., *Am. J. Botany,* **54**, 125–35 (1967)
22. Bowen, M. R., Hoad, G. V., *Planta,* **81**, 64–70 (1968)
23. Carns, H. R., *Ann. Rev. Plant Physiol.,* **17**, 295–314 (1966)
24. Carns, H. R., McMeans, J. L., Addicott, F. T., *Proc. Intern. Botan. Congr., 9th, Montreal,* **2**, 60 (1959)
25. Carr, D. J., *Advan. Sci.,* 186–92 (August 1966)
26. Cathey, H. M., *Proc. Am. Soc. Hort. Sci.* (In press)
27. Cherry, J. H., in *Biochemistry and Physiology of Plant Growth Substances* (See Ref. 5)
28. Chrispeels, M. J., Varner, J. E., *Nature,* **212**, 1066–67 (1966)
29. Chrispeels, M. J., Varner, J. E., *Plant Physiol.,* **42**, 1008–16 (1967)
30. Cooper, W. C., Henry, W. H., *Israel J. Agr. Res.,* **18** (In press, 1968)
31. Cooper, W. C., Rasmussen, G. K., Rogers, B. J., Reece, P. C., Henry,

W. H., *Plant Physiol.*, **43**, 1560–76 (1968)

32. Cooper, W. C., Rasmussen, G. K., Smoot, J. J., *Florida Citrus and Vegetable Magazine* (Sept. 1968)

33. Cooper, W. C., Young, R. H., Henry, W. H., *Proc. Intern. Citrus Symp., Riverside, Calif.* (In press)

34. Corcoran, M. R., West, C. A., *Plant Physiol.*, **43**, 859–64 (1968)

35. Cornforth, J. W., Draber, W., Milborrow, B. V., Ryback, G., *Chem. Commun.*, 114–16 (1967)

36. Cornforth, J. W., Mallaby, R., Ryback, G., *J. Chem. Soc.* (C), 1565–68 (1968)

37. Cornforth, J. W., Milborrow, B. V., Ryback, G., *Nature*, **206**, 715 (1965)

38. Cornforth, J. W., Milborrow, B. V., Ryback, G., *Nature*, **210**, 627–28 (1966)

39. Cornforth, J. W., Milborrow, B. V., Ryback, G., Rothwell, K., Wain, R. L., *Nature*, **211**, 742–43 (1966)

40. Cornforth, J. W., Milborrow, B. V., Ryback, G., Wareing, P. F., *Nature*, **205**, 1269–70 (1965)

41. Cornforth, J. W., Milborrow, B. V., Ryback, G., Wareing, P. F., *Tetrahedron, Suppl.* **8**, Part II, 603–10 (1966)

42. Davis, L. A., *Gas Chromatographic Identification and Measurement of Abscisic Acid and Other Plant Hormones in the Developing Cotton Fruit* (Doctoral thesis, Univ. Calif., Davis, Sept. 1968)

43. Davis, L. A., Heinz, D. E., Addicott, F. T., *Plant Physiol.*, **43**, 1389–94 (1968)

44. De Fossard, R. A., *Abstr. Australian Soc. Plant Physiol., 9th General Meeting, Canberra, May 1968*, 39

45. Dörffling, K., *Planta*, **60**, 390–412 (1963)

46. Dörffling, K., *Planta*, **60**, 413–33 (1964)

47. Dörffling, K., *Planta*, **70**, 257–74 (1966)

48. Dörffling, K., *Naturwissenschaften*, **54**, 23–24 (1967)

49. Dörffling, K., *Wiss. Z. Univ. Rostok*, **16**, 673–74 (1967)

50. Dörffling, K., Böttger, M., *Planta*, **80**, 299–308 (1968)

51. Eagles, C. F., Wareing, P. F., *Physiol. Plantarum*, **17**, 697–709 (1964)

52. El-Antably, H. M. M., Wareing, P. F., Hillman, J., *Planta*, **73**, 74–90 (1967)

53. Esashi, Y., Leopold, A. C., in *Biochemistry and Physiology of Plant Growth Substances* (See Ref. 5)

54. Evans, L. T., *Science*, **151**, 107–8 (1966)

55. Evans, L. T., in *The Induction of Flowering: Some Case Histories* (MacMillan, Australia, in press)

56. Ferrari, T. E., Varner, J. E., *Plant Physiol.* (In press)

57. Gabr, O. M. K., Guttridge, C. G., *Planta*, **78**, 305–9 (1968)

58. Glew, R. H., *Developmental Aspects of Lipid Metabolism in the Developing and Germinating Castor Bean Seed* (Doctoral thesis, Univ. Calif. Davis, Sept. 1968)

59. Goldschmidt, E. E., Monselise, S. P., *Plant Physiol.*, **43**, 113–16 (1968)

60. Graebe, J. E., *Science*, **157**, 73–75 (1967)

61. Hacskaylo, J., Moke, S. E., *Ohio Agr. Expt. Sta. Res. Circ.*, **133**, 3–18 (1964)

62. Hall, W. C., Herrero, F. A., Katterman, F. R. H., *Botan. Gaz.*, **123**, 29–34 (1961)

63. Hartmann, H. T., Heslop, A. J., Whisler, J., *Calif. Agr.*, **22**, 14–16 (1968)

64. Hashimoto, T., Ikai, T., Tamura, S., *Planta*, **78**, 89–92 (1968)

65. Hashimoto, T., Tamura, S., *Botan. Mag. Tokyo* (In press)

66. Heide, O. M., *Nature*, **219**, 960–61 (1968)

67. Hemberg, T., *Encycl. Plant Physiol.*, **14**, 1162–84 (1961)

68. Hemberg, T., *ibid.*, **15/2**, 669–98 (1965)

69. Hemberg, T., *Acta Chem. Scand.*, **21**, 1665–66 (1967)

70. Ina, K., Sakato, Y., *Tetrahedron Letters*, **23**, 2777–80 (1968)

71. Irving, R. M., *Plant Physiol., Suppl.*, **43**, S-49 (1968)

72. Irving, R. M., Lanphear, F. O., *Plant Physiol.*, **43**, 9–13 (1968)

73. Isogai, Y., Okamoto, T., Komoda, Y., *Chem. Pharm. Bull.* (Tokyo), **15**, 1256–57 (1967)

74. Jackson, G. A. D., in *Plant Growth Regulators* (Soc. Chem. Ind., Monogr. 31, in press)

75. Jackson, G. A. D., Blundell, J. B., *Nature*, **212**, 1470–71 (1966)

76. Jacobs, W. P., *Develop. Biol.*, **1**, 527–33 (1959)

77. Jacobs, W. P., Shield, J. A., Jr., Osborne, D. J., *Plant Physiol.*, **37**, 104–6 (1962)

78. Kaminski, W., *Acta Soc. Botan. Polon.*, **37**, 173–78 (1968)
79. Khan, A. A., *Nature*, **216**, 166–67 (1967)
80. Khan, A. A., *Plant Physiol.*, **43**, 1463–65 (1968)
81. Khan, A. A., *Physiol. Plantarum* (In press)
82. Koshimizu, K., Fukui, H., Mitsui, T., Ogawa, Y., *Agr. Biol. Chem.* (*Tokyo*), **30**, 941–43 (1966)
83. Koshimizu, K., Inui, M., Fukui, H., Mitsui, T., *Agr. Biol. Chem.* (*Tokyo*), **32**, 789–91 (1968)
84. Lang, A., *HortSci* (In press)
85. Lenton, J. R., Bowen, M. R., Saunders, P. F., *Nature*, **220**, 86–87 (1968)
86. Libbert, E., in *Régulateurs Naturels de la Croissance Végétale*, 387–405 (See Ref. 6)
87. Lipe, J. A., *Endogenous Hormonal Regulation of Pecan Abscission* (Master's thesis, Texas A & M Univ., College Station, Texas, Jan. 1968)
88. Lipe, W. N., Crane, J. C., *Science*, **153**, 541–42 (1966)
89. Liu, W., Carns, H. R., *Science*, **134**, 384–85 (1961)
90. Lott, H., *Vitis-Ber. Rebenforsch.*, **7**, 221–22 (1968)
91. MacMillan, J., Pryce, R. J., *Chem. Commun.*, 124–26 (1968)
92. Madison, M., Rappaport, L., *Plant Cell Physiol.* (*Tokyo*), **9**, 147–53 (1968)
93. Maheshwari, S. C. (Personal communication)
94. Martin, G. C., Mason, M. I. R., Forde, H. I., *HortSci*, **3**, 114 (1968)
95. Milborrow, B. V., *Planta*, **70**, 155–71 (1966)
96. Milborrow, B. V., *Planta*, **76**, 93–113 (1967)
97. Milborrow, B. V., in *Biochemistry and Physiology of Plant Growth Substances* (See Ref. 5)
98. Mousseron-Canet, M., Mani, J., Dalle, J., Olivé, J., *Bull. Soc. Chim. France*, **12**, 3874–78 (1966)
99. Nitsch, C., *Ann. Sci. Nat., Botan., Paris, Ser. 12*, **9**, 1–92 (1968)
100. Nitsch, J. P., in *Environmental Control of Plant Growth*, 175–93 (Academic Press, New York, 1963)
101. Nitsch, J. P., *Ann. N.Y. Acad. Sci.*, **144**, 279–94 (1967)
102. Nygaard, P., *Physiol. Plantarum*, **22** (In press, 1969)
103. Ohkuma, K., *Agr. Biol. Chem.* (*Tokyo*), **30**, 434–37 (1966)
104. Ohkuma, K., *J. Agr. Chem. Soc. Japan*, **40**, 45–52 (1966)
105. Ohkuma, K., Addicott, F. T., Smith, O. E., Thiessen, W. E., *Tetrahedron Letters*, **29**, 2529–35 (1965)
106. Ohkuma, K., Lyon, J. L., Addicott, F. T., Smith, O. E., *Science*, **142**, 1592–93 (1963)
107. Olmstead, C. E., *Botan. Gaz.*, **112**, 365–93 (1951)
108. Olney, H. O., *Plant Physiol.*, **43**, 293–302 (1968)
109. Osborne, D. J., *Nature*, **176**, 1161–63 (1955)
110. Osborne, D. J., *Trop. Agr.*, **35**, 145–58 (1958)
111. Osborne, D. J., in *Aspects of the Biology of Ageing*, 305–21 (Academic Press, New York, 634 pp., 1967)
112. Paleg, L. G., *Plant Physiol.*, **35**, 902–6 (1960)
113. Palmer, R. L., Hield, H. Z., Lewis, L. N., *Proc. Intern. Citrus Symp.* (In press)
114. Phillips, I. D. J., Wareing, P. F., *J. Exptl. Botany*, **10**, 504–14 (1959)
115. Pieniazek, J., Grochowska, M. J., *Acta Soc. Botan. Polon.*, **36**, 579–87 (1967)
116. Pieniazek, J., Rudnicki, R., *Bull. Acad. Polon. Sci., Ser. V.*, **15**, 251–54 (1967)
117. Pilet, P. E., *Compt. Rend. Paris Acad. Sci. Ser. D*, **267**, 1142–45 (1968)
118. Porter, N. G., Van Steveninck, R. F. M., *Life Sci.*, **5**, 2301–8 (1966)
119. Quail, P. H., *A study of the Biology and Control of Wild Oats (Avena fatua L., and A. ludoviciana Dur.)* (Doctoral thesis, Univ. Sidney, Australia, 1968)
120. Rappaport, L., Blumenthal-Goldschmidt, S., Hayashi, F., *Plant Cell Physiol.* (*Tokyo*), **6**, 609–14 (1965)
121. Roberts, D. L., Heckman, R. A., Hege, B. P., Bellin, S. A., *J. Org. Chem.*, **33**, 3566–69 (1968)
122. Robinson, P. M., Wareing, P. F., *Physiol. Plantarum*, **17**, 314–23 (1964)
123. Romberger, J. A., *Meristems, Growth and Development in Woody Plants* (U.S. Dept. Agr. Tech. Bull. No. 1293, 214 pp., 1963)
124. Rothwell, K., Wain, R. L., in

Régulateurs Naturels de la Crois-sance Végétale, 363–75 (See Ref. 6)

125. Rudnicki, R., Antoszewski, R., *Bull. Acad. Polon. Sci., Ser. V.*, **16**, 447–49 (1968)

126. Rudnicki, R., Machnik, J., Pieniazek, J., *Bull. Acad. Polon. Sci., Ser. V.*, **16**, 509–12 (1968)

127. Rudnicki, R., Pieniazek, J., Pieniazek, N., *Bull. Acad. Polon. Sci., Ser. V*, **16**, 127–38 (1968)

128. Sankhla, N., Sankhla, D., *Experientia*, **24**, 294–95 (1968)

129. Sankhla, N., Sankhla, D., *Naturwissenschaften*, **55**, 91–92 (1968)

130. Sankhla, N., Sankhla, D., *Z. Pflanzenphysiol.*, **58**, 402–9 (1968)

131. Sankhla, N., Sankhla, D., *Physiol. Plantarum*, **21**, 190–95 (1968)

132. Saunders, P. F., Poulson, R. H., in *Biochemistry and Physiology of Plant Growth Substances* (See Ref. 5)

133. Savich, M. S., *Izv. Timiryazev. Sel'skokhoz. Akad.* (U.S.S.R.), **2**, 14–23 (1968)

134. Scott, P. C., *Abscission as a Cellular Senescence* (Doctoral thesis, Purdue Univ., Lafayette, Ind., Jan. 1967)

135. Shantz, E. M., *Ann. Rev. Plant Physiol.*, **17**, 409–38 (1966)

136. Shell Intern. Res., Maatschappij, N. V., The Hague, Netherlands, *Pat. No. 67 03449* (Sept. 5, 1967)

137. Smith, O. E., Lyon, J. L., Addicott, F. T., Johnson, R. E., in *Biochemistry and Physiology of Plant Growth Substances* (See Ref. 5)

138. Söding, H., Dörffling, K., *Arch. Mikrobiol.*, **60**, 182–200 (1968)

139. Sondheimer, E., Galson, E. C., *Plant Physiol.*, **41**, 1397–98 (1966)

140. Sondheimer, E., Tzou, D. S., Galson, E. C., *Plant Physiol.*, **43**, 1443–47 (1968)

141. Steward, F. C., in *Growth and Organization in Plants*, 345 (Addison-Wesley, Reading, Mass., 1968)

142. Sumner, D. C., Lyon, J. L., *Planta*, **75**, 28–32 (1967)

143. Taylor, H. F., in *Plant Growth Regulators* (See Ref. 74)

144. Taylor, H. F., Smith, T. A., *Nature*, **215**, 1513–14 (1967)

145. Thimann, K., *Am. Naturalist*, **90**, 145–62 (1956)

146. Thomas, T. H., Wareing, P. F., Robinson, P. M., *Nature*, **205**, 1269–72 (1965)

147. Tomaszewska, E., *Arboretum Kor-nickie* (*Poland*), **13**, 177–219 (1968)

148. Tomaszewska, E., Tomaszewski, M., *Proc. 3rd Symp. Plant Growth Regulators, Copernicus Univ., Torun, Poland, Sept. 1968* (In press)

149. Van Overbeek, J., Loeffler, J. E., Mason, M. I. R., *Science*, **156**, 1497–99 (1967)

150. Van Overbeek, J., Loeffler, J. E., Mason, M. I. R., in *Biochemistry and Physiology of Plant Growth Substances* (See Ref. 5)

151. Van Overbeek, J., Mason, M. I. R., *Acta Botan. Neerl.* (In press)

152. Van Overbeek, J., Tukey, H. B., Went, F. W., Muir, R. M., *Plant Physiol.*, **29**, 307–8 (1954)

153. Van Steveninck, R. F. M., *J. Exptl. Botany*, **10**, 367–76 (1959)

154. Vegis, A., *Ann. Rev. Plant Physiol.*, **15**, 185–224 (1964)

155. Villiers, T. A., *Planta*, **82**, 342–54 (1968)

156. Walton, D. C., Sondheimer, E., *Plant Physiol.*, **43**, 467–69 (1968)

157. Wareing, P. F., *Encycl. Plant Physiol.*, **15/2**, 909–24 (1965)

158. Wareing, P. F., *Sci. Progr.*, **53**, 529–37 (1965)

159. Wareing, P. F., in *Trends in Plant Morphogenesis*, 235–52 (Longmans Green & Co., London, 329 pp., 1966)

160. Wareing, P. F., *British Pat. No. 1,103,000* (14 Feb. 1968)

161. Wareing, P. F., Eagles, C. F., Robinson, P. M., in *Régulateurs Naturels de la Croissance Végétale*, 377–86 (See Ref. 6)

162. Wareing, P. F., El-Antably, H. M. M., *Proc. Liege Conf. on Flowering, Liege, Belgium, 1967* (In press)

163. Wareing, P. F., Good, J., Manuel, J., in *Biochemistry and Physiology of Plant Growth Substances* (See Ref. 5)

164. Wareing, P. F., Good, J., Potter, H., Pearson, A., in *Plant Growth Regulators* (See Ref. 74)

165. Wellensiek, S. J., in *The Induction of Flowering: Some Case Histories* (See Ref. 55)

166. Wright, S. T. C., in *Biochemistry and Physiology of Plant Growth Substances* (See Ref. 5)

167. Zeevaart, J. A. D., Marushige, K., in *Physiology of Flowering in Pharbitis nil*, 121–38 (Imamura, S., Ed., Japan Soc. Plant Physiol., 1967)

PHYSIOLOGY OF RAPID MOVEMENTS IN HIGHER PLANTS

By Takao Sibaoka

Biological Institute, Faculty of Science
Tohoku University, Sendai, Japan

Among the various behaviors in higher plants, a peculiar one, that a part of the leaf or flower in certain plants shows very rapid movement upon stimulus, has invited the attention of a number of investigators since the beginning of botanical research. However, in spite of this long history of study, numerous fundamental aspects of the phenomena remain to be clarified. Since the definition of the rapid movement is still unclear, discussion in this review will be restricted to three types of the movements: (*a*) rapid response in the pulvini of the mimosas; (*b*) shutting movement in the traps of two carnivores, *Dionaea* and *Aldrovanda* (an aquatic plant); and (*c*) visible movements in the stamen and pistil of some plants upon stimulus. This review is not intended to be a comprehensive résumé of all published works on the movements. I intend to restrict my discussion to a consideration of various results in an attempt to discover a general mechanism underlying these movements, and will stress the relation between electrical response and the movement. Several reviews and monographs have been published that approach this problem from various points of view (18, 19, 24, 42, 101, 103), including the author's own works (11, 71). In this review I will return to some of the important older literature which provides a basis for understanding the mechanism.

PERCEPTION OF STIMULUS AND RESPONSE BEHAVIOR

Dionaea and Aldrovanda.—Features of perception of stimulus and the process of response in these two carnivorous plants (3) are essentially similar to each other, though their form, size, and habitat are quite different. Normally, six (three on each lobe) sensory hairs in *Dionaea muscipula* and 30 to 40 in *Aldrovanda vesiculosa* (3) are found on the upper surface of the trap-lobes. When a small animal touches the distal lever above the joint of a sensory hair, or when the lever is pushed slightly with a fine rod, the hair bends at the joint consisting of morphologically special cells. In *Dionaea*, the mechanical stimulus is received in the remaining part of the hair after removal of the distal lever (14). Deformation of the thin-walled joint cells in *Aldrovanda* by pinching with two fine glass rods results in shutting of the trap (4). The special cells at the joint (42) seem therefore to be mechanical receptors, but in *Dionaea* no direct evidence for this conclusion has yet been obtained.

In *Dionaea*, at moderate temperature a shutting of the trap usually follows two stimuli (22, 27), disturbing either the same hair twice or two dif-

ferent hairs at an interval of less than 20 sec (14, 71). At higher temperatures (35 to 40° C), however, the shutting frequently follows only one stimulus (14). The absolute refractory period for perception of the stimulus is
less than 1 sec (14, 70). Latent time between the second stimulus and onset
of the shutting, as well as the process of the movement, are independent of
the intervals of two stimuli less than 20 sec (71), so that the response
seems to obey an all-or-none principle. However, slow and partial closures
are caused with each of successive stimuli at longer intervals than 20 sec,
ultimately the trap making complete closure; the number of stimuli required
for complete closure depends upon the time intervals between the stimuli
(13, 14, 22). Also, the trap of *Aldrovanda* commonly closes after the sensory hair has been bent twice (4). There are few quantitative data about
the intervals of stimuli and number of bendings required because of experimental difficulties in *Aldrovanda*.

Jacobson (51) has found that when a sensory hair of *Dionaea* is bent,
an electrical potential change that is somewhat similar to the receptor potentials in mechano-receptor of animals appears in the hair stimulated.
When this potential goes over a certain magnitude, it generates a propagated
action potential. The magnitude of receptor potentials roughly depends
upon velocity of hair bending, but fast bending is rather ineffective. The
propagated action potential starts from the base of the hair stimulated and
spreads in all directions over the entire surface of the trap-lobes; a second
action potential elicited within 20 sec after the first one is followed by the
shutting of the trap (71). In the trap of *Aldrovanda,* one would expect that
the receptor potential and action potential should be generated prior to the
shutting, but no attempt has been made as yet to prove this.

In *Aldrovanda,* deformation of a few cells in the three-cell layered region which is the central part of the trap, and the zone where the cells active in closure are located, results in the shutting movement (4). When
some part of the trap-lobes of *Dionaea* is scratched or pricked with a nee-
dle, a propagated action potential (101) occurs, followed by shutting (14).
From the above results, it appears that mechanical stimuli are also received
directly by the cells of the trap-lobes.

An electrical stimulus is also effective in the trap of both *Dionaea* and
Aldrovanda. Ashida (4) has proved in *Aldrovanda* that the sensory hairs
are not the chief receptor of the electrical stimulus, while cells in the motor
zone are more sensitive than any other cells of the trap. A strong induction
shock is always sufficient to cause the mechanical response in *Aldrovanda*
(4) and in *Dionaea* (14). The strong current seems to stimulate more than
two points of the trap at the same time. Since in these experiments one of a
pair of stimulating electrodes is normally placed on the trap and the other
one on the petiole in the case of *Dionaea* (14), or relatively large stimulating electrodes are placed apart from each other into the water with the trap
of *Aldrovanda* positioned between them (4) the electric current must pass
through a substantial portion of the trap in the both cases. On the other
hand, when a pair of stimulating electrodes are positioned close to each

other on a part of the trap of *Dionaea,* each electric pulse above threshold strength elicits a propagated action potential, and the second action potential is followed by the shutting of the trap (71). Thus, two electrical stimuli, each of which elicits a propagated action potential, are required for the shutting of the trap, as has already been shown with mechanical stimuli.

A sudden rise or fall of temperature results in the shutting of the trap in *Aldrovanda* (4). The threshold temperature differences are smaller for a sudden fall than for a rise, the thresholds depending upon leaf age and initial temperature (5). Reaction time (2 to 50 sec) for the shutting with thermal shock is much longer than that with mechanical or electrical stimulus (about 0.1 sec) (5). It appears that when the trap is exposed to a new temperature, more than two excitations (action potential?) are elicited at certain intervals which depend on temperature differences, and then the shutting occurs.

It seems clear from the above results that in the *Dionaea* trap-lobes, and probably also in those of *Aldrovanda,* mechanical response (shutting movement) follows after a definite amount of accumulated effect. The mechanism of accumulation or memory is still unknown. There is no indication that the memory is closely associated with the receptor potential (51). The velocity of propagation of the second action potential is markedly larger than that of the first—within about 30 to 60 sec after propagation for the latter. In other words, the effect of the first propagated action potential remains in the trap for some time (70, 71). Recently, DiPalma et al. (28) found that if the lower surface or marginal ciliated part in the trap of *Dionaea* is stroked with a stiff-bristle brush several times, the number of bendings of the sensory hair required for the shutting of the trap after stroking becomes fewer than the number required without stroking. The investigators concluded that stellate trichomes which are distributed on the region just mentioned act as tactile receptors, and touching the trichomes results in some accumulated effect in the trap. The stroke causes a small nonpropagated potential change in the trap (28).

When several drops of 3 per cent NaCl solution are placed in the trap of *Dionaea,* a series of action potentials appears; a similar effect is obtained with equivalent osmotic quantities of other salts or even glucose, and also with juices from another trap that has captured an insect within 48 hr (8). These effects are followed by the shutting movement. In the process of digesting the captured insect, the trap shows spontaneous action potentials (8). This suggests a possible mechanism for keeping the trap closed during digestion. The closed trap reopens within about 10 hr if there is no insect in it, while the closure lasts for 10 or more days if the trap has captured an insect (58).

Mimosa.—While there has been much investigation of conduction phenomena, relatively little attention has been directed toward the nature and mechanism of stimulus perception in *Mimosa pudica* and its allied species. Among them, *M. pudica* (which is the most sensitive to stimulus) has been well investigated, so in this review our discussion will dwell mainly on *M.*

pudica and, unless specified otherwise, all references to *Mimosa* are to this plant. Shaking a whole *Mimosa* plant results in the almost simultaneous fall of each leaf and closure of each pair of leaflets, but little or no propagation is observable in this case. These responses must be generated through direct perception of mechanical stimulation by each pulvinus, perhaps with deformation of the pulvinus due to swaying of the leaves when the plant is shaken. It is well known that the lower surface of the main pulvinus of *Mimosa* is sensitive to the slightest touch, since the leaf falls immediately after touching, and usually this response is restricted within the stimulated pulvinus so that no propagation is seen. On the other hand, every part of the leaf and stem of *Mimosa* is receptive to many types of stimuli other than shaking, and a series of visible successive responses of pulvini (76, 92) or propagated action potential (45, 67, 93, 94) starts from the site stimulated. This means that excitable cells and their connections or other conduction systems extend throughout the whole plant, and the excitable cells may play the roles of both receptor and conductor.

Visible responses (rapid movements) occur only at the pulvini, whereas electrical responses (potential changes) can be observed not only at the pulvini but at points along the path of propagation such as stem, petiole, pinna-rachis, and leaflet. The propagated responses in the stem and leaf are analysed into three kinds from the patterns of electrical response, the propagation velocities, the type of blocks at which propagation is interrupted, and the variety of stimuli invoking a response (45, 62, 76, 92, 94, 101). Most research conducted earlier than the careful works of Snow (76) and Umrath (92) indicated that there was only one mechanism of conduction in the stem and leaf of *Mimosa,* so in some cases these early results appear conflicting.

The slowest propagation has a negative electrical potential irregular in shape and long in duration, and is produced by a wounding stimulus (cutting or burning) (45, 66, 105) or by tetanic stimuli from an inductor coil (100, 101). Among the three forms, only this wave can generally pass through the pulvini and propagate over a distance (45, 66). The rate of propagation depends upon the velocity of the water movement in vessels (45). This wave may correspond with the conduction mechanism found by Ricca (60) in the stem and leaf of *M. spegazzinii,* and with "normal" conduction in the stem of *M. pudica* proposed by Snow (76). These workers have shown that this conduction depends on a stimulating substance which is set free by wounding and carried along in the transpiration stream in the vessels. The electrical negative variation within this wave may depend on electrical potential changes generated by a moving stimultant in the neighboring living cells of the vessels (66).

The most rapid propagation is occasionally observed in the young leaf of intact plants, especially in damp air (45, 62), and frequently in a submerged "stem and leaf preparation," which is an isolated length of stem carrying a single leaf (76). Only the main pulvinus reacts 1 to 3 sec after cutting the pinna of the same leaf, and neither further propagations nor further visible responses are seen. This wave can pass through a cooled ($\sim 3°$) zone of the petiole but not a killed zone (45). When cutting the pinna causes this wave, the system exhibits at the same time the slowest and the moderate waves, both of which can be seen as electrical potential changes (45). Electrical changes associated with the most rapid propagation are not clear, since the mechanism of this wave has not been explored. Recently, Umrath (104) reported a small action potential associated with this wave, but this seems to be somewhat questionable.

The moderately rapid conduction, which is by means of an action potential, is produced everywhere in the leaf and the stem by every sort of stimulus (45, 67, 94, 101). The use of electrophysiological investigation with microelectrode technique, which can determine the kind of cells that generate action potentials (69), reveals that elongated parenchyma cells in the protoxylem and phloem of the petiole are excitable and that the same cells are very probably the pathway of propagation. The elongated parenchyma cells found in the pinna-rachis and stem seem to be excitable cells, but no direct evidence of this has yet been obtained. In the petiole of *M. himalayana* and *M. pigra,* the elongated parenchyma cells are found in both the protoxylem and phloem (54). Wound stimulation elicits this mechanism together with the slowest wave, whereas stimulation without wounding, such as rapid cooling or electrical current, produces an action potential alone (45, 66). Under normal conditions, transmission of the action potential is interrupted at the pulvini (45, 62), so that when elicited alone this response occurs solely within the length of the stimulated pinna, petiole, or stem. When the transmission is produced together with the slowest wave by a wounding stimulus, the former stops at the pulvinus, but the latter passes through it a little later and regenerates the transmission of an action potential on the other side of the pulvinus (45, 62). The same reaction can be observed at a killed (71) or cooled (45) region, because the action potential cannot pass through such a region although the slowest wave can pass through it. This transmission may correspond with the "protoplasmic excitation" propounded by Bose (12), the "high speed" conduction in the stem and "rapid phloem mechanism" in the leaf found by Snow (76), and the "rapid conduction" in the submerged stem explored by Ball (7).

When an action potential propagated basipetally through the petiole arrives at the joint between the slender part of the petiole and the main pulvinus, another type of action potential in the main pulvinus is elicited here after a latent period of about 0.2 sec (65). The pulvinar action potential which may be caused as a result of the stimulative effect of the petiolar action potential at the joint has a more sharply rising phase than that in the petiolar action potential (99) and also shows a propagated nature (65); its velocity is about twice the latter. Mechanical response of the main pulvinus (rapid fall of the leaf) begins about 0.1 sec after the occurrence of the pulvinar action potential (32, 65). Thus the mechanical response always follows the pulvinar action potential, but only the action potential is generated when the second stimulus is applied within about 1 min after the first (95, 99). This means that when the absolute refractory period for the pulvinar action potential is over, the pulvinus does not recover immediately from the mechanical response. What kind of cells generates the action potential in the pulvinus has not yet been determined, but motor cells (cortical parenchyma cells), occupying a large part of the pulvinus, are most likely to be the source of the action potential, because of considerable activity in the motor cells during the movement. In the subpulvinus and the pulvinule the action potential elicited prior to their rapid mechanical responses is not yet clear.

Snow (76) has observed that when the cut distal end of a petiole is dipped into NaCl solution (3.5 per cent or stronger) the main pulvinus responds usually after 3 to 5 sec, but no response is obtained with a concentrated sucrose solution. It seems that such a solution of NaCl can generate the action potential at the cut end because the reaction time of 3 to 5 sec may correspond to the transmission time of the action potential through the petiole. Response in a fresh section of the pulvinule occurs with the addition of more than 0.5 per cent NaCl solution (108); apparently the motor cells directly generate the action potential with such a solution. The effect of NaCl on the cells is not osmotic but seems to be related to an ionic correlation between both sides of the cell membrane.

Rapid response in the main pulvinus also occurs with a light stimulus (38). When plants placed in a dark room are irradiated by 400 to 500 mμ of light at 0.8 × 10^{-8} Einsteins cm^{-2} sec^{-1}, the petioles fall within 30 to 80 sec after the beginning of exposure; irradiation of 450 mμ is most effective (39). High intensity irradiation 0.5 × 10^{-6} Einsteins cm^{-2} sec^{-1} of 1 to 10 sec exhibits the same response as continuous exposure of the lower intensities mentioned above (39). Where the light stimuli are perceived is as yet unknown.

Both the perception of stimulus and response behaviors in *M. spegazzinii* (77, 93, 94, 101), *M. invisa* (97), *Neptunia plena* (94, 101), *Biophytum sensitivum* (41, 94, 96), and *Biophytum* sp. (72) are similar to those found in *M. pudica*.

Filaments of stamens.—Only the adaxial surface (that facing the flower center) at the base of the filaments of *Berberis vulgaris, B. thunbergii,* and *Mahonia aquifolium* can directly perceive touch stimulus. A rapid response, bending toward the flower center, occurs locally in the same region that has just received the stimulus: no further response is seen (15, 19). In *Sparmannia africana* and *Helianthemum vulgaris,* a bending movement away from the flower center at the filament base is caused by a touch stimulus only on the abaxial surface (that facing away from the center) of the base or with bending inwardly so that this surface may be stretched (15, 19, 26). In all these plants, both perception of stimuli and responses are restricted within a small portion at the filament base, and the bending response occurs in a definite direction. In *Portulaca grandiflora,* on the other hand, bending occurs everywhere through the length of the filament at stimulated sites, and the direction of the response is opposite to the bending direction for stimulus (47, 48). Trichomes or papillae distributed on the surface of the filaments of these plants do not seem to be part of the receptor apparatus (15, 49, 50). The perception mechanism of mechanical stimulus is not clear. No propagation of response is observed in the filament stimulated, but in *Sparmannia* some neighbors of the stimulated filament show the same response (15).

In *Sparmannia* and *Berberis,* a nonpropagated action potential (negative potential change) appears only at the base of the filament when stimulated (17). No difference in potential pattern is seen with different sorts of stimuli: mechanical, electrical, chemical, or thermal (17). The beginning of the action potential precedes the movement by 1 to 2 sec in *Sparmannia* (17). It seems that in *Berberis* also the electrical response is prior to the mechanical one. However, latent times for both electrical and mechanical responses are very short (0.03 to 0.07 sec), so that exact determination of time relation between the two responses is difficult (17, 101). Simultaneous records of action potential and movement in *Berberis thunbergii* (101) reveal that neither action potential nor movement appears within a 3-min period after the latest response, while a normal action potential with little or no movement appears within 7 min after the latest response. Thus, different refractory periods for electrical and mechanical responses are observed, as mentioned above for the main pulvinus of *Mimosa.*

Stigmas of pistils.—Bilobate stigmas in some plants are sensitive to mechanical stimulus and the lobe stimulated bends toward the other one. The stigma lobes in *Mimulus luteus* generally respond only to a pressure-stimulus on the inner surface (that facing the other lobe), but a simple touch is ineffective (23). Violent shaking of the pistil or strong bending of the lobe outside is effective (23). Accordingly, distortion of the inner surface cell layers must act as a stimulation. When a small part anywhere on the inner surface is stimulated gently, the response occurs locally at this part only, while with a strong stimulus the response occurs all over the surface of the lobe (23).

Recently, Sinyukhin & Britikov (75) found a propagated action potential in the sensitive bilobate stigmas of *Incarvillea grandiflora* and *I. delavayi.* The action potential caused by mechanical stimulus spread throughout the lobe stimulated but was blocked at the fork of the lobes. About 0.1 sec after the action potential spread throughout the lobe, the mechanical response occurred. If pollen is placed gently on a lobe so that there is no mechanical effect, no electrical potential change and no movement appear within 3 to 17 min after the pollination. An action potential is finally elicited after the generation of a slow potential change in the stigma lobe following the pollination, and hence movement occurs.

Action Potential and Its Transmission

As early as 1873, Burdon-Sanderson (20) found that deflection of a galvanometer connected with the *Dionaea* trap occurred when a fly creeping on the upper surface of the trap reached the sensory hairs and touched them. This was the first known observation of an action potential in plants. As described in the preceding section, the moderately rapid conduction from the stimulated part in the petiole, pinna-rachis, and stem of *Mimosa* is by means of transmission of an action potential (45, 62, 67, 94, 101); and an-

TABLE I
Action Potentials in Higher Plants

Species	Organ	Spike Height (mV)	Transmission (cm/sec)	Key References
Biophytum sensitivum	pinna-rachis	60	0.3–0.5	41, 94
Biophytum sp.	pinna-rachis	65–90	0.15–0.2	72
Biophytum sp.	peduncle	100–120	0.2	72
Clematis zeylanica	stem	—	0.15–0.25	46
Cucumis melo	tendril	30–80	(decrement)	98
Cucurbita pepo	stem	20 (80)[a]	6–1 (decrement)	6, 74
Dionaea muscipula	trap-lobes	40–60 (100)[a]	6–17	71
Incarvillea grandiflora	stigma-lobe	55	1.8	75
Incarvillea grandiflora	style	—	2.9	75
Mimosa pudica	pinna-rachis	80	0.3–0.7	64
Mimosa pudica	petiole	120 (140)[a]	2–3	67, 69
Mimosa pudica	stem	60	4–5	101
Mimosa spegazzinii	petiole	50	0.8	101
Neptunia plena	petiole	60	1	94
Vitis discolor	stem	—	0.2–0.7	45
Vitis gongylodes	tendril	—	0.6	45

[a] The values in the parentheses showed membrane action potential recorded in a single excitable cell.

other type of action potential triggered by the petiolar action potential starts at the entrance of the main pulvinus and propagates through it before onset of its mechanical response (65). An action potential starts at the sensory hair just stimulated and spreads over the whole surface of the trap-lobes of *Dionaea* (21, 27, 71, 81). Thus the transmission of the action potential plays an important role in the conduction of response in sensitive plants.

Table I summarizes the results of experimentation by many authors with action potentials and their transmission in the various higher plants. Some of the plants shown in the table do not exhibit any visible mechanical response; the role of action potential transmission in these plants is not understood. On the other hand, some plants show a propagated electrical potential change (101); but it appears that the change is not a true action potential but is an indication of the movement of a stimulating substance in the organ.

As far as we know, the most rapid transmission of action potential in higher plants is found in the trap of *Dionaea*. Within a few tenths of a second after stimulus an action potential spreads in all directions over the whole surface of the trap which consists of two lobes (71). The velocity of the spread is higher in the direction parallel to the vascular bundles than in the perpendicular direction (71). There is some variation in the form of the action potentials obtained from the upper and lower surfaces of the trap (70). Thus the patterns of action potential recorded from the surface of the trap are somewhat complicated, though the action potential recorded intracellularly from a single cell has a simple form (71). These differences may be the result of some distortion in the form of the action potential recorded from the surface due to dorsiventrality of the structure of the trap. The forms of action potential change successively with repeated excitation in relatively short time intervals (21). This seems to be an indication of the accumulated effects of repeated stimuli. The patterns of the diphasic recorded action potential (27, 81) must be largely modified by both the transmission velocity and the accumulated effects from repeated stimuli. No additional change in electrical potential in the trap can be found when a mechanical response (shutting of the trap) occurs (71). Accordingly, it appears that the mechanical changes occur in the same cells that generate the action potential immediately prior to the change; the relation between them recalls the mechanism of excitation-contraction coupling in muscle cells.

Excitable cells which generate an action potential and serve as the path of transmission in the petiole of *Mimosa* are found in the vascular bundles; the elongated parenchyma cells in protoxylem and phloem are excitable, and they form a number of cell rows along the longitudinal axis (69, 71). The membrane of the excitable cells is polarized; the cell interior is about 160 mV negative to the exterior, which is significantly larger than that in other insensitive cells found in the petiole, and during activity the potential changes transitorily about 140 mV toward the direction of depolarization (69). The latter is the membrane action potential of an excitable cell. This feature in the membrane is essentially similar to that in the axon, muscle fiber, and characeous internodal cell.

An action potential can be propagated over the whole length or the whole area of a certain region of the leaf, as stated previously. An approximate estimation based on the size of excitable cells and the transmission velocity shows that each excitable cell along a certain cell row in the *Mimosa* petiole successively generates the action potential with an interval of 4 to 6 msec (71). The mechanism of the transmission of the action potential from an excitable cell to another one remains unknown, but the results below suggest a possible mechanism.

When the petiole of *Mimosa* is entirely immersed in a large volume of salt solution having relatively high conductivity, a significant and reversible rise (15 to 60 per cent, depending on the concentration of the solution) in velocity of transmission of the action potential can be obtained (68). Since, under these conditions, the resultant resistance outside the excitable cells is expected to be much reduced by shunting with the low resistance of the solutions, these results strongly suggest not only that the conduction of the action potential along a single excitable cell but also the transmission from cell to cell may be mediated by local current which flows between the just activated part and the adjacent yet unexcited part.

Another piece of evidence about transmission can be obtained from microelectrode experiments (71). The electrode is inserted into an excitable cell along a certain row; the latter is surgically interrupted some distance from the stimulated site. In spite of the disconnection from the stimulation, the excitable cell in question normally generates an action potential. This means that the transmission must take place transversely from the rows connected with the stimulated point to those disconnected from it. Similar experiments reveal that the transverse transmission can also take place not only between the rows located within the large central vascular bundles but from the central bundles to two slender ones which are isolated from the former; the tissues between the slender and large bundles consist of only the unexcitable cortical tissue having some intercellular spaces. From the results above, it may be concluded that the excitable cells may be affected electrotonically by the action potentials in other cells located nearby and may elicit the action potentials by themselves, so that any chemical transmission scarcely needs consideration.

Thus, good evidence for the transmission of action potentials in higher plants may be afforded by the petiole and the pinna-rachis of *Mimosa*. The transmission velocity depends on temperature and maturity of the plant, but it is independent of the strength of stimulus except in the stimulated portion (63). At the point of stimulus, when the stimuli are weak, only local potential changes are observed, the size of which increase with increasing strength of the stimulus. When the strength exceeds a certain value and the local potential reaches a certain size, the transmitted action potential suddenly appears, showing all-or-none characteristics (67). Since size of the local potential change may depend on the number of activated excitable cells in the stimulated part, it appears that generating transmission requires the activation of a certain number of excitable cells, and thereafter excitation spreads transversely until all the excitable cells are suddenly activated.

The velocity of transmission also depends on the size of the petiole and pinna-rachis, that is, the number of excitable cells (63, 64). It seems that the greater the number of excited cells present in the petiole the stronger the electrotonic current that is generated. The latter may result in a shortening of the time interval between reception of the current and occurrence of excitation in each of the excitable cells that are not yet activated, and hence it may increase the velocity of transmission. Accordingly, the transmission in this plant takes place only as a result of the cooperation of many cells. In fact, the transverse spreading from the slender vascular bundles to the large ones does not occur, and transmission cannot take place very far along the slender bundle alone (63, 71). Decrement transmission of action potential in *Cucumis* and *Cucurbita,* as shown in the table, seems to occur because the number of excitable cells is too small for the transmission to the necessary distance.

STIMULATING SUBSTANCES

In 1916, Ricca (60) found important evidence of the propagation of a stimulating substance in *M. spegazzinii.* His research shows that a substance is released from cells wounded by stimulation, enters the vessels, moves an appreciable distance, and can stimulate the pulvini. The same phenomenon is observed in *M. pudica* (76). This is the second means of propagation of response in *Mimosa.* When the basal cut end of the petiole of a detached leaf is immersed into a water extract of other leaves, the pinnae eventually exhibit successive closures of the leaflet pairs; a 1:5000 dilution of the extract is still effective (36). More than a thousand substances have been tested for the pinna response in the same way: among them DL-alanine, DL-serine, DL-glutamic acid, and some derivatives of anthraquinone are effective to the response, but the threshold concentrations of them are as high as 10^{-3} to 10^{-4} M (36).

Several workers (9, 37, 43, 44, 78, 79) have made attempts at purification and determination of chemical structure of the stimulating substance in *Mimosa,* but so far no one has succeeded. An amorphous concentrate gives the pinna response at a dilution 1.5×10^8: the substance behaves as an oxy-acid containing nitrogen (4.5 per cent) with an estimated molecular weight between 300 and 450 (78). Supposing the molecular weight is 400, the threshold concentration could be as low as 5×10^{-9} M. Other results (43, 44) show that the extracted substances from the *Mimosa* plant are highly sensitive to oxygen and can turn easily into an inactive form, their chemical behavior being that of a reducing agent: meso-inositol is perhaps one of the primary compounds leading to the active substances. The reducing power of the active form seems to have a stimulating effect on the cells. When the extraction is carried out after applying an anesthetic to the *Mimosa* plant, the activity of the substance is reduced to one-fourth to one-tenth of the normal (79). This suggests that the cells contain the substance in an inactive form that may turn into the active form upon wounding stimulus.

A water extract from the stamen or leaf of *Berberis vulgaris* is effective to the response in the filament of this plant (102). Effectiveness of the extract is found in dilutions of more than about one-sixtieth; an extract from the leaf anesthetized previously with ether show about a half effect of that from the normal (102).

MECHANISM OF RAPID MOVEMENTS

Most of the literature concerning the mechanism of rapid movements in higher plants concludes that the movements are caused by the diminishing or sudden loss of turgor in the motor cells or decrease in their volume or both. This seems to explain the rapid movements satisfactorily, but the changes in turgor and volume of the motor cells must be brought about passively as a result of an action that is initiated in the cells when the response starts. This action is not precisely understood. Various facts, reported by many authors, of morphological and physiological changes in the motor cells during the movement will be considered below from such a point of view.

Excretion of water or cell sap.—There are several observations on the excretion of water or cell sap from the motor cells during response in plants exhibiting rapid movements. This phenomenon seems to be important for explaining the mechanism. In the stamen of *Sparmannia,* swelling of cell wall materials and formation of droplets over the wall surface are observed on the outer wall of the irritable cells after the movement occurs (16). Extrusion of liquid from the cells into the intercellular spaces of the tissue in the stigma-lobes of *Mimulus* is observable under the microscope when the lobe responds to stimulus (23).

Various observations of liquid movement in the pulvini of *Mimosa* during the rapid movements have been conducted. Expulsion of water from the main pulvinus during the movement, and reabsorption of water during recovery, can be seen by a micropotometer: the quantities of the water reabsorbed are always greater than those expelled (31). Long ago, Blackman & Paine (10) demonstrated that electrical conductivity of a small quantity of water which surrounds an excised main pulvinus is increased after its mechanical response. This seems to be a result of excretion of electrolytes from the cells in the pulvinus during the movement. They concluded that the amount of electrolytes exosmosed was far too small to account for the sudden decrease of turgor of the motor cells. However, the amount of electrolytes actually exosmosed during the movement must be larger than they reported, because it seems that the electrolytes just secreted from the excited cells could not move out quickly from the inside of the tissue to the surrounding water; thus only a fraction of those secreted from the cells near the cut surface contribute to changes in conductivity of the water. Electrical resistance measured longitudinally between both ends of the intact main pulvinus is decreased with the mechanical response: the amplitude of the response closely corresponds to the decrease of resistance (61). The electrical resistance of the intact pulvinus must depend mainly on the amount of electrolyte present in the liquid of the intercellular spaces rather than that in the cell interiors. Microscopic observation of the main pulvinus reveals that there are many air bubbles in the well-developed intercellular spaces which are localized at a certain zone in the motor tissue, but almost no bubbles are found after the pulvinus receives a stimulus (83). A juice containing tannins, potassium, and other substances issues from the cut surface of the main pulvinus under stimulus (83). Observation of the incinerated sections of the main pulvinus reveals that ashes are distributed homogenously over the cytoplasmic layer before a stimulus, but these ashes almost disappear in the cytoplasm and masses of ashes are located about the cell walls after a stimulus (86). Histochemically detectable potassium salts are found in the motor cells before response, but the large crystals of the salts appear in the intercellular spaces after response (84, 86). A liquid containing potassium salts is found to be present in the intercellular spaces in the section of the fresh main pulvinus upon stimulation: before stimulation and after recovery from the response such a liquid is not found (30). Tannin substances seen in a particular vacuole (tannin vacuole) in the motor cells of the pulvinus are also found in the peripheral cytoplasmic layer or the intercellular spaces after a stimulus (82, 83).

In the trap-lobes of *Aldrovanda,* a capillary-active substance, such as alcohol or acetone, rapidly enters the intercellular spaces at the motor zone only and drives out the air which filled them; and if the lobes are dipped in a solution of osmic acid, the cell contents in the motor zone becomes dark brown in color, although no other part shows this change in color (3). These facts indicate that the outer walls in the motor zone are particularly permeable to the liquids even during the rest period.

All of the above results clearly indicate that some of the cell sap escapes to the exterior during movement, and the excape may result in decrease of turgor in the motor cells. Explaining what causes the motor cells to move their cell sap out to the exterior should be a most important step toward understanding the mechanism of the rapid movements.

Increase of permeability.—Several authors (3, 16, 23, 61, 90) have proposed that the mechanical response in the motor cells, seen in the rapid movement, is caused by an increase in permeability of the cell membrane. There is, however, no conclusive evidence that a rise in permeability actually does occur when the mechanical response starts in the motor cells. Since a transient increase of membrane conductance which depends on the permeability to ions is seen to occur concomitantly with the action potential in the excitable cells of animals and characeous internodes, it may also occur in the motor cells of sensitive plants. However, this does not mean that the increase of permeability to ions during the action potential results directly in the changes in turgor, because movement of ions through the membrane during the action potential seems to be in insufficient quantity to account for the decrease of turgor and, as already described, there exists a certain time interval between the occurrence of the action potential and the mechanical response seen in the filament of *Sparmannia* (17), in the trap of *Dionaea* (71), and in the main pulvinus of *Mimosa* (32, 65). If the decrease in turgor of the motor cells were brought about directly by an increase in permeability to water or other liquid, the latter should be superimposed on the rise of permeability during the action potential. The actual existence of such a change in permeability has not yet been demonstrated.

Microscopically visible changes in the motor cells and tissues.—The attention of many investigators has been directed to the vacuoles in the motor cells and their changes during the response. Additional observations have been made concerning the difference in structure of the motor cells before and after the response and about morphological characteristics of the motor cells.

Weintraub (108) studied sections of the fresh pulvinule of *Mimosa*. In the motor cells, he found numerous small vacuoles (about 1 μ in diameter), which are not usually evident in the fixed material; these were in addition to the central and tannin vacuoles. Behavior of the small vacuoles is of great interest and suggests an explanation for the mechanism of the movement. During the response, the small vacuoles already present disappeared, but at the same time, rapid formation of new vacuoles of the same type and their subsequent disappearance were observed under the microscope. The number of small vacuoles present after the response was greatly diminished, and the sizes of both the cell and the central vacuole decreased during the response. After recovery, the number of small vacuoles and the size of the cells became nearly as great as the initial ones. When the section was immersed in a dilute solution of neutral red, the small vacuoles as well as the large central vacuole were stained; during the response, the newly formed small vacuoles contained none of the dye, unlike those already present, and the color of the stained central vacuole, which decreased in size, deepened. Weintraub concluded from these results that active contraction of the small vacuoles, as well as the formation of new vacuoles and their subsequent contraction, caused a sufficient decrease in water content in the motor cells to result in the lessening of their turgor.

In the main pulvinus of *Mimosa,* small contractile vacuoles are also observed in the motor cells in fresh sections; these are fewer in number and smaller in size than those found in the pulvinule (30). On stimulus these vacuoles disappear completely, the tannin vacuole becomes smaller in size, and a slight contraction of the cell wall occurs (30). During recovery, on the other hand, the small vacuoles reappear, and the tannin vacuole returns to its initial size (30). Upon electrical stimulation, the vacuole (probably the tannin vacuole) of the motor cells of the main pulvinus rapidly contracts, and at the same time deformation of the cell and decrease in cell volume also occur; no difference in this behavior is seen between the lower half—seemingly more sensitive than the upper—and the upper half of the main pulvinus (2). In one experiment, the large central vacuole of the motor cells in a freshly hand-sectioned main pulvinus was tinted violet with brilliant cresyl blue (25). When an extract from cut pulvini, which has a stimulating effect, was added on the medium in which the section was located, the violet color of the vacuole deepened in shade (25). Upon treatment with a glycerine solution, the vacuolar membrane crumpled, but after a while it recovered partially, and when water or pulvinar sap was added to the outside medium the recovery of the membrane was promoted (25).

All of the above results clearly indicate that the motor cells in *Mimosa* have contractile vacuoles whose activity causes liquid (probably cell sap) to be expelled from the motor cells, just like the contractile vacuoles seen in the protozoa; this activity may result in a decrease in turgor or volume of the motor cells.

Toriyama (82, 87, 89, 90) observed the variously fixed and stained sections of the main pulvinus of *Mimosa* and recognized some differences in structure and content in the motor cells before and after receiving a stimulus; he stressed changes of the tannin vacuole. Affinity of the tannin vacuole for basic dyes is higher during the rest period than after response (89, 90): the outline of this vacuole is clear before stimulus and somewhat obscure after response (89). In the sections fixed by Müller's fluid and stained by Ehrlich's haematoxylin, the peripheral cytoplasm is seen as a thin layer before the response, while it shrinks and becomes somewhat granular after the response (89). When the section is treated with chromium salts the granular contents are seen in the central vacuole during rest, but little is found after the section receives a stimulus (87). These observations indicate that the nature of the motor cells seems to change during the response, but its relationship with the mechanism of movement is not clear. There is no direct relationship between the presence of tannin vacuole and the occurrence of rapid movement, because no tannin vacuole is found in the motor cells of the very young plants in which the movement takes place normally (85). Recently Toriyama found a membrane structure surrounding the tannin vacuole (91).

Microscopic observations of the fresh motor cells of the filament of *Berberis vulgaris* reveal that the cell form changes greatly during response, but without a change in cell volume; the size of the central vacuole greatly decreases, while the peripheral cytoplasm thickens; and both granulation of cytoplasm and change in shape of the nucleus from spherical to spindly are seen (24).

Force of the movement.—The motor zone in the trap of *Aldrovanda* consists of three cell layers: both inner and outer epidermis and the middle layer. Ashida (3) proposed the following mechanism of rapid shutting movement and inward bending of the lobes in *Aldrovanda,* based on his own and other workers' results. Upon stimulus, an increase in the permeability of the inner epidermal cells occurs as the response, and then sap from these cells is pressed out by their own wall pressure and by the water deficit of the outer two layers, the latter not being irritable and remaining quite turgid. In other words, the motive force of this movement originates from inherent tissue water tension in the outer layers of the trap when the turgor (or volume) of the irritable cells in the inner epidermis suddenly decreases upon receiving a stimulus. The same mechanism of movement in *Dionaea* was suggested by him. Stuhlman (80) demonstrated the shutting process of the trap in *Dionaea* with a movie camera. The results reveal that the shutting is a typical dynamical action exhibiting a decrease in angular displacement proportional to the square of the time, namely $t^2 = a - b\theta$, where θ is angular separation of the lobes at $t,$ and a and b are constant.

From this fact, it follows that the increase in angular speed is proportional to the time elapsed since the start of the movement and that the angular acceleration is constant during the movement. This acceleration is attributed to the restoring forces such as tissue tension of the outer layer of the lobes, which comes into action when a pressure maintaining the lobes in open state is abruptly removed, causing a loss of turgor of the inner layer. Shutting forces of the traps in these plants are measured with a small silica dynamometer in *Aldrovanda* (3) and with a strain gauge transducer in *Dionaea* (27): the forces are 22 to 55 mg, depending on the leaf age, and about 7 dyn, respectively.

As shown in well-known classical experiments, fall of the petiole in *Mimosa* occurs weakly but otherwise normally when the upper half of the main pulvinus is surgically removed, while no movement occurs if the lower half is removed. Accordingly, it is widely accepted that the loss of turgor is caused only in the cells of the lower half, which are sensitive to stimulus, and the movement itself is caused by an extension of the opposite half (107). In the pulvinule (the pulvinus of leaflet), in fact, significant differences in shape, content, activity, and especially in nature of the cell walls are seen between upper and lower halves (108), and only the cells in the upper half seem to be irritable in this organ. In the main pulvinus, however, this simple explanation for the rapid movement seems to be somewhat questionable on the basis of the following results: (*a*) no differences in the affinity change for dyes and the change in size of the tannin vacuole during response are found in the cells of the two halves (83); (*b*) there is no difference in the threshold values of electrical stimulus for the contraction of the vacuole in both halves (2). By an improved recording apparatus, Aimi (1) proved that sensitive motor cells exist even in the upper half as well as the lower half of the main pulvinus. When the lower half is removed and the plant is inverted, the petiole bends downwardly (i.e., upwardly in normal position) on stimulus: the magnitude of bending in this case is almost the same as when the upper half is removed. Aimi (2) concluded that magnitude and direction of the petiolar movement in *Mimosa* is expressed by two forces antagonizing each other, each of which consists of bending force due to the contraction of one half and the tissue tension in the other half; normally, the force in a downward direction would be much greater than that the upward force. Some differences between the halves can be actually observed in the morphology and activity of the cells. The wall of cells in the upper half is thicker than that in the lower (83). The magnitude of the extracellular action potential in the main pulvinus, which occurs prior to the movement and the size of which may depend on the number of cells excited, is about fivefold greater in the lower half than that in the upper half (65).

Role of ATP and ATPase.—Recent results suggest that the rapid movement in *Mimosa* is caused by a reaction of the ATP-ATPase system. Poglazov (59) found first that ATPase activity in the fresh leaf of *Mimosa* is markedly stronger than that in the senile insensitive leaf as in the leaves of other plants which do not exhibit the rapid movement. No activation with addition of Mg^{++} and Ca^{++} but an inhibition with ethylenediaminetetraacetic acid (EDTA) are observed. The maximum activity is shown at pH 5 to 6. However, Lyubimova et al. (57) also found an ATPase in homogenates of the various tissues in *Mimosa* which is activated by Mn^{++} with the optimum pH at 6.5. This is widely distributed in the insensitive parts, such as leaflet, pinna-rachis, and petiole, but scarcely in the sensitive pulvini. They pointed out, therefore, that the ATPase seems not to be related to the mechanism of rapid movement, and this may be identical with results obtained by Poglazov (59). Lyubimova and associates extracted another ATPase found largely in the puvini (56), which is activated with Mg^{++} and Ca^{++} with an optimum pH between 8 and 9. The precise chemical nature and physiological function of the ATPase found in the pulvini are still unknown.

The ATPase activity can be demonstrated histochemically in the main pulvinus and the pulvinule of *Mimosa* (88). The activity is found homogenously through the peripheral cytoplasmic layer in the motor cells when Mg^{++} is present: sodium fluoride inhibits this activity. A section of the main pulvinus which is treated with 50 per cent glycerin for 2 hr exhibits contractions of the motor cells with addition of a solution containing ATP and Mg^{++} (56). The number of yellow crystals of ammonium phosphomolybdate which occur in the motor cells of the glycerol-treated main pulvinus section treated previously with ammonium molybdate is significantly larger with addition of ATP than those without ATP or with ATP and PCMB (106). This shows a liberation of inorganic phosphate from the added ATP caused by ATP-hydrolysing activity which is present in the glycerinated pulvinus.

The ATP contents, assayed by the firefly tail system, in the motor organs such as main pulvinus, subpulvinus, and pulvinule of *Mimosa* are three to four times greater than those in the pinna-rachis and petiole (55). After receiving a stimulus, the contents decrease to less than half their original value, and increase again during recovery (55). A marked decrease in ATP content in higher plant tissues is also demonstrated in the tendril of *Pisum sativum* during its coiling movement; at the same time, a remarkable increase in the endogenous inorganic phosphate is observed (52).

No direct evidence of the existence of contractile proteins in the motor cells of *Mimosa* and other plants exhibiting the rapid movements has yet been obtained. However, extracts with the Weber-Edsall solution of the tendril of *Pisum sativum* (53), the vascular bundles of *Cucurbita moschata* and *Nicotiana tabacum,* and the leaf blade of *Hydrilla* sp. (109) exhibit a transient reduction in their viscosity when ATP is added to them. The same extracts also show a liberation of inorganic phosphate from added ATP (53, 109). Driessche (29) showed an implication of contractile proteins in the movement of *Mimosa,* based on the following results. When the basal cut end of the petiole is immersed in the solutions of mersalyl and protamine sulfate (with a wetting agent), the pinnulae do not maintain the open position. Treatments with EDTA by the same method show no effect on maintaining the open position of the pinnulae, but the pulvinules of the treated leaf lose their motor response to shock stimulus. Driessche concluded from these results that maintenance of the open position in the pulvinar cells is dependent on the energy set free by ATP-hydrolysis in the pulvinule, which is blocked with mersalyl; this position corresponds to the elongated state of the contractile proteins, a state no longer possible in the presence of protamine sulfate, and divalent cations such as Ca^{++} and Mg^{++} play a role in the mechanical response in the pulvinule.

Concluding remarks.—The central problem concerning the mechanism of the rapid movements, that is, what does occur as the first mechanical change in the motor cells, is still far from a solution. From the preceding discussion, the liquid extrusion from the motor cell which has just received the stimulus seems to occur due to the activity of the contractile vacuoles, but not due to increase in permeability in the plasma membrane. It appears that the activity of the contractile vacuoles depends on a mechano-chemical reaction caused with an ATP-ATPase system.

It is well known that secondary response in the protoplasm, such as muscle contraction, is triggered by the electrical potential change (action potential) of the membrane. The same correlations are also seen in bioluminescent flash and tentacle movement in the dinoflagellate *Noctiluca miliaris* (33, 34), and in the shock stoppage of protoplasmic streaming in characeous internodal cells (73), etc. All of the motor organs which have been studied elecrophysiologically and discussed in this review exhibit the generation of an action potential prior to the rapid movement. It is therefore to be expected that an action potential elicited in the motor cell triggers mechanical or chemical changes or both in its protoplasm as a secondary response: the triggering seems to occur through ionic changes about the membrane. A direct effect of stimulus on the motor cells, or an effect of the propagated action potential which reaches them from the stimulated site, should cause the motor cell to generate a depolarization of the membrane and then an action potential. This may be the first response in the motor cells to stimulus.

How the liquid, which has been expelled into intercellular spaces during response, re-enters the cell interior is still unknown. Potassium and other salts are found in the intercellular liquid of *Mimosa* (84). Recovery of contracted central vacuole in the motor cell of the main pulvinus of *Mimosa* is promoted with addition of the pressed sap from cells to the external medium (25). Recently, it was found that the stomatal opening, involving an increase in volume of the guard cells, depends on an effect of active accumulation of potassium (35, 40), and ATP in the guard cells is involved in the uptake of potassium (40). An active accumulation of the salts or ions may take part in the recovery process of the motor cells.

RAPID MOVEMENTS IN HIGHER PLANTS 183

LITERATURE CITED

1. Aimi, R., *Botan. Mag. (Tokyo)*, **73**, 412–16 (1960)
2. Aimi, R., *ibid.*, **76**, 374–80 (1963)
3. Ashida, J., *Mem. Coll. Sci. Univ. Kyoto, Ser. B*, **9**, 141–244 (1934)
4. Ashida, J., *ibid.*, **11**, 55–113 (1935)
5. Ashida, J., *ibid.*, **14**, 353–86 (1939)
6. Auger, D., *Compt. Rend. Soc. Biol.*, **99**, 1822–24 (1928)
7. Ball, N. G., *New Phytologist*, **26**, 148–70 (1927)
8. Balotin, N. M., DiPalma, J. R., *Science*, **138**, 1338–39 (1962)
9. Banerji, B., Bhattacharya, G., Bose, D. M., *Trans. Bose Res. Inst. (Calcutta)*, **16**, 155–76 (1946)
10. Blackman, V. H., Paine, S. G., *Ann. Botany (London)*, **32**, 69–85 (1918)
11. Bose, D. M., *Proc. Natl. Inst. Sci. India, Pt. B*, **26** (Suppl.), 281–304 (1960)
12. Bose, J. C., *The Nervous Mechanism of Plants* (Longmans, London, 224 pp., 1926)
13. Brown, W. H., *Am. J. Botany*, **3**, 68–90 (1916)
14. Brown, W. H., Sharp, L. M., *Botan. Gaz.*, **49**, 290–302 (1910)
15. Bünning, E., *Z. Botan.*, **21**, 465–536 (1929)
16. Bünning, E., *Protoplasma*, **11**, 49–84 (1930)
17. Bünning, E., *Planta*, **22**, 251–68 (1934)
18. Bünning, E., *Ergeb. Biol.*, **13**, 235–347 (1936)
19. Bünning, E., in *Handbuch der Pflanzenphysiologie*, **17/1**, 184–238 (Ruhland, W., Ed., Springer, Berlin, 716 pp., 1959)
20. Burdon-Sanderson, J., *Proc. Roy. Soc. (London)*, **21**, 495–96 (1873)
21. Burdon-Sanderson, J., *Phil. Trans. Roy. Soc. (London), Ser. B*, **179**, 417–49 (1888)
22. Burdon-Sanderson, J., Page, F. J. M., *Proc. Roy. Soc. (London)*, **25**, 411–34 (1877)
23. Christalle, W., *Botan. Archiv.*, **34**, 115–45 (1931)
24. Colla, S., *Die kontraktile Zelle der Pflanzen* (Borntraeger, Berlin, 168 pp., 1937)
25. Datta, M., *Nature*, **179**, 253–54 (1957)
26. Dijkman, M. J., *Proc. Koninkl. Akad. Wetenschap. (Amsterdam)*, **34**, 1051–56 (1931)
27. DiPalma, J. R., Mohl, R., Best, W., Jr., *Science*, **133**, 878–79 (1961)
28. DiPalma, J. R., McMichael, R., DiPalma, M., *Science*, **152**, 539–40 (1966)
29. Driessche, T. V., *Ann. Physiol. Vegetale Univ. Bruxelles*, **8**, 101–12 (1963)
30. Dutt, A. K., *Nature*, **179**, 254 (1957)
31. Dutt, B. K., Guha-Thakurta, A., *Trans. Bose Res. Inst. (Calcutta)*, **21**, 51–59 (1957)
32. Dutt, B. K., Guha-Thakurta, A., *ibid.*, **25**, 181–98 (1962)
33. Eckert, R., *Science*, **147**, 1140–45 (1965)
34. Eckert, R., Sibaoka, T., *J. Exptl. Biol.*, **47**, 433–46 (1967)
35. Fischer, R. A., *Science*, **160**, 784–85 (1968)
36. Fitting, H., *Jahrb. Wiss. Botan.*, **72**, 700–75 (1930)
37. Fitting, H., *ibid.*, **83**, 270–314 (1936)
38. Fondeville, J. C., *90e Congr. Soc. Savantes, Nice 1965*, **2**, 391–401 (1965)
39. Fondeville, J. C., Schneider, M. J., Borthwick, H. A., Hendricks, S. B., *Planta*, **75**, 228–38 (1967)
40. Fujino, M., *Sci. Bull. Fac. Liberal Arts Educ. Nagasaki Univ.*, **18**, 1–47 (1967)
41. Guha-Thakurta, A., Dutt, B. K., *Trans. Bose Res. Inst. (Calcutta)*, **26**, 85–96 (1963)
42. Guttenberg, H., von, in *Handbuch der Pflanzenphysiologie*, **17/1**, 168–83 (Ruhland, W., Ed., Springer, Berlin, 716 pp., 1959)
43. Hesse, G., *Biochem. Z.*, **303**, 152–63 (1939)
44. Hesse, G., Banerjee, B., Schildknecht, H., *Experientia*, **13**, 13–19 (1957)
45. Houwink, A. L., *Rec. Trav. Botan. Néerl.*, **32**, 51–91 (1935)
46. Houwink, A. L., *Ann. Jard. Botan. Buitenz.*, **48**, 10–16 (1937)
47. Iwanami, Y., *Botan. Mag. (Tokyo)*, **75**, 133–39 (1962)
48. Iwanami, Y., *ibid.*, 289–95
49. Iwanami, Y., *ibid.*, 331–35
50. Iwanami, Y., *ibid.*, 371–76
51. Jacobson, S. L., *J. Gen. Physiol.*, **49**, 117–29 (1965)
52. Jaffee, M. J., Galston, A. W., *Plant Physiol.*, **41**, 1152–58 (1966)
53. Jaffee, M. J., Galston, A. W., *ibid.*, **42**, 845–47 (1967)

54. Kundu, B. C., Saha, B., *Experientia*, **24,** 287–88 (1968)
55. Lyubimova, M. N., Demyanovskaya, N. S., Fedorovich, I. B., Itomlenskite, I. V., *Dokl. Akad. Nauk SSSR*, **161,** 964–67 (1965)
56. Lyubimova, M. N., Demyanovskaya, N. S., Fain, F. S., Chumakova, L. P., *Zh. Evolyutsionnoi Biokhim. Fiziol.*, **2,** 139–44 (1966)
57. Lyubimova, M. N., Fain, F. S., Demyanovskaya, N. S., *Biokhimiya*, **31,** 805–14 (1966)
58. Lloyd, F. E., *The Carnivorous Plants* (Ronald, New York, 352 pp., 1942)
59. Poglazov, B. F., *Dokl. Akad. Nauk SSSR*, **109,** 597–99 (1956)
60. Ricca, U., *Nuova Giorn Botan. Ital.*, **23,** 51–170 (1916)
61. Sen, B., *Proc. Roy Soc. (London)*, *Ser. B*, **94,** 216–31 (1922)
62. Sibaoka, T., *Sci. Rept. Tohoku Univ.*, *Ser. IV*, **18,** 362–69 (1950)
63. Sibaoka, T., *ibid.*, 370–76
64. Sibaoka, T., *ibid.*, 521–26
65. Sibaoka, T., *ibid.*, **19,** 133–39 (1951)
66. Sibaoka, T., *ibid.*, **20,** 72–88 (1953)
67. Sibaoka, T., *ibid.*, 139–57 (1954)
68. Sibaoka, T., *ibid.*, **26,** 199–204 (1960)
69. Sibaoka, T., *Science*, **137,** 226 (1962)
70. Sibaoka, T., *Proc. Ann. Meeting Botan. Soc. Japan, 29th, Kanazawa, 1964*, p. 111
71. Sibaoka, T., *Symp. Soc. Exptl. Biol.*, **20,** 49–74 (1966)
72. Sibaoka, T., *Botan. Mag. (Tokyo)* (In press)
73. Sibaoka, T., Oda, K., *Sci. Rept. Tohoku Univ., Ser. IV*, **22,** 157–66 (1956)
74. Sinyukhin, A. M., *Izv. Timiryazev. Sel'skokhoz. Akad.*, **3,** 59–70 (1964)
75. Sinyukhin, A. M., Britikov, E. A., *Nature*, **215,** 1278–80 (1967)
76. Snow, R., *Proc. Roy. Soc. (London)*, *Ser. B*, **96,** 349–74 (1924)
77. Snow, R., *ibid.*, **98,** 188–201 (1925)
78. Soltys, A., Umrath, K., *Biochem. Z.*, **284,** 247–55 (1936)
79. Soltys, A., Umrath, K., Umrath, C., *Protoplasma*, **31,** 454–80 (1938)
80. Stuhlman, O., Jr., *Bull. Torrey Botan. Club*, **75,** 22–44 (1948)
81. Stuhlman, O., Jr., Darden, E. B., *Science*, **111,** 491–92 (1950)
82. Toriyama, H., *Cytologia (Tokyo)*, **18,** 283–92 (1953)
83. Toriyama, H., *ibid.*, **19,** 29–40 (1954)
84. Toriyama, H., *Botan. Mag. (Tokyo)*, **67,** 104 (1954)
85. Toriyama, H., *ibid.*, **68,** 203–8 (1955)
86. Toriyama, H., *Cytologia (Tokyo)*, **20,** 367–77 (1955)
87. Toriyama, H., *ibid.*, **22,** 184–92 (1957)
88. Toriyama, H., *Botan. Mag. (Tokyo)*, **76,** 79–80 (1963)
89. Toriyama, H., *Proc. Japan Acad.*, **43,** 541–46 (1967)
90. Toriyama, H., *ibid.*, 777–82
91. Toriyama, H., Sato, S., *Proc. Japan Acad.*, **44,** 528–32 (1968)
92. Umrath, K., *Sitz. Akad. Wiss. Wien, Math.-Naturw. Kl., Abt. I*, **134,** 21–44 (1925)
93. Umrath, K., *ibid.*, 189–208
94. Umrath, K., *Planta*, **5,** 274–324 (1928)
95. Umrath, K., *Z. Biol.*, **87,** 85–96 (1928)
96. Umrath, K., *Planta*, **7,** 174–207 (1929)
97. Umrath, K., *ibid.*, **13,** 169–92 (1931)
98. Umrath, K., *ibid.*, **23,** 47–50 (1934)
99. Umrath, K., *Jahrb. Wiss. Botan.*, **81,** 448–63 (1935)
100. Umrath, K., *ibid.*, 573–78
101. Umrath, K., *Ergeb. Biol.*, **14,** 1–142 (1937)
102. Umrath, K., *Protoplasma*, **37,** 346–49 (1943)
103. Umrath, K., in *Handbuch der Pflanzenphysiologie*, **17/1,** 24–110 (Ruhland, W., Ed., Springer, Berlin, 716 pp., 1959)
104. Umrath, K., *Z. Pflanzenphysiol.*, **55,** 445–48 (1966)
105. Umrath, K., Umrath, C., *Jahrb. Wiss. Botan.*, **85,** 698–705 (1937)
106. Watanabe, S., Sibaoka, T., *Proc. Ann. Meeting Japan Soc. Plant Physiol., 6th, Tokyo, 1965*, p. 122
107. Weidlich, H., *Botan. Arch.*, **28,** 219–54 (1930)
108. Weintraub, M., *New Phytologist*, **50,** 357–82 (1952)
109. Yen, L. F., Shih, T. C., *Acta Biochim. Biophys. Sinica*, **3,** 490–96 (1963)

THE ROLE OF PLANTS IN THE BIOREGENERATIVE SYSTEMS

By A. A. Nichiporovich

Laboratory of Photosynthesis, Institute of Plant Physiology of USSR Academy of Sciences, Moscow

Man requires vital resources, with food being primary, for normal activity and the maintenance of metabolism. The population of the world consumes about 600 million tons of organic matter as food every year, with about 2.5×10^{15} k/cal of energy stored in it. The biosphere and biological turnover are the source of food for man. The motive power of this cycle is sunlight and its initial stage is photosynthesis. The life of man is one of the routes of this cycle. Its overall scope and the portion man can divert from it for his vital needs determine the possible density of the population on earth and the well-being of the people.

Thus the biosphere, with the activity of living beings in it, constitutes a bioregenerative system; i.e., life in it is maintained by the constant renewal of vital resources (organic matter and oxygen) within the biological turnover. The capacity for enduring and continuing to function, based on the cycle and use of incident outer energy, is one of the most essential properties of bioregenerative systems, whether the system is the biosphere of the earth or a closed system to support man in space.

THE EARTH'S BIOSPHERE AS A BIOREGENERATIVE SYSTEM

Although the earth's biosphere took billions of years to develop and its "life" includes highly organized beings with many-sided, fine specialization and adaptability to various conditions, the relative effectiveness of the biosphere as a dynamic system has been low. Thus, the yearly influx of the energy of photosynthetically active radiation (PAR with λ from 380 to 720 nm) to the surface of the earth is $\sim 250 \times 10^{18}$ kcal (27). The quantity of the biomass produced yearly by autotrophic plants approximates 100×10^9 t (tons) (1–4) and the energy stored equals 400 to 450×10^{15} kcal. Thus, the mean quotient of utilization of the incident PAR energy in photosynthesis and for its accumulation in organic matter (E) is not great and amounts to only about 0.15 and 0.20 per cent. At the same time, crops with good structure that are well supplied with water and nutrients utilize and store in the continuously formed organic matter of the biomass 4 to 5 per cent, and in periods of highest activity 10 to 12 per cent, of PAR energy incident on the plants (5–7).

Measured in terms of human needs, again the effectiveness of the biosphere as a dynamic bioregenerative system is rather small; mankind consumes as nutrient only about 0.6 per cent of organic matter primarily formed by chlorophyllous plants. By contrast, on well-organized farms with a suitable combination of plant culture and cattle breeding, the quotient of utilization of initial photosynthetic production for food may reach 6 to 7 per cent.

Nor are there any good reasons for assuming that the artificial synthesis of organic substances may essentially compensate the natural photosynthesis as the source of food for man (4). Hence, man's future will to a great extent depend on his progress in solving the following problems: (*a*) an increase in the rate and the amount of photosynthetic production on earth; and (*b*) improvement of techniques and coefficient of utilization of this production in the food industry, including additional chemical treatment of the as yet not usable organic biomass of both plant and animal origin.

All other means will remain only as certain auxiliaries to the main function—present and future—of the photoautotrophic plants in bioregenerative systems.

FACTORS DETERMINING THE PRODUCTIVITY OF BIOREGENERATIVE PROCESSES
IN THE BIOSPHERE

The present scale of biological cycling on earth has been shaped over the course of billions of years and is attributed to many important causes which operated in its history.

Carbon dioxide and oxygen.—The early geologic epochs (Archean and early Proterozoic) were characterized by a relatively high content of CO_2 and low content of O_2 in the atmosphere. From the beginning of late Proterozoic and early Paleozoic epochs—with a warm, moist climate during the interglacial periods—there was luxurious development of autotrophic green plants with a great excess of new production of organic substances over their loss by oxidation processes.

During these geologic epochs, tremendous amounts of carbon from the CO_2 of the atmosphere and hydrosphere entered into the composition of organic substances which formed the deposits of combustible fossils.[1] The activity of some photosynthetic organisms resulted in the formation of great quantities of sedimentary carbonates which played an important role in the composition of the upper part of the earth's crust. Gradually the atmosphere became poor in CO_2 (on the average up to 0.03 per cent) and enriched with oxygen (on the average up to 21 per cent). All this stimulated the development of the world of heterotrophic organisms and, consequently, intensified the processes of oxidation and mineralization of organic substances. Fi-

---

[1] Organic debris of biological origin such as bitumen, combustible gases, combustible schists, petroleums, or coals.

nally, the present dynamic balance between the processes of new formation (P) and mineralization (Ox) became established on Earth.

Actually, the biosphere developed such conditions as are usual in a closed chamber with photosynthetic plants having a high initial content of CO_2 (C_{co_2}). As photosynthesis proceeds, the content of CO_2 (C_{co_2}) in the air of the chamber decreases and the concentrations of O_2 (C_{o_2}) increases. Both factors stimulate the respiration rate (Ox) and decrease the intensity of photosynthesis (P). Finally P and Ox become equal. This is a dynamic balance state between P and Ox, where P reaches a low though constant level corresponding to the CO_2 compensation point of the process (8, 9).

The present state of biological turnover on the earth exactly corresponds to this situation. We can thus infer that at present plants incompletely bring about their potential photosynthetic activity, being limited by the low content of CO_2 in the atmosphere. Proof of the latter is that the mean C_{co_2} values in the atmosphere are considerably lower than those (10) at which the P indices reach the level of saturation with CO_2 (usually at C_{co_2} of 0.1 to 0.3 per cent); and, further, that the artificial supply of plants with CO_2 improves their photosynthesis and productivity (11, 12). It is to be noted that C_{o_2} as high as 21 per cent considerably decreases the photosynthetic activity (13–15).

What are the possibilities then for increasing the rate and scale of photosynthetic production on earth? In principle, they could be increased by intensifying the processes of oxidation and the mineralization of organic substances, with free CO_2 augmenting its content in the atmosphere. However, the intensification of the cycling rate of the same amount of carbon in itself does not lead to an increase in the total life and, consequently, the amount of organic substances on earth. To increase it, additional amounts of carbon must be brought into biological cycling from tremendous sources of inorganic substances such as carbonates, crystal rocks, combustible fossils (as they are burned), and the reserves of CO_2 in the atmosphere and hydrosphere (16, 17).

In other words, to increase the total amount of life on earth it would be necessary to secure a condition where the dynamic balance of a complex system (shown in the diagram) for a certain period of time would be considerably shifted to the right. Later this balance would reach its new level at higher values of P and Ox:

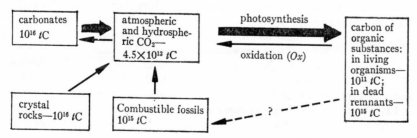

The possibility of increasing the photosynthetic productivity of plants in this way, even under the modern CO_2 and O_2 condition in the atmosphere and hydrosphere, can be illustrated by the following data: at each given moment the air within the canopy of a good crop of maize contains only 5 to 10 kg CO_2 per ha ($=$ hectar $= 10,000$ m^2). During 24 hr the soil evolves 30 to 70 kg CO_2 per ha (18).

Meanwhile, crops in the period of most intensive photosynthesis will daily accumulate 200 to 300 kg of dry matter per ha, and crops of good structure under optimal conditions will accumulate from 400 to 600 kg (5–7). To do so they must assimilate daily 500 to 750 to 1000 and even 1200 kg CO_2 per ha in the process of photosynthesis. Such a great inflow of CO_2 to the crops and biocoenosis is ensured by a turbulent exchange of air masses and turbulent diffusion of CO_2 (19).

An active role in this process belongs to the plants themselves. This role is proportionate to their photosynthetic activity. This is clearly manifested by the 24-hr changes of C_{CO_2} which considerably increases at night (up to 0.04 to 0.05 per cent) inside the crops; in the daytime this value decreases sharply (to 0.02 to 0.025 per cent) especially in the zone of photosynthetic organs (19, 20). By active photosynthesis, plants increase the vertical gradients of C_{CO_2}, thus promoting the supply of assimilating organs with the great quantities of CO_2, as mentioned above. The greater the photosynthetic activity of foliage, the wider the possibility of assimilation of great quantities of atmospheric CO_2.

The laws of turbulent exchange and diffusion are being studied intensely to clarify their mechanism and rate (19–24), as well as to develop a direct method for determining the photosynthesis of crops and biocoenoses as one integral system (19–24).

Thus, wide possibilities exist for increasing photosynthetic productivity even under the present CO_2 system on earth. Of paramount significance here is the task of activating the photosynthetic function of plants. One of the ways of coping with this task lies in the adjustment of the factors restricting photosynthesis, other than CO_2 concentrations. Modifying them can considerably increase the productivity of photosynthesis even with the present CO_2 system and the present potential activity of the plant photosynthetic apparatus.

Energy of radiation.—As was stated above, the average coefficient (E) of the incident PAR energy utilization by the entire flora of the earth is 0.2 per cent. The average E of the cultivated plants is approximately 1 per cent. Still, under identical irradiation conditions, such crops as have the optimal structure and resource provision do utilize PAR energy with an E as high as 4 to 5 per cent. The E amount can and must be the basic criterion of success of the effort to increase the productivity of plants. Thus, for instance, the utilization of PAR energy during the growing season by crops and biocoenoses with E up to 0.5 per cent indicates their low photosynthetic productivity, E of 1 to 1.5 per cent indicates medium productivity, E of 2 to

3 per cent indicates good productivity, and E of 4 to 5 per cent indicates high productivity approaching the theoretical limit (5, 6). Only in the autumn and winter months at the middle and higher latitudes, when 24-hr influx of PAR is lower than 500 kcal/m², its maximum intensity being 70×10^3 erg/cm² sec, is such a quantity of energy insufficient for normal photosynthesis and growth of plants (25). However, the quantities of such unutilized energy are insignificant as compared with the total amount of PAR flowing to the earth; but the PAR energy flowing to the earth in sufficient quantities can be well utilized by living organisms or plants for photosynthesis only when it is combined with a proper temperature regime, water supply, and good mineral nutrition.

For the assimilation by crops and biocoenoses of 1 per cent from each billion of PAR influx during the growth season, and at the same time, with the formation of 2.5 t of dry organic matter, plants and crops require for free transpiration and evaporation approximately 1.0 to 1.5×10^3 t/ha of water. In addition, 25 to 50 kg of available nitrogen and 150 to 250 kg of other mineral elements are required (5). Temperature conditions and photoperiod to suit a given plant are further essentials. However, the optimal and stable combination on earth of the above-mentioned natural factors of productivity is more of an exception than a rule.

Temperature relations.—The immense quantities of the incident PAR energy are rather nullified by the discrepancy between its influx and the temperature conditions, especially during the spring months in middle latitudes (5, 26, 28). Thus, in March, April, May, and early June the influx of sunlight energy is the optimum for very intensive photosynthesis, but because of low temperatures the land is either still empty or only sparsely covered by small plants. The incident PAR energy becomes sufficiently active as a factor in photosynthesis only when the mean daily air temperature is above +5 or +10°C.

Water.—A still greater discrepancy exists between the influxes (in time and space distribution) of sunlight energy and moisture. Vast masses of water (520×10^{12} m³) go through the turnover every year. However, 412 $\times 10^{12}$ m³ of it falls over the oceans and only 107×10^{12} m³ over the mainland (26).

A considerable portion of precipitation falls over areas unfit for plants (i.e., mountains, Antarctica, Greenland) or falls in the period unfavorable for photosynthesis and growth (winter, autumn). A great mass (36×10^{12} m³) drains into rivers, seas, and oceans, carrying away enormous quantities of substances valuable for plants. Some regions of the globe, such as deserts and semideserts, receive quite an insignificant quantity of water, and then the great influx of sunlight energy instead of being a life factor is an unfavorable or very often pernicious factor for plant life (26, 28, 29).

Only 16×10^{12} m³ of the water falling on the mainland is used up by plants for transpiration; 55×10^{12} m³ is wasted as unproductive surface evaporation from soil, inland waters, in industry and public utilities, etc.

Thus, moisture is one of the most crucial factors limiting the photosynthetic productivity of plants on earth.

Mineral nutrients.—Many types of soil have less nutrients available to plants than would be necessary for at least a 3 per cent utilization of incident PAR energy. Moreover, there is a continuous vast dissipation of nutrients because of soil erosion, many of them being carried away into seas and oceans with the run-off. The processes of denitrification are responsible for the continuous loss of the most important plant nutrient–nitrogen.

Some ecosystems (forests and grasslands) have their own particular turnover of mineral nutrients. The latter accumulate in plants, then are transferred to the litter, and by mineralization are utilized by plants anew. The photosynthetic productivity of such systems frequently depends on the nutrient quota involved in such a local cycle and on the rate of transport in it (30, 31). The situation is much more complicated where the removal of a product results in a massive dissipation of nutrients carried away with the harvest.

OCEANS

Other unfavorable combinations of factors exist in oceans. First of all, there is the extremely meager salt nutrition system. Huge quantities of nutrients brought down with run-off waters are either thinly scattered in the water mass (1.37×10^{18} m^3) or else concentrated in the mud and other sediment on the ocean bottom. Therefore, sufficiently high photosynthetic productivity is characteristic only of relatively small oceanic areas with an upward circulation of water and where the effect of chemical elements conveyed by the inflow of water from the land is still present. The major part of the oceanic area has a low photosynthetic efficiency; the total photosynthetic production of oceans nearly equals that of the land [approximately 50×10^9 t of dry biomass (32–35)], although the oceanic area is 2.5 times that of the land. Besides, the primary production of oceans, due to the most complicated trophic bonds, is a poor source of food for man (4); and, finally, the oceans offer great obstacles to any practical regulation or control on a wide scale.

POSSIBLE WAYS AND PRINCIPLES OF INCREASING PHOTOSYNTHETIC PRODUCTION ON EARTH

It is evident from the above that any uniform or overall increase of general photosynthetic production on earth as a human task is extremely difficult and, for all practical purposes, impossible. This would require radical alteration of climates and geochemical conditions of great regions of the globe. Thus, the efforts to increase photosynthetic production and improve the properties of the biosphere should be concentrated first of all on that phase of the biological cycle which is especially responsible for man's vital needs. This is the photosynthetic activity of food and fodder plants which are the primary source of not less than 70 per cent of the food consumed by man (4, 36).

PLANT AGRICULTURE AS A BIOREGENERATIVE SYSTEM

Today, cultivated crops occupy 1.5×10^9 ha. It is probably possible to increase the cultivated area by 1.5 to 2 times (36, 37). The mean influx of PAR energy onto the cultivated area during the growing season may be assumed as approximately equal to 3×10^9 kcal/ha, although in different latitudes it varies within 1.0 to 10×10^9 kcal (38, 39). The mean coefficient of incident PAR energy utilization for the future can be considered (5) as equal to 2 per cent (theoretically possible, $E = 5$ to 6 per cent). Assuming that the heat of the burned plant biomass averages 4×10^6 kcal/t a yearly future harvest of 45×10^9 t of total plant biomass on a cultivated area of 3×10^9 ha is to be expected.

Present total annual production of agricultural plants on an area of 1.5×10^9 ha amounts today to 6×10^9 t. (That means a possible sevenfold increase.) Along with this, the overall primary photosynthetic production on earth would increase by 35×10^9 t, or 35 per cent as against the present total for the biosphere. This will require an additional 15×10^9 t of carbon, 0.5×10^9 t of nitrogen, and 2 to 3×10^9 t of mineral nutrients to be involved into the biological cycling.

It should be recalled that the present yearly production of nitrogen fertilizers amounts only to about 20×10^6 t with a 20 per cent content of nitrogen. Production of other mineral fertilizers amounts to about 30×10^6 t (36, 37). Increasing the crop yield on an area of 3×10^6 ha apparently will require an additional 2 to 3×10^{12} m^3 of water (1000 m^3/ha as the mean). For comparison, today the cultivated areas are given through irrigation 0.5×10^{12} m^3 of water. Consequently, even such a "partial" increase of photosynthetic productivity, i.e., of cultivated plants alone, will require great effort. To this end, the essential procedure, at least on cultivated areas, should be the maximum synchronization and quantitative coordination of photosynthetic productivity factors, and these should be so regulated that the plants utilize the incident PAR energy for photosynthesis and store it in yields to a definite assumed coefficient: initially about 1 to 2, then 3, and in the future as an optimum, 4 and 5 per cent (5).

Accordingly, it will be necessary to include the preceding increased quantities of chemical elements within the life cycle of cultivated plants and to a maximum extent prevent their dissipation in the atmosphere and hydrosphere.

One way to do this is to concentrate, as much as possible, all nutrients in organic substance and to enrich soils with humus. In this state, nutrient elements are, as a rule, in optimal proportions. They are best protected from washing out, erosion, and other forms of dissipation. And, given optimal microbiological processes, they may be made available to plants at the rate optimal for their growth and development. The enrichment of soils with humus on the area of 3×10^9 ha of future crops will evidently call for an additional supply of at least 100 to 150×10^9 t of organic biomass. The greater portion of this must be produced by the cultivated plants themselves. At present they produce about 6×10^9 t of the total biomass per year, but the latter is only partially retained in the soil or returned to it after the utilization of yield.

Thus, creating such a fertility fund for cultivated plants on an area of 3.10^9 ha calls for extensive time limits. Still, these time limits will depend on the rate and scale of supplying the cultivated plants with nitrogen, mineral nutrients, and water. Thus, obtaining increased harvests and returning the residual organics to a maximum extent on the fields will considerably accelerate the humus accumulation of soils and augment the agricultural way of cycling while lessening its dependence on the disadvantages of the overall biological turnover in the biosphere. As was said earlier, the source of increasing the carbon supply for the biological turnover can be the extensive reserves of carbonates, crystal rocks, and combustible fossils (16, 17).

Increasing the amounts of nitrogen in turnover is possible at the expense of its great abundance in the atmosphere (4.10^{15} t), but it will be necessary to set up a large-scale industry of nitrogen fertilizers on the basis of atmospheric nitrogen, or to drastically increase the biological fixation of this element.

The other mineral nutrients—P,K,S . . . and trace elements—in contrast to carbon and nitrogen, are found on earth almost entirely in the solid state or in solutions. Their movement via the general biological turnover is mostly a one-way process. They are extracted from deposits or utilized by plants from soil or bedrock, go through a small number of local cycles, and they are mainly washed out and finally transported to the ocean where their efficiency in the increase of photosynthetic productivity is quite low. Moreover, the natural sources of P,K,S . . . for production of mineral fertilizers are not unlimited. It is this that gives special importance to the maximum possible accumulation of mineral nutrients (including nitrogen) in the soil humus and maximum syncronization of decomposition of soil organics with the processes of plant growth and nutrition.

THE PROPERTIES OF PLANT COMMUNITIES AS INTEGRAL PHOTOSYNTHETIC SYSTEMS

The level of efficiency of PAR energy utilization depends on a number of intrinsic properties of the functioning photosynthetic systems (biocoenosis, crops). They include characteristics[2] of the rate of growth of the photosynthetic apparatus (leaf area) and its optimal maximum possible size; the functioning period of this apparatus (5, 6, 23, 40–44); and the

---

[2] The terms characteristics and indices are used interchangeably.

losses of organic matter by respiration (45–49). In some cases we have to consider not only the photosynthesis of leaves but that of other green organs—stalks and stems, sheaths and ears (50).

Also important are characteristics of the geometric structure of biocoenoses and crops, leaf area spatial distribution, and orientation of leaf blades (51–59). These constitute the general optical properties of biocoenoses and crops, and determine their capacity to absorb greater or smaller quantities of incident PAR energy, and better or worse distribution of it in the foliage of different layers of the canopy. The latter property determines not only the degree of incident PAR energy absorption, but also the most effective utilization of the absorbed energy for photosynthesis (60–63).

Activity of Photosynthetic Apparatus Proper

A very important factor in productivity is the activity of the photosynthetic apparatus (leaves) proper. This is reflected in the differences between the slopes and saturation levels of light intensity—photosynthesis graphs.

These vary in plants of different systematic position and different ecological groups (64–69). They also vary depending on the leaf anatomy and CO_2 diffusion resistance (70), age of the plant and leaves (71), their nutritional status (72), water conditions (72) and salinity (74), temperature conditions (73), etc. The dark and light respiration systems are also very important to photosynthetic activity of leaves (75–78), as well as the presence and activity of specific enzymes of the photosynthetic apparatus (67–69, 79, 80) and of some cofactors. Finally, the state and properties of pigment systems are important factors in photosynthetic activity (81).

Also very important (though complicated) in the activity of the photosynthetic apparatus are the structural, molecular, and biochemical organization and properties of chloroplasts. Regular membranes are the basis of the structural organization of chloroplasts (82–87). Stroma and the heterogeneous structure of membranes, including thylakoids and lamella, grana, and quantasomes, create the spatial delimitation of light and dark reactions of photosynthesis and permit the complicated process of photosynthesis as a whole to occur (88, 89). The chemical components of the chloroplast structure are: the pigments, specific proteins and lipoproteins, lipids, enzymes, specific nucleic acids, and other active substances (90–92). These components form structures of different complexity and exist in the structures in different states and in various quantitative relations, determining the differential activity of chloroplasts. They vary in plants of different types (67, 85) during formation of the photosynthetic apparatus and depend on the plant age (85, 93, 94) and environmental and internal conditions (93–100). A role of no less importance in this phenomenon, however, is played by the interaction of the choroloplasts with components of the photosynthetic cell, leaf, or plant as a whole (101, 102) and by hereditary factors (67, 68, 85, 103–106).

Important factors of photosynthetic productivity are the composition and quality of products of photosynthesis and their participation in the formation of structures and constituents of the photosynthetic apparatus proper, as well as of cells, tissues, and various organs of plants. A number of important and physiologically active products are formed directly in the process of photosynthesis (107–109)—sugars, pigments, amino acids, specific nucleic acids, specific proteins, enzymes, etc. The composition and quantity of products of photosynthesis also depend on the plant species (110–112), their age, nutritional conditions (113, 114), intensity and spectral composition of light (115–118), and water conditions (119), or are induced by nonphotosynthetic or catalytic light reactions.

The rate and direction of photosynthetic product translocation (120, 121), and utilization of the photosynthates in formation of the photosynthetic apparatus proper and in processes of metabolism and growth of plant organs and the plant as a whole are also decisive processes in crop formation (122–125). Here, photosynthesis determines the process of growth and, conversely, the latter determines the state and operation of the photosynthetic apparatus itself. Such lability and easy adaptability of the photosynthetic apparatus held out great promise in working out the principles and means of rational control of the processes of photosynthesis and photosynthetic activity in crops. But the optimal responses of different physiological processes of plants to each environmental factor are not uniform; each has its own optimum. In this respect, under different conditions either one or the other of the physiological processes may be decisive in determining the crop yield, especially in plant communities.

PHOTOSYNTHETIC ACTIVITY IN PLANT COMMUNITIES

In a number of investigations, a positive correlation between the size of the photosynthetic apparatus—leaf area (L) or leaf area duration—and biological yields (Y_{biol}) (126–131) has been demonstrated. Frequently the increase of leaf area in crops via simple agronomical techniques proves to be the easiest and most effective way of raising the yields (5–7, 126–131). However, the increase of L in crops (e.g., increase of crop or plantation density) usually results in a decrease of the mean net assimilation index (NA) (132–136). The highest 24-hr amounts of total photosynthesis or accretion of dry biomass are obtained at optimal (for specific existing conditions) ratios of L and NA. In those cases, and for these conditions L is optimal (L_{opt}). But the greater the decrease of the NA index, due to the increase of L, or the lower they are in general the smaller the value of L_{opt} and, consequently, of the dry biomass (5).

The decrease of the NA index in crop canopy in proportion to the increase of L is the result of the decreased illumination of levels on the one hand and the increase of soil fertility on the other. Therefore, irrigation and fertilization often stimulate the increase of the NA value (137) and consequently result in the increase of L_{opt}, dry biomass, and gross yield.

Thus, in raising yields (while L is still less than L_{opt}) the means guaranteeing the increase of L may be highly effective. Afterwards, further progress will be possible only with the increase of photosynthetic intensity and of the NA index (5).

The possible effectiveness of increasing L in crops without simultaneous improvement of the efficiency of photosynthesis is limited also by the following: when the leaf area of crops amounts to 4 to 5 m^2/m^2, the latter absorb as much as 90 to 95 per cent (138) of PAR energy coming into the crop, and the further increase of L without activation of the photosynthetic apparatus proper is of little avail. An excessive increase of leaf area of crops is unfavorable for photosynthesis and, in addition, impairs the uptake of mineral nutrients and decreases the effectiveness of fertilization (139–141).

In crops with a high L, we frequently observe the decrease of the relative utilization of assimilates for the growth of reproductive (grain, fruits) and storage organs (tubers, root crops, etc.). This results in decreasing the economic effectiveness of the yields of plants cultivated for obtaining the above-mentioned organs (7, 142, 148). In fact, the value of L_{opt} of plants cultivated for total fodder biomass (e.g., corn) may be higher than when growing plants for grain (145). The rate and direction of utilization of photosynthates for the rational growth of different plant organs is an important factor for obtaining crop yields high in both quality and quantity (142–147).

Leaves are not only the photosynthetic organs, but the organs of transpiration as well. Consequently, the increase of leaf area in crops is not solely beneficial for photosynthetic efficiency, but also results in an increased water requirement. The water deficit plays a decisive role in determining the dynamics of leaf area (L) being secondary to L_{opt} at normal water supply (7, 155, 156).

Thus, the growth rate and size of leaf area in crops are among the most significant indices of photosynthetic activity and productivity, but the possibilities of increasing productivity on the basis of increasing these indices are limited. In this connection, theoretically and practically of great importance are the problems of increasing the activity of the photosynthetic apparatus, improving the qualitative characteristics of this activity, and establishing the conditions for the most advantageous and consistent (stable) utilization of assimilates for a rational and harmonious rate of general metabolism, growth, and organogenesis of plants.

The productivity of complex photosynthetic systems depends on multiple combinations and interactions of many processes and indices of photosynthetic activity (148–153). Therefore, to optimize their functioning it is necessary to solve problems with many factors. This calls for extensive application of new techniques.

For the quantitative relationships of factors, processes, and indices of productivity, statistical analyses are applied to mass data on photosynthetic

activity of crops in various geographical zones (154–156). The method
(though still limited) of mathematical planning of multifactor experiments
has been initiated (157–159). Mathematical models of terrestrial as well as
aquatic complex photosynthetic systems are being developed (160–167).
Such models make feasible the "weighting" of probable changes of various
indices of photosynthetic activity for total productivity. They permit a
rough calculation of possible productivity under various real sets of conditions and estimation of the most possible photosynthetic productivity under
the optimal conditions. But the principal role remains with the exact experiment. Only after wide experimental examination may a mathematical
model, within certain limits, serve as a tool for the solution of such problems which it would be more complicated and time-consuming to solve via
direct experiment. In this respect, of special significance is the development
of methods of registration and analysis of characteristics and processes of
photosynthetic activity in crops and biocoenoses, with accurate consideration of the conditions under which they proceed (168–178).

In the basic research on photosynthetic productivity, an important role
belongs to the modeling of complex photosynthetic systems in factoral and
completely controlled chambers, this allowing continuous monitoring of the
main physiological processes and control of the material and energy bal-
ances in different conditions (179, 180). A convenient, though simplified,
model for basic research on productivity of photosynthetic systems may be
found in unicellular algae suspensions in the intensive completely controlled
culture (5, 206, 207).

Theoretical elaboration of high productivity of photosynthetic systems,
primarily in cultivated crops, will acquire great significance in proportion to
the increase in the level of agriculture and plant breeding, a better supply
of crops with water and mineral nutrients, and multiplicity of cases where
the L indices approach L_{opt}. In these cases, such factors as efficiency and
qualitative patterns of the photosynthetic apparatus, activity and trend of
utilization of assimilates for metabolism and growth, and geometrical structure of crops and biocoenoses will be generally minimum factors of productivity, instead of such factors as fertility of soils and total optical density of
crops. Further efforts to increase productivity must be strictly subordinated
to the goal of optimization of these processes and characteristics.

As has been stated above, the field crops may, in highly optimal conditions, utilize the PAR flowing in during the actual growth period with the
quotient of efficiency equal to 3 to 4 and even 5 per cent. This highest quotient is determined by the fact that a good crop can absorb during the actual growth period up to 50 to 60 per cent of the incident PAR energy
(38). The energy absorbed may be utilized for photosynthesis with the quotient of efficiency of 10 to 12 per cent. About 20 to 25 per cent of the energy bound in the photosynthetic product is later wasted in respiration. It is
this that establishes the overall efficiency at 4 to 5 per cent (5, 42).

However, in a number of instances, the actual growth period of plants is much shorter than the maximum possible one characterized by adequate illumination and by a mean 24-hr temperature higher than +5 to +10°C. Plants of a short growth period even at high efficiency can utilize the PAR energy during the actual growth period with a coefficient 1.5 to 2 less than is possible. The situation may be sufficiently improved either by cultivation of plants with the longest possible growth period or by successive cultivation of winter crops, then summer or early summer crops, then after-harvest crops, etc. (129, 130).

Good results in increasing the efficiency value may be achieved by application of film cover for crops and plantations of the most valuable species in spring, when the light intensity is high but temperatures too low [April, May, and early June (5)]. Still more independent of the imperfection of biological cycling may be the crops on protected and warmed-up ground. If waste heat and purified industrial gases can be used for warming and supplying plants with additional CO_2, a plant culture will thus be enhanced. Besides, this opens the possibility of better utilization of as yet underestimated sources of possible plant productivity.

In the periods of inadequate natural illumination, the highly intensive cultivation of valuable plants may be carried out with the use of artificial light. Under normal natural conditions during the growth season, the diurnal incident PAR energy varies within 1000 to 3000 kcal/m², with the maximum intensity from 100 up to 420 erg/cm² sec. Growing plants under fluorescent tubes supplying the plants with light of 70 to 100×10^3 erg/cm² sec intensity and with a PAR dose of 1000 to 1500 kcal/m² for 16 to 18 hr, guarantees a level of plant productivity approaching that of "outdoor" culture (181, 182). However, this level does not approach the highest potential photosynthetic yield of plants. This is demonstrated by the cultivation of plants with an illumination supplying crops with 24-hr doses of PAR exceeding that found under natural conditions. For instance, using xenon tubes will supply plants with light of 150 to 200×10^3 erg/cm² sec intensity; 16 to 18-hr illumination provides daily doses of PAR energy of 2000 to 3200 kcal/m². With an energy supply that good, such plants as tomatoes, carrots, and radishes shorten their growth season to almost half with the yield twice as great in comparison with the field and garden culture: up to 20 kg/m² of tomatoes in 60 days, 15 kg of carrots in 65 days, and 8 kg of radishes in 15 days (182). In such cases, under fully favorable conditions, the quotient of utilization of PAR energy reaches 8 per cent (5).

The creation and use of photosynthetic bioregenerative systems ever more autonomous and independent of the lack of coincidence and the disadvantages of photosynthetic activity in the natural biosphere will probably play an increasingly important role in the food industry of the future.

CLOSED BIOREGENERATIVE SYSTEMS ISOLATED FROM BIOLOGICAL TURNOVER IN THE BIOSPHERE

As the ultimate case in the development of photosynthetic systems, independent of and isolated from the general turnover on earth, let us consider the systems now conceived or existing which are completely closed in mass exchange and have their own turnover, e.g., those aimed to provide for man in space (183–191).

The task here requires that the man under such conditions be guaranteed a daily ration of about 600 g of food and 3×10^3 kcal of chemically combined energy concentrated in it and biologically available, approximately 900 g of free oxygen, and 1500 g of drinking and 2000 g of sanitary water (188–191). The total weight of substances necessary for a 24-hr period for man in space amounts to about 5 kg.

Thus in case of a prolonged stay of man in isolated and closed space, the problem of supplying him with vital resources, without their regeneration and reproduction, is very complicated, or even unreal (187, 192, 193). It is still more complicated because, besides providing ample resources for man, it is necessary to eliminate the end products of his vital processes from immediate contact with him: every 24 hr about 1000 g of CO_2, 400 g of water resulting from the process of oxidation of organic substances, 2000 g of polluted sanitary water, about 1500 g of liquid and solid excretions, plus a certain quantity of volatile matter—the end products of metabolism.

A number of effective physical and chemical methods exist either for absorption of such substances (e.g., CO_2) or for purification (e.g., polluted water) or for their isolation or extraction from the system (e.g., excrements) (188–191). Also, the chemical conversion of the end products of metabolism is possible, e.g., electrolysis producing O_2 and H_2 from water. The method may be used for catalytic reduction of CO_2 by H_2, accompanied by the formation of C and H_2O as end products. H_2O can also be subjected to electrolysis to yield finally O_2 (the main aim of the reaction) and H_2, which is utilized for the reduction of new portions of CO_2. The process may be carried out either via CO formation (the Bosch reaction) or CH_4 (the Sabatier reaction) (192–197).

In this way, the H_2O and CO_2 produced from biological oxidation of organic substances can be utilized for regeneration of free oxygen in the isolated system. In addition, this largely solves the problem of eliminating surplus CO_2 and newly formed metabolic water.

Besides, the use of physicochemical systems of regeneration (purification) of drinking and sanitary water (from urine and polluted sanitary water) opens the possibility of considerable extension of the functioning period of isolated systems. It also permits the diminishing of quantities of water, oxygen, or reagents for elimination of CO_2, etc., taken from the earth (191–199). However, all this still leaves unsolved the problem of unlimited continuous functioning of these systems in that there are no chemical or physical means to regenerate standard food and the biologically active energy it contains out of the final metabolic products. The final criterion for the duration of functioning of the supply systems using the above means of H_2O and O_2 regeneration will be the length of time during which all carbon of the food reserves will shift to such "dead ends" of substance migration as solid and liquid human wastes, free carbon, or methane emerging in the Bosch and Sabatier reactions.

Nowadays, full-value food regeneration is possible only by means of autotrophic organisms, which, however, require as outer energy either light or chemical energy. The primary source for this may be either sunlight radiation or the energy produced by an atomic reactor within the system and transformed either into light or into chemical energy. Light energy may be directly utilized by photoautotrophs. Chemical energy may be readily produced via electrolysis of metabolic water. The emergent hydrogen can be used as a source of energy and agent of CO_2 reduction in chemosynthesis, e.g., *Hydrogenomonas* (200, 201).

The use of photoautotrophic organisms in the systems providing for man in closed space is advantageous because their action is polyfunctional: (*a*) absorbing CO_2, decomposing water, and excreting oxygen, the photosynthetic organisms in a single process of photosynthesis can regenerate air and eliminate surplus water from the system; (*b*) through immediate utilization or after preliminary treatment of waste water and liquid wastes of human vital processes, and by evaporating water via transpiration or from reactors with algae in the course of bubbling, the above organisms take part in distillation and, consequently, regeneration of drinking and pure sanitary water; (*c*) absorbing light energy (e.g., sunlight) the photoautotrophic plants convert it by photosynthesis into chemical energy and thus directly introduce biochemically active energy into the closed system; (*d*) utilizing immediately or after certain additional treatment the end products of human vital processes, the photoautotrophic plants are able to regenerate organic substances and consequently food.

This is sufficient ground for the utilization of photosynthetic organisms in the development of highly closed systems fit for unlimited prolonged functioning (183–187, 190, 191, 194, 202–207). However, this is only a concept, and its practical realization requires still greater effort. Primarily, we must overcome the following obstacles. The assimilation quotient of plant photosynthesis (CO_2/O_2) approaches 1.0, while the respiration quotient of man (CO_2/O_2) approaches 0.85. Nevertheless, this incongruity can be easily eliminated by means of appropriate nutrition of plants and man, and by other techniques (202). The requirements of man and plants for NaCl are also different. The way out may be found in the extracting of NaCl from the liquid excretions of man and returning it into his food cycle.

A number of obstacles related to an element such as nitrogen are also to be overcome in the system. Nitrogen can be transformed into the molecular state by the processes of biological denitrification or burning and mineralization of organic human wastes. The means are known (chemical and biological) for returning it to the forms of NH^3, NH^+_4, NO^-_3, or urea and its inclusion into plant nutrient media.

In designing artificial closed bioregenerative systems to supply humans, one has to consider the different requirements of plants and man for atmospheric concentrations of CO_2 and O_2. Apparently, this fact will necessitate the construction of separate isolated chambers for plants and man in a space vehicle (180).

Far from being simple is the problem of utilization of end products and wastes of human vital processes as the substrates for plant mineral nutrition. At any rate, these products are not utilizable in unchanged form, and their preliminary chemical, physical, or biological treatment and processing are inevitable (191, 207).

When unicellular algae are used as photosynthetic organisms, their combination in cultures with bacterial organisms may be more effective (207, 211). Here, in a set of reactors, processes may be effected in which the early steps, stimulated by algal photosynthesis, will be the intensive oxidation of organic wastes by bacteria, similar to the process of biological purification of sewage (208, 209). In the subsequent reactors with a complete prevalence of algae, the processes of CO_2 assimilation, evolving of O_2, and formation of algal biomass proper must occur.

The preparation of human waste for nutrition of higher plants requires different techniques (191, 211). After all, as far as the regeneration of the air and decomposition of human metabolic water is concerned, we can assume that the solution of this problem by means of photoautotrophic plants is quite feasible. However, this will require great effort, first of all in finding out rational ways and means for transferring the vital products from man to autotrophic plants.

Much more complicated is that phase of the hypothetical turnover in which the moving of substances from autotrophs to man should be realized. The ideal system might have been one in which autotrophic plants (e.g., algae) would yield full-value food for man. In this case, a simple two-or-three-stage closed system might be operated.

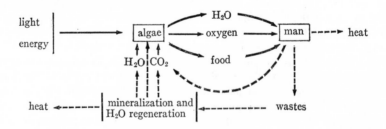

The total energetic efficiency of PAR in such a system with respect to the energy utilized by algae might be thus: 8 to 12 per cent of it might be utilized for photosynthesis (207, 210–212) and 80 per cent by man from alimentary algal biomass. In this case, the surface of the algal reactor moving in space, continuously illuminated by direct sunlight at a distance of 125 to 175 × 10⁶ km from the sun, might amount only to 5 to 6 m². However, the biomass of the present-day forms of unicellular green algae cannot furnish sufficient nutriment for man (213, 214); to reverse the situation, much work should be done in selection of algal forms yielding biomass with better alimentary qualities than those we know today.

Probably in this work the possibility of varying the biochemical composition of algae by changing the mineral content of the medium (207, 215–219, 222) or the temperature of the system will be important. This modifies the correlation between photosynthesis and growth and reproduction processes and, accordingly, the biochemical composition of the harvested biomass (215–219).

Another technique for utilizing algae as a component of life-sustaining systems is the introduction of an additional link between algae and man, these being heterotrophic organisms, e.g., yeast cultivated on hydrolytic products of the algal biomass. It is also possible to consider animals as an intermediate link. These could include herbivorous fishes, some invertebrates, or even vertebrates which, feeding on the algal biomass, would produce a complete food for man. However, the introduction of such linking intermediaries between algae and man apparently would strongly decrease the energetic efficiency of the system. It is too early to say which will be the optimum solution of the problem, particularly because in its modern form the algal or yeast biomass cannot be the only full-value food for animals, especially under the extreme conditions of cosmic flight.

The third possible way of solving the problem of food regeneration lies in the utilization in the isolated systems of higher plants which from ancient times have served as sources of food for man (203). However, their cultivation under the conditions of cosmic flight, in the absence of gravity, is rather complicated. The absence of gravitation might, in principle, be compensated by means of phototropism, by chemotropisms, or even by creation of artificial gravitation.

Certainly not all plants are utilizable for this purpose. Cereals and fruits yielding the most valuable food have the unfavorable peculiarity that in the period of formation and maturation of reproductive organs their photosynthetic activity decreases or even stops altogether. Yet at the same time, the processes of translocation and secondary conversion of substances continue. At this period, respiration considerably exceeds photosynthesis, which may result in considerable loss of formerly accumulated organic matter.

In addition, during yield formation such plants produce a sizable portion of woody biomass unfit for further use either as fodder or food. In this respect, more profitable are the plants with such valuable (in the alimentary sense) vegetative organs as tubers, roots, and especially leaves. The yields of such plants may be harvested in the period of still intensive growth without incurring relatively serious losses by respiration (180).

Thus, much work should be done in selection of the most appropriate forms and cultures of plants fit for supplying man with valuable food mainly with their vegetative organs, e.g., leaves. Besides, such forms must have the most advantageous morphology and physiology, possess a highly efficient photosynthetic apparatus, have the highest rate of growth and development, and be able to form biocoenoses with perfect structure (referring to photosynthesis and light energy utilization).

An advantage of algal utilization in closed systems is that algal suspensions are easily put through the necessary working cycle; for example, the optimum operation density of the suspension can be established and is then automatically kept at a constant level by extraction of biomass increment. The intensity of photosynthesis is automatically regulated by the intensity of the metabolism of man and, in particular, by the rate of CO_2 excretion (with the reactor having excessive power).

As to the higher plants, the state of their crops changes with time in the course of growth. The quantity of their product and the CO_2 absorption rate also vary. Thus it is impossible to introduce higher plant cultures into a closed system with each sowing having to be made anew after harvesting the previous yield.

Here is probably where the so-called "green conveyor" will come in. Then sowing can be done in small portions with short intervals. With the same rate, the ripening yield must be harvested. In such a case it is possible to continuously maintain this "green conveyor" as a whole in the mean unchanged and optimal state. The plants in a "conveyor" system can utilize PAR energy absorbed for photosynthesis, with a mean efficiency of about 10 per cent (221). However, the application and distribution of light energy in higher plant systems will be technically difficult, which is true for algal culture as well (223).

The problem of utilizing the "conveyor" plant products in food rations requires further investigation. These will determine the degree of completion of turnover in the provision system and, consequently, the possible duration of its functioning. Where a space vehicle or station has its own source of energy (which, e.g., is inevitable on the moon with a 28-day diurnal cycle, or in a flight away from the sun), then food regeneration by way of activity of hydrogen bacteria might be more profitable (200, 201). Hydrogen (H_2) produced by the electrolysis of water could provide nutriment with a good general biochemical composition. However, the extent to which this biomass may replace standard food for man is still questionable and requires experimental evidence (220).

In the experiments performed in the USSR at present, air and water were regenerated in the closed system with man by the combined activities of algae and bacteria (algo-bacterial complex). The experiment lasted for several months. Thus, the compatibility of life activities of man, of algae, and of bacteria in their gas and water exchange inside the closed system was demonstrated (191). Only food for man was given from the outside during the experiment.

We have touched on only a few of the specific important areas bearing on the potential utilization of autotrophic plants in creating life-supporting systems for man in space. The solution of all of them is equally determined by biological and technical problems. The life patterns of biological subjects, and first of all man, must be so suited to the technical possibilities and means of the flight that they form an integrated, self-regulating and self-operating, fully reliable system, automatically and cleverly reacting upon all the particulars and variables in the physiological activity of man. The life-provisioning systems in closed space cannot be a mere imitation of biological cycling in the biosphere. For this reason we must create far more effective, self-regulated systems utilizing few but very effective organisms thoroughly improved by special selective genetic means.

The creation of such systems must be based on many new principles which are missing in the natural biological cycling in the biosphere, but which, after testing and realization in artificially closed systems, may probably be used in the solution of food problems on earth.

For both of these goals we have to proceed from the assumption that neither today nor in the foreseeable future can complete food production and food resource problems be solved without autotrophic organisms and their photosynthetic activity as the primary source of the mass production of organic matter.

LITERATURE CITED

1. Rabinowitch, E., *Photosynthesis and Related Processes,* 1 (Interscience, New York, 1945)
2. Vallentyne, J. R., *Mem. Inst. Ital. Idrobiol.,* Suppl. 18, 309–11 (1965)
3. Duvigneaud, P., Ed., *Ecosystemes et Biosphèra,* 2 (Bruxelles, 1962)
4. Nichiporovich, A. A., *J. Priroda* (Russ), 6, 33–43 (1967)
5. Nichiporovich, A. A., *Photosynthetic Systems of High Productivity,* (Nauka, Moscow, 1966) [English version: *Photosynthesis of productive Systems,* Nichiporovich, A. A., Ed., 1–182 (Israel Progr. Sci. Transl., Jerusalem, 1967)]
6. Ustenko, G. P., *Photosynthetic Systems of High Productivity,* 178–92 (Nauka, Moscow, 1966)
7. Okanenko, A. S., *Ways of Photosynthesis Productivity Rising,* 3–23 (Naukova Dumka, Kiev, 1966)
8. Forrester, M. L., Krotkov, G. P., Nelson, C. D., *Plant Physiol.,* 41, 422–27 (1966)
9. Poskuta, J., *Physiol. Plantarum,* 21, 1129–36 (1968)
10. Gaastra, P., *Mededel. Landbouwhogeschool (Wageningen),* 5 (13), 1–68 (1959)
11. Wittwer, S. H., Robb, W., *Econ. Botany,* 18, 34–56 (1964)
12. Ford, M. A., Thorne, G. N., *Ann. Botany,* 31, 621–44 (1967)
13. Kutjurin, W. M., Voskresenskaya, N. P., Ulubekova, M. V., Crishina, G. S., *Fiziol. Rast.,* 1, 7–16 (1964)
14. Treguna, E. B., Krotkov, G. P., Nelson, C. D., *Physiol. Plantarum,* 19, 723–33 (1966)
15. Björkman, O., *Ann. Rept. Dept. Plant Biol.,* 1966–67, Carnegie Inst., 220–32 (1968)
16. Vernandskiy, V. T., *Biosphere* (Leningrad, 1926)
17. Vernandskiy, V. T., *Ocherki Biogeochim.* (Moscow-Leningrad, 1940)
18. Haber, W., *Flora,* 146, 107–57 (1958)
19. Inoe, E., in *Functioning of Terrestrial*

Ecosystems at the Primary Production Level, 359–66 (Eckardt, F. E., Ed., UNESCO, Liège, 1968)

20. Karpushkin, L. T., *Photosynthetic Systems of high Productivity*, 149–56 (See Ref. 5)

21. Lemon, E., *Harvesting the Sun*, 263–90 (Acad. Press, N.Y., 1967)

22. Monteith, J. L., in *Functioning of Terrestrial Ecosystems*, 349–58 (See Ref. 19)

23. *Photosynthesis and Utilisation of Solar Energy, Level III Experiments* (Japan. Natl. Subcomm. for IBP, Tokyo, 1968)

24. Kobak, K. J., in *Reports on Woody Plants Anatomy and Physiology*, 57–64 (Leningrad, 1967)

25. Kleshnin, A. F., *Light and Plant* (Acad. Sci. USSR, Moscow, 1956)

26. Kostin, S. J., Pokrovskaja, T. V., *Climatology*, 1–429 (Leningrad, 1953)

27. Kondratjev, K. J., *Radiant Solar Energy*, 1–599 (Leningrad, 1954)

28. *Atlas of Heat Balance* (Budyko, M. I., Ed., Leningrad, 1955)

29. Slayter, R. O., *Plant-Water Relationships*, 1–366 (Academic Press, London and New York, 1967)

30. Ovington, J. D. *Functioning of Terrestrial Ecosystems*, 95–104 (See Ref. 19)

31. Rodin, L. E., Bazilevich, H. U., *Dynamics of Organic Matter and Biological Turnover of Ash Elements and Nitrogen in Main Types of Earth's Vegetation* (Nauka, Moscow, Leningrad, 1965)

32. Steemann Nielsen, E., *Ann. Rev. Plant Physiol.*, **11**, 341–62 (1960)

33. Vinberg, G. G., *Primary Production of Bodies of Water*, 1–329 (Akad. Nauk Belorussk SSSR, Minsk, 1960)

34. Bogorov, W. G., *Okeanologia* (Russ), **7**, 839–59 (1967)

35. *Primary Productivity in Aquatic Environments* (*Mem. Inst. Ital. Idrobiol.*, Suppl. 18, 1965)

36. *Production Yearbook* FAO, **19** (Rome, 1965)

37. Kovda, V. A., *J. Agr. Biol. (Moscow)*, **1** (2), 163–77 (1966)

38. Berland, T. G., *Distribution of Solar Radiation on the Earth* (Leningrad, 1961)

39. Efimova, N. A., *Photosynthetic Systems of High Productivity*, 70–77 (See Ref. 5)

40. Watson, D. J., *Advan. Agron.*, **4**, 101–45 (1956)

41. Watson, D. J., *The Growth of Leaves*, 178–90 (Milthorpe, E. L., Ed., London, 1956)

42. Nichiporovich, A. A., *Photosynthesis and Theory of Obtaining of High Yields* (Acad. Sci. USSR, Moscow, 1956)

43. Nichiporovich, A. A., Strogonova, L. E., Chmora, C. H., Vlasova, M. P., *Photosynthetic Activity of Plants in Crops*, 1–133 (Acad. Sci. USSR, Moscow, 1961)

44. Welbank, P. J., French, S. A. W., Witts, K. J., *Ann. Botany*, **20**, 291–99 (1966)

45. Watson, D. J., Hayashi, K., *New Phytologist*, **64**, 38–47 (1965)

46. Watson, D. J., Wilson, J. H., Ford, M. A., French, S. A. W., *New Phytologist*, **65**, 500–8 (1966)

47. Yoda, K., *Nature and Life in Southeast Asia*, 93–148 (1967)

48. Strogonova, L. E., *Fiziol. Rast.* (Russ), **15**, 272–81 (1968)

49. Kira, T., *Functioning of Terrestrial Ecosystems*, 399–407 (See Ref. 19)

50. Torne, G. N., *Ann. Botany*, **29**, 317–28 (1965)

51. Tsunoda, S., *Japan. J. Breeding*, **9**, 237–44 (1959)

52. Monsi, M., Saeki, T., *Japan. Botan. J.*, **14**, 22–52 (1953)

53. Tzunoda, S., *Japan. J. Breeding*, **12**, 49–56 (1962)

54. Saeki, T., *Botan. Mag (Tokyo)*, **73**, 55–63 (1960)

55. Nichiporovich, A. A., *Fiziol. Rast. (Russ)*, **8**, 536–46 (1961)

56. Pearee, R. B., Brown, R. H., Blasser, R. E., *Crop Sci.*, **7**, 321–24 (1967)

57. *Photosynthesis and Productivity of Plant Canopy*, 1–135 (Acad. Sci. Eston. SSR, Tartu, 1968)

58. Ross, J. K., Nilson, T., in *Photosynthetic Systems of High Productivity*, 96–108, 109–25 (See Ref. 5)

59. Tooming, Ch., *Botan. Zh.* (Russ), **52**, 601–16 (1967)

60. Baumgartner, A., *Functioning Terrestrial Ecosystems*, 367–73 (See Ref. 19)

61. Kuroiwa, S., *Functioning of Terrestrial Ecosystems*, 391–98 (See Ref. 19)

62. Loomis, R. S., Williams, W. A., Duncan, W. G., *Harvesting The Sun*, 269–90 (See Ref. 21)

63. Phytoactinometric Researches of Plant Canopy, 1–178 (Akad. Sci. Eston. SSR, Tartu, 1967)

64. Hesketh, J. D., Crop Sci., 3, 493–96 (1963)

65. Homann, P. H., Schmid, G. H., Plant Physiol., 42, 1619–32 (1967)

66. Hesketh, J., Planta, 16, 371–74 (1967)

67. Björkman, O., Physiol. Plantarum, 21, 84–99 (1968)

68. Avratowščuková, N., Photosynthetica, 2 (3), 149–60 (1968)

69. Holmgren, P., Physiol. Plantarum, 21, 676–98 (1968)

70. Whiteman, P. C., Koller, D., Functioning of Terrestrial Ecosystems, 415–19 (See Ref. 19)

71. Wiecƙowski, S., Photosynthetica, 2 (3), 172–77 (1968)

72. Nichiporovich, A. A., Osipova, O. P., Nikolayava, M. K., Romanko, E. G., Fiziol. Rast. (Russ), 14, 849–59 (1967)

73. Hiesey, W. M., Björkman, O., Nobs, M., Ann. Rept. Direct. Dept. Plant Biol., Cranegie Inst. Yr. Bk., 65, 461–64 (1967)

74. Gale, J., Kohl, H. C., Hagan, R. M., Physiol. Plantarum, 20, 408–20 (1967)

75. Zelitch, I., Plant Physiol., 41, 1623–31 (1966)

76. Egle, K., Folk, H., Biochemistry of Chloroplasts, 2, 79–90 (Goodwin, T. W., Ed., Academic Press, N.Y., 1967)

77. El-Sharkawy, M. A., Loomis, R. S., Williams, W. A., Psysiol. Plantarum, 20, 171–86 (1967)

78. Björkman, O., Ann. Rept. Direct. Dept. Plant Biol., Carnegie Inst. Yr. Bk., 65, 446–54 (1967)

79. Feierabend, J., Pirson, A., Z. Pflanzenphysiol., 55, 235–45 (1966)

80. Berger, Ch., Feierabend, J., Physiol. Végetal., 5 (2), 109–22 (1967)

81. Plastidenpigmente und ihre Rolle im Photosyntheseprozess, Studia biophysica, 5, 89–164 (Sayromsky, H., Ed., Catersleben, 1967)

82. Calvin, M., Brookhaven Symp. Biol., 2, 160–80 (1959)

83. Mühletaler, K., Biochemistry of Chloroplasts, 1, 49–64 (Goodwin, T. W., Ed., Acad. Press, N.Y., 1966)

84. Park, R. B., Plant Biochemistry, 124–50 (Bonner, J., Ed., Academic Press, N.Y., 1965)

85. Wettstein, D., Harvesting the Sun, 153–90 (See Ref. 21)

86. Bogorad, L., Harvesting the Sun, 191–210 (See Ref. 21)

87. Boardman, N. K., Harvesting the Sun., 211–30 (See Reg. 21)

88. Arnon, D. I., Physiol. Rev., 47, 319–58 (1967)

89. Osipova, O. P., Mechanisms of Cell Metabolism Integrity, 66–102 (Nauka, Leningrad, 1967)

90. Goodwin, T. W., Ed., Biochemistry of Chloroplasts (See Ref. 83)

91. Weier, T. E., Benson, A., Am. J. Botany, 54, 389–402 (1967)

92. Weier, T. E., Am. J. Botany, 50, 604–11 (1963)

93. Feierabend, J., Planta, 71, 326–55 (1966)

94. Berger, Ch., Feierabend, J., Physiol. Vegetal., 5 (2), 109–22 (1967)

95. Döbel, P., Sagromsky, M., Die Kulturpflanzen, 14, 293–97 (Gatersleben, 1966)

96. Osipova, O. P., Ashur, N. I., Fiziol. Rast. (Russ), 11(3), 369–74 (1964)

97. Brandt, A. B., Tageeva, S. V., Optical Properties of Plants, 45–63 (Nauka, Moscow, 1967)

98. Champigny, M. L., Moyse, A., Z. Pflanzenphysiol., 57, 280–97 (1967)

99. Selga, M. P., Tageeva, S. V., Izv. Akad. Nauk Latv. SSR, 92–99 (1967)

100. Faludi-Daniel, A., Dubraviczky, D., Fiziol. Rast., 14, 232–36 (1967)

101. Heber, U. W., Biochemistry of Chloroplasts, 2, 71–78 (See Ref. 76)

102. Manton, J., in Biochemistry of Chloroplasts, 1, 23–48 (See Ref 83)

103. Schmid, C., Price, M., Gaffron, H., J. Microscopy, 5, 205–12 (1966)

104. Homann, P. H., Schmid, G., Plant Physiol., 42, 1619–32 (1967)

105. Schmid, G., Gaffron, H., J. Gen. Physiol., 50, 563–82 (1967)

106. Voskresenskaya, N. P., Oshmarova, I. S., Gostimskii, S. A., Genetica (Russ), 4, 41–49 (1968)

107. Biochemistry of Chloroplasts, 2, (See Ref. 76)

108. Bassham, J. A., Harvesting the Sun, 79–110 (See Ref. 21)

109. Nichiporovich, A. A., Proc. Intern. Congr. Biochem., 6, 352–63 (Pergamon, 1963)

110. Häcker, M., Planta, 16, 309–25 (1967)

111. Slack, C. R., Hatch, M. D., Biochem.

J., **103**, 660–65 (1967)

112. Gyldenholm, A. O., *Hereditas*, **59**, 142–68 (1968)

113. Moyse, A., *Mem. N.M. Syssakjan* (Moscow, 1968)

114. Karpilov, Y. S., Nedopekina, I. F., *Rept. Moldavien Res. Inst. Irrigation Farming*, **7**, 35–40 (Kishinev, 1965)

115. Voskresenskaja, N. P., *Photosynthesis and Spectral Composition of Light* (Nauka, Moscow, 1965)

116. Hess, J. L., Tolbert, N. E., *Plant Physiol.*, **42**, 1123–30 (1967)

117. Landenbach, B. *Der Einfluss von Farblicht auf den Kohlenhydratumsatz in Grünalgen* (Doctoral thesis, Pflanzenphysiol. Inst., Göttingen, 1968)

118. Buschbaum, A., *Vergleichend-physiologische Untersuchungen an Algen aus Blau-und Rotlichtkulturen* (Doctoral thesis, Pflanzenphysiol. Inst., Göttingen, 1968)

119. Tarchevsky, I. A., *Photosynthesis and Drought*, 1–197 (Kazan Univ., USSR, 1964)

120. Nelson, C. D., *Environmental Control of Plant Growth*, 149–74 (Evans, L. T., Ed., Academic Press, N.Y., 1963)

121. Mokronosov, A. T., *Photosynthetic Systems of High Productivity*, 157–61 (See Ref. 5)

122. Sweet, C. B., Wareing, P. F., *Nature*, **5031**, 77–79 (1966)

123. Hansen, P., *Physiol. Plantarum*, **20**, 382–94 (1967)

124. Stark, Z., *Acta Soc. Botan. Polon.*, **35**, 337–48 (1966)

125. Kursanov, A. L., *Izv. Akad. Nauk SSSR, Ser. Biol.*, **1**, 3–10 (1967)

126. Watson, D. J., French, S. A. W., *Ann. Appl. Biol.*, **50**, 1–17 (1962)

127. Birke, J., *Albrecht-Thaer Arch.*, **10**, 1111–26 (1966)

128. *Photosyntheses and Utilisation of Solar Energy, Level III Experiments* (See Ref. 23)

129. Pochinok, H. N., Culjaev, B. I., Okanenko, A. S., Makhovskaja, M. A., Pogolskaja, V. I., Smeljanskaja, É. I., *Photosynthesis and Pigments as Factors of Plant Productivity*, 21–47 (Naukova Dumka, Kiev, 1965)

130. Schatilov, I. S., Zamarajev, A. G., Chaikovskaja, G. B., *Izv. Timiryazev. Sel'skokhoz. Akad.*, **3**, 65–74 (1967)

131. Alexeenko, L. N., *Productivity of*

Meadow Plants in Relation to Environmental Conditions (Leningrad Univ., 1967)

132. Watson, D. J., *Ann. Botany*, **22**, 37–54 (1958)

133. Nichiporovich, A. A., Malofeev, V., *Fisiol. Rast.*, **12**, 1–10 (1965)

134. Ustenko, G. P., *Photosynthesis and Questions of Plant Productivity*, 37–70 (Acad. Sci. USSR, 1963)

135. Tsuno, Y., Fujise, K., *Bull. Natl. Inst. Agr. Sci. (Japan)*, **13**, 1–131 (1965)

136. Hiroi, T., Monsi, M., *J. Fac. Sci., Univ. Tokyo*, **9**, 241–85 (1966)

137. Patron, P. I., *J. Agr. Biol. (Moscow)*, **1** (4), 561–72 (1966)

138. Tooming, H. T., Guljaev, B. I., *Methods of Photosynthetic Active Radiation Measurements*, 1–95 (Nauka, Moscow, 1967)

139. Gubar, C. D., Kreizberg, O. E., Kristkalne, S. H., *Photosynthesis and Plant Productivity*, 17–42 (Zinatne, Riga, Latv. SSR, 1965)

140. Vitola, A. K., *Photosynthesis and Plant Productivity*, 45–54 (See Ref. 139)

141. Nichiporovich, A. A., Vija, N., *J. Agrokhim. (SSSR)*, **3**, 5–11 (1964)

142. Medinec, V. D., *Photosynthetic Systems of High Productivity*, 162–68 (See Ref. 5)

143. Thorne, G. N., Ford, M. A., Watson, D. J., *Ann. Botany*, **32**, 425–46 (1968)

144. Thorne, G. N., *Ann. Botany*, **32**, 79–95 (1968)

145. Anisimov, V. A., *Fiziol. Rast.* (Russ), **15**, 13–18 (1968)

146. Blackman, G. E., *Functioning of Terrestrial Ecosystems*, 242–59 (See Ref. 19)

147. Welbank, P. J., Witts, K. J., Thorne, G. N., *Ann. Botany*, **32**, 79–95 (1968)

148. Nichiporovich, A. A., *Functioning of Terrestrial Ecosystems*, 261–70 (See Ref. 19)

149. Cowan, J. R., Milthorpe, F. L., *Functioning of Terrestrial Ecosystems*, 107–28 (See Ref. 19)

150. *Rept. Welsh Plant Breeding Sta. 1966* (Aberystwyth, England, 1967)

151. Kumakov, D. A., Kusmin, K. M., *Fiziol. Rast.*, **15**, 41–46 (1968)

152. Army, T. J., Greer, F. A., *Harvesting the Sun*, 321–32 (See Ref. 21)

153. Decker, W. L., *Functioning of Ter-*

restrial Ecosystems, 375–79 (See Ref. 19)

154. Cherepnin, W. L., *Botan. Zh.* (Russ), **53,** 881–90 (1968)

155. Chirkov, J. I., *Photosynthesis and Questions of Plant Productivity,* 88–98 (Nauka, Moscow, 1963)

156. Chirkov, J. I., *Vestn. Sel'skokhoz. Akad. Nauk SSSR,* 15–25 (1967)

157. Harder, R. J., Harward, D. D., Mason, D. D., Moore, D. P., *Proc. Am. Soil Soc.,* **21,** 1–65 (1955)

158. Bogorov, V. G., Maksimov, V. N., Fedorov, V. D., *Dokl. Akad. Nauk SSSR,* **165,** 606–89 (1965)

159. Maksimov, V. N., Fedorov, V. D., *Izv. Akad. Nauk SSSR,* **6,** 864–77 (1966)

160. Monsi, M., *Functioning of Terrestrial Ecosystems,* 131–48 (See Ref. 19)

161. de Witt, C. T., *Photosynthesis of Leaf Canopies, Agr. Res. Rept. 663* (Wageningen, 1965)

162. Budyko, M. U., Gandin, L. S., *Dokl. Akad. Nauk SSSR Ser. Biol.,* **164,** 454–57 (1965)

163. Budagovskii, A. U., Ross, Y. K., *Photosynthetic Systems of High Productivity,* 51–58 (Nauka, Moscow, 1966)

164. *Actinometry and Atmospheric Optics.* Rept. 6th Symp. Actinometry and Atmospheric Optics. IV. Radiation and plants, 255–385 (Valgus, Tallin, Eston. SSR, 1968)

165. Eley, J. H., Jr., Myers, J., *Plant Physiol.,* **42,** 598–607 (1967)

166. Vinberg, G. G., Anisimov, S. I., *Photosynthetic Systems of High Productivity,* 213–23 (Moscow, 1966)

167. Vollenweider, R., *Primary Productivity in Aquatic Environments* (*Mem. Inst. Ital. Idrobiol.,* Suppl. 18, 427–57, 1965)

168. Vosnesensky, V. A., Zalensky, O. V., Semikhatova, O. A., *Methods of Study of Plant Photosynthesis and Respiration,* 1–305 (Nauka, Moscow, 1965)

169. Chmora, S. N., *Fiziol. Rast.,* **14,** 179–86 (1967)

170. *Methods of Studying Photosynthetic Production of Plants* (Sestak, Cataky, J., Eds., Czech. Acad. Sci., Praha, 1966)

171. Eckardt, F. E., Eds., *Functioning of Terrestrial Ecosystems,* 289–317 (UNESCO, Liège, 1968)

172. Bernard, E. A., *ibid.,* 67–83.

173. Gaastra, P., *ibid.,* 467–77

174. Inoe, E., *ibid.,* 359–65

175. Kira, T., *ibid.,* 399–408

176. Kuroiwa, S., *ibid.,* 391–98

177. Lemon, E. R., *ibid.,* 381–88

178. Whiteman, P. C., Koller, D., *ibid.,* 415–19

179. Tranquillim, W., *Angew. Botan.,* **41,** 1–12 (1967)

180. Nilovskaya, N. T., Bokovaja, M. M., *Fiziol. Rast.* (Russ), **15,** 258–66 (1968)

181. Lemon, V. M., *Course of Plant Cultivation Under Artificial Light,* 1–303 (Vysshaja Shkola, Moscow, 1961)

182. Moshkov, B. S., *Plant Cultivation Under Artificial Light,* 1–286 (Kolos, Leningrad, 1966)

183. Nichiporovich, A. A., *Cosmos I,* 25–55 (Acad. Sci. USSR, 1963)

184. Myers, J. E., *Conf. Nutr. Space Relat. Waste Probl.,* Tampa, Fla., 1964, 283–87 (NASA, Washington, D.C.)

185. Kraus, R., *Conf. Nutr. Space Relat. Relat. Waste Probl.,* Tampa, Fla., 1964, 289–97 (NASA, Washington, D.C.)

186. Goldman, Ch. R., *Conf. Nutr. Space Relat. Waste Probl.,* Tampa, Fla., 1964, 311–15 (NASA, Washington, D.C.)

187. Brown, A., *Space Biology,* 15–28 (Oregon State Univ. Press, Corvallis, 1964)

188. Smylie, R. S., Reumont, M. R., *Manned spacecraft: Engineering Design and Operation,* 137–59 (Fairchild, IHC, 1964)

189. Duca, M. C., Del Conecei, E. B., Ingelfinger, A. L., *Space Aeron.,* **41,** 81–91 (1964)

190. Macklin, M., *Aerospace Med.,* **37,** 1040–45 (1966)

191. *Problems of Closed Ecosystems Creation* (Russ), 1–259 (Nichiporovich, A. A., Lisovsky, G. M., Eds., Nauka, Moscow, 1967)

192. Mattson, H. W., *Intern. Sci. Technol.,* **54,** 28–37 (1966)

193. Popma, D. C., *Astronaut. Aerospace Eng.,* **1** (7) 53–56 (1963)

194. Oswald, W. J., Golueke, C. G., Norning, D. O., *Proc. Am. Soc. Civil Engrs.,* **81,** 23–46 (1965)

195. Smith, R. E., *Advan. Space Sci. Technol.,* **5,** 87–142 (1966)

196. Babinsky, A. D., *Aerospace Med.,* **36,** 623–28 (1965)

197. Neswald, R. C., *Space Aeron.,* **44,** 70–78 (1965)

198. Rudek, F. P., *Chem. Eng. Progr. Symp., Ser. 63,* 210–17 (1967)
199. Serjapin, A. D., Fomin, A. G., Chijov, S. V., *J. Cosmic Biol. Med.* (Russ), **I**, 298–329 (1966)
200. Foster, J. F., Litchfield, J. H., *Biotechnol. Bioeng.,* **6**, 441–56 (1964)
201. Bongers, L. H., *Aerospace Med.,* **35**, 139–44 (1965)
202. Myers, J., *Use of Algae for Support of Humans in Space* (Univ. Texas, 1964)
203. Golueke, C. G., Oswald, W. J., *Ann. Rev. Plant Physiol.,* **15**, 387–408 (1964)
204. Wilks, S. S., *Conf. Nutr. Space Relat. Waste Probl.,* 305–10 (NASA, Washington, D.C., 1964)
205. McDowell, M. E., Leveille, G. A., *Conf. Nutr. Space Relat. Waste Probl.,* 317–22 (1964)
206. *Controlled Culture of Microalgae* (Russ.), 1–152 (Lisovsky, G. M., Ed., Nauka, Moscow, 1964)
207. Materials of fifth meeting on the question of cycling in closed systems created on the base of life activity of microorganisms (Russ), 1–199 (Naukova Dumka, Kiev, 1968)
208. Oswald, W. J., *J. Air, Water Pollution,* **5**, 357–93 (1962)
209. Vinberg, G. G., Ostapenja, P. V., Sivko, T. N., Levina, R. I., *Biological Ponds in Practice of Sewage Purification,* 1–231 (Belaruss, Minsk, 1966)
210. Dean, B., Hobby, G., Gaucher, T., *Man's Dependence on Earthly Atmosphere,* 400–16 (McMillan, N.Y., 1962)
211. Terskov, N. A., Gitelson, J. J., Sidko, F. I., Kovrov, B. G., Batov, V. A., Beljanin, V. N., *Controlled Algae Cultivation,* 55–64 (Nauka, Moscow, 1964)
212. Semenenko, V. E., Vladimirova, M. G., Tzoglin, L. N., Tauts, M. I., Filippovisky, I. N., *Controlled Biosynthesis,* 75–86 (Nauka, Moscow, 1966)
213. Dam, R., Lee, S., Fry, P. C., Fox, H., *J. Nutrition,* **86**, 376–82 (1965)
214. Bychkov, V. P., Kondratjev, J. I., Ushakov, A. S., *Controlled Biosynthesis and Biophysics of Population,* 144–55 (Krasnojarsk, SSSR, 1965)
215. Klyachko-Gurvich, G. L., *Controlled Biosynthesis,* 116–21 (Nauka, Moscow, 1966)
216. Semenenko, V. E., Vladimirova, M. G., Orleanskaja, O. B., *Fiziol. Rast.,* **14**, 612–24 (1967)
217. Klyachko-Gurvich, G. L., Zhukova, T. A., *Fiziol. Rast.,* **13**, 15–24 (1966)
218. Abakumova, I. A., Kondratjeva, J I., Ushakov, A. S., *Controlled Biosynthesis and Biophysics of Population,* 115–20 (Moscow, 1965)
219. Kraut, H., Jeket, F., Pabst, W., *Nutr. Dieta,* **8**, 130–44 (1966)
220. *Space Food from Bacteria, Space Flight 10,* 124 (1968)
221. Dadykin, V. P., *Cosmic Farming* (Russ) (Moscow, 1968)
222. *Controlled Biosynthesis* (Russ), 1–370 (Ierusalimsky, N. D., Kovrov, B. G., Eds., (Nauka, Moscow, 1966)
223. Novosad, R. S., Dezur, R. S., *Am. Astronaut. Soc.,* **22**, 39–60 (1963)

MEMBRANE STRUCTURE

By Daniel Branton

Department of Botany, University of California, Berkeley, California

INTRODUCTION

The boundary of all living cells is delineated by a thin membrane which separates the living protoplasm from its environment. This membrane can be seen in the electron microscope as a positively stained layer, less than 100 Å thick (148, 187), and its physical existence is demonstrable by micromanipulation (140). Within the protoplasm the boundaries of numerous organelles such as vacuoles, chloroplasts, or mitochondria are also delineated by membranes. Many functional capabilities, including active transport, selective permeability, quantum conversion in photosynthesis, oxidative phosphorylation, and nerve conductivity, have been attributed to these biological membranes. The composition of many membranes has also been established. In general they contain both lipids and proteins whose proportions and detailed components have been the subject of a number of analyses (for reviews, see 8, 90, 130). In spite of this knowledge regarding function and composition, there is not one single case in which the physiological capabilities of a membrane can be explained in terms of the molecular ordering or structure of its biochemical components. In a sense our knowledge of membranes today stands where our knowledge of DNA stood in 1945. We know what many membranes do and we know of what they are made. But despite many efforts, there is no generally accepted explanation of biological membrane structure which provides a fundamental understanding of how different membranes carry out their respective functions.

There are certainly a number of reasons for this ignorance. In many cases detailed studies of membrane composition have only recently been possible; pure preparations of a given membrane type were not previously available. Membrane proteins tend to be insoluble and therefore difficult to characterize. More generally, membrane phenomena occur in or on a highly structured matrix and are therefore not amenable to standard techniques of solution chemistry. On the other hand, some of the most powerful tools which could be used for studying structures of this type depend upon averaging techniques such as measurements of X-ray diffraction, infrared spectroscopy, optical rotatory dispersion (ORD), nuclear magnetic resonance (NMR), and circular dichroism. Functionally important centers within a membrane may be too few or too transient to provide the structural organization or periodicity most easily detectable by these measurements. Thus,

209

averaging techniques might provide a clear picture of the overall membrane matrix without ever indicating much about the structure of functionally important sites within the matrix.

This review will first consider some of the models of membrane structure which have been proposed to account for the overall organization of the membrane matrix. Both plant and animal membranes are equally relevant to this issue and the question is of general biological concern. As a result this aspect of membrane biology has been reviewed extensively (90, 106, 149, 151, 154) and will occupy only the first part of this review. The remaining part will consider evidence for differentiation in the organization of the membrane matrix. The existence and significance of discontinuities or specialized elements in the plane of the membrane and their unique relation to specific plant membrane types will be emphasized.

The Membrane Matrix

It is generally agreed that the surface of the membrane is hydrophilic and that the interior of the membrane is hydrophobic. This agreement is based on surface tension measurements, knowledge of membrane composition, and considerations of permeability phenomena. Various methods have been devised for measuring the surface tension at membrane surfaces, and the results always show values at least an order of magnitude below those for a water/hydrocarbon interface (33, 71). These low values would not be found if the membrane exterior were hydrophobic, but they are consistent with a hydrophilic surface. On the other hand, it is clear also that most membranes are composed of proteins and lipids, both of which contain hydrophobic groups (48, 146). The surface tension measurements dictate that these hydrophobic groups must be buried within the membrane matrix. Finally, this conclusion is consonant with permeability measurements which in fact led Overton (132) to propose the lipoidal nature of cell membranes over 70 years ago. Overton measured the rates of plasmolysis reversal in *Hydrocharis* root hairs and found that the lipid solubility of various molecules was directly related to their ability to enter the cell. Comprehensive and accurate measurements of *Chara* assessing the variation of the permeability constant with the chemical structure of the penetrating species (26, 183) confirm Overton's results and remain among the more striking indications of the hydrophobic nature of the membrane interior. Lattice models for diffusion into and across the cell membrane (168) have recently been used to recalculate the diffusion data for a number of algae, red blood cells, and *Arbacia* eggs. The results imply that for entry into the membrane a nonelectrolyte must break all hydrogen bonds that its hydroxyl groups make with water when in an aqueous phase. This requirement tends to retard transfer through a membrane in proportion to the number of hydrogen-bonding acceptor or donor groups a molecule contains. On the other hand, bare $-CH_2-$ groups in the permeant molecules are seen to increase transfer

Fig. 1. Membrane models. Diagrams of (*a*) protein-lipid-protein (32, 148), (*b*) lipid-protein-lipid (98), and (*c*) subunit (63, 159, 184) schemes for the biological membrane.

rate. It therefore appears that a membrane with a hydrophobic interior provides an accurate molecular picture to account for the unspecialized permeability of the cell membrane.

Granting that the membrane has a hydrophobic interior and a hydrophilic surface, it is evident that these restrictions on the molecular groupings within a membrane allow wide latitude in any detailed model. Thus, models which have been proposed may be grouped according to whether they place protein on the outside, lipid on the inside (Fig. 1a, a protein-lipid-protein arrangement we shall abbreviate as PLP), or lipid on the outside, protein on the inside (Fig. 1b, LPL). A third type of membrane explicitly questions the lamellar continuity implicit in both of these models and proposes instead a membrane composed of distinct subunits (Fig. 1c).

Protein-lipid-protein membranes.—Of the former PLP type, the paucimolecular model suggested by Danielli & Davson (31, 32, 148) has had the most profound influence on the thinking of students of membrane structure. According to this model, the membrane lipids are arranged in a bilayer stabilized by hydrophobic interactions and covered by electrostatically interacting proteins on both surfaces. The basic PLP model is supported by a number of different lines of evidence.

(*a*) Polarization optics show that intact nerve myelin is positively birefringent with reference to its optic axis, whereas lipid-depleted myelin is negatively birefringent (156). These birefringence data indicate that the lipid molecules are oriented with their long axis radial to the axis of the nerve fiber, interspersed with sheets of protein. The relevance of these observations to the problem of membrane structure was demonstrated when it became clear that myelin was a membranous, spiraled infolding of the surrounding (Schwann) cell membrane (56).

(*b*) X-ray diffraction patterns of myelin are best interpreted as concentric alternating layers of protein and lipid with an approximately 85 Å PLP repeat corresponding to one membrane layer (43, 45, 157, 158). Similar X-ray diffraction images have recently been obtained from red blood cell ghosts, microsomal membranes, and isolated mitochondrial membranes packed by strong centrifugal forces (25, 46, 47, 176). The close similarities of the characteristic X-ray reflections support the essential similarities of structure for most membranes. The X-ray patterns suggest that they consist of a predominantly continuous bimolecular lipid bilayer with nonlipid components associated with both surfaces. However, X-ray diffraction patterns of chloroplast lamellae appear to differ from those of most other membranes and will be discussed in greater detail below.

(c) The lipid extracted from the membrane of a single red blood cell forms a monolayer with twice the surface area of the cell from which it was extracted (59). This classical demonstration has recently been confirmed by modern methods which show that there is adequate lipid to account for a bilayer within the red blood cell membrane (6). Although it has been objected that in many membranes the ratio of protein to lipid is different from that in red blood cells (16, 90), even mitochondria, which have a high protein:lipid ratio of about 80:20 (50), have enough lipid to form a bilayered membrane (86).

(d) Differential scanning calorimetry of *Mycoplasma laidlawii* cell membranes indicates that at least 60 per cent of the membrane lipids participate in reversible thermotropic gel-liquid crystal phase transitions similar to those shown by mesophase phospholipid dispersions (167). These results show that extensive hydrophobic lipid-protein associations in the native membrane are unlikely since the gel-liquid crystal phase transition results from cooperative association between hydrocarbon chains and would vanish or be profoundly perturbed by hydrophobic bonding.

(e) Electron microscopy shows that under appropriate fixation conditions, nearly all biological membranes appear as two approximately 20 Å wide, positively stained lines separated by an approximately 35 Å relatively unstained space (148–150). Robertson (148) called this characteristic image of the biological membrane a "unit membrane," a phrase designed to emphasize that all three lines—the two dark ones and the intervening light space—are part of one single membrane. This image could obviously support either a PLP or an LPL membrane depending upon whether the black lines correspond to stained lipid or stained protein. This has been investigated in model systems containing various lipid and lipid-protein dispersions in water. Although it was first believed that the dark lines represented the double bonds in the hydrocarbon portion of the lipid which had been stained by reacting with the fixative (170), subsequent comparison of heavy metal soaps (uranyl linolenate) and phospholipid brain extracts, dispersed in water to form myelin figures, demonstrated that the dark bands marked the position of hydrophilic ends of the lipid molecules (171). The main difference between the lamellae of myelin figures and the cell membrane is the lesser density and width of the outer layers in the former. When an appropriate protein is added to the solution in which the lipids are dispersed, the protein is absorbed onto the surface of the lipid layers, increasing the density and the width of the outer dark bands seen in the electron micrographs to 25 Å or more depending on the amount of protein present (173). It therefore follows that the structure of cell membranes observed in electron micrographs is consistent with a PLP hypothesis.

Although the chemical reactions between various fixatives, stains, and biological tissue are still under study in several laboratories (91, 92, 131, 147), it is probable that during fixation of biological material with osmium tetroxide, the unsaturated phospho- or galactolipid fatty acids are converted to stable glycol osmates (93). If this or any other fixative-hydrocarbon reaction is actually the major fixation product, it might be expected that the two dark lines seen in electron micrographs of membranes would not delineate the location of the protein, as noted above, but rather that of the lipid hydrocarbon groups. However, the reaction of osmium with unsaturated fatty acids in phospholipid monolayers most probably leads to subsequent reorientation of the osmium reaction product (37), so that the hydrophobic paraffin chain and attached osmium atom are pulled into the plane of the polar end of the membrane lipid molecule. Similar reorientation of osmium reaction products could occur during fixation of biological specimens, although this remains to be demonstrated. In any case, the staining patterns of a number of different membranes, including myelin (127) and mitochondria (49), are unchanged by lipid extraction, and there can be no doubt that the dark lines represent the location of the protein in these lipid-depleted membranes. Although redistribution of the protein component could occur during lipid extraction, this is rendered unlikely by glutaraldehyde fixation before lipid extraction (127), and the most reasonable conclusion to be drawn from these experiments is that the dark lines of the unit membrane correspond to the location of a substantial portion of the membrane protein.

(f) Work with model systems, including lipid dispersions in water or thin lipid membranes separating two aqueous phases, suggests that a bilayer of lipid modified by the addition of appropriate compounds can demonstrate a surprising range of "physiological" characteristics. For example, dispersions of phospholipids in water cause the formation of vesicles enclosed by concentric bimolecular lipid layers (4). The vesicles are highly permeable to water and anions, but much less permeable to cations (3–5, 36, 133). These characteristics are remarkably similar to those of living membranes. Work with a variety of lipid-water dispersions has demonstrated that the permeability of the vesicles is dependent upon lipid composition (4, 133) and can be further manipulated by addition of local anesthetics (3), steroids, or antibiotics (5).

Thin lipid membranes separating two aqueous phases have also been constructed by painting a layer of brain lipids suspended in hydrocarbon solvents across a small 1 or 2 mm pore in a polyethylene or teflon sheet separating two aqueous compartments (124). Other methods and lipids have also been used with success (178). The thickness, electrical resistance, water permeability, interfacial tension, and excitability of these thin lipid membranes produced from lipid extracts in the presence of some added proteins correspond closely to those of biological membranes (123, 125, 178). These remarkable properties of thin lipid films provide an exquisite model system for studying the properties and potentialities of thin lipid or lipoprotein layers under well-defined and controlled conditions, and study of these thin lipid membranes has done much to allay the objection that a PLP model of the biological membrane is unable to account for the varied physiological characteristics exemplified by the many different membranes found in nature. Nonetheless, the objection still exists. Biological membranes do show a range of compositional and physiological complexities not seen in lipid membranes, and it remains to be shown how thin lipid membranes can function as a matrix for reconstruction of enzymatic function or active transport. For this reason, alternative models for the biological membrane must be considered.

Lipid-protein-lipid membranes.—In order to place enzymatically active proteins in the interior of the membrane, it has been suggested that the lipids are on the outside with their hydrophilic, charged groups at the surface and their hydrophobic groups oriented inward where they interact extensively with hydrophobic portions of the centrally located proteins (Fig. 1b). A special case of the LPL model which has received considerable attention (9, 63) suggests further that the membrane is composed of hydrophobically interacting subunits (Fig. 1c). It should be noted that a major difference between the PLP membranes which were considered above and the LPL membranes which are being considered here is the nature of possible lipid-protein associations. The former envisages extensive polar bonding between lipid and protein, whereas the latter suggests extensive apolar bonding between these two major membrane components. Hence, identification of the bonding which holds together lipids and proteins within the membrane is crucial in deciding between PLP and LPL models. Support for an LPL model is found in the following kinds of observations:

(*a*) Surface tension properties of the biological membrane can be accounted for by an LPL model just as well as by a PLP model. One of the original reasons why Danielli & Davson suggested that the surface of the membrane was covered with protein was that the low surface tension properties could not be accounted for by comparison with surface tensions at oil-water interfaces (33). However, the oil-water interfaces used for comparison consisted of triglycerides which have no hydrophilic groups. In contrast, naturally occurring membrane lipids consist of amphiphilic phospholipids, galactolipids, and sulfolipids (8, 90). These surface-active membrane lipids are clearly capable of forming a low surface tension interface with water (30). Indeed, thin lipid membranes formed from pure lecithin dissolved in chloroform-methanol show surface tensions around 1 dyne/cm (177), which is within the range found for natural membranes (71).

(*b*) Optical rotatory dispersion and circular dichroism measurements of carcinoma (182), erythrocyte, *Bacillus subtilis* (98, 107, 108), mitochondrial (180), and chloroplast (84, 85) membranes are remarkably similar, and as a group they show spectra not usually found in simple protein systems. In general, the optical rotation spectra exhibit a form usually associated with an α-helix, but with the spectra shifted a number of micra toward longer wavelengths. This redshift has been explained as due to interaction of adjacent protein helices (98), extensive hydrophobic interaction between membrane proteins and lipids (182), or direct contributions of phospholipid to the complete spectrum (180). The last two explanations appear improbable since all of the characteristic optical rotation features of intact membranes are found in lipid-free preparations of membrane protein (166). It is therefore reasonable to assign the redshift to protein-protein associations, although the nature of these associations remains to be clarified.

Regardless of how the redshift is explained, it is generally agreed that the optical rotation data show a substantial amount of the membrane protein in α-helix and random conformations, with little or none in the β-conformation. This conclusion is consistent with infrared spectroscopy of erythrocyte membranes which also suggests that none of the membrane protein appears in the pleated sheet structure characteristic of the β-conformation (22, 107, 108).

The existence of helical proteins in membranes is consistent with an LPL model but not with some PLP models which assume unfolded polypeptide chains on the membrane surfaces (31, 82, 181). Although some of these unfolded polypeptide chains could be replaced by helices parallel to the membrane surface, it is also possible that aggregated ensembles of helices traverse the membrane [as suggested in (98, 166, 182)] and this will be discussed in greater detail below.

(c) Biochemical characterization of proteins derived from a number of different membrane systems including mitochondria (27), red blood cells, microsomes (10, 146), and chloroplasts (28) suggested the presence of a characteristic class of membrane proteins which are insoluble in water and which bind to phospholipid hydrophobically (60, 61). It is difficult to see how such extensive hydrophobic interaction between membrane lipids and proteins could occur if the lipids are in a bilayer at the center of the membrane (72). Thus, the presence of hydrophobic protein as a predominant feature of membrane systems argues against the PLP membrane and in favor of an LPL model.

Recent evidence shows, however, that membrane proteins can exhibit a surprising range of solubilities and binding modalities (62). One example of this is the discovery that structural protein[1] can be isolated from mitochondria by mild acetic acid treatment (190), whereas previous methods called for cholate and deoxycholate (27, 146). Unlike detergent "solubilized" protein, the acetic acid-extracted material does not bind hydrophobically with phospholipid.

An even more striking example of the solubility properties of membrane

---

[1] The term structural protein refers to preparations originally described by Green et al. (64) and Criddle et al. (27). Since standard preparations of the protein are grossly inhomogeneous (62), and since the name "structural protein" has subsequently been applied to a wide variety of different membrane proteins, the name may be confusing and will be avoided wherever possible.

protein is shown by the recent demonstration that up to 70 per cent of the red blood cell protein can be solubilized in distilled water if appropriate steps are taken to maintain low ionic environments around the cells (109, 112). Previous methods of solubilizing red cell proteins had been performed with a variety of reagents, including high ionic strengths, detergents, organic solvents, or urea (10, 106, 144, 146). The recent experiments with distilled water solubilization imply that protein structure in the living membrane may be poised conformationally between a state of maximum association (molecular rigor mortis) and a state of dissociation (12). Hence, the conditions under which the protein passes from the medium provided by the cell to that provided by the experimenter can determine whether the isolated material will become more stable and "insoluble" or less stable and "soluble." Preliminary evidence suggests that the water-solubilized erythrocyte protein does not bind hydrophobically with phospholipid and that its association with lipid may be polar in the living membrane (112).

It becomes evident that the solubility of red blood cell membrane proteins is in large part determined by their history. Ionic requirements for membrane stability could reflect the requirements of either or both lipid-protein or protein-protein associations. Red blood cell membrane proteins may appear as hydrophobic proteins following detergent treatment, or as hydrophilic proteins following distilled water treatment. Although it remains to be seen whether or not the dominant proteins of other membranes can also exhibit such remarkably chameleonic properties, it is clear that conclusions regarding the binding of lipid to protein, based on experiments with harshly solubilized membrane proteins, are inconclusive.

(d) Nuclear magnetic resonance spectroscopy of red blood cell ghosts suggests that the hydrocarbon chains of the lipids are considerably more immobilized in the membranes than in sonicated lipids extracted from the same membranes (20, 21). Spectral peaks normally associated with signals from $-CH_2-$ and $-CH=CH-$ groups of lipid hydrocarbon chains are weakened or absent in the membrane preparations. Cholesterol-phospholipid interaction could not account for the signal inhibition which has been interpreted as evidence for hydrophobic association of hydrocarbon chains with part of the membrane protein (21). In contrast, sharp signals from the methyl protons of the choline groups of membrane lipids suggest that polar ends of the phospholipid molecules are free to move. Infrared spectra of erythrocyte membranes in the 14 μ region due to $-CH_2-$ chains could also be explained as a result of hydrophobic lipid-protein interaction (39).

Unfortunately, most of the NMR and infrared results were obtained from membranes and lipid models which had been sonicated and freeze-dried before rehydration for analysis. Although some spectra were obtained with intact ghosts (20), the spectra were weak and variable (21). Hence, the effect of sonication and freeze-thawing on the NMR and infrared spectra remains to be assessed. Even though NMR indicates immobilization of fatty

acid chains, it does not indicate whether chains are immobilized by association with protein or by tight packing with other lipids. Nuclear magnetic
resonance studies of serum lipoproteins prepared without freeze-drying
show no evidence for extensive hydrophobic association between protein
and lipid (165).

(e) Various lipase treatments show that in several different membranes
the polar groups of the lipids are particularly susceptible to enzymatic attack. For example, in chloroplast membranes galactose is rapidly hydrolyzed
off the galactolipids in runner bean cell homogenates (155), and rapid enzymatic transformation of monogalactosyl diglyceride to acylgalactosyl diglyceride takes place during normal isolation of *Spinacea* chloroplasts (73).
In red blood cell ghosts, phospholipase *C,* which catalyzes the hydrolysis of
phospholipids to diglycerides and water-soluble phosphorylated amines,
causes the release of up to 74 per cent of the total membrane phosphorus
(99). Especially noteworthy is the observation that neither protein nor
other lipid components were released from the hydrolyzed membranes
which appeared intact in phase contrast microscopy. These demonstrations
of enzymatic cleavage and release of major fractions of the polar heads of
membrane lipids without disruption of membrane structure are certainly
among the most striking pieces of evidence in favor of an LPL membrane.
However, several questions about this approach remain unanswered. In the
first place, it appears that the susceptibility of any membrane component is
controlled by a number of factors which may have little or nothing to do
with their location in or on the membrane. Thus, the cell membranes of isolated *Avena* coleoptile protoplasts are resistant to enzymatic attack by a
wide range of both lipases and proteases (152), whereas the membranes of
lobster muscle fibers are sensitive to both lipases and proteases (54). In the
second place, it is evident that membrane lipids exchange with nonmembrane
lipids (188) so that regardless of its location within the membrane this component is continuously being plugged into and out of the membrane matrix
and it is not at all clear where in this process the phospholipase enzymes
are actually hydrolyzing the lipids. Finally, there is no evidence that the lipases could not penetrate part or all of the membrane to effect their attack
on the membrane lipids. Slight proteolytic activity of phospholipase could
alter enough of the protein coat so that the large enzyme can freely approach its substrate. The very fact that over 70 per cent of the membrane
phospholipids are hydrolyzed by phospholipase *C* (99) is in itself an indication that precisely such penetration may occur. The LPL models usually
assume that about half the lipid polar groups are exposed on each surface
(98). If the lipase were unable to penetrate the membrane protein, it would
hydrolyze only the lipid exposed on the outer surface of the intact red blood
cell ghost and less than 50 per cent of the lipid phosphorus should be removed. Thus, although it is indeed noteworthy that membranes are able to
remain intact even after hydrolysis of 70 per cent of their phospholipid

phosphoric acid residues, the enzymatic susceptibility of these groups may simply be a measure of the relatively loose, permeable meshwork formed by the membrane proteins, rather than an assay of lipid localization.

Subunit membranes.—An LPL membrane could be organized into subunits as shown in Figure 1c. The hypothesis that a membrane is composed of such subunits is supported by the following evidence:

(a) Electron microscopy of some of the first membranes examined in the electron microscope—red blood cells (189) and chloroplasts (79)—is not consistent with models which show the biological membrane as a continuous lipoprotein phase, but suggests instead mosaic structures (74) or arrays of micellar or globular subunits (53). Similar observations have now been extended to a wide variety of membranes by using several different fixation methods. Shadowing techniques have consistently demonstrated particulate structure in chloroplast membranes (134, 137, 138), and positive staining in standard thin sections reveals what appears to be substructure in chloroplast membranes (184) as well as in mitochondria (44), endoplasmic reticulum, and golgi membranes (159, 160). Some of the strongest support for a subunit model has come from negative staining results in mitochondria in which 90 Å wide subunits composed of head piece, stalk, and base piece can be seen (42). The head pieces appear to contain the membrane ATPases (42). Since they can be removed by a variety of techniques including sonication, they may simply be attached to the surface of the underlying lipoprotein membrane. According to the subunit model, the base pieces seen in these negatively stained preparations are the elements which actually make up the membrane continuum (44, 63, 65, 88). Subunits can also be seen in negatively stained plasma membrane (7), microsomal vesicles, and red blood cell membranes (29). The presence of subunits following a variety of fixative techniques argues against the probability that the electron microscope images are completely artifactual. Furthermore, subunit structure is not seen in all classes of membranes prepared by identical techniques or even in all classes of membranes in the very same micrograph (29, 185). Thus different membranes may differ in structure, chloroplast and mitochondrial membranes being among those in which substructure has most often been demonetrated by electron microscopy.

Although the substructure seen in electron microscope images may be related to inherent membrane architecture, the nature of this relation is open to considerable debate. For example, particles seen in shadowed preparations may simply be attached to the surface of the membrane. In positively stained thin sections the transverse densities across the membrane have been interpreted as lipoprotein (184) or globular subunits (159), although they may arise by aggregation of heavy metal atoms caused by electron bombardment in the microscope (174). These transverse densities may also be explicable in terms of a granular or fibrillar mosaic confined to the outside surfaces of the membrane and unrelated to any interruptions in the continuity of the hydrophobic center of the membrane (150). According to this argument, if the surface mosaic were in the form of a fairly regular lattice, it might appear as a regular series of dense granules in sections perfectly normal to the plane of the membrane. But, if the sections are not perfectly normal to the plane of the membrane, there might well exist some angle at which one edge of the membrane at the top of the section will overlap the opposite edge of the membrane at the bottom of the section. Experiments (150) show that this can produce an apparent transverse density and hence an apparent membrane subunit when the section is tilted little more than 5° to 10° from the vertical. Furthermore, such as overlap image artifact is inevitable for any curved membrane whose radius of curvature is less than about 0.5 μ (150). Therefore, globular membrane subunits may appear in the electron microscope image because of a surface mosaic rather than because of any lipoprotein or globular subunits within the membrane.

Negative staining has provided some of the clearest pictures of what could be interpreted as subunit membranes, but again the relation between electron microscope image and membrane architecture is difficult to establish. Even if one grants that negative staining produces an amorphous glass that preserves hydrated native structures (75), there remains the problem of labeling the negatively stained particles as lipoprotein subunits. Negatively stained dispersions of various mixtures of lecithin, lysolecithin, cholesterol, and saponin to which proteins have never been added can produce morphological assemblies similar to those which have been equated with lipoprotein subunits in membrane preparations (2, 57, 102).

Thus, electron microscopy using shadowing, thin sectioning, and negative staining techniques can provide images consistent with a subunit model of the biological membrane, but in each case substantive questions of interpretation preclude definitive decisions for or against this model.

(b) Physical isolation and separation of lipoprotein fragments from intact membranes (19, 60, 143) support the subunit hypothesis. The subunit model views the membrane as a continuum, one particle thick, made of fused or nesting subunits. It further assumes that the particles are lipoprotein macromolecules identical in form and size, although possibly comprised of a number of chemically and functionally different species (65). It is implicit in this model that intraunit bonding must be different from iterunit bonding and hence that it is possible to isolate macromolecular complexes [monomerized membrane (63)] which reflect the composition of the membrane as a whole. These basic assumptions of the subunit model are diagrammed in Figure 2a. Evidence showing both the disaggregation and the reaggregation steps has been obtained in a variety of membrane systems. Mitochondrial particles with a variety of enzymatic functions have been resolved with bile salts and have been seen to reaggregate upon removal of the bile salts (89). The cell membrane of *Mycoplasma laidlawii* has been disaggregated in sodium dodecyl sulfate (143). Reconstitution of membrane-like structures occurred when the sodium dodecyl sulfate was removed in the presence of Mg^{++}. Similar results, including both disaggrega-

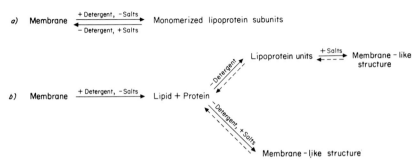

FIG. 2. Results of disaggregation studies. (*a*) As expected according to the subunit hypothesis (65). (*b*) As experimentally determined (39).

tion and reaggregation of the cell membrane, were observed in *Micrococcus lysodeikticus* (19, 66).

As a first approximation, it would appear that the above experiments confirm the validity of diagram Figure 2a, and hence the subunit membrane model. However, Figure 2a implies a reversible reaction which assumes the integrity of the lipoprotein subunits during aggregation and disaggregation. Several experiments contradict this assumption.

Comparison of the original membrane of *M. lysodeikticus* with the reaggregated product formed after removal of the sodium dodecyl sulfate showed that although they were similar chemically and morphologically, the former was sensitive to urea and guanidine whereas the latter was attacked preferentially by anionic detergent molecules (19). The results of these experiments implied that hydrogen bonding played an important role in stabilizing the *in vivo* membrane, whereas hydrophobic bonding became the dominant stabilizing factor in the reaggregated product. Thus, irreversible changes may have modified the lipid-protein or protein-protein interactions somewhere during the disaggregation-reaggregation cycle, and it cannot be assumed that the lipoprotein unit obtained upon dissolution of the membrane represented an *in vivo* subunit of the original membrane.

Even more crucial is the demonstration that during the disaggregation of *Mycoplasma laidlawii* the membrane is solubilized by sodium dodecyl sulfate into separate protein and lipid components (40), although it had originally been concluded that the primary breakdown product of the membrane was a lipoprotein of homogeneous size (104). The original conclusion was based on the appearance of a single schlieren peak upon analytical ultracentrifugation of the disaggregated membrane. Subsequent examinations of density gradient profiles show that in spite of the single peak, which has been used as a criterion in a number of membrane disaggregation studies (19, 44, 55, 161), the solubilized membrane material is composed of separate protein and lipid components. Further work (38, 39, 175) has shown that the solubilized components can interact in a variety of ways to produce a number of different reassociated structures (Fig. 2b). Only under a limited set of conditions (Fig. 2b) does the majority of the disaggregated material reaggregate to form assemblies which closely resemble the original membrane. It is of considerable interest that small, water-soluble lipoprotein aggregates can be assembled into a membranous structure but, as the complexities of Figure 2b show, the phenomenon of membrane formation by disaggregated lipoprotein units does not constitute adequate evidence for a lipid-protein subunit in the original material.

Finally, it should be noted that membrane-like structures and vesicles can be formed from a large variety of single or mixed lipids when exposed to many different proteins which are unrelated to membranes, such as total serum proteins, hemoglobins, serum albumin, and protamine (123). The principal role of protein in these vesicles appears to be to prevent the formation of concentric lamellae which phospholipids alone would form (4).

In summary, the data reviewed thus far provide evidence for the topological assignment of lipoidal and protein regions that is convincing in at least one membrane system—myelin—and persuasive in several others. Results from birefringence measurements, X-ray diffraction analysis, differential calorimetry, and electron microscopy are consistent with a PLP membrane. Further, we see that membrane lipids and their interaction with aqueous environments in model systems have received considerable attention and provide a concise starting point for hypothesis regarding the biological membrane. Put this way, the force of the argument for a PLP model can be seen. On the other hand, definitive proof has not been obtained (90). Furthermore, the study of proteins and protein-lipid interactions in hydrated membranes is in its infancy and efforts to demonstrate LPL or subunit models may flounder because of ignorance in this complex but nonetheless critical area.

DIFFERENTIATION WITHIN THE MEMBRANE MATRIX

Thus far we have examined evidence for the structure of the unspecialized portion of the membrane with the view that this matrix might constitute a suitable carrier and environment within which specialized, functionally significant elements may be inserted. Although subunit models usually invoke no structural element other than the repeating subunits to account for all the macromolecules contained within the membrane system (65), other models usually assume some differentiated regions within the plane of the membrane. Thus, a generalized LPL membrane such as shown in Figure 1b could in part be organized into subunits (98), and the classical Danielli model can include relatively permanent, polar protein pores (31, 169). Other suggestions for modifications with the framework of the PLP model have arisen with the realization that the amphiphilic membrane lipids may assume structures other than the smectic mesophase characteristic of the extended lipid bilayer postulated for the undifferentiated matrix of the PLP membrane. Depending upon temperature, concentration, and the type of lipids involved, X-ray diffraction analysis has shown that a number of configurations including lamellar and rodlike lipid in water or water in lipid micellar phases are possible (67, 104, 105, 145, 172). Although many of the micellar phases are three-dimensional structures of questionable relevance to membranes, a two-dimensional hexagonal network has recently been described in pure lecithin (103). More complicated arrays, including tubular, hexagonal, and helical structures, have been observed by negative staining in lecithin-cholesterol and saponin-lecithin-cholesterol dispersions (2, 102). In view of these observations it has been suggested that micellar lipid configurations might be in dynamic equilibrium with a bimolecular leaflet structure and that the adaptability and versatility of membranes may result from the utilization of both arrangements (101). A more elaborate model, in which the lipid micelles are capable of reversible transformations between broad, flat discs and tall, narrow pillars, has been invoked to account for a number of membrane properties including coalescence, contraction, expansion, and rotational movements (81–83). An inherent feature of these suggestions is the proviso for water-filled pores between the micelles. Whether or not such pores explain the results of permeability measurements in cell membranes remains unsettled (41, 68, 69; for review, see 168).

Specific concern with the diverse enzymatic properties linked to different types of membranes has led to the suggestion that enzymatically active proteins may be inserted into the membrane matrix (100, 101, 114, 118). According to this argument, the spatial anisotropy of the membrane can provide a vectorial character to what might otherwise be scalar processes (115, 116). Enzymes of metabolism, properly located within the hydrophobic matrix of the membrane might, for example, mediate transport, translocate protons, or couple metabolic oxidation to phosphorylation (117).

What evidence, if any, is there to support the idea that the relatively unspecialized membrane matrix is interrupted by differentiated, perhaps functionally active, centers? Because these centers may constitute only a small percentage of the total volume of some membrane systems, it is clear that many of the averaging techniques previously discussed in this review will be of little use in answering this question. Fortunately, during the last few years a new physical preparatory technique for electron microscopy has been developed which appears to be particularly well suited to the examination of membrane structure. This technique is called freeze-etching (121, 164).

Freeze-etching.—Unlike most other electron microscope preparatory techniques, freeze-etching does not require the use of chemical fixatives and dehydrating agents. Tissues are rapidly frozen and then fractured under vacuum. A small amount of ice may be sublimed from the fractured face, and this etched surface is then shadowed and replicated. Examination of the replica by usual electron microscopic techniques reveals extensive structures which evidently represent membranous portions of the tissue. As the fractures follow inherent planes of weakness within the tissue, the surfaces exposed in freeze-etching are three-dimensional cleavages in which spatially extended areas of membranes can be examined. One of the major advantages of this technique is that it appears to be a morphologically useful extension of biochemical approaches to fractionation and separation of membrane components. Many of these biochemical approaches are directed toward the weakening of hydrophobic associations followed by purification of components. Freeze-etching also appears to depend upon a weakening of hydrophobic interactions but is followed by examination of components using standard electron microscopic techniques. Biochemical approaches usually depend upon detergents to weaken hydrophobic bonds; freeze-etching utilizes the freezing process to accomplish the same end.

This is possible because unlike many types of polar bonding, hydrophobic bonding involves large entropy changes attributable to structural restrictions on water surrounding nonpolar groups (51, 80). Hydrophobic bonding is of little relevance in frozen specimens (35) where there is no question either of surrounding newly exposed polar groups with water or of structural reorganization in the frozen aqueous phase. One might expect that hydrophobically stabilized regions of cell membranes would be among the most easily cleaved structures inside a hydrated tissue since strong charge dipole interactions between hydrophilic portions of membranes and cytoplasmic components would not be much affected by freezing.

This reasoning has been confirmed by careful examination of freeze-etch replicas (11). A consistent feature in such preparations is a small ridge at the base of most exposed membrane faces. This small ridge is in fact continuous with and identical to one of the two ridges which form the characteristic freeze-etch image of a cross-fractured membrane (Fig. 3). This same type of fracture has been observed in freeze-etched preparations of a wide number of plant and animal membranes (11, 12, 15) and is interpreted (Fig. 4) to mean that during fracturing of frozen tissues, membranes are most likely to be split, which exposes either one or the other of the two inner, hydrophobic faces. If this interpretation is generally applicable, it implies that the fracture process of freeze-etching will expose neither the true membrane surface nor the surface of any materials contiguous to membranes. These implications have been verified by using membranes with known surface markers (11) and by experiments in which the fracture process has been combined with extensive etching to remove ice from around unfractured portions of membranes (17, 139).

Two further observations indicate that the membrane faces seen in freeze-etching are not outer membrane surfaces. (*a*) Aldehyde fixatives are known to effect cross-linkage of hydrophilic portions of proteins (70, 153). However, numerous aldehyde-fixed structures have been freeze-etched (15, 18, 78) and found to yield the same membrane faces as the unfixed controls. This suggests that the freeze-etch images of membrane faces are views of inner, hydrophobic areas and not those of the outer, hydrophilic glutar-

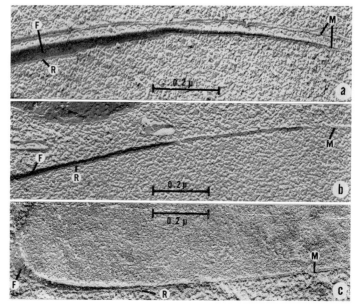

FIG. 3. Freeze-etched membranes in onion root-tip cells. (a) Endoplasmic reticulum. (b) Vacuolar membrane; view from inside vacuole. (c) Vacuolar membrane; view from outside membrane. In all cases, the fractures are tangent to the membrane on the left and almost perpendicular to the membrane surfaces on the right. The small ridge (R) at the base of an exposed membrane face (F) on the left is continuous with one of the two ridges which forms the typical freeze-etch image of a single membrane (M) on the right. From Branton (11).

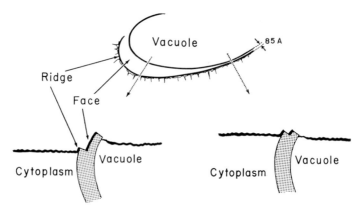

FIG. 4. *Top*, a representation of Fig. 3. *Bottom*, diagrams of imaginary sections perpendicular to the plane of the page through the fractured tissue along the *dashed arrows*. From Branton (11).

aldehyde-susceptible surfaces of these membranes. (*b*) On the other hand, lipid extraction of this aldehyde-fixed tissue completely removes the planes of weakness which give rise to the characteristic freeze-etch fractures. After extraction, breaks no longer occur along membrane faces, occurring instead at random through the frozen tissue (15). This is true even though other techniques show that lipid extraction does not destroy the general shape and morphology of the membranes (49, 127, 135). Hence, the presence of lipid appears to be necessary to establish planes of weakness in the frozen membranes and this supports the idea that cleavage occurs within the nonpolar interior of membranes. Although other interpretations of the fracture process have been proposed, they do not provide a consistent explanation for the observed results (for review, see 87).

The discovery that frozen membranes may be fractured to expose inner, hydrophobic membrane faces is consistent with either a PLP model or an LPL model but is extremely difficult to explain in terms of subunit models which would be expected to cleave the hydrophobically bonded subunits apart at right angles to the plane of the membrane rather than to cleave within the plane of the membrane, as observed. Freeze-etching therefore provides an additional criterion which makes a subunit model of the membrane matrix, such as shown in Figure 1c, highly improbable.

The ability to fracture membranes in their hydrophobic interior has been particularly useful in determining the extent and distribution of any differentiated regions within the membrane matrix. The possibility of examining structure in the hydrophobic plane of the membrane can obviously provide a direct answer to whether or not such differentiated elements exist. In most membrane systems such discontinuities do seem to exist and, as shown in Figure 5, they appear in freeze-etch replicas as small particles in the otherwise smooth continuum of the fractured membrane matrix. The tonoplast, plasmalemma, and chloroplast lamellae have been investigated most extensively.

Tonoplast.—In the tonoplast of both yeast and root tip cells the exposed vacuolar faces appear as a smooth background upon which are distributed particles 65 to 130 Å in diameter (Fig. 5). This range in diameter appears in part real, in part attributable to experimental variation, and in part due to which laboratory reports the results. Henceforth we shall refer to particles in this size range simply as small particles. The small particles usually appear to be randomly distributed within the plane of the membrane matrix, although they sometimes form fairly regular, circular patterns in some yeast vacuolar membranes (120). Similar particles are seen in smaller number on nuclear and endoplasmic reticulum membranes (Table I).

Plasmalemma.—In contrast to the tonoplast whose prime role appears to be that of a semipermeable membrane mediating transport into and out of the vacuole, the role of the plasmalemma is probably more complex. It functions not only as the major permeability barrier between the outside environment and the protoplasmic environment but also as the interface through

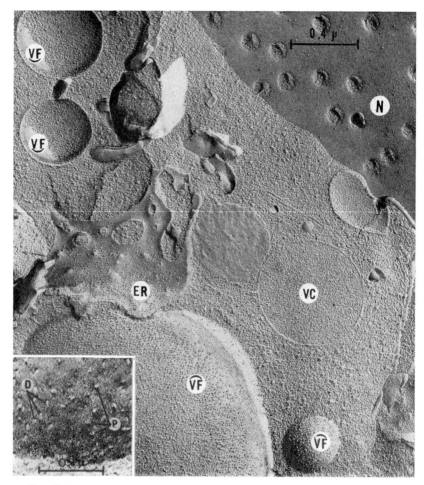

Fᴵɢ. 5. Freeze-etch views of various cell membranes in an onion root-tip cell. Both concave faces (V̲F̲) and convex faces (V͡F͡) of vacuolar membranes have been exposed, as well as the nuclear membrane (N) and endoplasmic reticulum (ER). Inset shows membrane particles (P) and depressions (D) from which some particles have been fractured. From Branton (11).

which cell wall components must pass and upon which they become organized as they are incorporated into the cell wall. Indeed particles in the plasmalemmas of root tip and yeast cells appear to be somewhat more organized than in vacuolar membranes.

    In the yeast plasmalemma the particles embedded in the membrane matrix are distinctly larger (150 to 180 Å in diameter) than in the tonoplast and are frequently concentrated in hexagonal arrays (120). It has been suggested that these arrays may play a role in cell wall formation (120). Between the hexagonally arrayed particles are a great number of randomly distributed single particles. Preliminary attempts to isolate these particles from the membrane matrix by detergent treatment and sonication suggest they are rich in protein and wall polysaccharide. Lipid analyses have not been reported (111).

In pea and onion root tips the plasmalemma contains numerous small particles mostly in random arrays, but sometimes organized into patterns of single or double rows (14, 128). Such patterns are never seen in tonoplast membranes.

In *Chlorella* small particles also appear randomly inserted into the membrane matrix. Here, linear, hexagonal, or other special arrays seen in root tip and yeast cells are lacking (162). On the other hand, correlation of cell age with the plasmalemma structure indicates that the number of particles reaches a maximum just before cell division and a minimum just after cell division. The observations have been used as a basis for conjectures that during interphase the particles are inserted into the membrane from the cytoplasm side and during mitosis move out of the membrane into the surrounding wall material (162).

Chloroplasts.—Because the internal membranes of chloroplasts can be readily isolated and purified, these lamellae have been more extensively investigated—both structurally and functionally—than any other plant membrane system. Studies using standard shadowing and sectioning electron microscopy, polarization optics, and X-ray diffraction techniques have been employed to investigate their molecular organization (for review, see 13). In the discussion of subunit membranes, above, we have already referred to the electron microscopic evidence for particulate structure in chloroplast lamellae. In addition, both the intrinsic birefringence (52) and dichroism (58) are very weak and show that the lipids are not highly ordered in the chloroplast lamellae. X-ray diffraction shows the membranes to be composed of lipid and protein layers but the results cannot be interpreted exclusively in terms of lamellar repeats (76, 94–96, 113). They can be explained in terms of a two-dimensional array of subunits within the membranes, suggesting that if chloroplast lamellae are PLP membranes, the interior of their matrix must be interrupted by such a large number of differential elements as to be detectable by the optical averaging techniques.

Evidence from freeze-etching experiments support this expectation (15, 126). Fracture faces through the hydrophobic interior of chloroplast lamellae show at least two classes of particles. The first type has an average diameter of 175 Å, and is at least 90 Å thick. These particles are sometimes densely packed, occasionally occur in regular arrays, and frequently appear to be composed of three or four substructures. This second type of particle is smaller, corresponding in dimension to the small particles seen in other membranes. These small particles form part of the embedding matrix around the large 175 Å units. Chloroplasts contain more particles per unit area of membrane than any other membrane system thus far examined (Table I).

Although the freeze-etch method provides a remarkably consistent image of the photosynthetic apparatus, interpretations of the resultant micrographs differ as to whether the particles are located within (15) or on (126) the lamellar membranes. Many of these difficulties have been resolved by recent experiments in which freeze-fracturing has been supplemented by extensive deep-etching (drying) to expose the dried membrane surface as well as the fracture face (136). The results (Fig. 6) suggest that particles are embedded within the membrane matrix but may protrude, giving the membrane surface a roughened appearance. The protrusions are easily distinguished from adhering, nonmembrane particles as the latter can usually be removed by EDTA washing (77).

The persistence of a continuous, albeit bumpy, fracture plane through the hydrophobic interior of choloroplast lamellae must reflect the existence of a continuum that holds the particles together. Thus, even chloroplasts appear to consist of a continuous matrix, and the lamellar structure can be interpreted as a continuous, PLP membrane interrupted by an unusually large number of differentiated elements.

Other membranes.—Data regarding particle density in a number of different systems, including those discussed above, are assembled in Table I. Included are results from phospholipid-water mixtures in which lecithin or lecithin-cholesterol mixtures are dispersed as bilayers separated by water. These bilayers are cleaved apart predominantly in the plane of their hydrocarbon tails (163) just as membranes are split in their hydrophobic interiors.

Although the value of a compilation such as that included in Table I is severely limited by haphazard pooling of data taken from different cells under different growth conditions and different stages of the cell cycle, some of the more striking trends are noteworthy.

In the first place, in every membrane system there is a marked and consistent asymmetry in the distribution of particles between the two faces created as a membrane is fractured. For example, most of the vacuolar membrane particles appear on the concave fracture faces whereas fewer particles appear on the convex faces. Thus, the vacuolar particles seem to be more strongly bound to one half of the membrane than to the other. As the two halves are cleaved apart, the particles on one face leave numerous, small, hard-to-discern holes or irregularities on the previously apposed face (11, 110). A similar asymmetry is seen in all other membranes and is diagramed in Figure 7. It is evident that the asymmetry of particle distribution reflects well-known membrane relationships—e.g., continuity between nuclear membrane and endoplasmic reticulum (148), between endoplasmic reticulum and tonoplast (110)—and even extends to chloroplast lamellae if one adopts the view that the inner of the two limiting chloroplast membranes is morphologically an autonomous plasmalemma.

TABLE I

PARTICLE DENSITY ON FRACTURED MEMBRANE FACES

Type of membrane	Number of particles per μ^2 of membrane face		Membrane area covered by particles[a]	Reference[b]
	(a) Densely populated face	(b) Thinly populated face	%	
Lecithin myelin forms	0	0	0	163*
Myelin	0	0	0	12*
Root-tip nuclear membrane	1790	420	12	14*
Plasmalemma				
Root tip	2030	550	15	14, 128*
Red blood cell	2800	1400	23	186*
Yeast	2600	—	63	111, 120*
Vacuole	3300	2480	32	11, 14, 110*
Mitochondria	2700	—	—	119, 122
Chloroplast	3860	1800	80	15, 126*

[a] Area covered by particles calculated from total number of particles [(a)+(b)] and measured diameter of individual particles. There is unfortunately too little information to complete the calculations for mitochondria.

[b] Where reference number is followed by an asterisk, particle counts made on the published photographs have been supplemented, for greater accuracy, by counts on similar unpublished photographs in the author's files.

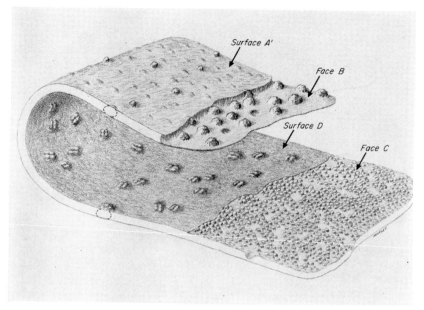

FIG. 6. Interpretation of freeze-etch studies of chloroplast thylakoids. The lamella matrix contains at least two types of differentiated elements which appear as two different-sized particles in the fractured membrane faces. Some of these elements protrude through the membrane surfaces, A′ and D. From Park & Pfeifhofer (136).

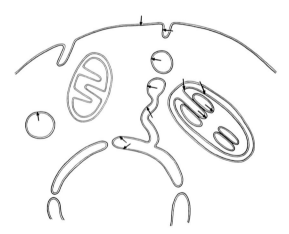

FIG. 7. Membrane asymmetry. Using the data compiled in Table I, the fracture face which always has the largest number of particles is shown by arrows.

                    a   *b*

Fig. 8. Molecular configurations which could account for the freeze-etch results. Particles seen in the fracture faces of frozen membranes are interpreted as (*a*) lipid micelles in equilibrium with a lipid bilayer (57), or (*b*) protein elements in the hydrophobic interior of the membrane. In each case the fractured membrane is on the left.

It is also noteworthy that the number of particles in the membrane matrix is greatest in "active" membranes such as the chloroplast lamellae, which perform the light reactions of photosynthesis (137, 179), and least in "inactive" membranes such as the myelin layers, which function primarily as metabolically inert insulators around the axon (34, 129). Such observations have led to the suggestions that functional complexity of a membrane might be directly related to number of particles (135), but unfortunately there is, as yet, no direct evidence that allows one to ascribe a unique function, or for that matter a defined composition, to the particles seen in the freeze-etched preparations.

Figure 8 shows several possible interpretations of the freeze-etch results. It is assumed in Figure 8a that the particles represent lipid micelles which may be in dynamic equilibrium with the bimolecular leaflet configuration (57, 83, 101, 105). This assumption appears to be unlikely since such micelles, even if present in the living membrane, would probably disappear as the temperature of the specimen is lowered in pareparation for the freeze-etch procedure. Below a critical transition temperature lipids undergo phase transitions to a crystalline lamellar gel (23, 97, 145). This does not rule out the possibility of micellar lipid arrangements *in vivo* but simply makes it unlikely that they can be studied with the freeze-etch technique.

A more likely interpretation of the freeze-etch results is indicated in Figure 8b. According to this model, the membrane matrix is interpenetrated with proteins or polypeptides which may interact hydrophobically with the membrane lipids. The presence of such proteins within the membrane would deflect the fracture plane, as shown, and might explain one important difficulty encountered with interpretations of freeze-etch images: there do not seem to be adequate depressions into which all of the particles can be fitted (24). This might be because some stretching or deformation of the interpenetrated protein is possible even at the −100° C temperatures used in freeze-etching (24). Deformations could exaggerate the apparent size of the particles or render the cavities from which they are torn hard to discern and irregular. Furthermore, if the lipids and protein within the differentiated membrane elements interact hydrophobically, as in Figure 8b, the presence of protein would not necessitate a full-particle size discontinuity in the lipid bilayer, but at most an increased space between the lipid molecules. Increased spacing, large enough to accommodate even several peptide chains, might not be clearly resolved as a hole by the shadow methods used in the freeze-etch technique. Thus the diagram of Figure 8b predicts that particles would be easier to detect than holes because the detailed regions of lipid-protein interdigitation would be distorted, irregular or unresolvable.

Some progress in specifying the location of specific chemical components within the membrane matrix has come from enzyme extraction experiments performed in chloroplast lamellae: treatments with lipase and protease caused unique morphological changes within the lamellae, and these changes were used to assign chemical composition to some of the structures revealed by freeze-etching (1). The results suggest that galactolipids make up the smooth regions of the membrane matrix and that chlorophyll as well as protein is associated with the large particles seen in photosynthetic membranes. A more promising approach is the direct separation and purification of the membrane particles. Detergent and sonication treatments have been used to liberate the particle-bearing membrane fragments from yeast plasmalemma (111). The preliminary results suggest that the particles may contain glycoproteins and play a role in the development of the cell wall. Separation and isolation of membrane fragments have been highly successful in conjunction with negative staining techniques to localize ATPase activity in particles attached to the surface of inner mitochondrial membranes (141, 142). However, the progress of similar approaches to identify differentiated regions embedded within the membrane has been slow. Now that the freeze-etch method provides a means of visualizing specialized regions inside the membrane matrix, it should be possible to relate functional differentiation of the membrane with internal structural modifications.

CONCLUSION

Awareness of the biochemical and functional diversity among different membrane systems has stimulated interest in the possibility of membrane structures other than that postulated in the classical Danielli-Davson PLP membrane. Nevertheless, a bimolecular lipid leaflet continues to provide the best explanation for the unspecialized properties of the membrane. Recent investigations in four critical areas are consistent with this conclusion. First, lipid extraction experiments have demonstrated that the staining patterns of membranes are unchanged by lipid extraction in spite of the fact that electron microscope fixatives react with the unsaturated fatty acids of membrane lipids. Thus, the two dark lines which form the electron microscope image of nearly all biological membrane surfaces remain intact after all lipid is removed. This shows that a substantial portion of the membrane protein must be on the membrane surface. Second, newer methods of solubilizing membrane proteins indicate that these proteins can present either hydrophobic or hydrophilic groups for interaction with other membrane components. Although hydrophobic bonding has been invoked to explain lipid-protein binding in isolated membrane components, polar bonding may dominate lipid-protein association in the unspecialized membrane matrix. Third, properly doped thin phospholipid membranes have properties comparable to those of living cell membranes. This shows that a lipid bilayer could provide the environment to support the functionally active groups that explain the many specialized properties of different membranes. Finally, freeze-etching yields face views of internally cleaved membranes. Such cleavage is compatible with fracture between the hydrocarbon tails of a bimolecular leaflet but is difficult to reconcile with a true subunit membrane. On the other hand, freeze-etching also shows that a range of substructural complexity can be accommodated within the hydrophobic interior of active membranes. This technique therefore provides the morphological basis for distinguishing an undifferentiated membrane matrix from what may be more specialized functional sites within this matrix.

It is obvious that conjectures which postulate differentiated elements within the membrane are of little use until bolstered by knowledge of their specific composition, mode of attachment, and function. Nevertheless, the hypothesis that only a small fraction of a given membrane may be relevant to a given function should emphasize the need for approaches which do not rely exclusively on average properties. Techniques which seek to separate and purify relevant fragments are required. Because membrane-associated functions may be dependent upon hydrophobic interactions favored within the membrane matrix, isolation procedures which preserve existing molecular relationships rather than synthesize *ad hoc* membrane units should provide the most rewarding insights linking membrane structure and function.

LITERATURE CITED

1. Bamberger, E. S., Park, R. B., *Plant Physiol.*, **41**, 1591–1600 (1966)
2. Bangham, A. D., Horne, R. W., *J. Mol. Biol.*, **8**, 660–68 (1964)
3. Bangham, A. D., Standish, M. M., Miller, N., *Nature*, **208**, 1295–97 (1966)
4. Bangham, A. D., Standish, M. M., Watkins, J. C., *J. Mol. Biol.*, **13**, 238–52 (1965)
5. Bangham, A. D., Standish, M. M., Weissmann, G., *J. Mol. Biol.*, **13**, 253–59 (1965)
6. Bar, R. S., Deamer, D. W., Cornwell, D. G., *Science*, **153**, 1010–12 (1966)
7. Benedetti, E. L., Emmelot, P., *J. Cell. Biol.*, **26**, 299–305 (1965)
8. Benson, A. A., *Ann. Rev. Plant Physiol.*, **15**, 1–16 (1964)
9. Benson, A. A., *J. Am. Oil Chemists' Soc.*, **43**, 265–70 (1966)
10. Blumenfeld, O. O., *Biochem. Biophys. Res. Commun.*, **30**, 200–5 (1968)
11. Branton, D., *Proc. Natl. Acad. Sci. U.S.*, **55**, 1048–56 (1966)
12. Branton, D., *Exptl. Cell Res.*, **45**, 703–7 (1967)
13. Branton, D., in *Photophysiology*, **3**, 197–224 (Giese, A. C., Ed., Academic Press, New York/London, 1968)
14. Branton, D., Moor, H., *J. Ultrastruct. Res.*, **11**, 401–11 (1964)
15. Branton, D., Park, R. B., *J. Ultrastruct. Res.*, **19**, 283–303 (1967)
16. Branton, D., Park, R. B., *Papers on Biological Membrane Structure* (Little, Brown, Boston, 311 pp., 1968)
17. Branton, D., Southworth, D., *Exptl. Cell Res.*, **47**, 648–53 (1967)
18. Bullivant, S., Ames, A., *J. Cell Biol.*, **29**, 435–47 (1966)
19. Butler, T., Smith, G. L., Grula, E., *Can. J. Microbiol.*, **13**, 1471–79 (1967)
20. Chapman, D., Kamat, V. B., DeGier, J., Penkett, S. A., *Nature*, **213**, 74–75 (1967)
21. Chapman, D., Kamat, V. B., DeGier, J., Penkett, S. A., *J. Mol. Biol.*, **31**, 101–14 (1968)
22. Chapman, D., Kamat, V. B., Levene, R. J., *Science*, **160**, 314–16 (1968)
23. Chapman, D., Williams, R. M., Ladbrooke, B. D., *Chem. Phys. Lipids*, **1**, 445–75 (1967)
24. Clark, A. W., Branton, D., *Z. Zellforsch.*, **91**, 586–603 (1968)
25. Coleman, R., Finean, J. B., *Biochim. Biophys. Acta*, **125**, 197–206 (1966)
26. Collander, R., *Physiol. Plantarum*, **2**, 300–11 (1949)
27. Criddle, R. S., Bouck, R. M., Green, D. E., Tisdale, H., *Biochemistry*, **1**, 827–42 (1962)
28. Criddle, R. S., Park, L., *Biochem. Biophys. Res. Commun.*, **17**, 74–79 (1964)
29. Cunningham, W. P., Crane, F. L., *Exptl. Cell Res.*, **44**, 31–45 (1966)
30. Danielli, J. F., *Proc. Roy. Soc. (London), Ser. B*, **122**, 155–74 (1937)
31. Danielli, J. F., *Colston Papers*, **7**, 1–14 (1954)
32. Danielli, J. F., Davson, H., *J. Cellular Comp. Physiol.*, **5**, 495–508 (1935)
33. Danielli, J. F., Harvey, E. N., *J. Cell. Physiol.*, **5**, 483–94 (1935)
34. Davison, A. N., Dobbing, J., *Biochem. J.*, **75**, 565–70 (1960)
35. Deamer, D. W., Branton, D., *Science*, **158**, 655–57 (1967)
36. Demel, R. A., Kinsky, S. C., Kinsky, C. B., Van Deenen, L. L. M., *Biochim. Biophys. Acta*, **150**, 655–65 (1968)
37. Dreher, K. D., Schulman, J. H., Anderson, O. R., Roels, O. A., *J. Ultrastruct. Res.*, **19**, 586–99 (1967)
38. Engelman, D. M., Morowitz, H. J., *Biochim. Biophys. Acta*, **150**, 376–84 (1968)
39. Engelman, D. M., Morowitz, H. J., *ibid.*, 385–96
40. Engelman, D. M., Terry, T. M., Morowitz, H. J., *Biochim. Biophys. Acta*, **135**, 381–90 (1967)
41. Fensom, D. S., Wanless, I. R., *J. Exptl. Botany*, **18**, 563–77 (1967)
42. Fernandez-Moran, H., *Circulation*, **26**, 1039–65 (1962)
43. Fernandez-Moran, H., Finean, J. B., *J. Biophys. Biochem. Cytol.*, **3**, 725–48 (1957)
44. Fernandez-Moran, H., Oda, T., Blair, P. V., Green, D. E., *J. Cell Biol.*, **22**, 63–100 (1964)
45. Finean, J. B., *Circulation*, **26**, 1151–62 (1962)
46. Finean, J. B., Coleman, R., Green,

W. G., Limbrick, A. R., *J. Cell Sci.*, **1**, 287–96 (1966)

47. Finean, J. B., Coleman, R., Knutton, S., Limbrick, A. R., Thompson, J. E., *J. Gen. Physiol.*, **51**, 19S–25S (1968)

48. Fleischer, S., Brierly, G., Klouwen, H., Slautterback, D. B., *J. Biol. Chem.*, **237**, 3264–72 (1962)

49. Fleischer, S., Fleischer, B., Stoeckenius, W., *J. Cell Biol.*, **32**, 193–208 (1967)

50. Fleischer, S., Klouwen, H., Brierly, G., *J. Biol. Chem.*, **236**, 2936–41 (1961)

51. Frank, H. S., Evans, M. W., *J. Chem. Phys.*, **13**, 507–32 (1945)

52. Frey-Wyssling, A., Steinmann, E., *Biochim. Biophys. Acta*, **2**, 254–59 (1948)

53. Frey-Wyssling, A., Steinmann, E., *Vierteljahresschr. Naturforsch. Ges.* (Zurich), **98**, 20–29 (1953)

54. Gainer, H., *Biochim. Biophys. Acta*, **135**, 560–62 (1967)

55. Gent, W., Gregson, N., Gammack, D., Raper, J., *Nature*, **204**, 553–55 (1964)

56. Geren, B. B., *Exptl. Cell Res.*, **7**, 558–62 (1954)

57. Glauert, A. M., *J. Roy. Microscop. Soc.*, **88**, 49–70 (1968)

58. Goedheer, J. C., *Optical Properties and In Vivo Orientation of Photosynthetic Pigments* (Proefschrift. Drukkerij Gebr. Janssen. Nijmegen, 1957)

59. Gorter, E., Grendel, F., *J. Exptl. Med.*, **41**, 439–43 (1925)

60. Green, D. E., Fleischer, S., *Biochim. Biophys. Acta*, **70**, 554–82 (1963)

61. Green, D. E., Fleischer, S., in *Metabolism and Physiological Significance of Lipids*, 581–618 (Dawson, R. M. C., Rhodes, D. N., Eds., Wiley, New York, 1964)

62. Green, D. E., Haard, N. F., Lenaz, G., Silman, H. I., *Proc. Natl. Acad. Sci. U.S.*, **60**, 277–84 (1968)

63. Green, D. E., Perdue, J. F., *Proc. Natl. Acad. Sci. U.S.*, **55**, 1295–1302 (1966)

64. Green, D. E., Tisdale, H. D., Criddle, R. S., Chen, P. Y., Bock, R. M., *Biochem. Biophys. Res. Commun.*, **5**, 109–14 (1961)

65. Green, D. E., Tzagoloff, A., *J. Lipid Res.*, **7**, 587–602 (1966)

66. Grula, E. A., Butler, T. E., King, R. D., Smith, G. L., *Can. J. Microbiol.*, **13**, 1499–1507 (1967)

67. Gulik-Krzywicki, T., Rivas, E., Luzzati, V., *J. Mol. Biol.*, **27**, 303–22 (1967)

68. Gutknecht, J., *Science*, **158**, 787–88 (1967)

69. Gutknecht, J., *Biochim. Biophys. Acta*, **163**, 20–29 (1968)

70. Habeeb, A., Hiramoto, R., *Arch. Biochem. Biophys.*, **126**, 16–26 (1968)

71. Harvey, E. N., *Protoplasmatologia*, **2**, E5, 1–30 (1954)

72. Haydon, D. A., Taylor, J., *J. Theoret. Biol.*, **4**, 281–96 (1963)

73. Heinz, E., *Z. Naturforsch.*, **20b**, 83 (1965)

74. Hillier, J., Hoffman, J. F., *J. Cellular Comp. Physiol.*, **42**, 203–47 (1953)

75. Horne, R. W., Whittaker, V. P., Bangham, A. D., *Nature*, **200**, 1340 (1963)

76. Hosemann, R., Kreutz, W., *Naturwissenschaften*, **12**, 298–304 (1966)

77. Howell, S. H., Moudrianakis, E. N., *J. Mol. Biol.*, **27**, 323–33 (1967)

78. Jost, M., *Arch. Mikrobiol.*, **50**, 211–45 (1965)

79. Kausche, G. A., Ruska, H., *Naturwissenschaften*, **28**, 303–4 (1940)

80. Kauzmann, W., *Advan. Protein Chem.*, **14**, 1–63 (1959)

81. Kavanau, J. L., *Nature*, **198**, 525–30 (1963)

82. Kavanau, J. L., *Structure and Function in Biological Membranes*, **1**, **2** (Holden-Day, San Francisco, 1965)

83. Kavanau, J. L., *Federation Proc.*, **25**, 1096–1107 (1966)

84. Ke, B., *Arch. Biochem. Biophys.*, **112**, 554–61 (1965)

85. Ke, B., *Nature*, **208**, 573–74 (1965)

86. Klingenberg, M., in *Mitochondrial Structure and Compartmentation*, 157 (Quagliariello, E., Papa, S., Slater, E. C., Tager, J. M., Eds., Adriatica Editrice, Bari, Italy, 1967)

87. Koehler, J. K., *Advan. Biol. Med. Phys.*, **12**, 1–84 (1968)

88. Kopaczyk, K., Asai, J., Allmann, D. W., Oda, T., Green, D. E., *Arch. Biochem. Biophys.*, **123**, 602–21 (1968)

89. Kopaczyk, K., Asai, J., Green, D. E., *Arch. Biochem. Biophys.*, **126**, 358–79 (1968)

90. Korn, E. D., *Science*, **153**, 1491–98 (1966)

91. Korn, E. D., *Biochim. Biophys. Acta*, **116**, 317–24 (1966)

92. Korn, E. D., *ibid.*, 325–35
93. Korn, E. D., *J. Cell. Biol.*, **34**, 627–38 (1967)
94. Kreutz, W., in *Biochemistry of Chloroplasts*, **I**, 83–88 (Goodwin, T. W., Ed., Academic Press, London/New York, 1966)
95. Kreutz, W., *Ber. Deut. Botan. Ges.*, **79**, 34–43 (1966)
96. Kreutz, W., Weber, P., *Naturwissenschaften*, **53**, 11–14 (1966)
97. Ladbrooke, B. D., Williams, R. M., Chapman, D., *Biochim. Biophys. Acta*, **150**, 333–40 (1968)
98. Lenard, J., Singer, S. J., *Proc. Natl. Acad. Sci. U.S.*, **56**, 1828–35 (1966)
99. Lenard, J., Singer, S. J., *Science*, **159**, 738–39 (1968)
100. Lowe, A., *Nature*, **219**, 934–36 (1968)
101. Lucy, J. A., *J. Theoret. Biol.*, **7**, 360–73 (1964)
102. Lucy, J. A., Glauert, A. M., *J. Mol. Biol.*, **8**, 727–48 (1964)
103. Luzzati, V., Gulik-Krzywicki, T., Tardieu, A., *Nature*, **218**, 1031–34 (1968)
104. Luzzati, V., Reiss-Husson, F., *J. Cell Biol.*, **12**, 207–19 (1962)
105. Luzzati, V., Reiss-Husson, F., Rivas, E., Gulik-Krzywicki, T., *Ann. N.Y. Acad. Sci.*, **137**, 409–13 (1966)
106. Maddy, A. H., *Intern. Rev. Cytol.*, **20**, 1–65 (1966)
107. Maddy, A. H., Malcolm, B. R., *Science*, **150**, 1616–17 (1965)
108. Maddy, A. H., Malcolm, B. R., *ibid.*, **153**, 213 (1966)
109. Marchesi, V. T., Steers, E., *Science*, **159**, 203–4 (1968)
110. Matile, P., Moor, H., *Planta*, **80**, 159–75 (1968)
111. Matile, P., Moor, H., Mühlethaler, K., *Arch. Mikrobiol.*, **58**, 201–11 (1967)
112. Mazia, D., Ruby, A., *Proc. Natl. Acad. Sci. U.S.* (In press)
113. Menke, W., in *Biochemistry of Chloroplasts*, **1**, 3–18 (See Ref. 94)
114. Mitchell, P., *Nature*, **180**, 134–36 (1957)
115. Mitchell, P., in *Membrane Transport and Metabolism*, 22–34 (Kleinzeller, A., Kotyk, A., Eds., Academic Press, London, 1961)
116. Mitchell, P., *Biochem. Soc. Symp.*, **22**, 142–68 (1963)
117. Mitchell, P., *Federation Proc.*, **26**, 1370–79 (1967)
118. Mitchell, P., Moyle, J., *Nature*, **182**, 372–73 (1958)
119. Moor, H., *Z. Zellforsch.*, **62**, 546–80 (1964)
120. Moor, H., Mühlethaler, K., *J. Cell Biol.*, **17**, 609–28 (1963)
121. Moor, H., Mühlethaler, K., Waldner, H., Frey-Wyssling, A., *J. Biophys. Biochem. Cytol.*, **10**, 1–13 (1961)
122. Moor, H., Ruska, C., Ruska, H., *Z. Zellforsch.*, **62**, 581–601 (1964)
123. Mueller, P., Rudin, D. O., *J. Theoret. Biol.*, **18**, 222–58 (1968)
124. Mueller, P., Rudin, D. O., Tien, H. T., Wescot, W. C., *Circulation*, **26**, 1167–73 (1962)
125. Mueller, P., Rudin, D. O., Tien, H. T., Wescot, W. C., in *Recent Progress in Surface Science*, 379–93 (Danielli, J. F., Parkhurst, K. G. A., Riddiford, A. C., Eds., Academic Press, New York, 1964)
126. Mühlethaler, K., Moor, H., Szarkowski, J. W., *Planta*, **67**, 305–23 (1965)
127. Napolitano, L., LeBaron, F., Scaletti, J., *J. Cell Biol.*, **58**, 817–26 (1967)
128. Northcote, D. H., Lewis, D. R., *J. Cell Sci.*, **3**, 199–206 (1968)
129. O'Brien, J. S., *Science*, **147**, 1099–1107 (1965)
130. O'Brien, J. S., *J. Theoret. Biol.*, **15**, 307–24 (1967)
131. Ongun, A., Thomson, W. W., Mudd, J. B., *J. Lipid Res.*, **9**, 416–24 (1968)
132. Overton, E., *Vierteljahresschr. Naturforsch. Ges.* (Zurich), **44**, 88–135 (1967)
133. Papahadjopoulos, D., Watkins, J. C., *Biochim. Biophys. Acta*, **135**, 639–52 (1967)
134. Park, R. B., Biggins, J., *Science*, **144**, 1009–11 (1964)
135. Park, R. B., Branton, D., *Brookhaven Symp. Biol.*, **19**, 341–52 (1966)
136. Park, R. B., Pfeifhofer, A. O., *J. Cell Sci.* (In press)
137. Park, R. B., Pon, N. G., *J. Mol. Biol.*, **3**, 1–10 (1961)
138. Park, R. B., Pon, N. G., *ibid.*, **6**, 105–14 (1963)
139. Park, R. B., Shumway, L. K., in *Comparative Biochemistry and Biophysics of Photosynthesis* (Shibata, K., Takamiya, A., Jagendorf,

A. T., Fuller, R. C., Eds., Univ. Tokyo Press, Tokyo, 1968)

140. Plowe, J. Q., *Protoplasma*, **12**, 196–221 (1931)

141. Racker, E., *Federation Proc.*, **26**, 1335–40 (1967)

142. Racker, E., Horstman, L. L., *J. Biol. Chem.*, **242**, 2547–51 (1967)

143. Razin, S., Morowitz, H. J., Terry, T. M., *Proc. Natl. Acad. Sci. U.S.*, **54**, 219–25 (1965)

144. Rega, A. F., Weed, R. I., Reed, C. F., Berg, G. G., Rothstein, A., *Biochim. Biophys. Acta*, **147**, 297–312 (1967)

145. Reiss-Husson, F., *J. Mol. Biol.*, **25**, 363–82 (1967)

146. Richardson, S. H., Hultin, H. O., Green, D. E., *Proc. Natl. Acad. Sci. U.S.*, **50**, 821–27 (1963)

147. Riemersma, J. C., *Biochim. Biophys. Acta*, **152**, 718–27 (1968)

148. Robertson, J. D., *Biochem. Soc. Symp.*, **16**, 3–43 (1959)

149. Robertson, J. D., *Soc. Study Develop. Growth*, **22**, 1–81 (1964)

150. Robertson, J. D., *Ann. N.Y. Acad. Sci.*, **137**, 421–40 (1966)

151. Rothfield, L., Finkelstein, A., *Ann. Rev. Biochem.*, **37**, 463–96 (1968)

152. Ruesink, A. W., Thimann, K. V., *Proc. Natl. Acad. Sci. U.S.*, **54**, 56–64 (1965)

153. Sabatini, D., Bensch, K., Barrnett, R. J., *J. Cell Biol.*, **17**, 19–58 (1963)

154. Salton, M. R. J., *Trans. N.Y. Acad. Sci.*, **29**, 764–81 (1967)

155. Sastry, P. S., Kates, M., *Biochemistry*, **3**, 1280–87 (1964)

156. Schmidt, W. J., *Z. Zellforsch. Mikroskop. Anat.*, **23**, 657–76 (1936)

157. Schmitt, F. O., Bear, R. S., Clark, G. L., *Radiology*, **25**, 131–51 (1935)

158. Schmitt, F. O., Bear, R. S., Palmer, K., *J. Cellular Comp. Physiol.*, **18**, 31–41 (1941)

159. Sjöstrand, F. S., *J. Ultrastruct. Res.*, **9**, 340–61 (1963)

160. Sjöstrand, F. S., Elfvin, L. G., *J. Ultrastruct. Res.*, **10**, 263–92 (1964)

161. Smith, E. L., Pickels, E. G., *J. Gen. Physiol.*, **24**, 753–64 (1941)

162. Staehelin, A., *Z. Zellforsch.*, **74**, 325–50 (1966)

163. Staehelin, A., *J. Ultrastruct. Res.*, **22**, 326–47 (1968)

164. Steere, R. L., *J. Biophys. Biochem. Cytol.*, **3**, 45–60 (1957)

165. Steim, J. M., Edner, O. J., Bargoot, F. G., *Science*, **162**, 909–11 (1968)

166. Steim, J. M., Fleischer, S., *Proc. Natl. Acad. Sci. U.S.*, **58**, 1292–98 (1967)

167. Steim, J. M., Reinert, J. C., Tourtellotte, M. E., McElhaney, R. N., Rader, R. L., *Proc. Natl. Acad. Sci. U.S.* (In press, 1969)

168. Stein, W. D., *The Movement of Molecules Across Cell Membranes* (Academic Press, New York/London, 369 pp., 1967)

169. Stein, W. D., Danielli, J. F., *Discussions Faraday Soc.*, **21**, 238–51 (1956)

170. Stoeckenius, W., *J. Biophys. Biochem. Cytol.*, **5**, 491–500 (1959)

171. Stoeckenius, W., *Proc. European Conf. Electron Microscopy*, **II**, 716–20 (Delft, 1960)

172. Stoeckenius, W., *J. Cell Biol.*, **12**, 221–29 (1962)

173. Stoeckenius, W., *Circulation*, **26**, 1066–69 (1962)

174. Stoeckenius, W., in *Principles of Biomolecular Organization*, 418–41 (Wolstenholm, G., O'Connor, M., Eds., Churchill, London, 1966)

175. Terry, T. M., Engelman, D. M., Morowitz, H. J., *Biochim. Biophys. Acta*, **135**, 391–405 (1967)

176. Thompson, J. E., Coleman, R., Finean, J. B., *Biochim. Biophys. Acta*, **135**, 1074–78 (1967)

177. Thompson, T. E., in *Cellular Membranes in Development*, 83–96 (Locke, M., Ed., Academic Press, New York/London, 1964)

178. Tien, H. T., Diana, A. L., *Chem. Phys. Lipids*, **2**, 55–101 (1968)

179. Trebst, A. V., Tsujimoto, H. Y., Arnon, D. I., *Nature*, **182**, 351–55 (1958)

180. Urry, D. W., Mednieks, M., Bejnarowicz, E., *Proc. Natl. Acad. Sci. U.S.*, **57**, 1043–49 (1967)

181. Vandenheuvel, F. A., *J. Am. Oil Chemists' Soc.*, **42**, 481–92 (1965)

182. Wallach, D. F. H., Zahler, P. H., *Proc. Natl. Acad. Sci. U.S.*, **56**, 1552–59 (1966)

183. Wartiovaara, V., Collander, R., in *Protoplasmatologia: Handbuch der Protoplasmaforschung*, **II**, c. 8d (Springer, Vienna, 1960)

184. Weier, T. E., Benson, A. A., *Am. J. Botany*, **54**, 389–402 (1967)

185. Weier, T. E., Engelbrecht, A. H. P.,
     Harrison, A., Risley, E. B., *J.
     Ultrastruct. Res.*, **13,** 92–111
     (1965)
186. Weinstein, R. S., Bullivant, S.,
     Blood, **29,** 780–89 (1967)
187. Whaley, W. G., Mollenhauer, H. H.,
     Leech, J. H., *Am. J. Botany*, **47,**
     401–49 (1960)

188. Wirtz, K. W. A., Zilversmit, D. B.,
     J. Biol. Chem., **243,** 3596–3602
     (1968)
189. Wolpers, C., *Naturwissenschaften*,
     29, 416–24 (1941)
190. Zahler, W. L., Saito, A., Fleischer,
     S., *Biochem. Biophys. Res. Commun.*, **32,** 512–18 (1968)

STRUCTURAL PROTEINS OF CHLOROPLASTS AND MITOCHONDRIA[1]

By R. S. CRIDDLE

*Department of Biochemistry and Biophysics, University of California
Davis, California*

Any discussion of chloroplast and mitochondrial structural proteins (SP) raises the questions: just what feature of a protein species distinguishes it as a structural protein; and does a class of proteins exist in such membrane systems which either has an exclusive structural role or which is central to the membrane structure while possibly being involved in some additional function?

In such comparatively simple units as the spherical plant viruses, one can readily obtain a structural protein fraction which has no other known function. In bacterial viruses, this fraction, with an equally well-defined role as structural or coat protein, in some cases also has a demonstrable enzymic function. Mitochondrial and chloroplast membranes, on the other hand, with their large array of components have no such obvious species to assign a structural role. In the simplest sense, all the membrane proteins are structural proteins as all contribute in some way to the structure. Further analysis makes it apparent that not all of these proteins are equally tightly associated with the membrane and that some obviously contribute much more to the structure than others. While this type of approach may be used to rule out weakly associating components as candidates for the key element of membrane structure, it offers no means of selecting a unique protein component and stating that this is a structural protein.

The claim for the existence of a unique structural protein class in mitochondria and chloroplasts was based mainly on the preparation of a protein fraction, accounting for nearly 50 per cent of the membrane protein, for which no other function could be detected and on analogy with other membrane systems which have structural protein.

Subsequent work on this membrane fraction has been largely aimed at investigation of its chemical and physical properties and at the study of any property which might define its structural role. It will be this work that is reviewed here. It will become evident to the reader that much of this review will deal with evidence that a class of structural proteins does exist and with a discussion of the properties of these proteins. While this may

---

[1] The following abbreviations will be used: SP (structural protein); MSP (mitochondrial structural protein); CSP (chloroplast structural protein); DNP (dinitrophenol).

seem a somewhat one-sided approach to the question, it must be kept in mind that it is very difficult to establish a structural role for a protein from such complex organelles, and even more difficult to rule out the existence of such a specific structural protein. The requirement for proof lies with the proponents of the structural protein, and it is this information which is assembled.

Methods of isolation of structural protein.—Structural protein (SP) was first isolated from mitochondria by ammonium sulfate fractionation of the mitochondrial preparation "solubilized" by a combination of the detergents cholate, deoxycholate, and sodium dodecyl sulfate (1, 2). From such detergent solubilized preparation, SP is generally precipitated at 12 to 14 per cent saturation with ammonium sulfate. After washing with buffer and removal of lipid, this material is essentially free of colored components and accounts for near 40 per cent of the mitochondrial protein.

Several subsequent methods of preparation have been proposed to obtain a product with different binding properties or with a higher degree of purity. Richardson et al. (3) eliminated the use of sodium dodecyl sulfate in their isolation procedure to obtain a preparation which had greater capacity to bind phospholipid. This preparation also would serve as Factor 4 in the partial reconstitution of the phosphorylating system of the electron transport chain (4). A modification of this procedure has subsequently been worked out by Allman et al. (5).

Other preparations of MSP (mitochondrial structural protein) fractions include potassium hydroxide solubilization and neutralization to precipitate SP (6), extraction of SP from mitochondria with 10 mM HCl (7), solubilization of the protein by succinylation (8), and solubilization of a protein fraction with 1.4 per cent acetic acid (9). Pinna & Wadkins solubilized the mitochondrial fraction with 8 M urea and 0.2 M mercaptoethanol and precipitated out SP by dialysis against dilute buffer (10). Some further fractionation of components isolated in these preparations by extraction with urea solutions has been reported by Lenaz et al. (7). The "Factor 4" studied by Racker and co-workers, which may have as a major protein component the same species isolated as SP, is isolated by extraction with 1.2 M ammonium hydroxide followed by ammonium sulfate fractionation (4).

Structural protein has been isolated from mitochondria with altered respiratory capacity prepared from petite yeast cells (11) and also from the promitochondrial fraction (12) of anaerobically grown yeast cells (13). In both of these cases, a SP fraction with the same general amino acid composition (11) or with the same pattern of electrophoretic mobilities on disc gel observed in wild type cells was found (13). Thus, even though major components of the electron transport chain are absent or at very low concentration in these mitochondria (13, 14), the pattern of SP is the same.

The yield of structural protein from all of these preparation procedures is in the range of 40 per cent of the total mitochondrial protein. The degree of homogeneity of the products from each procedure varies greatly and will be discussed below.

Fewer preparations of chloroplast structural proteins have been reported and correspondingly less work has been done in characterization of this material. Menke & Jordan described the extraction of soluble or readily solubilized protein from chloroplasts with dilute buffers to leave what was termed an insoluble membrane structural protein fraction (15).

Solubilization of chloroplast lamellae with various detergents and organic solvents has led to the description of a number of protein or protein-chlorophyll fractions. (For reviews see 16, 17). The fractions obtained are heterogeneous in nature and have been reported to have average molecular weights from approximately 20,000 to over one million. Bailey et al. (17) have described a fractionation of lamellae proteins with acetic acid extractions and have investigated the homogeneity of their preparation with disc gel electrophoresis.

Criddle & Park (18) carried out a fractionation of washed chloroplast lamellae using essentially the same procedures employed for isolation of the mitochondrial protein. This led to a preparation of a low molecular weight protein, with solubility properties resembling preparations of MSP.

SP from non-mitochondrial sources.—A structural protein fraction has been isolated from a large number of membrane sources. As several recent reviews in this area have been published (c.f. 19), these proteins will not be considered here. Of particular interest, however, is the report by Munkres & Woodward (20) of the isolation of the same structural protein from mitochondrial, microsomal, and nuclear membranes, as well as from the soluble fraction from *Neurospora*. The evidence for the identity of the protein isolated from each of these fractions is based upon amino acid analyses, peptide mapping, similar solubility properties, and immunological cross reaction. While this may still leave the question of exact identity open, the marked similarities are of great interest. It has been clearly established that mutations resulting in changes in SP amino acid composition from the mitochondrial source appear as identical changes in the protein from each of these sources. The recent observations of Attardi & Attardi (21) that an RNA produced in the mitochondria of HeLa cells may be exported to other membrane structures may account for the appearance of similar proteins in these different membranes.

The question of how an insoluble membrane protein can appear in the soluble phase following cell fractionation has puzzled many, but may be accounted for by the formation of SP complexes with other cell components. The ability to form such soluble complexes with other proteins or lipids has been noted (2, 3, 22). Just what role these soluble complexes may be playing and just what is the necessity of structural protein in such complexes is still unknown.

PROPERTIES OF SP PREPARATIONS

Molecular weight.—The molecular weight of MSP from beef heart was first measured by Criddle et al. (2) to be 22,000 by means of sedimentation equilibrium in solutions containing 0.05 per cent sodium dodecylsulphate. As was pointed out, these solution conditions gave rise to some experimental uncertainty in the exact value of this molecular weight, but other sources of information have yielded additional evidence supporting this value. This includes molecular weight measurements of SP complexes with cytochromes (2), with myoglobin (22), and combining weights of SP with these same components (22, 23). NADH has been reported to bind in a ratio of one molecule per 20,000 to 25,000 mol wt structural proteins (25, 26), and ATP is also bound stoichiometrically under appropriate conditions to give a minimal combining weight of 23,000 (24).

Structural protein from other mitochondrial sources yielded similar molecular weight values. *Neurospora* MSP, for example, has a molecular weight of 22,000 to 25,000 based on sedimentation equilibrium (6) and binds one mole of the mitochondrial enzyme malic dehydrogenase, one molecule of NADH, or one molecule of ATP per mole of SP (26).

The molecular weight of CSP (chloroplast structural protein) has also been measured at near 25,000 (18). Again the uncertainties of measurements on a marginally soluble material in a detergent-containing solution are apparent. In this instance, there is less direct supporting evidence available to establish the accuracy of this value. Secondary information does, however, come from the X-ray studies of Menke (27), which indicate a chloroplast membrane matrix made up of repeating units of this size.

It is interesting to note that SP from many other sources, i.e., virus

TABLE I

AMINO ACID COMPOSITION OF STRUCTURAL PROTEINS
MOLES AA PER MOLE PROTEIN (22,500 G/M)

Amino acid	Beef heart	Yeast	*Neurospora*
Ala	17.8	13.3	18.9
Arg	9.5	7.4	9.9
Asp	14.6	16.7	16.5
1/2 Cys	4.5	9.0	3.5
Glu	20.1	17.4	18.5
Gly	16.2	9.2	16.0
His	2.5	3.1	4.3
Ileu	9.7	9.7	9.8
Leu	17.1	15.3	16.0
Lys	11.9	13.1	11.7
Met	4.0	2.9	3.8
Phe	8.5	7.7	7.2
Pro	8.3	7.4	7.7
Ser	10.4	10.7	10.7
Thr	9.2	9.0	9.8
Tryp	1.8	1.8	2.5
Tyr	5.8	5.4	5.2
Val	12.9	10.3	13.1

coat proteins (28), bacterial membranes (29), and microsomal membranes (30) have molecular weights which fall in this general size range of 20,000 to 30,000 mol wt.

Recent studies on beef heart MSP in the laboratory of D. E. Green have suggested that the molecular weight of this protein is much higher than the previously reported values would indicate (31). These values, based on centrifugation studies in quanidinium hydrochloride solutions, indicate molecular weights in the range of 55,000 to 70,000. It is apparent that a gross heterogeneity of molecular sizes was present in the solutions analyzed in these studies, as the plot of mass distribution in the cell used for their calculations deviated from the ideal straight line such that: "In many of these experiments this plot resulted in a straight line for data points from the meniscus to about the midpoint of the solution" (31). The high values obtained certainly reflect in part this heterogeneity. When one notes that a molecular weight of 22,000 was obtained for lysozyme in these same studies [actual molecular weight 14,000 (32)], the accuracy of the high values reported becomes even more questionable.

Amino acid composition.—The amino acid compositions of structural proteins from a large number of sources have been investigated. The similarities among the various preparations have been noted (6). Table I indicates the amino acid composition of some SP preparations. While at one time a high percentage of nonpolar side chain amino acids relative to other known proteins was suggested as a characteristic of this material (2), as more membrane bound or slightly soluble proteins have been investigated for comparison, this value no longer appears exceptionally high.

The MSP amino acid composition of the cytoplasmic "pokey" mutants mi-1 and mi-3 from *Neurospora* have been shown to differ in amino acid composition by a single amino acid change from the wild type (6). Similar studies carried out on SP from cytoplasmic petite and wild type yeast cells, however, have shown no differences detectable within the experimental method of investigators (11). The techniques employed in this case, however, were not sufficiently sensitive to detect small differences in numbers of certain of the amino acids, so that one cannot conclude that no change exists. Other workers have indicated differences in SP from petite yeast in binding ATP and in gel electrophoretic pattern (33).

N-terminal amino acids.—Investigation of the N-terminal amino acids of beef heart structural protein initially indicated that no significant quantities of N-terminal DNP-amino acid could be detected (34). Analysis of this preparation did, however, show that acetyl serine could be isolated from the SP fraction with one mole of acetyl group per 22,000 to 26,000 grams of protein. It was postulated than an N-acetyl derivative could account for the absence of free amino terminal residues in the protein. The only other amino acid appearing in these analyses was alanine, which was estimated to be present at less than 5 per cent of the concentration of the peptide chains (34).

The free N-terminal amino acids of beef heart SP preparations have recently been restudied by Lenaz et al. (35) following application of a number of their fractionation procedures to the preparation. Determination of acetyl groups showed that a great variability in number of these groups was noted, depending upon the sample and means of isolation. This makes somewhat questionable the suggestion that the N-acetyl residues observed in previous studies are attached to the free amino end of the SP polypeptide. These workers, in addition, searched further for free N-terminal amino acids. Two major DNP derivatives, identified as DNP-alanine and DNP-aspartate were detected, and it was concluded that these were N-terminal residues of the major polypeptide chains of their different fractions. Careful analysis of the data reported, however, shows that even after application of a factor based on recovery of standard amino acids, to correct for recovery losses, a yield of only 0.02 to 0.05 moles of N-terminal amino acid were obtained per mole of structural protein. With a recovery level this low, one must conclude—as was done for previous studies with similar results (34) —that there has as yet been no clear demonstration of free N-terminal amino acids for MSP. Both glutamic acid and valine have been noted as N-terminal amino acids in preparations of yeast SP(36), and aspartic acid has been detected as the major free N-terminal amino acid of CSP from spinach (18).

Other components associated with SP.—During the process of isolation of SP, the protein is removed from a membrane containing many other chemical entities. Without some measurable criterion of activity related to its function in the mitochondrion, it is difficult to ascertain whether any of these components are an intrinsic part of functional structural protein. The final preparations of SP which are isolated are devoid of lipid, carbohydrate and nucleic acid. Pinna and Wadkins reported the presence of phosphate bound covalently as serine phosphate in SP from beef heart mitochondria (10). This is consistent with the observation by Zalkin & Racker (4) of a phosphate associated with his F_4 preparation. Structural protein is often isolated with free amino acids tightly bound, but these may be removed by repeated washing.

Binding properties of SP.—One of the basic factors in the initial postulate of a structural role for the SP fraction was the observed interaction of this protein with other components of the mitochondrion (2). Structural protein has been observed to combine stoichiometrically with the cytochromes *a, b* and *c* and with cytochrome oxidase (2, 22). It will also combine 1:1 with myoglobin but not with hemoglobin (23). A large number of non-mitochondrial proteins do not combine with the SP (2).

Some of the binding studies are of particular interest in determining the functional role for SP and whether SP as isolated has any properties in common with the protein in the intact membrane. The first suggestion of a functional role came from the studies of Goldberger, which showed that complex formation between isolated cytochrome *b* and structural protein resulted in a change of the oxidation-reduction potential of the enzyme in such a fashion that the complex resembled the intact mitochondrion in this property (37, 38).

The most direct evidence for the influence of SP on the catalytic activity of mitochondrial proteins comes from the recent studies on the mitochondrial malic dehydrogenase activity of wild type and respiratory deficient strains of *Neurospora* (6). It was found that mutants of malic dehydrogenase fell into two classes: one in whch the enzyme itself was altered and the other in which another component of the mitochondrial structure was altered in such a fashion as to affect the kinetic properties of the enzyme.

Two of the mutants studied in detail, mi-1 and mi-3, showing a cytoplasmic inheritance pattern, were found to have no alteration of the *in vitro* structure of malic dehydrogenase (MDH). Thus mutated MDH activity was observed only in the intact mitochondria or when MDH was associated with the membrane structure. In these two cases, the structural protein was mutated, mi-1 being characterized by a change in tryptophane to a cysteine, and in mi-3 a tryptophane replacement was made by an as yet unidentified amino acid. In contrast, nuclear mutants showed alteration of the activity of MDH *in vitro* and in some cases altered ability of the MDH to complex with the mitochondrial structural protein.

Binding studies on the isolated proteins showed that MDH could form a 1:1 complex with SP and that alteration of the SP affected its ability to bind MDH but not the soichiometry of binding. Mutation of the structural protein also affected the binding of ATP and NADH, resulting in a much lower affinity for these molecules (26).

A comparison of the kinetics of malate oxidation by MDH in the presence of mutant and wild-type structural proteins demonstrated that combination of enzyme with SP has a marked effect on activity. Table II indicates the changes in Michaelis constants of wild-type and mutant MDH's resulting from addition of wild-type and mutant MSP. This last example is the most direct evidence for the role of SP in the catalytic process of mitochondria by virtue of a structural effect on activity.

Binding of lipids to SP has been studied in detail (3). The preparation of Richardson et al. shows markedly different lipid binding capacity than does the original preparation of Criddle et al. (2). Richardson, Hultin & Fleischer (3) have studied this binding and have concluded that the interactions between these substances are nonpolar in nature. It is difficult to draw any conclusions concerning the importance of lipid binding to SP, as there is no readily measurable physiological property to serve as an indicator of lipid binding.

Other substances, in addition to ATP and NADH, shown to bind to SP include desaspidin (4), and atractyloside (39) (see Table III). The binding of nucleotides and other anions has been studied by Palmieri & Klingenberg (40). Their conclusion was that binding of these molecules and their displacement by atractyloside is a nonspecific anion effect.

A completely different line of evidence for the role of SP in mitochondrial enzyme functioning comes from studies on the mechanism of action of the murine toxin of *Pasteurella pestis* and diphtheria toxin. Those toxins inhibit the respiration of heart mitochondria (41, 42). While early observations suggested that the inhibition was due to toxin inhibition of cyto-

TABLE II

MICHAELIS CONSTANTS OF WILD-TYPE AND MUTANT MALIC DEHYDROGENASES
WITH WILD-TYPE AND MUTANT MITOCHONDRIAL STRUCTURAL PROTEINS[a]

MSP added	Michaelis constant for malate (K_m, mM)				
	Wild type	Mutant number			
		24	10	20	7
None	0.72	1.1	2.1	2.9	1.4
Wild type	0.72	3.3[b]	7[b]	10[b]	33[b]
Mutant					
Mi-1	500[b]	6[b]	3	3	1.4
Mi-3	40[b]	4[b]	1.7	1.2	4.5

[a] Data from Munkres and Woodward (7).
[b] Significantly different from the value measured in the absence of MSP.

TABLE III

SUMMARY OF BINDING STUDIES OF STRUCTURAL PROTEINS

Structural protein complexed with[a]	Stoichiometry	Comments	Reference
[1]Cytochrome c_1	1:1	Monomerizes c_1	2
[1]Cytochrome b	1:1	Solubilizes b	2, 37
[1]Cytochrome oxidase			2
[1]Cytochrome c	1:1	Dissociated by salt $Kd = 3 \times 10^{-7}$	22
[1,2]Myoglobin	1:1	$Kd = 5 \times 10^{-7}$	2, 23
[1]Phospholipid	$\sim$2 μg/mg protein	Amount bound depends upon solubilization procedure	3
[4]Desaspidin	50% inhibition at 5×10^{-7} M	[32]Pi-ATP exchange	4
[2]Malic dehydrogenase	1:1	$Kd = 9 \times 10^{-7}$	26
[1,2]DPNH	1:1	$Kd = 6 \times 10^{-7}$	26
[1,2]ATP	$\sim$1:1		3, 26
[3,4]Atractyloside		Inhibits ATP binding	39

[a] Structural protein from: [1]Beef heart; [2]*Neurospora*; [3]Yeast; [4]Liver.

chrome formation (43), more recent evidence suggests an alteration of mitochondrial structure by association of the toxins with SP.

Montanaro & Sperti (42) demonstrated that the diphtheria toxin is capable of solubilizing mitochondrial structural protein when the two are incubated together at pH 8. Maximum solubilization was obtained with excess toxin. Immunodiffusion and immunoelectrophoresis experiments were used to demonstrate actual complex formation between the two proteins.

Attempts to locate the site of inhibition by the plague toxin more precisely were made by Kadis & Ajl (44). They were able to show that this toxin inhibits primarily the enzymatic activity of Complex I of the electron transport chain [the NADH-CoQ reductase of Hatefi et al. (45)] in isolated beef heart mitochondria. No evidence could be found, however, for an effect of the toxin on any of the major individual electron transport components of this complex. Thus the activity of NADH dehydrogenase flavoprotein, nonheme iron, and coenzyme Q_{10} were not detectably altered by the toxin.

Kadis et al. (46) were, however, able to demonstrate a solubilization of SP with the plague toxin analogous to that with the diphtheria toxin. Again, complex formation was demonstrated by immunodiffusion experiments but was also studied by following the decrease in toxicity of the toxin as it was bound to the SP. At SP:toxin ratios approaching 20:1, the toxin had lost all its toxicity for mice and precipitin bands for free toxin could no longer be detected.

These experiments, while aimed at defining the mechanism of toxin inhibition, also indicate the requirement for SP in the ordered electron transport chain. It appears that when toxin reacts with the structural protein, the behavior of the catalytic components is altered, and this alteration is only observed in the particulate system. This is entirely consistent with what may be expected if SP serves in the capacity of an organizing and stabilizing entity of the membrane.

Optical rotatory dispersion measurements of membranes.—Recent studies of membrane structure using optical rotatory dispersion have shown that membrane systems as a class have spectral properties which distinguish them from soluble proteins or polypeptides (47). In membrane systems such as chloroplast fragments (48), *Bacillus subtilis* membrane (47), and mitochondrial vesicles (49), the entire Cotton effect show a red shift of 2 to 3 $m\mu$ (47). Steim & Fleischer have studied the effect of aggregation of MSP on this spectral change (50). It was observed that while the solubilized SP is observed to have an optical rotary dispersion (ORD) spectrum characteristic of a protein or polypeptide containing α-helical structure, aggregation resulted in the spectral shift. Steim & Fleischer therefore conclude that the typical ORD spectrum of mitochondrial membrane systems may be explained by SP interaction within the membrane.

Care must be taken in any extrapolation of this data not to suggest that this ORD shift is a specific property of interacting membrane proteins, as it was demonstrated by Cassim & Yang that similar ORD spectral shifts are observed upon aggregation of α-helical poly-L-glutamic acid (51). The relation of these measurements to membrane structure must yet be established.

Gel electrophoresis.—The application of disc gel electrophoretic techniques to the study of membrane protein has permitted a study of sample heterogeneity in detail not previously possible. This method, however, has a great many difficulties which currently make interpretation difficult. The first problem comes in selecting a buffer system which will solubilize the membrane protein, limit aggregation, and allow migration of individual discrete components. Several solvent systems have been proposed (52–54), but at present none is completely satisfactory. Membrane proteins dissolved in these systems still have only marginal solubility, so that aggregation, particularly during the boundary sharpening process, is marked. This is evidenced by a heavy layer of insoluble material at the remaining top of the gel (e.g., 7, 52). Other lower molecular weight polymers may still penetrate the gel under these conditions and appear as individual bands. While methods are available for determining differences between true heterogeneity and polymerization products on acrylamide gels by altering gel composition (55, 56), these have not been applied generally to studies of membrane proteins.

One of the major benefits of the use of gel electrophoresis on membrane proteins has been the demonstration by Green and co-workers (7) of a number of impurities in the standard SP preparations of beef heart MSP and the ability to remove these components in some cases by urea extraction. Other results cited in this same series of papers, however, are equally good examples of the necessity for careful consideration of the results obtained.

It is obvious in these studies that a large and undetermined amount of protein failed to penetrate the gel (6), yet one finds in the urea extracted sample only one migrating band. To reduce the amount of material at the origin, the samples were subjected to performic acid oxidation. The sample subsequently yielded three additional bands upon electrophoresis which, taken all together, were stated to be four species of MSP. The three additional species appear to be formed from the original single band and not from the insoluble material, as it was reported that the material held at the origin was identical to that which migrated into the gel.

At present, the origin of the three additional bands is not clear— whether they are separate protein species more clearly resolved after oxidation, whether they were produced by chemical side reactions during the performic acid treatment, or whether they correspond to some of the various conformation states proposed by these authors (57). It is apparent that these are not present in other solvent systems (7) and that they are not always observed. Liver MSP has been stated to have only one (58) and four components (7) by the same workers at different times.

Gel electrophoresis has been used successfully to demonstrate that protein synthesis in isolated mitochondria results in the incorporation of C^{14} amino acids into the membrane proteins (59). Some correspondence between the distribution of radioactive label and the major components of coupling Factor 4 proteins has been noted (60). With further development of this technique, it may become an important tool in studies allowing the description of products of mitochondrial syntheses (see below).

Role of SP in mitochondrial synthesis.—Recent widespread interest in SP has resulted from observations that *in vitro* incorporation of C^{14} amino acids into isolated mitochondria results in a rather specific labeling of the mitochondrial membrane proteins. A recent review of this subject may be found in the book by Roodyn & Wilkie (61). Here only the relation of these findings to structural protein will be discussed.

It was shown in 1961 by Roodyn et al. (59) that addition of labeled amino acids to a simple medium containing mitochondria, adenine nucleotide, Mg^{++}, and an energy source resulted in incorporation of label into proteins. The major radioactive product was shown to be insoluble protein associated with the membrane, while the soluble enzymes and cytochromes were labeled little, if at all (60, 62). Many recent studies have confirmed these original findings on isolated mitochondria. Neupert et al. (63) have indicated further that amino acid incorporation *in vitro* occurs only in the inner membrane.

In vivo studies following the time course of amino acid incorporation into mitochondrial fractions, and also studies using specific inhibitors of cytoplasmic or mitochondrial protein synthesis, have confirmed and extended the earlier conclusions that the mitochondrion is the site of synthesis of proteins from the mitochondrial membrane. (For review see 61).

The identification of the products of mitochondrial protein synthesis is not nearly so clear and reflects the difficulties apparent in solubilizing and characterizing the proteins of the membrane. The predominant site of the incorporation, however, is into the structural protein fraction. The work of Haldar et al. (60) has shown that SP prepared by the method of Richardson et al. (3) is labeled by *in vitro* synthesis. Their data show radioactive label in a number of components separable by gel electrophoresis from a SP preparation, indicating several products of synthesis. Kadenbach in similar experiments found that 65 per cent of the radioactivity was in the SP (64).

Wheeldon & Lehninger, following the time course of synthesis in isolated mitochondria, showed that while the initial labeling is rather uniform throughout their membrane fractions, as synthesis proceeded SP became relatively more radioactive (65). Kadenbach has pointed out the need for caution in interpreting such studies on radioactive incorporation when he showed that some of the radioactive product could be released from the membrane by treatment with phospholipase (64). A tight nonspecific adsorption of the labeled amino acids onto structural protein has also been observed (36) and thus further care is required in interpretation of these experiments. Strong support for the structural protein being at least one major product of mitochondrial protein synthesis comes from the work of Woodward & Munkres on the pokey mutants of *Neurospora crassa* (6). Certain such respiratory-deficient mutants in which an amino acid replace-

ment in the peptide chain of SP has been noted show a maternal or cytoplasmic inheritance pattern. The resulting change in the structural protein
alters its ability to combine with the enzyme malic dehydrogenase and with
nucleotides and may disrupt the system for mitochondrial assembly. Other
mutants requiring malate were studied to show that observed differences in
the properties of the malic dehydrogenase enzyme were dependent in part
on the malic dehydrogenase-SP complex which could be formed either *in
vivo* or from the isolated components. This latter observation was also cited
as strong support for a functional role for the SP in membrane function *in
vivo* and suggests that at least some of its specific properties are not lost in
the isolation process.

The evidence thus far accumulated strongly suggests that protein synthesis does occur in the mitochondria and that SP is one of the products of
this synthesis. It is of interest to note that evidence has also been presented
to suggest that the half life of structural protein in rat liver mitochondria
in situ is considerably longer than that of catalytic protein (66). While this
further suggests that SP may, therefore, be a direct gene product of a mitochondrial gene, there has as yet been no direct demonstration of this. Such
direct evidence can come only after more thorough analysis of the insoluble
structural protein fraction.

The observations that mitochondria from cytoplasmic petite mutants of
yeast may have a greatly altered DNA (67) and lack mitochondrial r-RNA
(68) and yet still make an apparently normal SP (11) are difficult to reconcile with the conclusion that SP is solely a product of the mitochondrial
gene, however, and a much more complicated relationship may exist.

While studies of the biosynthetic apparatus of chloroplasts have progressed further than corresponding studies in mitochondria (69), the identification of protein products of the chloroplast DNA-directed synthesis are
presently even more uncertain. There is evidence that some of the structural genes concerned with the synthesis of photosynthetic enzymes are located in the nucleus, but there is no such evidence that the structural gene
for any chloroplast protein is located in the chloroplast DNA (70). Isolated
chloroplasts are capable of incorporating C^{14} amino acids into acid insoluble
products (69). Again, as in mitochondria, much of this incorporation is into
the insoluble or membrane proteins. It has been reported, however, that incorporation into some of the soluble enzymes of the chloroplast may also
occur (71). Whether synthesis of chloroplast structural proteins is directed
by the chloroplast DNA is again a question that must await further study.

CONCLUSIONS

The mass of data accumulated to date allows us to conclude that a protein fraction termed SP can be isolated in large yield from mitochondrial or
chloroplast membranes by numerous procedures. While it is quite probable
that none of these procedures gives rise to a completely homogeneous preparation, and that all have a different group of contaminating species present

in varying amounts, the same major protein components are probably isolated in all cases.

It is difficult to assess the purity of these preparations when there is no means of determining a "specific activity" to follow the purification process, and when physical measurements are hampered by problems of solubility. The final demonstration of whether purified SP is one species or a family of closely related peptide components must yet be made. Nonetheless, the demonstrations of binding by structural protein and indications of its effect on enzymic activity lead to the conclusion that this material plays an important role in the structure of membrane systems. In addition, suggestive results of biosynthesis of SP by the protein synthesizing systems of mitochondria and chloroplasts points to an important role of this material in organization and assembly as well. It is clear that SP will be the subject of much future study and that these studies will be central to further studies on structure, assembly, and function of organelles.

LITERATURE CITED

1. Green, D. E., Tisdale, H. D., Criddle, R. S., Chen, P. Y., Bock, R. M., *Biochem. Biophys. Res. Commun.,* **5,** 109–13 (1961)
2. Criddle, R. S., Bock, R. M., Green, H., *Biochemistry,* **1,** 827–42 (1962)
3. Richardson, S. H., Hultin, H., Fleischer, S., *Arch. Biochem. Biophys.,* **105,** 254–60 (1964)
4. Zalkin, H., Racker, E., *J. Biol. Chem.,* **240,** 4017–22 (1965)
5. Allmann, D. W., Lauwers, A., Lenaz, G., *Methods in Enzymology,* **10,** 433–37 (1967)
6. Woodward, D. O., Munkres, K. D., *Proc. Natl. Acad. Sci.,* **55,** 872–80 (1966)
7. Lenaz, G., Haard, N. F., Allmann, D. W., Lauwers, A., Green, D. E., *Arch. Biochem. Biophys.* (In press, 1968)
8. MacLennan, D. H., Tzagoloff, A., Rieske, J., *Arch. Biochem. Biophys.,* **109,** 383–87 (1965)
9. Zahler, W. L., Saito, A., Fleischer, S., *Biochem. Biophys. Res. Commun.,* **32,** 512–18 (1968)
10. Pinna, L. A., Wadkins, C. L., *Biochem. Biophys. Res. Commun.,* **28,** 400–6 (1967)
11. Kato, T., Sanukida, S., *Biochem. Biophys. Res. Commun.,* **21,** 373–78 (1965)
12. Schatz, G., *Biochim. Biophys. Acta,* **96,** 342–45 (1965)
13. Criddle, R. S., Schatz, G., *Biochemistry,* **8,** 322–34 (1968)
14. Ephrussi, B., *Nucleo-Cytoplasmic Relations in Microorganisms* (Clarendon Press, Oxford, 1953)
15. Menke, W., Jordan, E., *Z. Naturforsch.,* **14b,** 393 (1959)
16. Criddle, R. S., in *Biochemistry of Chloroplasts,* **I,** 203–31 (Goodwin, T., Ed., Academic Press, London, 1966)
17. Bailey, J. L., Thornber, J. P., Whyborn, A. G., in *Biochemistry of Chloroplasts,* **I,** 243–55 (See Ref. 16)
18. Criddle, R. S., Park, L., *Biochem. Biophys. Res. Commun.,* **17,** 74–79 (1964)
19. Rothfield, L., Finkelstein, A., *Ann. Rev. Biochem.,* **37,** 463–96 (1968)
20. Woodward, D. O., Munkres, K. D., in *Organizational Biosynthesis,* 489–502 (Vogel, H. J., Lampen, J. O., Bryson, V., Eds., Academic Press, New York, 1967)
21. Attardi, G., Attardi, B., *Proc. Natl. Acad. Sci.,* **61,** 261–68 (1968)
22. Edwards, D. L., Criddle, R. S., *Biochemistry,* **5,** 588–91 (1966)
23. Edwards, D. L., Criddle, R. S., *ibid.,* 583–88
24. Hultin, H. O., Richardson, S. H., *Arch. Biochem. Biophys.,* **105,** 288–96 (1964)
25. Takayama, K., MacLennan, D., Tzagaloff, A., Stoner, C. D., *Arch. Biochem. Biophys.,* **114,** 223–30 (1966)
26. Munkres, K. D., Woodward, D. O., *Proc. Natl. Acad. Sci.,* **55,** 1217 (1966)
27. Menke, W., in *Biochemistry of*

Chloroplasts, **I**, 3–18 (See Ref. 16)

28. Fraenkel-Conrat, H., in *The Proteins*, **III**, 99–151 (Neurath, H., Ed., Academic Press, New York, 1965)

29. Salton, M. J. R., Freer, J. H., *Biochim. Biophys. Acta*, **107**, 531–38 (1965)

30. Kaplan, D., *Isolation and Partial Characterization of Structural Protein from the Endoplasmic Reticulum of Rat Liver* (Doctoral thesis, Univ. Oregon, 1968)

31. Blair, J. E., Lenaz, G., Haard, N. F., *Arch. Biochem. Biophys.* (In press, 1968)

32. Sophianopoulos, A. J., Rhodes, C. K., Holcomb, D. N., Van Holde, K. E., *J. Biol. Chem.*, **237**, 1107–12 (1962)

33. Tuppy, H., Swetly, P., *Biochim. Biophys. Acta*, **153**, 293–95 (1968)

34. Criddle, R. S., Edwards, D. L., Petersen, T. P., *Biochemistry*, **5**, 578–82 (1966)

35. Lenaz, G., Haard, W., Silman, H. I., Green, D. E., *Arch. Biochem. Biophys.* (In press, 1968)

36. Criddle, R. S., Willemot, J., in *Protides of the Biological Fluids*, **15**, 55–67 (Peeters, H., Ed., Elsiver, Amsterdam, 1967)

37. Goldberger, R., Pumphrey, A., Smith, A., *Biochim. Biophys. Acta*, **58**, 307 (1962)

38. Deeb, S. S., Hagear, L. P., *J. Biol. Chem.*, **239**, 1024–32 (1964)

39. Moret, V., Lorini, M., Fotia, A., Siliprandi, N., *Biochim. Biophys. Acta*, **124**, 433–35 (1966)

40. Palmieri, F., Klingenberg, M., *Biochim. Biophys. Acta*, **131**, 582–85 (1967)

41. Packer, L., Rust, J. H., Ajl, S. J., *J. Bacteriol.*, **78**, 658 (1959)

42. Montanaro, L., Sperti, S., *Biochim. Biophys. Acta*, **100**, 621–23 (1965)

43. Pappenheimer, A. M., *Symp. Soc. Gen. Microbiol.*, **5**, 40 (1955)

44. Kadis, S., Ajl, S. J., *J. Biol. Chem.*, **241**, 1556–61 (1966)

45. Hatefi, Y., Haavik, A. B., Griffiths, D. E., *J. Biol. Chem.*, **237**, 1676–80 (1962)

46. Kadis, S., Trenchard, A., Ajl, S. J., *J. Biol. Chem.*, **241**, 5605–9 (1966)

47. Lenard, J., Singer, S. J., *Proc. Natl. Acad. Sci.*, **56**, 1828–35 (1966)

48. Ke, B., *Arch. Biochem. Biophys.*, **112**, 554–61 (1965)

49. Urry, D. W., Mednieks, M., Bejnarowicz, E., *Proc. Natl. Acad. Sci.*, **57**, 1043–49 (1967)

50. Steim, J. M., Fleischer, S., *Proc. Natl. Acad. Sci.*, **58**, 1292–98 (1967)

51. Cassim, J. Y., Yang, J. T., *Biochem. Biophys. Res. Commun.*, **26**, 58–64 (1967)

52. Takayama, K., MacLennan, D. H., Tzagaloff, A., Stoner, C. D., *Arch. Biochem. Biophys.*, **114**, 223–30 (1966)

53. Davis, B. J., *Ann. N. Y. Acad. Sci.*, **121**, 404–14 (1964)

54. Duesberg, P. H., Rueckert, R. R., *Anal. Biochem.*, **11**, 342–61 (1965)

55. Hedrick, J. L., Smith, A. J., *Arch. Biochem. Biophys.*, **126**, 155–64 (1968)

56. Shapiro, A. L., Vinuela, E., Maizel, J. V., Jr., *Biochem. Biophys. Res. Commun.*, **28**, 815–20 (1967)

57. Green, D. E., Haard, N. F., Lenaz, G., Silman, I., *Arch. Biochem. Biophys.* (In press, 1968)

58. Lenaz, G., Lauwers, A., Haard, N., *Federation Proc.*, **26**, 283 (1967)

59. Roodyn, D. B., Reis, P. J., Work, T. S., *Biochem. J.*, **80**, 9–21 (1961)

60. Haldar, D., Freeman, K., Work, T. S., *Nature*, **211**, 9–12 (1966)

61. Roodyn, D. B., Wilkie, D., *The Biogenesis of Mitochondria* (Methuen Ltd., London, 1968)

62. Roodyn, D. B., Suttie, J. W., Work, T. S., *Biochem. J.*, **83**, 29–40 (1962)

63. Neupert, W., Brdiczka, D., Buecher, Th., *Biochem. Biophys. Res. Commun.*, **27**, 488–93 (1967)

64. Kadenbach, B., *Biochim. Biophys. Acta*, **134**, 430–42 (1967)

65. Wheeldon, L. W., Lehninger, A. L., *Biochemistry*, **5**, 3533–45 (1966)

66. Beattie, D. S., Basford, R. E., Koritz, S. B., *J. Biol. Chem.*, **242**, 4584 (1967)

67. Mounolou, J. C., Jakob, H., Slonimski, P., *Biochem. Biophys. Res. Commun.*, **24**, 218–24 (1966)

68. Wintersberger, E., *Z. Physiol. Chemie*, **348**, 1701–4 (1967)

69. Eisenstadt, J., in *Biochemistry of Chloroplasts*, **II**, 341–49 (See Ref. 16)

70. Kirk, J. T. O., in *Biochemistry of Chloroplasts*, **I**, 320–40 (See Ref. 16)

71. Smillie, R. M., Graham, D., Dwyer, M. R., Grieve, A., Tobin, N. F., *Biochem. Biophys. Res. Commun.*, **28**, 604–10 (1967)

PLANT MICROTUBULES[1,2]

By Eldon H. Newcomb

Department of Botany and Institute of Plant Development
University of Wisconsin, Madison, Wisconsin

Current evidence suggests that microtubules constitute a class of morphologically and chemically closely related filamentous elements of general occurrence in plant and animal cells. Microtubules are of special interest at present because they are being implicated in an ever greater variety of important subcellular structures and functions. They compose the fibers of mitotic spindles, the tubular structures in centrioles and basal bodies, and the 9 + 2 array of axonemal filaments in cilia and flagella. As further examples, they occur in the sperm manchette, in elongated animal cells including neurons, and as the marginal band in erythrocytes. They are found in numerous structures in the protista, including the long, slender microspikes.

Microtubules probably function in a variety of ways. They participate in a motile system in cilia and flagella, and in movement of a different sort in the mitotic spindle. In many cases they are believed to perform a cytoskeletal role in the production and maintenance of cell asymmetries. In other cases they may aid in the movement of cytoplasmic materials. The uncertainties as to function are well illustrated by Figure 1, which shows microtubules in association with the pellicular ridges in *Euglena gracilis*. These microtubules could have a skeletal function, or could be involved in the body flexures ("metaboly"), in the movement of cytoplasmic materials, or in other ways.

Recognition of the widespread occurrence of microtubules followed upon the introduction of glutaraldehyde as a fixative several years ago (123). Use of glutaraldehyde followed by osmium tetroxide made the preservation of microtubules possible in many structures in which they had been destroyed previously by fixation either in osmium tetroxide alone, or in permanganate. The wide distribution and importance of microtubules in animal cells were stressed in 1963 by Slautterback (131). In the same year, Ledbetter & Porter (71) published their classic paper on microtubules as components of plant cells. Owing to its technical excellence and effective presentation, this contribution did much to direct attention to microtubules as important elements of cells generally.

[1] The following abbreviations have been used: ER, endoplasmic reticulum; GTP, guanosine triphosphate.

[2] I thank Mr. William P. Wergin for help in preparing the illustrative micrographs. The preparation of this review was supported in part by Grant GB-6161 from the National Science Foundation.

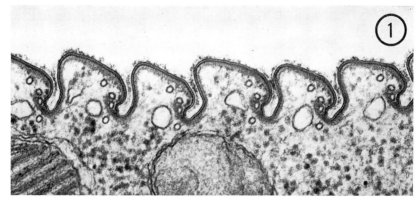

FIG. 1. Cross section of microtubules associated with the pellicular ridges in *Euglena gracilis*. ×86,000. Micrograph by Dr. Martin W. Steer, University of Wisconsin.

The present review is devoted largely to microtubules in higher plants, although some work on lower plants has been included where particularly relevant to higher plant problems, e.g., microtubules in relation to deposition of wall microfibrils. A brief description of recent work on the protein chemistry of microtubules from animal systems has been included because of its obviously great general significance. Several recent reviews on cilia and flagella are available (cf. 42); no attempt is made here to review the botanical literature on the fine structure of these motile organs. Porter (112) has written a general review of cytoplasmic microtubules, while Bracker (18) has covered the occurrence of microtubules in fungi. Mühlethaler (85) has discussed the cytoplasm in relation to the cell wall in a recent review in this series.

MORPHOLOGY AND DISTRIBUTION OF PLANT MICROTUBULES

Microtubules are slender unbranched cylindrical structures frequently encountered in the cytoplasm of both higher and lower plants. Their reported diameters usually fall between 180 Å and 300 Å, the average value being about 240Å. Because of technical and biological variations, ordinarily no great significance can be assigned to reported differences in diameter. Although their lengths are difficult to determine, some microtubules can be followed for many microns. In some cases they run circumferentially around the cell in the cytoplasm near the plasmalemma (Fig. 4), probably forming complete rings or hoops. Viewed longitudinally (Figs. 2 & 8), they exhibit a less-dense space bounded by two dark lines.

In cross section (Figs. 1 & 7), microtubules reveal an electron-lucent core about 100 Å in diameter bounded by an electron-opaque cortex or wall about 70 Å thick. The nature of the material occupying the core is unknown. The walls of clusters of microtubules viewed in cross section are not in contact, but are separated by a space of about 200 Å or more; also, in sections normal to the cell surface, microtubules near the cell wall usually appear to be located 100 Å or more from the plasmalemma. In longitudinal view a clear zone is commonly observed along the sides of microtubules. These observations suggest that each tubule may be surrounded by a specialized zone or layer of material (70, 71). Microtubules appear to be rather stiff and rigid structures, and usually follow straight or gently curving paths through the cytoplasm (Figs. 4, 5 & 8).

Employing Markham's rotation technique, Ledbetter & Porter (72) showed that the wall of plant microtubules is probably composed of 13 filamentous subunits which have a center-to-center spacing of about 45 Å. Subsequent images obtained at improved resolution permitted direct confirmation of these results (70). Several recent studies of microtubules isolated from various sources, including a plant (12), have shown that the filaments of the walls are composed of a series of globular subunits each about 40 Å in diameter (11, 12, 46, 138). Microtubules are known to be composed in large part of protein (1, 13, 138).

A variety of tubular structures have been reported from plant cells whose morphological characteristics set them apart from typical microtubules as described above. These tubules may be much more sinuous than microtubules, markedly different in size, etc. Among them are the two sizes of tubules derived from the ER in bean leaf glands (91, 137), the P-proteins of sieve elements (31), tubular projections on "spiny" vesicles (87), meandering tubular structures outside the plasmalemma in primary and secondary walls (27, 88), microtubule-like structures in plastids (106), tubules in cells of leaf Beltian bodies (117), and plasmodesmatal "desmotubules" (118). These structures are not discussed further in this review, although it is conceivable that some of them may be closely related to microtubules in substructure and chemical composition. Experiments (137) on the tubules of bean leaf glands, using the agents employed by Behnke & Forer (13) to distinguish four classes of microtubules, have shown clearly that the gland tubules are not similar to conventional microtubules, however.

Microtubules compose the mitotic and meiotic spindle fibers, and the phragmoplast fibers of dividing cells. They occur in the cytoplasm next to the growing primary wall, and similarly overlie the developing bands of secondary wall. They are occasionally encountered also in small numbers elsewhere in the cytoplasm of interphase cells. Microtubules are also important structural components of centrioles and basal bodies found in many lower plants, and constitute the "9 + 2" axonemal elements in the flagella of motile plant cells.

Although in animal and protistan cells microtubules are believed to play a prominent cytoskeletal role in controlling cell asymmetries (112), the cytoskeletal function of microtubules would appear to be much less important in plant cells possessed of rigid, supportive walls. However, microtubules may nevertheless be responsible for cell asymmetries in plants if they control the pattern of deposition of the wall microfibrils.

A case of great interest where microtubules do indeed appear to play a direct cytoskeletal role in controlling the shape of a higher plant cell has been reported recently by Sanger & Jackson (125). Early in pollen development in *Haemanthus,* the spherical generative cell becomes ellipsoidal, and this change in shape is accompanied by the appearance along the generative cell wall of a sheath of microtubules running parallel to the long axis of the cell. The effects of colchicine and cold are consistent with the hypothesis that the change in shape of the generative cell is controlled by the appearance and orientation of microtubules.

Protein Chemistry of Microtubules

A brief review of some of the recent work on the comparative protein chemistry of microtubules is included here, for while this work is not based on the study of plant materials, it is clear that it is of general applicability and of the utmost importance for an eventual understanding of microtubule assembly and function. These studies and the closely related biochemical work on the microtubules of cilia, protozoan flagella, and sperm tails (42) now provide considerable evidence that similar actin-like proteins are present in many kinds of microtubules.

In their successful chemical work on microtubules, Taylor and his colleagues (1, 16, 17, 129, 130) have taken advantage of the long-standing observation that colchicine and related compounds are highly active in disrupting the mitotic spindle. They reasoned that if the spindle is a labile structure maintained by a dynamic equilibrium (59), then colchicine might cause its depolymerization by forming a complex with the subunit protein of which the microtubules are composed.

Borisy & Taylor (16) found that tritiated colchicine, when applied to cultured mammalian cells both *in vivo* and *in vitro,* was bound specifically and non-covalently to a protein with a sedimentation coefficient of 6S. Two kinds of evidence indicated that the 6S protein to which the colchicine binds is a subunit of the microtubules. First, a survey indicated that the high colchicine-binding activity is characteristic not only of rapidly dividing cells rich in spindle protein, but also of various other materials rich in microtubules, including cilia, sperm tails, and nerve cells. On the other hand, slime molds have few if any microtubules, and bind very little colchicine. Second, Borisy & Taylor (17) found that when the sea urchin mitotic apparatus is extracted, the microtubules disappear and the soluble extract contains the 6S colchicine-binding protein. Furthermore, Shelanski & Taylor (129, 130) found that the 6S colchicine-binding protein is also the major component of the central pair of microtubules of sea urchin sperm flagella.

Thus, although Behnke & Forer (13) have provided evidence that different classes of microtubules can be distinguished on the basis of their sensitivity to colchicine and other treatments, it can be hypothesized that colchicine binding is a property of the subunit protein of microtubules generally (1). Borisy & Taylor (16, 17) proposed that colchicine acts by binding to subunit protein and preventing its polymerization into microtubules. If the polymerization is an equilibrium process, nucleated perhaps by the centrioles and kinetochores, then its equilibrium can be shifted in favor of the subunits by complexing them with colchicine.

The colchicine-binding proteins from brain cytoplasm (1), the proteins from the microtubules of sea urchin sperm (129), and the proteins from the outer doublet tubules of *Tetrahymena* cilia (114), although from three widely different sources, are quite similar, and consist of a dimer with a molecular weight of 110,000 to 120,000 which is convertible into a monomer with a molecular weight of 55,000 to 60,000 (1). This monomer is believed to be the 40 Å globular subunit resolved in the microtubule with the electron microscope (11, 12, 46, 138). One mole of colchicine is bound per dimer unit. The amino acid compositions of the proteins are quite similar (1, 138) and closely resemble that of muscle actin (114, 138).

Of great interest is the discovery that, like actin, the microtubule proteins have the ability to associate with a nucleotide. Stephens et al. (140) have shown that outer doublet tubules of cilia and flagella contain 1 mole of a guanine nucleotide per 60,000 g of protein, while Adelman et al. (1) have reported that either ATP or GTP is necessary to preserve the colchicine binding site of microtubule protein. Each dimer is believed to have two non-equivalent GTP binding sites.

Adelman et al. (1) have pointed out that the data now available indicate that microtubules from sperm tails, cilia, cytoplasm, and mitotic spindles in widely separated animal phyla have subunits which constitute a well-defined group of closely related proteins. These proteins, called "tubulin," all have a molecular weight of *ca.* 120,000, a sedimentation constant of 6S, two binding sites for GTP, and one for colchicine. Furthermore, the ability of colchicine to block mitosis and disrupt microtubule structure generally in plants and animals implies that similar proteins are present in many kinds of microtubules.

Stephens (139) has recently reported the successful reassociation *in vitro* of microtubule subunits into several fibrous forms. Nucleation in the form of tubule fragments was necessary for the polymerization, and it is possible that this is related to the role of orienting centers in the formation of microtubules *in vivo*.

Mitosis

As is well known from studies with the light microscope, the birefringent fibers of the mitotic apparatus seen in living cells consist of chromosomal fibers running from the kinetochores to the poles, and continuous fibers running from pole to pole (61, 80). It was shown in the late 1950's (126, 127) that these appear as fine filamentous elements in the electron microscope. Their microtubular nature in root tip cells in anaphase and telophase was clearly described in 1963 by Ledbetter & Porter (71), who suggested that the fibers which are resolved optically consist of bundles of microtubules. In 1964 Manton published exceptionally fine micrographs of microtubules in the mitotic spindle of a chrysophycean flagellate, *Prymnesium* (76), and in the mitotic and meiotic spindles of a lower vascular plant, *Equisetum* (77). It soon became obvious from these and similar observations that the microtubules in the different fibers of the spindle and phragmoplast are quite similar in appearance, and also resemble one another in a wide range of organisms, plant and animal. It was also apparent that as the chromosomes move to the poles in anaphase, the microtubules attached to the kinetochores become shorter without thickening or otherwise changing in appearance, suggesting that they are not contracting but are being digested at the poles.

Lability and dynamics of spindle microtubules.—The identification of spindle fibers as bundles of microtubules and the exploration of the protein chemistry of microtubule subunits has allowed thinking in more concrete terms about the many observations and experiments made by optical techniques on the mitotic apparatus in living cells (4, 5, 8–10, 39, 40, 59–62, 79, 80). Some of the most important results and conclusions of this work are given here, since they contribute much to our understanding of microtubule dynamics.

Ultraviolet microbeam experiments and other observations have gone far toward identifying the centrioles and kinetochores as centers of nucleation out of which grow, respectively, the continuous fibers (bundles of microtubules) and chromosomal fibers of the spindle (10, 39, 40, 59). In plant cells it appears that the cell plate region subsequently nucleates the growth of the phragmoplast fibers (61). A long series of experiments on birefringence supports the hypothesis developed particularly by Inoué (59, 61) that the fibers are highly labile structures existing in a dynamic equilibrium with a large pool of unassociated subunits available to the nucleation centers.

This equilibrium can be shifted toward depolymerization of the fibers by low temperature or high hydrostatic pressure, and toward polymerization by an increase in temperature or the addition of heavy water (59, 79). For example, spindle birefringence is destroyed in a matter of seconds by treatment with low temperature, and reappears in minutes by a return to normal temperature, after which chromosome movement can continue (59). (Related to this is the absence or dearth of microtubules frequently observed in electron micrographs of material fixed in the cold.) At low temperatures the protein subunits are believed to be insulated by shells of bound water molecules which at higher temperatures are dispersed, permitting the subunits to associate more closely and come into alignment to form the polymer (61).

The effect of high concentrations of D_2O in "freezing" mitosis or over-stabilizing the gel structure of the spindle (47, 79) is of great interest. For example, when 45 per cent D_2O is applied during mitosis, spindle birefringence may increase at least twofold and the volume occupied by the spindle as much as tenfold (62). The effect of D_2O is virtually instantaneous and completely reversible. Possible molecular mechanisms that might be involved in the rigidification caused by heavy water have been considered by Gross & Spindel (47).

The above results illustrating the great lability of the spindle and its ability to recover rapidly from disruption strongly suggest that the subunits from which the fibers are constructed during mitosis have already been synthesized and are readily available from a pool (59, 61). This view is strengthened by the observation that recovery of the spindle from disruption is not hindered by inhibitors of protein synthesis (61).

Experiments with low concentrations of colchicine are also instructive. As is well known, a high concentration of this drug completely disrupts the spindle (80) and destroys the spindle microtubules (99). However, Inoué has shown that a low concentration causes the chromosomes to be pulled poleward, and electron micrographs reveal that the microtubules have simply shortened (61). It can be assumed that in combining with free subunits the inhibitor in low concentration shifts the equilibrium only sufficiently to cause a slow depolymerization of the microtubules at the poles, resulting in their contraction. This action of colchicine may closely resemble the process taking place in the polar regions during normal anaphasic movement of the chromosomes.

The main hypothesis that has emerged from Inoué's observations is, briefly, that the fluctuation of birefringence during normal mitosis and cytokinesis represents the assembly and disassembly of the same protein subunits sequentially at the different nucleation centers. During anaphase, digestion of the ends of the chromosomal fibers takes place near the poles, accompanied by further growth and elongation of the continuous fibers, both processes being involved in the poleward movement of the chromosomes (61). A similar hypothesis has been proposed by Pickett-Heaps (103) in his ultrastructural study of mitosis in *Chara*.

Subirana (143) has proposed a molecular model to account for chromosome movements in mitosis based on production of active shearing forces at the surface of the microtubules either by an actin-myosin-like interaction or by a similar mechanism involving a single protein. His model implies a different polarity in the continuous tubules on the two sides of the spindle, hence a change in polarity at the midpoint. He also suggests that the chromosome-to-pole microtubules are of opposite polarity to the pole-to-pole microtubules, allowing the latter to act as "pumping units" helping the chromosomal microtubules in their anaphase movement.

A different suggestion is that the continuous microtubules emanating from one pole might be of opposite polarity to those from the other (142), since there is evidence that some of these microtubules associate as doublets (69). However, microtubules running from the kinetochores to the poles do not appear to pair with the pole-to-pole microtubules, and it has been suggested that this might be important in allowing the kinetochore microtubules to slide along the pole-to-pole microtubules during anaphase (142).

The kinetochore.—The kinetochore, like the centriole, serves as a point of attachment for microtubules. But more than this, it is believed to be the site from which the microtubules grow by the addition of monomers at their bases during late prophase and metaphase (19, 59, 61, 80, 142). Harris & Bajer (49) have shown that in *Haemanthus* endosperm a chromosomal fiber consists of a bundle of 50 to 100 microtubules connected to the kinetochore. Some studies suggest that the kinetochore of animal cells contains dense plate-like structures (68, 69) but there is also evidence for a fibrous nature (19). Electron micrographs of the kinetochore at meiotic metaphase in *Tradescantia* and *Lilium* pollen mother cells, published respectively by Wilson (146) and Dietrich (35), show that the microtubules arise in a large region that is less electron-opaque than other parts of the chromosome. Wilson (146) believes that the kinetochores in *Tradescantia* are composed of 70 to 80 Å granules rather than fibrils as reported for animal cells, and points out the need for further work.

The structure of the kinetochore is of prime importance for an understanding of the origin of microtubules and of the mitotic events leading to poleward migration of the anaphase chromosomes. It is, however, a difficult region to study in the electron microscope. Portions of the kinetochores at mitotic metaphase in a bean root tip cell are shown in Figure 2. Microtubules emanating from kinetochores are also shown at high magnification in papers by Manton (77), Harris & Bajer (49), Pickett-Heaps & Northcote (109), and Cronshaw & Esau (32).

Jokelainen (66) has presented evidence that kinetochore differentiation is affected by low concentrations of colchicine, while Krishan (68) has shown that fibroblast cells arrested in mitosis by vinblastine sulfate have prominent kinetochores showing details of fine structure usually not seen in untreated cells. It should be rewarding to use these drugs in exploring kinetochore structure in plant cells.

The centriole and basal body.—The centriole is found only in a few gymnosperms and not at all in the angiosperms, and while it occurs generally among the lower vascular plants it is restricted in these to a brief phase of the life cycle. For this reason, the quite limited objective of this section is to place this organelle in perspective in considering the nature of the orienting centers for microtubules in higher plants. An exhaustive review of the classical literature of light microscopy on the centriole in plants was published by Lepper (73).

In animal cells (80) and in those of some algae (65) and fungi (18) the centriole serves as an organizing center for the growth of microtubules comprising the continuous fibers of the spindle, and in many cases appears to give rise directly to them (142). Also, in the form of the basal body the centriole produces the microtubules comprising the familiar "9 + 2" structure of cilia and flagella. Stubblefield & Brinkley (142) consider that the centriole is a highly specialized organelle for microtubule production and also serves as a temporary scaffolding to anchor the poles toward which the chromosomes move in mitosis. It is a cylindrical body with a remarkably

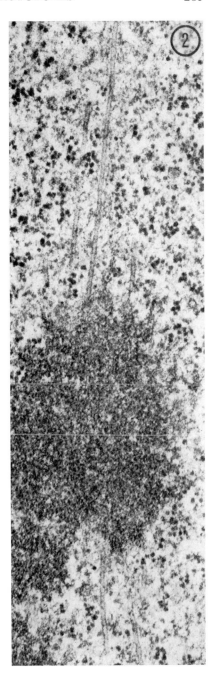

FIG. 2. Kinetochores with associated chromosomal microtubules at metaphase in a dividing cell in a leaf of corn (*Zea mays*). ×62,000. Micrograph by William P. Wergin, University of Wisconsin.

elaborate architecture, which may include both DNA and RNA. Its outer wall consists of a ring of nine evenly spaced triplet microtubules. The microtubules of the mitotic apparatus originating in the centriole appear to grow out from its side wall toward the opposite pole (142). Presumably this occurs by addition of monomers to the microtubule bases at the centriole.

In lower eukaryotic plants, there are wide variations in the occurrence and manner of participation of a centriole or centriole-like body in the organization of spindle microtubules. In several recently investigated cases in which the nuclear envelope remains intact, so that an intranuclear or "closed" spindle apparatus is formed, a centriole, or a pair of centrioles, lies just outside the envelope and the spindle microtubules do not penetrate the envelope but terminate in a dense region just inside (18). Ichida & Fuller (58) have studied this type of apparatus in a water mold (Fig. 3). Lessie & Lovett (74) have shown that vegetative nuclear division in the water mold *Blastocladiella emersonii* is similarly intranuclear. In yeast (119), microtubules radiate from the centriole into the cytoplasm, and "centriolar plaques" located at the nuclear envelope serve as polar foci for the spindle apparatus.

The nuclear envelope in the fungus *Armillaria* (84) is discontinuous at the poles where the spindle penetrates the nucleus. The spindle microtubules appear to be attached at the poles to centriole-like bodies that lack the organization of typical centrioles. Johnson & Porter (65) have demonstrated that the nuclear envelope of the alga, *Chlamydomonas reinhardi*, similarly develops discontinuities at the poles. The spindle microtubules arise just beyond these openings in a specialized region of the cytoplasm devoid of organelles. Although centrioles are present in the cell, they are involved not with the mitotic spindle but with formation of cytoplasmic microtubules that participate in cytokinesis.

In surveying the distribution of centrioles in the plant kingdom, basal bodies must be included since they have typical centriole structure and are generally considered to be centrioles that produce the microtubules for the shaft of the cilium or flagellum of motile cells. These microtubules arise as direct extensions of particular microtubules from one end of the centriole, and thus differ in their manner of production from those made by the centriole for the mitotic apparatus (142).

The origin of basal bodies from centrioles or procentrioles has been observed in a number of studies (14, 74, 83, 105, 115, 122). In an ultrastructural investigation of the fungus *Allomyces macrogynus,* Renaud & Swift (115) discovered that the basal body in the gamete is derived from a small centriole detectable in the tip of a vegetative hypha before it undergoes gametogenesis.

Centrioles or basal bodies occur not only in many algae and fungi, but also in all plants above these that produce flagellated sperm, including mosses and liverworts, all of the lower vascular plants including the ferns, and finally the cycads and ginkgos among the gymnosperms (73). They are not known to occur, however, in other gymnosperms or in angiosperms, and

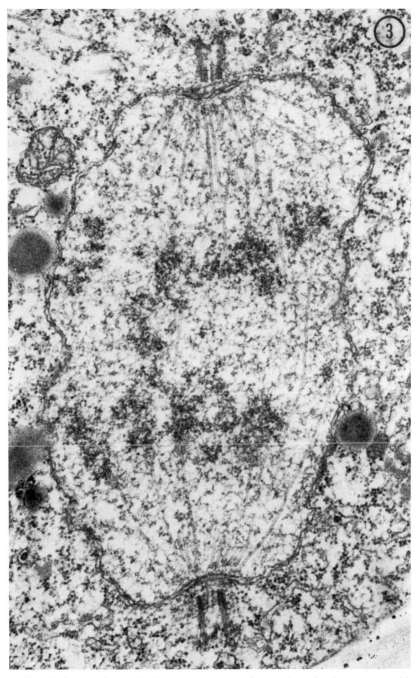

Fig. 3. Intranuclear mitotic apparatus at early anaphase in the water mold, *Catenaria anguillulae*. Centrioles, chromosomal microtubules, continuous microtubules, and chromosomes are evident. ×37,000. Micrograph courtesy of Drs. A. A. Ichida & M. S. Fuller (58).

in those plants above the algae and fungi in which they do occur, they generally appear only during gametogenesis and their origins are obscure. Mizukami & Gall (83) have studied ultrastructurally the origin of the numerous basal bodies from procentrioles present in the large spherical blepharoplast in the sperm of the fern, *Marsilea,* and the cycad, *Zamia.*

The fine structure of the very large multiflagellated sperm of *Zamia* has been explored by Norstog (89). In addition to the flagella and greatly elongated basal bodies, he has described a spiral system of microtubules underlying the plasmalemma in flagellated regions. He suggests that contraction of the microtubules in this system may account for the "euglenoid" movements characteristic of the apical portion of the sperm body. In two notable series of papers, microtubular structures involved in the developing and mature sperm of a moss, *Polytricum,* have been described by Paolillo and associates (93–96), and of a liverwort, *Marchantia,* by Carothers & Kreitner (24, 25).

Origin of pole-to-pole microtubules in plant cells.—Ultrastructural studies of mitosis in plant cells have made it clear that some of the microtubules of the spindle arise in the polar regions despite the absence of centrioles (2, 109). If, as suggested (142), the intricate structure of the centriole serves to make it a highly effective machine for the production (and disassembly?) of microtubules, as well as a scaffolding for chromosome movement to the poles, its loss from most plant cells is difficult to understand. Stubblefield & Brinkley (142) stress the role of the centriole as a supportive structure in suggesting that the need for it in plant mitosis is eliminated because the spindle microtubules are embedded in the end walls, which supply the necessary support. Although there is no evidence that spindle microtubules of plant cells are connected in any way to the cell walls, nevertheless the rigidity provided by the walls is conceivably related to the loss of the centriole generally except in those plants and at that point in the life cycle where a motile stage requires formation of a basal body.

If the polar regions of dividing plant cells are examined for clues to the nature of the nucleation centers from which microtubules arise, no unusual structures are encountered. However, Pickett-Heaps & Northcote (109) have observed that elements of endoplasmic reticulum, much of it smooth, become conspicuous at the poles at the onset of mitosis. As they have suggested, these elements may be producing the protein subunits needed for the assembly of microtubules. The occurrence of smooth endoplasmic reticulum at the poles immediately preceding and during mitosis of wheat cells has been reported also by Burgess & Northcote (22), who have suggested that this system may transport microtubule subunits and play a part in their aggregation. An increased amount of finely granular, moderately electron-dense material in the matrix surrounding the endoplasmic reticulum has also been observed (23). Apparently, then, it is to the endoplasmic reticulum and to this material that we must look for the orienting centers replacing the centrioles in the organization of the pole-to-pole microtubules in plant cells. In *Chara*, Pickett-Heaps (103) has noted that some spindle microtubules end at small, electron-dense, diffuse bodies.

The discovery of a "preprophase band" of microtubules by Pickett-Heaps & Northcote (109) may shed light on the origin of spindle microtubules in some cells. In ultrastructural studies of mitosis in roots, coleoptile tissue, and young leaves of wheat, these workers found that a dense band of 150 or more microtubules encircling the nucleus appeared in the cells just before they entered prophase. The microtubules were oriented at right angles to the axis of the future mitotic spindle and occurred several units deep in the equatorial region where fusion of the future cell plate would be expected. During prophase the microtubules in the band disappeared and spindle microtubules appeared, suggesting that the band might be contributing microtubules to the developing spindle.

A similar preprophase band has been reported in roots of *Phleum* (22) and in young leaves of tobacco (32), and presumably will prove to be of widespread occurrence. A preprophase band in a leaf cell of wheat is shown in Figure 4.

Burgess & Northcote (23) have also made observations on wheat that suggest that the preprophase band may serve as a source of material for spindle microtubules. Preceding mitosis, numerous elements of smooth endoplasmic reticulum surrounded by an amorphous matrix material containing some microtubules appear in the cytoplasm along the side walls where the band of microtubules arises. Smooth endoplasmic reticulum is also observed here at the start of prophase when microtubules are disaggregating in the band and appearing at the poles. Conceivably, microtubules or portions of them migrate from the band to the poles, where they are reutilized (22).

The results of Hepler & Jackson (52) with isopropyl N-phenyl carbamate are related to this question of centers of nucleation. When dividing endosperm cells of *Haemanthus* are treated with this chemical, a number of scattered spindles appear, each with a cluster of microtubules radiating in all directions from the poles. Some of the microtubules can be traced to the kinetochores of nearby chromosomes. Since the microtubules are normal in appearance, as are other cytoplasmic components, it appears that the chemical may be sufficiently specific in its action to prove useful in further study of the nature of polar nucleating centers.

CYTOKINESIS

During mitotic telophase, cell plate formation is commonly initiated by the accumulation of vesicles midway between the daughter nuclei. As these fuse and additional vesicles accumulate and consolidate at the margins, the plate grows laterally until it reaches and joins the side walls. The participation of a fibrous structure, the phragmoplast, lying at the margins of the plate and appearing successively farther out as the plate expands, has been known from light microscopic investigations on fixed and stained cells for a century (141). In recent years, living cultured cells of the endosperm of the

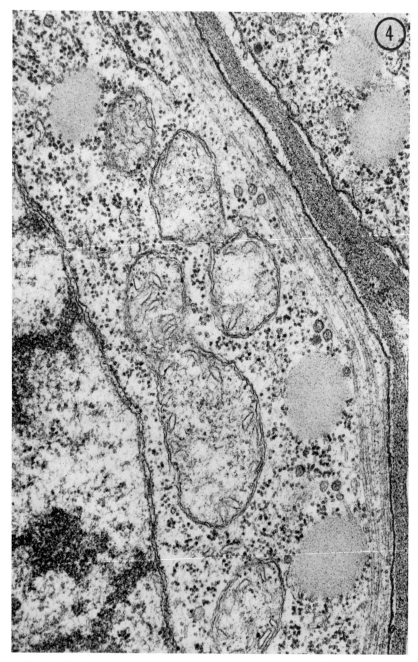

Fig. 4. Portion of a preprophase band of microtubules lying next to a cell wall and forming a ring around the cytoplasm. Individual microtubules can be traced for a micron or more. Leaf cell from 3-day-old seedling of wheat (*Triticum vulgare*). ×55,000. Micrograph by William P. Wergin, University of Wisconsin.

African blood lily, *Haemanthus katherinae,* have been used in light micro-scopic investigations of cell plate formation by Bajer and associates (4–6, 8–10, 60) and Jackson (63). Observations made on this material with a va-riety of optical systems (polarized light, phase contrast, and Nomarski dif-ferential interference contrast) have revealed that the phragmoplast con-sists of fibrillar elements which arise at the plate and radiate outward more or less normal to its plane, and numerous cytoplasmic droplets which are moved to and incorporated into the plate (5, 9, 60).

The fibrillar structure of the phragmoplast was recognized in the elec-tron microscope by Sato in 1958 (126, 127). Ledbetter & Porter (71) subse-quently observed microtubules among which vesicles were accumulating be-tween telophasic nuclei in an early stage of plate formation in dividing cells of root tips. Detailed ultrastructural studies employing fixatives which pre-serve the microtubules have now been made on cell plate formation in a variety of plant materials, including meristematic cells of root tips (54, 100, 109, 144), cambial and procambial cells (38), meristematic cells of the wheat coleoptile (109), dividing cells of young leaves (32), cells giving rise to the stomatal apparatus in leaves (110), orchid microspores forming the generative cell (55), and cultured endosperm cells of *Haemanthus* (7, 51). These studies have confirmed that the birefringent fibrillar elements pre-viously noted in the light microscope are microtubules similar in appearance to those of the spindle.

The microtubules of the phragmoplast first appear in the midregion of the cell in early stages of plate formation when some spindle tubules, con-tinuous through the plate region, are still present. At this time numerous vesicles begin accumulating and fusing in the plane of the future plate. Cin-emicrographic studies (5) indicate that in *Haemanthus* endosperm the plate may form in two or more places simultaneously and then grow cen-tripetally until it is consolidated in the center of the cell, after which it grows centrifugally as it does in most dividing plant cells.

According to Inoué & Sato (61) the phragmoplast microtubules arise at the plate, i.e., they are assumed to be polymerized at initiating centers within the incomplete plate and at its margins, from which they grow out in opposite directions into the cytoplasm of the developing daughter cells. This view is supported by ultraviolet microbeam experiments (59). Irradiation of the phragmoplast specifically at the plate destroys both the birefringent elements and the capability for formation of new elements, while irradia-tion of the phragmoplast in areas away from the plate destroys the birefrin-gent elements but not the reforming capability.

Inoué & Sato (61) have suggested, from observations with the polariz-ing light microscope, that near the end of mitosis the spindle microtubules may depolymerize into their protein subunits, which then move to the re-gion of the young cell plate where they are repolymerized into microtubules of the phragmoplast. Similarly, it seems likely that as the plate grows there is successive depolymerization of the older microtubules and incorporation of their subunits into new ones undergoing synthesis at the plate periphery. The lengths of the tubules vary with the stage of plate formation, commonly being shorter at more advanced stages as the side walls are approached (51, 54).

The base of the phragmoplast microtubule, which may be anchored in the plate region and to which new subunits are assumed to be added as the microtubule grows outward, occasionally appears to be enlarged or bulbous and surrounded by electron-opaque, amorphous material (Fig. 5) (51, 54). Hepler & Jackson (51) suggest that this material may contribute to the growth of the microtubules.

As might be expected if they arise at the plate and grow in opposite directions, the microtubules of one developing daughter cell are not continuous through the plate with those of the other (51, 54). The rare cases in which the microtubules do appear to be continuous are probably due to the contiguity or superimposition of the bases of tubules that arise near one another but grow in opposite directions. In *Haemanthus* the microtubules are interdigitated or overlapping at the plate, since those running into one developing daughter cell arise just beyond the plate in the other daughter cell (Fig. 5) (51).

It is generally agreed that the phragmoplast microtubules assist in establishing the zone along which the plate forms, and facilitate the movement of vesicles to this zone. The morphogenetic role of microtubules is best illustrated in certain asymmetric cell divisions, particularly in the formation of the subsidiary cells of the stomatal complex (110) and of the generative cell in pollen (55), where the orientation of the microtubules toward the pole produces a strongly curved plate.

In cinemicrographic analyses, Bajer (5) and Bajer & Allen (9) have observed swellings or droplets sliding along the phragmoplast filaments (clusters of microtubules) and fusing with the plate. It was first postulated by Whaley & Mollenhauer (145), based on a study of permanganate-fixed material, that the vesicles accumulating at the plate are derived from dictyosomes. Their view was soon affirmed by Frey-Wyssling et al. (41), and has been supported by several more recent studies, in which use of glutaraldehyde fixation has permitted observations on the relationship of the microtubules to dictyosomes and to the vesicles arising from them.

On the other hand, several investigators have commented on the abundance of ER elements aligned between the microtubules leading to the plate (7, 32, 51, 122). Some of these elements may become transformed into plasmodesmata (32, 54), but the possibility has been recognized that others may contribute material to the plate itself. Hepler & Jackson (51) pointed out that the aligned chains of vesicles near the plate in *Haemanthus* (Fig. 5) are derived from a cytoplasmic matrix rich in elements of the ER and sparse in dictyosomes. Also Pickett-Heaps (100), studying incorporation of tritiated glucose into the cell plate, found that there was as much or more label over elements of the ER as over dictyosomes. Cronshaw & Esau (32)

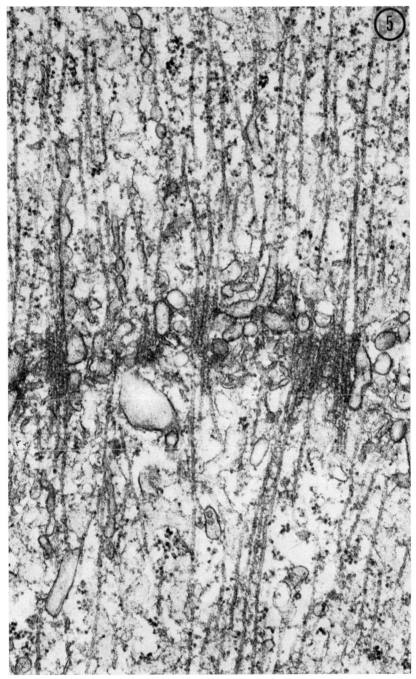

Fig. 5. Portion of a developing cell plate in endosperm of *Haemanthus kath-erinae*. Vesicles are aggregating in large numbers between clusters of microtubules. ×52,000. Micrograph courtesy of Drs. P. K. Hepler & W. T. Jackson (51).

and Bajer (7) have also suggested that the ER may be a source of plate material although subordinate to the dictyosomes.

Generally, ribosomes, elements of the ER, and vesicles occur within the phragmoplast but dictyosomes and other large organelles are excluded, and occur only at its margins and beyond (32, 54). Dictyosomes at the periphery of the phragmoplast commonly have an associated cloud of small vesicles, some of which are surrounded by a reticulate coat (32, 54, 102) and closely resemble in size and surface investment the vesicles previously described from growing root hairs (15). Smooth-surfaced and coated vesicles occur abundantly in the plate region, and both types can be observed fusing with the plate (32, 54, 102). However, there are ordinarily relatively few vesicles in the intervening region of the phragmoplast between the peripheral dictyosomes and the plate. Presumably, undulatory or vibratory motions (64) of the microtubules convey the vesicles rapidly plateward from the dictyosomes. Toward their bases, if the microtubules are anchored in the plate region, the undulations would diminish and the vesicles would come to rest. Undulate phragmoplast microtubules have been reported (32), but the possibility that they may represent fixation artifacts must be recognized. The periodically spaced interconnections observed by Hepler & Jackson (51) between the bases of closely adjacent microtubules are interpreted as cross-bridges which may serve to stabilize the microtubules and thus help to define the plane of the plate.

Schmitt (128) has borrowed the sliding-filament theory of muscle action to suggest how microtubules might function in moving vesicles. The microtubule is assumed to contain subunits bearing the energy source (ATP or GTP), while the vesicle walls contain a binding site for the microtubule subunit and a nearby site with ATPase. With the vesicle and microtubule in contact, the ATP is hydrolyzed, energy is coupled, and conformational changes occur which provide a thrust, moving the vesicle so that a different site is in apposition with a different subunit of the microtubule. As the thrusting process is repeated, the vesicle moves or jerks along the microtubule in a direction dependent on the sense of the microtubule helix.

Hepler & Newcomb (54) searched for evidence of an association between microtubules and vesicles in cross sections of the phragmoplast, but could detect no consistent grouping of microtubules around the vesicles or structural association between the two. Bajer (7), however, has observed an association in *Haemanthus*.

Considering the well-known effects of colchicine on microtubules, it is not surprising to find that its application inhibits cell plate formation. The spindle and phragmoplast microtubules disappear (99), and the vesicles fail to accumulate properly in the plate region (33, 144). If colchicine acts on a cell in which cytokinesis is well advanced, a poorly positioned plate with swollen ends is commonly obtained. The daughter nuclei may be close together, suggesting that the phragmoplast microtubules normally play a cytoskeletal role in keeping the chromosome masses apart (99).

Caffeine is of particular interest because it appears to be a specific inhibitor of cytokinesis. It apparently has little effect on mitosis, and does not destroy the microtubules, yet inhibits cell plate formation. Several groups have shown that the vesicles collect in the plate region in caffeine-treated cells, yet fail to coalesce into a plate (34, 75, 108, 144). This curious effect of caffeine certainly merits further study, as it might lead to a deeper analysis of events in plate formation. Mesquita (81) has found that in dividing cells of *Allium* root tips acenaphthene causes the formation of scattered, wandering sheets of cell plate material even though microtubules are present during their formation. Vincaleucoblastine also causes formation of highly irregular plates, and again microtubules are present, so that this drug appears to be more closely related to acenaphthene than to colchicine in its mode of action (82).

Finally, attention should be called to the distinctive type of cytokinesis described by Johnson & Porter (65) in a superbly illustrated study of *Chlamydomonas reinhardi*. Cytokinesis is accomplished by appearance of an array of microtubules oriented along the cleavage plane, and then passage of a furrow between them. The authors suggest that the microtubules may facilitate cytokinesis by providing a rigid framework on the opposing sides of the furrow against which cytoplasmic furrowing can take place.

Asymmetrical cell divisions.—Ordinarily, cells that differentiate do so after arising from more or less symmetrical divisions of meristematic cells. However, in a number of cases differentiation starts with a parent cell which itself becomes structurally polarized preceding mitosis (21, 134–136). Displacement of the nucleus to one end of the cell results in production of an eccentrically oriented mitotic spindle. The new cell plate then forms midway between the spindle, so that the genetically equivalent daughter nuclei resulting from the division are localized in different cytoplasmic environments. It has been assumed that some difference in cytoplasmic organization underlies the asymmetric division and the subsequent differences that develop between the two daughter cells, and that study of the phenomenon will aid in understanding the basis of differentiation (3, 134–136). Examples of differentiated cells that are initiated by asymmetric divisions in this way include root hair cells, the stomatal complexes in many monocots, the siliceous-suberous cell pairs in barley leaves, the tube and generative cells of the pollen grain, leaf cells in *Sphagnum,* and sclereids in *Monstera* (21).

The first ultrastructural investigation of an asymmetrical mitosis was that by Avers (3) on formation of the root hair initial in *Phleum,* made before introduction of glutaraldehyde as a fixative. The subsequent discovery by Pickett-Heaps & Northcote (109, 110) that a dense band of microtubules appears at least in many plant cells just before mitosis has expanded considerably our knowledge of the fine structure of asymmetric divisions, although just how basic the presence of the band may be in determining subsequent events is in question.

In monocots the "stomatal complex" consists of a pair of guard cells and may also include one to several pairs of surrounding subsidiary cells, depending on the genus. Ordinarily these complexes arise in rows, with the older stages in development being located farther from the meristem at the leaf base. Stebbins and colleagues (134–136) have discussed the influence which apparently emanates from the guard mother cell and induces the epidermal cells on either side to divide asymmetrically to give the subsidiary cells.

Pickett-Heaps & Northcote (110) studied the development of the stomatal complex in wheat, which at maturity consists of a pair of guard cells each flanked by a subsidiary cell. Three cell divisions are involved in development of the complex; the first and second divisions are asymmetrical, while the third is symmetrical (Fig. 6). They found that the band of microtubules which appeared preceding mitosis in each asymmetric division was asymmetrically located, and that its position predicted the plane and position of the future cell plate. In Figures 6a, c, and d, each microtubular band is shown as two short heavy lines, representing a median section through the band normal to its plane.

Preceding the asymmetric first division, the nucleus migrates to one end of the cell and in preprophase the microtubules form a band next to the wall around the nucleus (Fig. 6a). The asymmetric second division, which produces the two subsidiary cells, is particularly interesting because prior to mitosis the nuclei of the flanking epidermal cells come to rest against the wall shared with the guard mother cell, and the preprophase band appears adjacent to this wall and off to one side of the nucleus (Fig. 6c). It also lies perpendicular to the plane of the band that preceded the first division. Subsequently the cell plate forms in an arc that joins the walls of the cells immediately above and below the guard mother cell, adjacent to the former position of the band (Fig. 6d, e). The last division, in which the two guard cells are formed, is symmetrical (Fig. 6e), but the wall between the guard cells remains incomplete (Fig. 6f) (20).

Further investigations have raised some doubts about the relevance of the premitotic band to the subsequent plane and position of cell plate formation. Burgess & Northcote (22) investigated cell division in *Phleum* roots and found preprophase microtubular bands, but surprisingly, they were symmetrically disposed in the cells, as were the preprophase nuclei, even when the subsequent metaphase plates (3) and cell divisions were asymmetric. Furthermore, Pickett-Heaps (103) has investigated asymmetric divisions in *Chara* and ascertained that although microtubules are present, they do not show the preprophase grouping equivalent to what is observed in *Triticum*. There is also now available a study by Heslop-Harrison (55) of the asymmetric division giving the generative cell in orchid pollen. Although the spindle itself is asymmetrically located and the cell plate that is formed subsequently is hemispherical, no premitotic grouping of microtubules is observed in the expected regions.

In pursuing further the morphogenetic significance of the preprophase

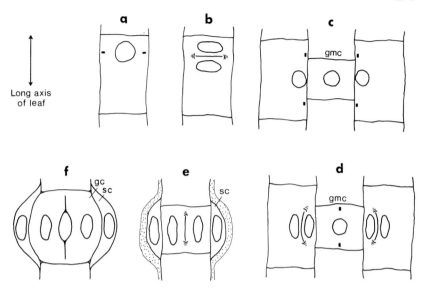

FIG. 6. Development of stomatal complex in *Triticum*.

a. Polarized primary stomatal mother cell. The two short, thick lines represent a group of microtubules in cross section and indicate the position and plane of the preprophase band.

b. The asymmetrical first division. The primary stomatal mother cell is dividing to give an epidermal cell and a smaller guard mother cell.

c. Guard mother cell (gmc) flanked by two epidermal cells. The two short thick lines in each cell represent the preprophase band of microtubules seen in section.

d. The asymmetrical second division. Lateral subsidiary cells are arising by asymmetric divisions in epidermal cells. Position and plane of preprophase band shown by short thick lines in the guard mother cell (gmc).

e. Symmetrical third division. The guard mother cell is producing two guard cells. S.c., subsidiary cell.

f. Two guard cells, each flanked by a subsidiary cell.

band, Pickett-Heaps (108) has treated dividing cells of wheat with caffeine, which inhibits cytokinesis. Examination of multinucleate cells produced in this way showed that the position of microtubular bands appearing in prophase was not noticeably affected by the size, shape, position, or number of nuclei in the cell. Thus, in Pickett-Heaps' view, the preprophase grouping may be a result rather than a cause of polarization. It may not be determinative in the preprophase positioning of the nucleus, but like the latter, simply an expression of a particular cytoplasmic environment. Quite possibly, formation of the microtubular band represents a preparatory step for mitosis, at the onset of which the microtubules or their subunits are incorporated into the spindle.

MICROTUBULES AND DEPOSITION OF CELL WALL MICROFIBRILS

Primary wall growth.—For many years, students of wall structure and growth have recognized that the orientation of the cellulose microfibrils at the time of deposition determines the manner of cell enlargement and the shape of the cell, and that this orientation is under cytoplasmic control (44, 85, 120). Discovery of microtubules in the cytoplasm adjacent both to the growing primary wall (71) and to the developing thickenings of secondary wall (53) has been of special interest because their orientation parallels that of the microfibrils. It has been widely supposed that the microtubules directly or indirectly control this orientation. Of course, if this role is attributed to the microtubules, then it becomes necessary to ask how they accomplish this, and what determines the sites at which the microtubules appear along the wall, and the orientation they themselves assume.

Ledbetter & Porter (71) observed that in elongating cells of *Phleum* and *Juniperus* root tips, microtubules were present in the cytoplasm close to the plasmalemma and ran parallel to the cell surface. Along the side walls, where they were one to three units deep, they ran transversely and parallel to one another and to the cellulose microfibrils outside the plasmalemma. In sections normal to the protoplast surface, the microtubules were never observed in contact with the plasmalemma, but were always separated from it by about 100 Å or more. At the end walls, both the microtubules and the wall microfibrils were randomly oriented.

Examples of the appearance of microtubules adjacent to the side walls of elongating cells are shown in Figures 7, 8 and 11.

Although microtubules near the primary wall in growing cells have undoubtedly been very widely observed since the publication of Ledbetter & Porter's original observations, they have generally received only passing notice, usually in connection with studies of secondary wall deposition in differentiating cells (e.g., 30, 132). There are a few reports of microtubules adjacent to the primary walls of algae. Pickett-Heaps (102) observed microtubules near the plasmalemma corresponding in alignment to the wall microfibrils in *Chara*. Nagai & Rebhun (86) found microtubules near the wall in *Nitella*, but whether they were aligned parallel to the microfibrils is not clear from the micrographs. Kiermayer (67) has reported microtubules running parallel to the cell surface and to one another beneath the plasmalemma in the desmid *Micrasterias*.

Although dividing cells have been the subject of study in a number of laboratories, these have yielded little or no information about microtubules in relation to the primary wall, since microtubules never occur next to the side or end walls in cells undergoing mitosis or cytokinesis. Pickett-Heaps & Northcote (109, 110) did, however, observe microtubules adjacent to the primary walls in premitotic cells of wheat (cf. Fig. 4).

With the evidence available, it seems likely that microtubules may be required next to primary walls in order for cellulose microfibrils oriented parallel to one another to be deposited. At any rate, whenever parallel microtu-

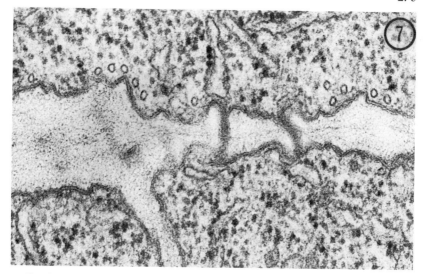

Fig. 7. Microtubules adjacent to side wall (primary wall) in a meristematic cell from a root tip of white sweet clover (*Melilotus alba*). ×76,000. Micrograph by the author.

bules are seen in the cytoplasm next to the primary wall, the most recently deposited wall microfibrils always appear to be similarly oriented. Whether microtubules also are associated typically with the random deposition of microfibrils is not clear; as discussed later, they are not in some cases.

Unfortunately, information on the occurrence of microtubules localized next to the wall is available for very few of the cell types classified (120) according to the pattern of microfibril deposition and manner of wall growth. The observations of Ledbetter & Porter (71), and most of those since, have been made on tissue cells which grow predominantly in length. Cells of this type include young vascular elements, fibers of various tissues, fusiform cambial initials, and parenchyma cells of apical meristems (120). The newly deposited microfibrils in these cells are usually oriented in a direction transverse to the root or shoot axis. Since the greatest coherence is along the axis of the transversely oriented microfibrils and the wall yields most readily to the turgor pressure perpendicular to this, the cells consequently elongate in the direction normal to that of the newly deposited microfibrils (44, 120).

The observations available on this type of cell indicate that the microtubules next to the lateral walls are always oriented transversely like the newly deposited microfibrils (Fig. 8). Individual microtubules frequently can be traced for several microns, and it seems likely that they run continuously around the cell "like hundreds of hoops" (71). Green & King (45) have pointed out that it is remarkable for the synthesis of cellulose to be

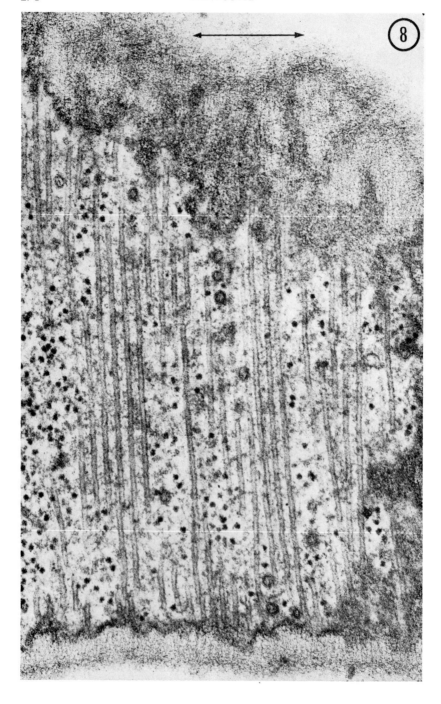

continued in the transverse direction in the face of an extreme longitudinal distortion of the cell. They have suggested that the resistance of the wall synthesizing machinery of the cytoplasm to strain orientation could be explained by a band-like arrangement of microtubules, since until they were broken, the bands could not be pulled out into the longitudinal direction.

More or less isodiametric growth is characteristic of many tissue parenchyma cells, callus cells of tissue cultures, and freely growing cells or cell parts like the globular cells of leaf glands and the sporangium of *Phycomyces*. The microfibrillar structure is known to be random in some cases (120). Little is known concerning the presence or orientation of microtubules in this type of cell despite its frequency of occurrence and importance in physiological studies. Halperin & Jensen (48) have reported that in carrot cell cultures, microtubules are not present when the cells are grown in the presence of auxin (2,4-D), but appear when the auxin is removed. It would be interesting to know whether random and parallel microfibrils are deposited, respectively, under the two conditions.

Root hairs, pollen tubes, fungal hyphae, and the rhizoids of algae and fungi are examples of freely growing tubular cells or parts of cells with tip growth only. Both root hairs and pollen tubes have been studied ultrastructurally, permitting a comparison to be made of the relationship of microtubules to their patterns of microfibril deposition. In both, microfibrils are deposited in a random network at the tip, and then are pushed aside and become part of the side wall as the tip extends. Since the side wall does not extend, the random position of these microfibrils is not altered subsequently. Microtubules do not occur at the tip either in the root hair (88) or the pollen tube (121), hence are not involved in the random deposition of the microfibrils which takes place at the growing tip.

In the pollen tube, no deposition of microfibrils occurs along the side wall, nor are microtubules known to occur in the adjacent cytoplasm (121). In the root hair, however, reinforcing microfibrils are deposited axially on the inner face of the wall, starting some distance from the tip (detectable at about 25μ from the tip in radish). Newcomb & Bonnett (88) found that *axially* oriented microtubules occur in the cytoplasm next to the side wall

---

←—⟨⟨⟨⟨

Fig. 8. Microtubules running parallel to one another immediately beneath a primary wall. Note that the microfibrils of the wall are oriented parallel to the microtubules. The axis of cell elongation (indicated by the arrow) is at right angles to the orientation of the microtubules and microfibrils. Vesicles can be seen among the microtubules. From root tip of bean (*Phaseolus vulgaris*). ×77,000. Micrograph by the author.

where the axial microfibrils are being deposited. Although the microtubules extend forward into the region where only random microfibrils occur in the wall, they can have no influence on these microfibrils, which were deposited at the tip and remain immobilized thereafter. This point needs to be stressed, lest it be concluded that random deposition occurs in the presence of axially oriented microtubules. Probably the presence of microtubules in this region simply means that they are more easily detected than are the beginnings of axial microfibril deposition. The results furnish additional support for the hypothesis that, at least in higher plants, parallel deposition of microfibrils requires the presence of similarly oriented microtubules.

It is interesting to note that the *Phycomyces* sporangiophore resembles root hairs in depositing a reinforcing layer of axially oriented microfibrils (of chitin, not cellulose) on the inner surface of the side wall back of the growing tip (120). Although the fine structure of *Phycomyces* has been investigated (78, 97), no microtubules have been reported.

Secondary wall deposition.—Numerous studies have demonstrated that oriented microtubules occur in the cytoplasm adjacent to the developing secondary wall thickenings of differentiating xylem elements. The relationship was first shown by Hepler & Newcomb (53) for parenchyma cells undergoing redifferentiation into tracheary elements in wounded *Coleus* stem, and shortly thereafter by Wooding & Northcote (149) for secondary xylem elements differentiating from cambial initials in *Acer pseudoplatanus*. Other studies include those by Cronshaw & Bouck (30) on differentiating xylem in *Avena* coleoptiles; Cronshaw on xylem derived from cambium in *Acer rubrum* (27, 28) and on tracheids differentiating from parenchyma cells in tobacco pith cultures (29); Esau, Cheadle & Gill (37) on tracheary elements differentiating with helical thickenings in *Beta* and *Cucurbita;* Pickett-Heaps & Northcote (111) on differentiating xylem cells in the coleoptile and root of wheat; and Srivastava & O'Brien (133) on xylem differentiating from cambium in *Pinus*. In addition, Pickett-Heaps has used experimental approaches in contributing to the study of microtubules in xylem differentiation, namely by application of colchicine to wheat seedlings (99) and by the use of radioisotopes to follow incorporation into the secondary wall thickenings of differentiating xylem in the same material (98, 101, 107).

Considered collectively, these studies present a remarkably consistent picture, and one which is essentially similar to that found for the primary wall. Except, apparently, for the earliest stages, microtubules are invariably present in the cytoplasm adjacent to the secondary wall thickenings or bands throughout their development. Moreover, the microfibrils within the bands run parallel to the microtubules, and since the microfibrils parallel the direction taken by the bands, the microtubules and bands likewise follow the same course. (It should be remembered that the microfibrils of a particular layer of the secondary wall retain their parallel orientation throughout development, in contrast to those of the primary wall which are gradually reoriented deeper in the wall as cell elongation occurs.)

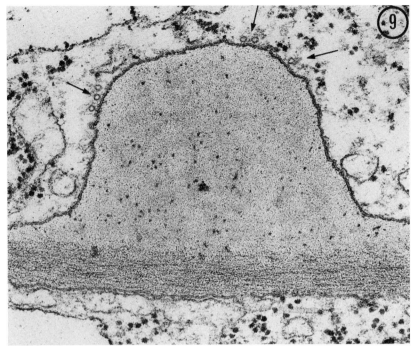

Fig. 9. Microtubules adjacent to a secondary wall thickening, both seen in transverse section. In tracheary element in leaf of *Petunia hybrida.* ×77,000. Micrograph by William P. Wergin, University of Wisconsin.

In transections of a cell, the microtubules are seen to follow gently curving paths conforming to the curves of the wall thickenings. It seems likely that the microtubules associated with annular thickenings form complete circumferential rings in the cytoplasm. Whether in the case of a helical wall thickening the particular group of microtubules seen at any one level follows the course of the thickening for the entire length of the cell or only for a relatively short distance has not been determined.

As in the case of the primary wall, in suitable sections the microtubules usually appear to be separated from the plasmalemma by at least 100 Å (Fig. 9). They are not as concentrated as they sometimes are along the primary wall, but are rather sparsely and irregularly distributed around the thickenings, and most frequently only one unit deep. They are remarkably persistent, considering the lability of microtubules as a class, and can still be found around the secondary wall thickenings at late stages of differentiation when the cytoplasm is obviously undergoing degradation. Both smooth-surfaced and coated vesicles derived from the cytosomes are commonly observed among them (Fig. 10). Other cytoplasmic bodies, however,

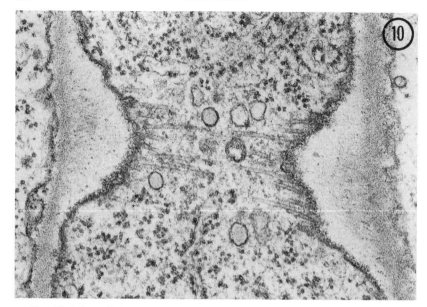

Fig. 10. Microtubules and vesicles in the cytoplasm adjacent to a secondary wall band. The plane of section passes through the band in the central region, revealing the microtubules. Note that the microtubules and microfibrils are oriented parallel to one another and transversely. In tracheary element of root tip of *Arabidopsis thaliana*. ×60,000. Micrograph by William P. Wergin, University of Wisconsin.

do not appear to be associated with the microtubules or noticeably concentrated in the vicinity of the thickenings.

Pickett-Heaps & Northcote (111) discovered that at an early stage in differentiation of a xylem element, when the thickenings of secondary wall first become evident, the microtubules occur along the primary wall between the thickenings, and do not appear over the thickenings until later. Possibly the presence of microtubules only along the primary wall at this stage indicates that secondary wall formation has not yet proceeded far enough to stop primary wall growth, and that initiation of secondary wall formation in a particular pattern over the primary wall surface involves a corresponding temporary disappearance of the microtubules.

The initial stages in the development of the secondary wall thickenings in the endothecial cells of the lily anther, studied by Heslop-Harrison (56), differ from the above account for xylem (111). The thickenings in the endothecial cells consist of a basal plate of cellulose from which arise branching bars on the lateral walls. Before visible thickenings appear, oriented files of microtubules define zones that delimit the prospective sites of the bars. During the thickening process, the microtubules are restricted entirely to the vicinity of the bars. As expected, the cellulose microfibrils are oriented in the direction of the bars and microtubules.

Remarks on microtubules in relation to microfibril deposition.—From the observed correlation of orientation between microtubules and the newly deposited cellulose microfibrils in both primary and secondary walls, it has been widely assumed that microfibrillar orientation at time of deposition is under microtubular control. Although Ledbetter & Porter (71, 72) suggested that this control might be achieved through the influence of the microtubules on cytoplasmic streaming, more recent evidence implicates much finer cytoplasmic filaments in streaming in a number of organisms. In the slime mold *Physarum,* which exhibits vigorous streaming, most investigators have been unable to find microtubules, but have observed numerous filaments about 50 Å in diameter (26, 113, 116, 147, 148). Since these closely resemble the muscle filaments 50 to 70 Å in diameter that are built from the globular protein actin, and since a protein has been isolated from slime mold that resembles actin closely and forms 50 Å filaments (1, 50), there is good reason to believe that actin or actin-like filaments may be of wide occurrence and may underlie the streaming phenomenon.

In the alga *Nitella,* whose growth has been analyzed intensively by Green (43, 44), Nagai & Rebhun (86) have also concluded that microfilaments are involved in developing the motive force for streaming. They found that bundles of microfilaments, each 50 Å in diameter and many microns long, were oriented parallel to the direction of streaming in the interface between the moving endoplasm and stationary ectoplasm where the site of motive force for streaming is believed to be located. The microtubules, however, were located near the wall in the stationary ectoplasm, where they could not be involved in streaming in any direct way.

Similar bundles of microfilaments were discovered in epidermal and parenchymatous cells of the oat coleoptile by O'Brien & Thimann (92), and in cells of *Chara* by Pickett-Heaps (102, 104). Their appearance in an elongate differentiating cell of a bean root is shown in Figure 11. (It should be noted that the bundle of microfilaments is axially oriented while the microtubules along the side walls are transversely oriented.)

The bundles observed by O'Brien & Thimann (92) were composed of microfilaments 50 to 70 Å wide and of indefinite length. They paralleled the long axis of the cell and the direction of streaming, while the microtubules sometimes observed in the same cell were transversely oriented. The authors recognized the possibility that the microfilaments might be subunits of microtubules, and that if so, they would participate in streaming as microfilaments, but primarily in controlling shape when part of the microtubule.

Recently Hohl et al. (57) have reported microfilaments of similar dimensions in the cytoplasm of *Acytostelium,* a cellular slime mold, where again they have been implicated in streaming. Microtubules are also encountered in the cytoplasm of *Acytostelium,* but are not numerous and are randomly

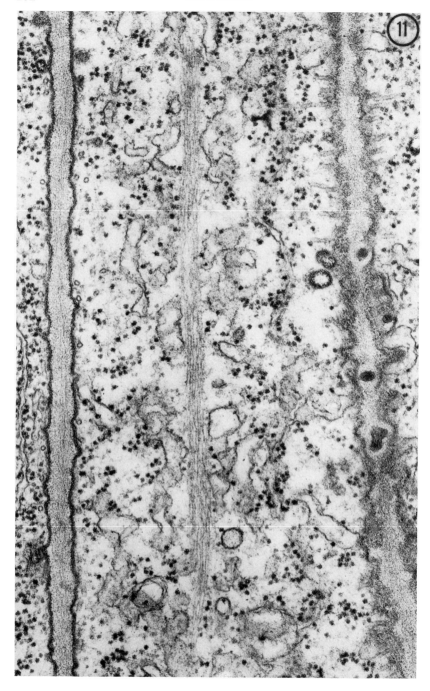

oriented. On the other hand, Sabnis & Jacobs (124) have shown that in the coenocytic alga *Caulerpa,* the streaming endoplasm is filled with bundles of numerous, evenly spaced, oriented microtubules. They suggest that the microtubules may provide the framework, or may delimit areas of cytoplasmic substrate, upon which the motive force responsible for streaming is generated.

On balance, then, it appears that there is accumulating evidence for the presence of microfilaments in plant cells, but it is by no means clear that they will prove to be common cytoplasmic components. There is also the possibility, in view of the previously reviewed information, that microfilaments and microtubules are composed of chemically identical or closely related subunits (1, 92).

Although there appears to be no evidence or support for the view that microtubules adjacent to the wall participate in the enzymatic synthesis of the cellulose microfibrils, it is generally agreed that they are involved "directly or indirectly" in orienting the microfibrils as they are deposited. This hypothesis has been greatly strengthened by experiments with colchicine, which has the same effect on microtubules located near the walls as it does on those of the spindle (99). In work on *Nitella,* where the microfibrils are deposited transversely, Green (43, 44) pointed out that in a simple mechanism to account for continued transverse synthesis, the orientation of new microfibrils could be based on that of pre-existing ones. When colchicine was applied, the cytoplasm was induced to put down a layer of random microfibrils, but then after removal of the drug, it was able again to deposit transverse microfibrils. Thus he showed that the order was in the synthetic machinery, not in the pre-existing microfibrils, and that this order could be re-established after removal of the drug.

The uniformity of spacing usually observed between the plasmalemma and the microtubules closest to it suggests that the two components may be attached, and several investigators have reported visual evidence for the presence of a connecting substance between them (29, 67, 72). Ledbetter & Porter (72) suggested that the point of attachment might anchor a portion of the microtubule so that any undulations along it would induce a streaming motion. Ledbetter (70) subsequently suggested that a stimulus arising

FIG. 11. Bundle of microfilaments oriented longitudinally in an elongating cell. Note that the microtubules associated with the side walls are oriented transversely. The wall and microtubules on the right have been sectioned obliquely. From root tip of bean (*Phaseolus vulgaris*). ×62,000. Micrograph by the author.

from the microtubules might be transmitted in some way by the plasma-lemma to the growing wall. Pickett-Heaps & Northcote (111) suggested, as one of the possible roles of the microtubules, that they might exert specific directional control of particular enzyme systems especially concerned with formation of the organized wall microfibrils. A proposal along similar lines was made by Cronshaw (29), who reasoned that microtubules attached to the inner surface of the plasmalemma might, through movement, bring about the orientation of cellulose synthesizing enzymes located on the outer surface, resulting in the deposition of oriented microfibrils.

How and in what form the cellulosic component reaches the cell surface from the cytoplasm remains unknown, however. There is now considerable autoradiographic evidence that vesicles derived from the dictyosomes contribute materials to both primary and secondary walls (90, 98, 100, 107, 111). Also, dictyosome vesicles have been widely observed in abundance near both types of wall, and in some instances an apparent fusion of dictyosome vesicles with the plasmalemma has been reported. Nevertheless, it has not been claimed in the autoradiographic studies that cellulose precursors reach the wall via dictyosome vesicles. During secondary wall deposition the dictyosomes at least for a time are quite active in producing numerous large smooth-surfaced vesicles (36), but whether these contain cellulose precursors is unknown.

If the vesicles were to contain cellulose precursors, then the microtubules could conceivably function by collecting these vesicles in particular regions, thus controlling the places in which new wall material were deposited. Although it is difficult to see how this could influence microfibril orientation, it might explain how the banded patterns of secondary wall arise. Experiments by Pickett-Heaps (99) with colchicine suggest, in fact, that the microtubules may play this role. When colchicine was applied to wheat seedlings, virtually all microtubules disappeared from the differentiating xylem, but deposition of secondary wall continued. However, the thickenings that appeared were malformed and lacked any regularity in size or distribution along the wall. It appeared also that within the thickenings the oriented microfibrillar texture was preserved.

This suggests that for the secondary wall the microtubules may not control the orientation of the microfibrils, but rather determine where the thickening will occur, perhaps by serving as tracts where vesicles and other cytoplasmic constituents are collected and deposited (107). Initially deposited microfibrils of the secondary wall might serve as templates in orienting those deposited subsequently. This does not rule out the influence of microtubules in determining the initial direction of orientation, however.

CONCLUDING REMARKS

Two remarkable interrelated properties appear to distinguish microtubules from other elements of cytoplasmic fine structure. First, they seem to play a directive role in morphogenesis, either by controlling the movement and positioning of other cellular structures, or by serving as cytoskeletal agents to bring about and maintain cell asymmetry. Second, as highly labile structures that are believed to exist in dynamic equilibrium with a pool of readily available subunits, they can be polymerized or depolymerized rapidly at different intracellular loci as conditions change during growth and differentiation. It is not surprising that their study currently occupies the center of attention among cell biologists.

LITERATURE CITED

1. Adelman, M. R., Borisy, G. G., Shelanski, M. L., Weisenberg, R. C., Taylor, E. W., *Federation Proc.*, **27**, 1186–93 (1968)
2. Allen, R. D., Bowen, C. C., *Caryologia*, **19**, 299–342 (1966)
3. Avers, C., *Am. J. Botany*, **50**, 140–48 (1963)
4. Bajer, A., *Chromosoma*, **16**, 381–402 (1965)
5. Bajer, A., *Exptl. Cell Res.*, **37**, 376–98 (1965)
6. Bajer, A., *J. Cell Biol.*, **33**, 713–20 (1967)
7. Bajer, A., *Chromosoma*, **24**, 383–417 (1968)
8. Bajer, A., Allen, R. D., *Science*, **151**, 572–74 (1966)
9. Bajer, A., Allen, R. D., *J. Cell Sci.*, **1**, 455–62 (1966)
10. Bajer, A., Molé-Bajer, J., *Exptl. Cell Res.*, **25**, 251–67 (1961)
11. Barnicot, N. A., *J. Cell Sci.*, **1**, 217–22 (1966)
12. Barton, R., *J. Ultrastruct. Res.*, **20**, 6–19 (1967)
13. Behnke, O., Forer, A., *J. Cell Sci.*, **2**, 169–92 (1967)
14. Berlin, J. D., Bowen, C. C., *Am. J. Botany*, **51**, 650–52 (1964)
15. Bonnett, H. T., Newcomb, E. H., *Protoplasma*, **62**, 59–75 (1966)
16. Borisy, G. G., Taylor, E. W., *J. Cell Biol.*, **34**, 525–33 (1967)
17. Borisy, G. G., Taylor, E. W., *ibid.*, 535–48
18. Bracker, C. E., *Ann. Rev. Phytopath.*, **5**, 343–74 (1967)
19. Brinkley, B. R., Stubblefield, E., *Chromosoma*, **19**, 28–43 (1966)
20. Brown, W. V., Johnson, S. C., *Am. J. Botany*, **49**, 110–15 (1962)
21. Bünning, E., *Protoplasmatologia*, **8**, 1–86 (1957)
22. Burgess, J., Northcote, D. H., *Planta*, **75**, 319–26 (1967)
23. Burgess, J., Northcote, D. H., *ibid.*, **80**, 1–14 (1968)
24. Carothers, Z. B., Kreitner, G. L., *J. Cell Biol.*, **33**, 43–51 (1967)
25. Carothers, Z. B., Kreitner, G. L., *ibid.*, **36**, 603–16 (1968)
26. Crawley, J. C. W., *J. Roy. Microscop. Soc.*, **85**, 313–22 (1966)
27. Cronshaw, J., *Can. J. Botany*, **43**, 1401–7 (1965)
28. Cronshaw, J., in *Cellular Ultrastructure of Woody Plants*, 99–124

29. Cronshaw, J., *Planta*, **72**, 78–90 (1967)
30. Cronshaw, J., Bouck, G. B., *J. Cell Biol.*, **24**, 415–31 (1965)
31. Cronshaw, J., Esau, K., *J. Cell Biol.*, **34**, 801–15 (1967)
32. Cronshaw, J., Esau, K., *Protoplasma*, **65**, 1–24 (1968)
33. Dauwalder, M., Whaley, W. G., *J. Cell Biol.*, **27**, 24A (1965)
34. Deysson, G., Benbadis, M.-C., *J. Microscopie*, **5**, 511–18 (1966)
35. Dietrich, J., *Compt. Rend. Acad. Sci., Paris*, **266**, 579–81 (1968)
36. Esau, K., Cheadle, V. I., Gill, R. H., *Am. J. Botany*, **53**, 756–64 (1966)
37. Esau, K., Cheadle, V. I., Gill, R. H., *ibid.*, 765–71
38. Esau, K., Gill, R. H., *Planta*, **67**, 168–81 (1965)
39. Forer, A., *J. Cell Biol.*, **25**, 95–117 (1965)
40. Forer, A., *Chromosoma*, **19**, 44–98 (1966)
41. Frey-Wyssling, A., López-Sáez, J. F., Mühlethaler, K., *J. Ultrastruct. Res.*, **10**, 422–32 (1964)
42. Gibbons, I. R., *Ann. Rev. Biochem.*, **37**, 521–46 (1968)
43. Green, P. B., *Science*, **138**, 1404–5 (1962)
44. Green, P. B., in *Cytodifferentiation and Macromolecular Synthesis*, 203 (Locke, M. J., Ed., Academic Press, N.Y., 1963)
45. Green, P. B., King, A., *Australian J. Biol. Sci.*, **19**, 421–37 (1966)
46. Grimstone, A. V., Klug, H., *J. Cell Sci.*, **1**, 351–62 (1966)
47. Gross, P. R., Spindel, W., *Ann. N.Y. Acad. Sci.*, **84**, 745–54 (1960)
48. Halperin, W., Jensen, W. A., *J. Ultrastruct. Res.*, **18**, 428–43 (1967)
49. Harris, P., Bajer, A., *Chromosoma*, **16**, 624–36 (1965)
50. Hatano, S., Oosawa, F., *Biochim. Biophys. Acta*, **127**, 488–98 (1966)
51. Hepler, P. K., Jackson, W. T., *J. Cell Biol.*, **38**, 437–46 (1968)
52. Hepler, P. K., Jackson, W. T., *Plant Physiol.*, **43**, S–3 (1968)
53. Hepler, P. K., Newcomb, E. H., *J. Cell Biol.*, **20**, 529–33 (1964)
54. Hepler, P. K., Newcomb, E. H., *J.*

(Côté, W. A., Jr., Ed., Syracuse Univ. Press, Syracuse, N.Y., 1965)

Ultrastruct. Res., **19**, 498–513 (1967)

55. Heslop-Harrison, J., *J. Cell Sci.*, **3**, 457–66 (1968)

56. Heslop-Harrison, J., in *27th Growth Symposium of the Society for Developmental Biology* (Locke, M. J., Ed., Academic Press, N.Y., 1969)

57. Hohl, H. R., Hamamoto, S. T., Hemmes, D. E., *Am. J. Botany*, **55**, 783–96 (1968)

58. Ichida, A. A., Fuller, M. S., *Mycologia*, **60**, 141–55 (1968)

59. Inoué, S., in *Primitive Motile Systems in Cell Biology*, 549–98 (Allen, R. D., Kamiya, N., Eds., Academic Press, N.Y., 1964)

60. Inoué, S., Bajer, A., *Chromosoma*, **12**, 48–63 (1961)

61. Inoué, S., Sato, H., *J. Gen. Physiol.*, **50**, 259–92 (1967)

62. Inoué, S., Sato, H., Tucker, R. W., *Biol. Bull.*, **125**, 380–81 (1963)

63. Jackson, W. T., *Physiol. Plantarum*, **20**, 20–29 (1967)

64. Jarosch, R., in *Primitive Motile Systems in Cell Biology*, 599–620 (See Ref. 59)

65. Johnson, U. G., Porter, K. R., *J. Cell Biol.*, **38**, 403–25 (1968)

66. Jokelainen, P. T., *J. Cell Biol.*, **39**, 68a (1968)

67. Kiermayer, O., *Planta*, **83**, 223–36 (1968)

68. Krishan, A., *J. Ultrastruct. Res.*, **23**, 134–43 (1968)

69. Krishan, A., Buck, R. C., *J. Cell Biol.*, **24**, 433–44 (1965)

70. Ledbetter, M. C., *J. Agr. Food Chem.*, **13**, 405–7 (1965)

71. Ledbetter, M. C., Porter, K. R., *J. Cell Biol.*, **19**, 239–50 (1963)

72. Ledbetter, M. C., Porter, K. R., *Science*, **144**, 872–74 (1964)

73. Lepper, R., *Botan. Rev.*, **22**, 375–417 (1956)

74. Lessie, P. E., Lovett, J .S., *Am. J. Botany*, **55**, 220–36 (1968)

75. López-Sáez, J. F., Risueño, M. C., Giménez-Martín, G., *J. Ultrastruct. Res.*, **14**, 85–94 (1966)

76. Manton, I., *J. Roy. Microscop. Soc.*, **83**, 317–25 (1964)

77. Manton, I., *ibid.*, 471–76

78. Marchant, R., Peat, A., Banbury, G. H., *New Phytologist*, **66**, 623–29 (1967)

79. Marsland, D. A., Zimmerman, A. M., *Exptl. Cell Res.*, **38**, 306–13 (1965)

80. Mazia, D., in *The Cell*, **3**, 77–412 (Brachet, J., Mirsky, A. E., Eds., Academic Press, N.Y., 1961)

81. Mesquita, J. M., *Compt. Rend. Acad. Sci., Paris*, **265**, 322–25 (1967)

82. Mesquita, J. M., Mangenot, S., *Compt. Rend. Acad. Sci., Paris*, **265**, 1917–19 (1967)

83. Mizukami, I., Gall, J., *J. Cell Biol.*, **29**, 97–111 (1966)

84. Motta, J. J., *Mycologia*, **59**, 370–75 (1967)

85. Mühlethaler, K., *Ann. Rev. Plant Physiol.*, **18**, 1–24 (1967)

86. Nagai, R., Rebhun, L. I., *J. Ultrastruct. Res.*, **14**, 571–89 (1966)

87. Newcomb, E. H., *J. Cell Biol.*, **35**, C17–C22 (1967)

88. Newcomb, E. H., Bonnett, H. T., *J. Cell Biol.*, **27**, 575–89 (1965)

89. Norstog, K., *Am. J. Botany*, **54**, 831–40 (1967)

90. Northcote, D. H., Pickett-Heaps, J. D., *Biochem. J.*, **98**, 159–67 (1966)

91. O'Brien, T. P., *J. Cell Sci.*, **2**, 557–62 (1967)

92. O'Brien, T. P., Thimann, K. V., *Proc. Natl. Acad. Sci. U.S.*, **56**, 888–94 (1966)

93. Paolillo, D. J., *Can. J. Botany*, **43**, 669–76 (1965)

94. Paolillo, D. J., *Trans. Am. Microscop. Soc.*, **86**, 428–33 (1967)

95. Paolillo, D. J., Kreitner, G. L., Reighard, J. A., *Planta*, **78**, 226–47 (1968)

96. Paolillo, D. J., Kreitner, G. L., Reighard, J. A., *ibid.*, 248–61

97. Peat, A., Banbury, G. H., *New Phytologist*, **66**, 475–84 (1967)

98. Pickett-Heaps, J. D., *Planta*, **71**, 1–14 (1966)

99. Pickett-Heaps, J. D., *Develop. Biol.*, **15**, 206–36 (1967)

100. Pickett-Heaps, J. D., *J. Ultrastruct. Res.*, **18**, 287–303 (1967)

101. Pickett-Heaps, J. D., *Protoplasma*, **64**, 49–66 (1967)

102. Pickett-Heaps, J. D., *Australian J. Biol. Sci.*, **20**, 539–51 (1967)

103. Pickett-Heaps, J. D., *ibid.*, 883–94

104. Pickett-Heaps, J. D., *ibid.*, **21**, 255–74 (1968)

105. Pickett-Heaps, J. D., *ibid.*, 655–90

106. Pickett-Heaps, J. D., *Planta*, **81**, 193–200 (1968)

107. Pickett-Heaps, J. D., *Protoplasma*, **65**, 181–205 (1968)

108. Pickett-Heaps, J. D., *J. Cell Sci.* (In press)

109. Pickett-Heaps, J. D., Northcote, D. H., *J. Cell Sci.*, **1,** 109–20 (1966)
110. Pickett-Heaps, J. D., Northcote, D. H., *ibid.*, 121–28
111. Pickett-Heaps, J. D., Northcote, D. H., *J. Exptl. Botany*, **17,** 20–26 (1966)
112. Porter, K. R., in *Ciba Foundation Symposium on Principles of Biomolecular Organizations*, 308–45 (Wohlstenholme, G. E. W., O'Connor, M., Eds., J. & A. Churchill, London, 1966)
113. Porter, K .R., Kawakami, N., Ledbetter, M. C., *J. Cell Biol.*, **27,** 78A (1965)
114. Renaud, F. L., Rowe, A. J., Gibbons, I. R., *J. Cell Biol.*, **36,** 79–90 (1968)
115. Renaud, F. L., Swift, H., *J. Cell. Biol.*, **23,** 339–54 (1964)
116. Rhea, R. P., *J. Ultrastruct. Res.*, **15,** 349–79 (1966)
117. Rickson, F. R., *J. Cell Biol.*, **38,** 471–74 (1968)
118. Robards, A. W., *Nature*, **218,** 784 (1968)
119. Robinow, C. F., Marak, J., *J. Cell Biol.*, **29,** 129–51 (1966)
120. Roelofsen, P. A., *Advan. Botan. Res.*, **2,** 69–149 (1966)
121. Rosen, W. G., *Ann. Rev. Plant Physiol.*, **19,** 435–62 (1968)
122. Roth, L. E., Wilson, H. J., Chakraborty, J., *J. Ultrastruct. Res.*, **14,** 460–83 (1966)
123. Sabatini, D. D., Bensch, K., Barrnett, R. J., *J. Cell Biol.*, **17,** 19–34 (1963)
124. Sabnis, D. D., Jacobs, W. P., *J. Cell Sci.*, **2,** 465–72 (1967)
125. Sanger, J. M., Jackson, W. T., *J. Cell Biol.*, **39,** 117a (1968)
126. Sato, S., *Cytologia*, **23,** 383–94 (1958)
127. Sato, S., *ibid.*, **24,** 98–106 (1959)
128. Schmitt, F. O., *Proc. Natl. Acad. Sci. U.S.*, **60,** 1092–1101 (1968)
129. Shelanski, M., Taylor, E. W., *J. Cell Biol.*, **34,** 549–54 (1967)
130. Shelanski, M., Taylor, E. W., *ibid.*, **38,** 304–15 (1968)
131. Slautterback, D. B., *J. Cell Biol.*, **18,** 367–88 (1963)
132. Srivastava, L. M., *J. Cell Biol.*, **31,** 79–93 (1966)
133. Srivastava, L. M., O'Brien, T. P., *Protoplasma*, **61,** 257–76 (1966)
134. Stebbins, G. L., in *Trends in Plant Morphogenesis*, 115–26 (Cutter, E. G., Ed., John Wiley & Sons, N.Y., 1966)
135. Stebbins, G. L., Jain, S. K., *Develop. Biol.*, **2,** 409–26 (1960)
136. Stebbins, G. L., Shah, S. S., *Develop. Biol.*, **2,** 477–500 (1960)
137. Steer, M. W., Newcomb, E. H., *Protoplasma* (In press)
138. Stephens, R. E., *J. Mol. Biol.*, **32,** 277–83 (1968)
139. Stephens, R. E., *ibid.*, **33,** 517–19 (1968)
140. Stephens, R. E., Renaud, F. L., Gibbons, I. R., *Science*, **156,** 1606–8 (1967)
141. Strasburger, E., *Zellbildung und Zelltheilung* (Gustav Fischer, Jena, 1880)
142. Stubblefield, E., Brinkley, B. R., *Symp. Intern. Soc. Cell Biol.*, **6,** 175–218 (1967)
143. Subirana, J. A., *J. Theoret. Biol.*, **20,** 117–23 (1968)
144. Whaley, W. G., Dauwalder, M., Kephart, J. E., *J. Ultrastruct. Res.*, **15,** 169–80 (1966)
145. Whaley, W. G.,, Mollenhauer, H. H., *J. Cell Biol.*, **17,** 216–21 (1963)
146. Wilson, H. J., *Planta*, **78,** 379–85 (1968)
147. Wohlfarth-Bottermann, K. E., *Protoplasma*, **54,** 514–39 (1962)
148. Wohlfarth-Bottermann, K. E., in *Primitive Motile Systems in Cell Biology*, 79–109 (See Ref. 59)
149. Wooding, F. B. P., Northcote, D. H., *J. Cell Biol.*, **23,** 327–37 (1964)

SILICON AND PLANT GROWTH[1]

By Joyce Lewin

Department of Oceanography
University of Washington, Seattle, Washington

AND Bernhard E. F. Reimann

Department of Biology
New Mexico State University, Las Cruces, New Mexico

INTRODUCTION

More than a hundred years ago, Julius Sachs (53), one of the early pioneers of plant nutrition studies, asked in his article, "Ergebnisse einiger neuerer Untersuchungen über die in Pflanzen enthaltene Kieselsäure," the following questions: ". . . whether silicic acid is an indispensable substance for those plants that contain silica, whether it takes part in the nutritional processes, and what is the relationship that exists between the uptake of silicic acid and the life of the plant?" These questions are still relevant today. A hundred years ago, however, the methods of plant physiology and biochemistry were not well enough advanced to find a definitive answer to the questions that Sachs asked. He concluded on the basis of nutrition experiments on *Zea mays* and morphological observations made by Mohl (44) that ". . . silicic acid is insignificant for the nutritional process of the maize plant." During the intervening years, many plant nutrition studies involving the use of water cultures have been made, and evidence both pro and con relative to Sachs' questions has accumulated. Today, the tendency of authors of textbooks on plant physiology is to dismiss silicon as being of little importance in plant nutrition. For example, Epstein (12) in his chapter on mineral metabolism devotes only a single paragraph to silicon in higher plants, concluding, "There seem to have been no physiological studies, like those with diatoms, that would throw light on the metabolic and biochemical events resulting in these silica depositions in higher plants." On the other hand, if one surveys the published research appearing during the past 10 years, it is obvious that investigations seeking a possible role for silicon in plant nutrition are still continuing quite vigorously. Some rather new approaches have been tried and new data have been forthcoming which are certainly of interest, worth reviewing at this time, and which offer enough encouragement to make further investigations well worthwhile.

[1] Contribution No. 480 from the Dept. of Oceanography, University of Washington. Work supported by National Science Foundation Grants GB-4456, GB-7096, and GB-7373.

An interest in a possible metabolic role of silicon in living organisms seems obvious because of the abundant occurrence of silicon in nature. Silicon in the form of silica gel is deposited in the epidermal cells and cell walls of many plant species, most strikingly in species of Equisetaceae, Cyperaceae, Gramineae, and Urticaceae. Very often it occurs as special morphological skeletal structures (spines, spicules, needles). In many plants where no skeletal structures are recognizable, silicon may, nevertheless, constitute a high proportion of the ash. Among the unicellular plants, silicon in the form of silica gel structures occurs in the cell walls of diatoms (Bacillariophyceae) and certain silicified flagellates (Chrysophyceae). Two major groups of animals also utilize silicon to form skeletal structures composed of silica gel, namely the radiolarians (belonging to the Protozoa) and the sponges (Porifera). The striking similarity of the depositional product among all of these plant and animal groups suggests the likelihood of a common mechanism of formation. For this reason, it is probably an unnecessary restriction to consider silicon only in relation to its possible role in higher plants, instead, a physiologist interested in silicon metabolism would be well advised to adopt a comparative approach.

CHEMICAL FORMS OF SILICON IN PLANTS

Studies on the physical and chemical properties of plant silica, using modern techniques, confirm and add to earlier observations. The studies by Jones & Milne (24) show that silica in the oat plant is noncrystalline and isotropic. It contains 13.5 per cent bound water [compare with 9 to 10 per cent bound water in the silica from a freshwater diatom, and 5 to 13 per cent bound water in sponge spicules; see Lewin (31, 33)], a specific gravity of 2.04, a refractive index of 1.427 to 1.440, and a surface area (by ethyl alcohol adsorption) of 14.4 m^2/g [compare with surface areas of 89 and 123 m^2/g for silica from diatoms measured by a nitrogen gas adsorption method; see Lewin (32)]. Infrared absorption studies (70), as well as studies on rates of dissolution (32, 70), show that the form of amorphous silica present both in higher plants and in diatoms is that of a silica gel (i.e., a form of hydrated amorphous silica, $SiO_2 \cdot nH_2O$, or polymerized silicic acid). Plant silica has been usually referred to as "opal," but its behavior is more like that of a silica gel than like the mineral opal deposited by geological processes.

Dry ashing produces changes in the physical and chemical properties of plant silica [shown very nicely in the study by Jones & Milne (24)], so that the silica is no longer of the same nature as it was in the plant originally. Any studies purporting to demonstrate properties of plant silica based on a dry-ash method are unacceptable, for example (27). Nitric acid (or a mixture of nitric and perchloric acids) can safely be used for wet digestion without causing any changes in the chemical and physical properties of the silica. On the other hand, sulfuric acid, being a dehydrating acid, cannot be used for wet digestion without changing the properties of the silica.

Silica gel is the most prevalent form of silicon in plants constituting 90 to 95 per cent of the total silicon in the rice plant, but the element is also present in other forms (72). The content of silicic acid in the rice plant ranged from 0.5 to 8.0 per cent of the total silicon, varying with parts of the plant analyzed, while the content of colloidal silicic acid ranged from 0 to 3.3 per cent of the total silicon (72). Silicon in the xylem sap has been shown to be entirely in the form of monosilicic acid (3, 14). Infrared absorption studies (70) gave no indications of any absorption bands due to organo-silicon compounds in the rice plant; however, the results did not exclude the possibility that a minute amount of silicon might exist in the form of organic compounds. Engel (11) presented evidence for the presence in rye straw of silicon-galactose complexes. However, it is well known that molecules of silicic acid readily complex with many substances [both with simple molecules such as polyhydric alcohols and organic acids and with complex molecules such as methemoglobin, albumin, collagen, gelatin, insulin, nylon, pepsin, and laminarin (7, 8, 18, 19)]. Because of this tendency to bind so readily with various organic molecules, it is difficult to put much faith in reports of complexes, such as a silicon-galactose complex, which could have been present as such in the plant but also might have been formed during the extraction process. There are reports that part of the silica in plants is strongly bound to the cellulose framework and can only be separated after the cellulose has been dissolved (11). Also, there are reports of silica present in higher plants in combination with proteins [see Umemura (59) for references]. Werner (62) has fractioned the silicon compounds present in the cells of a marine diatom and has found 96 to 98 per cent of the silicon in the form of cell wall or shell silica (silica gel), whereas 2 to 4 per cent of the silicon occurred as silicic acid either free or bound to cytoplasmic constituents.

Experiments show that silica gel, once it is solidified and deposited, is henceforth immobile and does not act as a source of silicon supply for other parts of the plant in the advent of a later period of silicon deficiency (72). The same may be said for the silica shell of diatoms, which remain intact as long as the cells are alive and only begin to dissolve upon death of the cells (32).

DISTRIBUTION OF SILICON IN PLANTS AND ITS LOCALIZATION WITHIN CERTAIN PLANT TISSUES

In some plants silicon is apparently distributed rather uniformly between shoots and roots, while in other plants it may accumulate to a greater extent in the shoots than in the roots. Occasionally, it may even be present at a higher concentration in the roots than in the shoots. In plants such as tomato, radish, green onion, and Chinese cabbage, all of which have a rather low silicon content, the silicon content of the roots was equal to or higher than that of the shoots (47). In *Trifolium incarnatum* the concentration of silicon in the roots was about eight times that in the tops (14).

In plants where the overall content of silicon is high, then silicon appears to occur mostly in aerial parts (leaf blade, leaf sheath, stem nodes, etc.). This distribution was clearly shown to be the case for rice plants (47, 58, 71) as well as for oat plants (23, 35). The amount of silica in roots of oat plants was less than 2 per cent of the silica in the whole plant (23).

A very beautiful study of the distribution of silica in oat plants (25) revealed that walls of all types of outer or abaxial epidermal cells, except for cork cells, were impregnated with silica. Walls of cells in the hypodermal layer, vessels, and fibers were likewise impregnated with silica (a more highly hydrated form), as were those of tracheids in the roots. The study revealed that silica had been deposited in intimate association with other constituents of the cell walls. The authors concluded that silica in the middle lamella and primary walls could have been deposited after the walls had been laid down, but that silica in the secondary walls could only have been deposited at the same time as the cellulose.

A similar study of the localization of silicon within the various tissues of rice plants has been made (73–75). In the leaf blade, silicon was localized in the epidermis, vascular bundles plus bundle sheath, and sclerenchyma. In the leaf sheath and stem, it was found mainly in the outer epidermis, vascular bundles, and along cell walls in parenchyma. In the root it was found in all tissues, in contrast with the leaf blade. The authors reported a combination of silica with cellulose in the epidermal cells of the leaf blade, above this a layer of silica, and then on the outside a very thin cuticle. They attributed great significance to this double layer (i.e., a cuticle layer plus a layer of silica) in limiting unnecessary water loss through the epidermis, as well as for protection against penetration of fungal hyphae.

The silica content varies with the age of the plant. Mature plants and older leaves have a higher silicon content than do younger plants and leaves, as shown for rice plants (22, 47, 58) and for horsetails (6). Substantial portions of the leaf blade were silicified in 6-week-old oat plants (25), but this deposition did not prevent the subsequent extension of immature cells, suggesting to the authors that the silica is not a rigid deposit when it is just laid down.

EFFECT OF SILICON ON PLANT GROWTH (DEVELOPMENT OF DEFICIENCY SYMPTOMS)

Earlier investigations.—A large number of the earlier published investigations clearly demonstrated that silicon was responsible for "improved growth" of a wide variety of plant species, both monocotyledons and dicotyledons. In many cases, various symptoms developed when silicon was absent or present in only small amounts. It was generally agreed that it played a role in the resistance of plants to fungus attacks, and for this reason it was difficult to decide whether the effect of silicon on plant growth was direct or indirect. Thus, silicon has been regarded as a beneficial or essential element by some (21, 39, 46, 48, 57, 61) and as a nonessential element by others (67; see also 41). Because of the lack of completely silicon-free culture techniques, some of the earlier studies were difficult to interpret.

More recent investigations.—The recent availability of plastic containers and pipettes has made more critical studies possible than could be carried out with the paraffin-coated glass containers (61) or asphalt-painted iron containers (49) of earlier workers.

Experimental objects for the more recent studies have usually consisted of plants that normally deposit rather considerable amounts of silica when growing under natural conditions: for example, rice plants (5 to 20 per cent of their dry weight); various other grasses such as oats, barley, wheat (around 2 to 4 per cent of their dry weight); and horsetails (up to 16 per cent of the dry weight in *Equisetum arvense*).

In some instances a clear-cut response to a lack of silicon in the culture medium has been noted, whereas in other cases no clear deficiency symptoms have developed. Thus, Tanaka & Park (58) found no effect of silicon concentration on growth rate and only a slight effect on final weight of the various organs of rice plants. The general appearance of 4-week-old rice plants grown with 0 and with 100 mg SiO_2 per liter was essentially the same. By growing tomato plants with purified salts in nutrient solutions held in polyethylene containers under a dust-free atmosphere, Woolley (69) showed that addition of silicon to the culture solution did not increase the growth of the plants. Neither did the silicon supply influence the yield of tomato, radish, green onion, or Chinese cabbage plants grown in polyethylene containers (47).

On the other hand, Yoshida, Ohnishi & Kitagishi (71) and Mitsui & Takatoh (42), also employing plastic containers, found that Si-deficient rice plants developed necrosis in their leaves and were retarded in growth, while the latter workers also found that silicon-deficient rice shoots exhibited reduced fertility. Okuda & Takahashi (47) also showed that silicon influenced the growth of rice plants kept in plastic containers. Both roots and shoots were longer in the presence of silicon, and the grain yield was greater. At harvest, the dry weights of ears from minus silicon plants were half or two-thirds those of plus silicon plants. Silicon also dramatically increased the yield of *Eq. arvense* grown in plastic containers (6). Symptoms of silicon deficiency in rice plants and horsetails were surprisingly similar, and the necrosis that developed in the leaves was similar to that reported by earlier workers. Both rice plants and horsetails also exhibited a "weeping willow" habit of growth under Si-deficient conditions (6, 71). Withering of the leaves and wilting of the plants were other symptoms frequently observed in Si-deficient plants (6, 47, 49, 71). Yields of species of Gramineae (barley, oats, wheat, and rye) were substantially decreased when the plants were grown in the absence of silicon (60).

It can be concluded that although silicon seems not to be indispensable for vegetative growth of most plants, nevertheless the indications are that it is necessary for the healthy development of many plants and may be considered to be an essential element for those plants with high silicon contents, such as rice and other grasses and horsetails.

UPTAKE OF SILICIC ACID

Silica in solution at pH's below 9 in soil solution and natural waters exists as uncharged monosilicic acid (= orthosilicic acid), $Si(OH)_4$ (see 2, 20, 23, 26). This is the form of silicon taken up by higher plants and by diatoms (23, 33).

Plants take up different amounts and proportions of silicon from culture solution, depending on the species and the concentration of dissolved silicic acid present. The proportion of silica, for example, in gramineous species is 10 to 20 times that found in leguminous species (23). Bean plants absorb relatively far more silicic acid than do pea plants (3). The amount of silica present in the plants (as percent of dry weight) increases in direct proportion to the amount of silicic acid dissolved in the soil solution or culture medium, as shown for rye and sunflower plants (67), for oat plants (23), for rice plants (47, 58), and for horsetails (6).

The facts presented so far in this discussion would be good evidence for the passive uptake of silicic acid in the transpiration stream and its subsequent distribution throughout the plant following the transpiration stream. A number of investigators have reached this conclusion. Yoshida, Ohnishi & Kitagishi (72) concluded that the rice plant could be regarded as an "evaporating dish" where silicic acid is constantly supplied by absorption through the roots and where silica constantly accumulates in the aerial parts, particularly in the epidermis, as water is lost by transpiration. Jones & Handreck (23) reasoned that knowing the concentration of silicic acid in the soil solution and the amount of water transpired, it should then be possible to calculate the amount of silica in the plant. The calculated amounts turned out to agree very closely with the amounts found by actual analysis, leading the authors to conclude that the uptake of silicic acid was passive, at least in the gramineous species studied. (However, they mention that other species containing relatively low proportions of silica must have some mechanism for rejecting it at the root surface.) *Trifolium incarnatum* is an example of such a plant with a low concentration of silica in its shoots, and it is apparently able to exclude monosilicic acid from its transpiration stream either within the root or at its external surface (14).

Although the initial entry of silicic acid into the free space of excised barley roots appeared to conform to the passive diffusion of a nonpolar solute (55), the movement of silicic acid across the root into the transpiration stream could not be explained by passive diffusion and mass flow in water (3). Except under conditions of very low humidity, silicic acid was found to enter barley roots at a relatively greater rate than the water lost in transpiration (by a factor of two to three times), and its concentration in the xylem sap of bean plants was found to be greater than in the external solution (3). In rice plants, the silicon concentration in the sap was several hundred times as high as that in the external solution (47), while in the xylem sap of oat plants the concentration in the sap was similar to that in the external solution (14); in tomatoes it was lower than in the external solution (47). Silicic acid appeared to be entering the xylem sap of bean and rice shoots against a concentration gradient. Barber & Shone (3) showed that the xylem exudate of bean plants was negative with respect to the culture solution by a potential of about 50 mV. Passive movement of positively charged ions or complexes into the xylem against a concentration gradient was therefore possible, but it seemed unlikely that the nonpolar molecule of monosilicic acid could acquire a positive charge.

Some experiments carried out with rice plants support the idea that silicic acid is absorbed independently of the rate of water absorption (43, 47, 58). It was found that (a) plants previously cultivated at low levels of silicon had a greater capacity to absorb silicic acid than those plants cultivated at higher levels; (b) excised roots had a greater capacity than excised shoots to absorb silicic acid; and (c) although transpiration rates were greater in the light than in the dark, there was no significant difference in the amount of silicic acid absorbed under the two situations. However, distribution of silica through the plant was found to be influenced by the rate of transpiration.

The influence of various metabolic inhibitors on the uptake of silicic acid has been studied. Transpiration and uptake of silicic acid were found to respond independently to the effects of metabolic inhibitors (2,4-dinitrophenol and Na azide) and temperature, suggesting that silicic acid was actively transported across the roots of those plants investigated (3). Silicon uptake by rice plants was severely inhibited by NaCN, NaF, 2,4-D, iodoacetate, D-glucosamine, and 2,4-dinitrophenol (43, 47) but not by phloridzin or by Na malonate (47). These workers concluded that energy from aerobic respiratory reactions in the roots, perhaps in the form of high energy phosphate, was necessary for silicic acid absorption. Okuda & Takahashi (47) also noted that silicon uptake seemed to be connected with anaerobic glycolysis but that it was not connected with the first step of glycolysis (glucose→glucose-6-phosphate) or the TCA cycle. Silicic acid uptake by diatoms was also demonstrated to be linked to aerobic respiration, since it could be inhibited by respiratory inhibitors (cyanide, fluoride, iodoacetate, arsenite, azide, and fluoroacetate) (30). Respiration rate was doubled by 2,4-dinitrophenol, and at the same time silicic acid uptake was inhibited, implicating ATP in silicic acid uptake (30).

MANGANESE AND IRON TOXICITY UNDER CONDITIONS OF SILICON DEFICIENCY

The accumulation of higher concentrations of mineral nutrients in aerial parts of silicon-deficient plants than in aerial parts of control plants has been reported by various investigators (47, 58, 61, 71). In particular, the accumulation of manganese and iron in leaves of rice plants seemed to be most striking. [Rice plants normally contain five to ten times as much Mn in their leaves as other grasses (60).]

Barley plants grown in standard nutrient solutions in the absence of silicon developed necrotic spots on their leaves which increased in severity when the Mn concentration was increased and decreased in severity when the Mn concentration was lowered. The addition of silicon caused a disappearance of the symptoms (68). Using ^{54}Mn, it was found that silicon affected the microdistribution of Mn in barley leaves (68). In a later study (60), it was shown that barley, rye, rice, and ryegrass all showed the brown spotting characteristic of Mn toxicity (oats and wheat did not), and in all four of the species, silicon prevented the development of necrotic spots. The effect of the silicon was to decrease the Mn content of the tissues. The authors thought that this might be explained by a dilution effect, i.e., the much greater growth of the plants in the presence of silicon might account for the lower Mn content (60). Since silicon caused an increase in yield beyond that increase in yield accounted for by overcoming of Mn toxicity, a function for silicon beyond that of preventing Mn toxicity was postulated.

Okuda & Takahashi (47) demonstrated that the effects of silicon supply on alleviation of iron and manganese toxicity in rice plants resulted from a decrease in uptake of iron and manganese by the plants. They showed that Fe^{++} and Mn^{++} were readily oxidized by rice roots, rendered insoluble, and precipitated on the surface of the roots. The effect was greater in plants supplied with silicon than in silicon-deficient plants. Thus, silicon promoted the oxidation power of rice roots with the resulting deposition of iron and manganese oxides on the root surface. The effect depended on silicon within the rice plants rather than in the external solution. In silicon-deficient plants, iron and manganese were transported to the aerial parts. To demonstrate this, ^{59}Fe was used. Increased oxygen supply to the roots in the presence of silicon in the plants depended on intact plants. When the tops were excised, the oxygen supply from the top of the root was shut off, and silicon had no effect on the oxidation power of the excised root and root extract.

INCREASED RATE OF TRANSPIRATION ASSOCIATED WITH SILICON DEFICIENCY

One recent finding that can help to explain some of the symptoms associated with silicon deficiency is that the rate of transpiration of Si-deficient rice plants was increased by about 30 per cent over the rate of control plants (71). (Rates were measured as grams of water lost through transpiration per gram of dry weight per day.) Okuda & Takahashi (47) obtained a similar result with rice plants, but found that in barley the effect was small (less than 10 per cent difference between Si-deficient and control plants). These observations suggested a role for silicon in the water economy of the plant. An increased rate of transpiration in Si-deficient plants could explain the wilting that may occur, particularly under conditions of low humidity, and could also help to explain the increased accumulation of manganese and other mineral nutrients in the aerial parts of Si-deficient plants. The rate of transpiration is presumably influenced by the amount of silica gel associated with the cellulose in the cell walls of epidermal cells. Hence a well-thickened layer of silica gel should help to retard water loss, while epidermal cell walls with less silica gel will allow water to escape at an accelerated rate.

RELATIONSHIP OF SILICON TO METABOLISM OF OTHER INORGANIC NUTRIENTS (PHOSPHORUS AND BORON)

Hydroxyl groups of silicic acid can condense with those of sugars (and other molecules) just as the hydroxyl groups of phosphoric, sulfuric, and boric acids do (45). This similarity in chemical behavior presents the possibility that silicic acid may replace or interfere with the metabolism of one of these other elements or that it may function in the cell similarly to one or another of them. However, silicon is not capable of forming double bonds. In this respect, it differs from sulfur and phosphorus, which like carbon are capable of forming double bonds (45).

Phosphorus.—In certain chemical respects, orthosilicic acid resembles orthophosphoric acid (for example, both react with ammonium molybdate to form yellow complexes). There have been earlier references to the effect that part of the phosphorus requirement of plants might be spared by silicon (see 15, 20), but it is now clear that the beneficial effects were due to replacement of phosphate ions by silicic acid in the soil itself (47).

Possible phosphorus-silicon interactions have been looked for. In two investigations, radioactive [31]Si was used to study uptake of silicic acid in the presence and absence of phosphoric acid (43, 52). The uptake of silicic acid was only very slightly depressed (probably not by a statistically significant amount) in the presence of phosphate, whereas the uptake of phosphorus was slightly enhanced when silicic acid was present (52). The authors concluded that there was a close relationship in the metabolism of the two elements. However, Mitsui & Takatoh (43) found that most of the [31]Si absorbed by rice roots was translocated rapidly into the shoots, while most of the ^{32}P remained in the roots. Most of the ^{32}P absorbed by wheat plants also remained in the roots. Okuda & Takahashi (47), using ^{32}P, concluded that silicon seemed to retard the excessive uptake of phosphorus by rice plants and to promote the translocation of phosphorus into the grain. Their experiments suggested that the role of silicon in rice is unique and not explained by partial substitution for phosphorus.

The two elements also behaved quite differently in response to metabolic inhibitors. For example, there was no inhibitory effect of malonate or phloridzin on silicon uptake by young rice seedlings, whereas phosphorus uptake was substantially decreased by these two inhibitors (43, 47). Iodoacetate, sodium cyanide, antimycin A, and 2,4-dinitrophenol depressed the rate of silicic acid uptake and translocation more than that of phosphorus

(43, 47). The effects of sugars, organic acids, and light on silicon uptake differed from their effect on phosphorus uptake (47). These results seemed to indicate that the metabolic pathways concerned with phosphorus metabolism were quite different from those concerned with silicon.

Boron.—It has been known for 50 years that boron was essential for growth of higher plants, but its mode of action is still not certain. Some of the recent studies on function of boron in plans implicate the element in RNA metabolism (1, 54), in the biosynthesis of sucrose (10), and as a modulator determining the level of activity of the pentose shunt due to the formation of a 6-phosphogluconate borate complex (28). There are several earlier studies giving evidence for its role in sugar translocation and the synthesis of cell wall material (see 56). This elusiveness of boron is due to the same reason that makes silicon so elusive, i.e., its capacity to form complexes readily with polyhydroxy compounds.

It is of particular interest that diatoms require both boron and silicon for growth (34) and thus resemble higher plants. Species of *Chlorella* and various fungi have no boron or silicon requirement (4, 5). Because of their chemical similarities, a competition between the two elements might be expected. In a culture medium with a high Si:B ratio, the growth rate of a marine diatom was reduced, showing that silicon interfered with the uptake or utilization of boron (35).

GERMANIC ACID, A SPECIFIC INHIBITOR OF SILICON METABOLISM

Germanium is the next higher analogue of silicon in the main subgroup of Group IV of the periodic table of elements. It has recently been shown that germanic acid acts as a specific inhibitor of silicic acid metabolism, and that only those organisms having a requirement for silicon are sensitive to germanium (36, 62, 63). For diatoms and higher plants, germanium is extremely toxic at low concentrations. In these plants germanium acts as a competitive inhibitor of silicon, since addition of higher concentrations of silicon is able to reverse the inhibitory effect (36, 62, 63). It was demonstrated by Werner (63) that growth of *Sinapsis alba, Lemna minor, Wolffia arrhiza, Nicotiana tabacum, Tradescantia* sp., *Zinnia elegans,* and *Secale cereale* was depressed by germanium and that the inhibition could be reversed by silicon addition. On the other hand, a wide variety of algae (belonging to the Chlorophyceae, Rhodophyceae, Phaeophyceae, and Cyanophyceae) and a wide variety of bacteria and fungi were not inhibited in their growth by germanic acid at much higher concentrations (36, 62, 63).

The appearance of plants affected by germanic acid was characterized by a variety of symptoms (63). In general, growth was significantly reduced. In *S. alba,* the plants withered. In *Tradescantia* sp., the axes of the sprouts were bent down and subsequently dried out, whereas in *N. tabacum* there were macroscopically discernible lesions as primary damage spread to the leaves. As a secondary effect, the leaves of many plants exhibited a localized bluish discoloration, interpreted by Werner as due to an accumulation of anthocyanin. Of particular interest was the complete cessation of root growth in *L. minor* and *Lycopersicon pimpinellifolium*. However, germination of *S. cereale* was not inhibited even by higher concentrations of germanic acid. Only when the plants exceeded a length of 5 cm did inhibition of growth become evident, and then plants treated with germanium did not grow taller than 8 to 10 cm. The same effect was observed in *S. alba*. If a competitive inhibition of silicon by germanium is assumed, then there are apparently early developmental stages in certain plants for which silicon is not an essential growth factor, whereas the same plants need silicon in later developmental stages.

A study of the site of germanium inhibition has been made by Werner (62, 64) using a marine diatom species, *Cyclotella cryptica*. Germanium apparently does not inhibit uptake of silicic acid into the cell, but interferes with further reactions of silicic acid within the cell. Chlorophyll synthesis and protein synthesis were both inhibited more drastically than in cells whose growth was limited by silicon deficiency (64). Respiration, photosynthetic oxygen production, and synthesis of carbohydrate were not directly influenced by germanic acid (36, 64); however, breakdown of carbohydrate in the dark was distinctly inhibited (64). Werner (64) also studied the activities of three enzymes in response to the inhibitor. The specific activity of $NADP^+$-dependent glyceraldehyde-3-phosphate dehydrogenase was inhibited by germanic acid, whereas NAD^+-dependent glyceraldehyde-3-phosphate dehydrogenase and lactic acid dehydrogenase were not inhibited.

SILICON METABOLISM IN DIATOMS
CHANGES IN DIATOM CELLS UPON DEPRIVATION OF SILICIC ACID IN THE CULTURE MEDIUM

Metabolic and physiological changes.—In a medium without silicic acid cell division in diatoms ceases (33). Werner (62) found that in *Cyclotella cryptica* in a silicic acid-free medium, syntheses became blocked in the following sequence: protein- chlorophyll- DNA- RNA- xanthophyll- lipid- photosynthesis. Chlorophyll became much more difficult to extract, and there was an abrupt shift from carbohydrate accumulation to lipid accumulation, whereas deficiency of nitrogen or phosphorus first caused a storage of carbohydrate. Enzymes behaved differently in response to silicic acid deficiency, depending on their metabolic role; e.g., synthesis of aldolase continued after protein synthesis had stopped, whereas the enzyme glutamate-oxalacetate transaminase did not increase. In *Navicula pelliculosa*, a freshwater diatom, synthesis of RNA, protein, carbohydrates, and chlorophyll ceased 5 to 7 hr upon deprivation of silicic acid in the medium, while synthesis of DNA and lipid continued for some hours longer (9).

Respiratory quotients of diatoms have been shown to be affected by silicon deficiency. The respiratory quotient (R.Q.) of silicon-deficient cells of

N. pelliculosa decreased from 0.8-0.9 to 0.3 after 4 days of starvation in darkness, whereas the R.Q. of nondeficient cells decreased from 0.93 to 0.75 after 4 days in the dark. Addition of silicic acid raised the R.Q. of dark-starved Si-deficient cells from 0.3 to 0.5, due to a 25 per cent stimulation of oxygen uptake along with a 90 per cent stimulation of carbon dioxide evolution. These changes give a further indication of the influence of silicic acid on cellular composition. One would not have expected this kind of response if the only function of silicon was as a constituent of the silica shell.

Additional support for a significant relationship between silicon and protein metabolism in *C. cryptica* has been demonstrated by Werner (65). In a silicic acid-free medium, the α-ketoglutarate content of the cells decreased to a third of the normal value within 60 min, the glutamic acid pool decreased within 3 hr to a third of the original value, the aspartic acid and nucleoside diphosphate pools were reduced by about 20 per cent, while pools of nucleoside triphosphates and glycerol-1-phosphate remained unaffected. A decrease in the glutamic acid pool preceded the inhibition of total protein synthesis. The acetyl co-A pathway (enhanced fatty acid synthesis) was not inhibited. These results suggested that silicic acid was involved with reactions between the condensing enzyme (acetyl co-A and oxalacetate) and α-ketoglutarate.

Lewin & Chen (37) studied uptake of silicic acid by a colorless marine diatom and found that certain amino acids (aspartic acid, glutamic acid, and glutamine) were important in restoring the ability of washed cells to take up silicic acid. A large number of other amino acids and other compounds were without effect.

Morphological changes.—There do not appear to be any reports on changes in the fine-structural organization of higher plants under conditions of silicon deficiency. A beginning in this direction, however, has been made with diatoms. As has been stated previously, cell division comes to a stop in the absence of silicic acid. However, diatom cells remain viable under such conditions if kept in dim light or darkness (33). Cells maintained in this way demonstrated morphological changes in the siliceous parts of their cell walls. In *Cylindrotheca fusiformis* there were cells present that exhibited normal siliceous skeletons, others having one theca with normally-developed siliceous elements and with the corresponding hypotheca having much thinner siliceous parts, and finally cells with a significant reduction of the siliceous parts on both thecae. This contradicts the assumption of Werner & Pirson (66) that the deposited shell could be considered as a possible site for a silica reserve. Cell walls completely lacking siliceous parts have never been observed by the present authors even after a culture period of more than one month under conditions of silicon deficiency. On the other hand, silica from the walls of dead cells has been corroded to various degrees. This seemed to suggest that the siliceous cell wall components remain intact as long as the cell is alive even in silicon-deficient media.

If diatoms were kept in the absence of silicic acid under higher light intensities, various metabolic syntheses still took place even though the cells did not divide. The ultrastructural organization underwent dramatic changes as shown by Reimann & Lewin (38). As could be seen with the light microscope, cells of *C. fusiformis* increased in volume six times over that of normal cells. Electron micrographs showed that the siliceous cell wall parts were greatly reduced. The most significant changes occurred in the size of the chromatophores, in the number of mitochondria, the structure of the endoplasmic reticulum and the nuclear area, and in the amount of osmiophilic substances excreted into the vacuole. The picture that emerged was one of total intracellular disorganization rather than that of a reduction of the various cellular components, as might have been expected had the silicon starvation state been comparable with resting stages as suggested by Werner (65).

UPTAKE OF SILICIC ACID IN THE DARK BY DIATOMS

When Si-deficient diatoms were harvested from Si-depleted cultures, placed in a medium containing silicon but lacking an assimilable nitrogen or phosphorus source, and kept in the dark, the cells continued to remove silicic acid from the medium (29), even though the cells did not divide under these conditions. Actually, the cells absorbed silicic acid until the silicon concentration per cell had doubled. This means that they had taken up enough to make the two new silica shells which would be formed if the cells were to divide. The silicic acid taken up was firmly bound inside the cells as it was not released if the cells were killed. It could be accounted for chemically with the solid silica fraction, but on the other hand, the number of silica valves had not increased. Lewin (29) concluded that the original silica shells must have become thicker, although it now seems that other explanations are more probable. Colorless (nonphotosynthetic) diatoms taken from Si-depleted cultures also absorbed silicic acid from a medium lacking an assimilable nitrogen, phosphorus, or carbon source, and continued to do so until their silica content had doubled (37).

Werner & Pirson (66) found that the silica content of *C. cryptica* (non-Si deficient cells) increased by about 50 per cent after the cells were placed in the dark. In minor part, this was due to cell divisions that continued in the dark, but in addition, there was a silicic acid fraction which could be used by the cells if they were put into a silicon-free medium and returned to the light. Based on these investigations, it can be concluded that cells are capable of taking up silicic acid in the dark under "nongrowing" conditions (doubling their silica content if they are Si-deficient cells), and when returned to the light or to a growth medium with necessary nutrients present, the cells can then go ahead and divide, completing their new, solidified shells. The form in which silicic acid is present in the cells before it ends up in the silica shell is not yet known.

DEPOSITION OF SILICA INSIDE THE DIATOM CELL

Although the final solidified silica shell ends up as part of the cell wall in diatoms, the actual process of the deposition and formation of the shell takes place within a membrane-bound vesicle within the cell (50, 51). The silica scales of a chrysophycean flagellate were also formed within vesicles inside the cell and later moved to the outside (40). Apparently no one has looked for the analogous situation in cells of higher plants that deposit silica as part of their cell-wall structure. Since solidified silica structures of very specific shapes are often formed in higher plants, we would predict that these would also be most likely formed within the cells themselves, perhaps in similar membrane-bounded vesicles.

This specialized membrane responsible for the one-way transport of silicic acid into the vesicle has been called the "silicalemma" by Reimann (38, 51). Nothing is known of its chemical nature. While the silica shell is growing during the process of its deposition, the membrane that tighly surrounds the growing shell must also be simultaneously rapidly growing, and the synthesis of this membrane must be very closely tied to the silicon metabolism of the cell. Where the membrane is initiated within the cell is still not known. Golgi vesicles may be the source (50).

Although silica ends up associated with cellulose in the cell walls of higher plants, there is no cellulose present in diatom cell walls. The carbohydrate material characteristic of the diatom cell wall is a sulfated glucuronomannan (13). Whether this is a component of the silicalemma or is deposited in the cell wall later after the shell is fully formed is still not known.

SILICON METABOLISM IN BACTERIA

A series of biochemical and physiological investigations concerned with silicic acid uptake and "silicon metabolism" in *Proteus mirabilis* have been made by Heinen (see 17). However, this bacterium does not require silicon for growth. These studies with bacteria do not seem to relate directly to the studies made with diatoms and higher plants. Werner (62) was of the same opinion.

LITERATURE CITED

1. Albert, L. S., *Plant Physiol.*, **40**, 649–52 (1965)
2. Alexander, G. B., *J. Phys. Chem.*, **58**, 453–55 (1954)
3. Barber, D. A., Shone, M. G. T., *J. Exptl. Botany*, **17**, 569–78 (1966)
4. Bowen, J. E., Gauch, H. G., Krauss, R. W., Galloway, R. A., *J. Phycol.*, **1**, 151–54 (1965)
5. Bowen, J. E., Gauch, H. G., *Plant Physiol.*, **41**, 319–24 (1966)
6. Chen, C., Lewin, J., *Can. J. Botany* (In press)
7. Clark, S. G., Holt, P. F., *Trans. Faraday Soc.*, **53**, 1509–15 (1957)
8. Clark, S. G., Holt, P. F., Went, C. W., *Trans. Faraday Soc.*, **53**, 1500–8 (1957)
9. Coombs, J., Darley, W. M., Holm-Hansen, O., Volcani, B. E., *Plant Physiol.*, **42**, 1601–6 (1967)
10. Dugger, W. M., Humphreys, T. E., *Plant Physiol.*, **35**, 523–30 (1960)

11. Engel, W., *Planta*, **41**, 358–90 (1953)
12. Epstein, E., in *Plant Biochemistry*, 438–66 (Bonner, J., Varner, J. E., Eds., Academic Press, N.Y., 1054 pp., 1965)
13. Ford, C. W., Percival, E., *J. Chem. Soc.*, **1965**, 7042–46 (1965)
14. Handreck, K. A., Jones, L. H. P., *Australian J. Biol. Sci.*, **20**, 483–85 (1967)
15. Heinen, W., *Arch. Mikrobiol.*, **41**, 229–46 (1962)
16. Heinen, W., In *Moderne Methoden der Pflanzenanalyse*, **6**, 4–20 (Linskens, H. F., Tracey, M. V., Eds., Springer, Berlin, 1963)
17. Heinen, W., *Arch. Biochem. Biophys.*, **110**, 137–49 (1965)
18. Holt, P. F., Bowcott, J. E. L., *Biochem. J.*, **57**, 471–75 (1954)
19. Holt, P. F., Went, C. W., *Trans. Faraday Soc.*, **55**, 1435–40 (1959)
20. Iler, R. K., *The Colloid Chemistry of Silica and Silicates* (Cornell Univ. Press, Ithaca, N.Y., 324 pp., 1955)
21. Ishibashi, H., *J. Sci. Soil Manure, Japan*, **10**, 244–56 (1936)
22. Ishizuka, Y., In *The Mineral Nutrition of the Rice Plant*, 199–217 (Proc. Symp. Intern. Rice Res. Inst., Feb. 1964, Johns Hopkins Press, Baltimore, Maryland, 494 pp., 1965)
23. Jones, L. H. P., Handreck, K. A., *Plant Soil*, **23**, 79–96 (1965)
24. Jones, L. H. P., Milne, A. A., *Plant Soil*, **18**, 207–20 (1963)
25. Jones, L. H. P., Milne, A. A., Wadham, S. M., *Plant Soil*, **18**, 358–71 (1963)
26. Krauskopf, K. B., *Geochim. Cosmochim. Acta*, **10**, 1–26 (1956)
27. Lanning, F. C., Ponnaiya, B. W. X., Crumpton, C. F., *Plant Physiol.*, **33**, 339–43 (1958)
28. Lee, S., Aronoff, S., *Science*, **158**, 798–99 (1967)
29. Lewin, J. C., *J. Gen. Physiol.*, **37**, 589–99 (1954)
30. Lewin, J. C., *ibid.*, **39**, 1–10 (1955)
31. Lewin, J. C., *Can. J. Microbiol.*, **3**, 427–33 (1957)
32. Lewin, J. C., *Geochim. Cosmochim. Acta*, **21**, 182–98 (1961)
33. Lewin, J. C., In *Physiology and Biochemistry of Algae*, 445–55 (Lewin, R. A., Ed., Academic Press, N.Y., 938 pp., 1962)
34. Lewin, J., *J. Phycol.*, **2**, 160–63 (1966)
35. Lewin, J. C., *J. Exptl. Botany*, **17**, 473–79 (1966)
36. Lewin, J., *Phycologia*, **6**, 1–12 (1966)
37. Lewin, J., Chen, C., *J. Phycol.*, **4**, 161–66 (1968)
38. Lewin, J. C., Reimann, B. E., Busby, W. F., Volcani, B. E., in *Cell Synchrony* (Cameron, I. L., Padilla, G. M., Eds., Academic Press, N.Y., 392 pp., 1966)
39. Lipman, C. B., *Soil Sci.*, **45**, 189–98 (1938)
40. Manton, I., Leedale, G. F., *Phycologia*, **1**, 37–57 (1961)
41. Meyer, B. S., Anderson, D. B., *Plant Physiology* (Van Nostrand, D., N.Y., 487 pp., 1952)
42. Mitsui, S., Takatoh, H., *Soil Sci. Plant Nutr. (Tokyo)*, **9**, 7–11 (1963)
43. Mitsui, S., Takatoh, H., *ibid.*, 12–16 (1963)
44. Mohl, H. v., *Botan. Z.*, Nr. 30, 31, 32, 42 (1861)
45. Needham, A. E., *The Uniqueness of Biological Materials* (Pergamon Press, Oxford, 593 pp., 1965)
46. Okawa, K., *J. Sci. Soil Manure, Japan*, **10**, 95–110, 415–19 (1936)
47. Okuda, A., Takahashi, E., in *The Mineral Nutrition of the Rice Plant*, 123–46 (Proc. Symp. Intern. Rice Res. Inst., Feb. 1964, Johns Hopkins Press, Baltimore, Md., 494 pp., 1965)
48. Raleigh, G. J., *Plant Physiol.*, **14**, 823–28 (1939)
49. Raleigh, G. J., *Soil Sci.*, **60**, 133–35 (1945)
50. Reimann, B. E. F., *Exptl. Cell Res.*, **34**, 605–8 (1964)
51. Reimann, B. E. F., Lewin, J. C., Volcani, B. E., *J. Phycol.*, **2**, 74–84 (1966)
52. Rothbuhr, L., Scott, F., *Biochem. J.*, **65**, 241–45 (1957)
53. Sachs, J., *Flora*, **20**, 31–38, 49–55, 65–71 (1862)
54. Shkol'nik, M. Ya., Solov'eva, E. A., *Botan. Zh.*, **46**, 161–73 (1961)
55. Shone, M. G. T., *Nature*, **202**, 314–15 (1964)
56. Skok, J., in *Trace Elements*, 227–43 (Lamb, C. A., Bentley, O. G., Beattie, J. M., Eds., Academic Press, N.Y., 410 pp., 1958)
57. Sommer, A. L., *Univ. Calif. (Berkeley) Publ. Agr. Sci.*, **5**, 57–81 (1926)
58. Tanaka, A., Park, Y. D., *Soil Sci. Plant Nutr. (Tokyo)*, **12**, 23–28 (1966)

59. Umemura, Y., Nishida, J., Akazawa, T., Uritani, I., *Arch. Biochem. Biophys.*, **92,** 392–98 (1961)
60. Vlamis, J., Williams, D. E., *Plant Soil,* **27,** 131–40 (1967)
61. Wagner, F., *Phytopathol. Z.*, **12,** 427–79 (1940)
62. Werner, D., *Arch. Mikrobiol.*, **55,** 278–308 (1966)
63. Werner, D., *Planta,* **76,** 25–36 (1967)
64. Werner, D., *Arch. Mikrobiol.*, **57,** 51–60 (1967)
65. Werner, D., *Z. Naturforsch.*, **23,** 268–72 (1968)
66. Werner, D., Pirson, A., *Arch. Mikrobiol.*, **57,** 43–50 (1967)
67. Whittenberger, R. T., *Am. J. Botany,* **32,** 539–49 (1945)
68. Williams, D. E., Vlamis, J., *Plant Physiol.*, **32,** 404–9 (1957)
69. Woolley, J. T., *Plant Physiol.*, **32,** 317–21 (1957)
70. Yoshida, S., Ohnishi, Y., Kitagishi, K., *Soil Plant Food (Tokyo),* **5,** 23–27 (1959)
71. Yoshida, S., Ohnishi, Y., Kitagishi, K., *ibid.*, 127–33
72. Yoshida, S., Ohnishi, Y., Kitagishi, K., *Soil Sci. Plant Nutr. (Tokyo),* **8,** No. 3, 15–21 (1962)
73. Yoshida, S., Ohnishi, Y., Kitagishi, K., *ibid.*, No. 1, 30–35
74. Yoshida, S., Ohnishi, Y., Kitagishi, K., *ibid.*, No. 1, 36–41
75. Yoshida, S., Ohnishi, Y., Kitagishi, K., *ibid.*, No. 2, 1–5

ACTION SPECTRA AND ENERGY TRANSFER IN PHOTOSYNTHESIS[1]

By David C. Fork

Carnegie Institution of Washington, Department of Plant Biology Stanford, California

and Jan Amesz

Biophysical Laboratory of the State University Leiden, The Netherlands

Introduction

This review will consider recent contributions which measurements of action spectra have made to the understanding of the photosynthetic process. The first section will cover certain aspects of the techniques of the measurements themselves; the following sections will discuss some recent results that have been obtained with photosynthetic bacteria, algae, and higher plants. Consideration will be given to mechanisms of energy transfer between molecules of photosynthetic pigments and to the transfer of energy between photosynthetic units and pigment systems. A review by Halldal (1) covers action spectra for ultraviolet effects, so this area will not be included here. A recent review by Hoch & Knox (2) presents a detailed discussion of primary processes and energy transfer in photosynthesis. The review article by Allen (3) gives a discussion of the techniques used for the measurement of action spectra and also includes a section on the interpretation of action spectra. Reviews by Smith & French (4) and Blinks (5) cover developments in this field up to 1964, and since then so many papers have appeared which are concerned with action spectra and energy transfer in photosynthesis that only certain ones could be selected for inclusion in the present review. Undoubtedly, many important papers have been omitted.

The Measurement of an Action Spectrum

According to the general definition, an action spectrum gives the reciprocal of the (relative) number of light quanta needed to bring about an effect of a certain size, as a function of wavelength or wavenumber of the actinic light. The word "relative" is inserted here, because action spectra often are plotted on a relative, rather than an absolute scale. An action

[1] The following abbreviations will be used: CMU [3-(chlorophenyl)-1, 1-dimethylurea]; DCMU [3-(3,4-dichlorophenyl)-1, 1-dimethylurea]; DCIP (dichlorophenol-indophenol); PMS (*N*-methylphenazonium methosulfate); P700 (pigment absorbing at 700 nm).

spectrum is often divided by the absorption spectrum, and then it gives the relative or absolute activity for absorbed quanta as a function of wavelength.

Under conditions where the response is linear with the intensity, an action spectrum may simply be plotted as the size of the effect induced by a certain number of incident light quanta as a function of wavelength. When the response is not linear with intensity, the action spectrum can be obtained by comparing at each wavelength the response induced by a certain light intensity with a response-versus-intensity curve made at a standard wavelength (6). An automatic apparatus for measuring action spectra of photosynthesis of algae has been described by French, Myers & McLeod (7). Oxygen production is measured polarographically by means of a platinum electrode which is in contact with a thin layer of algae and which gives an electrical current proportional to the rate of O_2 evolution. A servomechanism regulates the intensity of actinic light to keep the current at a constant value as the spectrum is transversed, and the reciprocal of the intensity is plotted as a function of wavelength after correction for the wavelength dependence of the photocell. A similar apparatus might be used to measure action spectra of fluorescence or of other phenomena where the response can readily be converted into an electric potential or current, and where the response of the organism is not so slow as to make the method impractical. A condition is that the response of the servosystem is slower than that of the organism; otherwise oscillations will result.

In order to convey quantitatively meaningful information, the shape of an action spectrum should be independent of the intensity at which each point of the spectrum has been obtained. This condition is fulfilled only when the response-versus-intensity curves at different wavelengths are proportional to each other. A disproportionality may be caused by the interaction of more than one primary process on the effect measured. An example is the action spectrum for cytochrome oxidation in an oxygen-evolving photosynthetic organism. As illustrated by Olson & Smillie (8, Fig. 2), the intensity curves for cytochrome oxidation in the blue-green alga *Anacystis nidulans* at 680 and 620 nm are different because of interaction of photosystems 1 and 2, and consequently, the shape of the action spectrum would depend on the light intensities chosen. Different time courses (kinetics) at different actinic wavelengths (6, 9) may also suggest the interaction between two or more primary reactions. Addition of an inhibitor which stops the reduction of the cytochrome by system 2 abolishes these effects and enables one to measure a better-defined action spectrum for the oxidation (9, 10). It should be noted, however, that a disproportionality of the intensity curves or different kinetics at different wavelengths of actinic light does not necessarily indicate the interaction of more than one primary reaction. With strongly absorbing samples, the effects may be caused by a different penetration into the sample of light of different wavelengths. Clayton (11, chapter 11) has discussed the effect of depth of penetration of the actinic light in the measurement of light-induced absorption changes, especially in relation to the geometry of actinic and measuring beams. An action spectrum of fluorescence can be distorted even though the fluorescence may be linearly proportional to the exciting light at every wavelength, when there is self-absorption of fluorescence, because the extent of self-absorption will depend on the depth of penetration of the exciting light. The effect can be minimized by the use of a thin layer or dilute solution or suspension and by a judicious choice of filters between sample and detector.

Unfortunately, these points have not always been taken into account sufficiently, and a number of action spectra which can be found in the literature may be suspected to be distorted by one or more of the effects mentioned above.

Photosynthetic Bacteria

Purple bacteria contain as photosynthetic pigments carotenoids and, except for one or a few species of *Rhodopseudomonas* (12, 13), bacteriochlorophyll-*a* [nomenclature after Jensen, Aasmundrud & Eimhjellen (12)]. Depending on the species, two to five different absorption bands of bacteriochlorophyll-*a* occur in the near infrared (14–16) with maxima at about 800, 820, 850, and 870 to 890 nm, respectively. These different maxima are probably caused by interaction between bacteriochlorophyll molecules, and possibly also by binding to lipoproteins or other cell constituents (15, 17–22).

The action spectra of bacteriochlorophyll fluorescence and of phototaxis [the latter presumed to be proportional to those of photosynthesis (23)], were measured by Duysens (24) for a number of species of purple bacteria. The results indicated that light energy absorbed by carotenoids and "shortwave" bacteriochlorophyll-*a* bands is transferred to the longest wavelength bacteriochlorophyll-*a*, absorbing at 870 to 890 nm (B890), before being used in photosynthesis. The efficiency of transfer of energy from carotenoids to bacteriochlorophyll-*a* is usually (cf. 25) only about 40 per cent. The efficiency of transfer of energy between different bacteriochlorophyll types was found to be much higher, close to 100 per cent. In agreement with this, B890, unless removed or altered by rather drastic treatments, was found to be the only bacteriochlorophyll type that showed fluorescence (24, 26). Recently, however, fluorescence from other bacteriochlorophyll types has also been observed, even upon excitation of B890 (27), suggesting that at least in some instances a measurable rate of transfer from longer-wavelength to shorter-wavelength bacteriochlorophyll can occur. Action spectra of B890 fluorescence indicate less than 100 per cent efficiency of transfer to B890 for some bacteriochlorophyll types in a number of species (28). The data suggested that different pools of light-harvesting bacteriochlorophyll may exist, in line with results of experiments on fractionation of chromatophore preparations (29–33).

A few species or strains of *Rhodopseudomonas,* two of which were designated *Rhodopseudomonas* sp. NTHC 133 (12) and *Rps. viridis* (13, 34) do not contain bacteriochlorophyll-*a,* but contain bacteriochlorophyll-*b* instead, which is probably related. A comparison of the absorption spectra of these pigments in acetone is given in (12). The bacteria have an absorption maximum at 1017 to 1020 nm, and a weak band at 830 to 835 nm (13, 15, 35, 36). Action spectra of bacteriochlorophyll-*b* fluorescence indicate an efficiency of energy transfer from carotenoids to bacteriochlorophyll-*b* of about 25 per cent (35).

The so-called "green bacteria" contain, besides carotenoids, *Chlorobium* chlorophyll 660 or 650 (12, 37) and small amounts of bacteriochlorophyll-*a* (12, 38). Energy transfer from carotenoids and *Chlorobium* chlorophyll to bacteriochlorophyll-*a* proceeds with an estimated efficiency of about 60 to 70 per cent (39). Emission spectra (40) of delayed light and of light-induced changes in fluorescence suggest that back transfer from bacteriochlorophyll-*a* to *Chlorobium* chlorophyll also occurs.

There are various lines of evidence that the excitation energy is ultimately transferred to a so-called reaction center, which contains the primary photooxidant and reductant and other compounds, including one or more cytochrome molecules. The identity of the primary photooxidant is not established yet, although there are indications that it may be ubiquinone (41–44). The primary photoreductant is probably a special type of bacteriochlorophyll constituting a few per cent of the total amount of bacteriochlorophyll and which is oxidized (bleached) upon illumination (31, 33, 43, 45–58). According to the location of its near infrared maximum, the primary photoreductant has been designated P890 or P870 for purple bacteria containing bacteriochlorophyll-*a* (49, 59), P840 for green bacteria (50), and P985 for *Rhodopseudomonas* sp. NTHC 133 (56). For the sake of simplicity, we shall use the designation P890 for both P890 and P870, irrespective of the exact location of the absorption maximum.

The bleaching of P890 and P985 is accompanied by a shift towards shorter wavelengths (blue shift) of a bacteriochlorophyll type absorbing at about 800 nm (P800) and 830 nm (P830), respectively. No such blue shift was observed in the green bacterium *Chloropseudomonas ethylicum* (50). Experiments with chromatophore preparations from *Rps. spheroides* and *Rhodospirillum rubrum,* in which all bacteriochlorophyll except P890 and P800 had been destroyed by treatment with oxidizing agents or removed by detergent treatment, indicate that these pigments occur in a ratio of two P800 to one P890 molecule (22, 31, 43, 60). Action spectra for P985 and cytochrome oxidation in *Rhodopseudomonas* sp NTHC 133, for P890 oxidation in a *Rps. spheroides* mutant, and for bacteriochlorophyll fluorescence suggest that the transfer of energy from P830 and P800 to P895 and P890, respectively, is more efficient than to the bulk of bacteriochlorophyll (36, 61). Efficient energy transfer from P800 to P890 was also observed in bleached chromatophore preparations which contained no other bacteriochlorophyll (43). These observations and optical rotatory dispersion and circular dichroism spectra (22) suggest that P830 and P800, in a complex with P890 and P985, are part of the reaction center.

Vredenberg & Duysens (49) and Clayton (57, 62) observed a correlation between the fluorescence of bacteriochlorophyll and the bleaching of P890. These experiments, which will be more fully discussed in another section, indicate transfer of energy from the lowest singlet excited state to the reaction center. P890 does not normally emit fluorescence, but its fluorescence was observed in the presence of dithionite (62), which inhibits its photooxidation (55, 62).

In many but not all species of purple bacteria, a second type of light-induced infrared absorption change, not related to P890 or P800, has been observed (63, 64, 65). These changes should probably be interpreted as small shifts, generally to longer wavelengths, of some of the absorption bands of part of the "bulk" bacteriochlorophyll. In some species these shifts are accompanied (64, 65) by shifts in carotenoid bands [discovered earlier (66)]. Clayton's original hypothesis (63) that these changes in pigment absorption would be caused by a reduction of bacteriochlorophyll in a separate primary photochemical reaction, has been recently revived and extended by Cusanovitch, Bartsch & Kamen (33). However, pending further evidence, a more plausible explanation (16, 64, 65) appears to be that the effects, which can be produced with very high quantum efficiency [in the order of 15 molecules shifting their absorption bands per quantum absorbed (16, 65)], are more secondary phenomena brought about by changes in the environment of the pigment molecules, and possibly related to phosphorylation (67). They may be similar to the 515 nm absorption change, the carotenoid changes (next chapter), and the recently observed absorption changes in the chlorophyll-a region (68) in algae.

With the exceptions mentioned above, it has been more or less generally assumed until recently that photosynthetic bacteria contain only one type of pigment system, analogous to photosystem 1 in algae and higher plants, with one type of primary photochemical reaction. The evidence for this was partly of a negative nature [the absence of O_2 evolution and of Emerson enhancement effects (69)], partly based on the similarity of the action spectra for bacteriochlorophyll fluorescence and various other processes [intracellular NAD reduction (70), cytochrome 553 (C423.5) oxidation (28), and shift in carotenoid absorption (28)]. Recently, however, results have been published which were interpreted as evidence for the existence of more than one pigment system. The possibility of different photochemical systems for cyclic phosphorylation and noncyclic electron transport has been considered (71, 72) in view of an observed mutual independence of the rates of these processes. Such an explanation is more convincing for these results at nonsaturating light intensities (71) than at higher ones, since under the latter conditions the results may be explained by the assumption of different rate-limiting steps for the two processes. Morita (73) reported different action spectra for cytochrome 553 (C423.5), cytochrome cc', and for cytochrome 555 (C422) oxidation in *Chromatium*. The first two spectra differed only slightly and, in view of the experimental error usually encountered in these measurements, possibly not significantly. The third spectrum, however, measured in aerobic cells or at high light intensity, was clearly different. One interpretation (73) of these results is that oxidation of cytochrome 555 is brought about by a different pigment system with either the same (cf. 74) or a different primary reaction. However, this explanation is not easily reconciled with other evidence: viz. the proportionality of the action spectra for cytochrome 553 oxidation and bacteriochlorophyll fluorescence (28) of *Chromatium;* the correlation between bacteriochlorophyll fluorescence and P890 oxidation (57); the correlation between the reaction kinetics of P890 and cytochrome 555 (52, 53, 55); and the observed quantum requirements for cytochrome 553 and 555 oxidation, both close to unity (75, 76). A different way to explain the results would be to assume the existence of different cells in the sample, e.g., young and old ones, with different pigment compositions and different rates of dark reduction of the cytochromes, or the existence of an analogous inhomogeneity within the cells. A third possibility that canot be discounted on the basis of present evidence (cf. 57, 65) is that aerobiosis or a high light intensity, conditions which favor the accumulation of oxidized cytochrome 555, change the efficiency of energy transfer between bacteriochlorophyll molecules.

Sybesma & Fowler (77, 78) reported different action spectra for oxidation of cytochrome C428 and C420 in *R. rubrum,* which were interpreted as evidence for the existence of two different pigment systems. It should be noted, however, that both action spectra have in common a low activity at 880 nm which is difficult to explain in terms of the "normal" activity of B890 in the action spectra for phototaxis (79, 80), inhibition of oxygen uptake (81), and for B890 fluorescence (28), which match the absorption spectrum much more closely. Sybesma & Fowler also made the interesting observation that low intensity illumination, which gave mainly C428 and little C420 oxidation, caused a bleaching at 880 nm accompanied by only a small blue shift at 800 nm. At higher light intensities, a second, slower phase in the absorption change was observed which showed a larger shift at 800 nm. This may indicate that two different types of reaction centers exist: the first type containing P890 but not P800, and associated with C428; the second one containing both P890 and P800, and associated with C422.

ALGAE AND HIGHER PLANTS

The experiments to be mentioned in this chapter will be discussed in terms of the well-known two photosystems "series" scheme for photosynthesis, which has been reviewed repeatedly in earlier volumes of these reviews and elsewhere (e.g., 11, 82–84).

Action spectra for various light-induced processes provide information on the one hand about the pigment composition of photosystems 1 and 2 (terminology after 85) and about energy transfer between pigments in these systems, and on the other hand they may give evidence about the mechanism of photosynthesis by identifying the photosystem which is responsible for a given process.

Fluorescence action spectra.—There are various lines of evidence (see, e.g., 24, 86–89) to suggest that most of the chlorophyll fluorescence emitted by algae and higher plants comes from system 2. The yield of this fluorescence can be enhanced by light mainly absorbed by system 2 and decreased by light mainly absorbed by system 1 (86, 87, 90, 91). Duysens & Sweers (86) proposed that excitation energy is transferred between chlorophyll-*a* molecules belonging to system 2 until it is trapped by a reaction center (called "Q" for quencher). Since the reduced reaction center, QH, can no longer trap excitation energy, fluorescence is increased. Reoxidation of QH takes place in the dark and upon excitation of photosystem 1. Action spectra for the fluorescence decrease in a green leaf, measured by Butler (92), had a peak at 700 to 720 nm. An effect driven in one direction by one pigment and in the other direction by another pigment can give action spectra that do not correspond to the absorption spectrum of either pigment but come nearer to representing the ratio of the absorption of the two pigment systems. Thus, this long wavelength peak is probably the wavelength at which the ratio of system 1 to system 2 activity has its maximum (see chapter on oxygen evolution and dye reduction).

Experiments of Duysens and co-workers (86, 93, 94) indicate that Q or QH may be converted into a photochemically inactive form called Q', which is also a quencher. Excitation of system 2 stimulates the inactivation; excitation of system 1 stimulates reactivation. This inactivation process is different from that studied by Joliot (95, 96). The latter process occurs in darkness and is reversed more rapidly and by smaller amounts of, presumably, system-2 light.

Fluorescence emission spectra (see 89 for a recent review), although different for different species, at room temperature usually show only one clear maximum, located at about 685 nm. Emission in this band results upon excitation of system 2 (88, 97–100). Upon cooling to the temperature of liquid nitrogen, two and often three emission bands are observed around 685, 695, and 720 nm. The band at about 720 nm is usually the strongest one. Goedheer (101) has estimated the half-width values for these bands to be 10, 15, and 28.5 nm respectively in red and blue-green algae. The widths of the 685 and 695 nm bands are comparable to those of chlorophyll-*a* in organic solvents. The broad 720 nm band may represent the fusion of two or more overlapping bands. It has recently been reported (94) that the shape and intensity of the low-temperature emission spectrum depend upon the intensity and wavelength of preillumination at room temperature.

Action spectra of red and blue-green algae cooled to 77°K indicate that the fluorescence bands at 685 and 695 nm are produced upon excitation of system 2 (101–103). The fluorescence band at 720 nm is apparently produced by both systems (101, 102).

Although at room temperature the major part of the fluorescence appears to originate in system 2, some fluorescence must also come from system 1. The fluorescence near 720 nm is polarized, indicating a high degree of orientation of the chlorophyll molecules *in vivo* emitting this fluorescence

(104). Action spectra for excitation of polarized fluorescence have been reported (100, 105) to show participation of system 1. In some species of red algae, excitation of system 1 gives rise to a fluorescence band dominant at 720 to 730 nm, and system 2 excitation gives relatively stronger emission at shorter wavelengths (100, 106). The relative size of changes in fluorescence yield upon excitation with system 1 or system 2 light upon photoreduction of Q similarly indicates that system 1 also emits fluorescence (86).

Digitonin treatment of spinach chloroplasts, followed by differential centrifugation according to the procedures of Boardman & Anderson (107, 108), leads to a partial separation of systems 1 and 2. The large particles sedimenting at 10,000 g are apparently enriched in system 2 because they are active in DCIP but not NADP reduction, contain only about 1 P700 per 700 chlorophyll molecules (109–111), show hardly any absorbance changes caused by cytochrome f (109), and are highly fluorescent (88). The changes with time of the fluorescence yield of the chlorophyll associated with system 2 (86, 112), which are seen upon illumination of intact algae and chloroplasts, are also seen in these heavy particles. At 77°K, fluorescence bands of these particles appear at 683, 693 and 735 nm (88). The intensity of the 735 nm band in the large particles, relative to that in the small ones, indicates that both system 2 and system 1 have an emission band at this wavelength and that the emission at 735 nm in the heavy particles is not, or only partly, due to "contamination" by system 1 (88, 110). In the red alga *Porphyra perforata* which has strong emission at 730 nm, even at room temperature, the relative heights of the bands in the emission spectra with and without DCMU likewise suggest that energy transfer from a chlorophyll-*a* type fluorescing at 684 to the pigment fluorescing at 730 nm occurs in system 2 as well as in system 1 (113).

Goedheer (114) has recently made a comprehensive examination of fluorescence action spectra at room temperature and 77°K of various algae and of greening bean leaves. The fluorescence at wavelengths longer than 705 nm was recorded. In contrast to spectra obtained at room temperature, the low temperature action spectra of most species showed two or more chlorophyll bands in the red region. In the blue-green alga *Synechococcus cedrorum* and in the red alga *Porphyridium cruentum,* the activity of light absorbed by chlorophyll-*a* relative to that absorbed by phycobilins was considerably higher at 77°K than at room temperature, which suggests that at low temperature a relatively larger proportion of the fluorescence at wavelengths longer than 705 nm comes from system 1. No bands attributable to carotenoids were seen at room temperature with these algae, whereas the low-temperature spectrum showed bands at 475 and 510 to 520 nm. Absorption and action spectra of algal preparations which had been extracted with organic solvents (101) suggested that these bands may belong to β-carotene, and that in red and blue-green algae β-carotene transfers energy only to the chlorophyll of system 1, while xanthophyll does not transfer energy to either system. Similar experiments with the xanthophyte *Tribonema aequale* and with spinach chloroplasts indicated transfer of energy from carotenes to both system 1 and 2 and again no activity of the xanthophylls. The room-temperature action spectrum for fluorescence for *Chlorella pyrenoidosa* had peaks at 674 and 440 nm, a shoulder around 650 nm (from chlorophyll-*b*), and a broad shoulder from 470 to 490 nm probably produced both by chlorophyll-*b* and carotenoid(s). Low temperature produced a peak at 650 and a double chlorophyll band with a shoulder at 672 and a peak at 682 nm (114).

Interesting changes could be seen by Goedheer in the action spectra for fluorescence during the development of the photosynthetic apparatus of greening bean leaves. An etiolated leaf which had been in the light for 15 min showed peaks in the action spectrum only at the chlorophyll maxima of 670 and 440 nm. The carotenoids present in the leaf shortly after the conversion of protochlorophyll to chlorophyll had taken place did not contribute to chlorophyll fluorescence (see also 115, 116) even though they exhibited strong absorption. The major fraction of the carotenoids present at this stage of greening are xanthophylls. Carotenes are formed later (88). After 4 hr of greening, bands occurred at 470 and 520 nm in the low-temperature action spectrum, which possibly were due in part to the formation of carotene. The leaves were first capable of photosynthesis after 4 hr of greening.

The DCIP-Hill reaction.—The reduction of DCIP, like ferricyanide reduction, apparently occurs not only upon excitation of system 2 but also upon excitation of system 1. Kok et al. (117) have shown that in a short flash of light the photoreductant of system 1 reduces DCIP very rapidly. The reduction was followed by a somewhat slower reoxidation, and finally by another still slower reduction. The reoxidation was interpreted as being caused by oxidized P700, cytochrome *f*, or plastocyanin, the final slow reduction as a reduction of DCIP by products of system 2. The rapid reduction by system 1 was not affected by DCMU and did not occur in particles from Bishop's *Scenedesmus* mutant No. 8 which lacks a functional system 1. Ke (118) has also observed reduction of DCIP by system 1 in chloroplast particles prepared by fractionation with the detergent Triton X-100. Small particles that had activities associated with photosystem 1 (P700 oxidation, the rapid ESR signal, NADP photoreduction with added electron donor) reduced DCIP rapidly (within 10^{-4}sec) upon onset of flash illumination. In whole chloroplasts illuminated with a broad band of red light which excited both photosystems, Ke found a biphasic response in DCIP reduction. The rapid initial reduction produced by system 1 could still be produced in far-red light and was insensitive to DCMU. A slower, larger dye reduction, mediated by system 2, was produced in red light and abolished upon addition of DCMU.

The action spectrum for DCIP reduction had been shown earlier by Sauer & Park (119) to be characteristic of system 2. The quantum requirement of this reaction was found to be 2 quanta per electron transferred from water to DCIP. One of the factors needed for an efficient reaction was low actinic light intensity. No enhancement of DCIP reduction was seen upon combination of light of 688 and 650 nm. These results can be understood in terms of the above-mentioned evidence. The action spectrum is that of the slow system 2 mediated reaction, and excitation of system 1 merely gives rise to a cycling of electrons via DCIP. On the other hand, Joliot & Joliot (120), using modulated light (discussed later), reported enhancement for the DCIP-Hill reaction. This suggests that at least under certain conditions DCIP cannot compete effectively with the "natural" components of the chain between the two light reactions.

Ferricyanide-Hill reaction.—The results of measurements made by several workers on the Hill reaction with ferricyanide as oxidant have been interpreted on one hand to show participation only of system 2 and on the other hand participation of both systems 1 and 2. Biggins & Sauer (121) reported a maximum at 650 nm in the quantum efficiency spectrum for ferricyanide reduction and suggested that only system 2 functioned under their conditions. The action spectrum of Horio & San Pietro (122) had a peak at 665 nm and a shoulder at 680 nm. They also interpreted the results to demonstrate activity of system 2 alone in this reaction. Mayne & Brown (123) were unable to see the Emerson-enhancement effect using ferricyanide and also suggested that only one photoreaction participates in this reaction.

The action spectrum for ferricyanide reduction, measured (124) with the automatic recording procedures developed by French and his collaborators (7, 125), had a peak at 678 and a shoulder near 650 nm and was interpreted as indicating the cooperation of two light reactions, since it was shifted to longer wavelengths than the action spectrum for the oxygen-evolution burst in chloroplasts without added oxidants. The latter action spectrum had a peak near 650 nm and a shoulder around 680 nm. Govindjee & Bazzaz (126) observed enhancement in the ferricyanide-Hill reaction in spinach chloroplast fragments exposed to red (650 nm) and far-red (700 nm) light at high intensities which were below saturation. At very low intensities, the Emerson-enhancement effect was not seen. They suggested that at low intensities ferricyanide is reduced by system 2 alone and that at high intensity it is reduced at a different site which requires the cooperation of both photochemical systems. Joliot & Joliot (120) similarly concluded that both photosystems may interact in ferricyanide reduction. Schmidt-Mende & Witt (127) suggested that ferricyanide at $10^{-4}M$ is reduced by system 2; at $10^{-6}M$ it was reported to react only with system 1 (128). Avron & Ben-Hayyim (129) also suggested that ferricyanide ($5 \times 10^{-4}M$) reacted only at the level of system 2. They also reported quantum yields for ferricyanide reduction as high as 1.0 and 0.35 equiv./hν at 640 and 715 nm respectively. These high yields, especially that at 640 nm, are hard to explain in terms of the mechanisms currently envisaged.

NADP reduction.—Quantum yields for the photoreduction of NADP by spinach chloroplasts have been reported by Hoch & Martin (130) and more recently by Schwartz (131), by Sauer & Biggins (132), and by Avron & Ben-Hayyim (129). In chloroplasts that were inhibited with DCMU and provided with the donor couple, DCIP-ascorbate, Schwartz found a quantum yield of about 0.33 equiv./hν above 700 nm, i.e., about

3 quanta absorbed for each electron transferred. At shorter wavelengths, the yield dropped to 0.17 equiv./hν. Hoch & Martin (130) and Sauer & Biggins (132) determined by extrapolations to zero light intensity a value of about 0.5 equiv./hν for the quantum yield above 690 nm. Avron & Ben-Hayyim (129) reported a quantum yield, extrapolated to zero intensity, of 1.0 at 715 and 0.40 at 640 nm. It is not clear why, except for the data given by Avron & Ben-Hayyim (129), the quantum yields in the near-infrared for a reaction which presumably involves only system 1 are lower than the expected value of close to 1 equiv./hν.

Oxygen evolution and dye reduction in modulated light.—Joliot & Joliot (120) have recently developed a new approach to amperometric measurement of photochemically produced oxygen or reductants which employs modulated illumination with both phase and frequency sensitive ac signal detection. A thin layer of the experimental material is held in place over a bare platinum electrode by a dialysis membrane. A buffer medium containing oxygen and an appropriate Hill oxidant flows over this thin layer of cells or chloroplasts. "Dark" reduction or oxidation of the Hill oxidant at the electrode gives no problems because this reaction produces a dc signal which is not detected. A second compartment, separated by a dialysis membrane from the compartment containing the Hill oxidant, contains the silver chloride reference electrode over which flows buffer with KCl. This arrangement prevented troublesome reactions of the Hill oxidants at the silver chloride reference electrode. For measurement of oxygen evolution, the platinum electrode was polarized negatively with respect to the reference electrode; positive polarization was used to determine production of reduced substances, such as reduced methyl viologen, reduced DCIP and ferrocyanide.

By choosing appropriate conditions, Joliot et al. (120, 133) were able to use the modulated method so that it responded exclusively to one of the two photosystems. Background light, which could theoretically be of any wavelength, was used to maintain the traps of systems 1 and 2 at a particular steady-state concentration. The intensity of the modulated detecting beam had to be low enough (2 per cent of the background beam) so as not to disturb the concentration of active traps. For measurements of the action spectrum for system 2, negative polarization was used in order to measure O_2 evolution and NADP was used as the electron acceptor. A continuous 720 nm background light was chosen to give maximum sensitivity. The action spectrum for system 2 of spinach chloroplasts determined under these conditions had a maximum at 677 nm and a shoulder at 650 nm (chlorophyll-*b*). This spectrum is like that reported earlier by Joliot (95) for system 2 in *Chlorella pyrenoidosa,* in which the rate of O_2 evolution at the onset of illumination was measured. Joliot's spectrum is also similar to that reported earlier (134) for the production of the 515 nm absorbance change in spinach chloroplasts which had been treated with a concentration of ferricyanide sufficiently high to oxidize P700. The action spectrum for system 1 was determined in a similar way by measuring the action spectrum for methyl viologen reduction with positive polarization. The background light was 650 nm. This spectrum showed a peak at 681 nm and extended further into the near infrared than the action spectrum of system 2, as could be expected.

Ratios between the action spectra of systems 1 and 2 were plotted based on the assumption of equal active absorption at 680 nm. This ratio was 0.7 at 650 nm and had a maximum of 12 at 720 nm. At wavelengths longer than about 720 nm, the ratio decreased again. A similar decrease in enhancement was also found by Myers & Graham (135) and by Govindjee (136) when the far-red beam had wavelengths greater than about 720 nm.

Phosphorylation.—Experiments of Schwartz (137) indicate that phosphorylation is sensitized both by system 1 and system 2. The quantum yield as a function of wavelength for ATP formation with reduced PMS as a catalyst differed markedly from that obtained when either ferricyanide or NADP were used as oxidants to support O_2 evolution in a Hill reaction. Reduced PMS increased the long-wavelength sensitized phosphorylation and decreased short-wavelength phosphorylation. Likewise, the action spectrum determined by Yin et al. (138) for photophosphorylation in a suspension of sweet potato leaf cells using ferricyanide as an oxidant showed a red drop at wavelengths greater than 680 nm, while that determined with PMS (probably oxidized) had a high efficiency at 700 nm. The latter action spectrum appears to reflect the activity of both photosystems because PMS can act (with reduced efficiency) as a Hill oxidant as well as catalyze cyclic phosphorylation (137).

Schwartz (139) has recently used a rapid and sensitive pH electrode to show that the link between light-induced electron transport and ATP synthesis is the electrochemical gradient produced when protons are taken up across chloroplast membranes. It appears that a proton translocation site is located in the electron-transport sequence between the two photosystems. Schwartz (140) found by using methyl viologen as oxidant and modulated 650 nm actinic light that the modulated rate of steady-state proton uptake was suppressed upon addition of weak nonmodulated 710 nm light. And conversely, the modulated rate of proton uptake in weak, modulated 710 nm light was increased with addition of nonmodulated 650 nm light. When pyocyanine was used as a cofactor, no such increases in the modulated rates of proton uptake were seen, since cyclic electron transport with this cofactor involves only system 1 (137, 141). Dilley & Vernon (142) had shown earlier that proton transport can be mediated by system 1.

Action spectra for changes in pigment absorption.—The identity of the compound producing the light-induced increase of absorbance at 515 nm which was discovered in 1954 by Duysens (143) has received considerable attention during the last few years (134, 144–148). A number of compounds have been suggested to be involved in this reaction: chlorophyll-*b,* a plastoquinone complex, a carotenoid, and chlorophyll-*a.* DCMU has been shown to have only a partially inhibiting effect on the 515 nm change (144, 147, 149–153). Contrary to these findings, however, is the report that Witt and co-workers (154) found complete inhibition by DCMU. The participation of both light reactions has been claimed for this reaction (134, 144–148, 155, 156). It is now clear that the conflicting reports arose because it was not understood that the change is sensitized by both systems. Action spectra of *Ulva lobata* showed (148) that both the steady-state change in the presence of DCMU and the rate of formation of the change in the presence and absence of DCMU are sensitized by system 1. These action spectra which had a peak at about 680 nm matched that of cytochrome oxidation, a well-known system-1 reaction (10, 85). They were also similar to that of oxygen uptake in the presence of DCMU (157). Thus in *Ulva*, at least, the fast component is produced by system 1 only. A second, slower, 515 nm change appears at higher intensities which, judging from the action spectrum, is caused by system 2 and which is inhibited by DCMU. Experiments with *Chlorella* (153) support these conclusions. The difference spectra for both the system 1 and the system 2-induced changes are identical, exhibiting negative bands at 475 and 650 nm and a positive band at 515 nm (148, 158). As suggested by Rumberg (158), the location of these bands indicates that these changes are produced by chlorophyll-*b*. Moreover, in a barley mutant which lacks chlorophyll-*b* (159), these characteristic changes are not seen (148) but other changes are seen, probably caused by a carotenoid, which have maxima at 447, 475, and 512 nm and minima at 475 and 493 nm (160).

Similar difference spectra with maxima and minima separated by about 30 nm, presumably due to a shift in the location of the absorption bands of a carotenoid, were seen in red, brown, and yellow-green algae (160, 161). The kinetic properties of these absorbance changes were remarkably similar to those produced by chlorophyll-*b* described above. In both cases, excitation of system 1 gave a fast, transitory change upon illumination, while excitation of system 2 produced a slow but sustained absorbance change, followed by a reversal upon darkening. Action spectra (162) for the fast component in the yellow-green alga *Botrydiopsis alpina* indicate that it is mediated by system 1. Excitation of system 2 produced a sustained carotenoid shift in the presence of far-red background light. Since one of the positive bands of the carotenoid change occurs in many plants at 515 to 520 nm (161), it is possible that the confusion concerning the origin of this change may be caused partly by overlapping of carotenoid and chlorophyll-*b* absorption changes in this region. Junge & Witt (163) have recently reported evidence that the chlorophyll-*b* change may reflect a development of a potential across a membrane, related to hydrogen ion transport and phosphorylation. This would agree with the evidence discussed in the previous section that both photosystems can mediate these processes.

Photoreduction.—Gingras (164) developed an electrode assembly that simultaneously measured the relative rates of O_2 and CO_2 exchange in small samples of algae. This technique was used to determine with the same samples the action spectra for photosynthesis and for photoreduction of CO_2 with concomitant H_2 uptake. The apparatus was sensitive enough to permit the use of very thin layers of algae so that distortion of action spectra could be avoided. Gingras compared photosynthesis and photoreduction in the red alga *Porphyridium cruentum*. Emerson enhancement was seen with paired 560 and 690 nm beams in photosynthesis, but not in photoreduction in hydrogen-adapted *Porphyridium*. Gingras' action spectra show very clearly that photosynthesis and photoreduction are driven by different photosystems. The action spectrum for oxygen evolution is typical of the type found originally by Haxo & Blinks (165) for red algae: green light, predominantly absorbed by the phycobilins, was about twice as effective as blue and red light, absorbed by chlorophyll. By contrast, the action spectrum for photoreduction (in the presence of DCMU) had a maximum at 680 nm and showed maximum activity in the red and blue spectral regions. The activity of phycobilins amounted to 88 per cent of that of the red band of chlorophyll. The action spectrum for photoreduction was similar to that reported for the oxidation of the *f*-type cytochrome in *Porphyridium* by Duysens & Amesz (10) and in *Anacystis* by Amesz & Duysens (9).

Action spectra and quantum requirements determined recently by Bishop (166) also suggest that photoreduction is driven by system 1. The action spectrum for photoreduction of hydrogen-adapted *Scenedesmus* treated with DCMU (measured manometrically) had a peak at 691 nm and extended farther into the near-infrared than that for photosynthesis. The lowest quantum requirement for photoreduction found in the region around 710 nm was more than 10 einsteins per mole CO_2, a relatively high value when one assumes that almost no energy is lost by absorption by system 2 at this wavelength. Action spectra similar to those obtained with DCMU-treated *Scenedesmus* were found for mutants of this alga (#11 and a') that are unable to evolve O_2.

TRANSFER OF ENERGY BETWEEN PHOTOSYNTHETIC UNITS AND PIGMENT SYSTEMS

A question receiving attention during recent years is that of the possibility of transfer of excitation energy between photosynthetic units or reaction centers for conversion of excitation energy into chemical energy. Such transfer would reduce loss of excitation energy when part of the reaction centers are inoperative for some reason.

Energy transfer between photosynthetic units belonging to the same pigment system.—In 1963, Vredenberg & Duysens (49) showed that in *Rhodospirillum rubrum* the photoinduced bleaching of the reaction-center pigment P890 was correlated with an increase in the yield of bacteriochlorophyll fluorescence. These observations indicated that fluorescence and energy transfer to (unbleached) P890 are competitive processes. A linear relation between the reciprocal of the fluorescence yield and the amount of bleached P890 was observed, which was explained by a simple model in which the rate of transfer from the bulk bacteriochlorophyll to the reaction centers was proportional to the concentration of unbleached P890. This implied in principle that the photosynthetic units in this bacterium were not separate, and that energy could be transported between them over distances several times the size of one unit. The same conclusion could be drawn from experiments with *Chloropseudomonas ethylicum* (50).

Clayton (57, 62, 167) extended these experiments with different species of purple bacteria and with chromatophore preparations. The same type of relationship between P890 (or P985) bleaching and fluorescence as found by Vredenberg & Duysens was observed in aerobic cell suspensions of various species. A closer analysis (167) of data obtained with *Rhodopseudomonas spheroides* indicated that the range of energy transfer extended over at least 7 molecules of P890. However, deviations were observed in anaerobic cell suspensions and in preparations of chromatophores. In some instances, these deviations were tentatively explained by an effect of the oxidation-reduction state of the primary photooxidant on the yield of fluorescence or by an inhomogeneity in the preparation. With some chromatophore preparations, an approximately linear relation between the fluorescence yield (rather than the reciprocal of this yield) and P890 bleaching was observed, suggesting the absence of energy transfer between photosynthetic units. The last conclusion followed also from experiments of Parson (55), who observed, with a chromatophore suspension of *Chromatium,* an exponential relationship between the amount of P890 or cytochrome oxidized and the amount of light energy given by a laser flash to bring about the oxidation.

Energy transfer between system-2 units in algae and higher plants was studied with a somewhat different approach by Joliot, Joliot & Kok (133, 168, 169) by measuring the relative efficiency of photochemistry as a function of the fraction of reaction centers that are operative under a given set of conditions. For system 2 in *Chlorella pyrenoidosa* and in spinach chloroplasts, the oxidation-reduction state of the primary photooxidant [Q in Duysens' terminology (86)] was varied by illuminating with light of different wavelengths and intensities, or by the use of CMU and DCMU as specific poisons; its redox state was determined by measuring the amount of oxygen evolved by a short, saturating flash of light. The photochemical efficiency was determined by measuring rates of oxygen evolution. By analysis of the data in terms of a simplified model where energy transfer within one photosynthetic unit occurs essentially without losses, and where transfer to a second unit occurs only when the reaction center in the first unit is inoperative and unable to trap energy, a probability of transfer (p) of 0.5 to 0.6 from an inoperative unit to a second unit was derived. The same number was derived from an analysis of fluorescence yield as a function of total light energy absorbed after onset of illumination in the presence of substances such as CMU that inhibit reoxidation of accumulated QH. Energy transfer between photosynthetic units in such an experiment should result in an initially slower fluorescent rise than the exponential rise expected in the absence of such transfer.

It should be noted that in the model of Joliot & Joliot (168), the "base" fluorescence observed when all traps of system 2 are open is an independent experimental value. Since the model predicts absence of fluorescence when all traps are open, this fluorescence must be assumed to be emitted by some special fraction of the chlorophyll which is inactive or less active photosynthetically (167, 170). In the model of Vredenberg & Duysens for purple bacteria (49), the base fluorescence enters into the equations, and the ratio between the yields with open and with closed traps is directly related to the photosynthetic efficiency (11, 167, 170). For a more detailed discussion of this point and a more general treatment, we may refer to (167) and (170). The assumption of an "independent" base fluorescence is not supported by experiments of Tumerman & Sorokin (171), who reported a constant ratio between the yield and the lifetime of chlorophyll fluorescence in *Chlorella*, independent of variations in both these quantities brought about by illumination or addition of CMU. Results of Müller & Lumry (172) similarly indicate an approximately constant ratio. These observations indicate the absence of "energy" barriers between photosynthetic units, as well as the absence of more than a small amount of fluorescence from special pools of chlorophyll. The accuracy is probably not sufficient to rule out the existence of a small amount of system-1 fluorescence (see chapter on fluorescence action spectra). Müller, Lumry & Walker (172, 173) did not obtain evidence for the existence of more than one exponentially decaying excited chlorophyll species at any light intensity from experiments in which fluorescence was excited with light modulated at different high frequencies. They showed, however (173; and Müller, personal communication), that the method at the frequencies employed would not have been of sufficient accuracy to distinguish different lifetimes of chlorophyll located in "separate" photosynthetic units.

Measurements of Fork & Amesz (174) to compare the relative efficiency of oxygen production and the fraction of P700 that was in the oxidized state at various intensities of predominantly system-2 light in the red alga *Cryptopleura violacea* indicated energy transfer between photosynthetic units of system 1 in this alga, with an estimated p of 0.5 to 0.6 or more. Comparison of the sum of the net rates of P700 and cytochrome f oxidation with the oxidation level of P700 in the red alga *Iridaea splendens* suggested about the same number for p (175). Experiments with some other species of algae were inconclusive (174). On the other hand, Joliot, Joliot & Kok (133) found, in experiments where the rate of methyl viologen reduction and the amount of methyl viologen reduced in a flash were measured with isolated spinach chloroplasts, a linear relation between these two quantities, suggesting that in these chloroplasts either the system-1 units are separated or that light energy is trapped not only by active, but also by inactive reaction centers (or by chlorophyll connected to them).

Transfer between units belonging to different pigment systems ("spillover").—Almost immediately after the two-photosystem model for photosynthesis had been developed, the possibility was considered of energy transfer between the two pigment systems (135, 176–179). "Spill-over" (terminology after 135) from system 2 to system 1 under conditions where system 2 receives more light energy than could be used efficiently has been advanced as an attractive hypothesis to explain the approximately constant quantum yield of photosynthesis at wavelengths with predominant system 2 absorption, as has often (e.g., 165, 180–182) but not in all cases (183) been observed in a variety of algae. The same applies to the approximately constant yield of NADP reduction with coupled oxygen evolution in spinach chloroplasts at wavelengths below 680 nm (see previous chapter). Also, the observation (181) that the action spectrum of oxygen evolution measured on a background of green (system 2) light of some red algae matches closely, except in the carotenoid region, the absorption spectrum would appear to be more easily explained in terms of a "spill-over" mechanism than of a so-called "separate package" mechanism, in which no transfer of energy—or at least no enhanced rate of energy transfer—from system 2 to system 1 can occur. A closer analysis of these and similar data led Malkin (184) to the conclusion that at least in some species of green and red algae and diatoms efficient spill-over from system 2 to system 1 takes place.

It should be noted that the arguments listed above are based on the (tacit) assumption that the difference between the E_0' of the primary photooxidant of system 2 and of the primary reductant of system 1 is large, so that the first one can be almost completely oxidized while the second one is almost completely reduced. If not, in both systems part of the units will be inoperative at any wavelength of illumination, even in the system that receives less than a balanced amount of excitation energy (185). From flash experiments of the type discussed in the first part of this chapter, Joliot, Joliot & Kok (133) deduced an E_0' difference of about 40 mV for spinach chloroplasts, on the basis of which they calculated that the relative efficiency for a reaction requiring both photosystems (e.g., NADP reduction with oxygen evolution) should be nearly independent of wavelength from 610 to 680 nm in the absence of spill-over. For intact cells of red and blue-green algae, however, preliminary results of spectrophotometric measurements (Amesz, Dirks & Nooteboom, unpublished) suggest a much higher E_0' difference.

Clayton (178) suggested that the extent of spill-over would be regulated by the oxidation state of P700, by postulating direct transfer from system 2 to P700. In predominantly system-2 light, less P700 would be oxidized and bleached than in light predominantly absorbed by system 1, so that in the first case more energy would be transferred from system 2 to P700. However, experiments of Duysens (186) to check this hypothesis showed the fluorescence yield of system 2 in the presence of DCMU, and thus energy transfer from system 2 to system 1, to be independent of the oxidation-reduction state of P700.

If spill-over from system 2 to system 1 occurs, one of the factors correlated with this spill-over should be the fluorescence yield of system 2, and a decrease in fluorescence yield should be associated with a decrease in the rate of spill-over. Amesz, Nooteboom & Spaargaren (68) compared the relative activity of light absorbed by phycobilins and by chlorophyll-a in bringing about photochemical reactions of system 1 (P700 and cytochrome oxidation) in the presence of DCMU, which gave a high yield of fluorescence, and after subsequent addition of 1,4-naphthoquinone, which quenched this fluorescence. No significant changes in relative activity were found with various species of red algae, but a decrease was observed in the blue-green alga *Anacystis nidulans*. These results indicate the absence of spill-over in red algae, but may suggest the occurrence of spill-over in *Anacystis*. Gingras (164), however, explained the constant yield for photoreduction in *Porphyridium cruentum* between 610 and 705 nm by spill-over from system 2 to 1. Murata, Nishimura & Takamiya (102), from the action spectrum of the long-wavelength chlorophyll fluorescence at 77°K, concluded that spill-over occurred in *Porphyra yezoensis*. Williams (187) found no evidence for spill-over in *Chlorella* by comparing data on CMU poisoning [Gingras, Lemasson & Fork (188)] with the action spectrum of photosynthesis (7) or with fluorescence data.

Data obtained with isolated spinach chloroplasts partly favor the spill-over and partly the separate package model. As noted already, the approximately constant quantum yield for NADP reduction with concomitant oxygen evolution below 680 nm, observed by many authors (130, 132, 189, 190), and similar data for DCIP reduction (119) would be in line with the spill-over model. However, with DCMU, ascorbate and DCIP as electron donor system, the quantum yield for NADP (130, 132, 189) and cytochrome *c* (191) reduction has been reported to be roughly twice as low at wavelengths below 680 nm as in the near infrared region, indicating the absence of spill-over. Moreover, the sum of the quantum efficiencies for the latter reaction and for DCIP reduction is close to 1.0 at any wavelength (191). Absence of spill-over was also suggested by experiments of Joliot, Joliot & Kok (133), who found that addition of DCMU and diaminodurol and ascorbate as electron donor system had no effect on the shape of the action spectrum for methyl viologen reduction, measured with modulated light (see previous chapter). Avron & Ben-Hayyim (192) reported that, in contrast to NADP reduction with ascorbate and DCIP as electron donor, which gave the pattern mentioned above, the reduction of diquat or FMN under the same conditions proceeded with a quantum yield of 1.0 both at 640 and 715 nm, and interpreted this result as showing complete spill-over. To explain these divergent (and other) results, they made the hypothesis that the extent of spill-over can be strongly influenced by internal and external factors, such as the composition of the medium or the nature of the electron acceptor. Interestingly, for the ferricyanide-Hill reaction, a quantum yield of 1.0 at 640 nm was reported. This high yield was explained by spill-over from system 1 to system 2.

MECHANISMS OF ENERGY TRANSFER

Mechanisms of transfer of excitation energy between molecules of photosynthetic pigments have been reviewed and discussed in recent years by various authors (2, 11, 83, 193–195). For this reason, only a short review will be given here with emphasis on recent developments.

When pigment molecules are not located too distant from each other, transfer of excitation energy between them can occur by way of so-called induced resonance between dipoles. This type of energy transfer has been treated quantum mechanically by Förster (196, 197) and in a classical way by Förster (197) and by Hoch & Knox (2). The Förster theory predicts that the rate of energy transfer is proportional to the sixth power of the reciprocal of the distance, and proportional to the overlap between the fluorescence emission spectrum of the emitting and the absorption spectrum of the receiving molecule, provided there is "weak interaction" between the pigment molecules, i.e., provided the rate of transfer is low compared to the time the energy-receiving molecule needs to reestablish thermal (vibrational) equilibrium or to lose its excitation energy or to convert it into another form of energy.

Because of the small shift of the emission relative to the absorption spectrum, the overlap between these spectra is unusually high for chlorophyll-a, which makes it a very suitable intermediate for transfer of absorbed energy to the reaction centers. Good overlap also exists between the absorption spectrum of chlorophyll-a and the emission spectra of chlorophyll-b and phycocyanin, which explains the high efficiencies of energy transfer from these pigments to chlorophyll-a (24). The same is true for the various bacteriochlorophyll types in purple bacteria.

For transfer between chlorophyll-a molecules, various values have been computed (83, 198–200) for R_0, the distance at which transfer of energy is equally as probable as loss of energy by fluorescence. The accepted "theoretical" value, obtained from absorption and emission spectra in ethanol solution, is 70 Å (83, 199). However, the "experimental" value, deduced from experiments on concentration quenching of fluorescence polarization, may lie anywhere from 65 Å to 92 Å (201).

Because the rate of transfer depends on the sixth power of the reciprocal of the distance, at distances somewhat shorter than R_0, transfer by induced resonance will compete very effectively with other processes, and the efficiency of transfer will be very high. It has been shown (83, 195, 202) that at an average distance of about 15 to 20 Å between chlorophyll molecules (the most probable distance in the chloroplast), the rate of transfer is sufficiently high to account for an efficient transfer of energy from chlorophyll to reaction centers present at a concentration of one per several hundred chlorophyll molecules.

It is a matter of dispute (2, 193–195) whether the Förster mechanism operates at distances as close as 15 to 20 Å. According to Robinson (193, 194), the interaction energy is too strong, and consequently the rate of energy transfer between molecules is too high to apply the Förster theory, but his views are contested by others (2, 195). Robinson (194) estimated that the transfer time would be about 100 times smaller than the time needed to convert excitation energy into "chemical" energy in a reaction center. If so, this could imply that a reaction center has little capacity to trap energy transferred to it and therefore has to be visited by the energy a large number of times before there is a good chance that the energy will be converted into chemical energy. However, experiments of Olson, Clayton & Sistrom (36, 61), mentioned earlier in this review, would not seem to favor this assumption for purple bacteria. These experiments indicate that, at least in two species of *Rhodopseudomonas,* quanta absorbed by bacteriochlorophyll types P800 or P830 are more active in bringing about P890 or P985 oxidation than in exciting bacteriochlorophyll fluorescence. Unless separate pools of fluorescent bacteriochlorophyll are assumed, this result implies a high trapping efficiency of the reaction center.

LITERATURE CITED

1. Halldal, P., *Photochem. Photobiol.,* **6,** 445–60 (1967)
2. Hoch, G., Knox, R. S., in *Photophysiology,* **3,** 225–51 (Giese, A. C., Ed., Academic Press, N.Y., 1968)
3. Allen, M. B., in *Photophysiology,* **1,** 83–110 (Giese, A. C., Ed., Academic Press, N.Y., 1964)
4. Smith, J. H. C., French, C. S., *Ann. Rev. Plant Physiol.,* **14,** 181–224 (1963)
5. Blinks, L. R., in *Photophysiology,* **1,** 199–221 (Giese, A. C., Ed., Academic Press, N.Y., 1964)
6. Duysens, L. N. M., in *Progr. Photobiol., Proc. Intern. Congr. Photobiol., 3rd, Copenhagen, 1960,* 135–42 (1961)
7. French, C. S., Myers, J., McLeod, G. C., in *Comparative Biochemistry of Photoreactive Systems,* 361–65 (Allen, M. B., Ed., Academic Press, N.Y.—London, 437 pp., 1960)
8. Olson, J. M., Smillie, R. M., in *Photosynthetic Mechanisms in Green Plants,* 56–65 (Natl. Acad. Sci., Natl. Res. Council, Washington, D.C., 766 pp., 1963)
9. Amesz, J., Duysens, L. N. M., *Biochim. Biophys. Acta,* **64,** 261–78 (1962)
10. Duysens, L. N. M., Amesz, J., *Biochim. Biophys. Acta,* **64,** 243–60 (1962)
11. Clayton, R. K., *Molecular Physics in Photosynthesis* (Blaisdell Publ., N.Y., Toronto, London, 1965)
12. Jensen, A., Aasmundrud, O., Eimhjellen, K. E., *Biochim. Biophys. Acta,* **88,** 466–79 (1964)
13. Drews, G., Giesbrecht, P., *Arch. Mikrobiol.,* **52,** 242–50 (1965)

14. Wassink, E. C., Katz, E., Dorrestein, R., *Enzymologia,* **7,** 113–29 (1939)
15. Olson, J. M., Stanton, E. K., in *The Chlorophylls,* 381–98 (Vernon, L. P., Seely, G. R., Eds., Academic Press, N.Y.—London, 1966)
16. Vredenberg, W. J., Amesz, J., *Biochim. Biophys. Acta,* **126,** 244–53 (1966)
17. Krasnovsky, A. A., *Photochem. Photobiol.,* **4,** 641–55 (1965)
18. Krasnovsky, A. A., *Intern. Congr. Photosyn. Res., June, 1968, Freudenstadt, W. Germany* (In press)
19. Olson, J. M., in *The Chlorophylls,* 413–25 (Vernon, L. P., Seely, G. R., Eds., Academic Press, N.Y.—London, 1966)
20. Dratz, E. A., Schultz, A. J., Sauer, K., in *Energy Conversion by the Photosynthetic Apparatus, Brookhaven Symp. Biol.,* **19,** 303–18 (1967)
21. Sauer, K., Lindsay Smith, J. R., Schultz, A. J., *J. Am. Chem. Soc.,* **88,** 2681–88 (1966)
22. Sauer, K., Dratz, E. A., *Intern. Congr. Photosyn. Res., June, 1968, Freudenstadt, W. Germany* (In press)
23. Thomas, J. B., *Biochim. Biophys. Acta,* **5,** 186–96 (1950)
24. Duysens, L. N. M., *Transfer of Excitation Energy in Photosynthesis* (Doctoral thesis, Univ. Utrecht, Utrecht, Netherlands, 96 pp., 1952)
25. Goedheer, J. C., *Biochim. Biophys. Acta,* **35,** 1–8 (1959)
26. Bril, C., *Studies on the Photosynthetic Apparatus of Some Purple Bacteria* (Doctoral thesis, Univ. Utrecht, The Netherlands, 96 pp., 1964)

27. Zankel, K. L., Clayton, R. K., *Biophys. J., Soc. Abstr.,* **8,** A-151 (1968)

28. Amesz, J., Vredenberg, W. J., *Biochim. Biophys. Acta,* **126,** 254–61 (1966)

29. Garcia, A., Vernon, L. P., Mollenhauer, H., *Biochemistry,* **6,** 2399–2407 (1966)

30. Garcia, A., Vernon, L. P., Mollenhauer, H., *ibid.,* 2408–16

31. Garcia, A., Vernon, L. P., Ke, B., Mollenhauer, H., *Biochemistry,* **7,** 326–32 (1968)

32. Erokhin, Yu. E., *Studia Biophysica (Berlin),* **5,** 171–74 (1967) (In Russian)

33. Cusanovitch, M. A., Bartsch, R. G., Kamen, M. D., *Biochim. Biophys. Acta,* **153,** 397–417 (1968)

34. Giesbrecht, P., Drews, G., *Arch. Mikrobiol.,* **54,** 297–330 (1966)

35. Olson, J. M., Nadler, K. D., *Photochem. Photobiol.,* **4,** 783–91 (1965)

36. Olson, J. M., Clayton, R. K., *Photochem. Photobiol.,* **5,** 655–60 (1966)

37. Stanier, R. Y., Smith, J. H. C., *Biochim. Biophys. Acta,* **41,** 478–84 (1960)

38. Olson, J. M., Romano, C. A., *Biochim. Biophys. Acta,* **59,** 726–28 (1962)

39. Olson, J. M., Sybesma, C., in *Bacterial Photosyn. Symp., Yellow Springs, Ohio, 1963,* 413–22

40. Clayton, R. K., *J. Gen. Physiol.,* **48,** 633–46 (1965)

41. Zaugg, W. S., Vernon, L. P., Tirpack, A., *Proc. Natl. Acad. Sci. U.S.,* **51,** 232–38 (1964)

42. Clayton, R. K., *Biochem. Biophys. Res. Commun.,* **9,** 49–53 (1962)

43. Beugeling, T., *Biochim. Biophys. Acta,* **153,** 143–53 (1968)

44. Ke, B., Vernon, L. P., Garcia, A., Ngo, E., *Biochemistry,* **7,** 311–18 (1968)

45. Duysens, L. N. M., Huiskamp, W. J., Vos, J. J., van der Hart, J. M., *Biochim. Biophys. Acta,* **19,** 188–90 (1956)

46. Arnold, W., Clayton, R. K., *Proc. Natl. Acad. Sci. U.S.,* **46,** 769–76 (1960)

47. Duysens, L. N. M., in *The Photochemical Apparatus; Its Structure and Function, Brookhaven Symp. Biol.,* **11,** 10–25 (1959)

48. Kuntz, I. D., Loach, P. A., Calvin, M., *Biophys. J.,* **4,** 227–49 (1964)

49. Vredenberg, W. J., Duysens, L. N. M., *Nature,* **197,** 355–57 (1963)

50. Sybesma, C., Vredenberg, W. J., *Biochim. Biophys. Acta,* **75,** 439–41 (1963)

51. Sybesma, C., Vredenberg, W. J., *Biochim. Biophys. Acta,* **88,** 205–7 (1964)

52. Beugeling, T., Duysens, L. N. M., in *Currents in Photosynthesis, Proc. West.-Eur. Conf. Photosyn., 2nd, Zeist, Neth., 1965,* 49–55 (1966)

53. Duysens, L. N. M., in *Currents in Photosynthesis, Proc. West.-Eur. Conf. Photosyn., 2nd, Zeist, Neth., 1965,* 263–71 (1966)

54. Clayton, R. K., *Photochem. Photobiol.,* **1,** 201–10 (1962)

55. Parson, W. W., *Biochim. Biophys. Acta,* **153,** 248–59 (1968)

56. Holt, A. S., Clayton, R. K., *Photochem. Photobiol.,* **4,** 829–31 (1965)

57. Clayton, R. K., *Photochem. Photobiol.,* **5,** 807–21 (1966)

58. Reed, D. W., Clayton, R. K., *Biochem. Biophys. Res. Commun.,* **30,** 471–75 (1968)

59. Clayton, R. K., in *Bacterial Photosyn. Symp., Yellow Springs, Ohio, 1963,* 377–95

60. Clayton, R. K., *Photochem. Photobiol.,* **5,** 669–77 (1966)

61. Clayton, R. K., Sistrom, W. R., *Photochem. Photobiol.,* **4,** 661–68 (1966)

62. Clayton, R. K., *Photochem. Photobiol.,* **5,** 679–88 (1966)

63. Clayton, R. K., *Proc. Natl. Acad. Sci., U.S.,* **50,** 583–87 (1963)

64. Vredenberg, W. J., Amesz, J., Duysens, L. N. M., *Biochem. Biophys. Res. Commun.,* **18,** 435–39 (1965)

65. Amesz, J., Vredenberg, W. J., in *Currents in Photosynthesis, Proc. West.-Eur. Conf. Photosyn., 2nd, Zeist, Neth., 1965,* 75–83 (1966)

66. Smith, L., Ramírez, J., *J. Biol. Chem.,* **235,** 218–25 (1960)

67. Fleischman, D., Clayton, R. K., *Photochem. Photobiol.,* **8,** 287–98 (1968)

68. Amesz, J., Nooteboom, W., Spaargaren, D. H., *Intern. Congr. Photosyn. Res., June 1968, Freudenstadt, W. Germany* (In press)

69. Blinks, L. R., van Niel, C. B., in *Studies on Microalgae and Photosynthetic Bacteria,* Special Issue of *Plant Cell Physiol.,* 297–308 (Univ. Tokyo Press, Tokyo, 636 pp., 1963)

70. Amesz, J., *Biochim. Biophys. Acta,* **66,** 22–36 (1963)

71. Zaugg, W. S., Vernon, L. P., Helmer,

G., *Arch. Biochem. Biophys.*, **119**, 560–71 (1967)

72. Klemme, J. H., *Hydrogenase und Photosynthetischer Elektronentransport bei Rhodospirillum rubrum und Rhodopseudomonas capsulata* (Doctoral thesis, Georg-August-Universität, Göttingen, 123 pp., 1967)

73. Morita, S., *Biochim. Biophys. Acta*, **153**, 241–47 (1968)

74. Hind, G., Olson, J. M., *Ann. Rev. Plant Physiol.*, **19**, 249–82 (1968)

75. Olson, J. M., *Science*, **135**, 101–2 (1962)

76. Vredenberg, W. J., Duysens, L. N. M., *Biochim. Biophys. Acta*, **79**, 456–63 (1964)

77. Sybesma, C., Fowler, C. F., *Biophys. J.* (Society abstr.), **8**, A-149 (1968)

78. Sybesma, C., Fowler, C. F., *Intern. Congr. Photosyn. Res., June 1968, Freudenstadt, Germany* (In press)

79. Manten, A., *Anthonie van Leeuwenhoek, J. Microbiol. Serol.*, **14**, 65–86 (1948)

80. Clayton, R. K., *Arch. Mikrobiol.*, **19**, 107–24 (1953)

81. Fork, D. C., Goedheer, J. C., *Biochim. Biophys. Acta*, **79**, 249–56 (1964)

82. Vernon, L. P., Avron, M., *Ann. Rev. Biochem.*, **34**, 269–96 (1965)

83. Duysens, L. N. M., *Progr. Biophys. Mol. Biol.*, **14**, 1–104 (1964)

84. Duysens, L. N. M., Amesz, J., in *Comprehensive Biochem.*, **27**, *Photobiology, Ionizing Radiations*, 237–66 (1967)

85. Duysens, L. N. M., Amesz, J., Kamp, B. M., *Nature*, **190**, 510–11 (1961)

86. Duysens, L. N. M., Sweers, H. E., *Studies on Microalgae and Photosynthetic Bacteria* (Ed. by Japan. Soc. Plant Physiol., 353–72, Univ. Tokyo Press, 1963)

87. Butler, W. L., Bishop, N. I., *Photosynthetic Mechanisms of Green Plants*, 91–100 (Natl. Acad. Sci.-Natl. Res. Council, Publ. 1145, Washington, D.C., 1963)

88. Boardman, N. K., Thorne, S. W., Anderson, J. M., *Proc. Natl. Acad. Sci. U.S.*, **56**, 586–93 (1966)

89. Govindjee, Papageorgiou, G., Rabinowitch, E., in *Fluorescence Theory, Instrumentation, and Practice*, 511–64 (Guilbaut, G. G., Ed., Marcel Dekker, Inc., N.Y., 1967)

90. Govindjee, Ichimura, S., Cederstrand, C., Rabinowitch, E., *Arch. Biochem. Biophys.*, **89**, 322–23 (1960)

91. Teale, F. W. J., *Biochem. J.*, **85**, 14P (1962)

92. Butler, W. L., *Biochim. Biophys. Acta*, **66**, 275–76 (1963)

93. Duysens, L. N. M., Talens, J., *Intern. Congr. Photosyn. Res., June, 1968, Freudenstadt, Germany* (In press)

94. Donze, M., Duysens, L. N. M., *Intern. Congr. Photosyn. Res., June, 1968, Freudenstadt, Germany* (In press)

95. Joliot, P., *Biochim. Biophys. Acta*, **102**, 116–34 (1965)

96. Joliot, P., *ibid.*, 135–48

97. Bergeron, J. A., *Photosynthetic Mechanisms of Green Plants*, 527–36 (Natl. Acad. Sci.-Natl. Res. Council, Publ. 1145, Washington, D.C., 1963)

98. Krey, A., Govindjee, *Biochim. Biophys. Acta*, **120**, 1–18 (1966)

99. Kok, B., Rurainski, H. J., *Biochim. Biophys. Acta*, **126**, 584–87 (1966)

100. Govindjee, *Currents in Photosynthesis*, 93–103 (Thomas, J. B., Goedheer, J. C., Eds., Ad. Donker, Rotterdam, Neth., 1966)

101. Goedheer, J. C., *Biochim. Biophys. Acta*, **153**, 903–6 (1968)

102. Murata, N., Nishimura, M., Takamiya, A., *Biochim. Biophys. Acta*, **126**, 234–43 (1966)

103. Bergeron, J. A., Olson, J. M., *Biochim. Biophys. Acta*, **131**, 401–4 (1967)

104. Olson, R. A., Jennings, W. H., Butler, W. L., *Biochim. Biophys. Acta*, **88**, 331–37 (1964)

105. Lavorel, J., *Biochim. Biophys. Acta*, **88**, 20–36 (1964)

106. Duysens, L. N. M., *Nature*, **168**, 548–50 (1951)

107. Boardman, N. K., Anderson, J. M., *Nature*, **203**, 166–67 (1964)

108. Anderson, J. M., Boardman, N. K., *Biochim. Biophys. Acta*, **112**, 403–21 (1966)

109. Anderson, J. M., Fork, D. C., Amesz, J., *Biochem. Biophys. Res. Commun.*, **23**, 874–79 (1966)

110. Vredenberg, W. J., Slooten, L., *Biochim. Biophys. Acta*, **143**, 583–94 (1967)

111. Kok, B., Rurainski, H. J., *Biochim. Biophys. Acta*, **126**, 584–87 (1966)

112. Vredenberg, W. J., Duysens, L. N. M., *Biochim. Biophys. Acta*, **94**, 355–70 (1965)

113. Amesz, J., Fork, D. C., *Biochim. Biophys. Acta*, **143**, 97–107 (1967)

114. Goedheer, J. C., *Biochim. Biophys. Acta*, **102**, 73–89 (1965)
115. Butler, W. L., *Biochem. Biophys. Res. Commun.*, **2**, 419–22 (1960)
116. Goedheer, J. C., *Biochim. Biophys. Acta*, **51**, 494–504 (1961)
117. Kok, B., Malkin, S., Owens, O., Forbush, B., *Energy Conversion by the Photosynthetic Apparatus*, 446–59, *Brookhaven Symp. Biol.*, **19**, (1967)
118. Ke, B., *Plant Physiol.*, **42**, 1310–12 (1967)
119. Sauer, K., Park, R. B., *Biochemistry*, **4**, 2791–98 (1965)
120. Joliot, P., Joliot, A., *Biochim. Biophys. Acta*, **153**, 625–34 (1968)
121. Biggins, J., Sauer, K., *Biochim. Biophys. Acta*, **88**, 655–57 (1965)
122. Horio, T., San Pietro, A., *Proc. Natl. Acad. Sci. U.S.*, **51**, 1226–31 (1964)
123. Mayne, B. C., Brown, A. H., *Studies on Microalgae and Photosynthetic Bacteria* (Ed. by Japan. Soc. Plant Physiol., 347–52, Univ. Tokyo Press, Tokyo, 1963)
124. Fork, D.C., *Plant Physiol.*, **38**, 323–32 (1963)
125. French, C. S., Fork, D. C., Brown, J. S., *Carnegie Inst. Wash. Yearbook*, **60**, 362–63 (1961)
126. Govindjee, Bazzaz, M., *Photochem. Photobiol.*, **6**, 885–94 (1967)
127. Schmidt-Mende, P., Witt, H. T., *Z. Naturforsch.*, **23b**, 228–35 (1968)
128. Rumberg, B., *Z. Naturforsch.*, **19b**, 707–17 (1964)
129. Avron, M., Ben-Hayyim, G., *Intern. Congr. Photosyn. Res., June, 1968, Freudenstadt, Germany* (In press)
130. Hoch, G., Martin, I., *Arch. Biochem. Biophys.*, **102**, 430–38 (1963)
131. Schwartz, M., *Biochim. Biophys. Acta*, **131**, 559–70 (1967)
132. Sauer, K., Biggins, J., *Biochim. Biophys. Acta*, **102**, 55–72 (1965)
133. Joliot, P., Joliot, A., Kok, B., *Biochim. Biophys. Acta*, **153**, 635–52 (1968)
134. Müller, A., Fork, D. C., Witt, H. T., *Z. Naturforsch.*, **18b**, 142–45 (1963)
135. Myers, J., Graham, J. R., *Plant Physiol.*, **38**, 105–16 (1963)
136. Govindjee, *Photosynthetic Mechanisms of Green Plants*, 318–34 Natl. Acad. Sci.-Natl. Res. Council, Publ. 1145, Washington, D.C., 1963)
137. Schwartz, M., *Biochim. Biophys. Acta*, **131**, 548–58 (1967)
138. Yin, H. C., Fan, I. J., Shen, G. M., Li, T. Y., Shen, Y. K., *Sci. Sinica (Peking)*, **14**, 1184–92 (1965)
139. Schwartz, M., *Nature*, **219**, 915–19 (1968)
140. Schwartz, M. (Personal communication)
141. Hill, R., Walker, D. A., *Plant Physiol.*, **34**, 240–45 (1959)
142. Dilley, R. A., Vernon, L. P., *Proc. Natl. Acad. Sci. U.S.*, **57**, 395–400 (1967)
143. Duysens, L. N. M., *Science*, **120**, 353–54 (1954)
144. Kok, B., Cooper, B., Yang, L., *Studies on Microalgae and Photosynthetic Bacteria*, 373–96 (Univ. of Tokyo Press, 1963)
145. Rumberg, B., *Nature*, **204**, 860–62 (1964)
146. Govindjee, Govindjee, R., *Photochem. Photobiol.*, **4**, 793–801 (1965)
147. Rubinstein, D., *Biochim. Biophys. Acta*, **109**, 41–44 (1965)
148. Fork, D. C., Amesz, J., Anderson, J. M., *Energy Conversion by the Photosynthetic Apparatus, Brookhaven Symp. Biol.*, **19**, 81–94 (1967)
149. Kok, B., Hoch, G., *La Photosynthèse*, 93–107 (Centre Natl. Rech. Sci., Paris, 1963)
150. de Kouchkovsky, Y., Fork, D. C., *Carnegie Inst. Yearbook*, **63**, 441–47 (1964)
151. Rubinstein, D., *Abstr. WH 13 Biophys. Soc. Meeting, 9th, San Francisco, 1965*
152. Fork, D. C., Urbach, W., *Proc. Natl. Acad. Sci. U.S.*, **53**, 1307–15 (1965)
153. Rubin, L., *Biol. Nauki*, **3**, 60–66 (1967)
154. Witt, H. T., Müller, A., Rumberg, B., *La Photosynthèse*, 43–73 (Centre Natl. Rech. Sci., Paris, 1963)
155. Rubinstein, D., Rabinowitch, E., *Biophys.. J.*, **4**, 107–13 (1964)
156. Fork, D. C., de Kouchkovsky, Y., *Photochem. Photobiol.*, **5**, 609–19 (1966)
157. Vidaver, W., French, C. S., *Plant Physiol.*, **40**, 7–12 (1965)
158. Rumberg, B., *Nature*, **204**, 860–62 (1964)
159. Highkin, H. R., Frenkel, A. W., *Plant Physiol.*, **37**, 814–20 (1962)
160. Fork, D. C., Amesz, J., *Carnegie Inst. Wash. Yearbook*, **66**, 160–65 (1967)

161. Fork, D. C., Amesz, J., *Photochem. Photobiol.*, **6**, 913–18 (1967)
162. Fork, D. C., *Carnegie Inst. Wash. Yearbook*, 67 (In press)
163. Junge, W., Witt, H. T., *Intern. Congr. Photosyn. Res., June, 1968, Freudenstadt, W. Germany* (In press)
164. Gingras, G., *Physiol. Végétale*, **4**, 1–65 (1966)
165. Haxo, F. T., Blinks, L. R., *J. Gen. Physiol.*, **33**, 389–422 (1950)
166. Bishop, N. I., *Photochem. Photobiol.*, **6**, 621–28 (1967)
167. Clayton, R. K., *J. Theoret. Biol.*, **14**, 173–86 (1967)
168. Joliot, A., Joliot, P., *Compt. Rend.*, **258**, 4622–25 (1964)
169. Joliot, A., *Biochim. Biophys. Acta*, **126**, 587–90 (1966)
170. Duysens, L. N. M., in *Energy Conversion by the Photosynthetic Apparatus, Brookhaven Symp. Biol.*, **19**, 71–80 (1967)
171. Tumerman, L. A., Sorokin, E. M., *Molekulyarnaya Biologiya*, **1**, 628–38 (1967)
172. Müller, A., Lumry, R., *Proc. Natl. Acad. Sci. U.S.*, **54**, 1479–85 (1965)
173. Müller, A., Lumry, R., Walker, M. S., *Photochem. Photobiol.* (In press)
174. Fork, D. C., Amesz, J., *Biochim. Biophys. Acta*, **143**, 266–68 (1967)
175. Amesz, J., Fork, D. C., *Photochem. Photobiol.*, **6**, 903–12 (1967)
176. Myers, J., in *Photosynthetic Mechanism of Green Plants*, 301–17 (Natl. Acad. Sci.-Natl. Res. Council, Washington, D.C., Publ. 1145, 766 pp., 1963)
177. Bannister, T. T., Vrooman, M. J., in *Photosynthetic Mechanisms of Green Plants*, 391–99 (Natl. Acad. Sci.-Natl. Res. Council, Washington, D.C., Publ. 1145, 766 pp., 1963)
178. Clayton, R. K., *J. Theoret. Biol.*, **5**, 497–99 (1963)
179. Kok, B., in *Photosynthetic Mechanisms of Green Plants*, 45–55 (Natl. Acad. Sci.-Natl. Res. Council, Washington, D.C., Publ. 1145, 766 pp., 1963)
180. Emerson, R., Lewis, C. M., *Am. J. Botany*, **30**, 105–78 (1943)
181. Fork, D. C., in *Photosynthetic Mechanisms of Green Plants*, 352–61 (Natl. Acad. Sci.-Natl. Res. Council, Washington, D. C., Publ. 1145, 766 pp., 1963)
182. Haxo, F. T., in *Comparative Biochemistry of Photoreactive Pigments*, 339–60 (Allen, M. B., Ed., Academic Press, N.Y.—London, 437 pp., 1960)
183. Brody, M., Emerson, R., *J. Gen. Physiol.*, **43**, 251–64 (1959)
184. Malkin, S., *Biophys. J.*, **7**, 629–49 (1967)
185. Eley, J. H., Jr., Myers, J., *Plant Physiol.*, **42**, 598–607 (1967)
186. Duysens, L. N. M., *Arch. Biol. (Liège)*, **76**, 251–75 (1965)
187. Williams, W. P., *Biochim. Biophys. Acta*, **153**, 484–89 (1968)
188. Gingras, G., Lemasson, C., Fork, D. C., *Biochim. Biophys. Acta*, **69**, 438–40 (1963)
189. Schwartz, M., *Biochim. Biophys. Acta*, **131**, 559–70 (1967)
190. Fewson, C. A., Black, C. C., Gibbs, M., Gordon, S. A., Elliwanger, P., *Plant Physiol.*, **37**, Suppl. lxiii (1962)
191. Kelly, J., Sauer, K., *Biochemistry*, **4**, 2798–802 (1965)
192. Avron, M., Ben-Hayyim, G., *Intern. Congr. Photosyn. Res., June, 1968, Freudenstadt, W. Germany* (In press)
193. Robinson, G. W., *Ann. Rev. Phys. Chem.*, **15**, 311–48 (1964)
194. Robinson, G. W., in *Energy Conversion by the Photosynthetic Apparatus, Brookhaven Symp. Biol.*, **19**, 16–45 (1967)
195. Pearlstein, R. M., in *Energy Conversion by the Photosynthetic Apparatus, Brookhaven Symp. Biol.*, **19**, 8–14 (1967)
196. Förster, T., *Ann. Physik.*, **2**, 55–75 (1948)
197. Förster, T., *Fluoreszenz Organischer Verbindungen* (Vandenhoeck und Ruprecht, Göttingen, 312 pp., 1951)
198. Weber, G., in *Comparative Biochemistry of Photoreactive Systems*, 395–411 (Allen, M. B., Ed., Academic Press, N.Y.—London, 437 pp., 1960)
199. Pearlstein, R. M., *Proc. Natl. Acad. Sci. U.S.*, **52**, 824–30 (1964)
200. Tweet, A. G., Bellamy, W. D., Gaines, G. L., Jr., *J. Chem. Phys.*, **41**, 2068–77 (1964)
201. Knox, R. S., *Physica*, **39**, 361–86 (1968)
202. Bay, Z., Pearlstein, R. M., *Proc. Natl. Acad. Sci. U.S.*, **50**, 1071–78 (1963)

STOMATAL CONTROL

By Israel Zelitch

Department of Biochemistry, The Connecticut Agricultural Experiment Station, New Haven

Since this subject was last reviewed here in 1963 (1), the striking demonstration of the importance of leaf stomata in transpiration and photosynthesis, and the ability to exercise relatively specific biochemical control of stomatal apertures, has stimulated considerable experimental work and discussion about stomatal physiology. In 1965, in *Biological Reviews* (2), I summarized the work with chemical inhibitors and reviewed the evidence for the role of glycolic acid metabolism in stomatal opening in the light. In the same issue of that journal, Meidner & Mansfield (3) concluded that the CO_2 concentration in the intercellular spaces of leaves near the guard cells largely controls stomatal activity. Heath, Mansfield & Meidner (4) have stressed the "complexity" of stomatal movement and disputed the suggested participation of glycolic acid in stomatal opening. Pallas (5) also doubted that a universal mechanism could account for the observations at hand. Others (6–8) have independently called attention to the error in the so-called perimeter law, which has been learned for years by students of botany, and demonstrated that, except in still air, stomatal diffusive resistance controls transpiration at all stomatal apertures. Such control may be used to alter the hydrologic cycle in nature (7). Most recently, and further confirming that the control of stomatal opening and closing is an exciting and lively subject, Levitt (9) has rejected all current interpretations and has loyally returned to the ideas of a former teacher in his search for the truth.

It is curious that the mechanism of stomatal movement should stimulate so much controversy, and one must admit at the outset that the mechanism cannot presently be given with precision. This is likely not because the process is unusually complex. It is probably simpler than many other physiological processes that are already better understood. Part of the difficulty in the interpretation of experiments with guard cells comes from the fact that guard cell function is dependent to some degree on other cells, and some of the difficulty also arises because many research workers have failed to use adequate controls and thus have observed indirect effects on stomatal movement.

Guard cells occupy a small portion of the epidermis, and either intact leaf tissue or, at best, epidermal strips must be used as experimental material. Stomatal opening depends on an increase in turgor in the guard cells relative to the adjacent epidermal cells. Thus the difference between the osmotic value in the two neighboring cells determines the degree of stomatal opening, as has been emphasized recently by Stålfelt (10). In most species, stomatal opening and increased osmotic value in the guard cells occurs in the light. This may result from photosynthetic production of organic solutes by the chloroplasts of the guard cells or from the "pumping" of ions or other solutes into the guard cells from adjacent cells. The turgor of the guard cells at any time is also dependent on the cell membranes through which water must pass. Under some conditions, stomatal opening may result from decreased turgor in adjacent epidermal cells (10).

Most of the factors that affect photosynthesis and the water relations in leaves also influence stomatal movement. One must take care to insure that stomatal changes observed were not caused, for example, by water deficits rather than by the factor under investigation. In this paper, I will examine some of the apparently conflicting results on stomatal control and attempt to sort out some of the misunderstandings in the literature. Finally, the evidence in favor of a potassium ion "pump" to account for stomatal opening in the light will be summarized.

Measurement of Stomatal Apertures

Several rapid and reliable methods for the assay of stomatal width have become available in recent years, but no single technique is best for all plant species. The casting of leaf impressions in silicone rubber, followed by the preparation of replicas of the cast with a cellulose acetate film, was invented by Sampson (11) and has been used extensively in this laboratory for the measurement of stomatal dimensions (12). By this method, numerous diverse leaf samples, including leaf disks, may be observed at the same time without affecting the leaf environment. The impressions provide a permanent record, and the stomatal widths can be measured accurately at one's convenience. With care, such casts can be made repeatedly on the same area of a leaf without visible damage to the tissues. Its simplicity has no doubt led to its widespread use as a method of observing and recording stomatal movement by university undergraduates and research workers and even by school children. The major limitation of the silicone rubber technique is that it cannot be used with accuracy when the apertures are much narrower than 1 μ, or with species in which the stomata are recessed in pits rather than being located on the plane of the leaf surface.

Other methods of preparing leaf replicas have been used by several groups recently. Stoddard (13) characterized the epidermis of various leaves directly from cellulose acetate films. Others (14, 15) have made excellent leaf impressions with plastic films. Such materials require considerable time to set before the films can be stripped from the leaf surface, during which stomatal widths may change. They also usually cause damage to the tissue being examined.

In addition to these indirect but visual methods, some new types of porometers, in particular a convenient diffusion porometer, have been described that have advantages for certain purposes. The rapid estimation of stomatal aperture is now possible with a device that senses the humidity gradient next to a leaf, as described by Wallihan (16). This technique was modified by Turner & Waggoner (17) to observe stomatal changes in needles of red pine (*Pinus resinosa*). It was not possible to do this easily by any other method in pine needles except by the relatively crude procedure of observing the degree of penetration by organic solvents. However, even the solvent infiltration method may be useful, as was shown by Moreshet & Stanhill (18), who found a linear relation between infiltration index and porometer measurements in cotton leaves in the greenhouse and outdoors.

A viscous-flow porometer that permit measurement of the rate of air pressure drop through a leaf in a convenient manner was invented by Alvim (19). Waggoner (20) showed with barley leaves that such an instrument acts according to predicted physical diffusion theory, and that the results with the porometer are well correlated with stomatal width in the range from 0.8 μ to 4.2 μ, as determined from silicone rubber impressions (20, Fig. 4).

Nevertheless, Glinka & Meidner (21) considered porometers, which do not reveal stomatal dimensions directly but measure diffusive resistance, superior and have written that "detailed investigations into the mechanism of stomatal movements cannot be carried out with silicone-rubber impressions, however useful a tool for approximate studies they may be." They also incorrectly attribute to me the opinion that in the impression method "anything up to 2 μ is practically indistinguishable from a closed pore." Besides the contrary evidence with barley leaves already mentioned (20), Shimshi (22, Fig. 1) had earlier found an excellent correlation ($r = 0.938$) in maize leaves between stomatal apertures in the range between 0.8 μ and 6 μ obtained from silicone impressions and permeability as determined with an Alvim porometer. Another confirmation of such a relationship in the range between 1.2 μ and 3.0 μ is shown for tobacco leaf tissue in Figure 1. Thus a lack of good methods for evaluating stomatal movement does not now seem to be limiting progress in understanding how guard cells function or in finding better methods of controlling their movement.

EFFECT OF WATER RELATIONS

Since the opening of stomata depends primarily on an uptake of water by the guard cells, it is understandable that severe water stress will inhibit stomatal opening. To avoid this pitfall, many investigators have used the technique of floating leaf disks on water, a circumstance under which water deficits cannot exist. Under such conditions (12, 23), stomata in tobacco leaf disks in the light in air open at about the same rate and to the same extent as is usually observed in the intact leaf. When disks on water with open stomata are placed in the dark, the stomata close more rapidly than

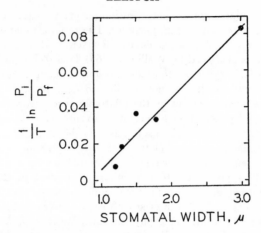

FIG. 1. Comparison of leaf permeability (Alvim porometer) and mean stomatal width (silicone rubber impressions) in tobacco leaf disks. Pairs of disks from a leaf kept in darkness were floated on water at 30° and 2000 ft-c and duplicate samples were taken at various times for the two kinds of determinations. In the porometer measurements (21), the initial pressure (P_i) was 200 mm Hg, and the final pressure (P_f) was determined after 10 sec.

they open, and when returned to the light a second time, the stomata open again at their initial rate. Thus the opening in the light and closing in the dark is an easily reversible process, in contrast to other types of stomatal movement that can be induced and which will be discussed later. In addition, Stålfelt (24) has shown in leaf disks of *Vicia faba* and *Rununculus repens* that stomatal opening can occur readily in the dark in a CO_2-free atmosphere only if the leaf tissue has a slight water deficit. This also serves to distinguish this kind of stomatal opening from the normal opening that occurs in the light in fully turgid leaf tissue.

When plants encounter a drought, the osmotic value of the epidermal cells may become higher than that of the guard cells even in the light, and stomata may not open at all (10). The midday closure of stomata is a common occurrence in many species. It may occur even in a wet soil environment because of the water deficit in the leaves caused by a greater water loss by transpiration than can be supplied by the roots. Macdowall (25) showed that midday closure in tobacco leaves occurs more readily in older leaves. In a comparison of the effect of drought on stomatal movement in sorghum and maize leaves, Glover (26) showed that after a period of one week only sorghum stomata opened. After two weeks of drought, the stomata in maize were permanently damaged, although there was still only a slight effect in sorghum stomata as evidenced by an almost complete recovery 5 days after the plants were watered. Thus the ability of stomata to recover from a severe water deficit may be an important factor in apparent drought resistance. Bannister (27) found that the relative leaf turgidity in a given species at which stomata will close may vary with the habitat in which the plant grows. All of these studies serve to emphasize that when the stomatal mechanism is under investigation, the leaf tissue should either by turgid or at least the water status of the leaf must be kept constant while other variables are studied.

Light Requirement for Stomatal Opening

Need for photosynthesis.—It has never been shown that guard cells devoid of chloroplasts are capable of opening in the light. Virgin (28) observed that the development of the stomatal light response in etiolated wheat leaves, after a short light exposure needed to initiate chloroplast formation, closely followed the increase in chlorophyll-*a* content of the tissue. This suggested that the photosynthetic process must be concerned with the increase in turgor of the guard cells. Recently, Poskuta & Tomczyk (29) carried out similar experiments with etiolated onion leaves, in which no starch is synthesized in the guard cells. Stomata did not open well until 3 or 4 days after the period of illumination that initiated chloroplast development, when the chlorophyll concentration was about 75 per cent of that of green control leaves.

Several investigations have also been carried out on the effect of wavelength of light on the opening of stomata. The most significant study of this kind was described by Kuiper (30), who did his experiments on the maintenance of already open stomata in light with epidermal strips of *Senecio odoris* that were essentially devoid of mesophyll cells. The light was supplied by a high intensity spectrograph. Maximal opening occurred at 432 mμ and at 675 mμ, the same maxima as were found in the absorption spectrum of spinach chloroplasts. This work provides strong evidence that photosynthesis in the guard cells themselves is responsible for the maintenance of stomatal opening in the light. With these epidermal strips, 2(3,4-dichlorophenyl)-1,1-dimethyl urea (DCMU) at 10^{-5} M, a well known inhibitor of Photosystem II and noncyclic photophosphorylation (31), closed the stomata completely in the light. This observation raises the question of whether photosynthesis is needed to produce carbon compounds in the guard cells or is primarily required for the production of ATP in the light.

Stomata up or down.—Stålfelt (32) described experiments from which he concluded that net CO_2 uptake (the "production effect") played an important part in light opening. He measured stomatal opening in leaf sections from three species which contain stomata only on their lower surface, either when the stomata were floated down against the water or up facing the

TABLE I

EFFECT OF CHANGES IN THE GAS PHASE ON STOMATAL OPENING IN
ROSE LEAF DISKS IN LIGHT

Expt. No.	Time in Light, *min*	Gas Phase	Increase in Stomatal Width, μ	
			Stomata Up	Stomata Down
1	30	Still air	0.4	0.2
	90	Still air	1.1	0.3
	240	Still air	4.5	2.5
2	90	Flowing air	2.5	1.5
	90	Flowing CO_2-free air	2.2	1.8
3	120	Flowing air	2.8	
	120	Flowing CO_2-free air	2.5	

Pentafoliate rose leaves (stomata are present only on the lower surface in this species) were excised and kept with their petioles in water in the dark for 1 hr. Leaf disks (1.6 cm diameter) were cut from the three terminal leaflets and floated in pairs in 2 ml of water with the stomata either facing the gas phase (stomata up) or against the water (stomata down). At the end of the times shown at 30° and 1000 ft-c (a mirror reflected approximately the same light to the lower surface), impressions of the lower epidermis were cast in silicone rubber to determine stomatal widths.

In Experiment 1, the disks were floated in partly-covered beakers (12). In Experiments 2 and 3, moistened air or CO_2-free air was passed through the atmosphere over the disks in 25 ml Erlenmeyer flasks at a rate of several flask volumes per minute (23), starting 5 min before the light was turned on.

atmosphere. When stomata were down there could be little net photosynthesis, and indeed he found that stomata opened two to three times as wide in from 3 to 6 hr when the stomata were up (32).

Table I, Experiment 1, shows a similar result with leaf disks from still another species, the rose. However, when the stomata were up (Experiments 2 and 3), they opened nearly as well in flowing CO_2-free air as in normal air, showing that lack of net photosynthesis did not greatly inhibit stomatal opening in this tissue. This suggests that sufficient photosynthesis can occur in guard cells from internally derived CO_2 to permit good rates of stomatal opening in the light, and the poorer opening when the stomata were down must have been for a different reason, such as the poorer availability of oxygen (23), rather than from a lack of net CO_2 fixation.

Opening of stomata in the dark.—Wide opening of stomatal pores in the dark is characteristic of crassulacean plants, whose metabolism is geared to net CO_2 fixation in the dark, as was shown by Nishida (33). Even in such species, dark opening occurred only after a light period, and the magnitude of the opening was related to the duration of illumination in the preceding day. A slight "endogenous" diurnal opening of stomata takes place in the dark in normal air in some species, as Stålfelt found in intact leaves of *Vicia faba* (34). When the leaves were excised, however, opening in the dark occurred only in an atmosphere of CO_2-free air, suggesting that this kind of opening differs from the usual opening in the light that takes place readily in excised leaves. Another difference was that the dark opening (34) was also very much smaller after the first 24-hr period. The "endogenous" dark opening was less than 20 per cent of that in the light, and in the absence of a water deficit was only 2 per cent as great (35). Dark opening occurs best in the presence of a water deficit (24), providing another distinguishing characteristic from the light opening which takes place so readily in fully turgid tissue (12).

Mansfield (36) has described dark stomatal opening in CO_2-free air in *Xanthium* leaves and showed that the pores were always smaller than in normal air in the light. He also indicated that, in continuous darkness, stomata closed partially several hours after reaching a maximal aperture. In contrast, stomata that open in the light remain fully open under continuous illumination for at least 10 hr (12, 23). Thus it would appear that in all cases where opening in the dark has been observed, its characteristics are sufficiently different from the normal light opening to suggest that a different mechanism operates in the dark, and it may bear little relation to the light-requiring process that is common to all but plants with crassulacean type metabolism.

Effects of blue light.—Mansfield & Meidner (37) examined stomatal opening in *Xanthium* at low light intensities in a closed system at the CO_2 compensation point. There was little difference between red and blue light on the compensation point (110 to 115 ppm CO_2 at 21°), but stomatal opening was greater in blue light. Blue light was also more effective in *Allium cepa* (38). Raschke (39) investigated opening in *Vicia faba* in CO_2-free air in blue light. When the pores were open maximally, a change to an atmosphere of nitrogen produced a much increased stomatal opening. When the gas phase was changed back to CO_2-free air, they returned to their former opening, but then a second exposure to nitrogen produced very little increase in width. Since opening in the light is inhibited in an atmosphere of nitrogen (23), and opening in light and closing in darkness is freely reversible (12), the blue light effect may also be related to the dark opening processes, but does not appear to be important in the normal opening mechanism in the light.

CO_2 CONCENTRATION IN THE INTERCELLULAR SPACES

Stomatal opening in CO_2-free air in darkness.—During the last 20 years, considerable attention has been paid to the hypothesis that opening in the light results from the lowering of the CO_2 concentration in the substomatal spaces, and closing in the dark is caused by the increase in CO_2 from dark respiration. The greatest support for this view comes from the observations that, in some species, stomatal opening occurs in the dark and is sometimes accelerated in a CO_2-free atmosphere. As indicated earlier, such dark opening appears to differ in a number of respects from the opening normally observed in the light, and in any case no reasonable biochemical explanation for such a CO_2 hypothesis has yet been suggested.

A slow (7-hr) stomatal opening by leaf disks of *Vicia faba* in the dark in CO_2-free air was described by Stålfelt (40), who also found that the increase in the surplus in the osmotic value of the guard cells over that in the epidermal cells was well correlated with the increase in pore width. Longuet (41) showed how critical the CO_2 concentration is in order to obtain dark opening of *Pelargonium zonale* stomata. At 0.03 per cent CO_2 in air the stomata were closed, but when lower than 0.02 per cent or greater than 2 per cent to 4 per cent CO_2, the stomata opened. These experiments further emphasize difficulties in accepting a hypothesis of stomatal movement based largely on the CO_2 concentration.

Stomatal closure by high CO_2 concentration in light.—In spite of the uncertainties about the role of internal CO_2 concentration in the normal range on opening in the dark (or light), the effect of high concentrations of CO_2 on stomatal closure in the light is an easily observable phenomenon. Pallas (42) studied the effect of increasing CO_2 levels on transpiration of several species, and found, based on the concentration at which the transpiration rate remained constant with further increases of CO_2, that stomata were closed at the following concentrations: tomato, 0.1 per cent; cotton, 0.1 per cent; maize, 0.2 per cent; and sorghum, 0.3 per cent. In tobacco leaf disks floated on water in the light, CO_2 levels above 0.2 per cent in air also inhibit stomatal opening (43). High concentrations of CO_2 such as these are known to greatly alter the nature of the products formed in photosynthesis (2, 44), particularly the synthesis of glycolic acid and hence its metabolic products, and this could be responsible for stomatal closure.

Raschke (45) used leaf sections of *Zea mays* to show that the linear light intensity requirement for stomatal opening is the same in atmospheres of air, CO_2-free air, and nitrogen. He therefore concluded that opening is not dependent on CO_2 assimilation. Such an interpretation is uncertain because there is a constant supply of CO_2 present from respiration (and including photorespiration in most species) inside leaves. Moreover, the CO_2 concentration inside a leaf would be considerable at the beginning of a period in the light no matter what the atmosphere might be outside. I have also observed with maize and tobacco leaf disks floating on water that the rate and extent of stomatal opening in the light is the same in air as in CO_2-free air (46). In intact maize leaves, however, Moss (47) found that stomatal

TABLE II

CO₂ CONCENTRATION AT MID-STOMA IN A SIMULATED TOBACCO LEAF AT 30°
(From Waggoner, 51)

CO₂ Conc. in Atmosphere, ppm	CO₂ Concentration at Mid-Stoma, ppm Light Intensity, $ly\ min^{-1}$		
	0.1	0.4	1.2
100	95	93	95
300	260	252	253
600	516	491	488
	CO₂ Compensation Point, ppm		
	71	61	76
	Net Photosynthesis at 300 ppm CO₂, $mg\ dm^{-2}\ hr^{-1}$		
	7.9	14.6	15.9

opening is inhibited as the CO_2 concentration is raised from zero to 400 ppm, and the inhibition is greatest at higher leaf temperatures and disappeared at 14°. Thus the closing at warmer temperatures in intact leaves may also have been related to leaf water deficits.

Changing CO₂ concentration inside leaves in light.—Stomatal opening can be studied in leaves of different species that vary greatly in their CO_2 compensation point, the steady state concentration of CO_2 in a closed, illuminated system. In leaves or leaf disks of maize, the CO_2 compensation point is less than 10 ppm (21, 48, 49), while in most species such as tobacco leaf tissue this figure is at least 50 ppm under usual conditions (21, 50). The CO_2 compensation point characteristically increases greatly with rise in leaf temperature in species like tobacco (50). Since the concentration of CO_2 is the same inside and outside the leaf at the CO_2 compensation point, and it is easily measured by comparing stomatal opening in an open system (in flowing air) with that in a closed system (at the CO_2 compensation point), one can observe if there is any effect at widely differing internal CO_2 concentrations.

Estimates of the CO_2 levels inside maize and tobacco leaves in an open and closed system have been presented (46), and a more detailed analysis is available in Table II. These results were obtained from a rational model of a leaf, similar to tobacco, which was constructed by Waggoner (51) to account for net photosynthesis by incorporating the effects of such factors as light, temperature, CO_2 concentration, respiration, etc. This model simulates the activity of real leaves in a number of ways. It also shows that the CO_2

concentration at mid-stoma is always considerably greater in normal air than at the CO_2 compensation point at light intensities from one-tenth to that of full sunlight. In maize, these differences would be still greater. Nevertheless, I found that stomata in leaf disks open at the same rate and to the same extent in moving air as at the CO_2 compensation point in both species (46). Stomata also open wider at warmer temperatures in a closed system in spite of the higher internal concentration of CO_2 (46). Hence the CO_2 concentration inside leaves in the normal range need not have a pronounced effect on stomatal opening in the light.

If stomatal closing in the dark resulted from an increased CO_2 concentration in the substomatal spaces, closing in the dark should be inhibited by CO_2-free air. However, it was found (37) that the initial rate of closing in *Xanthium* is the same in both atmospheres, although the final extent of closing is less in the absence of CO_2. These experiments also indicate that CO_2 concentration does not have an important role in the normal opening and closing of stomata.

Inhibitors of Stomatal Movement

Experiments with biochemical inhibitors of stomatal movement have provided crucial evidence of the relation between stomatal aperture and rates of net photosynthesis and transpiration, and they have provided some insight into the biochemical mechanism responsible for this movement. It was realized in the beginning that since guard cells are located on the outer surfaces of leaves, the greatest chance of achieving specificity in controlling stomata with inhibitors would likely be by supplying such compounds as a spray on leaves or by floating leaf tissue in solutions (12, 52, 53). Allowing substances to reach guard cells through roots, stems, or petioles, and hence making it more likely that inhibitors will affect mesophyll cells as well as guard cells, introduces unnecessary complications in studies on the mechanism of stomatal action. It also seems obvious that, in biochemical studies with inhibitors, one should use a compound at the lowest possible effective concentration, for the shortest time necessary. One should then confirm by using independent chemical measurements that the biochemical changes expected are indeed being carried out. It is unfortunate that in a number of recently published papers few of these precautions were considered, and hence there is serious doubt about the conclusions derived from such work.

If a substance acts specifically on the guard cells of a leaf to close stomata, it can be shown from diffusion theory (52) that the transpiration rate should be inhibited to a greater extent than net photosynthesis. On the other hand, if photosynthesis in the mesophyll cells is also seriously interfered with by an inhibitor that also closes stomata, the decrease in photosynthesis would be greater than that of transpiration. Thus a comparison of these two processes provides a simple test of the specificity of a substance on guard cell metabolism.

One group of workers (4) has been dismayed by the array of substances that interfere with stomatal movement and considers this broad range a part of the evidence that there is no primary mechanism of stomatal opening. However, oxygen uptake in dark respiration is carried out by the cytochrome oxidase reaction, but respiration may be interfered with by many different kinds of inhibitors that may affect glycolysis, the citric acid cycle, or the cytochrome oxidase reaction itself. Inhibitors, when used judiciously, should help to unravel the stomatal mechanism just as they have the respiratory process.

Inhibitors are known that interfere with stomatal opening, prevent closing of already open stomata in the dark, and substances are known that even stimulate opening. The action of many of these compounds has already been summarized (7, 23, 43, 46). Only those inhibitors about whose action a great deal is known, or whose unusual properties have only recently been described, will be discussed here.

Inhibitors of photosynthesis and phosphorylation.—The substituted ureas DCMU and CMU, which are herbicides and inhibit the Hill reaction at low concentrations (31), close stomata in the light in epidermal strips (30) and in leaf disks (46) at concentrations less than 5×10^{-5} M. Allaway & Mansfield (54) supplied CMU at 1×10^{-4} M through the petiole to excised leaves of *Rumex* and *Vicia faba* after the stomata were opened in light. The leaves continuously absorbed the CMU for at least several hours, and the stomata closed to various extents in normal air. When CO_2-free air was then passed under pressure through the leaves treated with CMU, the stomata opened somewhat in comparison to those of leaves provided with normal air. However, no leaf was treated with CO_2-free air in the light in the absence of CMU for comparison. If opening was in fact greatly stimulated by CO_2-free air under conditions that appear to have been so adverse for photosynthesis and photophosphorylation by all leaf cells, it might indicate that the enhancement of opening by CO_2-free air bears little connection with the normal process of stomatal opening in the light and might be caused by indirect effects on cells other than guard cells.

Stomatal closure in the light is also caused by atrazine (2-chloro-4-ethylamino-6-isopropylamino-s-triazine), another herbicide that inhibits the oxygen-evolving reactions of photosynthesis. Smith & Buchholtz (55) showed that this substance inhibits transpiration and closes stomata when sprayed on bean leaves. This inhibitor diminished transpiration in cotton, maize, and soybean plants when supplied in the nutrient solution (56), and practically stopped transpiration within several hours when sprayed on leaves of *Vicia faba* (57).When applied to the soil at herbicidal concentrations immediately after planting, stomata of maize were unaffected by atrazine (58). No publications indicate whether transpiration was inhibited more than photosynthesis when stomata were closed by treatment of leaves with atrazine.

Growth regulators.—Another growth regulator, 2,4,5-trichlorophenoxy-acetic acid, may be added to the list of those already known to inhibit stomatal opening. When sprayed on apricot leaves at low concentrations (59), stomata were closed, and the effect persisted for about two weeks. Kozinka (60) showed that stomata were closed and transpiration was decreased in barley seedlings sprayed with the potassium salt of 2-methyl-4-chlorophenoxyacetic acid at concentrations from 10^{-3} M to 10^{-6} M.

Livnè & Vaadia (61) made the interesting observation that when excised barley seedlings were placed in the light in a solution of 10^{-5} M kinetin, stomatal opening was greatly enhanced within 2 hr. These results were confirmed by Meidner (62) and by Luke & Freeman (63). The latter group indicated that wheat and oat leaves were more sensitive than barley. The wider stomatal opening induced by kinetin resulted in an increase in net photosynthesis of 12 per cent (62), as might be expected from the decreased stomatal diffusive resistance (52).

Inhibitors acting directly on membranes.—Water must pass through cell membranes in order to make the guard cells turgid, and cell organelles also play an essential part in the opening of stomata. Alkenylsuccinic acids and their derivatives, CH_3-$(CH_2)_n$-$CH=CH$-CH_2-$CH(COOH)$-CH_2COOH, are surface-active agents that effectively close stomata in leaf disks (64). Kuiper has shown (65, 66) that these compounds at low concentrations enhance the permeability of bean roots to water, and the same chemical structures required to demonstrate this activity are needed to inhibit stomatal opening. These inhibitors probably act on membranes through the activity of their hydrocarbon chain of appropriate length on the lipid portion of membranes. Siegenthaler & Packer (67) observed that the monomethyl ester of decenylsuccinic acid, between 10^{-3} M and 10^{-4} M inhibits electron transport and photophosphorylation as well as changes in the volume of chloroplast membranes in isolated spinach chloroplasts in the light. Baddeley & Hanson (68) observed that the same compound at 10^{-4} M and 10^{-5} M acts as an uncoupler of oxidative phosphorylation in isolated mitochondria from maize shoots and is similar in its mode of action to linoleic acid. Thus these inhibitors function on cellular organelles, as would be expected if they interfered with the behavior of the lipids of membranes.

The inhibitor most used in studies on decreasing transpiration through stomatal control is phenylmercuric acetate (52, 53). It probably forms mercaptides with the sulfhydryl groups of the protein in membranes, and this may account for the longer lasting inhibition than is usually observed with alkenylsuccinic acids. In isolated spinach chloroplast preparations, phenylmercuric acetate inhibits NADP reduction and accompanying non-cyclic photophosphorylation at concentrations between 10^{-4} M and 10^{-6} M (67). Rao, Fallin & Fang (69) observed with Hg^{203}-labeled phenylmercuric acetate supplied to pea roots that this substance is concentrated in the mitochondrial fraction in comparison with similarly labeled mercuric acetate. Mercuric acetate, in comparison with phenylmercuric acetate, has little effect on stomata (70).

Mansfield (71) apparently still retains the view that even substances like phenylmercuric acetate act on guard cells by inhibiting photosynthetic CO_2 uptake and thus increasing the CO_2 concentration inside the leaf. To test this, he carried out some experiments in which inhibitors were supplied through the cut petiole, a hazardous technique with reactive inhibitors for reasons already discussed. Other experiments were done with epidermal strips of *Vicia faba*. In an atmosphere of CO_2-free air, the stomata closed more slowly in 10^{-4} M phenylmercuric acetate than in normal air. Evidence, to be discussed later under antitranspirants, makes it highly unlikely that when phenylmercuric acetate is sprayed on leaves, the mechanism by which it closes stomata can be related to that suggested by Mansfield. Instead, its action must be primarily on the guard cells themselves, and these relatively few cells could hardly provide any large contribution to the total release or uptake of CO_2 inside a leaf.

Graniti (72) discovered that the fungus *Fusicoccum amygdali*, a pathogen causing almond and peach canker, when grown in submerged culture produces a substance that alters the water relations of plants. This compound, Fusicoccin A, has been characterized (73) and its structure is reminiscent of a substituted sterol glycoside (MW 680). When supplied to cut tomato leaves through the stem at 10^{-5} M, this natural product doubled the transpiration rate and increased stomatal opening much as has been mentioned for kinetin. It also slowed stomatal closure in the dark (A. Graniti & N. Turner, personal communication), in a manner similar to higher concentrations of azide (23).

Mansfield & Heath (74) indicated that natural "smog" had a small inhibitory effect on stomatal opening *Xanthium* leaves which was not permanent. Todd & Propst (75) found that ozone in the air reduced transpiration in bean, tomato, and *Coleus* leaves. It is possible that ozone will react with unsaturated groups in the lipid portion of membranes to induce a temporary stomatal closure.

Glycolic Acid Metabolism in Stomatal Opening

Since α-hydroxysulfonates, which are effective competitive inhibitors of the glycolate oxidase reaction, were found to inhibit stomatal opening in the light or to close already open stomata (12, 52), it seemed important to investigate the possible role of glycolate metabolism in stomatal movement. Experiments with these inhibitors, as well as a comparison of several environmental factors that affect the synthesis of glycolate and its oxidation, were first carried out by Zelitch & Walker (43) and have been extended more recently in order to examine the relation of these factors to stomatal opening in the light. The results are consistent in every instance with the postulated importance of glycolate metabolism and may be summarized as follows:

(a) The concentration of α-hydroxy-2-pyridinemethanesulfonic acid required to inhibit by 50 per cent the stomatal opening in tobacco leaf disks was about the same as that needed to inhibit glycolate synthesis 50 per cent under the same conditions (43).

(b) After stomata were opened in the light in leaf disks, 10^{-3} M sodium 1-hydroxy-1-decanesulfonate effectively closed stomata (in sodium tartrate buffer at pH 4.6), and this closure was reversed in a competitive manner by sodium glycolate (also buffered at pH 4.6). On the other hand, solutes like glucose, malate, or potassium chloride did not reverse the effect of the inhibitor under the same conditions. Glycolate also did not reverse stomatal closure induced by another inhibitor, phenylmercuric acetate, again emphasizing the specific nature of the action of this α-hydroxysulfonate and its connection with glycolate metabolism.

(c) The rate of stomatal opening by leaf disks in light was greater in air than in an atmosphere of nitrogen (23), and the synthesis of glycolate by the same tissue was likewise greatly stimulated in air in comparison with nitrogen (43).

(d) The rate and extent of stomatal opening in the light in leaf disks floating on water was the same in CO_2-free air as in normal air (46), while the rate of glycolate synthesis was only slightly less (27 per cent) in CO_2-free air compared with normal air (44). Stomatal opening was much less at CO_2 concentrations in the gas phase greater than about 0.2 per cent (42, 43), and marked inhibition of glycolate biosynthesis also occurred at concentrations of CO_2 above 0.2 per cent (43, 44).

(e) The closure of stomata in the light induced by 1.8 per cent CO_2 was reversed only by sodium glycolate in a comparison with a large number of metabolites and salts (43).

A number of lines of evidence thus indicate that glycolate metabolism plays an important part in the opening of stomata. This may result because glycolate metabolism serves to reoxidize NADPH, especially at low CO_2 concentrations, and hence to stimulate noncylic phosphorylation needed for a "pump" where glycolate may function in catalytic concentrations, or perhaps because glycolate acts as an intermediate in the synthesis of carbohydrate (2, 43, 70).These interpretations of the role of glycolate have been criticized, however, and in order to clear up some misunderstandings in the literature, I will discuss some of the objections that have been raised.

Meidner & Mansfield (3) stated that there was no evidence that glycolate synthesis is better at low (zero) CO_2 concentrations and, to bolster their argument, cited work on the excretion rather than the synthesis of glycolate in *Chlorella* cells (76). These latter workers did not examine the excretion of glycolate at "zero" CO_2 but did in fact observe a severe inhibition of 0.25 per cent CO_2. In tobacco leaf tissue, the rate of synthesis of glycolate in light is not much less at "zero" CO_2 than in normal air (44). They (3) also cited an apparent paradox since glycolic acid (10^{-2} M) inhibited stomatal opening slightly (12), whereas it was used by us in reversal experiments to bring about opening. Glycolic acid is a fairly strong acid, pK = 3.83, hence there is a decided difference between the use of the free acid at a low pH and the conditions used in the reversal experiments (pH 4.6).

These workers (4) repeated the objections already mentioned, and further stated that "at zero carbon dioxide there can be little if any photosynthetic formation of glycolate, and on Zelitch's hypothesis illuminated stomata should therefore show closure in carbon dioxide-free air." This is in error, since glycolate synthesis in tobacco leaf tissue is little affected by the absence of CO_2 in the atmosphere(44), because under such environmental conditions there is a considerable turnover of CO_2 inside the leaf arising from dark respiration and photorespiration (50). In fact, this turnover of carbon may be so great in "zero" CO_2 that only one-third of the CO_2 generated by photorespiration may be released into a rapid stream of CO_2-free air outside the leaf even when the stomata are open (77).

Meidner & Mansfield (78) continuously supplied excised tobacco and *Xanthium* leaves through the petioles with 10^{-2} M α-hydroxy-2-pyridine methanesulfonic acid in the light for 90 min. With stomata closed, the CO_2 compensation point in *Xanthium* increased from 36 ppm to 121 ppm because of inhibition of photosynthesis. In CO_2-free air, stomata closed by the inhibitor opened, and in 0.2 per cent CO_2 they closed. The investigators concluded that stomatal closing is not related to inhibition of glycolate oxidation, but results from the increase in CO_2 concentration in the intercellular spaces. However, I have found that when leaf disks were floated on the same inhibitor solution for periods up to 20 min or longer, depending on the temperature, net photosynthesis is not affected and is even enhanced under certain conditions in tobacco (44, 50), although glycolate oxidation was clearly interfered with since glycolate accumulated. I have also recently found (unpublished) that when an α-hydroxysulfonate is supplied to tobacco leaves in a manner more likely specifically to affect guard cells, and not through the petiole, stomata closed with no change in the CO_2 compensation point, indicating that the CO_2 concentration inside the leaf is not involved. Thus I conclude that the results described by Meidner & Mansfield (78) were not necessarily caused by an increase in the CO_2 concentration inside the leaf, but that coincidentally all chloroplasts, including those in the guard cells, were adversely affected by the manner in which the inhibitor was supplied. Thus effects on stomatal widths induced by lowering the normal CO_2 concentration (78) still appear to be unrelated to the primary mechanism of stomatal opening in the light.

Mouravieff (79) found that when leaf tissue of *Leucanthemum* was floated on a solution of α-hydroxy-2-pyridinemethanesulfonic acid, the stomata closed, but the inhibitor failed to close stomata in *Veronica* tissue. An attempt to reverse the closing with glycolic acid also failed. However, in the original reversal experiment (43), a different inhibitor was used and the pH was controlled.

Levitt (9) repeated some of the misunderstandings about glycolate metabolism already discussed. He also expressed skepticism that glycolate could even penetrate cells in commenting on the reversal experiments (43), although there are many experiments in the literature showing how readily sodium or potassium glycolate is metabolized when supplied to leaf tissues (50).

USE OF INHIBITORS OF STOMATAL OPENING AS ANTITRANSPIRANTS

A leaf disk assay has been described (12) that facilitates the search for compounds that close stomata, and methods of selecting inhibitors that are highly specific on guard cells have also been discussed by Waggoner & Zelitch (7). The most reliable inhibitor used thus far is phenylmercuric acetate. Zelitch & Waggoner (52) first used this substance on excised tobacco leaves in experiments designed to test whether stomatal diffusive resistance was a greater part of the total diffusive pathway for transpiration than for net photosynthesis, as was predicted by Fick's law of diffusion. Several properties make phenylmercuric acetate useful in model studies. It closes stomata when sprayed on leaves at low concentrations (10^{-4} M); it affects only the stomata in the area where it is sprayed, hence it is not likely to be translocated and to affect cells other than guard cells; and one treatment inhibits stomatal opening for at least 14 days without apparent toxicity in many species. The poor translocation of this inhibitor was confirmed in studies on transpiration in *Vicia faba* leaves (80).

We found (52) that closure of stomata in excised leaves resulted in a greater inhibition of transpiration than of photosynthesis, indicating that the inhibitor affected primarily stomatal diffusive resistance. Also when sprayed on intact tobacco plants in the greenhouse, phenylmercuric acetate diminished transpiration from 16 per cent to 43 per cent for 16 days, depending on the concentration of the inhibitor used, and the effect on growth was small (53). These results are consistent with the considerable evidence that, except in still air, diffusion of water vapor and CO_2 through stomata affects transpiration and photosynthesis at all stomatal widths in leaves as well as in artificial pores whose dimensions simulate those of natural stomatal cavities (7, 8, 81, 82). Hence experiments with phenylmercuric acetate indicate that transpiration and CO_2 uptake must be negligible through the cuticle in comparison with stomatal diffusion.

Shimshi (22, 83) also found that, when sprayed on maize leaves, phenylmercuric acetate closed stomata and more adversely affected transpiration than photosynthesis in a chamber. A single treatment on sunflower plants outdoors closed stomata for 37 days, transpiration was decreased by 14 per cent, and growth was essentially unaffected. Slatyer & Bierhuizen (84, 85) showed that dipping the foliage of cotton plants in a greenhouse into 10^{-4} to 10^{-5} M phenylmercuric acetate closed stomata and inhibited transpiration proportionately more than photosynthesis.

Waggoner, Monteith & Szeicz (86) first demonstrated the role of stomatal diffusive resistance under field conditions with barley plants that were sprayed with the monomethyl ester of nonenylsuccinic acid (10^{-3} M). A reduction in transpiration of 20 per cent cent to 30 per cent was observed that persisted for several days, only as long as the stomata were closed by the inhibitor. Fulton (87) was able to close stomata in potato leaves growing outdoors by spraying them with 10^{-3} M monomethyl ester of decenylsuccinic acid. He claimed no effect on transpiration. However, a comparison of the stomatal widths in treated and control leaves with their respective rates of evapotranspiration shows that water loss was inhibited when the stomatal differences were greatest.

Granger & Edgerton (88) observed that spraying phenylmercuric acetate on apple leaves closed stomata, but there was variable damage to the leaves. Toxicity was also found by Keller (89), who sprayed this inhibitor on spruce foliage outdoors at 10^{-4} M. Transpiration of 30 per cent less for 30 days, but there was a greater inhibition of photosynthesis, suggesting that mesophyll cells were also adversely affected in this tissue in addition to the guard cells.

Davenport (90) sprayed 10^{-3} M decenylsuccinic acid or phenylmercuric acetate on creeping red fescue (*Festuca rubra*) growing in a lysimeter in the field, and found transpiration was inhibited 5 per cent and 10 per cent respectively without measurable affect on growth of the grass. Finally, the potential importance of controlling stomata on increasing stream flow in watersheds was clearly shown by Waggoner & Bravdo (91) in one summer season, and this was confirmed the following season by Turner & Waggoner (17). They sprayed the foliage of 16 m tall red pine trees in a forest with 10^{-3} M phenylmercuric acetate at the beginning of the summer, observed increased stomatal diffusive resistance in the treated trees during daylight hours, and found a significantly higher soil moisture content around the treated trees at the end of the summer.

Genetic Control

I have previously cited an example of a drought-resistant grass in which the stomata failed to open even in a wet environment (2). Brown & Pratt (92) observed inactive stomata in many of the 69 species of grasses examined, although it is uncertain whether this was a genetic or an environmental effect. Waggoner & Simmonds (93) studied a potato mutant ("Droopy") in which the stomata remained open even when the leaves wilted. When sprayed with 10^{-3} M phenylmercuric acetate, however, the stomata closed, and transpiration was inhibited to the same level as in normal leaves treated in a similar manner. Tal (94) likewise described three mutants of tomato in which excessive wilting occurred because transpiration was greater and stomata remained open. With these plants, 10^{-4} M phenylmercuric acetate closed stomata very poorly in comparison with normal tomato leaf disks.

Zelitch & Day (95) noted that stomata of a yellow mutant of tobacco, first described by Burk & Menser (96), open in the light at about twice the rate of wild type tobacco. Thus plants are known in which both the rate and extent of stomatal opening are genetically controlled, although no biochemical explanations for these interesting aberrations are yet known.

Ions and a Potassium Ion "Pump" in Light Opening

Several mineral deficiencies have recently been shown to retard stomatal opening, presumably because of adverse effects on photosynthesis and phosphorylation. Shimshi (97) showed that withholding nitrogen and iron caused reduced stomatal apertures in several species, and these inhibitions were well correlated with a decrease in chlorophyll concentration. Wallace & Frolich (98) found poor stomatal opening in phosphorous-deficient tobacco leaves, and Buczek (99) observed decreased transpiration in nitrogen-deficient tomato plants. Peaslee & Moss (100) showed a more specific effect of potassium deficiency on stomata in maize leaves; normal leaves opened about 6.5 μ, while the widths in deficient stomata were less than 1 μ. Moreover, the resulting lower net photosynthesis was similar to that found when normal stomata were closed with a spray of phenylmercuric acetate. Hence it appeared that guard cells could not compete very well with mesophyll cells in obtaining potassium ions.

Fujino (101), with use of cytochemical methods, made the important observation that guard cells of several species contain large concentrations of potassium when they are open in the light and relatively small quantities when they are closed in the dark. In epidermal strips of Commelina communis, which were floated on phosphate buffer at pH 5.6 containing 5×10^{-2} M potassium chloride, stomata opened 7 μ in 120 min in light, and the potassium content of the guard cells increased. When he added 10^{-2} M ATP to the medium, the stomata opened 14 μ in the same time, and a still greater quantity of potassium accumulated in the guard cells. The possibility that the increase in potassium ions in the guard cells is related to the functioning of an ATP-operated pump that increased the osmotic value was suggested by these experiments.

Fischer (102) independently described experiments on the uptake of potassium ions (or ^{86}Rb$^+$ as a substitute) in epidermal strips of *Vicia faba* floated on a medium containing buffer and 10^{-2} M potassium chloride. Although this epidermal tissue was a good choice since the stomatal opening was stimulated in light, it was also an unfortunate system because stomata in this tissue atypically open to some extent in the dark, and this caused high blank values for potassium uptake. Opening in the light in CO_2-free air in this system was accompanied by a decrease in solute potential (increase in solute concentration), and maximal stomatal opening in the dark required a ten-fold higher potassium concentration in the medium (103). From measurement of the ^{86}Rb$^+$ uptake in the light, on the assumption that it took place in the guard cells, there would have been an increase in potassium concentration of 0.3 M, enough to account for the opening observed (102).

In these interesting experiments with *Vicia faba* epidermal strips, an atmosphere of CO_2-free air in the light was compared with one of normal air in the dark, although it appeared that CO_2-free air offered very little advantage (104). More recently, these experiments have been extended by Humble & Hsiao (105), who found that rubidium and potassium ions are much more effective in light opening than lithium, sodium, or calcium ions, and preliminary evidence was obtained that potassium ions move out of the guard cells when the stomata close.

Pallaghy (106) measured the potential between the guard cells and the external medium in epidermal strips of tobacco in the light in open stomata. When potassium chloride was in the medium, the greatest change in the electrochemical potential was observed indicating that potassium ions were accumulating. However, the stomata in this system did not close well in the dark or in the presence of high concentrations of CO_2, hence this is a limitation in work with this tissue.

Thus, in spite of the absence of as precise quantitative data as one would wish for, there is good evidence that stomatal opening in the light is mediated by an inward potassium ion pump that concentrates this ion in guard cells. If this hypothesis holds true, then stomatal opening in the light would require only small amounts of photosynthetic CO_2 fixation in the guard cells—just enough perhaps to maintain a catalytic concentration of glycolate so that its metabolism could stimulate noncyclic photophosphorylation and thus provide the energy of ATP for the pump (2). The potassium ions might come from the adjoining epidermal cells, or perhaps from the chloroplasts in the mesophyll, or even to some extent from the chloroplasts in the guard cells themselves. It is also likely that carbon compounds produced in photosynthesis would contribute to the increase in osmotic value in the guard cells, especially at the later stages of stomatal opening, since there are clear differences with respect to the requirement for oxygen in the atmosphere between the initiation and the maintenance of stomatal opening in the light (23).

ACKNOWLEDGMENTS

I wish to thank Dr. H. B. Vickery for his helpful counsel, and Bonnie Gambs for assistance in the search of the literature.

LITERATURE CITED

1. Ketellapper, H. J., *Ann. Rev. Plant Physiol.*, **14**, 249–70 (1963)
2. Zelitch, I., *Biol. Rev.*, **40**, 463–82 (1965)
3. Meidner, H., Mansfield, T. A., *Biol. Rev.*, **40**, 483–509 (1965)
4. Heath, O. V. S., Mansfield, T. A., Meidner, H., *Nature, 207*, 960–62 (1965)
5. Pallas, J. E., Jr., *Quart. Rev. Biol.*, **41**, 365–83 (1966)
6. Meidner, H., *Symp. Soc. Exptl. Biol.*, **19**, 185–203 (1965)
7. Waggoner, P. E., Zelitch, I., *Science*, **150**, 1413–20 (1965)
8. Lee, R., *Water Resources Res.*, **3**, 737–52 (1967)
9. Levitt, J., *Planta*, **74**, 101–18 (1967)
10. Stålfelt, M. G., *Physiol. Plantarum*, **19**, 241–56 (1966)
11. Sampson, J., *Nature*, **191**, 932–33 (1961)
12. Zelitch, I., *Proc. Natl. Acad. Sci. U.S.*, **47**, 1423–33 (1961)
13. Stoddard, E. M., *Conn. Agr. Expt. Sta., Cir. 227*, New Haven (1965)
14. Gloser, J., *Biol. Plant.*, **9**, 28–33 (1967)
15. Horanic, G. E., Gardner, P. E., *Botan. Gaz.*, **128**, 144–50 (1967)
16. Wallihan, E. F., *Plant Physiol.*, **39**, 86–90 (1964)
17. Turner, N. C., Waggoner, P. E., *Plant Physiol.*, **43**, 973–78 (1968)
18. Moreshet, S., Stanhill, G., *Ann. Botany*, **29**, 625–33 (1965)
19. Alvim, P. de T., *Symposium on Methodology of Eco-Physiology*, 325–29 (UNESCO, Montpellier, France, 1962)
20. Waggoner, P. E., *Agr. Meteorol.*, **2**, 317–29 (1965)
21. Glinka, Z., Meidner, H., *J. Exptl. Botany*, **19**, 152–66 (1968)
22. Shimshi, D., *Plant Physiol.*, **38**, 713–21 (1963)
23. Walker, D. A., Zelitch, I., *Plant Physiol.*, **38**, 390–96 (1963)
24. Stålfelt, M. G., *Physiol. Plantarum*, **14**, 826–43 (1961)
25. Macdowall, F. D. H., *Can. J. Botany*, **41**, 1289–1300 (1963)
26. Glover, J., *J. Agr. Sci.*, **53**, 412–16 (1960)
27. Bannister, P., *J. Ecology*, **52**, 151–58 (1964)
28. Virgin, H. I., *Physiol. Plantarum*, **10**, 445–53 (1957)
29. Poskuta, J., Tomczyk, J., *Experientia*, **24**, 184–85 (1968)
30. Kuiper, P. J. C., *Plant Physiol.*, **39**, 952–55 (1964)
31. Wessels, J. S. C., Van der Veen, R., *Biochim. Biophys. Acta*, **19**, 548–49 (1956)
32. Stålfelt, M. G., *Physiol. Plantarum*, **17**, 828–38 (1964)
33. Nishida, K., *Physiol. Plantarum*, **16**, 281–98 (1963)
34. Stålfelt, M. G., *Physiol. Plantarum*, **16**, 756–66 (1963)
35. Stålfelt, M. G., *ibid.*, **18**, 177–84 (1965)
36. Mansfield, T. A., *Nature*, **205**, 617–18 (1965)
37. Mansfield, T. A., Meidner, H., *J. Exptl. Botany*, **17**, 510–21 (1966)
38. Meidner, H., *J. Exptl. Botany*, **19**, 146–51 (1968)
39. Raschke, K., *Naturwissenschaften*, **54**, 73 (1967)
40. Stålfelt, M. G., *Physiol. Plantarum*, **20**, 634–42 (1967)
41. Longuet, P., *Physiol. Vegetale*, **3**, 345–53 (1965)
42. Pallas, J. E., Jr., *Science*, **147**, 171–73 (1965)
43. Zelitch, I., Walker, D. A., *Plant Physiol.*, **39**, 856–62 (1964)
44. Zelitch, I., *J. Biol. Chem.*, **240**, 1869–76 (1965)
45. Raschke, K., *Planta*, **68**, 111–40 (1966)
46. Zelitch, I., *Am. Scientist*, **55**, 472–86 (1967)
47. Moss, D. N., *Stomata and Water Relations in Plants*, 86–101 (Conn. Agr. Expt. Sta. Bull. 664, New Haven, 1963)
48. Moss, D. N., *Nature*, **193**, 587 (1962)
49. Meidner, H., *J. Exptl. Botany*, **13**, 284–93 (1962)
50. Zelitch, I., *Plant Physiol.*, **41**, 1623–31 (1966)
51. Waggoner, P. E., *Crop Sci.* (In press, 1969)
52. Zelitch, I., Waggoner, P. E., *Proc. Natl. Acad. Sci. U. S.*, **48**, 1101–8 (1962)
53. Zelitch, I., Waggoner, P. E., *ibid.*, 1297–99
54. Allaway, W. G., Mansfield, T. A., *New Phytologist*, **66**, 57–63 (1967)
55. Smith, D., Buchholtz, K. P., *Plant Physiol.*, **39**, 572–78 (1964)

56. Willis, G. D., Davis, D. E., Funder-burk, H. H., Jr., *Weeds*, **11**, 253–55 (1963)

57. Sivadjian, J., Ricardo, C. P., *Bull. Soc. Botan. France*, **112**, 119–21 (1965)

58. Pallas, J. E., Jr., Bertrand, A. R., *Agron. J.*, **59**, 139–42 (1967)

59. Marei, N., Crane, J. C., Bradley, M. V., *Proc. Am. Soc. Hort. Sci.*, **89**, 61–71 (1966)

60. Kozinka, V., *Biologia*, **19**, 809–19 (1964)

61. Livnè, A., Vaadia, Y., *Physiol. Plantarum*, **18**, 658–64 (1965)

62. Meidner, H., *J. Exptl. Botany*, **18**, 556–61 (1967)

63. Luke, H. H., Freeman, T. E., *Nature*, **215**, 874–75 (1967)

64. Zelitch, I., *Science*, **143**, 692–93 (1964)

65. Kuiper, P. J. C., *Science*, **143**, 690–91 (1964)

66. Kuiper, P. J. C., *Mededel. Landbouwhogeschool. Wageningen*, **67-3**, 1–23 (1967)

67. Siegenthaler, P.-A., Packer, L., *Plant Physiol.*, **40**, 785–91 (1965)

68. Baddeley, M. S., Hanson, J. B., *Plant Physiol.*, **42**, 1702–10 (1967)

69. Rao, A. V., Fallin, E., Fang, S. C., *Plant Physiol.*, **41**, 443–46 (1966)

70. Zelitch, I., *Stomata and Water Relations in Plants*, 18–42 (See Ref. 47)

71. Mansfield, T. A., *New Phytologist*, **66**, 325–30 (1967)

72. Graniti, A., *Proc. Symp. Host-Parasite Rel. Plant Path. Budapest*, 211–17 (1964)

73. Ballio, A., Brufani, M., Casimovi, C. G., Cerrini, S., Fedeli, W., Pelliciari, R., Santurbano, B., Vaciago, A., *Experientia*, **24**, 631–35 (1968)

74. Mansfield, T. A., Heath, O. V. S., *Nature*, **200**, 596 (1963)

75. Todd, G. W., Propst, B., *Physiol. Plantarum*, **16**, 57–65 (1963)

76. Pritchard, G. G., Griffin, W. J., Whittingham, C. P., *J. Exptl. Botany*, **13**, 176–84 (1962)

77. Zelitch, I., *Plant Physiol.*, **43**, 1829–37 (1968)

78. Meidner, H., Mansfield, T. A., *J. Exptl. Botany*, **17**, 502–9 (1966)

79. Mouravieff, I., *Compt. Rend. Acad. Sci.*, **261**, 4487–89 (1965)

80. Sivadjian J., *Bull. Soc. Botan.*, **114**, 1–4 (1967)

81. Lee, R., Gates, D. M., *Am. J. Botany*, **51**, 963–75 (1964)

82. Holmgren, P., Jarvis, P. G., Jarvis, M. S., *Physiol. Plantarum*, **18**, 557–73 (1965)

83. Shimshi, D., *Plant Physiol.*, **38**, 709–12 (1963)

84. Slatyer, R. O., Bierhuizen, J. F., *Agr. Meteorol.*, **1**, 42–53 (1964)

85. Slatyer, R. O., Bierhuizen, J. F., *Australian J. Biol. Sci.*, **17**, 131–46 (1964)

86. Waggoner, P. E., Monteith, J. L., Szeicz, G., *Nature*, **201**, 97–98 (1964)

87. Fulton, J. M., *Can. J. Plant Sci.*, **47**, 109–11 (1967)

88. Granger, R. L., Edgerton, L. J., *Proc. Am. Soc. Hort. Sci.*, **88**, 48–51 (1966)

89. Keller, T., *Forstwiss. Zentr.*, **85**, 65–79 (1966)

90. Davenport, D. C., *J. Exptl. Botany*, **18**, 332–47 (1967)

91. Waggoner, P. E., Bravdo, B.-A., *Proc. Natl. Acad. Sci. U. S.*, **57**, 1096–1102 (1967)

92. Brown, W. V., Pratt, G. A., *Southwestern Natur.*, **10**, 48–56 (1965)

93. Waggoner, P. E., Simmonds, N. W., *Plant Physiol.*, **41**, 1268–71 (1966)

94. Tal, M., *Plant Physiol.*, **41**, 1387–91 (1966)

95. Zelitch, I., Day, P. R., *Plant Physiol.*, **43**, 1838–44 (1968)

96. Burk, L. G., Menser, H. A., *Tobacco Sci.*, **8**, 101–4 (1964)

97. Shimshi, D., *New Phytologist*, **66**, 455–61 (1967)

98. Wallace, A., Frolich, E., *Nature*, **208**, 1231 (1965)

99. Buczek, J., *Acta Soc. Botan. Polon.*, **36**, 379–86 (1967)

100. Peaslee, D. E., Moss, D. N., *Crop Sci.*, **8**, 427–30 (1968)

101. Fujino, M., *Sci. Bull. Fac. Educ., Nagasaki Univ.*, **18**, 1–47 (1967)

102. Fischer, R. A., *Science*, **160**, 784–85 (1968)

103. Fischer, R. A., Hsiao, T. C., *Plant Physiol.*, **43**, 1953–58 (1968)

104. Fischer, R. A., *Plant Physiol.*, *ibid.*, 1947–52

105. Humble, G. D., Hsiao, T. C., *Plant Physiol.* (In press, 1969)

106. Pallaghy, C. K., *Planta*, **80**, 147–53 (1968)

MEASUREMENT OF THE WATER STATUS OF PLANTS

By J. S. Boyer

Department of Botany, University of Illinois, Urbana, Illinois

The measurement of the state of water in plants is an old and frequently studied subject. Methods have ranged from those based on the plant itself to those associated with various properties of the plant environment. Those based on the environment (1–8), though physically straightforward, are often difficult to interpret because of the dynamic nature of the soil-plant-atmosphere system. The plant is rarely, if ever, in equilibrium with its surroundings and, consequently, measurements of the surroundings may not reflect conditions within the plant. Methods based on the plant have become increasingly important for physiological work and during the last few years have developed rapidly, due partly to a greater understanding of the nature of the water flow system and partly to a redefinition of the concepts of plant water status.

The purpose of this article will be to describe some of the recent advances in techniques for measuring plant water status. The reader is referred to excellent, comprehensive reviews already available for a description of some of the older methods (9–13) and for some of the physiological consequences relating to water in plants (10, 14).

State of Water in Plants

To be useful, any measure of plant water status should represent as many aspects as possible of the role of water in transport and metabolism. Several means of describing water status have been suggested. Generally, they have been based on some aspect of the energy associated with water or with the quantity of water in the plant. Since water transport in plants follows gradients of decreasing free energy, energy concepts seem more useful than quantity concepts for this process. Growth also is affected by the energy status of water. Metabolism, on the other hand, is as yet poorly understood with regard to the role of water in enzymatic processes. Considerably more is known about water as a reactant than is available to explain how water affects enzyme activities. It is clear that metabolic patterns may be altered when water availability decreases, but beyond this there is little evidence to decide whether the free energy of water per se is an important factor, or whether other changes associated with water availability are involved. Nevertheless, measurements based on energy concepts provide a

351

convenient means of characterizing water status because, in contrast to measurements based on water quantity, they are relatively unaffected by physiological and morphological variation between samples. Consequently, several recent metabolic studies dealing with plant water have used this type of measurement (15–20).

Terms that have been applied to what have basically been free energy concepts concerning water in plants are suction force, suction tension, diffusion pressure deficit, net influx free energy, and more recently, water potential. The last of these has been derived from thermodynamic ideas currently in use and will be the term adopted here (21–23).

Water potential (ψ_w) is defined in terms of the Gibbs free energy of water expressed as chemical potential (μ) in ergs mole^{-1}. Since literature dealing with plant water traditionally uses pressure concepts, water potentials are often given in pressure units rather than ergs mole^{-1} by dividing the chemical potential by the partial molal volume of water (V, cm^3 mole^{-1}):

$$\psi_w = (\mu - \mu_0)/\overline{V} \qquad\qquad 1.$$

For purposes of convenience, the pressure units are usually stated as the bar (10^6 ergs cm^{-3}) or the atmosphere (0.987 bar). Since absolute values of chemical potential are unknown, a reference is adopted which for work with plants is the chemical potential of pure free water at atmospheric pressure and the same temperature as the system being considered (μ_0). The water potential of this reference state is defined as zero.

For many plant studies, it is of interest to divide the water potential into component potentials which are suitable for measurement. The most important of these are the osmotic, matrix, pressure, and gravitational components:

$$\psi_w = \psi_s + \psi_m + \psi_p + \psi_g \qquad\qquad 2.$$

where s, m, p, and g refer to the effects of solutes, matrix, pressure, and gravity, respectively. The osmotic component represents the forces due to free solutes, whereas the matrix component represents the adsorptive and surface tension effects associated with solid surfaces. Both solute and matrix forces reduce the chemical potential of water. In some instances, the distinction between solute and matrix forces becomes somewhat arbitrary as, for example, for macromolecules which may show readily reversible changes from the solution to the gel state. In such cases, matrix and solute forces should be carefully defined and correlated with the means of measurement. In contrast to the lowering of potential brought about by solute and matrix forces, external pressure may either raise or lower the chemical potential of water depending on whether the molecules concerned are subjected to pressures above or below atmospheric. The same is true of the gravitational component which has a sign determined by the gravitational position of the reference. The effects of gravity are important for water having considerable vertical extent, such as the water columns of trees, but are usually negligible in laboratory studies.

Free energy, though providing a means of characterizing plant water, is often more difficult to measure than the quantity of water in plant tissues, and consequently, tissue water content is sometimes used to estimate the availability of water to the plant. The two have often been related to each other by measuring water potential at various tissue water contents. Terms used to describe tissue water content are relative water content [relative turgidity (24)], water deficit (25), or simply water content per unit fresh or dry weight. The values are usually expressed as percentages, with relative water content being the most frequently used because it corrects for differences in dry weight between samples.

In a discussion of terminology dealing with plant water, mention should be made of hydrature, since it combines concepts both from the energy and the quantity points of view (26). Walter & Stadelmann (27) have shown by means of models that the hydration of a gel is dependent on the osmotic potential of a solution with which it is in equilibrium across a semipermeable membrane. Hydrature is a measure of hydration in this system and is determined as the ratio of the vapor pressure of the solution to that of pure water under the same conditions of temperature and pressure. The concept is similar to that in water potential terminology dealing with surface effects (matrix potential) but has not been widely adopted because it results in uncertainties with regard to the effects of pressure (28) and requires the assumption that no solutes are present in the gel matrix (27).

METHODS OF MEASURING WATER POTENTIAL AND COMPONENT POTENTIALS

Most methods of measuring water potential take advantage of the fact that at equilibrium chemical potentials throughout any aqueous system are the same. Solution techniques (29–31), for example, require exchange of water between the tissue and a series of surrounding solutions. The one in which no exchange occurs is assumed to be at equilibrium with the tissue, and the water potential is obtained from the potential of the equilibrium solution. This type of method is difficult to interpret, however, because the possibility of solute exchange between the tissue and the medium may cause errors to arise (30, 32). Several recent techniques have not required that tissue be in contact with solutions and, since they are less subject to error due to exchange, this review will deal primarily with them.

Vapor pressure techniques.—Vapor pressure is a sensitive indicator of the chemical potential of water and has been used for determining water potentials as well as most of the component potentials. Since potentials are measured in the vapor phase, solute exchange is not a problem. For water potentials in the physiological range, vapor pressures are close to those at saturation, and methods must be capable of detecting small changes in this property. Water potential is related to vapor pressure by the equation:

$$\psi_w = \frac{RT}{\overline{V}} \ (ln \ e/e_0) \qquad\qquad 3.$$

where R is the gas constant (cm^3 bars $mole^{-1}$ deg^{-1}), T is the Kelvin temperature, e is the vapor pressure of water in the tissue, and e_0 is the vapor pressure of pure water at atmospheric pressure. As with solutions, vapor in equilibrium with tissue has a chemical potential which is the same as that of the tissue. The high sensitivity of vapor pressure to changes in temperature requires that the methods have some form of temperature control to assure equilibrium, a restriction that generally makes them unsuitable for field measurements.

The demonstration by Spanner (33), that sensitive measurements of water potential could be obtained from the vapor phase with thermocouples, has led to considerable effort to develop thermocouple psychrometers as tools for research. The method has the advantage of great sensitivity and requires only small amounts of tissue. The equipment consists of a thermocouple sealed in a chamber with plant tissue that has equilibrated with the chamber atmosphere (Fig. 1). Constant temperature is maintained by immersing the chamber in a water bath. For a determination, a small amount of water is condensed on the thermocouple by passing an electric current through the junction for a short time in a direction which causes cooling (Peltier effect) and then allowing the condensate to evaporate to the air in the chamber. The rate of evaporation is determined by the water potential of the system and calibration is carried out with solutions of known potential.

Richards & Ogata (34) suggested a modification which required that a small water drop be placed on the thermocouple to replace the need for Peltier cooling, thereby increasing the stability of the system. Approximately 3 to 5 μl of water were placed on a specially designed ring thermocouple which was then sealed in the chamber for a determination. After an initial period, the evaporation of water from the thermocouple and its absorption by the tissue reached a steady rate which could be calibrated in the same way as the Spanner system.

Both methods have been used and modified by various workers (35–41). The modifications have included the use of miniature chambers (40), rapid sample changers (36), and a direct measurement of the volume of water evaporating to the chamber contents (38). The instruments have been used for measuring soil water potentials as well as plant water potentials, (34) and the first instance of the adaptation of these psychrometers to field measurements has recently been reported for a soil instrument (42).

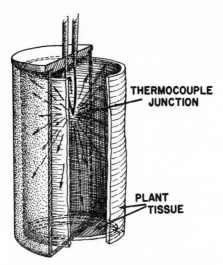

FIG. 1. Spanner thermocouple, plant tissue, and psychrometer chamber for measuring water potential. The chamber top is sealed to the chamber bottom with a rubber O-ring. For a measurement, water is condensed on the junction and then allowed to evaporate, cooling the thermocouple junction. The amount of cooling is related to the water potential of the chamber contents.

The latter equipment tolerates slow drifts in temperature and appears suitable for measuring soil water potentials *in situ*.

Although much of the utility of thermocouple psychrometers is associated with determination of water potential, component potentials can also be distinguished by altering some of the factors in Equation 2. This is done in such a way that certain components become zero or are not sensed by the thermocouple. In plant tissue, pressure effects may be reduced to zero by freezing and thawing the tissue to disrupt cell membranes (43). The magnitude of the pressure component is then obtained from the difference in potential before and after freezing. Solute and matrix forces remain after this treatment (43, 44, 47, 49) and may be distinguished in the Richards and Ogata system by placing cell sap expressed from the same sample on the thermocouple ring. Since the osmotic effect of solutes then becomes the same on the thermocouple and in the tissue sample, thermocouple output depends only on matrix forces (45). Matrix forces are often assumed to be negligible in water potential measurements (11, 12, 46), and appear to be small in plant tissues composed of highly vacuolated cells. However, they may be appreciable in young tissue (47) or tissue having a considerable amount of cell wall (48–50) and should be measured in most determinations of component potentials.

Psychrometer measurements, although free of solute exchange error, are subject to three other sources of error. These are caused by the resistance of plant tissue to vapor transfer, the heat produced by respiration, and the adsorption of water by chamber walls. The first of these errors was pointed out by Rawlins (51), who concluded that the rate of water transfer between the tissue and the thermocouple of the Richards and Ogata system was reduced because of the resistance of the tissue to diffusion transfer of water. Subsequently, Boyer & Knipling (35) showed that this error extended to the Spanner system as well, but to a lesser degree. They demonstrated that the transfer of water in a Richards and Ogata system could be described by the equation:

$$dm/dt = -\mathrm{k} \ (\psi_o - \psi_l) \qquad\qquad 4.$$

where dm/dt is the rate of transfer from the thermocouple (gm sec^{-1}), ψ_o is the water potential of water on the thermocouple (bars), and ψ_l is the water potential of the leaf. The proportionality factor, k (gm bar^{-1} sec^{-1}), includes the effect of the tissue resistance to diffusive transfer and may be different for each tissue sample. The resistance has no effect on the system only when dm/dt is zero and ψ_o equals ψ_l, i.e., when the thermocouple and the tissue are at thermodynamic equilibrium. They point out, however, that the equilibrium point may be obtained by extrapolation from the slope of the line representing Equation 4. Since the method gives an equilibrium value, it was termed an isopiestic method because of its similarity to an equilibrium vapor pressure method of the same name used in physical chemistry (52).

Resistance error is a function of the tissue water potential (Eq. 4) and may be as great as 15 to 20 per cent of the water potential of the sample (35). However, heat produced in tissue metabolism (53, 54), the second type of error, is usually smaller and appears to be relatively unaffected by tissue water potential. The heat affects determinations by warming the thermocouple but the amount of warming varies considerably with the physiological state of the tissue. The effect may be corrected by noting the heating of a dry thermocouple and adding this to the output of the wet thermocouple, as long as the effect of the tissue heat on the wet and dry thermocouples is identical (55).

The third psychrometer error is associated with transfer of water to chamber walls and results in spurious water loss from the thermocouple. Water is apparently adsorbed by the wall material (56) but may also be taken up if there are contaminating substances present (57). The tendency for water to collect on the walls is influenced by the materials used in constructing the chamber, metal surfaces causing the smallest amount of uptake. In practice, the problem is minimized by covering the wall with a single layer of the tissue being measured. For samples such as root segments or conifer needles which are not wide enough to mask wall surfaces easily, adsorption may be reduced to a negligible amount by coating the walls with melted and resolidified petrolatum (56).

In addition to the three errors mentioned above, an additional error recently has been described for leaf tissue that is saturated with water (58, 59). Measurements with the psychrometer would be expected to be zero under these conditions but are not. The lack of zero potential has been attributed to cell expansion or water loss after the tissue has been removed from the plant. Nevertheless, more recently it has been shown that in well-watered plant tissue remaining on the plant, the tissue does not reach zero water potential as long as growth can occur (45). Thus, it appears that water potentials of −1 to −4 bars, which have been reported for water-saturated tissue, may be characteristic of the growth process rather than due to measurement error.

When effects of resistance, metabolic heat, and adsorption are corrected, thermocouple psychrometers are capable of quite accurate measurements. In one instance, a psychrometer gave values within ± 0.1 bar of the water potential of leaf tissue that had been equilibrated above solutions of known water potentials (60).

In addition to the accuracy of the technique, part of the attractiveness of thermocouple psychrometry lies in its possible use for intact plant measurements (61–65). The instrument has been adapted to intact leaves by enclosing a whole leaf in a psychrometer chamber with the petiole sealed in a hole in the chamber wall (61, 62). These methods have not had wide usage because of long equilibration times (61) or a large amount of variability in measurements (62). Recently, however, a design has been described which may avoid these drawbacks and which appears to be capable of following rapid changes in leaf water potentials (45).

Thermocouple psychrometers designed for intact leaves generally determine water potentials under nontranspirational conditions because the blade is enclosed in an air-tight, temperature-controlled chamber. Gradients in potential which are present during transpiration become reduced so that water potentials probably reflect an average for the leaf blade rather than a potential at a specific point in the flow pathway. Comparisons between intact leaf measurements and those requiring excised leaf tissue show that the two are essentially the same (45, 62). Thus, the presence of an intact but non-flowing transpiration stream does not appear to affect the accuracy of water potentials measured in intact leaves. Of special interest in this regard is a recently described psychrometer which measures water potentials of intact leaves during transpiration (66, 67). The equipment is similar to that used for field measurements of soil potentials but is attached to only one side of the leaf, the other side remaining free to lose water.

In addition to thermocouple psychrometers, there are other methods

which use vapor pressures to estimate water potential, most notably the gra-
vimetric vapor equilibration technique described by Slatyer (68). Since the
equipment required for a measurement is less complex than that required
with thermocouple psychrometers, the method has been widely used. It involves the equilibration of a series of tissue samples for several hours in
the atmosphere above solutions of known water potential. The solution
causing no gain or loss in weight of the tissue is considered to have a water
potential equal to that of the tissue. Except that the method requires temperature control, it is a logical extension of solution techniques with the advantage that solute exchanges can not take place. The major sources of
error are loss in weight during manipulation of the tissue and heat production by respiration (60, 69). Respiratory heat brings about warming of the
tissue and excessive water loss so that water potentials may be too high by
as much as several bars (69).

   Pressure techniques.—Since the effect of pressure on water potential is
thermodynamically equivalent to the effect of solutes and other components
of water potential, it may be used as a measure of water potential. Pressure
changes in proportion to the Kelvin temperature so that measurements are
relatively insensitive to temperature and are suitable for field work.

   Scholander and co-workers (70, 71), recalling early experiments by
Dixon (72) and Haines (73), have used a pressure chamber for measuring
potentials in trees. They interpret their measurements to indicate only the
pressure component acting on xylem sap (74), but the method has also been
used to estimate leaf water potentials (56, 75).

   Measurements of leaf water potentials are made by sealing the petiole
of a leaf (or the stem of a leafy branch) in the chamber top so that the cut
end of the petiole projects to the outside and the leaf blade is subjected to
pressure on the inside (Fig. 2). As pressure is applied to the blade, the
water potential of the cell sap rises until it equals that of the sap in the
xylem vessels at atmospheric pressure. At this point, the xylem sap appears
at the cut surface of the petiole. The cut surface acts as a reference representing the position of the xylem sap just before excision.

   The pressure required to return the sap to this point is then related to
the water potential of the leaf cells by :

$$\psi_w = P + \psi_s{}^{\mathrm{xylem}} \hspace{3cm} 5.$$

where P represents the negative component of the water potential of the
xylem sap measured as a positive pressure in the pressure chamber. $\psi_s{}^{\mathrm{xylem}}$
is the osmotic effect of solutes in the xylem sap. P and $\psi_s{}^{\mathrm{xylem}}$ represent
the forces in the vascular system tending to remove water from the leaf
cells, whereas ψ_w represents the force tending to cause water to enter the
leaf cells. At the balance point, when no flow is occurring during a measurement, these two forces are equal to each other and opposite in direction. Since the osmotic potential of xylem sap is generally higher than

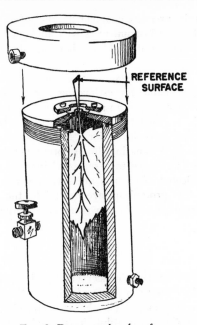

FIG. 2. Pressure chamber for measuring leaf water potential. The reference surface is the original point of excision from the plant and represents the position of the xylem sap prior to excision. Water and a baffle to prevent splashing are usually present on the bottom of the chamber but are not shown in the diagram. The water moistens the nitrogen entering the chamber and reduces drying of the tissue.

—3 bars (56, 76), estimates of water potential may be obtained without accounting for $\psi_s{}^{xylem}$ in some studies. Accurate determinations require a knowledge of $\psi_s{}^{xylem}$, however, which is particularly important when saline conditions are encountered.

Water potentials measured with the apparatus tend to vary in accuracy from species to species (56). The effect appears to be due at least partly to variable compression of the tissue under pressure and possibly to filling of tissue other than xylem with sap during a measurement. Comparisons with the thermocouple psychrometer show that some of the variability is in a direction to cause measurements which are too wet at high potentials and too dry at low potentials. Over much of the water potential range, however, measurements with the pressure chamber parallel those with the psychrometer sufficiently so that the instrument is well adapted to experiments which compare one water potential with another but do not require accurate values in the absolute sense.

At the present time, the pressure technique is probably the most rapid and simple method available for estimating water potential. At the same time, it offers higher accuracy than most other methods that are suitable for the field. There is little doubt that it will gain increasing use in the future.

Although more time is required for a measurement, the pressure chamber also can be used for estimating the osmotic potentials of leaves (70, 71, 77). The leaf blade is exposed to a series of increasing pressures and the expressed sap is collected after each pressure interval. Assuming that matrix effects in the leaf protoplasm are negligible, the reciprocal pressures are plotted versus the volume of sap remaining in the tissue according to the equation:

$$1/p = V/nk - V_0/nk \qquad\qquad 6.$$

where p is the pressure in the chamber (assumed equal and opposite to the leaf water potential), V is the volume of cell sap that has been removed by the pressure treatment (cm^3), V_0 is the original volume of cell sap in the leaf, n is the number of moles of solute in the leaf, and k is a factor for converting concentration to potential (bar cm^3 mole^{-1}). The volumes are usually calculated after removal of the main veins. After enough cell sap has been expressed to reduce tissue turgor to zero, Equation 6 gives a straight line (Fig. 3). The line may be extrapolated to any water content and represents the osmotic potential of the tissue at that water content.

Extrapolation of the x axis of Figure 3 appears to be a measure of the volume of water outside the protoplasts (49, 71). Supporting evidence for this interpretation comes from correlations between cell wall volume and the volume represented by the extrapolation (49). The measurement is probably valid because the sorption isotherms for wall and protoplast are quite different (47, 50). Cell walls appear to lose considerable quantities of water with the application of small pressures, after which wall water content varies only slightly (47). The protoplast volume, however, is proportional to the reciprocal pressure, and measurements are conducted at relatively high pressures where wall water content changes little. Thus, the straight line portion of Figure 3 probably represents the behavior of protoplasts with little effect from walls; and the extrapolation to the x axis would indicate that 90 per cent of the interveinal water is in protoplasts and 10 per cent is between protoplasts at the original tissue water content.

Matrix potentials may also be measured with the pressure chamber (49) or pressure membrane apparatus (47) after freezing and thawing the plant material. Here, the tissue consists of a matrix of cell walls enclosing small volumes of disorganized cell sap. As pressure is applied to the system,

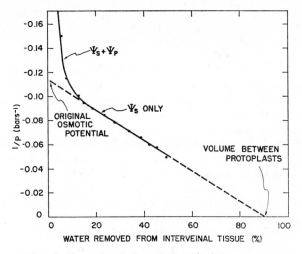

F_{IG.} 3. Example of the relationship between pressure and the water content of a leaf as measured with a pressure chamber. The curve is divided into two parts, one with turgor present and one with turgor absent. The straight-line portion of the curve provides an estimate of the osmotic potential of the tissue at various water contents as well as an estimate of the volume of water outside the leaf protoplasts (10%).

water and soluble components exude from the cut end of the petiole. Adsorptive forces on both water and solutes, as well as the effects of surface tension, tend to keep the sap within the matrix. All of them contribute to the matrix potential of the tissue (49, 78) and should be of similar magnitude in living cells (49). Although surface forces are undoubtedly present in organelles or particles in the cytoplasm, evidence for leaf tissue so far suggests that the largest matrix forces are associated with cell walls (49).

A further interesting, but untested, procedure to which the pressure chamber may be adapted in the future is seen by re-expressing Equation 6 in nonreciprocal form. The expression then gives a relationship between Ψ_w and the volume of water in the tissue which is essentially the same as the relative water content-water potential isotherm which has found considerable use in studies of plant water. The shape of the curve is related to the elastic modulus of the cell walls of the tissue (46) and should permit determination of both the water content-potential relationship and the elastic properties of leaf cell walls from a single sample.

W_{ATER} C_{ONTENT} M_{ETHODS}

Relative water content (24), which expresses water content as a per cent of the turgid water content of the tissue, is probably the most widely accepted way of expressing the quantity of water in plant tissue (79). It requires little equipment and, if calibrated in terms of potential, may be used to estimate plant water potential (46, 80, 81). The validity of the determination depends on the stability of the calibration (82), the degree of injection of the tissue with water during soaking for turgid weights (10), and on the definition of turgid tissue itself (24, 83–85). Some plant tissues undergo growth by cell enlargement when turgor rises above a certain level and, at least in the case of leaf tissue, the cells may not become fully turgid in the sense of having zero water potential (45). Temperature also may have an effect (86). Nevertheless, the simplicity of the method has resulted in its wide usage in spite of these drawbacks, and carefully standardized calibration can yield considerable information about the water potential of plant tissue.

β-ray gauging.—This method for determining the relative water content of intact leaves is based on the tendency for a stream of β particles to be attenuated as the mass of the particle pathway increases (87). In leaves, an increase in water content results in an increase in leaf mass which may be detected by positioning a leaf with a source of β particles on one side and a detector on the other. Several β sources have been used (^{14}C, ^{147}Pm, ^{99}Tc), all being of intermediate energy and long half-life (19, 87–89). Counts are detected with a Geiger-Muller counter and may be calibrated by a simplified method (90). The system is affected by its position with respect to the leaf, but with ^{147}Pm as a source, Nakayama & Ehrler (88) have obtained estimates of relative water content that are accurate to ± 0.25 per cent. Others have reported somewhat more variability (87, 90, 91).

With a knowledge of the relationship between relative water content and ψ_w, the water potential of intact leaves may be followed. Gardner & Nieman (19) have successfully used the β gauge to demonstrate the diurnal pattern of leaf water potential as soil dries. A particularly attractive aspect of the method is the possibility of estimating water potential without enclosing the leaf. Most thermocouple psychrometers, because of the nature of the measurements, alter the potential gradients during determinations. The β gauge permits measurements to be made with a minimum of disturbance to the flow system.

LITERATURE CITED

1. Briggs, L. J., Shantz, H. L., *Botan. Gaz.*, **53**, 229–35 (1912)
2. Thornthwaite, C. W., *Ecology*, **21**, 17–28 (1940)
3. Huffaker, C. B., *Am. Midland Naturalist*, **28**, 486–500 (1942)
4. Wadleigh, C. H., Gauch, H. G., *Plant Physiol.*, **23**, 485–95 (1948)
5. Wadleigh, C. H., *Soil Sci.*, **61**, 225–38 (1946)
6. Richards, L. A., *Soil Sci.*, **68**, 95–112 (1949)
7. Veihmeyer, F. J., Hendrickson, A. H., *Ann. Rev. Plant Physiol.*, **1**, 285–304 (1950)
8. Denmead, O. T., Shaw, R. H., *Agron. J.*, **54**, 385–90 (1962)
9. Kramer, P. J., Brix, H., *UNESCO Arid Zone Res.*, **25**, 343–51 (1965)
10. Slatyer, R. O., *Plant-Water Relationships* (Academic Press, N.Y., 366 pp., 1967)
11. Bennett-Clark, T. A., Water relations in cells. In *Plant Physiology, **2**, 105–92 (Steward, F. C., Ed., Academic Press, N.Y., 758 pp., 1959)
12. Crafts, A. S., Currier, H. B., Stocking, C. R., *Water in the Physiology of Plants* (Chronica Botanica Co., Waltham, Mass., 240 pp., 1949)
13. Kramer, P. J., *Plant and Soil Water Relationships* (McGraw-Hill, N.Y., 347 pp., 1949)
14. Vaadia, Y., Raney, F. C., Hagan, R. M., *Ann. Rev. Plant Physiol.*, **12**, 265–92 (1961)
15. Barnett, N. M., Naylor, A. W., *Plant Physiol.*, **41**, 1222–30 (1966)
16. Boyer, J. S., *Plant Physiol.*, **40**, 229–34 (1965)
17. Brix, H., *Physiol. Plantarum*, **15**, 10–20 (1962)
18. Gale, J., Kohl, H. C., Hagan, R. M., *Physiol. Plantarum*, **20**, 408–20 (1967)
19. Gardner, W. R., Nieman, R. H., *Science*, **143**, 1460–62 (1964)
20. Plaut, Z., Ordin, L., *Physiol. Plantarum*, **14**, 646–58 (1961)
21. Taylor, S. A., Slatyer, R. O., *UNESCO Arid Zone Res.*, **16**, 339–49 (1962)
22. Slatyer, R. O., Taylor, S. A., *Nature*, **187**, 922–24 (1960)
23. Kramer, P. J., Knipling, E. B., Miller, L. N., *Science*, **153**, 889–90 (1966)
24. Weatherley, P. E., *New Phytologist*, **49**, 81–97 (1950)
25. Stocker, O., *Ber. Deut. Botan. Ges.*, **47**, 126–29 (1929)
26. Walter, H., *Ber. Deut. Botan. Ges.*, **76**, 40–71 (1963)
27. Walter, H., Stadelmann, E., *BioScience*, **18**, 694–701 (1968)
28. Slatyer, R. O., *Z. Pflanzenphysiol.*, **56**, 91–94 (1967)
29. Ursprung, A., Blum, G., *Ber. Deut. Botan. Ges.*, **34**, 525–39 (1916)
30. Knipling, E. B., Kramer, P. J., *Plant Physiol.*, **42**, 1315–20 (1967)
31. Gaff, D. F., Carr, D. J., *Ann. Botany (London)*, **28**, 351–68 (1964)
32. Slatyer, R. O., *Protoplasma*, **62**, 34–43 (1966)
33. Spanner, D. C., *J. Exptl. Botany*, **2**, 145–68 (1951)
34. Richards, L. A., Ogata, G., *Science*, **128**, 1089–90 (1958)
35. Boyer, J. S., Knipling, E. B., *Proc. Natl. Acad. Sci. U.S.*, **54**, 1044–51 (1965)
36. Campbell, G. S., Zollinger, W. D., Taylor, S. A., *Agron. J.*, **58**, 315–18 (1966)
37. Dalton, F. N., Rawlins, S. L., *Soil Sci.*, **105**, 12–17 (1968)
38. Macklon, A. E. S., Weatherley, P. E., *J. Exptl. Botany*, **16**, 261–70 (1965)
39. Monteith, J. L., Owen, P. C., *J. Sci. Instr.*, **35**, 443–46 (1958)
40. Waister, P. D., *Israel J. Botany*, **12**, 192–96 (1963)
41. Zollinger, W. D., Campbell, G. S., Taylor, S. A., *Soil Sci.*, **102**, 231–39 (1966)
42. Rawlins, S. L., Dalton, F. N., *Proc. Soil Sci. Soc. Am.*, **31**, 297–301 (1967)
43. Ehlig, C. F., *Plant Physiol.*, **37**, 288–90 (1962)
44. Warren Wilson, J., *Australian J. Biol. Sci.*, **20**, 329–47 (1967)
45. Boyer, J. S., *Plant Physiol.*, **43**, 1056–62 (1968)
46. Gardner, W. R., Ehlig, C. F., *Plant Physiol.*, **40**, 705–10 (1965)
47. Wiebe, H. H., *Plant Physiol.*, **41**, 1439–42 (1966)
48. Gaff, D. F., Carr, D. J., *Australian J. Biol. Sci.*, **14**, 299–311 (1961)

49. Boyer, J. S. *Plant Physiol.*, **42**, 213–17 (1967)
50. Teoh, T. S., Alymore, L. A. G., Quirk, J. P., *Australian J. Biol. Sci.*, **20**, 41–50 (1967)
51. Rawlins, S. L., *Science*, **146**, 644–46 (1964)
52. Daniels, F., Alberty, R. A., *Physical Chemistry* (Wiley, N.Y., 744 pp., 1955)
53. Barrs, H. D., *Nature*, **203**, 1136–37 (1964)
54. Barrs H. D., *Australian J. Biol. Sci.*, **18**, 36–52 (1965)
55. Knipling, E. B., *Comparison of the Dye Method with the Thermocouple Psychrometer for Measuring Leaf Water Potentials* (Doctoral thesis, Duke Univ., Durham, No. Carolina, 1966)
56. Boyer, J. S., *Plant Physiol.*, **42**, 133–37 (1967)
57. Rawlins, S. L., *Agr. Meteorol.*, **3**, 293–310 (1966)
58. Tinklin, R., Weatherley, P. E., *New Phytologist*, **65**, 509–17 (1966)
59. Tinklin, R., *New Phytologist*, **66**, 85–88 (1967)
60. Boyer, J. S., *Science*, **154**, 1459–60 (1966)
61. Lambert, J. R., van Schilfgaarde, J., *Soil Sci.*, **100**, 1–9 (1965)
62. Lang, A. R. G., Barrs, H. D., *Australian J. Biol. Sci.*, **18**, 487–97 (1965)
63. Manohar, M. S., *J. Exptl. Botany*, **17**, 44–50 (1966)
64. Manohar, M. S., *ibid.*, 51–56
65. Manohar, M. S., *ibid.*, 231–35
66. Hoffman, G. J., Splinter, W. E., *Trans. Am. Soc. Agr. Engrs.*, **11**, 38–40 (1968)
67. Hoffman, G. J., Splinter, W. E., *Agron. J.*, **60**, 408–13 (1968)
68. Slatyer, R. O., *Australian J. Biol. Sci.*, **11**, 349–65 (1958)
69. Kaufmann, M. R., Kramer, P. J., *Plant Physiol.*, **42**, 191–94 (1967)
70. Scholander, P. F., Hammel, H. T., Hemmingsen, E. A., Bradstreet, E. D., *Proc. Natl. Acad. Sci.*

71. *U. S.*, **52**, 119–25 (1964)
71. Scholander, P. F., Hammel, H. T., Bradstreet, E. D., Hemmingsen, E. A., *Science*, **148**, 339–46 (1965)
72. Dixon, H. H., *Transpiration and the Ascent of Sap in Plants* (Macmillan, London, 216 pp., 1914)
73. Haines, F. M., *Ann. Botany (London)*, **49**, 213–38 (1935)
74. Gardner, W. R., Rawlins, S. L., *Science*, **149**, 920 (1965)
75. Waring, R. H., Cleary, B. D., *Science*, **155**, 1248–54 (1967)
76. Scholander, P. F., Bradstreet, E. D., Hammel, H. T., Hemmingsen, E. A., *Plant Physiol.*, **41**, 529–32 (1966)
77. Hammel, H. T., *Plant Physiol.*, **43**, 1042–48 (1968)
78. Bolt, G. H., Frissel, M. J., *Neth. J. Agr. Sci.*, **8**, 57–78 (1960)
79. Hewlett, J. D., Kramer, P. J., *Protoplasma*, **57**, 381–91 (1963)
80. Weatherley, P. E., Slatyer, R. O., *Nature*, **179**, 1085–86 (1957)
81. Ehlig, C. F., Gardner, W. R., *Agron. J.*, **56**, 127–130 (1964)
82. Knipling, E. B., *Physiol. Plantarum*, **20**, 65–72 (1967)
83. Barrs, H. D., Weatherley, P. E., *Australian J. Biol. Sci.*, **15**, 413–28 (1962)
84. Slatyer, R. O., Barrs, H. D., *UNESCO Arid Zone Res.*, **25**, 331–42 (1965)
85. Čatský, J., *UNESCO Arid Zone Res.*, **25**, 353–60 (1965)
86. Millar, B. D., *Science*, **154**, 512–13 (1966)
87. Mederski, H. J., *Soil Sci.*, **92**, 143–46 (1961)
88. Nakayama, F. S., Ehrler, W. L., *Plant Physiol.*, **39**, 95–98 (1964)
89. Rolston, D. E., Horton, M. L., *Agron. J.*, **60**, 333–36 (1968)
90. Jarvis, P. G., Slatyer, R. O., *Science*, **153**, 78–79 (1966)
91. Whiteman, P. C., Wilson, G. L., *Australian J. Biol. Sci.*, **16**, 140–46 (1963)

CELL MORPHOGENESIS[1]

By Paul B. Green

Department of Biology, University of Pennsylvania
Philadelphia, Pennsylvania

The plant cell is typically delimited by its wall. There are potentially two kinds of cell morphogenesis for such cells because new wall surface can be generated either by formation of a new cross-wall or by expansion involving the pre-existing wall. In the first case, new cells of varying proportions and reduced volume are relatively instantaneously produced by the completion of a cross-partition after mitosis. In the other case, which will be of primary concern here, cell proportions are gradually changed (or magnified) by an enlargement of cell volume and surface already present. This generation of new volume by the yielding of the cell wall to the stresses within it is termed growth by the present reviewer.

Each mode of generating cell shape (partitioning versus expanding a given volume) is readily recognized when it occurs alone. For example, in the regeneration of vascular strands, new phloem cells are "cut out" of parenchyma cells solely by cell division [Sinnott (141)]. No deformation of wall structure appears to be involved; wall synthesis is obviously required. On the other hand, the elongation of a root hair or the inflation of a giant algal cell such as the internode of *Nitella* has its immediate basis in the expansion of pre-existing surface. This is shown by the fact that marks put on the pre-existing surface separate from one another. That such movement ultimately requires synthesis is unquestioned. The overt morphogenetic phenomenon is, however, a rheological one and must be dissected into its various physical components before meaningful ties to synthesis and other factors, such as wall stresses, can be made.

Because cell division, viewed here as a partitioning process, cannot contribute significant new volume to a developing system, its involvement in organ morphogenesis must be indirect. A particular division pattern could promote, through altered cell physiology and cell physics, a particular pattern of deformation of cell volume which would generate on organ or complex form. The development of the red alga *Callithamnion* provides a striking example [Konrad-Hawkins (74)]. Each cell in the simple uniseriate main axis may expand to produce a single outgrowth or branch. Successive cells alternate in making the outgrowth on the left versus the right side to give the flat thallus a feather-like appearance (Fig. 1). The swellings or

[1] Preparation supported by N.S.F. grant GB 6055X.

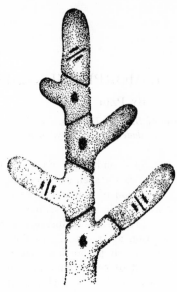

Fig. 1. Shoot tip of the red alga *Callithamnion*. Alternating oblique mitoses in the tip cell produce cells with one long side. This side produces the lateral. Hence the pattern of surface expansion is coupled to previous mitotic events. (After Konrad-Hawkins.)

outgrowths arise on the longest part of the cylindrical surface of the axial cells. The alternating (left versus right) location of this long side in successive cells has its origin in an alternating oblique mitosis of the apical cell. Recently made apical cells form only transverse cross-walls, so there is no long side in the derived cell; in this case no outgrowths arise. In this plant the geometry of wall deformation reflects a previous pattern of mitosis. In organs already initiated, however, there is evidence that cell division relates to histological pattern (as it must in any situation) but is not involved in the course of organ morphogenesis. The normally occurring transverse cross-walls are eliminated when developing leaves of wheat seedlings have received gamma-irradiation [Haber (50)]. The geometrical course of leaf enlargement is normal despite the fact that leaf histological pattern is altered by the presence of abnormally long cells. In this case, the enlargement of cells by distortion (stretching) of the side walls is a sufficient mechanism for the morphogenesis of the organ.

The mode of cell morphogenesis based on cell expansion is thus generally significant in plant development and will form the basis of this review.

For simplicity, it will be examined when it occurs unaccompanied by cell division. We will start to examine the links between cell deformation and its ultimate basis in structure, metabolism, and genetics by considering the immediate cause of change of shape.

The indirect origin of form from cell structure.—A few model examples will show that it is essential to resolve the gross change in shape of a cell into a pattern of local deformations of cell surface before proceeding to deeper questions of mechanism. In the models the shape is always a figure of revolution, and the local deformation behavior is always the same around a given circumference. In this way a 3-dimensional structure can be analysed in terms of only 2 variables, height and radius. In Figure 2, a model cylindrical cell becomes transformed into a trumpet shape.

The pattern of expansion, as resolved into the behavior of small subdivisions of surface, cannot be deduced from the change in cell outline; it must be derived from analysis of material points (wall ornamentation, applied marks, etc.). In the diagram the pattern of local surface change is revealed by the deformation of circles attached to the surface. In *a* the morphogenesis is achieved by a gradient in the rate of surface expansion, the circles remaining circles as they enlarge at different rates. This mode of shape change, a gradient in the rate of isotropic (equal in all directions) surface expansion, is generally the first one to come to mind. Such a pathway for shape change has its obvious potential mechanism in gradients of substances that promote or inhibit expansion rate. As sequence *b* shows, however, the above mode of expansion is not the only one that will produce the same shape change—by the same route of intermediate cell outlines. In *b* we observe a gradient in the direction of surface expansion, the transverse component being strong at the top and weak at the bottom, and the longitudinal component behaving in the opposite way. There is no gradient in the rate of area expansion in this example [Green (47)]. Clearly, many intermediate mixtures of these two extreme pathways could bring about the same change in form.

It is important to note that the second pathway involves variation in direction of maximal expansion. Change in shape brought on by oriented local expansion generally has no obvious immediate explanation in terms of diffusing agents (inhibitors, stimulators, or gene products in any simple sense), but rather must be based on oriented features of the cell such as stress anisotropy or organized wall texture. This oriented stretching or expansion may align cytoplasmic structures such as chloroplasts and microtubules and thus may have effects in addition to the obvious one relating to the shape of the cell. In studying a change in form, it is therefore fruitful on several grounds to first resolve the observed change in cell outline into the behavior of small subdivisions or elements of the cell surface. It is this behavior, not cell form, which can be expected to relate to the details of cell structure and cell physiology.

That local behavior cannot be inferred from the character of cell outline

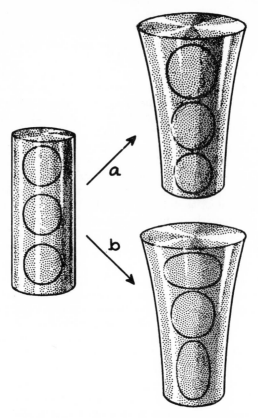

Fig. 2. Two extreme pathways for the deformation of a cylinder to a flaring trumpet shape. Local regions of surface are delimited by circles. In *a* shape change occurs in response to a gradient in the rate of expansion of area. The circles enlarge at varying rates but remain circles. In *b* there is no gradient in rate of expansion (final circle and the elipses have the same area) but there is a gradient in the direction of expansion. (After Green.)

(unless it has natural makings) is also evident in tip-growing cells where expansion is confined to a roughly hemispherical growth zone (hyphae, pollen tubes, root hairs). Such zones continually produce a cylinder at their base. Each point between the very tip and the base of the dome undergoes an apparent migration away from the tip (growth above any such point appears to move it downward). The character of surface distortion of a small region on the hemispherical dome could take many forms, all indistinguishable unless marks on the surface are followed. A small region may be continually enlarged without distortion (Fig. 3A), may be stretched out along the cell axis (Fig. 3B), or may even be primarily stretched laterally along the cell circumference as in Figure 3C [Green & King (49)]. The same possibilities appear present in the initiation of a new axis of growth either in a germinating structure or in the branching of a cylindrical cell. Techniques for measuring extension (and rate of cell division) along one axis are given by Erickson & Sax (35). The 2-dimensional analysis of growing cell surfaces was pioneered by Castle (22). Additional methodology is given by Green (47) and Erickson (34).

In brief, a mechanism of cell morphogenesis must account for a succession of forms, not form per se. The geometrical course of development of a cell can be viewed as the integral, through space and time, of the behavior of small districts of the cell surface. Such behavior, which is described in terms of both the rate and directionality of expansion, will in turn have its origin in the distribution of structural and physiological parameters throughout the cell. Analysis of this sort, traced backwards through the surface behavior generating form, will be attempted for various types of cell morphogenesis.

Related reviews.—Particularly useful reviews of cell wall structure are those by Albersheim (1), Frey-Wyssling (39), Northcote (102), Preston (110–114), Roelofsen (124, 125), Setterfield & Bayley (133), and Wilson (161). Cell walls are discussed in the recent book by Frey-Wyssling & Mühlethaler (38). Aronson (2) and Bartnicki-Garcia (8) have reviewed fungal cell walls. Nickerson & Bartnicki-Garcia (99) have reviewed morphogenesis in lower plants, as has Jaffe (56). Related environmental stimuli are reviewed by Haupt (52). The cytoplasmic structures most closely related to wall formation have been reviewed by Newcomb (96) and by Mühlethaler (91). The Golgi apparatus, reviewed by Mollenhauer & Morré (88), and microtubules, reviewed by Newcomb in this volume, are involved in wall formation. Articles on differentiation [Stange (147, 148); Heslop-Harrison (53)], pollen [Rosen (127)], and stem elongation [Sachs (129)] are apropos.

Scope of the review.—To a somewhat unusual degree, discussion will center around the morphogenesis of cells with exposed surfaces (plant hairs, filamentous and unicellular lower plants). The writer is more familiar with these systems, and they permit more ready analysis because the relation between shape change and local distortion of surface is more readily determined. Also, the stresses within the wall are generated primarily by the cell itself rather than by adjacent tissues.

Cells in tissues are potentially subject to tissue tensions whose magnitude and role are hard to evaluate. For example, the stellate pith cells of *Juncus* have radiating arms connected to other cells via arm tips. It is not clear whether the cells are "pulled out" into this configuration by growth of the epidermis or whether they "push," end-to-end, to increase the diameter of the epidermis. The first alternative is favored by the observation that rapid epidermal growth in stamen filaments can tear the inner cells apart [Schoch-Bodmer (130)]. A pushing role is favored by the finding of a transverse arrangement of cell wall microfibrils typical of actively elongating cells [Mass Geesteranus (78)]. Uncertainty as to the origin of the physical forces deforming the cell delays further analysis.

A strong possibility of tissue effects is found in the development of the palisade layer of leaves where a nearly spherical cell elongates into a cylinder. Slow growth in area of the two surfaces of the leaf would inhibit side-wise expansion of these cells and promote, if not cause, the directed character of their expansion. Excised palisade cells do not elongate but tend to swell in the middle [Joshi & Ball (66)]. This would favor "imposed" directionality of the previous elongation. On the other hand, the elongating cells do have the cell wall fine structure normally associated with independent elongation [von Witsch (163)].

A further variable associated with tissue cells is a more complex wall structure. Thick outer walls of epidermal cells differ in structure from walls in adjacent parenchyma [Roelofsen (124)]. Parenchyma cells themselves contain longitudinal "ribs" of aligned microfibrils. It has been suggested that these ribs are the result of synthesis of cellulose inside the wall [Bayley et al. (12)]. Roelofsen (124, 128), however, has argued that these microfibrils reach their unusual position by a sliding process brought on by tissue tensions. The ribs are missing in the exposed arms of the *Juncus* stellate pith cell, supporting Roelofsen's position. Further, Ray (121) found little or no synthesis of cellulose in the interior of the *Avena* epidermal wall; this may be general. These questions are reviewed by Wilson (161).

THE ELONGATING CYLINDRICAL SURFACE

Many cylindrical cells shift their proportions in favor of increased length by virtue of highly directed (anisotropic) surface expansion occurring along the entire length of the cell. This has been demonstrated with marking studies for the epidermis of *Avena* [Castle (21)] and for the internode of *Nitella* [Green (41)]. An important study of the number and spacing of primary pits in deeper plant tissues by Wilson (159, 160) established this pattern of expansion for cortical cells, in two aquatic angiosperms (at least in the later stages of growth). It may well characterize dividing cells.

The directed aspects of expansion can be characterized in some cases by a single constant: the ratio of the relative growth rates, each expressed as (fraction/time), in the axial and transverse directions. A constant ratio found in both *Nitella* and *Hydrodictyon* correlates with a constancy in the wall's transverse microfibrillar alignment as measured by the quotient (retardation in polarized light/optical thickness) [Green (44)]. The constant wall texture presumably gives the wall a constant anisotropic yielding quality. This, when integrated over space (the cell surface) and time, gives the cell its characteristic shift in proportions during development.

As discussed in the earlier reviews, the typical wall structure for such elongating surfaces has, in parenchyma and certain algal cell walls, an over-all transverse (hoop-like) arrangement of birefringent cellulose microfibrils. It has long been known that the stress pattern in a cylindirical wall favors increase in girth. Therefore the transverse arrangement of microfibrils must so strongly reinforce the wall in that direction that most of the expansion occurs in the axial direction. This has received direct support in a study by Probine & Preston (118, 119) of the mechanical properties of isolated longitudinal and transverse wall strips of *Nitella*. Microfibrils appear to govern the directionality of growth and thus the shape of the cell.

Since the classical work of the late Professor Roelofsen and collaborators (see 124), it has been recognized that the over-all transverse microfibrillar arrangement is actually a steady-state condition—a balance between continual deposition of transverse microfibrillar material at or near the wall inner surface and the realigning action of cell extension, "multi-net growth." Once a given group of microfibrils has been deposited, it suffers both thinning and eventual passive realignment into the longitudinal direction. There is a gradient in microfibrillar orientation from transverse to longitudinal as the growing wall is examined from the inner surface to the outer [Green (43); Probine & Preston (118)]. The transition to longitudinal orientation occurs near the wall outer surface, so the over-all orientation is transverse. The microfibrils thus rotate in a plane tangent to the cell surface; they apparently do not rotate around their own long axis because one crystallographic plane (6.1 A) is typically found parallel to the cell surface (Preston (111)).

That the observed microfibrillar pattern on the wall inner surface is adequate to maintain the less well ordered over-all arrangement in *Nitella* cell walls has been shown by Probine & Barber (117). They examined the possible frictional relation between the microfibrils and the matrix in light of the directed growth of the cell and physical properties of isolated strips of wall. The relation of Bingham flow (linear increase in rate of flow above a threshold value of stress) gave the best fit. Their analysis led to the prediction that at low turgor a cell should grow broader in proportions than at high turgor. That is, cell shape would be a function of the wall stress in excess of the yield stress, but not of the viscosity of the matrix.

A major exception to the correlation between elongating cylindrical surfaces and transverse wall texture is found in the alga *Chaetomorpha*. The cell wall here has two kinds of lamellae which alternate within the wall. One kind has well-ordered microfibrils lying in a slow spiral, and the other has a steep spiral. In some species, a third kind of lamella with microfibrils at an intermediate angle can be detected [Preston (110)]. This kind of wall structure is called "crossed fibrillar" and is common in certain groups of algae, including the ovoid cells of *Valonia*. It may explain the twisting growth in *Chaetomorpha*. It has received intensive study in the laboratory of Preston (109, 112).

While the most widespread crystalline microfibrillar component is cellulose, in fungi chitin (and possibly other aminopolysaccharides) contributes to wall structure. Mannan and xylan are the major structural elements of walls in certain algal groups and in endosperm [Preston (111)]. In certain fungal walls, X-ray diffraction shows that crystallinity appears only after chemical treatment [Kreger (75)]. In cellulose walls, microfibrillar alignment correlates well with the alignment of microtubules in the adjacent cytoplasm (77).

Loss of the normal directionality in elongating cylindrical surfaces: loss of microtubules?—There are several instances of elongating cylindrical surfaces—growing along their length—changing their expansion pattern so as to produce a spherical cell. In *Hydrodictyon africanum* this occurs in normal development and is accompanied by a shift in wall structure, as determined with polarized light, from a predominantly transverse arrangement to a configuration with no over-all orientation [Green (44)]. In *Nitella* a similar loss of the capacity for axially directed expansion and the same shift in wall texture is brought on by growth in colchicine (44), a drug which breaks up microtubules [Pickett-Heaps (106)] and disorganizes secondary wall synthesis. The drug had long been known to produce gross swellings and relatively isodiametric cells in plants [Eigsti & Dustin (33)]. That change in texture was brought on directly by the drug (i.e., it was not a consequence of shape change) has been shown by the drug-induced production of randomly oriented microfibrils on the inner wall surface of cells mechanically restrained from changing form [Green (45)]. This implicated structures of spindle-fiber character (microtubules) in the control of oriented cellulose synthesis.

Many chemically diverse compounds produce a sphering effect. Only rarely has an investigator followed the shift in expansion direction, the ultrastructure, and the chemical composition in one system. Benzimidazole, in the presence of auxin, causes cells of the pea epicotyl to elongate less than normal and to increase in diameter considerably more than normal [Galston et al. (40)]. Probine (116) found that wall chemistry was not appreciably abnormal, but wall structure showed an accumulation of many new longitudinal microfibrils in the region of the longitudinal "ribs" typical of dense tissue parenchyma. This kind of reinforcement could explain the shift in direction of growth provided the longitudinal cellulose bears stress adequately. It was concluded that the drug induced deposition of longitudinally oriented cellulose in the interior of the wall. Since deposition in the wall's interior appears not to occur when directly tested in the normal development of *Avena* coleoptile cells [Ray (121)], other explanations may apply for the pea epicotyl's response. By analogy with the above-mentioned cases in exposed cells, the low negative retardation between ribs—as seen in polarized light—could reflect disorientation of cellulose. This might cause the unusual increase in girth.

There is little structural information on the "sphering up" of cylindrical cells brought on by other reagents. High concentrations of auxin apparently promote increase in diameter at the expense of length in *Helianthus* hypocoty tissue [Diehl et al. (31)]. There is no strong reason to suspect an action on microtubules, although in tissue culture auxin does appear to suppress the formation of microtubules in carrot cells [Halperin & Jensen (51)]. Generally, auxin is believed to "loosen" the matrix components of the wall, so it is possible that excessive loosening diminishes the interaction between microfibrils so that, even though their initial alignment is nearly normal, the effective anisotropy of strength of the wall is lowered and this results in sphering. The herbicide trifluralin, a mitotic poison, causes swollen cells in higher plants [Schultz et al. (131); Bayer et al. (11)]. In *Nitella* it produces spherical cells from young cylindrical internodes. The surface behavior during the transition has not been followed, but the wall texture does shift from predominantly transverse to random (all microfibrils lying in the plane of the wall).

Ethylene, whose production may be a consequence of auxin action [Burg (19)], produces swollen cells; it also promotes the initiation of root hairs [Chadwick & Burg (24)]. Malformin, isolated from fungi, causes cell swelling, probably by the induction of ethylene formation [Curtis (28)].

Because heavy water stabilizes and enhances the birefringence of the mitotic spindle [Inoue & Sato (55)], it might be expected that it would counteract the effects of reagents like colchicine and, if simply included in a normal growth medium, it might be expected to increase the directionality of growth. The reverse effect, however, a swelling of the organ, appears typical [Stein & Forrester (145, 146)]. The forces aligning microtubules in the cell cortex and the spindle may be different.

The surface behavior converting elongation to spherical inflation has apparently not been studied in the above cases. This behavior probably presents one of the simpler entries into experimental morphogenesis for structural-physiological investigation.

Control of oriented cellulose synthesis.—The few studies relating mitotic poisons (which disrupt spindle fibers) to the sphering up of cells implicate microtubules in cellulose orientation despite the fact that the cellulose and microtubules lie on opposite sides of the cell membrane. This situation need not preclude an orienting role for microtubules because the geometrical details of microfibril synthesis and the attendant membrane behavior, with or without specific orientation, are unknown in eukaryotic plants.

Certain particulate structures have been proposed to govern cellulose synthesis and orientation. These are reviewed by Mühlethaler (90, 91). In freeze-etch preparations, 80 Å particles are seen on the outer surface of the membrane and in some cases in the cell wall itself. Fibrous extensions from the particles appear to be microfibrils, although similar extensions are occasionally seen in plastid particles [Staehelin (143, Fig. 23)]. The cell types where these particles were first described (yeast, *Chlorella*, and blue-green algae) do not have well-oriented microfibrillar patterns, so a correlation between microfibrillar orientation and particle alignment (comparable to that between microtubules and cellulose) could not be made. Recently, Northcote & Lewis (103) have seen aligned particles on the outer surface of the plasmalemma in root cells with oriented cellulose. The strands of particles appeared to vary more in orientation and to be very sparse compared to microtubules or microfibrils. Fields showing both abundant parallel microfibrils and membrane (their Fig 12) or abundant microtubules and membrane (their Fig. 14) showed no obvious corresponding aligned pattern of particles on the membranes. The particles were also noted on fractured starch grains.

A clear correlation with larger (500 Å) cytoplasmic elements is seen, however, in shadow-cast replicas of *Chaetomorpha* walls from which the cytoplasm has been removed by plasmolysis [Preston (110)]. Here linear aggregates of cytoplasm (particles or clumps) are seen parallel to the prospective orientation of the next layer of aligned cellulose. It is conceivable, however, that plasmolysis removed a thin wall layer and that the particles reflect rather than anticipate wall orientation.

A diversity of roles has been proposed for the particles seen in or near cell walls. They could serve as initiation centers for microfibrils [Moor & Mühlethaler (89)], as cross-linking *Haftpunkte* between microfibrils (91), or as elements of a three-dimensional lattice through which microfibrillar elongation would proceed only in preferred directions [Preston (110)]. In the last view, the particles would have the property of catalyzing the addition of residues to microfibrils along any of three lines through the particle. In a tight lattice this would permit synthesis to proceed without movement of microfibril or enzyme, but would require truly remarkable catalytic properties for the 500 Å particle.

The particles seen in freeze-etch material have been proposed by Mühlethaler (91) as the form in which a cell wall protein "extensin," described by Lamport (76), is present in walls. This hydroxyproline rich material is thought to be specific to cell walls and involved in their growth. This view has been challenged recently by Steward et al. (149), who found that radioactive proline is not found to be concentrated in cell walls of carrot.

In brief, a role for particles in wall synthesis cannot be excluded, but a strong particle alignment with a relation to known microfibrillar orientation is seen only for large particles in *Chaetomorpha*. In many walls with aligned microfibrillar texture, there is a parallel arrangement of microtubules and cellulose microfibrils. This suggests a causal role for the former in oriented synthesis, and thereby in the succession of cylindrical forms assumed in elongation.

De novo origin of elongating cylindrical cell walls.—The wall-less and motile swarmer cells of *Hydrodictyon* assemble into a net pattern on the inner wall surface of the parent cell. The cells elongate as cylinders from points of contact and appear, in polarized light, to have walls with transverse texture [Diehl et al (31); Green (44)]. It is not known if there is a transitory first-formed wall with random microfibrils as found in germlings of *Chaetomorpha* and *Cladophora* [Nicolai & Preston (101)]. Wall texture in *Hydrodictyon* may have its origin in some structural feature of the swarmer; directionality based on stresses generated by cell-versus-cell "pushing" [McReynolds (80)] seems unlikely because the net could bend before appreciable stresses could be produced.

Origin from apical cells.—The surface of the *Nitella* internode comes ultimately from that of a single apical cell. Assuming that surface elongation is based on transverse microfibril deposition and that this in turn is somehow controlled by a transverse arrangement of microtubules [Nagai & Rebhun (94); Pickett-Heaps (105)], there are two major questions: (*a*) How do the microtubules retain a transverse position in the face of longitudinal surface extension; and (*b*) how do they initially achieve this position? Only highly tentative answers can be given.

Conceivably, retention of orientation could be based on a hoop-like arrangement of the microtubules. As long as the microtubules, singly or in aggregate, ringed the cell vacuole, they could not be strain-oriented into the longitudinal direction without breaking or extending as chords through the cell interior. This method of maintaining transverse alignment in spite of longitudinal strain was suggested long ago for microfibrils by Diehl et al (31).

The elongating surface of an internode is derived from the surface of the apical cell. This cell has a random pattern of microfibrils [Green (42)] and presumably a random arrangement of microtubules in the cell cortex. Marking experiments show a predominating transverse stretch at the base of this cell [Green & King (49)]; this could be the process which first gives the microtubules their preferred orientation. Once transversely aligned, they would be expected to be associated with transverse microfibrils whose presence would redirect expansion into its definitive longitudinal character. Microtubular details over these stages are unknown, but transversely oriented cellulose can be detected *in vivo* shortly after the temporary circumferential stretch. This stretch could in turn have its origin in a gradient of wall thickness or extensibility in the apical cell wall [Green & King (49)].

This view that oriented strains can establish the normal transverse microfibril synthesis is bolstered by the observation that a new (branch) axis of growth—with wall structure appropriate to that axis—can be mechanically induced in *Nitella* internodes [Green (44)].

Consequences of oriented expansion of cylindrical surfaces.—The directed stretching of cell surfaces can influence the subjacent cytoplasm. In *Nitella* internodes a slightly oblique (nealy transverse) wall texture is capable of explaining the twisting aspect of elongation characteristic of that cell [Probine & Preston (115)]. The total amount of twist measured on the wall surface corresponds to that shown in the parallel chloroplast files [Green (41)], so the surface growth pattern appears to strain-align the chloroplast files. Parallel to the plastid files, and just interior to them, microfilaments can be seen in the electron microscope (Nagai & Rebhun (94)]. They are apparently at the site of the motive force for the protoplasmic stream [Kamiya (68)]. Therefore the strain pattern of the wall, acting to align the plastid layer, would ultimately establish the helical streaming pattern. That the stream direction is a determining agent in the orientation of cellulose deposition, rather than a remote consequence of it as suggested here, has also been proposed by Probine (115).

Chloroplasts in a young cell which has been mechanically inhibited from expanding lose both the directed character of their expansion and their capacity to divide [Green (46)]. Thus the oriented behavior of certain organelles can be shown to be ultimately dependent on the oriented behavior of the cell wall. The apparent helical alignment of phytochrome in *Mougeotia* could be based on previous helical growth of cell surface [Haupt (52)], possibly extending this generalization to the molecular level.

In cells which are both elongating and dividing, cross-walls are usually at right angles to the direction of maximum expansion. This correlation is valid for both long and short cells in rib meristems, the cambium, etc., so some connection between these two directed aspects of development could be sought.

The exceptional case of the normal division of the guard mother cell of stomata can be brought into conformity with this generalization after chemical treatment. Stebbins (144) has suggested that the effective reagents alter the timing of preceding mitosis, thereby altering subsequent cell shapes and strain patterns. By exaggerating longitudinal extension, gibberellic acid appears occasionally to reorient a division plane in *Avena* stomate formation [Kaufman (69, Fig. 10)]. The site of junction of a future cross wall and the side wall is marked by microtubules before division [Pickett-Heaps & Northcote (107, 108)].

In summary, the directed expansion of cylindrical cell surfaces appears based on continuous oriented wall synthesis which is related to transversely aligned microtubules. The origin and maintenance of this alignment is far from certain. A correlation between a transitory circumferential stretch and the origin of transverse wall texture can be seen, however, in early developmental stages in *Nitella*. The oriented growth of the internode is thus traceable, in principle only, back to oriented events in the apical cell. The consequences of oriented expansion in cylindrical cells are more clear. In *Nitella* they include not only the typical shift in proportions seen in cell development but also an aligning action on the chloroplast files, an action which influences their growth and division and also the direction of the cytoplasmic stream.

It is thus evident that many oriented features of development may be the result of long chains of transfer of information pertaining to direction. The transfer could involve strain alignment, crystallization, or possibly other processes such as electrophoresis. The role of the genome in this aspect of development appears not to involve a simple coding of directional information but rather the specification of a complex cytoplasm capable of responding to external and internal directional "cues" (including mechanical ones) and capable of compounding this information to control the geometrical course of cell development.

TIP GROWTH

KINETIC AND STRUCTURAL CHARACTERIZATION

Tip growth designates the activity in a dome-shaped growth zone which typically generates a cylindrical cell surface at its base. The best studied examples are tips of pollen tubes, hyphae, and root hairs. Ordinarily the cylindrical part of a tip-growing cell does not change shape except to initiate branches. An exceptional secondary inflation of the cylindrical part is seen, however, in ring closure of nematode-trapping fungi. The tripling of cell volume takes 0.1 sec [Higgins & Pramer (54)]. Formation of arthrospores in fungi also involves a rounding up of hyphal segments.

It is sometimes assumed that the essential feature of tip growth in cylindrical cells is the restriction of surface expansion to a terminal region of the cell. Restriction per se is clearly not a sufficient explanation because this is compatible with growth producing a variety of shapes at the cell tip. In *Phycomyces,* for example, both the steady elongation of the tip of the cylindrical sporangiophore in the early stages and the later swelling of the tip into the round sporangium involve a restricted apical growth zone in the same cell [Castle (23)]. The particular surface behavior needed to insure that a hemispherical growth zone does generate a cylinder at its base has been described in part by de Wolff & Houwink (30) and by Green & King (49). Assuming the growth is radially symmetrical, there are three interacting parameters: shape of the growth zone, the gradient in local rate of area expansion (at different distances down the dome), and directionality of this expansion. If, for example, expansion is to be the same in all directions (isotropic as in Fig. 3A) and in all regions, and if the shape is to stay hemispherical, then the gradient in local relative rate of expansion of area must decrease as a cosine function as points are examined from the tip of the dome (maximum rate) to its base (line m in Fig. 3A). Rate would be proportional to the cosine of the angle (α in Fig. 3B) whose vertex is the center of curvature of the dome and whose arms connect this point to the tip of the dome and to the point in question. This stems from the finding that isotropic expansion requires a point to move down the profile (m in Fig. 3A) with a velocity proportional to its distance (r in Fig. 3A) from the cell's axis of rotation, a sine function [Green & King (49)]. The relative elemental rate of extension of a short meridional line segment through the point would be the derivative of this, with respect to distance down the profile, a cosine function. The relative rate of increase in the area around the point would be twice this if growth were undirected. This area rate gradient, therefore, would be a cosine function as one considered the descending rate from the tip of the dome to its base. The gradient in the rate at which small regions expand will take different forms depending upon the directed character of expansion (see Fig. 3).

Rate gradients within the tip growth zone.—Several types of evidence indicate that the expansion rate is maximal at the extreme tip of the zone and that expansion is approximately isotropic (the same in all directions in the plane of the wall) at the tip and sometimes transverse at the base: (*a*) When pairs of marks are seen along the profile of the zone, they often do not show separation from each other as they move from lower regions of the dome to the cylindrical part. Since diameter at the region of the marks does increase during this movement, expansion must be primarily along lines of cell circumference (Fig. 3C). Because the extension along the meridian (profile) has ceased, and the relative increase in circumference is small, the over-all growth rate at the base must be small also. Marks behaving this way are seen in hyphal tips [Reinhardt (122); Stadler (142)], and on the surface of *Nitella* apical cells [Green (47)]. (*b*) The microfibrillar texture on the inner surface of such growth zones is either isotropic or slightly transverse, the outer surface being either isotropic or slightly longitudinally aligned [Roelofsen (125)]. There is thus little evidence for well-ordered deposition of fibrils and there is only weak passive alignment of microfibrils (some of it possibly in the flattening required to make metal-shadowed preparations). Strunk (151, 152) reports a concentric arrangement on a hyphal tip, but a random arrangement appears typical in fungi [Scurfield (132); Manocha & Colvin (84)]. The failure of Rosen (126) to find morphogenetic effects of colchicine on pollen tube development also weighs against a significant role for microtubules and oriented cellulose in growth of this cell type. Rosen & Gawlik (128) found no microtubules in lily pollen. These observations speak for nearly isotropic expansion, a condition coupled to a gradient from high expansion rate at the tip to low at the base. (c) In the tropistic response, tip growth zones generally grow toward increasing concentrations of growth stimulants [Rosen, on pistil factor and pollen (126)] and away from increasing concentrations of growth retardants [Stadler, on hyphae (142)]. Stimulants apparently bring on bulging at the very tip, in the direction of the stimulant; if growth took place primarily in subapical collars, the cell would grow away from the side rich in the stimulant (142). Curiously, in snapdragon pollen, Ca^{++} is a natural attractant [Mascarenhas & Machlis (86, 87)] and presumed stimulant even though in *Avena* parenchyma cells it is a "wall hardener" [Tagawa & Bonner (153)]. (*d*) Autoradiographic studies show maximum incorporation of wall precursor at the very tip of hyphae of *Mucor* [Bartnicki-Garcia & Lippman (9)]. Presumably, incorporation reflects rate of wall expansion as well as synthesis.

The maintenance of a steep descending gradient in relative rate of area expansion within the apical dome appears to be the essential basis for the generation of cylindrical form in tip-growing cells. While the formation of a secondary wall in the cylindrical part could account for the cessation of expansion at the base of the dome, this is not a general explanation because the secondary wall is first clearly seen only several cell diameters below the tip [Newcomb & Bonnett (97)] in the radish root hair, and because this wall is missing in *Neurospora* [Manocha & Colvin (83)].

The rate limiting process.—If tip growth is maintained through a specific gradient in rate of expansion of surface, it is significant to inquire how expansion rate is controlled. It could be controlled by wall thickness, but no obvious gradient is seen in hyphae [McClure et al (79)] or root hairs [Bonnett & Newcomb (14)]. Given constant wall thickness, the stresses tending to expand the wall would actually be greater at the base of the dome than at tip, so the observed opposite gradient in rate must reflect complex control of wall yielding.

While in principle a wall could yield in a viscous fashion to turgor stresses without any active loosening by the cell, a concurrent lytic action is highly probable. The coordinated turning and subsequent fusion of hyphae suggest that controlled wall dissolution is a part of normal growth in fungi. The germination of walled spores and zygotes must involve local wall softening. All forms of delayed cell branching (e.g., root hair formation) suggest a weakening of the wall. Experimentally it can be shown that the cytoplasm of *Nitella* acts upon the wall to lower its yield threshold when growth is stopped osmotically. The "softened" wall can resume growth at reduced turgor even though wall thickness apparently increases [Green (48)]. This suggests that in the absence of elongation the loosening action predominates over the addition of new wall mass, giving a net weakening of the wall. To account for the obvious balance between these two processes during normal elongation, the phenomenon of strain-hardening (increase in strength in response to being stretched) may be invoked [Cleland (25)]. If this is a property of the intact cell wall, it would counteract excessive growth rate. The preponderant softening action during osmotic inhibition may be the natural activity which promotes growth when the rate is low. Such a scheme could incorporate stability into the yielding process.

Tip growth can withstand certain perturbations of the environment (small changes in osmolarity of the medium), but in fungi the internal controls, whatever they may be, cannot accommodate large shifts in turgor [Robertson (123)]. The original growth zone often becomes inextensible and cannot resume activity when turgor is restored and a new zone appears below it. The opposite effect—excessive loosening—is seen under anaerobiosis where tip-growth zones can soften to the point of bursting [Frey-Wyssling (39)].

In view of the stability of tip growth, within limits, it may be an oversimplification to seek a single reaction or enzyme as the key governing factor in determining rate. The simplest functional unit of growth may be a process as complicated as the fusion of small vesicles into the wall and cell membrane.

Cytoplasmic structure.—Most of the major cell organelles (mitochondria, nuclei, Golgi apparatus, endoplasmic reticulum) are relatively excluded from the dome-shaped part of the tip-growing cell. In the subapical part of a single *Chara* rhizoid, however, Sievers (136) estimates there are 25,000 dictyosomes! Golgi are rare in hyphae [Bracker (15)], so the vesicles seen in growth zones presumably come from the endoplasmic reticulum. The growing region in root hairs is rich in ribosomes and, most strikingly, in vesicles of various sorts [Newcomb & Bonnett (97); Bonnett & Newcomb (14)]. This corresponds to cytochemical findings of RNA and polysaccharides by Dashek & Rosen (29).

Microtubules appear to be prominent only when there is a parallel textured secondary wall. They are seen in the cylindrical part of *Chara* rhizoids [Sievers (136, 137)] but are absent in many hyphae [McClure et al. (79)]. In radish root hairs, microtubules extend further toward the cell apex than does the secondary wall (97). This observation opposes the generalization that aligned microtubules are associated with oriented wall synthesis. It is possible, however, that here the microtubules adjacent to the random cellulose are not yet mature enough to have an orienting role; that no wall synthesis occurs in this part of the cell (between the dome and apical end of the secondary wall); or that some oriented synthesis does occur but cannot be detected in sectioned material (shadowed wall surfaces are more diagnostic in this regard).

Vesicles in tip growth zones.—The vesicles prominent in tip growth zones have a diameter of 50 to 200 mμ and appear to originate in the Golgi complex [Sievers (134)] or, in fungi, in other membranous structures [Bracker (15); Marchant et al. (85)]. Smooth vesicles, which show only a single line boundary after glutaraldehyde-osmium preparation, appear to empty their contents directly into the cell wall (also contributing their membrane to the plasmalemma) or into somewhat diffuse "fibrous inclusions" which often lack a limiting membrane [Bonnett & Newcomb (14)]. Presumably, these inclusions ultimately become part of the growing wall. There appears to be a maturation of vesicle contents, including increased stainability [Sievers (135–137)], and the development of a fibrous appearance (14) along the apparent route of migration from the dictyosome to the wall. Other vesicles take on a coated appearance after budding from larger vesicles associated with the dictyosomes. These are also found near the cell wall, but the appearance of fusion with it is only rarely encountered. There is evidence from other systems that the coated vesicles are involved in protein transport, and in the radish root hair it has been suggested that they transport enzymes to sites of both primary and secondary wall synthesis (14). In rhizoids of *Chara,* the "microvesicles" (diameter 50 mμ) are abundant in the tip regions [Sievers (138)]. They appear to be identical with "coated visicles" of root hairs and arise from multivesicular bodies

[Sievers (139)]. In hyphae, multivesicular bodies and "lomasomes" may be involved in synthesis [Marchant et al. (85)]. Similar structures appear in algae [Barton (10); Crawley (27)].

In a noteworthy series of papers, Sievers has shown that variation in the path of Golgi vesicles correlates with the early stages of the geotropic response of the rhizoid of *Chara* (136–140). When the rhizoid is made horizontal, statoliths in proximal regions of the dense cytoplasm near the growing tip fall toward the lower wall. Their accumulation appears to deflect upward the path of Golgi vesicles as they move from their origin in proximal dictyosomes to their usual site of fusion at the tip of the growth zone. The deflection yields an abundance of vesicles fusing with the wall in regions unusually distant from the tip of the cell. Thus if vesicle-to-wall fusion is considered a rate-limiting step in growth, the growth zone is not only made asymmetrical in its activity but is also made unusually long in the upper part of the cell. These adjustments require 5 to 10 min and precede actual curvature. It thus appears that a vesicle may contain lytic enzymes to loosen and expand the wall. The same vesicle may also contribute enough mass to the wall to maintain wall thickness and strength after the expansion.

The material covered so far, the kinetics of the cell wall expansion rate, and the prominance of vesicles in the adjacent cytoplasm, suggest certain possible interactions. Migration (or fusion) rate could be a function of growth rate. Since the vesicles show various stages of maturation of their contents en route to the wall [Sievers (136)], variation in the migration time of vesicles might therefore automatically change the chemical nature of the materials being added to the wall. Conceivably, these variations might stiffen the wall under conditions of rapid growth (the vesicles would be immature) or soften the wall when growth was slow (the vesicles would be overripe). The accumulation of vesicles is actually visible *in vivo* in certain fungi as a *Spitzenkörper* [McClure et al. (79)]. After a growth arrest, reformation of this body precedes any elongation—suggesting that vesicles might serve to loosen the wall only after a period of maturation. Such speculation would have more merit if the kinetics of vesicle fusion could be quantitatively related to wall expansion rate. Unfortunately, the relative abundance of vesicle fusion figures in electron micrographs does not unequivocally relate to the frequency of fusions. (It could equally well reflect the duration of the fusion process in various parts of the cell.) Awareness of the unsolved questions and complex possibilities already raised may aid in the evaluation of experimental work on tip growth.

Experimental Modification of Tip Growth

The literature on this subject reveals two large classes of experimentation. In one, an oriented factor (unilateral light, pH gradients, etc.) is brought to bear on growing or germinating cells, and a correlation with the orientation of subsequent growth is sought. In the other, a nondirected variable, either environmental (pCO_2, osmotic pressure, unusual nutrients, etc.) or internal (a particular form of a gene) can be made present or absent. Correlations with the presence or absence of a particular cell form are obtained. Details about intermediate steps, such as altered chemistry of wall formation, are often sought.

Experimental study of the orientation of growth.—These are often termed "polarity" experiments; many are reviewed by Haupt (52) and Jaffe (56, 59). Experiments of this sort may be screened for data which would relate the perception (interaction within the cell) of the orienting agent to the gradient in local growth rate which is believed to characterize tip growth. With orientation by light, there are several cases which do present an intriguing parallel. Polarized light, falling vertically on the growing hypha tips of *Penicillium glaucum,* brings on elongation at right angles to the vibration plane of the light [Etzold (36)]. Assuming that tip growth here involves the already described gradient in growth rate down the dome-shaped growth zone (rate decreases as a cosine function as points farther down the dome are examined, as in Fig. 3A), a direct parallel between local rate of growth and the amplitude of light absorbed is possible. Oriented dichroic photoreceptors in the cell cortex are typically involved in the response of spores to polarized light [Jaffe (57); Jaffe & Etzold (60)]. If in the cortex of these hyphae such photoreceptors were oriented parallel to the cell surface, then in the horizontal plane at least there would be a fall-off in the relative amplitude of light absorbed (as a function of distance down the dome-shaped cell) which would also decrease as a cosine function. Intensity would decrease as cosine.[2] Local growth rate, in light, could thus be a simple function of the amount of light absorbed. A similar relationship could be present in the chloronema of the moss *Funaria* [Jaffe & Etzold (61)].

There is considerable evidence that many orienting agents active on spores or zygotes do not work directly through a gradient in their interaction within the cell, as could be the case above. Rather, the interaction is highly amplified to give the response, or, to put it another way, the applied influence acts on a metastable cell cortex to trigger a growth response. The evidence follows: (*a*) In the action of light gradients on germinating cells, increasing the steepness of the gradient improves the degree of statistical orientation of the outgrowths, but does not obviously alter the size or shape of the germinating structure. This is true when the gradient is light working on zygotes of *Fucus* [Jaffe (57)] or a diffusing agent working on germinating *Botrytis* spores [Müller & Jaffe (92)]. The orienting agent thus appears to contribute little in the way of energy or information needed for protrusion formation per se but merely signals where the protrusion will be made. The fact that germination can occur in the absence of the experimental orienting agent supports this view. (*b*) The area of the outgrowth initially involves only a few percent of the cell cortex. The gradient of light absorption within this small area would probably be too small to be effec-

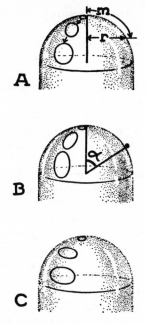

FIG. 3. The various modes of surface enlargement possible in a hemispherical growth zone. Depending upon
the pattern of the velocity of a small
area moving down m, in relation to
its distance r from the axis of rotation, a small area may be enlarged
without distortion as in A, extended
longitudinally as in B, or extended
transversely as in C. Some hyphae
and the *Nitella* apical cell behave as
in C. Most tip-growing cells behave
approximately as in A. (After Green
& King.)

tive. Presumably, the intensity gradient across the whole cell is perceived,
then the protrusion is triggered at a low point in the gradient. The equivalence of oriented response between half-illuminated cells and cells illuminated with plane polarized light strongly indicates that at least 90° of the
cell perimeter is involved in perception, even though only a small fraction is
involved in the response [Jaffe & Etzold (60)]. (c) In *Botrytis* spores subjected to intense unilateral illumination, the outgrowth often appears midway between two regions where it would be expected on the basis of the
response to weaker light. This appears to reflect summation, in this region,
of influences from the two centers (60). Here again the geometry of the

protrusion itself is quite restricted compared to the large regions of the cell cortex involved in perception.

Müller & Jaffe (92) have shown that a diffusing macromolecule may be involved in the control of oriented germination in *Botrytis*. When subjected to slow flow of the aquatic environment, the stationary spores germinate downstream, the direction in which the molecule would accumulate. If this same molecular gradient were essential to continued growth, the absence, not presence, of the molecule would have to correlate with high growth rate because the environment of the hyphal tip pushing through the medium would be equivalent to the upstream side of a stationary but unilaterally irrigated spore.

While gradients of light and of large molecules seen in flow studies are active in orienting germination, their direct involvement in the physics of tip growth is considered unlikely. Electrical currents and ion gradients, however, appear not only to act to orient germination but may be involved in the normal tip-growth mechanism as well. Jaffe (58) has shown that an electrical current flows through the germinating *Fucus* zygote as the protrusion (rhizoid) elongates. The current might suffice to concentrate particles in the size range 0.01 to 0.1 μ at the rhizoid tip. Golgi vesicles might be influenced. Bentrup et al. (13) have oriented *Fucus* eggs by potassium and hydrogen ion gradients. They concluded that the gradients act by establishing a voltage gradient across the cytoplasm. In general terms, it is possible that the current, through an electrophoretic action on cell contents, promotes the process which causes it. These general possibilities are reviewed by Jaffe (59) and Neuscheler & Jaffe (95). On the basis of turning maneuvers seen in hyphae tips, Park & Robinson (104) propose that hyphae continuously emit a growth retardant (to explain the "repulsion" of an approaching tip by a mature hypha) and also remove it locally at the very tip (to explain the "attraction" and fusion sometimes seen between two hyphal tips). The question of what maintains the gradient in expansion rate in tip-growth zones contains the subquestion of whether the basic mechanism includes components outside the cell membrane (but possibly in the cell wall, as in aerial hyphae). The above studies suggest that they do.

Experimental study of the form of tip-growing cells.—Experimental variables in this category do not contain an oriented or vectorial component. They include genetic, nutritional, and environmental factors.

Genetic analysis.—The chain of causation between gene and morphological expression in tip-growing forms can be approached, from the gene end, by the analysis of mutations. In *Neurospora* about 100 morphological mutants are known. These differ from the traditional metabolic mutants in being relatively autonomous; they are less subject to modification by environmental factors, and the deficiency is not usually restorable by an exogenous supply of gene product [Tatum & Luck (154)], although exceptions will appear below.

Certain poorly growing mutants have been shown to be non-nuclear in nature, the character being transferrable by cytoplasmic injections. An abnormal type of mitochondrion, replicating more rapidly than the normal, appears to be the effective agent (154).

In a thorough investigation of a nuclear mutation more closely related to form, Brody & Tatum (16) showed that the earliest identifiable gene product associated with an abnormal mycelial type was an abnormal form of glucose-6-phosphate dehydrogenase (G6PDH). The mutant, *col*, had slow-growing dense colonies with bulbous cells rich in branch points; it had a form of the enzyme that was more heat labile and that had a different affinity for substrates. Strains with this form of the enzyme invariably had high levels of glucose-6-phosphate (G6P). Genetic reversion of colony form coincided with a reversion to the normal form of the enzyme, indicating that the *col* locus is the structural gene for the enzyme. The same colony form could be found, however, with wild-type nuclei, provided they were grown on sorbose. Other nuclear mutations give the *col* growth form but not the mutant form of the enzyme, as judged by the normal level of G6P. This shows that the *col* growth habit does not cause the abnormal enzyme but also that other genetic and nutritional variations lead to the same morphological peculiarity. It is likely that some late step in the carbohydrate chemistry of the cell wall (perhaps only indirectly influenced by levels of G6PDH) is altered by the diverse treatments that can lead to the *col* morphology. Mahadevan & Tatum (81) found that one cell wall fraction (one containing glucan, galactosamine, and amino acids) varied in *col* relative to normal mycelia. The direction of variation from normal was, however, not consistent. Analyses were of whole mycelia rather than the growing regions. Later it was shown that this form-related chemical fraction comes from a outer wall layer of thick fibrils. This layer might be wall present in the growth zone. An inner layer contains thin fibrils of chitin [Mahadevan & Tatum (82)].

Generally, difficulty of analysis of a mutation increases rapidly with greater distance (in terms of steps) from the gene. In related work on the Basidiomycete *Schizophyllum*, Wessels & Niederpruem (158) have correlated the activity of a wall glucan degrading enzyme with the operation of one genetically determined developmental sequence (alteration in septum structure and stability) governing dikaryon formation [Raper & Raper (120)]. In the same genus, cellobiose (but not maltose) induces wavy and highly branched hyphae. Cellobiose derepresses a glucanase which apparently lowers the proportion of a β-1, 3 glucan in the wall [Wilson & Niederpruem (162)]. The link between these chemical-enzymatic studies and the physical nature of tip growth has not been elucidated in detail.

Interconversion between filamentous tip growth and budding.—Johnson & Gibson (64, 65) have shown wall precursors to be incorporated primarily in one growing end in fission-yeasts and in the distal region of buds in budding yeasts. Assuming this incorporation (into β-3 glucan) reflects surface expansion, many fungi seem to show localized growth. Certain mutant forms of the yeast *Candida albicans* show filamentous rather than budding growth. Normal and mutant growth behavior is often described by the contrasting terms "dividing" and "divisionless." Much of the literature on this "dimorphism" implies fundamental differences in growth mechanism, including a difference in the chemistry of the rate-limiting reaction in the cell wall [Falcone & Nickerson (37); Nickerson & Falcone (100)].

The two modes of growth appear, however, to be very closely related and can give about the same rate of growth [Ward (156)]. A budding cell can bud repeatedly at or near the same end, so it would appear to involve only a minor modification in growth pattern to have periodic budding, at the same relative position of a cell, give rise to a beaded filament. As the periodic nature of budding became continuous, the filament would lose the periodic bulging appearance and resemble a hypha. All of these intermediate forms are seen in the mutant strain when it is cultured on the same agar with the normal form (156). The local expansion behavior of the growing surface in the two forms has not been described.

The diffusing factor which restores budding to the filamentous mutant appears to involve reduced organic sulfur because it can be replaced by cysteine or reduced glutathione (156). The filamentous form can reduce dyes very effectively (more so than the normal strain) but seems unable to carry out some reduction, presumably involving sulfur, needed for budding. In *C. albicans,* Nickerson has shown that the hyphal form has a lower level of an enzyme, protein disulphide reductase, than is found in the yeast form. Moreover, the wall contains a gluco-mannan-protein complex rich in sulfur which is partly oxidized to disulfides [Falcone & Nickerson (37)]. While the enzyme is found in mitochondria and the assay involves previous chemical oxidation of the protein in the wall, it has been suggested that wall softening by enzymatic reduction of the disulfides is the essential basis for budding. How the wall softening is accomplished in the filamentous form, which grows at the same rate and which also contains gluco-mannan-protein in similar amount [Nickerson (98)], is not clear. It seems at least equally reasonable to suggest that the differences in sulfur metabolism between the two strains deals not with a fundamental difference in the nature of the rate-limiting reaction of surface expansion, but rather with the control of the spatial distribution of a yielding process which may be identical in the two forms.

Yeast-like and mycelial forms of *Histoplasma* and *Saccharomyces* can be produced by nutritional variations. The yeast-form walls were relatively high in chitin but low in mannose and amino acids. Of 17 amino acids detected, only methionine (trace amounts in both) contained sulfur [Dormer, Hamilton & Harkin (32)]. The keratin-like protein of *C. albicans* was apparently absent. The wall of *Saccharomyces* appears to lack sulfhydrils [Mundkur (93)]. The glucan-galactosamine-peptide in the wall of *Neurospora* appears to lack sulfur [Mahadevan & Tatum (81)]. Thus, few tested cell types appear to contain wall structure with the disulfide bonds and sulfhydril groups needed to give a protein disulfide reductase a possible general direct role in wall alteration. The assays may, however, suffer from breakdown of sulfur amino acids during hydrolysis.

In the mold *Mucor,* a conversion of the typical filamentous elongation to a budding growth habit can be brought on by high concentrations of CO_2. A clear and well-illustrated review is provided by Bartnicki-Garcia (7). Concentrations of CO_2 (pCO_2 of 0.3 atm or more) are most effective if oxygen is excluded from the mixture. Pure nitrogen yields the filamentous form. The morphogenetic effects correlate well with the actual uptake of CO_2, presumably by the malic enzyme whose optimum pCO_2 is near the peak concentration for the developmental response. The main product is a 4 carbon dicarboxylic acid. The major chemical difference in wall composition between the two forms involve greater mannan and protein in the yeast form. It is suggested, therefore, that the CO_2 fixation enhances mannan-protein production (7). While yeast-form walls appear thicker (and double-layered) in the electron microscope, the over-all wall synthesis is roughly comparable on a weight basis. It is not clear whether the difference in mannan and protein, found for whole walls, also characterizes the small fraction of the wall undergoing expansion. The metabolic alterations bringing on budding may therefore involve the control and distribution of the expansion process, rather than a drastic change in its chemical nature (7). This is supported by the highly localized incorporation of radioactive wall precursor in the tip of hyphae, compared to a more scattered pattern in the yeast form [Bartnicki-Garcia & Lippman (9)].

In related yeast, Johnson (62, 63) has shown lysis at the growing region to be brought on by 2-deoxy-glucose. He suggests that rupture occurs because this glucose analogue interferes with the intercalation of new residues in the midregions of glucan chains. All cell wall polymers are believed, however, to grow at one or both ends, not in the middle [Roelofsen (125)], so matrix substances are probably involved.

Origin of Tip Growth

Tip-growing cell surfaces commonly originate from spherical spores or zygotes, from the sides of cylindrical cells, or, in the remarkable case of the desmids, from the cross-wall of the previous cell division.

The maintenance of tip growth involves the perpetuation of certain types of gradients in local expansion rate down the dome-shaped growth zone. The origin clearly involves the initial establishment of such gradients. Very little kinetic data appears available for the conversion of a flat area into a hemisphere. This phenomenon has been only crudely explored in simple models by Green & King (49). A rubber membrane, fixed like a drumhead over a cup, can be deformed into a near-hemispherical shape by evacuating the cup. Markings on the membrane show that when the membrane is of uniform thickness, there is a gradient in amount of isotropic expansion from the center to the rim, the maximum being in the center. When the membrane initially has a thickness gradient from the center to the rim, the deformation is no longer isotropic because circles drawn on the membrane are pulled out along lines of longitude on the dome-shaped structure. A thickness gradient falling from the rim to the center gives the opposite effect: circles are pulled out along lines of latitude. This latter effect, which is actually observed in the initial swelling of leaf apical cells in *Nitella,* could serve to align microtubules into the transverse orientation, an alignment which they maintain in cylindrical cells of this genus [Pickett-Heaps (105)]. The coupling between a gradient in yielding rate and a specific orientation of distortion of surface in a swelling structure may be of some significance in the generation of oriented textures in biological systems [Green & King (49)].

Two major unanswered questions about the origin of tip growth appear to be: (*a*) what initially delimits the base of the swelling; and (*b*) what ensures that the swelling does not balloon up into a vesicle (bud) but rather extends as a cylinder with a diameter about equal to the base of the swelling.

Origin from the spore or zygote.—This subject was discussed under the control of tip growth by oriented aspects of the environment. Appropriate reviews are by Jaffe (56), Haupt (52), and Bünning (17). Most recently it has been shown that the electrical current which approximately coincided with the appearance of the rhizoid in *Fucus* actually precedes the protrusion in the germination of *Pelvetia* [Jaffe (59)]. This current may be an intermediate between the light stimulus which orients development and the physical manifestation of growth.

Origin from the sides of cylindrical cells.—The most studied process of this sort is the origin of the root hair which, in grasses, occurs just prior to the cessation of elongation of the epidermal cell. Avers and associates (3–6) have applied cytochemical tests for various kinds of enzymatic activity in prospective hair-bearing and hairless cells. In some grasses these cell types are identifiable after an asymetrical division in the young epidermis; in other grasses a prediction is not possible. Their survey, limited by the availability of tests, did not discover any one enzyme universally correlated with root hair production. In the class with the asymmetrical division, some enzymes appeared prominent in the prospective hair-bearing cell while at least one enzyme appeared relatively excluded.

The role of calcium in the initiation and growth of root hairs has been reviewed and debated [Street (150)]. Ethylene definitely promotes the formation of root hairs [Burg (18); Chadwick & Burg (24)]. At the same time, it brings on the production of relatively isodiametric cortical and epidermal cells [Burg & Burg (20)]. Whether the promotion of initiation of tip growth is based on the condition of the wall or the unusual proportions of the cell (presumably brought on by the previous condition of the wall) is unknown.

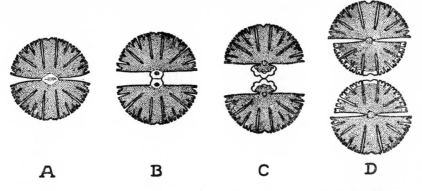

A   B   C   D

FIG. 4. Sequence of stages in the formation of new semicells in desmids.
(After Waddington.)

Origin in the cross wall.—In the desmids, the new cross-wall splits into two lamellae, one for each daughter cell. Each such lamella becomes, in effect, a primary wall which then expands enormously to form an entire new semicell (Fig. 4). A cross-wall thus becomes a side wall. The opposite relation occurs in cocci where a localized band on the side of the cell grows in so as to "pinch" the cell into two [Cole & Hahn (26)]. Waris & Kallio (157) have recently reviewed this morphogenesis in desmids. Mutants, almost certainly of a cytoplasmic sort because they can be formed in relatively high yield by mild techniques such as cold treatment and centrifugation, lack one or two lobes of the three that characterize each semicell. It has been postulated that three cytoplasmic "axes" pass through the isthmus and govern the formation of the lobes. Mutation is thought to be the loss of an axis and reversion to be its restoration by duplication of an unaffected axis and the subsequent relocation of the extra axis to re-establish normal form. Attempts to find structural evidence for the axes, however, have yielded little [Waddington (155)]. The future lobes appear to have their earliest manifestation in the form of thickness variations in swollen form of the cross-wall which appears when growth is osmotically inhibited [Kiermayer (72)]. Thin regions in it correspond to prospective major indentations between lobes [Kiermayer & Jarosch (73)]. These minima correspond to attachment-sites of the plasmolysed protoplast [Kiermayer (70)], suggesting that at least the main outlines of cell form correlate with cell membrane properties immediately after division. The wall appears to be semifluid and the indentations of the septum can be seen to suddenly "evert" smoothing the outline of septum (72). Kiermayer suggests that this results from the breakage of certain cytoplasmic strands which can be seen penetrating the wall, particularly at thickness minima (71). Upon return to normal turgor, the wall is compressed nearly to its normal thickness, but subsequent development is abnormal. While some growth does occur along lines between indentations and the isthmus, most extension occurs in the lobes [Kiermayer & Jarosch (73)].

Although excellent time-lapse photographs of semicell formation exist, they do not permit analysis of local growth rate within the lobes. The lobe tip, with its apparent greater attachment to the membrane, may be either a rate minimum or a maximum. Bifurcation of the lobes appears promoted by high nuclear/cytoplasmic ration and is prominent in polyploid forms [Kallio (67)].

In septa developing at some distance from a nucleus—due to experimental manipulation—the degree of bifurcation is less than normal. The semicell form in growing anucleate cells may consist of only the major lobes in simple outline [Waddington (155)]. While this may reflect loss of a direct morphogenetic influence of the nucleus, it may be a side effect of low turgor in the enucleate cell. Low turgor in general leads to simplified cell outline [Kiermayer (70)].

Summary Statement

Cell deformation is a physical process. The information relating metabolic and genetic alterations to form can take on causal meaning only when the alterations can be specifically connected to components of the physical mechanisms of growth. The two most general physical characteristics of a small region of a growing cell surface are (a) the rate at which it expands, and (b) and the directionality of its expansion.

In tip-growing cells, the extension of form primarily involves gradients, within the growth zone, of the rate of expansion. Two major questions are: what is the chemical reaction (or physical process) in the wall which limits rate; and what establishes and maintains the proper gradient of rate. The most significant ultrastructural body associated with these gradients appears to be a small vesicle which may contribute both mass and "loosening" factors to the wall. The controls governing the origin, migration, and biochemical activity of these vesicles appear central to the mechanism of tip growth. Migration and fusion behavior may be influenced by chemical and electrical factors and even by the pre-existing expansion pattern (vesicles may more easily reach and more easily fuse with an expanding membrane). Experimental variables could alter controls of the gradient or the nature of rate-limiting process itself, or both. Few experiments are discriminatory on this matter.

In cylindrical cells which display extension all along their length, gradients in rate of area expansion are not prominent. Here the form-generating phenomenon is directed expansion of surface, a process with an apparent immediate explanation in terms of transversely oriented microfibrils in the wall. The cytoplasmic component most clearly identified with oriented synthesis is the microtubule. These structures may be absent when synthesis is random but tend to run parallel to oriented cellulose. Drugs which break up microtubules destroy the orientation of synthesis but not synthesis per se. Disoriented synthesis typically leads to a sphering of the cell. Such a strong correlation between ultrastructure and normal-abnormal morphogenesis has not yet been established for certain particles proposed to be active in controlling microfibril synthesis.

The general plea of this review is that a morphogenetic response in a cell should generally be quantitatively dissected into its two components of surface behavior (rate and directionality of expansion). Then the influence of any variable which alters form can be more meaningfully connected to the physical phenomenology of morphogenesis.

LITERATURE CITED

1. Albersheim, P., in *Plant Biochemistry*, 151–86, 298–321 (Bonner, J., Varner, J. E., Eds., Academic Press, N.Y., 1965)
2. Aronson, J. M., in *The Fungi*, 1, 49–76 (Ainsworth, G., Sussman, A. S., Eds., Academic Press, N.Y./London, 1965)
3. Avers, C. J., *Am. J. Botany*, 50, 140–48 (1963)
4. Avers, C. J., Grimm, R. B., *Exptl. Cell Res.*, 16, 692–95 (1959)
5. Avers, C. J., Grimm, R. B., *J. Exptl. Botany*, 10, 341–44 (1959)
6. Avers, C. J., Grimm, R. B., *Am. J. Botany*, 46, 190–93 (1959)
7. Bartnicki-Garcia, S., *Bacteriol. Rev.*, 27, 293–304 (1963)
8. Bartnicki-Garcia, S., *Ann. Rev. Microbiol.*, 22, 87–108 (1968)
9. Bartnicki-Garcia, S., Lippman, E., *Bacteriol. Proc.*, 31 (1968)
10. Barton, R., *Nature*, 205, 201–2 (1965)
11. Bayer, D. E., Foy, C. L., Mallory, T. E., Cutter, E. G., *Am. J. Botany*, 54, 945–52 (1967)
12. Bayley, S. T., Colvin, J. R., Cooper, F. P., Martin-Smith, C. A., *J. Biophys. Biochem. Cytol.*, 3, 171–82 (1957)
13. Bentrup, F., Sandan, T., Jaffe, L. F., *Protoplasma*, 64, 254–66 (1967)
14. Bonnett, H. T., Newcomb, E. H., *Protoplasma*, 62, 59–75 (1966)
15. Bracker, C. E., *Ann. Rev. Phytopathol.*, 5, 343–74 (1967)
16. Brody, S., Tatum, E. L., *Proc. Natl. Acad. Sci. U.S.*, 56, 1290–97 (1966)
17. Bünning, E., *Protoplasmatologia*, 8 (9a), 1–86 (1958)
18. Burg, S. P., *Ann. Rev. Plant Physiol.*, 13, 265–302 (1962)
19. Burg, S. P., Burg, E. A., *Proc. Natl. Acad. Sci. U. S.*, 55, 262–69 (1966)
20. Burg, S. P., Burg, E. A., *Science*, 148, 1190–96 (1965)
21. Castle, E. S., *Proc. Natl. Acad. Sci. U. S.*, 41, 197–99 (1955)
22. Castle, E. S., *Quart. Rev. Biol.*, 28, 364–72 (1953)
23. Castle, E. S., *J. Gen. Physiol.*, 41, 913–26 (1958)
24. Chadwick, A. V., Burg, S. P., *Plant Physiol.*, 42, 415–20 (1967)
25. Cleland, R., *Planta*, 74, 197–209 (1967)
26. Cole, R. M., Hahn, J. J., *Science*, 135, 722–24 (1962)
27. Crawley, J. C. W., *Nature*, 205, 200–2 (1965)
28. Curtis, R. W., *Plant Physiol.*, 43, 76–80 (1968)
29. Dashek, W. V., Rosen, W. G., *Protoplasma*, 61, 192–204 (1966)
30. de Wolff, P. M., Houwink, A. L., *Acta Botan. Neerl.*, 3, 396–98 (1954)
31. Diehl, J. M., Gorter, C. J., van Iterson, G., Kleinhoonte, A., *Rec. Trav. Botan. Neerl.*, 36, 709–98 (1939)
32. Dorner, J., Hamilton, J., Harkin, J., *J. Bacteriol.*, 94, 466–74 (1967)
33. Eigsti, O. J., Dustin, P., *Colchicine* (Iowa State College Press, Ames, Iowa, 1955)
34. Erickson, R. O., *J. Exptl. Botany*, 17, 390–403 (1966)
35. Erickson, R. O., Sax, K., *Proc. Am. Phil. Soc.*, 100, 499–514 (1956)
36. Etzold, H., *Exptl. Cell Res.*, 25, 229–45 (1961)
37. Falcone, G., Nickerson, W. J., in *Biochemistry of Morphogenesis*, 65–70 (Nickerson, W. J., Ed., Pergamon Press, N.Y., 1958)
38. Frey-Wyssling, A., Mühlethaler, K.,

Ultrastructural Plant Cytology (Elsevier, N.Y., 377 pp., 1965)

39. Frey-Wyssling, A., *Die Pflanzliche Zellwand* (Springer Verlag, Berlin, 367 pp., 1959)
40. Galston, A., Baker, R. S., King, J. W., *Physiol. Plantarum*, **6**, 863–72 (1953)
41. Green, P. B., *Am. J. Botany*, **41**, 403–9 (1954)
42. Green, P. B., *J. Biophys. Biochem. Cytol.*, **4**, 505–16 (1958)
43. Green, P. B., *ibid.*, **7**, 289–96 (1960)
44. Green, P. B., in *Meristems and Differentiation*, 203–15 (Brookhaven Symp. Biol., **16**, 1963)
45. Green, P. B., in *Cytodifferentiation and Macromolecular Synthesis*, 203–34 (Locke, M., Ed., Academic Press, N.Y./London, 1963)
46. Green, P. B., *Am. J. Botany*, **51**, 334–42 (1964)
47. Green, P. B., *J. Cell Biol.*, **27**, 343–63 (1965)
48. Green, P. B., *Plant Physiol.*, **43**, 1069–84 (1968)
49. Green, P. B., King, A., *Australian J. Biol. Sci.*, **19**, 421–37 (1966)
50. Haber, A. H., *Am. J. Botany*, **49**, 538–46 (1962)
51. Halperin, W., Jensen, W. A., *J. Ultrastruct. Res.*, **18**, 428–43 (1967)
52. Haupt, W., *Ann. Rev. Plant Physiol.*, **16**, 267–90 (1965)
53. Heslop-Harrison, J., *Ann. Rev. Plant Physiol.*, **18**, 325–48 (1967)
54. Higgins, M. L., Pramer, D., *Science*, **155**, 345–46 (1967)
55. Inoue, S., Sato, H., *J. Gen. Physiol.*, **50**, 259–92 (1967)
56. Jaffe, L. F., *Ann. Rev. Plant Physiol.*, **9**, 359–84 (1958)
57. Jaffe, L. F., *Exptl. Cell Res.*, **15**, 282–99 (1958)
58. Jaffe, L. F., *Proc. Natl. Acad. Sci. U. S.*, **56**, 1102–9 (1966)
59. Jaffe, L. F., *Advan. Morphogenesis*, **7**, 295–328 (1968)
60. Jaffe, L. F., Etzold, H. J., *J. Cell Biol.*, **13**, 13–31 (1962)
61. Jaffe, L. F., Etzold, H. J., *Biophys. J.*, **5**, 715–42 (1965)
62. Johnson, B. F., *Exptl. Cell Res.*, **39**, 613–24 (1965)
63. Johnson, B. F., *J. Bacteriol.*, **95**, 1169–72 (1968)
64. Johnson, B. F., Gibson, E. J., *Exptl. Cell Res.*, **41**, 297–306 (1966)
65. Johnson, B. F., Gibson, E. J., *ibid.*, 580–91

66. Joshi, P. C., Ball, E., *Develop. Biol.*, **17**, 308–25 (1968)
67. Kallio, P., *Bull. Torrey Botan. Club.* **80**, 247–63 (1953)
68. Kamiya, N., *Ann. Rept. Sci. Works, Fac. Sci., Osaka Univ.*, **8**, 13–41 (1960)
69. Kaufman, P. B., *Physiol. Plantarum*, **18**, 703–24 (1965)
70. Kiermayer, O., *Protoplasma*, **59**, 76–132 (1964)
71. Kiermayer, O., *Planta*, **66**, 216–20 (1965)
72. Kiermayer, O., *Protoplasma*, **64**, 481–84 (1967)
73. Kiermayer, O., Jarosch, H., *Protoplasma*, **54**, 382–420 (1962)
74. Konrad-Hawkins, E., *Protoplasma*, **58**, 42–59 (1964)
75. Kreger, D. R., in *Symposium über Hefe-protoplasten*, 81–88 (Akademie-Verlag, Berlin, 1967)
76. Lamport, D. T. A., *Advan. Botan. Res.*, **2**, 151–218 (1965)
77. Ledbetter, M., Porter, K., *Science*, **144**, 872–74 (1964)
78. Maas Geesteranus, R. A., *Proc. Koninkl. Akad. Wetenschap. Amsterdam*, **44**, 481–88 (1941)
79. McClure, W. K., Park, D., Robinson, P. M., *J. Gen. Microbiol.*, **50**, 177–82 (1968)
80. McReynolds, J. S., *Bull. Torrey Botan. Club*, **88**, 397–403 (1961)
81. Mahadevan, P. R., Tatum, E. L., *J. Bacteriol.*, **90**, 1073–81 (1965)
82. Mahadevan, P. R., Tatum, E. L., *J. Cell Biol.*, **35**, 295–302 (1967)
83. Manocha, M. S., Colvin, J. R., *J. Bacteriol.*, **94**, 202–12 (1967)
84. Manocha, M. S., Colvin, J. R., *ibid.*, **95**, 1140–52 (1968)
85. Marchant, R., Peat, A., Banbury, G. H., *New Phytologist*, **66**, 623–29 (1967)
86. Mascarenhas, J. P., Machlis, L., *Plant Physiol.*, **39**, 70–77 (1964)
87. Mascarenhas, J. P., Machlis, L., *Nature*, **196**, 292–93 (1962)
88. Mollenhauer, H. H., Morré, D. J., *Ann. Rev. Plant Physiol.*, **17**, 27–46 (1966)
89. Moor, H., Mühlethaler, K., *J. Cell Biol.*, **17**, 609–28 (1963)
90. Mühlethaler, K., in *Cellular Ultrastructure of Woody Plants*, 51–60 (Coté, W. A., Jr., Ed., Syracuse Univ. Press, Syracuse, N.Y., 1965)
91. Mühlethaler, K., *Ann. Rev. Plant Physiol.*, **18**, 1–24 (1967)

92. Müller, D., Jaffe, L. F., *Biophys. J.*, **5**, 317–35 (1965)
93. Mundkur, B., *Exptl. Cell Res.*, **34**, 155–81 (1964)
94. Nagai, R., Rebhun, L., *J. Ultrastruct. Res.*, **14**, 571–89 (1966)
95. Neuscheler, W., Jaffe, L. F., *Develop. Biol.*, **19** (In press, 1969)
96. Newcomb, E. H., *Ann. Rev. Plant Physiol.*, **14**, 43–64 (1963)
97. Newcomb, E. H., Bonnett, H. T., *J. Cell Biol.*, **27**, 575–89 (1965)
98. Nickerson, W. J., *Bacteriol. Rev.*, **27**, 305–24 (1963)
99. Nickerson, W. J., Bartnicki-Garcia, S., *Ann. Rev. Plant Physiol.*, **15**, 327–44 (1964)
100. Nickerson, W. J., Falcone, G., in *Sulfur in Proteins*, 409–24 (Benesch, R., Ed., Academic Press, N.Y., 1959)
101. Nicolai, E., Preston, R. D., *Proc. Roy. Soc. (London), Ser. B*, **151**, 244–55 (1959)
102. Northcote, D. H., *Intern. Rev. Cytol.* **14**, 223–65 (1963)
103. Northcote, D. H., Lewis, D. R., *J. Cell Sci.*, **3**, 199–206 (1968)
104. Park, D., Robinson, P. M., in *Trends in Plant Morphogenesis*, 27–44 (John Wiley & Sons, N.Y., 1966)
105. Pickett-Heaps, J. D., *Australian J. Biol. Sci.*, **20**, 539–51 (1967)
106. Pickett-Heaps, J. D., *Develop. Biol.*, **15**, 206–36 (1967)
107. Pickett-Heaps, J. D., Northcote, D. H., *J. Exptl. Botany*, **17**, 20–26 (1966)
108. Pickett-Heaps, J. D., Northcote, D. H., *J. Cell. Sci.*, **1**, 121–28 (1966)
109. Preston, R. D., *Intern. Rev. Cytol.*, **8**, 33–60 (1959)
110. Preston, R. D., in *Formation of Wood in Forest Trees*, 169–88 (Academic Press, N.Y., 1964)
111. Preston, R. D., *Endeavour*, **23**, 153–59 (1964)
112. Preston, R. D., in *Biosynthetic Pathways in Higher Plants* (Pridham, J. B., Swain, T., Eds., Academic Press, N.Y./London, 1965)
113. Preston, R. D., *Advan. Sci.*, **22**, 1–15 (1965–66)
114. Preston, R. D., *Sci. Am.*, **218**, 102–8 (1968)
115. Probine, M. C., *J. Exptl. Botany*, **14**, 101–13 (1963)
116. Probine, M. C., *Proc. Roy. Soc. (London) Ser. B*, **161**, 526–37 (1965)
117. Probine, M. C., Barber, N. F., *Australian J. Biol. Sci.*, **19**, 439–57 (1966)
118. Probine, M. C., Preston, R. D., *J. Exptl. Botany*, **12**, 261–82 (1961)
119. Probine, M. C., Preston, R. D., *ibid.*, **13**, 111–17 (1962)
120. Raper, J. R., Raper, C. A., *J. Elisha Mitchell Sci. Soc.*, **84**, 267–73 (1968)
121. Ray, P. M., *J. Cell Biol.*, **35**, 659–74 (1967)
122. Reinhardt, M. O., in *Botanishche Untersuchungen* (Schwendener Festschrift, Borntraeger, Berlin, 1898)
123. Robertson, N. F., *Ann. Botany (London)*, **22**, 159–73 (1958)
124. Roelofsen, P. A., *The Plant Cell Wall* (Gebrüder Borntraeger, Berlin, 1959)
125. Roelofsen, P. A., *Advan. Botan. Res.*, **2**, 69–149 (1966)
126. Rosen, W. G., *Am. J. Botany*, **61**, 889–95 (1961)
127. Rosen, W. G., *Ann. Rev. Plant Physiol.*, **19**, 435–66 (1968)
128. Rosen, W. G., Gawlik, S. R., *Protoplasma*, **61**, 181–91 (1966)
129. Sachs, R. M., *Ann. Rev. Plant Physiol.*, **16**, 73–96 (1965)
130. Schoch-Bodmer, H., *Planta*, **30**, 168–240 (1939)
131. Schultz, D. P., Funderburk, H. H., Jr., Negi, N. S., *Plant Physiol.*, **43**, 265–73 (1968)
132. Scurfield, G., *Nature*, **214**, 740–41 (1967)
133. Setterfield, G., Bayley, S. T., *Ann. Rev. Plant Physiol.*, **12**, 35–62 (1961)
134. Sievers, A., *Protoplasma*, **56**, 188–92 (1962)
135. Sievers, A., *Z. Naturforsch.*, **18b**, 830–40 (1963)
136. Sievers, A., *Z. Pflanzenphysiol.*, **53**, 193–213 (1965)
137. Sievers, A., in *Funktionelle und morphologische Organization der Zelle, Sekretion and Exkretion*, 89–118 (Wohfarth-Bottermann, K. E., Ed., Springer, Berlin/Heidelberg/New York, 1965)
138. Sievers, A., *Naturwissenschaften*, **10**, 252–53 (1967)
139. Sievers, A., *Protoplasma*, **64**, 225–53 (1967)
140. Sievers, A., *Z. Pflanzenphysiol.*, **57**, 462–73 (1967)
141. Sinnott, E., *Plant Morphogenesis* (McGraw-Hill, New York, 1960)
142. Stadler, D. R., *J. Cellular Comp. Physiol.*, **39**, 449–74 (1952)

143. Staehelin, A., *Histochemie,* **74,** 325–50 (1966)
144. Stebbins, G. L., in *Control Mechanisms in Cellular Processes,* 113–35 (Locke, M., Ed., Academic Press, N.Y., 1968)
145. Stein, O. L., Forrester, G. M., *J. Exptl. Botany,* **15,** 146–59 (1962)
146. Stein, O. L., Forrester, G. M., *Planta,* **60,** 349–59 (1963)
147. Stange, L., *Advan. Morphogenesis,* **4,** 111–54 (1964)
148. Stange, L., *Ann. Rev. Plant Physiol.,* **16,** 119–40 (1965)
149. Steward, F. C., Israel, H. W., Salpeter, M. M., *Proc. Natl. Acad. Sci. U. S.,* **58,** 541–44 (1967)
150. Street, H. E., *Ann. Rev. Plant Physiol.,* **17,** 315–44
151. Strunk, C., *Z. Allgem. Mikrobiol.,* **3,** 265–74 (1963)
152. Strunk, C., *Arch. Mikrobiol.,* **60,** 255–61 (1968)
153. Tagawa, T., Bonner, J., *Plant Physiol.,* **32,** 207–12 (1957)
154. Tatum, E. L., Luck, D. L., in *Control Mechanisms in Developmental Processes,* 32–42 (Locke, M., Ed., Academic Press, N.Y./London, 1967)
155. Waddington, C. H., *New Patterns in Genetics and Development* (Columbia Univ. Press, N.Y., 277 pp., 1962)
156. Ward, J. M., in *Biochemistry of Morphogenesis* (Nickerson, W. J., Ed., Pergamon Press, N.Y., 1958)
157. Waris, H., Kallio, P., *Advan. Morphogenesis,* **4,** 45–80 (1964)
158. Wessels, J. G., Niederpruem, D. J., *J. Bacteriol.,* **94,** 1594–1602 (1967)
159. Wilson, K., *Ann. Botany (London),* **21,** 1–11 (1957)
160. Wilson, K., *ibid.,* **22,** 449–56 (1958)
161. Wilson, K., *Intern. Rev. Cytol.,* **17,** 1–49 (1964)
162. Wilson, R. W., Niederpruem, D. J., *Can. J. Microbiol.,* **13,** 1663–79 (1967)
163. von Witsch, H., *Planta,* **31,** 638–52 (1941)

MORPHOGENESIS IN CELL CULTURES

By Walter Halperin

Department of Botany, University of Massachusetts
Amherst, Massachusetts

The basic assumption of cell and organ culture as an experimental method is that many of the interactions essential to organismic control of cell behavior can be sorted out and made to occur independently of each other. The first step consists of working with "cuttings," i.e., isolated organs or organ systems. When this is done under sterile conditions, the method is referred to as "organ culture." Organ culture is not reviewed here since its methods and results require separate consideration in conjunction with the many unrelated problems which have been studied by this means with such notable success. In contrast, "cell culture" hangs together as a coherent subject susceptible to review because of its few successes and its concentration on technical problems. Included in the term cell culture are the following: "callus" (clumps on static media), "suspensions" (single cells and clumps in agitated liquid media), "plate cultures" (individually identifiable single cells and clumps on agar plates), and "microcultures" (one or several cells grown in chambers which facilitate microscopic observation). The term "tissue culture" has traditionally been used as an inclusive name for both organ and cell culture.

Cell culture may be regarded as the ultimate step in sorting out interactions, since the raw material consists of a disorganized population of cells in which normal histological patterns are suppressed, or allegedly so, until the proper environment is introduced for invoking selected morphogenetic processes. Current techniques emphasize the application of suspected morphogenetically active chemicals to hopefully totipotent cells. The difficulty with this approach is that it overlooks the importance of physical factors and also the crucial difference between totipotence and competence. Grobstein (72) has pointed out, for example, that "while the zygote is thought of as totipotent, its capacity as a cell is very low, probably zero." The capacities of individual cells in culture are usually unpredictable. Thus, while we have made advances in identifying chemical stimuli which evoke a particular morphogenetic response, the cells which are competent to respond are few in number and are generally not identifiable in advance. Elucidation of the nature of competency has been overlooked since the identification of chemical morphogens requires nothing more than the observation of a limited morphological response to alterations in the nutrient medium.

Throughout this review, the terms *differentiation* and *morphogenesis* will be used in the traditional imprecise way, the former referring to chemical and structural changes in individual cells as they depart from the features defined as eumeristematic (56) and take on other specializations, and the latter to any and all morphological changes, subcellular or supracellular. The precise definitions of these terms (46), which have emerged from microbial genetics and biochemistry, are not yet applicable to multicellular organisms.

A painstaking review of nearly all aspects of plant tissue culture prior to 1959 may be found in Gautheret's monumental *La Culture des Tissus Végétaux* (67). In addition, a number of excellent reviews dealing with various aspects of morphogenesis in cell cultures have appeared in the last 5 years (29, 68, 69, 187, 198). Accordingly, no attempt has been made here to review the literature exhaustively. Selected problems are discussed, primarily from a methodological standpoint, with emphasis on cytological rather than physiological data.

PRIMARY CULTURES

Primary cell cultures, i.e., those established directly from the organism, ideally should consist of one cell type with well-defined developmental potentialities. Theoretically, this result might be achieved in at least three ways: (*a*) short-term culture of a population of progenitor cells committed to a known fate; (*b*) culture of specialized cells which retain their differentiated features through successive mitotic cycles; (*c*) establishment of a meristematic cell population uncommitted to any course of differentiation but capable of many.

Progenitor cells.—A prime example of the use of progenitor or "blast" cells in following the final stages of differentiation *in vitro* is the well-known work on myogenesis and chondriogenesis (89, 114) with animal tissue cultures. With the notable exception of meiocytes (90), embryonic cells which are the equivalent of blast cells cannot be obtained from plants.

Specialized cells.—The inevitable question arises concerning the ability of cells to re-enter the mitotic cycle and retain specialized functions. In a recent review in this series (88), Heslop-Harrison provided a lucid discussion of the evidence from cell cultures which bears on this problem. He concluded that the transmission of differentiated states by single cell cloning had not been demonstrated. Retention of such states through single cell cloning would eliminate the possibility that they were dependent upon interactions between cells, a situation which has been referred to as "group stability" (72).

The recognition of differentiated states depends upon three properties of cells: morphological features, physiological or chemical features, and latent capacities. Characteristic morphological features are not likely to survive repeated cell divisions, although there are exceptional cases. Tulecke reported, for example, that cells in callus derived from *Taxus* pollen grow "in an elongated manner typical of growing pollen tubes," with the nucleus and cytoplasm located at one end (202). On the other hand, Joshi & Ball (102) followed the cytological changes accompanying a renewal of cell division *in vitro* in palisade cells of *Arachis hypogea* and observed that "no derivative had any morphological resemblance to the original palisade parenchyma cell." Whether or not the derivatives retained any physiological features which might be peculiar to palisade cells is an open question.

Where good chemical criteria exist, as in animal cells, it has been possible to demonstrate the continued synthesis in long-term cultures of tissue and organ-specific products (45, 47, 147, 220). In at least four cases, the cell strains were derived from single cell clones (220). Surprisingly enough, we know very little about specific products of specialized plant cells. The production of alkaloids and other secondary compounds occurs in some cultures (34, 171, 172), but their synthesis in the intact plant normally occurs in meristems (97, 134) and is therefore not a differentiated function in the sense of belonging to cells outside the mitotic cycle. A special case of stable chemical differentiation may be seen in the tannin cells which "breed true" during both normal ontogeny and induced regeneration in *Ricinus* (14). Bloch interpreted the arrangement of such cells as evidence that single differentiated initials divided to yield identical progeny. His attempts to culture such cells were unsuccessful for technical reasons, but he did conclude that they were irreversibly differentiated (13). Ball (7) observed similar cells reproducing true to type in *Sequoia* callus, but found some evidence that they dedifferentiated when incorporated into bud primordia. A now classic case of the retention of physiological features peculiar to the parent explant was the discovery by Stoutemeyer & Britt (185) that callus cultures derived from either the adult or juvenile phases of *Hedera helix* maintained characteristic differences indefinitely.

Examples of the retention of latent capacities may be found in the studies of European workers on *in vitro* induction of flower buds in vernalized or photoinduced cuttings (1, 130, 140, 149, 153), and studies by Bauer on regeneration of mosses (10). The flowering studies of interest are those where, following induction, a considerable period of callus growth ensued before floral primordia were organized. A particularly striking example of this was the formation of flowers in tumors induced by injecting *Agrobacterium tumefaciens* into the internodes of *Nicotiana tabacum* (2). However, in all the above cases, the buds were formed in callus still attached to the parent cutting, and the influence of the remaining mitotically inactive tissue is uncertain. The logical extension of this kind of experiment, namely subculturing of the callus, has been performed by Bauer in his unique studies of regenerating moss sporogonia (10). Explants removed from young sporogonia regenerated in different ways, depending upon the region of excision. Some segments gave rise to protonema which in turn produced leafy plants, or protonema which produced sporogonia directly. Other segments yielded callus which remained unorganized in the light but produced sporogonia in the dark. Under the proper conditions, the sporogonial factor was stable through a number of subcultures. Other cases are known of stable morphological or metabolic features which arise only after callus has been subcultured for a period of time and which cannot be referred to some aspect of the tissue of origin (e.g., 142). These may be of no relevance for understanding normal mechanisms of differentiation, since stability of this kind probably arises from selection of a mutant population.

None of the above cases of stable differentiated states have been subjected to single cell cloning, a critical step as pointed out by Heslop-Harrison (88). Since single cells of both lower and higher plants can be cultured (5, 91, 109, 120, 135, 144, 164), it should be possible to perform more critical analyses. A theoretical basis for clonal transmission of the differentiated state exists, namely the "paragenetic" mechanisms for gametic transmission of the functional state of particular gene loci (22, 23). In the case of higher plant cell cultures, however, the issue will be confused by the considerable variation within secondary clones derived from a single parent cell (164).

Meristematic cells.—The ideal situation would be a primary culture of meristematic cells which can be induced en masse to yield specialized cells or organ primordia of one type. However, it is doubtful that a uniform population of meristematic cells can be obtained directly from the plant. The diversity of structural types within a single meristem has been emphasized (56). More significantly, studies of the periodicity of division in roots (101) led to the conclusion that there is no meristematic cell existing "as a distinct cell type whose function is primarily the production of new cells . . ." This conclusion was based on the finding that mitosis was a property of cells in radial and longitudinal enlargement in a region where tissue patterns had already been blocked out. This suggests that if it were possible to dissociate meristems and obtain a population of meristematic cells directly, one might have a mixture of subpopulations which were the functional equivalent of different kinds of blast cells. Regardless of the validity of this argument, it is not possible at present to dissociate plant tissues in the same way as animal tissues by enzymatic means or by chelation (148), although recent work with hydrolytic wall enzymes in obtaining living protoplasts suggests that the technical problems may be overcome (36, 160, 192). In practice, cultures have been started by inducing cell division in relatively massive explants consisting largely or entirely of cells which have ceased to divide as a result of normal maturation. The first steps in growth of such cultures involved a series of regressive cytological changes referred to as dedifferentiation (32) or embryonization (173, 174). It remains to be seen whether or not it will be possible by this method to produce a uniform population of meristematic cells.

Dedifferentiation.—The term embryonization has been preferred by some workers to describe this process since it does not imply a loss of functional specialization (173). There is some justification for this view since, as discussed earlier, certain differentiated functions of the primary explant may persist through considerable subculturing. This may be the rule rather than the exception for animal cells (73). However, the term dedifferentiation in most cases of the renewal of growth in mature plant cells accurately describes a fundamental alteration in the differentiated state, since the daughter cells commonly show the ability to redifferentiate into cells of another type than the parent.

Buvat's (30, 31) early investigation of the renewal of growth in mature cells from a variety of tissues and organs remains the most extensive to date. The limit of the dedifferentiative process is reached when, by virtue of division proceeding more rapidly than enlargement, small, densely cytoplasmic (eumeristematic) cells are produced. However, Buvat found that dedifferentiation involved at least one intermediate stage beyond which certain kinds of regressing cells could not, or at least did not, pass. According to later workers, this phenomenon of partial dedifferentiation was characteristic of young lignified cells such as fibers, collenchyma, or of immature vessels and immature sieve tubes (151, 152, 194). Gautheret (69) emphasized that the subsequent morphogenetic potential of such partially dedifferentiated cells is restricted to histogenesis, whereas cells which are derived from parenchyma, companion cells, secretory cells, or cambium regain a potential for organogenesis. It is not clear whether the inability of certain cells to dedifferentiate fully in the studies cited above was the result of a permanent block, possibly genetic, or of other factors. The fundamental implication of these findings requires that they be substantiated in an unambiguous way.

It is evident that a complex explant necessarily gives rise to a culture initially consisting of an extremely heterogeneous mixture of cell types. The difficulties inherent in the use of such material are obvious. Nevertheless, a considerable number of important generalizations have emerged from studies of the histological changes occurring during induction of growth in complex explants. For a detailed discussion of all aspects of this work, the reader is referred to the excellent reviews by Gautheret (66–69). In addition to these histological studies, there is a vast background of work on the physiology of newly excised tissues. These data cannot be covered here and will be discussed only in so far as they bear directly on subsequent morphogenetic events in established cell strains.

DIFFERENTIATION

The majority of cells in any culture have gross cytological features similar to thin-walled ground parenchyma of the intact plant, but the resemblance does not include a regularity of shape. A variety of shapes, many quite bizarre, occurs due to random yielding of wall areas and irregular orientation of cell plates. The significance of this fact for classical concepts of growth and cell division has been discussed in considerable detail by Steward (181). In addition, cells of *Picea* in culture show an unprecedented range of dynamic activities, including the ability to extrude a variety of large drops, strands, fibers, etc., through the cell wall. Whether or not these activities are representative of normal processes which go unobserved in the intact plant is uncertain, although White believed this to be the case (215). The greatest interest naturally attaches to definition of the circumstances under which irregular cell growth is succeeded by normal patterns of growth and differentiation. The reassertion of such patterns is usually restricted to the development of cambia, vascular tissue, and organs.

One difficulty in interpreting the circumstances necessary for normal growth arises out of the fact that the same substances which are required to initiate and maintain callus growth are also implicated in the initiation of organized structures. While this has obvious significance, it is undesirable experimentally. Thus when one finds the statement that a particular culture was "undifferentiated" at the start of an experiment, one usually has to revise this mentally to read "no organs or other structures were visible to the naked eye." Unorganized eumeristematic loci which can be carried through a number of subcultures have been described by Gautheret as "méristèmes dégradés" (67). One example is the proembryogenic mass which can be present unnoticed in cell cultures and will not produce an embryo until the auxin level is lowered (84, 87). In addition, organized primordia which cannot develop further because of inhibiting auxin levels may be present. It is clear that assumptions cannot be made about the role of growth substances or metabolites in organogenesis or cell differentiation unless a thorough histological study of the culture has been made before the experimental treatment begins. This is seldom done.

CAMBIA

Gautheret noted that the circumstances surrounding cambium development in cell cultures were fundamentally similar to those in intact plants. He concluded (68) that "cambiums naissent toujours à la limite de deux tissus de nature différente." The major types of cambia found are the phellogen-like tissues which arise where parenchymatous cells border the periphery of the explant or callus, and the vascular cambia which usually arise in relation to pre-existent tracheids or sieve tubes. The cell types produced by vascular cambia vary with the origin of the primary explant (69, 96) and the nutrient medium (213). According to Gautheret (69), the functioning of newly formed cambia is initially "conditioned by the nature of the surrounding tisse." Thus, cambia regenerated at the periphery of an explant will produce phloem towards the interior and xylem towards the exterior if the explanted tissue consists of phloem, whereas the reverse orientation occurs if the explanted tissue is xylem. Aspects of this kind of directed differentiation, known as homeogenetic induction, are discussed in some detail by Lang (117). The data from cell cultures and other experimental systems have been used by Wilson & Wilson (217) in their "gradient induction" hypothesis, which attempts to account for both the locus at which a cambium originates and its orientation with respect to production of xylem and phloem. Also of relevance are the ingenious *in vitro* experiments of Brown & Sax on the role of mutual cell pressures in cambial function (24, 25).

VASCULAR TISSUE

Few reports in the literature of cell culture fail to mention the random differentiation of xylem, indicating that the conditions necessary for differentiation of tracheary cells are easily met under culture conditions. Phloem is less frequently reported. Whether this is due to more exacting requirements for sieve tube differentiation or to the difficulty of detection is uncertain. Recent work favors the latter interpretation (63, 103). The cases with which we are most concerned are not the random observations but those in which systematic attempts have been made to control vascularisation.

Chemical control of vascular tissue differentiation.—In the 1950's, Jacobs and his co-workers demonstrated a quantitative relationship between indoleacetic acid concentration and the differentiation of tracheary cells in both wound regeneration (92) and normal ontogeny (94, 95) in *Coleus*. Subsequent work with the same experimental system established a similar relationship for sieve tube regeneration (116). French workers had earlier observed that buds regenerating in callus (64) or grafted into callus or cuttings (33) induced the vascularization of subjacent tissue. Camus (33) found that auxins could, to a certain extent, replace the bud effect. Wetmore and his associates (213, 214) subsequently showed that the effect of buds grafted into callus of *Syringa* was fully replaceable by sugar and auxins, although they were unable to observe in their system the correlation between auxin concentration and quantity of vascular tissue as described for *Coleus* stems. The sucrose concentration determined the amount and type of vascular tissue formed, low sugar favoring xylem, high sugar favoring phloem, and intermediate levels favoring a balance of the two.

The response of *Syringa* to sugar may be a general one, since similar results were found with other species (98, 99, 133, 158). Jeffs & Northcote (99) found that vascularized nodules (associations of phloem, cambium, and xylem) were induced in *Phaseolus* callus only by "disaccharides which contain an α-glucosyl radical at the nonreducing end." They cited the work of Van Lith-Vroom et al. (203) as further evidence of the same phenomenon. However, the histological studies performed by the latter workers on differentiation in crown gall cultures of *Nicotiana tabacum* seem more contradictory than supporting. Growth of the tissue on glucose produced large vascularized nodules, complete with phloem, xylem, and cambia, whereas on starch media (which presumably yields maltose, an α-glucosyl disaccharide) the cultures had "a parenchymatic character with few and very scattered lignified elements." Ball (8) found that the most effective sugars in inducing vascularized nodules in *Sequoia* callus were a monosaccharide (raffinose) and a β-galactosyl disaccharide (lactose). Although other differences in the media may have played a role in these conflicting results, it appears that the effect of α-glucosyl disaccharides on *Phaseolus* may not be a general one.

In some cases (11, 199), a large number of individual tracheids are induced, apparently unassociated with cambia or phloem. According to Bergmann (11), kinetin increases the general level of lignification in parenchymatous callus cells of *Nicotiana* and also the percentage of tracheids. Chemical analyses showed that kinetin promoted lignification at the expense of other wall components (107) by shifting carbohydrate metabolism into the pentose phosphate pathway (11, 108), thereby promoting synthesis of the phenylpropane precursors of lignin. A similar inductive effect of lignin precursors on xylem differentiation was proposed by Jensen on the basis of auxin-induced peroxidase activity in roots of *Vicia faba* (100). However, Fosket & Miksche (60) have argued that lignin precursors are not likely to be involved in the control of secondary wall patterns, citing evidence of others that xylem elements differentiate before detectable lignification occurs. Geissbuhler & Skoog (70) made essentially the same point 10 years ago in discussing the illogicality, in the absence of chemical data, of referring to the differentiation of tracheid-like cells as "lignification." Unfortunately, this is still a common practice. In view of the multiple physiological effects of kinins (122), there is no need to assume that the chemical and structural differentiations are caused by the same mechanism.

Since all the substances shown to influence vascular tissue differentiation have been hormones or metabolites which play a basic role in cell growth and division, considerable uncertainty exists with regard to the specificity of such substances in particular pathways of differentiation. Unequivocal separation of the growth function and the possible inductive function has not been accomplished.

Cell division and differentiation.—The most controversial conclusion reached by Wetmore and his associates was their interpretation of the conditions necessary for cell differentiation. They state (214) that "whether there is an elongation phase of little or great extent, that is, whether there is a procambial phase or not, the induction of phloem and xylem can happen if and whenever the necessary biochemical agents are available in appropriate concentrations." This hypothesis is obviously at odds with the concept, gained from studies of both plant and animal cells, that the ability of a cell to differentiate in a particular way is a temporal affair which comes and goes (58, 72, 178). For example, Shininger (163) has recently shown that decapitated *Xanthium* plants will continue to form relatively normal secondary xylem if the cut end of the stem is fed naphthalene acetic acid. If application of the auxin is delayed, the cambial derivatives which form in the absence of auxin will remain undifferentiated regardless of subsequent auxin applications. This result suggests that the period of competence had passed (although the possibility of inadequate translocation of the stimulus cannot be overlooked). Of equal significance is the fact that carrot cultures consisting entirely of proembryogenic cells never contain vascular tissue although they are grown in the same nutrient medium on which control cultures not containing proembryogenic cells form the usual vascularized nodules (84). Wetmore and his co-workers based their hypothesis of the nonessentiality of procambium in the subsequent differentiation of xylem and phloem on the assumption that the only role of the procambium is to block out the shape of the stele. Yet they recognized (214) that in callus the cells at the center of the actively dividing nodules were "biochemically favorable for induction and differentiation of vascular tissue." On the strength of their own observation, it can be argued that the divisions in nodules yield cells which are the physiological equivalent of procambium, although there is no obvious morphological resemblance, and that this physiological state is essential to subsequent overt differentiation of xylem and phloem. The argument for the nonessentiality of procambium would seem to require the demonstration that mature parenchyma cells can be caused to differentiate into vascular cells without an intervening mitosis. There have been reports that wound xylem may differentiate from parenchyma cells by direct transformation (93, 165), but a completely convincing documentation of this point does not seem to exist.

In a recent carefully controlled study of differentiation in stem segments of *Coleus,* Fosket (61) concluded that "cells must divide in order to initiate wound-vessel member differentiation." Jeffs & Northcote (99), using the experimental techniques devised by Wetmore & Rier (213), also concluded that "mitosis immediately precedes differentiation." Recent studies with differentiating animal cells led to the conclusion that immediately prior mitoses were frequently essential to expression of a particular phenotype (57). Apparently in some cases there are molecular events essential to subsequent differentiation which can occur only during or immediately following mitosis. This kind of interpretation is not new, since it was hypothesized some time ago that the florigenic stimulus was not effective unless it arrived at an apex where cell divisions were occurring (221).

ORGANOGENESIS

The evolution of hormone and nutritional hypotheses in organogenesis has recently been reviewed by Dore (54), including extensive data from cell and organ cultures which bear on this problem. It is only necessary here to review the methodological advantages and disadvantages of cell cultures in studying organogenesis and to discuss recent contributions of basic interest.

The structural polarity of organ formation in intact plants and in regenerating cuttings is usually explained on the basis of chemical gradients which are experimentally demonstrable. The organogenetically active substances hypothesized by Bouillienne (18) or Went (209, 210) were deduced from studies of correlative phenomena which required the transport of unidentified substances from one part of the plant to another. Identification of such substances would be simplified if the experimental system permitted direct application of test substances to target cells without the intervention of a transport step. This method would not yield direct information on the integrated control of organogenesis by the whole plant, but it might be useful in obtaining information at the intracellular level. The transition to this kind of system was effectively pioneered by Skoog in his use of callus cultures as a method of bioassay for substances involved in organ formation (169).

When cell cultures are subjected to experimental media, the results are generally measured in terms of the kind and number of organs appearing after a considerable delay, without regard to immediate biochemical and cytological effects of test substances or alterations in the medium. Few reports of organogenesis in cell culture fail to conform to the same unrewarding generalization: establishment of the primary culture is followed, after one or more subcultures during which unknown cytological and physiological changes are occurring, by the production of roots on relatively high auxin levels and of shoots on relatively low auxin levels with or without a cytokinin. No adequate experimental system exists at present in which it is not only possible to control the time and place of initiation of organ primordia but also to isolate them for biochemical and ultrastructural studies during successive stages of development. Organ formation proceeding from extremely small clumps in suspension or plate cultures is a step in this direction (55, 84, 113, 180, 205).

Organ Initiation

Elucidation of the factors controlling organogenesis at the intracellular level will require knowledge of the metabolism peculiar to eumeristematic cells. A limited amount of information is available from biochemical analyses (179, 188) and from studies of the growth requirements of excised apices (9, 195). The formation of eumeristematic growth centers in callus occurs when parenchymatous cells undergo a shift in metabolism to the "mitosis-determined" condition. This term was devised by Stebbins (175) to describe the situation in which the relative rates of cell division and enlargement are such that successive generations of cells become progressively smaller until the eumeristematic condition is reached. This terminology is useful since it describes what happens at the gross cytological level during organ initiation without implying anything about the causal molecular events. The opinion of Haber & Foard (76; see also 59) that the extent and orientation of cell division do not play an essential role in the initiation or subsequent polarized growth of organs is not at issue here. In cell cultures, potential organ-producing cells are usually not identifiable and are therefore not susceptible to study prior to the eumeristematic stage (one exception will be discussed).

Hypotheses with regard to the origin of growth centers are scarce. Torrey (198) suggested that all organized structures in callus have a common origin in "activated" single cells which he called "meristemoids," a term devised by Bünning. Bünning (26) long ago pointed out an impressive number of cases where the critical feature preceding the appearance of a specialized cell (e.g., trichoblasts, guard cells, sclereids) was unequal division of a polarized cell. Of the two daughter cells, the one with the denser cytoplasm was termed a "meristemoid" since it had increased capacity for further cell division or for developing into a specialized cell.

Whether or not meristemoids, *sensu* Bünning, are involved in the origin of all organized structures in callus is unknown. There does seem, however, to be a fundamental distinction in the cytological events giving rise to organ primordia and vascularized nodules, since they may be separated experimentally in several ways. For example, habituated (65) or senescent (200) cultures may be incapable of organ formation but will continue to form growth centers containing vascular tissue. Although organs may originate in association with the cambia of vascularized nodules (35, 71, 131, 162, 180), they also arise directly by dedifferentiation of parenchymatous cells unassociated with vascular tissue (7, 55, 136, 196). Murashige (136) found that exposure of tobacco callus to gibberellins prevented organogenesis without interfering with the development of vascularized nodules. It seems possible that gibberellin promoted vascularization of growth centers which might otherwise have become organ primordia, since gibberellins have been shown to promote vascularization in a variety of experimental systems (4, 48, 159). The inhibition of organ formation in crown gall tumors was suggested by Kupila to be caused by this mechanism (115). However, Thorpe & Murashige (193), on the basis of histological studies, suggested that gibberellins prevented the development of bud primordia in tobacco callus by causing breakdown of the starch specifically associated with prospective bud-forming cells. Since intermediate cytokinin/auxin ratios also prevent organogenesis in tobacco callus (169), it would be of interest to have comparable data on the status or even recognizability of prospective organ-forming cells in such cultures. Although excellent histological studies of organ formation in cultured tobacco stem segments were carried out 20 years ago by Sterling (176, 177), the equivalent studies do not seem to have been made for organogenesis in subcultured tobacco callus. Other cases of gibberellin inhibition of organ formation are known. On the basis of the fact that pre-existent primordia were not inhibited by applications of gibberellic acid, Brian et al. (21) hypothesized that gibberellins prevented the initial divisions leading to organization of root primordia in pea and bean stem cuttings. A similar mechanism might be operating in the gibberellin-induced inhibition of floral initiation, since floral development is not prevented if the gibberellin is applied to the apex after the floral stimulus has arrived (161). It appears that this hormone constitutes a potentially valuable tool in studying the initial unique steps of organ formation.

Determination of Organ Type

When a particular treatment induces *de novo* formation of organs, root and bud primordia may be initially indistinguishable (16, 106). The question naturally arises as to when organ type is determined. Morphogenetic plasticity of organ primordia has been demonstrated in both Pteridophytes and Angiosperms. Surgical experiments on fern apices demonstrated that young leaf primordia could be converted to buds (40, 41). Similar experiments on Angiosperm apices were unsuccessful (189). Apparently, in Angiosperms a critical feature of the initiation of determinate organs is irreversibility as to organ type. Essentially similar conclusions may be drawn from Cusick's demonstration that developing floral primordia pass through a series of physiological states which are irreversible (39). There is evidence, however, that indeterminate primordia in Angiosperms go through a period of morphogenetic plasticity (16, 52, 53). Bonnett & Torrey (15) found that young bud and root primordia in cultured *Convolvulus* roots were histologically indistinguishable. Appropriate culture conditions made it possible to obtain buds at presumptive root sites. They proposed (15) that "these responses may be due to the initiation of a large number of primordia by auxin, which can then develop into either buds or roots depending on subsequent auxin levels." The proposal of a two-step formation of organs with the first step producing a generalized primordium and the second step determining organ type is not a new notion, since similar ideas can be traced back to Sachs (as cited in 208). Cutter (42) proposed that two separate sets of factors might control organogenesis: "phyllotactic factors" which determine the site of organ initiation, and "organogenic factors," which determine organ type, since in *Nymphaea,* identical sites in the genetic spiral may be occupied by leaves, vegetative buds, or flower buds.

To relate the information from *Convolvulus* or *Nymphaea* studies, one need only assume that the two sets of factors proposed by Cutter are qualitatively identical (i.e., same chemical species) but quantitatively unlike. This assumption is fundamentally similar to the conclusions reached by Skoog & Miller on the basis of extensive studies of organogenesis in tobacco cultures (169). The same hormones required to initiate and maintain mitosis and cell division in excised tobacco pith (44)—indoleacetic acid and a cytokinin—are also involved in the initiation and determination of organ types (169), although there is an extensive interaction of hormones with phosphates (168) and other substances, phenolic compounds in particular (118, 119, 201). The relationship between cytokinins and budding, discovered originally with tobacco callus, has since been observed in other experimental systems involving both seed plants (43, 51, 150, 154, 204) and lower plants (Bopp, 17). The main thrust of Skoog & Miller's argument (169) was that "quantitative interactions" among a common set of factors, and not unique morphogens, were involved in the regulation of "all types of growth investigated from cell enlargement to organ formation." Support for this position may be found in Hagen's studies (79) of the regulation of growth and organogenesis in tobacco hybrid tumors by the nitrogen/hormone ratio. The dual role played by hormones and metabolites in regulating both cell division and organ type in *Nicotiana* callus is essentially similar to the dual role of such substances in regulating cell division and vascular tissue type in *Syringa* or *Phaseolus* callus (see section on Differentiation).

EMBRYOGENESIS

Reports of the regeneration of whole plants in cell cultures have been numerous during the past 5 years. A variety of structures ranging from well-formed dicotyledonous embryos to obvious clumps of callus bearing both buds and roots to poorly defined forms of uncertain affinity have been reported under a bewildering variety of names. The suggestion has been made that any asexually produced structure, *in vivo* or *in vitro,* be called an "embryoid," reserving the term embryo for sexually produced structures (207). This proposal, in addition to relegating to second-class citizenship all taxa which yield perfectly good embryos apomictically, overlooks the crucial point that the problem is not one of terminology but of technique. It is irrelevant, for example, what name is applied to the various kinds of embryonic propagules functioning in the normal life cycle of a species (viz. foliar embryos in *Kalanchoe,* bulbils in *Lilium,* protocorms in orchids) since they are understood and recognized in terms of their distinctive ontogeny and final form. The only forms which are difficult to categorize by any means are teratological ones, and it is in this category that most of the plants formed *in vitro* must be placed. Many such structures were discovered in callus or suspensions after the culture had been through a succession of transfers on several kinds of media, often complex, during which time the developing organs were subjected to the deforming effects of high levels of growth substances. In the absence of a thorough study of organ ontogeny, including histological details, under the optimal circumstances for forming such organs, it is impossible to assess the significance of the results obtained.

The current need is to winnow this mass of data for the essential points regarding which cell types of the mature plant show embryological competence, the necessary chemical and physical factors involved, and the ontogeny of regenerated plants.

ORIGIN OF EMBRYOLOGICALLY COMPETENT CELLS

Few cases have been reported in which the specific cells of the explant giving rise to embryos can be unequivocally identified. Embryos have been reported in higher plant cultures started from excised seed embryos (38, 128, 183, 219), hypocotyls or stems (105, 112, 216), storage root phloem or xylem (84), leaf mesophyll (110), floral buds (111), nucellar tissue (155), etc. This is not intended to be a complete list, but it suffices to indicate the range of organs and tissues in a wide variety of Angiosperm species, including monocots (38, 216), which can yield embryos. In addition, both haploid and diploid embryos have been obtained from several different cultured tissues of Cycads (143).

Perhaps the best identification of embryo origin from a specific cell type involves the epidermal cells of *Ranunculus sceleratus* (112) and *Daucus carota* (105). However, the most interesting reports are those which claim the origin of haploid embryos from pollen grains. This phenomenon has been reported for *Datura innoxia* (75) and *Nicotiana tabacum* (139). It has been known for many years that developing microspores had the remarkable ability to yield embryo sac-like forms (129, 184). It is apparent, therefore, that microspores may yield the male gametophyte, female gametophyte, or sporophyte. The ready interconvertibility of Pteridophyte generations thus has its counterpart in the Angiosperms. In *Hyacinth*, embryo sac-like forms were apparently unable to develop from microspores after the generative nucleus had differentiated (184). However, Guha & Maheshwari (75) reported that in *Datura*, mature pollen grains with thick walls underwent internal proliferation to produce the embryo. It was apparently not known whether one or both nuclei of the pollen grain participated. In *Nicotiana*, the embryos were derived from microspores at the tetrad stage (139).

The ability of cells derived from so many tissues and organs to produce embryos is often taken as evidence for the generalization that differentiation of plant cells does not involve loss or permanent inactivation of genetic material. However, tissues of the mature plant contain large numbers of relatively simple parenchymatous cells which contribute to a developing callus and which may be largely responsible for the production of embryos. Final conclusions cannot be drawn about the genetic status of the full spectrum of mature cell types.

ONTOGENY OF REGENERATED PLANTS

Three basic variations are found, or are reputed to be found, in the manner in which roots and shoots come into association with each other to form a plant. In one method, the regeneration of buds in callus is followed by formation of adventitious roots on the stem as the bud develops (167), or the regeneration of roots in callus is followed by the formation of adventitious buds on the root (55). These cases are of no significance for embryogenesis. Secondly, independent regeneration of roots and buds in callus is followed by their integration into one axis. This phenomenon has been assumed to occur on a number of occasions (104, 154, 180), but there are no histological studies showing the intermediate stages involving union of the two organs. In any event, use of the term "embryoid" to describe clumps bearing only roots (207) is pointless. Use of the same term to describe callus bearing both roots and leaves is equally meaningless unless the organs have been shown to be integrated and capable of functioning as an embryonic plant.

The third mode of whole plant formation is embryogenesis, i.e., formation of an integrated root-shoot axis by stages resembling the ontogeny of seed embryos. Review of this phenomenon necessarily involves a brief trip through the history of carrot cell culture. Nobécourt in 1946 (141) reported the appearance of "de minuscules tiges portant chacune deux petites feuilles ovales, opposées, resemblant à de petits cotyledons" at three different places on a root which had grown from callus. The shoots appeared only in "cultures âgées." Levine (123, 124) a few years later, observed roots in carrot callus grown on simple media containing auxin. Transfer of the callus to media lacking auxin resulted in the appearance of plantlets which bore "primitive" or cotyledon-like leaves. In the late 1950's, studies by Steward and his co-workers (180) and Reinert (156) again led to the discovery of entire plants in carrot cultures, but differing ontogenetic sequences were proposed. Steward et al. (180) observed the regeneration of roots from cambium-like cells in clumps growing in liquid media. The entire plants which subsequently appeared were assumed to have arisen by formation of a bud at a point on the clump opposite the root. Reinert's work (156) with carrot callus led him to state that the shoots which were formed in his cultures were "fast ausschlieslich aus Adventivembryonen." Interpretation of his data is difficult because of the complexity and sequence of several kinds of media used, the extended time interval between transfers and the appearance of new morphological forms (3 to 5 months), and the grossly deformed nature of the organs found. Similar difficulties beset the carrot culture system reported by Butenko and her co-workers in Russia (27, 170). Although claims were made by all these workers that various components of the media were significant in inducing formation of organs, the only observation which seemed consistent was that roots appeared on auxin-containing media and that lowering of the auxin content in the culture was essential to subsequent appearance of shoots. It should be noted that although these shoots were frequently assumed to have been derived from buds, histological studies demonstrating an unequivocal bud in carrot callus have never been published. The significance of this fact is uncertain, unless it indicates that such cultures never form buds and that all shoot systems are derived from embryos.

In any case, subsequent studies in a number of laboratories provided adequate documentation for the formation of normal dicotyledonous embryos in carrot callus and suspension cultures (81, 104, 182, 211). Hypothetical ontogenetic sequences were proposed in which putative single cell progenitors gave rise directly to globular proembryos (104, 182) or to both filamentous and globular stages (83). It was found that continued exposure of proembryos to high auxin levels did not inhibit growth but caused them to proliferate randomly, forming disorganized starch-filled "proembryogenic masses" which could be carried through numerous subcultures (84, 87).

Wetherell & Koukkari (212) found these stable proembryogenic cells to have an extremely high phytochrome content. The heavy concentration of starch is also of interest, since the same phenomenon has been reported for nucellar embryo initials in some species (74, 145) and bud-forming cells in tobacco callus (193). In the case of carrot proembryogenic clumps, when the auxin level is lowered by transfer to auxin-free media, cells at the periphery of the clump utilize their starch and divide rapidly to form one or more embryos per clump (84, 87). The development of multiple embryos in this fashion resembles cleavage polyembryony (129) and is similar to the manner in which adventive embryos develop from experimentally damaged zygotic embryos of *Eranthis hiemalis* (77, 78). In carrot suspension cultures, the proembryogenic clumps small enough to pass a 45μ sieve gave rise to normal dicotyledonous embryos within 10 days on auxin-free media (86), a fact which emphasizes the difficulty in interpreting experiments where a period of weeks or months intervenes between transfer of callus to auxin-free media and the appearance of embryos. The possible failure of single cells to produce embryos in sieved suspension cultures (86) was not assigned any significance beyond the well-established fact that few single cells divide in suspension cultures (121, 186, 190, 197), a phenomenon which may be due to excessive leakage of metabolites into the medium or to the need for attachment to a solid substratum (another cell?), as demonstrated by Joshi & Ball (102).

Specific Factors Inducing Embryogenesis

Since readily expressed totipotency is a conspicuous feature of at least some higher plant cells, there seems to be no theoretical obstacle to the development of experimental methods similar to those used in studying embryogenesis of the sea urchin or *Fucus*. The present obstacles are practical ones—namely, our inability to isolate a homogeneous population of embryologically competent cells and to establish a starting point through the introduction into the culture of some factor or factors which approximate fertilization. In the most extensive studies to date of the metabolism of carrot callus in relation to organ formation, Syono (191) found that the callus passed through four distinct physiological phases which were characterized by formation of different kinds of organs and different responses to test media. Here again, however, detection of the organs depended upon transfer of the callus to auxin-free media, a procedure which permits further development of inhibited primordia but yields no information as to when or how they were induced. The inducing factors in embryogenesis are still not known, although several hypotheses have been advanced.

The crucial issues were first identified by Steward in 1958 (180) in a hypothesis which needs little description here. It consisted essentially of the proposal that exposure of cultured cells to coconut milk was a situation similar to the exposure of the fertilized egg to the endosperm and had, therefore, the same morphogenetic results. This hypothesis was of considerable heuristic value, although subsequent experimental work proved it to be erroneous (80, 84). The embryogenic role of endosperm in the ovule, a necessary corollary of Steward's hypothesis, is not on sound theoretical ground either (see 85 for discussion of this point). The question remains: what substances, if any, induce cultured cells to behave like zygotes? In considering this question, it is well to keep in mind that the entire ovule is peculiarly embryogenic in nature, since cells of the nucellus and integuments commonly serve as embryo initials either in place of the egg or in competition with it in some taxa. Other tissues of the carpel do not behave in this way, pointing up the fact that information on the unique physiology of ovules is badly needed.

Recent studies with carrot cultures have emphasized the inorganic components of the medium. Halperin & Wetherell obtained data indicating that ammonium ions played a role in the induction of embryogenesis in wild carrot cultures (82). Later work indicated that the requirement was not absolute, since embryos were induced on other forms of reduced nitrogen but were fewer in number than in ammonium-grown controls (84). It was proposed that ammonium ions might have developmentally significant effects not related to nitrogen metabolism. This hypothesis was consistent with the subsequent finding that cations (157) or high salt concentrations (28) were effective in inducing embryogenesis. A cation or salt effect is interesting in view of the demonstration by Braun & Wood (20, 218) that ions may be involved in activation of hormone biosynthetic systems. The role of reduced nitrogen remains unclear at present. Kato & Takeuchi found that yeast extract was as effective as ammonium in inducing embryo development from cultured hypocotyl segments of carrot (105). Linser & Neumann (127) found that reduced nitrogen was essential to carrot embryogenesis, but concluded that nitrogen and hormones influenced morphogenesis only indirectly through their effect on the rate of cell division. Reinert and his co-workers (157) confirmed that ammonium was more efficient than other nitrogen sources in inducing carrot embryogenesis, but concluded that reduced nitrogen was not essential since cultures grown on nitrate alone would produce embryos. Unfortunately, none of these results from different laboratories are readily comparable, since they involved different varieties and organs of carrot, different basic media, different culture conditions, and inadequate quantitative methods of measuring embryogenesis.

The remaining factor which has been cited as playing a causal role in embryogenesis is that of cell isolation. Steward (182), in particular, has emphasized that isolation of single cells from the controlling influence of other cells, via the breaking of plasmodesmata, is a *sine qua non* for the expression of totipotency. Cases where the breaking of intercellular connections causes a dramatic change in growth pattern are well known, particularly in filamentous algae (132; see 166 for discussion) and fern gametophytes (91). However, embryos in subcultured callus or suspension cultures are usually derived from proembryogenic masses whose origin in the explant is unknown. In cases where embryos develop directly on the primary explant, histological studies may reveal an extremely tenuous relationship between the embryo and subjacent tissues (105, 112), indicating a possible single cell origin, or the embryos may be attached by a broad band of cells to the subjacent tissue (206), giving the impression that more than one initiating cell was involved. Definitive studies have not been performed, and it remains uncertain whether the induction of embryogenesis in primary explants necessarily involves physical isolation (breaking of plasmodesmata) of single initiating cells, or whether some other form of physiological isolation of one or more cells is sufficient. Electron microscope studies of the initiation of nucellar embryos might be enlightening in this respect. It would also be informative to compare at the electron microscope level the initial stages of embryo development from hypocotyl epidermal cells of carrot or *Ranunculus* (105, 112) with the initial stages of bud regeneration from hypocotyl epidermal cells of decapitated flax, *Linum usitatissimum* (126), or cranberry, *Vaccinium macrocarpon* (6). One frequently finds the misleading statement that such buds are derived from single epidermal cells. Mitoses may be restricted initially to one cell and its derivatives, but cell divisions eventually spread to the adjacent tissues as a vascular connection is established. Embryos do not induce vascularization of subjacent tissue in the explant.

LOSS OF ORGANOGENETIC ABILITY

The putative loss of ability to form organs may be associated with other changes in the cell strain involving growth rate, friability, nutrient requirements, and chromosome constitution (137, 138, 200). Cultures which show an increased growth rate, increased friability, and growth in the absence of exogeneous hormones are referred to as "habituated" (65). Cultures exhibiting a decline in growth rate and decreased friability have been referred to as senescent (137). Habituation is a gradual process of tumorization, since habituated tissues grafted into normal plants cause varying degrees of tumor development (125) and, like tumor cells, are autonomous with respect to the synthesis of growth-regulating hormones (19, 65). Symptoms of tumorization frequently precede obvious chromosome abnormalities (49). It is significant, therefore, that cultures which show some of the symptoms of habituation or tumorisation but which are still in the diploid or tetraploid condition remain capable of producing organs (62). Even when the etiology of tumorization is clearly genetic but does not involve aneuploidy or high levels of polyploidy, as in certain *Nicotiana* hybrids, the tumors are quite capable of producing roots and buds (3, 79). Conversely, habituated cultures which do show a predominance of aneuploid mitoses are incapable of organ formation (135). It appears that genomic imbalance due to aneuploidy or high levels of ploidy is one direct cause of the inability of some cultures to form organs, a conclusion also reached by Torrey (200) and Murashige & Nakano (138) on the basis of studies with nonhabituated callus strains. The low polyploid condition is, however, not incompatible with organogenesis *in vitro* (12, 138, 200, 216).

Other causes of a failure in organ formation undoubtedly exist. It has been suggested (69) that derived strains lose the ability to synthesize specific factors required for organogenesis, although the existence of such substances has always been problematic in the absence of chemical identification. There are numerous reports of species which never produce organs at any time in their culture history, but few have been subjected to extensive analysis. Doering & Ahuja (50) reported, for example, that callus cultures derived from both tumorous and nontumorous segregants of *Lycopersicon* hybrids fail to produce organs, even when transferred to media lacking auxins or other growth regulators which might suppress organogenesis. It would be of value to have detailed information on the chromosome constitution and histology of both explants and derived cultures of such species. Some cell strains have been reported to remain diploid for years (37, 146, 190), but the relationship of this fact to organogenetic potential was not made clear. Stable nonmutational changes occur during aging of plants which show distinct phase changes during their life cycle (22, 23). Cuttings from these plants during their adult phase show a decreased capacity for regeneration. Similar nonmutational changes may occur *in vitro*.

LITERATURE CITED

1. Aghion, D., *Compt. Rend.*, **255**, 993–95 (1962)
2. Aghion-Prat, D., *Nature*, **207**, 1211 (1965)
3. Ahuja, M. R., Hagen, G. L., *Develop. Biol.*, **13**, 408–23 (1966)
4. Ahuja, M. R., Doering, G. R., *Nature*, **216**, 800–1 (1967)
5. Arya, H. C., Hildebrandt, A. C., Riker, A. J., *Plant Physiol.*, **37**, 387–92 (1962)
6. Bain, H. F., *Botan. Gaz.*, **101**, 872–80 (1940)
7. Ball, E., *Growth*, **14**, 295–325 (1950)
8. Ball, E., *Annee Biol.*, **31**, 281–305 (1955)
9. Ball, E., *Growth*, **24**, 91–110 (1960)
10. Bauer, L., *J. Linn. Soc. Botany*, **58**, 343–51 (1963)
11. Bergmann, L., *Planta*, **62**, 221–54 (1964)
12. Blakely, L. M., Jennings, H. K., Turner, B. B., *Am. J. Botany*, **55**, 711 (1968)
13. Bloch, R., *Science*, **106**, 320–22 (1947)
14. Bloch, R., *Growth*, **12**, 271–84 (1948)
15. Bonnett, H. T., Torrey, J. G., *Plant Physiol.*, **40**, 1228–36 (1965)
16. Bonnett, H. T., Torrey, J. G., *Am. J. Botany*, **53**, 496–507 (1966)
17. Bopp, M., *Ann. Rev. Plant Physiol.*, **19**, 361–80 (1968)
18. Bouillenne, A., *Annee Biol.*, **54**, 597–628 (1950)
19. Braun, A. C., *Proc. Natl. Acad. Sci. U. S.*, **45**, 932–38 (1959)
20. Braun, A. C., Wood, H. N., *Proc. Natl. Acad. Sci. U S.*, **48**, 1776–82 (1962)
21. Brian, P. W., Hemming, H. G., Lowe, D., *Ann. Botany*, **24**, 407–19 (1960)
22. Brink, R. A., *Quart. Rev. Biol.*, **37**, 1–22 (1962)
23. Brink, R. A., Styles, E. D., Axtell, J. O., *Science*, **159**, 161–70 (1968)
24. Brown, C. L., Sax, K., *Am. J. Botany*, **49**, 683–91 (1962)
25. Brown, C. L., in *The Formation of Wood in Forest Trees*, 389–404 (Zimmerman, M. H., Ed., Academic Press, New York, 1964)
26. Bünning, E., *Surv. Biol. Progr.*, **2**, 105–40 (1952)
27. Butenko, R. G., Yakovleva, Z. M., *Biol. Abstr.*, **42**, 11640 (1963)
28. Butenko, R. G., *Dokl. Akad. Nauk SSSR*, **175**, 1179–81 (1967)
29. Butenko, R. G., *Plant Tissue Culture and Plant Morphogenesis* (Acad. Sci. USSR, Moscow, 1964; Engl. Transl., Fed. Clearing House, Springfield, Va., 1968)
30. Buvat, R., *Ann. Sci. Nat. Botan.*, **5**, 1–130 (1944)
31. Buvat, R., *ibid.*, **6**, 1–119 (1945)
32. Buvat, R., in *Encyclopedia of Plant Physiology*, **15**(1), 100–45 (Lang, A., Ed., Springer-Verlag, New York, 1965)
33. Camus, G., *Rev. Cytol. Biol. Vegetales*, **11**, 1–198 (1949)
34. Carew, D. P., Staba, E. J., *Lloydia*, **28**, 1–26 (1965)
35. Chen, H-R., Galston, A. W., *Physiol. Plantarum*, **20**, 533–39 (1967)
36. Cocking, E. C., *Planta*, **68**, 206–14 (1966)
37. Cooper, L. S., Cooper, D. C., Hildebrandt, A. C., Riker, A. J., *Am. J. Botany*, **51**, 284–90 (1964)
38. Curtis, J. T., Nichol, M. A., *Bull. Torrey Botan. Club*, **75**, 358–73 (1948)
39. Cusick, F., *Trans. Roy. Soc. Edinburgh*, **63**, 153–66 (1956)
40. Cutter, E. G., *Nature*, **173**, 440–41 (1954)
41. Cutter, E. G., *Ann. Botany*, **20**, 143–65 (1956)
42. Cutter, E. G., *Phytomorphology*, **8**, 74–95 (1958)
43. Danckwardt-Lilliestrom, C., *Physiol. Plantarum*, **10**, 794–97 (1957)
44. Das, N. K., Patau, K., Skoog, F., *Physiol. Plantarum*, **9**, 640–51 (1956)
45. Davies, L. M., Priest, J. H., Priest, R. E., *Science*, **159**, 91–93 (1968)
46. Davis, B. D., *Medicine*, **43**, 639–49 (1964)
47. Deftos, L. J., Rabson, A. S., Buckle, R. M., Aurbach, G. D., Potts, J. T., *Science*, **159**, 435–36 (1968)
48. DeMaggio, A. E., *Science*, **152**, 370–72 (1966)
49. deTorok, D., *Cancer Res.*, **28**, 608–14 (1968)
50. Doering, G. R., Ahuja, M. R., *Planta*, **75**, 85–93 (1967)
51. Doerschug, M. R., Miller, C. O., *Am. J. Botany*, **54**, 410–13 (1967)
52. Dore, J., *Ann. Botany*, **19**, 127–37 (1955)

53. Dore, J., Williams, W. T., *Ann. Botany*, **22**, 231–49 (1956)
54. Dore, J., in *Encyclopedia of Plant Physiology*, **15(2)**, 1–91 (See Ref. 32)
55. Earle, E. D., Torrey, J. G., *Am. J. Botany*, **52**, 891–99 (1965)
56. Esau, K., *Plant Anatomy* (Wiley, New York, 1965)
57. Fleischmajer, R., *Science*, **157**, 1472–82 (1967)
58. Flickinger, R. A., *Science*, **141**, 608–14 (1963)
59. Foard, D. E., Haber, A. H., Fishman, T. N., *Am. J. Botany*, **52**, 580–90 (1965)
60. Fosket, D. E., Miksche, J. P., *Physiol. Plantarum*, **19**, 982–91 (1966)
61. Fosket, D. E., *Proc. Natl. Acad. Sci.*, **59**, 1089–96 (1968)
62. Fox, J. E., *Physiol. Plantarum*, **16**, 793–803 (1963)
63. Galavazi, G., *Acta Botan. Neerl.*, **13**, 420–21 (1964)
64. Gautheret, R., *Sciences (Paris)*, **40**, 95–128 (1942)
65. Gautheret, R., *Rev. Gen. Botan.*, **62**, 1–107 (1955)
66. Gautheret, R., *J. Natl. Cancer Inst.*, **19**, 555–90 (1957)
67. Gautheret, R., *La Culture des Tissus Végétaux* (Masson & Cie, 1959)
68. Gautheret, R., *Rev. Cytol. Biol. Vegetales*, **27**, 99–220 (1964)
69. Gautheret, R., in *Cell Differentiation and Morphogenesis*, 55–71 (North-Holland, Amsterdam, 1966)
70. Geissbuhler, H., Skoog, F., *Tappi*, **40**, 256–62 (1957)
71. Goldacre, P. L., Unt, H., Kefford, N. P., *Nature*, **193**, 1305–6 (1962)
72. Grobstein, C., in *The Cell*, **1**, 437–96 (Brachet, S., Mirsky, A. E., Eds., Academic Press, New York, 1959)
73. Grobstein, C., *Am. Scientist*, **50**, 46–58 (1962)
74. Guerin, P., *Ann. Sci. Nat. Botan.* (Ser. b), **19**, 225–65 (1937)
75. Guha, S., Maheshwari, S. C., *Nature*, **212**, 97–98 (1966)
76. Haber, A. H., Foard, D. E., *Am. J. Botany*, **50**, 937–44 (1963)
77. Haccius, B., *Z. Naturforsch.*, **146**, 206–9 (1959)
78. Haccius, B., *Phytomorphology*, **13**, 107–15 (1963)
79. Hagen, G. L., *Develop. Biol.*, **4**, 569–79 (1962)
80. Halperin, W., *Science*, **146**, 408–10 (1964)
81. Halperin, W. *Embryogenesis in Cell Cultures and the Wild Variety of Daucus carota* (Doctoral thesis, Univ. Connecticut, 1965)
82. Halperin, W., Wetherell, D. F., *Nature*, **205**, 519–20 (1965)
83. Halperin, W., Wetherell, D. F., *Science*, **147**, 756–58 (1965)
84. Halperin, W., *Am. J. Botany*, **53**, 443–53 (1966)
85. Halperin, W., *Science*, **153**, 1287–88 (1966)
86. Halperin, W., *Exptl. Cell Res.*, **48**, 170–73 (1967)
87. Halperin, W., Jensen, W. A., *J. Ultrastruct. Res.*, **18**, 428–43 (1967)
88. Heslop-Harrison, J., *Ann. Rev. Plant Physiol.*, **18**, 325–48 (1967)
89. Holtzer, H. H., in *Synthesis of Molecular and Cellular Structure*, 35–87 (Rudnick, D., Ed., Ronald Press, New York, 1961)
90. Ito, M., Stern, H., *Develop. Biol.*, **16**, 36–53 (1967)
91. Ito, M., *Botan. Mag. Tokyo*, **75**, 19–27 (1962)
92. Jacobs, W. P., *Am. J. Botany*, **39**, 301–9 (1952)
93. Jacobs, W. P., *Am. Naturalist*, **90**, 163–69 (1956)
94. Jacobs, W. P., Morrow, I. E., *Am. J. Botany*, **44**, 823–42 (1957)
95. Jacobs, W. P., in *Recent Advances in Botany*, 786–90 (Univ. Toronto Press, 1961)
96. Jacquiot, C., *Compt. Rend.*, **244**, 1246–48 (1957)
97. James, W. O., *Nature*, **158**, 377–78 (1946)
98. Jeffs, R. A., Northcote, D. H., *Biochem. J.*, **101**, 146–52 (1966)
99. Jeffs, R. A., Northcote, D. H., *J. Cell Sci.*, **2**, 77–88 (1967)
100. Jensen, W. A., *Plant Physiol.*, **30**, 426–32 (1955)
101. Jensen, W. A., Kavaljian, L. G., *Am. J. Botany*, **45**, 365–72 (1958)
102. Joshi, P. C., Ball, E., *Develop. Biol.*, **17**, 308–25 (1968)
103. Karstens, W. K. H., in *Proc. Intern. Congr. Plant Tissue Culture*, 309–20 (White, P. R., Grove, A. R., Eds., McCutchan, Berkeley, 1963)
104. Kato, H., Takeuchi, M., *Plant Cell Physiol.*, **4**, 243–45 (1963)
105. Kato, H., Takeuchi, M., *Sci. Papers Coll. Gen. Educ., Univ. Tokyo*, **16**, 245–54 (1966)

106. Kauppert, M., *Z. Botan.*, **46**, 383–416 (1958)
107. Koblitz, H., *Faserforsch. Textiltech.*, **13**, 231–34 (1962)
108. Koblitz, H., *ibid.*, 310–17
109. Kohlenbach, H. W., *Naturwissenschaften*, **46**, 116–17 (1959)
110. Kohlenbach, H. W., *Planta*, **64**, 37–40 (1965)
111. Konar, R. N., Nataraja, K., *Phytomorphology*, **14**, 558–63 (1965)
112. Konar, R. N., Nataraja, K., *ibid.*, **15**, 132–37 (1965)
113. Konar, R. N., Nataraja, K., *ibid.*, 206–11
114. Konigsberg, I., *Science*, **140**, 1273–84 (1963)
115. Kupila, S., *Cancer Res.*, **23**, 497–509 (1963)
116. Lamotte, C. E., Jacobs, W. P., *Develop. Biol.*, **8**, 80–98 (1963)
117. Lang, A., in *Encyclopedia of Plant Physiology*, **15(1)**, 409–23 (See Ref. 32)
118. Lee, T. T., Skoog, F., *Physiol. Plantarum*, **18**, 386–402 (1965)
119. Lee, T. T., Skoog, F., *ibid.*, 577–85
120. Lehmann, H., *Planta*, **71**, 240–56 (1966)
121. Lescure, A. M., *Exptl. Cell Res.*, **44**, 620–23 (1966)
122. Letham, D. S., *Ann. Rev. Plant Physiol.*, **18**, 349–64 (1967)
123. Levine, M., *Bull. Torrey Botan. Club*, **74**, 321–28 (1947)
124. Levine, M., *Am. J. Botany*, **37**, 445–58 (1950)
125. Limasset, P., Gautheret, R. J., *Compt. Rend.*, **230**, 2043 (1950)
126. Link, G., Eggers, V., *Botan. Gaz.*, **107**, 441–54 (1946)
127. Linser, H., Neumann, K. H., *Physiol. Plantarum*, **21**, 487–99 (1968)
128. Maheshwari, P., Baldev, B., *Nature*, **191**, 197–98 (1961)
129. Maheshwari, P., *An Introduction to the Embryology of Angiosperms* (McGraw-Hill, New York, 1950)
130. Margara, J., *Compt. Rend.*, **260**, 278–81 (1965)
131. Mehta, A. R., *Experientia*, **22**, 300 (1966)
132. Miehe, H., *Ber. Deut. Botan. Ges.*, **23**, 257–64 (1905)
133. Mlodzianowski, F., *Bull. Soc. Amis Sci. Lettres Poznan*, **6**, 1–20 (1965)
134. Mothes, K., in *The Alkaloids*, **6**, 1–29 (Manske, R. H. F., Ed., Academic Press, New York, 1960)

135. Muir, W. H., in *Proc. Intern. Congr. Plant Tissue Culture*, 485–92 (See Ref. 103)
136. Murashige, T., *Physiol. Plantarum*, **17**, 636–43 (1964)
137. Murashige, T., Nakano, R., *Am. J. Botany*, **52**, 819–27 (1965)
138. Murashige, T., Nakano, R., *ibid.*, **54**, 963–70 (1967)
139. Nakata, K., Tanaka, M., *Japan. J. Genet.*, **43**, 65–71 (1968)
140. Nitsch, J. P., Nitsch, C., *Bull. Soc. Botan. France*, **111**, 299–304 (1964)
141. Nobécourt, P., *Compt. Rend. Soc. Biol.*, **140**, 953–54 (1946)
142. Nobécourt, P., Hustache, G., *Intern. Botan. Congr., 8th*, 192–93 (1954)
143. Norstog, K., Rhamstine, E., *Phytomorphology*, **17**, 374–81 (1967)
144. Ootaki, T., *Botan. Mag. Tokyo*, **80**, 1–10 (1967)
145. Osawa, I., *J. Coll. Agr., Imp. Univ. Tokyo*, **4**, 83–116 (1912)
146. Partanen, C. R., in *Developmental Cytology*, 21–45 (Rudnick, D., Ed., Ronald Press, New York, 1957)
147. Patillo, R. A., Gey, G. O., Delfs, E., Mattingly, R. F., *Science*, **159**, 1467–69 (1968)
148. Paul, J., *Cell and Tissue Culture* (Williams & Wilkins, Baltimore, 1961)
149. Paulet, P., Nitsch, J. P., *Ann. Physiol. Vegetale*, **6**, 333–45 (1964)
150. Paulet, P., Nitsch, J. P., *Bull. Soc. Botan. France*, **106**, 426–41 (1959)
151. Paupardin, C., *Compt. Rend.*, **258**, 1024–27 (1964)
152. Paupardin, C., *ibid.*, **259**, 3345–47
153. Pierik, R. L. M., *Regeneration Vernalization and Flowering in Lunaria Annua L. in Vivo and in Vitro* (Veeman & Zonen, Wageningen, 1967)
154. Pilet, P. E., *Ber. Schweiz. Botan. Ges.*, **71**, 189–208 (1961)
155. Ranga Swamy, N. S., *Phytomorphology*, **11**, 109–27 (1961)
156. Reinert, J., *Planta*, **53**, 318–33 (1959)
157. Reinert, J., Tazawa, M., Semenoff, S., *Nature*, **216**, 1215–16 (1967)
158. Rier, J. P., Breslow, D. T., *Botan. Gaz.*, **128**, 73–77 (1967)
159. Roberts, L. W., Fosket, D. E., *New Phytologist*, **65**, 5–8 (1966)
160. Ruesink, A. W., Thimann, K. V.,

Proc. Natl. Acad. Sci. U.S., **54,** 56–64 (1965)

161. Sachs, R. M., Kofranek, A. M., Shyr, S.-Y., *Am. J. Botany,* **54,** 921–29 (1967)

162. Schroeder, C. A., Kay, E., Davis, L. H., *Science,* **138,** 595–96 (1962)

163. Shininger, T., *Secondary xylem differentiation in* Xanthium (Doctoral thesis, Univ. Massachusetts, 1969)

164. Sievert, R. C., Hildebrandt, A. C., *Am. J. Botany,* **52,** 742–50 (1965)

165. Sinnott, E. W., Bloch, R., *Am. J. Botany,* **32,** 151–56 (1945)

166. Sinnott, E. W., *Plant Morphogenesis* (McGraw-Hill, New York, 1960)

167. Skoog, F., *Am. J. Botany,* **31,** 19–24 (1944)

168. Skoog, F., Tsui, C., in *Plant Growth Substances,* 263–85 (Skoog, F., Ed., Univ. Wisconsin Press, 1951)

169. Skoog, F., Miller, C. O., in *The Biological Action of Growth Substances,* 118–31 (Porter, H. K., Ed., Academic Press, New York, 1957)

170. Smirnov, A. M., Butenko, R. G., *Akad. Nauk SSSR Vestnik,* **2,** 73–79 (Engl. Transl. in U. S. Govt. JPRS, **19,** 762, 1963)

171. Staba, E. J., *Develop. Ind. Microbiol.,* **4,** 193–98 (1963)

172. Staba, E. J., Laursen, P., Büchner, S., in *Proc. Intern. Congr. Plant Tissue Culture,* 191–210 (See Ref. 103)

173. Stange, L., *Advan. Morphogenesis,* **4,** 111–53 (1964)

174. Stange, L., *Ann. Rev. Plant Physiol.,* **16,** 119–40 (1965)

175. Stebbins, G. L., in *Genetic Control of Differentiation, Brookhaven Symp. Biol.,* **18,** 204–21 (1965)

176. Sterling, C., *Am. J. Botany,* **37,** 464–70 (1950)

177. Sterling, C., *ibid.,* **38,** 761–67 (1951)

178. Stern, H., Hotta, Y., in *Meristems and Differentiation, Brookhaven Symp. Biol.,* **16,** 59–72 (1963)

179. Steward, F. C., Wetmore, R. H., Thompson, J. F., Nitsch, J. P., *Am. J. Botany,* **41,** 123–34 (1954)

180. Steward, F. C., Mapes, M. O., Mears, K., *Am. J. Botany,* **45,** 705–8 (1958)

181. Steward, F. C., *Am. J. Botany,* **45,** 709–13 (1958)

182. Steward, F. C., Mapes, M. O., Kent, A. E., Holsten, R. D., *Science,* **143,** 20–27 (1964)

183. Steward, F. C., Kent, A. E., Mapes, M. O., in *Current Topics in Developmental Biology,* **1,** 113–54 (Moscona, A. A., Monroy, A., Eds., Academic Press, New York, 1966)

184. Stow, I., *Cytologia,* **1,** 417–39 (1930)

185. Stoutemeyer, V. T., Britt, O. K., *Am. J. Botany,* **52,** 805–10 (1965)

186. Street, H. E., Henshaw, G. G., *Symp. Soc. Exptl. Biol.,* **17,** 234–56 (1963)

187. Street, H. E., in *Cells and Tissues in Culture,* **3,** 631–89 (Willmer, E. N., Ed., Academic Press, New York, 1966)

188. Sunderland, N., Heyes, J. K., Brown, R., *J. Exptl. Botany,* **8,** 55–70 (1957)

189. Sussex, I. M., in *Meristems and Differentiation, Brookhaven Symp. Biol.,* **16,** 1–12 (1963)

190. Sussex, I. M., in *Proc. Intern. Congr. Plant Tissue Culture,* 383–91 (See Ref. 103)

191. Syono, K., *Plant Cell Physiol.,* **6,** 403–19 (1965)

192. Takebe, I., Otsuki, Y., Aoki, S., *Plant Cell Physiol.,* **9,** 115–24 (1968)

193. Thorpe, T. A., Murashige, T., *Science,* **160,** 421–22 (1968)

194. Toponi, M., *Compt. Rend.,* **253,** 1482–84 (1961)

195. Torrey, J. G., *Plant Physiol.,* **29,** 279–87 (1954)

196. Torrey, J. G., Shigemura, Y., *Am. J. Botany,* **44,** 334–44 (1957)

197. Torrey, J. G., Reinert, J., Merkel, N., *Am. J. Botany,* **49,** 420–25 (1962)

198. Torrey, J. G., *Advan. Morphogenesis,* **5,** 39–91 (1966)

199. Torrey, J. G., *Am. J. Botany,* **53,** 611 (1966)

200. Torrey, J. G., *Physiol. Plantarum,* **20,** 265–75 (1967)

201. Tryon, K., *Science,* **123,** 590 (1957)

202. Tulecke, W., in *Reproduction: Molecular, Subcellular, and Cellular,* 217–41 (Locke, M., Ed., Academic Press, New York, 1965)

203. Van Lith-Vroom, M. L., *Acta Botan. Neerl.,* **9,** 275–85 (1960)

204. Vardjan, M., Nitsch, J. P., *Bull. Soc. Botan. France,* **108,** 363–74 (1961)

205. Vasil, I. K., Hildebrandt, A. C.,

Riker, A. J., *Science,* **146,** 76–77 (1964)

206. Vasil, I. K., Hildebrandt, A. C., *Am. J. Botany,* **53,** 869–74 (1966)

207. Vasil, I. K., Hildebrandt, A. C., *ibid.,* 860–69

208. Went, F. W., Thimann, K. V., *Phytohormones* (MacMillan, New York, 1937)

209. Went, F. W., *Plant Physiol.,* **13,** 55–80 (1938)

210. Went, F. W., in *Plant Growth Substances,* 287–98 (Skoog, F., Ed., Univ. Wisconsin Press, 1951)

211. Wetherell, D. F., Halperin, W., *Nature,* **200,** 1336–37 (1963)

212. Wetherell, D. F., Koukkari, W. L., *Plant Physiol.,* **42,** 302–3 (1967)

213. Wetmore, R. H., Rier, J. P., *Am. J. Botany,* **50,** 418–30 (1963)

214. Wetmore, R. H., DeMaggio, A. E., Rier, J. P., *Phytomorphology,* **14,** 203–17 (1964)

215. White, P. R., *Am. J. Botany,* **54,** 334–53 (1967)

216. Wilmar, C., Hellendoorn, M., *Nature,* **217,** 369–70 (1968)

217. Wilson, J., Wilson, M. P., *New Phytologist,* **60,** 63–73 (1961)

218. Wood, H. N., Braun, A. C., *Proc. Natl. Acad. Sci. U. S.,* **12,** 1907–13 (1961)

219. Yamada, T., Nakagawa, H., Sinoto, Y., *Botan. Mag. Tokyo,* **80,** 68–74 (1967)

220. Yasumura, Y., Tashjian, A. H., Jr., Sato, G. H., *Science,* **154,** 1186–89 (1966)

221. Zeevaart, J. A. D., *Science,* **137,** 723–37 (1962)

FREEZING INJURY IN PLANTS[1]

By Peter Mazur

Biology Division, Oak Ridge National Laboratory
Oak Ridge, Tennessee

Two groups of biologists are chiefly interested in freezing injury and its prevention: those concerned with the use of low temperatures for the long-term preservation of animal tissues and microorganisms, and those concerned with the problem of how plants in nature survive subzero temperatures. Both groups have amassed large volumes of data, but neither has made much effort to study the results obtained by the other or to incorporate the results into more effective concepts of freezing injury.

Part of the lack of communication is due to the different experimental approaches used by the two groups. Those concerned with preservation have devoted most of their effort to improving survival by the addition of protective solutes; and they have devoted some effort to manipulating the physical variables involved in freezing, especially cooling velocity. They have generally used single cells or isolated pieces of animal tissue rather than intact animals, paying little attention to the biochemical and physiological differences underlying the wide variations in susceptibility to freezing shown by various species. On the other hand, botanists concerned with frost injury have been chiefly interested in the marked changes in sensitivity to freezing that occur seasonally in many plants, and in correlating these changes with biochemical and physiological alterations. But they have devoted little effort to uncovering the relation between survival and changes in physical factors such as cooling and warming velocity; and they usually define injury in terms of the median lethal temperature for plants subjected to single cooling and single warming velocities, velocities that are one to four orders of magnitude lower than those used by investigators concerned with preservation. Comparatively little effort has been devoted to simpler single-cell plant systems, and, as far as I know, none to plant material in tissue culture.

The purpose of this review is to identify and circumscribe these differences in concepts, approaches, and results, at the same time pointing out the common features involved in the freezing of all living systems. The review will not be a synopsis of recent data on freezing injury and hardiness in plants: instead, it will begin with a discussion of the physical and chemical

[1] Research sponsored by the U. S. Atomic Energy Commission under contract with the Union Carbide Corporation.

events occurring in cells at subzero temperatures and will attempt to relate cell survival to those events that occur in cells frozen under laboratory conditions different from those occurring in nature. These results will then be contrasted with those obtained in higher plants under conditions mimicking nature. The review will conclude with a consideration of some of the current theories of freezing injury.

I. PHYSICOCHEMICAL EVENTS DURING FREEZING

Understanding the mechanisms underlying injury requires an awareness of the events to which a cell is subjected during freezing and thawing. Briefly, these events are the following:

1. Both cells and their external medium supercool initially, but ice soon forms in the medium. However, the cell membrane keeps the ice from seeding the cell interior at temperatures above about $-10°$ C, so the cell remains unfrozen and supercooled.

2. As the temperature falls, an increasing fraction of the extracellular solution is converted to ice. The concentration of all extracellular solutes rises and the aqueous vapor pressure falls. Since the cell is supercooled, its aqueous vapor pressure exceeds that of the extracellular water, and water flows out of the cell and freezes extracellularly. The resulting dehydration concentrates the intracellular solutes, small and large, and decreases the spatial separation between macromolecules. If the cell is sufficiently permeable to water or if cooling is sufficiently slow, the cell will dehydrate to the extent required to maintain equilibrium between the intra- and extracellular aqueous vapor pressures, and intracellular freezing will not occur. But if the cell is not sufficiently permeable to water, or if it is cooled too rapidly, it will not remain in equilibrium, but will continue to supercool until it eventually equilibrates by internal freezing.

3. As more and more water is converted to ice during cooling, the solubility of some electrolytes, whether intra- or extracellular, will be exceeded, and they will precipitate. If their solubilities differ, the differential precipitation may result in large changes in pH.

4. Below a certain temperature (referred to as the eutectic point) or range of temperatures (eutectic zone), all free water will be converted to ice and all solutes precipitated. A cell held above these temperatures will be immersed in, and will contain, a highly concentrated solution, whose ionic composition and pH are likely to be far different from normal.

5. Small or nonspherical crystals of ice have higher surface free energies than large spherical crystals. There will be a tendency, therefore, for the former to be converted into the latter, a process known as recrystallization or grain growth. Recrystallization does not require the existence of liquid; i.e., it can occur in the solid state below the eutectic point.

6. During warming the events will essentially be reversed. The progressive melting of the external solution will begin above the eutectic point or

zone and will cause the external aqueous vapor pressure to rise above that of cells that have dehydrated during cooling. As a result, water will flow into the cell at a rate dependent on both the warming velocity and the permeability of the cell to water.

Some of these points need elaboration:

Lowered temperature.—Many animals, microorganisms, and plants can be killed by being cooled to suboptimum temperatures, but, with the exception of animals with highly developed homeostatic mechanisms, injury usually develops only after hours or days of exposure to lowered temperature (40, 85). There is, however, another class of injury, produced by rapid chilling, that results in immediate lethality and is called thermal shock. Thermal shock occurs in relatively few species (Sherman, personal communication, 1968), and even in these it occurs only after rapid chilling and only if the cell is in a susceptible physiological state (63). It occurs, for example, in rapidly cooled log phase *Escherichia coli* but not in stationary (77).

The causes of chilling injury and thermal shock are unknown, but Brandts (4) has recently suggested protein denaturation as a possible physical-chemical basis. Because hydrophobic interactions are important contributors to the stability of native proteins, and because they become weaker at reduced temperatures, the native form can become less stable when cooled. In support of this thermodynamic argument, he has observed the low-temperature denaturation of several proteins (5).

Although there are instances of damage from low temperature per se, most microorganisms and higher plant cells survive supercooling to temperatures as low as -20 C (24, 40, 43, 63, 68). The insects furnish a dramatic example. Some supercool without injury to below $-25°$ C (100, 107).

The ability of plant and animal cells to supercool even in the presence of extracellular ice is well established. Observations to this effect have been reviewed by Levitt (43) and Mazur (62, 63). Excellent descriptions of the phenomenon in plants were reported by Luyet & Gibbs (54), Asahina (3), Modlibowska & Rogers (78), and Salcheva & Samygin (98). Although the cell surface can block the seeding of cytoplasm above about $-10°$ C, it apparently loses this ability at lower temperatures, for cells surrounded by ice do not supercool as extensively as do cells surrounded by supercooled water (62). One explanation for the ability of the plasma membrane to prevent seeding by external ice above certain temperatures is that ice crystals small enough to grow through the aqueous channels believed by some to exist in membranes have melting points far below $0°$ C (56, 57, 62, 99). For example, an ice crystal 30 Å in radius will melt above $-10°$ C.

Dehydration.—If a supercooled cell is surrounded by ice or by a solution in equilibrium with ice, if the solutions are considered ideal, and if there is no diffusion of solutes across the cell membrane, the ratio of the internal to external vapor pressures of water (p_i/p_e) would increase with decreasing temperature (T) according to the relation

$$\frac{d \ln (p_i/p_e)}{dT} = \frac{d \ln x_1}{dT} - \frac{L_f}{RT^2} \qquad 1.$$

where L_f is the latent heat of fusion, R the gas constant, and x_l the mole fraction of water in the cell. Because of this vapor pressure gradient, water will flow out of the cell; and if no permeating solutes are present, the rate of efflux will be

$$-\frac{dV}{dt} = L_p A (\pi_e - \pi_i) = \frac{L_p A RT}{\overline{V}_1} \ln (p_i/p_e) \qquad 2.$$

where V is the volume of cell water, t time, L_p the permeability of the cell to water, $\overline{V}_l$ the molar volume of water, A the area of the cell surface, and π_i and π_e the internal and external osmotic pressures. If one knows the values of L_p, A, and the cooling velocity, it is possible to calculate the amount of water remaining in the cell at any given temperature, and the extent to which it is supercooled (60). Calculations for yeast show that cells cooled at 10° C/min or slower will contain no supercooled water below −15° C; that is, they will have dehydrated to the equilibrium value. But cells cooled faster than 10° C/min will contain increasing quantities of supercooled water, and the likelihood of intracellular freezing will become high. Measurements of the volumes of the freeze-substituted yeast support these predictions; they indicate that cells cooled slower than 10° C/min are shrunken and contain no intracellular ice, whereas cells cooled at 100° C/min are much less shrunken and do contain ice (58, 65). The prediction for mammalian red blood cells is similar except that because of their high permeability to water, the critical cooling velocity is calculated to be about 3000° C/min instead of 10° C/min (66). Electron micrographs by Rapatz, Nath & Luyet (88) support the prediction.

Two conclusions emerge from these results. One is that intracellular freezing becomes possible only above a certain cooling velocity. The other is that the numerical value of the critical velocity can differ greatly in different cells, and depends chiefly on the permeability of the cell to water. The higher the permeability, the higher the critical velocity.

The preceding treatment assumes the absence of a hydrostatic pressure difference across a cell membrane, an assumption that can be invalid in the case of higher plant cells. The rate of water movement out of a cell permeable only to water depends on the difference in chemical potentials of the intra- and extracellular water ($\Delta\mu_1$). According to Katchalsky & Curran (25) and Dainty (7),

$$\Delta\mu_1 = \overline{V}_1(\Delta P - \Delta\pi) \qquad 3.$$

and the rate of water movement is

$$\frac{dV}{dt} = L_pA(\Delta P - \Delta\pi) \qquad\qquad 4.$$

where P refers to the hydrostatic pressure.

Space will not permit a detailed analysis of how the substitution of Equation 4 for Equation 2 will affect the rate of water loss and the water content of cells as freezing proceeds. But two aspects need to be mentioned: As the external medium freezes, the unfrozen cell will begin to shrink even before the external osmotic pressure has become higher than the internal. This shrinkage will result from the elastic response of the cell wall to the reduction in turgor pressure that accompanies the increasing extracellular osmotic pressure. By the time the temperature has dropped to -2 or $-3°$ C, the external osmotic pressure will usually exceed the internal. A second question concerns the ensuing response of the cell. If the cell wall offers no resistance against shrinkage or if plasmolysis can occur easily, the hydrostatic pressure term in Equation 4 will disappear, and the protoplast will shrink in accordance with Equations 1 and 2. At the other extreme, if the cell wall were completely resistant to shrinkage and the plasmalemma strongly adherent to it, and if cavitation did not occur, reduction of the chemical potential of the intracellular water would come about not by water loss, but by the establishment of negative hydrostatic pressures. However, the tension required to reduce the chemical potential of intracellular water to equilibrium would soon become high; e.g., it would be about -100 atm at $-10°$ C. Gardner & Ehlig (10) have shown that negative turgor pressures are not produced in leaves of cotton, sunflower, trefoil, or pepper. Although this does not exclude the possibility in other cells, the ability of most cells to maintain tensions of 100 atm would seem remote.

Changes in pH.—Evidence that progressive freezing of a solution causes not only an increase in concentration of solutes but also a change in its composition and pH has been furnished by the work of van den Berg (115) and van den Berg & Rose (116) on solutions containing phosphate salts and sodium or potassium chloride. Changes approaching two pH units were noted in some instances as one or more of the components precipitated.

Complete solidification.—When a simple solution cools below its final eutectic point and solidifies completely, its electrical resistivity becomes very high. Using resistivity as the criterion, Rey (90), Mazur (61), and Greaves & Davies (13) have shown that cytoplasm and solutions of macromolecules do not exhibit unique eutectic points, but rather progressive solidification down to about $-35°$ C or $-40°$ C. Calorimetric measurements on yeast and *E. coli* (61, 109, 118) indicate that approximately 90 per cent of the cell water is frozen at $-20°$ C. The residual 10 per cent remains unfrozen at $-70°$ C, and is, therefore, considered "bound." Krasavtsev's (31) measurements on the twigs of several trees, however, show somewhat higher unfrozen water contents at $-20°$ C ($\sim$ 24 to 50 per cent of the

normal water content) and a progressive decline with falling temperature
(9 to 20 per cent unfrozen at $-60°$ C). The difference may be related to
the lower water content of the twigs at normal temperatures (1 g H_2O/g
solids vs. 3 g H_2O/g solids in yeast), or to the fact that much of the water
in twigs is associated with woody components.

Recrystallization.—The mutability in the size and shape of ice crystals
at low temperatures is well documented. Recrystallization can occur in
pure water at $-100°$ C (72), but in concentrated solutions of nonelectrolytes or proteins and in cells, it usually takes place above $-50°$ C (53, 63,
87).

II. RELATION OF CELL INJURY TO PHYSICAL EVENTS DURING FREEZING

Since freezing and thawing involve a number of interdependent events,
the task of determining which event is responsible for injury is formidable.
The chief tools available for the dissection are the functional relations between the survival, metabolism, and structure of a cell and the temperature,
phase state, cooling rate, exposure time, warming rate, and extracellular solutes to which it is exposed. Fortunately, these experimental variables do
provide information, for they affect the various physical events in different
ways. Thus, a comparison of the survival of supercooled cells with that of
frozen cells at the same temperature will tell whether injury is due to lowered temperature per se or to some consequence of ice formation. The response of a cell to cooling velocity should tell something about the extent to
which injury is the result of intracellular freezing or is the result of dehydration and the consequent alterations in solution properties. The reason for
this is that the probability of intracellular ice formation rises with cooling
velocity, whereas damage from concentrating solutes ought to rise with increasing exposure time and, therefore, with decreasing cooling rate. Other
examples will be given in the ensuing discussion.

Figure 1 shows the survival of the yeast *Saccharomyces cerevisiae* as a
function of cooling velocity to $-70°$ C. The three solid curves show the results for three warming rates. The dashed curve shows the calculated relation between cooling rate and the degree to which the cell water is supercooled at $-15°$ C (see Section I). The existence of an optimum cooling velocity means that at least two factors are affecting survival, and the fact
that slow warming is more deleterious to rapidly cooled cells than to slowly
cooled cells implies the involvement of at least a third factor. The best interpretation of these results seems to be the following: The low survivals at
low cooling velocities result from long exposures to critical concentrations
of solute or to critical levels of dehydration. Faster cooling shortens the exposure and hence causes a rise in survival, but still faster cooling increases
the probability of intracellular freezing. At cooling velocities above 10°
C/min, the deleterious consequences of internal ice rapidly overcome the
beneficial action of shorter exposure, and survival drops to an extent depen-

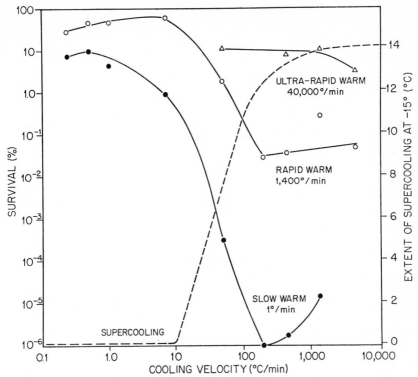

FIG. 1. Survival and supercooling of *Saccharomyces cerevisiae* as a function of cooling velocity. Cells in distilled water were cooled at various rates to —70° C, transferred to liquid nitrogen, and warmed at the indicated rates. The supercooling curve is calculated. From Mazur (65).

dent on the warming velocity. The influence of warming velocity is believed to be through its effect on recrystallization: slow warming maximizes recrystallization and thus maximizes injury. Evidence supporting these statements has been published elsewhere (63, 65, 69).

Similar survival curves have been obtained for the bacterium *Pasteurella tularensis* (70), mammalian red blood cells (11, 55, 66), higher plant cells (97), and recently mouse bone marrow stem cells (39). In the case of the red blood cells and plant tissues, there is direct electron microscopic evidence that cooling rates higher than optimum do in fact result in the formation of intracellular ice (88, 96).

The conclusion that low cooling rates injure by solute concentration or by dehydration and that high cooling rates injure by intracellular freezing may be of general validity; but the numerical values of "low" and "high" can vary widely depending on the sensitivity of the cell to solute concentration and on its ability to avoid intracellular freezing by losing water. Thus, the unprotected red cell, highly sensitive to high concentrations of electrolyte and extremely permeable to water, exhibits optimum survival at a cooling velocity of about 3000° C/min (55, 66) in contrast to 10° C/min for yeast (2, 65, 69) and mulberry parenchymal cells (97). As a consequence, a cooling rate of 100° C/min is adversely "slow" for red cells and adversely "rapid" for yeast and mulberry.

If nontoxic solutes such as glycerol or sucrose are present in the cell or in the extracellular fluid, they can affect the optimum cooling velocity by affecting the extent to which potentially deleterious solutes concentrate during freezing (50). They may also influence it by affecting the likelihood of intracellular freezing, the percentage of intracellular water that freezes, and the extent to which the formation of a given amount of ice will be lethal (9). Glycerol, for example, produces large shifts in the optimum cooling velocity of red cells (86) and marrow stem cells (39). In both cases, the higher the concentration of protective solute present, the lower the optimum rate.

Two points should be emphasized in summary. One is that the general outlines of the functional relation between survival and cooling and warming velocity are beginning to emerge; the other is that it is risky to base mechanistic conclusions on the survivals obtained for a single velocity, and it may be erroneous to conclude that the factors that kill a cell at one cooling velocity will kill the same cell at a different velocity or will kill a different cell at the same velocity.

Similar warnings apply to drawing conclusions from survival measurements based on freezing to a single temperature. As shown in Figure 2, the survivals of yeast, the bacterium *Pasteurella tularensis,* and bacteriophage T4B as a function of temperature are markedly different. Further, the shapes of the curves depend to a large extent on conditions such as the cooling and warming rate, the concentration of electrolytes in the suspending medium, and the time the cells are held at a given temperature. Explanations for the shapes of these curves have been given elsewhere (38, 69, 70).

Unfortunately, few studies on plant cells have involved sufficient ranges of cooling velocity, warming velocity, and temperature to permit definitive conclusions as to which physical factors are associated with injury. The in-

---

≫≫→

Fɪɢ. 2. Survival of *S. cerevisiae, Pasteurella tularensis,* and bacteriophage T4B as a function of temperature. Slow cooling and warming were about 1° C/min. Rapid cooling varied from 15 to 250° C/min and rapid warming from 500 to 1400° C/min, depending on the temperature. The data on yeast are from Mazur & Schmidt (69); those on *P. tularensis* are modified from Mazur, Rhian & Mahlandt (70); and those on T4B are modified from Leibo & Mazur (38).

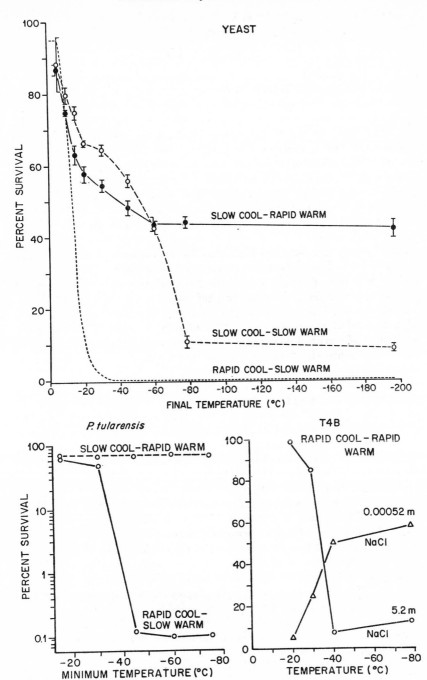

formation available on the fungi has been reviewed elsewhere (67). In addition, there is some information on the cells of algae and higher plants.

ALGAE

The most thorough study on the interactions of cooling velocity, temperature, and warming velocity is that of Leibo & Jones (35) on the unicellular red alga *Porphyridium cruentum*. Suspensions of cells in artificial sea water were frozen at −20°, −30°, −45°, or −76° C, either rapidly (20–50° C/min) or slowly (1° C/min), held 10 to 100 min, and warmed rapidly (150–500° C/min) or slowly (1° C/min). There was little damage at −20° C regardless of cooling rate, exposure time, and warming rate; but betlow −20° C, rapid cooling was decidedly more injurious than slow, and rapid warming slightly less injurious than slow. However, regardless of the rates, some injury occurred between −20° and −45° C, with −30° C being especially critical. Exposure time had little effect on cells held at −20°, −45°, and −76° C: at −20° C, injury remained low; at −45° and −76° C, injury was nearly as high after 10-min exposure as after 100 min. But at −30° C, injury increased progressively with time.

The protective effect of slow cooling is consistent with (but not proof of) the view that the greater injury after rapid cooling was associated with intracellular ice. Temperature was an even more important factor, however, with the critical range between −20° and −45° C probably reflecting the attainment of a critical concentration of solute, a critical extent of dehydration, or an approach to complete solidification rather than an influence of temperature per se.

Deleterious effects from rapid cooling have also been noted for green algae. Holm-Hansen (18) cooled suspensions of five unicellular species in air at −25° C and in liquid baths at −10°, −30°, −70°, and −196° C. The cooling velocities increased in the order given, and survival as determined by colony formation on agar plates was found to decrease. Unfortunately, because of the confounding of rate and temperature, one cannot evaluate the relative contributions of the two factors.

Hwang & Horneland's (19) experiments did not confound cooling rate and temperature (suspensions either were cooled at 1° C/min to −30° C followed by immersion in a bath at −79° C or were cooled at about 100° C/min by immersing room-temperature samples directly in a bath at −79° C), but the survival assay was less precise than that used by Holm-Hansen. They determined the number of cells after various lengths of time in growth medium. In all of the genera tested (*Ankistrodesmus, Chlamydomonas, Chlorella, Scenedesmus,* and *Euglena*), rapidly cooled samples yielded fewer cells after a given growth period than did slowly cooled samples although in some cases the difference was slight. In this work, unlike that of Leibo & Jones and of Holm-Hansen, the suspending medium contained 10 per cent glycerol.

Interestingly, the survival of blue-green algae in general does not appear to correlate with either temperature or cooling rate. Holm-Hansen (18) found, for example, the viability of *Schizothrix* to be good with all temperature-rate combinations and that at *Phormidium tenue* to be high only with rapid-cooling low-temperature, whereas that of *Nostoc* was highest with a slow-cooling high-temperature treatment.

Terumoto (112) froze fresh water and marine algae at 3° C/min. He observed that cells cooled at this rate did not undergo intracellular freezing, so that injury must have been associated with the solution effects of freezing; that is to say, with solute concentration or cell dehydration. However, certain aspects of his results are difficult to explain. For example, when filaments of the fresh water alga *Aegagropila* were frozen at −15° C for 2 hr in 0.1 to 1.0 M $CaCl_2$, the cells plasmolyzed but survived. When they were frozen to −15° C in water or in dilute salt solutions, they underwent no plasmolysis and little shrinkage, and they survived; but when they were frozen in sodium salt solutions above 0.01 M, they dehydrated without plasmolysis and were killed. Since the chemical potential of extracellular water equilibrated at −15° C has a single value that is independent of the concentration or type of solute present, the lack of shrinkage of cells frozen in dilute solutions would have to be caused by (a) a low permeability to water preventing attainment of intracellular equilibrium during the period of observation, (b) attainment of equilibrium by the establishment of a hydrostatic tension in the cells, or (c) an increase in permeability of the plasma membrane permitting equilibration by the inflow of solutes. All three explanations have their difficulties.

Injury to the various algae studied by Terumoto appears to be related in some way to the manner in which the protoplast shrinks (i.e., whether by contraction of the cell or by different types of plasmolysis) and to the extent of shrinkage. Survival tended to be high when shrinkage was minimal or when it occurred by normal types of plasmolysis. The findings may indicate that injury can be produced both by physical stresses associated with cell shrinkage or plasmolysis and by chemical stresses related to the concentration of intracellular solutes.

Higher Plant Cells

Both Sakai and Krasavtsev have carried out extensive studies on the response of various twigs cooled to −196° C at different rates. They found that although twigs would not survive direct immersion in liquid nitrogen, they would survive if they were immersed in baths at higher temperatures for several minutes before being transferred to liquid nitrogen (31, 92, 94). For example, when mulberry twigs were initially cooled to 0, −10, −20, −25, −30, or −70° C before transfer, survivals were 0, 10, 40–60, 60–70, 100, and 100 per cent, respectively. Furthermore, 100 per cent survived cooling from 25 to −90° C at the low rate of 0.5° C/min (92). The interpretation offered by Sakai for these results is that cooling to −30° C, for example, is sufficiently slow to permit the cells to equilibrate by dehydration

and extracellular freezing rather than by intracellular freezing, and that
−30° C is sufficiently low for nearly all freezable water to be removed
from the cells by exosmosis. This interpretation is qualitatively consistent
with the predictions from Equations 1 and 2, and with the calorimetric
studies on yeast (118) and *E. coli* (109), which show all free water to be
frozen below about −20° C. Krasavtev's (31) calorimetric measurements
on twigs, however, indicate that 9 to 21 per cent of the free water is still
unfrozen at −30° C.

Interestingly, twigs from hardy plants survived the transfer to liquid nitrogen from higher subzero temperatures than did nonhardy twigs (e.g.,
−15° C vs. −30° C for hardy and nonhardy willow) (94). This may reflect
the well-known fact that hardy cells have a higher permeability to water
(40, 43), for the higher permeability would permit them to be cooled more
rapidly without undergoing intracellular freezing (60, 62).

The suggestion that freezing in two steps protects by preventing intracellular ice formation has been supported by detailed studies of Sakai and
his co-workers on cortical parenchymal cells in tissue slices from hardy
mulberry twigs. Plots of survival (as measured by plasmolysis and staining
with neutral red) versus cooling rate were similar to the results shown for
yeast in Figure 1; i.e., at cooling rates below 10° C/min, survival was high
and independent of warming rate. But as the cooling velocity was raised
towards 100° C/min, survival dropped abruptly, and the drop became more
extensive when warming was slow than when it was rapid (97). When
cooling rates exceeded $10^{4°}$ C/min, survival after rapid warming rose
toward 100 per cent but survival after slow warming was zero, findings
that confirm similar observations made by Tumanov & Krasavtsev (114)
on thin slices of bark parenchyma. The major loss in survival during rapid
cooling (400–1000° C/min) occurred between −10° and −20° C, as with
yeast (Fig. 2). To obtain high survivals after rapid cooling, the parenchymal cells had to spend no more than 2 sec between −55° and −25° C
during warming, a time period very similar to that recently reported for
rapidly cooled yeast (69). The major damage during slow warming occurred between −40° and −30° C.

These data are consistent with the view expressed elsewhere (64, 65)
that abrupt drops in survival above a certain cooling velocity (10° C/min
in the cases discussed here) are associated with the formation of intracellular ice, and that the lethality of the intracellular ice depends on the
amount of recrystallization occurring during warming, with slow warming
producing the greater amount. Sakai & Otsuka (96) made an electron
microscopic examination of parenchymal cells cooled at various rates and
freeze-substituted, and demonstrated the presence of intracellular ice crystals
when the cooling rates were such as to produce low survivals in other
samples treated in parallel. Samples cooled very rapidly to −60° C or
below showed no evidence of intracellular ice and were 100 per cent viable

after rapid warming. But when similar samples were warmed from −60°
to −30° C for 10 min, the results were different: samples subsequently
freeze-substituted at −78° C showed evidence of large intracellular ice
crystals, and samples subjected to rapid thawing from −30° C contained
no viable cells.

In conclusion, injury of these hardy mulberry cells appears to be determined chiefly by two factors: the formation of intracellular ice and the subsequent growth of that ice during warming. Injury in slowly cooled yeast is
influenced by a third factor, the adverse effects of solute concentration or
dehydration, and in mammalian cells this third factor becomes even more
important than the other two. The more fragmentary data on other cells
suggests that the overall survival curve for cells cooled at rates between 1
and 10,000° C/min may in general be determined by these three factors and
by the relative contribution that each exerts at various cooling and warming
rates.

III. FROST INJURY AND FROST HARDINESS IN HIGHER PLANTS

BASIS OF MEASURING FROST INJURY

Most experimentation on freezing injury in higher plants involves
approaches and methodologies different from those described in the preceding section. In the first place, the measure of injury in the plant is
usually the median lethal temperature (LT_{50}). Secondly, the LT_{50} is determined by cooling plants at a single very low rate to various temperatures
and by warming them at a low rate, the rationale presumably being to
mimic the situation in nature.

Some numerical values will emphasize the differences. In the studies discussed in the preceding section, cooling and warming rates ranged for the
most part from 1° to 10,000° C per min, so that cells spent less than 1 min
to no more than 1 hr between 0° and −30° C. In work with higher plants,
cooling rates are usually about 1°–4° C/hr (0.016 to 0.06° C/min) and
warming rates are usually several degrees per hr (43), so that plants spend
as much as 30 to 40 hr between 0° and −30° C. The low rates and long
times can have important consequences:

1. Unless the plant cells have extremely low permeabilities to water or
the plant supercools extensively before freezing, calculations based on
Equations 1 and 2 suggest that intracellular freezing would be unlikely to
occur when cooling is slower than 0.1° C/min (64). According to Levitt
(40, 43) experiments have generally borne out this prediction. However, intracellular ice can form at surprisingly low velocities. Salcheva & Samygin
(98), for example, observed it in winter wheat cooled at about 0.3 C/min
(20° C/hr), and Samygin & Matveeva (101) observed it in cabbage cooled
at only 0.16° C/min (10° C/hr). Furthermore, supercooling is a possibility,
and Levitt (43) describes cases in which supercooled plants eventually un-

dergo intracellular freezing even when cooled as slowly as 0.08° C/min (5° C/hr).

2. Although intracellular ice cannot be ruled out at a cause of injury in all cases, it seems probable that frost killing of very slowly cooled plant material is usually a consequence of alterations in the extracellular and intracellular solutions produced by extracellular freezing, the chief alterations being the concentration of solutes and cellular dehydration. This view is strengthened by the close parallel between frost hardiness and drought hardiness (40). But it is not justifiable to conclude from this that the factors responsible for lethal injury in a plant cell spending 30 hr between 0° and −30° C are the same as those in a cell spending only 10 min to 1 hr in the same temperature range. There is ample evidence in the literature, for microorganisms at least, that the rate of killing in the first few minutes at a given temperature may be higher or lower than that occurring during subsequent storage at that temperature (63).

3. In view of the very low cooling rate used, the question arises as to the significance of a median-lethal temperature. It could represent the attainment of a critical temperature, a critical concentration of solute, a critical length of exposure to various concentrations or to some threshold concentration, or a critical level of dehydration or critical minimum cell volume. One type of experiment that would reduce the severe confounding of temperature, time, and rate would be to cool sections of plant tissue at much higher rates (but slowly enough to avoid intracellular freezing) to various temperatures for various lengths of time.

4. A corollary difficulty in using an LT_{50} as the sole measure of freezing injury is its inability to give information on the functional relations between survival and temperature. As noted in discussing Figure 2, these relations can vary widely; nevertheless, they must be accounted for by any mechanistic explanation of freezing injury. Furthermore, when hardening lowers an LT_{50}, it would be useful to know whether it produces a parallel shift of the survival versus temperature curve or a change in the shape of the curve. Unfortunately, such information is rarely reported.

FACTORS RESPONSIBLE FOR FREEZING INJURY

Partly because it is difficult to dissect out the relative influence on survival of the several events occurring during slow freezing, and chiefly because little attempt has been made to do so, there has been little progress in experimentally determining the physical-chemical factors associated with frost injury in higher plants. There is evidence [reviewed by Levitt (43)] that some plant cells are killed when a certain fraction of their water is frozen and that hardy cells will endure having a greater fraction frozen than will nonhardy. Of course, correlated with the freezing of a certain fraction of cell water will be a corresponding increase in solute concentration and a corresponding decrease in cell volume. Levitt (41, 43) also found that tissue of cabbage and *Saxifraga* cooled to or below their LT_{50} underwent a decrease in sulfhydryl centent and an increase in disulfide content, changes that form part of the evidence for his sulfhydryl-disulfide hypothesis of injury to be discussed later. Krasavtsev (30) observed that when parenchymal bark cells of elder or cherry were cooled slowly to $-55°$ C, they fluoresced a different color and were dead after thawing. Cells cooled to only $-20°$ to $-35°$ C showed no changes in color and were viable after thawing. Ths implication is that the cells were killed during freezing to $-55°$ C rather than during thawing.

Yet one of the interesting aspects of freezing injury in higher plants is that the measured LT_{50} is often influenced by the warming rate (40, 43). As discussed in Section II, rapidly cooled higher plant cells, like rapidly frozen animal cells (73) and microorganisms (63), are injured more when warming is slow than when it is rapid. Slow warming is also more deleterious, or equally deleterious, to slowly frozen animal cells and microorganisms; but the response of very slowly frozen plant cells (e.g., $\sim$ 0.01 to 0.1 ° C/min) stands in sharp contrast. Slow warming is apparently never deleterious, and is often less harmful than rapid warming (43), even in a given plant that responds oppositely to warming rate when freezing has been rapid (31, 114). Two other findings on the influence of warming rate are interesting. One is Parker's report (82) that leaves survived cooling to $-45°$ C when warmed at 5° C/hr, but failed to survive when warmed just twice as rapidly. The other is Tumanov & Krasavtev's (114) observation that the deleterious action of rapid warming on birch and cherry twigs was not associated with a rapid change of subzero temperatures from $-60°$ to $-5°$ C, but with the rapid appearance of liquid water between $-5°$ and $0°$ C. This is precisely opposite to the situation for slowly cooled yeast, where practically all the deleterious action of slow warming occurs below $-20°$ C (69).

The contrast between the effects of warming rate on higher plant cells and on animal cells and microorganisms could possibly be due to the fact that much lower cooling velocities are used with the former than with the latter. This possibility should be tested, especially since Meryman (75) recently reported that human red cells suspended in 0.5 to 1 M glycerol and cooled at 0.3° C/min showed much less hemolysis when warmed at 0.3° C/min than when warmed at several hundred degrees per minute, a complete reversal of the situation that occurs in rapidly cooled unprotected red blood cells (49).

An alternative possibility is that the difference in the response to warming rate reflects some fundamental difference between plant and animal cells, the most likely being the presence of a stiff cell wall in the former. As noted in Section I, a stiff cell wall could exert considerable influence on the manner in which equilibration occurs during slow freezing. The difficulty is that microorganisms do not respond like plant cells to warming rate, even though they too possess cell walls. However, their cell walls are generally less rigid, and many of them, especially gram-positive cells, are difficult to plasmolyze (59, 89).

Since slow warming produces much longer exposure to concentrated intra- and extracellular solutes than rapid warming, it is unlikely that the deleterious effects of rapid thawing are due to adverse biochemical consequences of solute concentration. They appear rather to be associated with the rapid rehydration of a dehydrated cell. Interestingly, as reviewed elsewhere (67), adverse effects from rapid rehydration have also been noted for some (but by no means all) freeze-dried fungi; that is, the percentage survivals of such spores after freeze-drying are much higher if they are first rehydrated by vapor-phase equilibration before placing them in contact with liquid water. Slow rehydration also greatly enhances the survival of *Escherichia coli* cells that have been freeze-dried in glucose. Record, Taylor & Miller (89) account for this in terms of osmotic shock. They found that the cells became plasmolyzed in concentrated glucose or sucrose solutions, which indicates that the sugars permeated the cell wall but not the plasma membrane. If abruptly transferred to dilute media, the cells were converted to spheroplasts, presumably because the cell wall ruptured as water entered the space between the wall and the plasma membrane faster than the sugar could diffuse out. Spheroplast formation did not occur if the sugar-containing suspending medium was diluted by dialysis, or if the original concentration of the sugar was kept below 0.5 M.

Similarly, Leibo & Mazur (37, 38) found that the osmotically sensitive bacteriophage T4B will survive freezing if thawing is slow and will survive suspension in concentrated salts above $0°$ C if dilution is slow, but is inactivated if either thawing or dilution is rapid. Here, too, the mechanism of inactivation has been shown to be osmotic shock. Changes in the buoyant density of T4B after exposure to concentrated electrolytes such as NaCl or CsCl indicate that electrolytes can permeate the head. Presumably, similar permeation of extracellular electrolytes occurs during freezing: As a consequence, when the bacteriophage is then rapidly thawed, water moves into the head faster than solutes can diffuse out, and the head ruptures as a result of the transient osmotic pressure developed. Furthermore, rapid thawing inactivates a greater fraction of the bacteriophage when prior cooling is slow than when it is rapid, a fact interpreted to mean that slow cooling allows more time for solute permeation than does rapid. Perhaps the greater sensitivity of very slowly frozen plant cells and red blood cells to rapid thawing has an analogous explanation. But clearly, whatever the explanation, there is a need for further studies on the role played by the rate of addition of water to cells that have been dehydrated by freezing.

It must be recognized, however, that most slowly frozen plant cells are killed below some temperature, even when they are warmed at very low rates (43). Frozen cells that are killed by rapid warming but survive slow warming must be killed by events during warming and thawing, but cells that are killed regardless of warming velocity could well have been killed by events during freezing. At least there is no basis for assuming that death in this case is caused by the same mechanisms responsible for the injurious effects of rapid thawing. The recent work of Heber & Santarius on isolated chloroplast fragments, for instance, strongly suggests that a different mechanism is involved in the inactivation of photophosphorylation by freezing and thawing. They have analyzed the enzymatic changes occurring in chloroplast membrane vesicles after freezing to $-25°$ C for 3 hr. Freezing destroyed the ability of the vesicles to respond osmotically and to carry out photophosphorylation, but it could actually stimulate electron transport (15, 17). In contrast to the situation for intact plant tissues, rapid freezing and rapid thawing were less damaging than slow freezing and slow thawing, results suggesting that injury was proportional to the exposure time at subzero temperatures. The soluble coupling factor required for photophosphorylation was not damaged by freezing. Rather, the damage appeared to be localized in the insoluble membrane structure, and Heber (15) suggests that freezing alters the permeability properties of chloroplast membranes in such a way as to prevent the formation of the proton gradient required for photophosphorylation.

He and his co-workers also found that even though sucrose does not penetrate the membrane vesicles, it could prevent the damage resulting from freezing. The amount of surcose required was almost stoichiometrically dependent on the concentration of electrolytes present in the system; e.g., 0.8 M sucrose permitted 50 per cent retention of photophosphorylation after freezing in the presence of 0.8 M NaCl ($\sim$ 1.6 osmolar). Similar protection was provided by glucose and raffinose. Furthermore, sucrose protected against several electrolytes (NaCl, KCl, $MgCl_2$, or Na_2SO_4) when the ratio of its osmolarity to that of the salts was about 1:2.

Heber interprets the data to indicate that loss in ability to photophosphorylate is a consequence of dehydration. However, if this were the case, the loss ought to be inversely proportional to the initial concentration of sucrose and electrolytes, for the amount of dehydration at any temperature, i.e., the fraction of water converted to ice, is inversely related to the initial concentration of solutes in the solution (62). Thus, solutions containing equiosmolar concentrations of sucrose and NaCl would have approximately 84 per cent of the water converted to ice at $-10°$ C if the total osmolarity were 1.6, and 99.5 per cent converted to ice if the total osmolarity were 0.05; yet membranes suspended in solutions of either composition were able to photophosphorylate at the normal rate after freezing and thawing. Moreover, chloroplasts frozen to $-25°$ C in equiosmolar concentrations of KCl and sucrose were still able to photophosphorylate after thawing, even though $-25°$ C is 11 to 14 degrees below the eutectic point of both solutes (-11 and $-13.9°$ C, respectively) and should have resulted in the freezing of all free water. Also, the capacity of the membranes to photophosphorylate survived freeze-drying over P_2O_5 when sucrose was present (16).

Although the data are not consistent with the view that dehydration

causes the damage and that sucrose protects by reducing the extent of dehydration, they are consistent with the view that damage is caused by the attainment of a critical electrolyte concentration in the unfrozen solution during freezing; for the total osmolal concentration of solute in a partially frozen solution is not dependent on the initial concentration, but only on temperature. To a first approximation, in other words, the data are consistent
with Lovelock's (49, 50) suggestion that damage (to mammalian red cells)
occurs when the electrolyte concentration exceeds a certain value and
that additives protect colligatively by reducing the electrolyte concentration
at any temperature. However, other factors must be involved both in the
injury and in its prevention by additives. For one thing, various electrolytes
of equal osmolarity did not produce exactly the same loss in ability to photophosphorylate (17). For another, Heber & Ernst (16) recently found
that a heat-stable protein or nucleoprotein extracted from hardy spinach
leaves is able to protect chloroplast membranes when its concentration is as
low as 0.1 per cent. Clearly, the protection in this case cannot be colligative.

Still needed for clear interpretation of the response of chloroplasts is
the relation between loss of photophosphorylation and subzero temperature.
If this were known, one could calculate the concentrations of electrolytes
and other solutes at the various temperatures, and then determine the relation of survival to these concentrations. Such information would permit one
to decide whether the loss of photophosphorylation after freezing is associated with the attainment of critical electrolyte concentrations at temperatures above the eutectic point, or with the solidification of the system below
the eutectic point. The former possibility is supported by Packer & Barnard's (80) finding that spinach chloroplasts in NaCl-Tris media lost all
ability to photophosphorylate when stored at $-20°$ C for 1 day, for $-20°$ C
is above the eutectic point of the system.

FROST HARDINESS

The preponderance of research on frost injury in higher plants has
been concerned with the physiological factors that induce hardiness (lowered LT_{50}) and the biochemical changes that accompany it.

It seems well established that hardiness is induced by factors that reduce
plant growth, especially temperatures near or below $0°$ C and short photoperiods (20, 21, 27, 34, 48, 81, 95, 105, 110, 113). Furthermore, gibberellin reduces or inhibits the establishment of hardiness; and compounds
that exhibit growth-retarding properties, such as Amo 1618 and abscisic
acid, permit the induction of hardiness under conditions in which hardiness
does not ordinarily appear, such as long photoperiods (21).

Changes in hardiness in many cases have also been found to correlate
closely with changes in the levels of certain substances in plant cells. One
of the better correlations is between hardiness and high concentrations of
sugar, especially sucrose (40, 48, 83, 84, 95, 119). Moreover, the resistance

to freezing of some plant tissues can be enhanced by immersing them in solutions of penetrating or nonpenetrating sugars (45, 93).

Siminovitch & Briggs (104) some 15 years ago observed a relation between hardiness of the bark of the black locust tree and soluble protein content of the tissues. Recent studies have confirmed and extended this in the locust (105) and demonstrated it in alfalfa (12, 22, 23) and other plants (48). The rise in soluble protein content is often accompanied by a rise in RNA (22, 23, 105).

Although these are the major components of plant tissues for which correlations exist, others that have been mentioned include DNA (22, 23), nicotinamide adenine dinucleotide (34), anthocyanins (84), certain organic acids (26, 48), and lipids (105). In addition, Levitt and his collaborators have found a number of correlations (both positive and negative) between sulfhydryl (SH) and disulfide contents of tissues and frost resistance. Usually, sulfhydryl content increases during early stages of hardening but sometimes decreases in later stages (28, 29, 46, 47, 102).

A number of investigators have reported increases in the levels of two or more tissue components with increases in hardiness. The rise of both soluble protein and RNA has already been mentioned. Other multiple correlations (both positive and negative) include pH and soluble protein (23), sugars and anthocyanins (84), phosphorus, proteins, amino acids, and organic acids (48), dehydroascorbic acid and protein SH (117), and sugars and SH content (43).

Despite these correlations, the question remains as to their interpretation and significance. None of them is perfect. Thus, Levitt (43) points out that sugar cane with its high sucrose content is among the most frost-sensitive of plants, and Siminovitch, Gfeller & Rheaume (105) have reported that hardiness in the black locust is not related to sugar content. On the other hand, Parker (84) found that hardiness of *Hedera* correlates poorly with the concentration of soluble proteins. Where several factors do correlate with hardiness, it is often implied or stated that only one of these is the primary correlate and the others are spurious. This question, unfortunately, is difficult to answer.

Underlying the studies on hardiness seems to be the assumption that a diligent search will uncover a single biochemical alteration or sequence of alterations responsible for all hardiness, which in turn implies that frost hardiness is a discrete property of plant cells, capable of protecting them against a discrete type of injury. Although this would be convenient, it seems to me unlikely. We have seen that freezing involves multiple events and that various events may cause cell death, depending on the nature of the cell and the conditions of freezing and thawing. There may be one prime target of injury (probably membranes), but the available information favors the idea that a number of factors can produce injury and a number of factors protect against it. For example, Heber & Santarius' work indicates that high concentrations of electrolytes or of specific ions damage chloroplast membranes. Sucrose may protect colligatively by reducing the concentrations of electrolytes, but the protein might act by protecting sensitive sites on the membrane against the action of high levels of certain ions. Possibly, frost hardiness in some plants is due to the presence of sucrose, in others to the presence of certain proteins, and in still others to the presence of other substances; but until there is better understanding of the causes and nature of the lesions produced by freezing, the basis of hardiness will probably remain obscure.

In addition to biochemical correlations, there are also physiological ones, the most interesting and general of which is the higher permeability of hardy cells to water (43). Also, Kuiper (32, 33) has reported that application of decenylsuccinic acid and its carbonamides to plants increases their permeability to water and produces significant increases in their resistance to freezing. It would be easy to explain the protective effect of higher water permeability if intracellular freezing were the cause of frost killing (see Section I), but the weight of the evidence seems to argue against this supposition. Alternative possibilities are that more permeable membranes are, for unknown reasons, more resistant to the potentially injurious events produced by freezing, or that the injurious event itself somehow arises because of the presence of a membrane with low permeability to water. Explaining these differences in permeability may be of central importance to an understanding of frost injury.

IV. MECHANISMS OF FREEZING INJURY

THEORIES OF FREEZING INJURY

Several current theories are unitary in that they ascribe all freezing injury to a single physical or chemical event such as the attainment of a critical electrolyte concentration (49), the removal of "stabilizing" water (75), the reduction of cell volume below a critical level (76), or the formation of disulfide bonds (41). The theories basically relate freezing injury to dehydration. Furthermore, they usually make no fundamental distinction between the killing associated with intracellular freezing and that associated with extracellular freezing. Since intracellular freezing is generally much more damaging, proponents of these theories are forced to argue that dehydration by intracellular freezing is more extensive than that by extracellular freezing. The difficulty with such an argument is thermodynamic. The chemical potential of large ice crystals at one atmosphere has a single value at a given temperature regardless of whether the ice is outside or inside the cell. Given sufficient time at that temperature, all unfrozen cellular water of greater chemical potential will be converted into ice. In other words, at equilibrium a cell will be dehydrated to the same extent regardless of whether this be by intracellular freezing or by the flow of water out of the cell and its subsequent freezing extracellularly. To infer, then, that the greater damage from intracellular freezing is a result of greater dehydration is to imply that an extracellularly frozen cell has not become equilibrated.

There is evidence against this view. First of all, yeast cells cooled rapidly enough to contain intracellular ice are killed if the total exposure between 0° and −70° C exceeds 6 sec. In contrast, cells cooled slowly enough to prevent intracellular freezing survive exposure times of 150 min (69). Sakai & Yoshida (97) obtained similar results for hardy mulberry parenchyma cells: cells cooled rapidly enough to contain intracellular ice were killed with exposure times between 0° and −60° as short as 3 sec; yet the same cells survived at least four days at various temperatures between 0° and −70° C when cooling was slow enough to prevent internal ice formation (91). Accordingly, supporters of unitary theories would be required to argue that intracellular freezing produces greater dehydration in a few seconds than extracellular freezing does in many hours or days. A second point is that yeast cells will survive the removal of more water at above-zero temperatures than is removed by freezing under conditions that result in the formation of intracellular ice (65).

An alternative and I think more likely possibility is that intracellular ice kills cells because, in an attempt to achieve its most stable state (large volume and spherical shape), it produces sufficient forces to rupture cell organelle membranes. This suggestion has been elaborated elsewhere (63, 65).

If one restricts the discussion to freezing injury that occurs in the absence of intracellular freezing, a unitary theory is conceivable. But it should be remembered that although intracellular ice can be prevented by slow cooling, the numerical values of rates low enough to preclude it vary over at least a 15,000-fold range, a fact that makes it risky to assume its absence without corroborating evidence. As mentioned in Section II, the cooling rates used to determine frost resistance in higher plants are probably low enough in most cases to ensure that all ice formation is extracellular, but this may not be true in every case.

TARGET OF INJURY IN CELLS

Nucleic acids apparently are not damaged by freezing; freezing produces no significant alterations in the optical density of DNA (103), and it is not mutagenic (63). Many soluble enzymes are also resistant to freezing, both with respect to their conformation and activity; others, however, lose activity, often by being dissociated into subunits (6). Levitt (44) has pointed out that susceptible enzymes contain SH groups. Perhaps more significant is the fact that soluble enzymes in general are much more resistant to freezing than are processes that require membranes or membrane-localized enzymes. A good example is the work on chloroplast membranes already discussed. Photophosphorylation is more readily inactivated by freezing than is electron transport (17). Similarly, oxidative phosphorylation by yeast mitochondria is much more readily inactivated by freezing than are dehydrogenase reactions (14).

Heber (15) concluded from biochemical evidence that the inactivation
of photophosphorylation by freezing is due more to damage to the chloroplast membranes than to inactivation of the membrane-associated enzymes.
Lovelock (51) suggested that alterations in permeability are responsible for
the hemolysis of red blood cells by freezing and thawing. Furthermore,
there is considerable evidence that microorganisms (59, 62, 108) and
plants (106) that are killed by freezing become permeable to solutes that
are normally nonpenetrating. If membranes are, in fact, the chief target of
freezing injury, then the relevance of studies on isolated soluble proteins to
freezing injury becomes a serious question.

Theories of Injury from Extracellular Freezing

Most cryobiologists agree that extracellular ice does not injure by direct
mechanical effects [(40); but see Olien (79) for an opposing view]. As
mentioned, three theories ascribe injury to the dehydration and concentration of solutes produced by freezing, and a fourth emphasizes the role of
temperature. Space will not permit a detailed analysis of the strengths and
weaknesses of each, but certain aspects require discussion.

Injury from low temperatures.—Reference was made earlier to Brandts'
hypothesis and demonstration (4, 5) that some proteins can be denatured as
effectively at low temperatures as at high, the low-temperature denaturation
being a consequence of the important role played by hydrophobic bonds in
the stability of the native form.

In some cases denaturation has been shown to proceed according to the
two-step reaction $N \rightleftarrows D \rightarrow A$; i.e., a reversible denaturation of the native
structure, followed often (but not always) by an irreversible aggregation
(4). In many cases, the first step is an unfolding of the protein, with consequent exposure to the solvent of groups previously buried in the interior of
the protein. Brandts has been concerned with this first step and has shown
that both the extent and rate of appearance of the reversibly denatured
form are increased in cerain marginally stable proteins at subzero temperatures (5). However, he is unable to make quantitative predictions about the
second step, irreversible aggregation, and it is that step that is critical in
injury.

Since most cells are not injured by supercooling (Section I), one is
forced to conclude either that the proteins essential to cell survival are not
denatured by low temperature per se, or else that they are not irreversibly
denatured. However, as freezing progresses, pH and ionic strength of the
extra- and intracellular milieu change drastically, and since Brandts has
shown that the influence of temperature on the extent and rate of the $N \rightarrow$
D reaction is affected by these factors, the possibility remains that lowered
temperatures play an important role in injury.

Injury from dehydration.—As pointed out in Section I, the dehydration
that accompanies extracellular freezing produces at least six consequences:

removal of liquid water, increased concentration of intra- and extracellular solutes, decreased volumes of cells, decreased spatial separation of macromolecules, precipitation of solutes, and changes in pH. In no living cells have the six events been disentangled to the point where their relative contributions to injury can be even approximately determined. There are instances, however, in which one or more events can be excluded, and there are instances for subcellular particles in which the probable injurious event can be identified. To cite a few examples:

(a) Injury to chloroplast membranes does not appear ascribable to the removal of liquid water or to a decreased spatial separation of macromolecules. (See Section III.)

(b) Inactivation of the osmotic-resistant bacteriophage T4Bos during freezing appears to be associated with the precipitation of certain electrolytes below the eutectic point and not with the other factors listed (38).

(c) Inactivation of β-lipoprotein appears to be related to the eutectic point of the suspending medium (52).

(d) Inactivation of mammalian red blood cells, smooth muscle, and mouse stem cells does not appear to be associated with the precipitation of solutes (8, 39, 49).

(e) Inactivation of the chromoprotein phycoerythrin by freezing does not appear to be accounted for by any one of the six events taken singly (36).

For other examples, the reader is referred to two recent compilations (74, 111).

Injury from concentrated electrolytes.—The most widely known and generally accepted theory of freezing injury is that developed by Lovelock (49) to account for freezing hemolysis of the red cell. It states that the injurious event is the concentration of intra- or extracellular electrolytes above a critical value. The theory accounts for many facts about the hemolysis of red cells by freezing, provided that certain additional assumptions are made [e.g., osmotic factors are involved in the damage and not all electrolytes are damaging (63, 76)]. But, since a buildup of salt concentration during freezing must be accompanied by a concomitant reduction in cell water content and cell volume, one cannot exclude the possibility that these are the factors actually responsible for hemolysis (75, 76).

The role of electrolyte concentration in the freezing injury of higher plants is uncertain. It is strongly implicated in the destruction of photophosphorylation (see Section III), but it is difficult to make any general statements about its role in intact plants or plant cells. Levitt (43) rejects electrolyte concentration as a factor, saying

The salt precipitation theory is completely unable to explain the greater resistance of the plant to extracellular than to intracellular freezing since the concentration of the salts would be the same in both cases at any one temperature. It is also incapable of explaining even a small protective effect by plasmolysis in sugar solutions and the existence of thawing as well as freezing injury. Attempts to show a lower salt content in hardy than in nonhardy cells, and a greater resistance of the proteins to salt precipitation when in the hardened state, have both failed.

The first three objections are valid only if a single factor is assumed to be responsible for all freezing injury, but the weight of the evidence is against such an assumption. Also, the second objection is predicated on the assumption that if damage were due to concentrated electrolytes, a protective additive would have to be able to permeate the cell and thereby reduce the concentration of intracellular electrolytes as well as extracellular. But the studies of Heber and his co-workers on chloroplasts and the recent work by Leibo et al. (39) and Mazur et al. (71) on mouse stem cells and Chinese hamster cells suggest that protection can be achieved with nonpenetrating additives, which cannot prevent the concentration of intracellular solutes. The protection, however, may be less effective than that produced by permeating additives. As to the fourth point, there is no reason to assume a lower salt content in hardy cells, since the salt concentration produced during freezing will be the same at any temperature regardless of the initial concentration. Finally, hardiness does not require a salt-tolerant protein; it merely requires, as Lovelock's theory states, the presence of nontoxic materials like sucrose in sufficient concentration to reduce the salt concentration at any temperature; or it requires the presence of some specific compound, such as a protein, capable of protecting sensitive sites against the action of high concentrations of electrolyte or against high concentrations of a specific ion.

Injury from thawing and rehydration.—The point was made in Section III that some freezing injury in higher plants may be associated not with dehydration during freezing but with rehydration during thawing. A clear example of rehydration damage is found in bacteriophage T4B. As mentioned, the phage survives freezing much better if thawing is slow than if it is rapid, and the basis of the damage from rapid thawing has been shown to be osmotic shock (38).

Osmotic events of this sort may play more of a role in the freezing injury of cells than is now appreciated. Their involvement would be implicated by a finding that slow thawing is less damaging than rapid; unfortunately, however, the effect of very low warming rates has not been studied in animal cells, with the exception of the work of Meryman referred to earlier (75), nor has it been studied in microorganisms.

The disulfide hypothesis of freezing injury.—In 1962 Levitt (41) proposed a theory of freezing injury that is the only complete molecular description to date. Basically, it ascribes injury to a combination of events during dehydration and rehydration. He proposed that as water is converted into ice during freezing, structural proteins are forced into closer proximity. Because of this compaction, exposed sulfhydryl groups in adjoining proteins, or in adjoining strands of the same protein, may become linked by disulfide bonds. When water returns to the cell during thawing, competition between hydration forces and the newly formed disulfide bonds causes the protein to become denatured. He argues that (*a*) the theory can account for nearly all observations on freezing injury; (*b*) other theories of freezing injury do not; (*c*) biochemical alterations in cells killed by freezing and thawing are consistent with the hypothesis; (*d*) the biochemical changes accompanying frost hardening are those which would tend to reduce the likelihood of disulfide bond formation; and (*e*) the ability of certain compounds to protect cells is explicable on the basis of the theory. The points are discussed in detail in the original paper and in a recent review (43).

There are, however, a number of difficulties with the hypothesis, the chief of which are the following:

1. Although Levitt presents evidence that the number of disulfide bonds can increase with freezing injury, there is no evidence that disulfide bond formation preceded injury, as the theory requires. He and his co-workers have demonstrated that the disulfide-bond content of the model compound Thiogel increases during storage in the partly frozen state at $-8°$; but Thiogel is already denatured (1, 42). Ordinarily, disulfide bond formation is considered to be one of the important steps resulting in the irreversible aggregation of a previously denatured protein, but not the cause of denaturation. If so, increases in the number of disulfide bonds in frozen-thawed cells may be the result of freezing injury rather than its cause.

2. It is not clear how the disulfide hypothesis can both explain the fact that rapid thawing benefits all rapidly cooled cells studied and many slowly cooled animal cells and microorganisms as well, and also explain the fact that it is often detrimental to very slowly cooled plant cells. As Levitt states (41), it could account for the latter if the stresses occurring during the rehydration of proteins that have become cross-linked by disulfide bonds during freezing are less with slow reentry of water than with rapid. But how can it account for the many cases in which rapid warming protects?

3. It seems difficult to explain Heber & Santarius' data on the freezing of the chloroplast membranes on the basis of the disulfide hypothesis, especially their finding that protection depended on the molar ratio of nonpermeating sugar to electrolyte, and not on the total osmolarity, and their finding that small quantities of a protein extract can protect. Furthermore, as mentioned above, there are increasing instances of cells being protected by nonpermeating solutes such as sucrose and by high molecular weight compounds such as polyvinyl pyrrolidone, which are incapable of permeating the cells and which are too large to exert much colligative effect. Since nonpenetrating compounds cannot prevent cell shrinkage during freezing, it is difficult to see how they could prevent disulfide bond formation and thus prevent consequent killing of the cell.

4. Levitt applies his theory to injury from both intra- and extracellular freezing. The arguments against such a view have already been discussed.

The chief difficulties with the theory arise when attempts are made to have it account for all freezing injury in animals and microorganisms as well as in higher plants. It can more satisfactorily account for the injury observed when higher plants are frozen very slowly and thawed rapidly, but even in this instance it is not proven.

CONCLUSIONS

This review has emphasized the rather paradoxical fact that freezing produces straightforward, well-understood physicochemical events; and yet, because of the interaction of the various events, it is a complex process biologically. But, though it is difficult, establishing the relation between event and biological consequence seems essential to understanding the bases of freezing injury. To date, success in this venture has been modest, mostly because too few attempts have been made. However, some of the efforts cited and other not cited permit certain conclusions.

Except when cooled at the highest of velocities, cells approach equilibrium during freezing. However, the fate of the cell is importantly influenced by whether it approaches equilibrium by intracellular freezing, or by dehydration and extracellular freezing. The former is almost always damaging, especially if warming is slow enough to permit recrystallization. Damage from intracellular ice at present seems due to direct interaction of ice crystals with membrane systems rather than to indirect effects associated with the loss of liquid water. Cooling velocity and permeability of the cell to water are the primary factors determining whether intracellular ice will form and to what extent, and the required cooling velocity can vary from below 1° C/min to more than 3000° C/min.

Cells that are cooled too slowly to freeze intracellularly, as for example most plant cells subjected to the usual methods for evaluating frost hardiness, equilibrate by dehydration. Dehydration produces at least six types of physical alterations: concentration of solutes, precipitation of solutes, reduction in cell water content, cell shrinkage or plasmolysis, changes in pH, and reduction in the spatial separation of macromolecules. Several of these (especially changes in ionic strength, in concentration of specific electrolytes, in pH, and in concentration of protein) can lead to irreversible denaturation of proteins at subzero temperatures as well as at elevated temperatures. Four of them (alterations in electrolyte concentration, removal of essential water, cell shrinkage, and reduction in the spatial separation of macromolecules) have been the bases of unitary theories of freezing damage. None, in my opinion, is successful. The lack of success is not surprising since cells and cell constituents can clearly be injured under appropriate conditions by almost every one of the physical and chemical alterations produced by freezing.

It may well be that certain consequences of dehydration are more important than others in a wide variety of cells frozen under a wide variety of conditions. It is almost certain that some consequences of dehydration are more important than others when specific cells are frozen under specific conditions, but relatively few experimental studies have clearly demonstrated which specific consequence is the culprit and which portion of the cell is the target. Further such studies are clearly needed both to better our understanding of mechanisms of injury and to devise methods of circumventing or preventing that injury.

Note added in proof.—Quatrano [*Plant Physiol.*, **43**, 2057 (1968)] has recently frozen cultured flax cells suspended in 10 per cent dimethylsulfoxide. After cooling at 5 to 10° C/min to −50° C and thawing rapidly, 14 per cent of the cells were viable, as judged by their ability to reduce a tetrazolium dye.

LITERATURE CITED

1. Andrews, S., Levitt, J., *Cryobiology*, **4**, 85–89 (1967)
2. Araki, T., Nei, T., *Low Temp. Sci., Ser. B (Sapporo)*, **20**, 57–68 (1962)
3. Asahina, E., The freezing process of plant cell, *Contrib. Inst. Low Temp. Sci.*, Hokkaido Univ., Sapporo, Japan, No. 10, 83–126 (1956)
4. Brandts, J. F., Heat effects on proteins and enzymes, *Thermobiology*, 25–72 (Rose, A. H., Ed., Academic Press, London and New York, 653 pp., 1967)
5. Brandts, J. F., *Cryobiology* (In press)
6. Chilson, O. P., Costello, L. A., Kaplan, N. O., *Federation Proc.*, **24**, Suppl. 15, S55–S65 (1965)
7. Dainty, J., *Advan. Botan. Res.*, **1**, 279–326 (1963)
8. Farrant, J., *Nature*, **205**, 1284–87 (1965)
9. Farrant, J., Woolgar, A. E., *Cryobiology*, **4**, 248 (1968)
10. Gardner, W. R., Ehlig, C. F., *Plant Physiol.*, **40**, 705–10 (1965)
11. Gehenio, P. M., Rapatz, G. L., Luyet, B. J., *Biodynamica*, **9**, 77–82 (1963)
12. Gerloff, E. D., Stahmann, M. A., Smith, D., *Plant Physiol.*, **42**, 895–99 (1967)
13. Greaves, R. I. N., Davies, J. D., *Ann. N.Y. Acad. Sci.*, **125**, 548–58 (1965)
14. Hansen, I. A., Nossal, P. M., *Biochim. Biophys. Acta*, **16**, 502–12 (1955)
15. Heber, U., *Plant Physiol.*, **42**, 1343–50 (1967)
16. Heber, U., Ernst, R., A biochemical approach to the problem of frost injury and frost hardiness, in *Cellular Injury and Resistance in Freezing Organisms*, 63–77 (Proc., **2**, Intern. Conf. Low Temp. Sci., August 14-19, 1966; Asahina, E., Ed., Inst. Low Temp. Sci., Hokkaido Univ., Sapporo, 257 pp., 1967)
17. Heber, U., Santarius, K. A., *Plant Physiol.*, **39**, 712–19 (1964)
18. Holm-Hansen, O., *Physiol. Plantarum*, **16**, 530–40 (1963)
19. Hwang, Shuh-Wei, Horneland, W., *Cryobiology*, **1**, 305–11 (1965)
20. Irving, R. M., Lanphear, F. O., *Plant Physiol.*, **42**, 1191–96 (1967)

21. Irving, R. M., Lanphear, F. O., *ibid.*, **43**, 9–13 (1968)
22. Jung, G. A., Shih, S. C., Shelton, D. C., *Cryobiology*, **4**, 11–16 (1967)
23. Jung, G. A., Shih, S. C., Shelton, D. C., *Plant Physiol.*, **42**, 1653–57 (1967)
24. Kaku, S., *Botan. Mag. (Tokyo)*, **77**, 283–89 (1964)
25. Katchalsky, A., Curran, P. F., *Nonequilibrium Thermodynamics in Biophysics* (Harvard Univ. Press, Cambridge, Mass., 248 pp., 1965)
26. Ketchie, D. O., *Am. Soc. Hort. Sci.*, **88**, 204–7 (1966)
27. Kohn, H., Levitt, J., *Plant Physiol.*, **40**, 476–80 (1965)
28. Kohn, H., Levitt, J., *ibid.*, **41**, 792-96 (1966)
29. Kohn, H., Waisel, Y., Levitt, J., *Protoplasma*, **57**, 556–68 (1963)
30. Krasavtsev, O. A., *Soviet Plant Physiol.*, **9**, 282–88 (1962)
31. Krasavtsev, O. A., Frost hardening of woody plants at temperatures below zero, in *Cellular Injury and Resistance in Freezing Organisms*, 131–38 (See Ref. 16)
32. Kuiper, P. J. C., *Science*, **146**, 544–46 (1964)
33. Kuiper, P. J. C., *Mededel. Landbouwhogeschool Wageningen*, 67–3, 1–23 (1967)
34. Kuraishi, S., Arai, N., Ushijima, T., Tazaki, T., *Plant Physiol.*, **43**, 238–42 (1968)
35. Leibo, S. P., Jones, R. F., *J. Cellular Comp. Physiol.*, **62**, 295–302 (1963)
36. Leibo, S. P., Jones, R. F., *Arch. Biochem. Biophys.*, **106**, 78–88 (1964)
37. Leibo, S. P., Mazur, P., *Biophys. J.*, **6**, 747–72 (1966)
38. Leibo, S. P., Mazur, P. (Submitted for publication)
39. Leibo, S. P., Farrant, J., Mazur, P., Hanna, M. F., Jr., Smith, L. H. (In preparation)
40. Levitt, J., *The Hardiness of Plants. Agronomy*, **6** (Academic Press Inc., New York, 278 pp., 1956)
41. Levitt, J., *J. Theoret. Biol.*, **3**, 355–91 (1962)
42. Levitt, J., *Cryobiology*, **1**, 312–16 (1965)
43. Levitt, J., Winter hardiness in plants, *Cryobiology*, 495–563 (See Ref. 74)

44. Levitt, J., *Cryobiology*, **3**, 243–51 (1966)

45. Levitt, J., Hasman, M., *Plant Physiol.*, **39**, 409–12 (1964)

46. Levitt, J., Sullivan, C. Y., Johansson, N. O., *Plant Physiol.*, **37**, 266–71 (1962)

47. Levitt, J., Sullivan, C. Y., Johansson, N. O., Pettit, R. M., *Plant Physiol.*, **36**, 611–16 (1961)

48. Li, P. H., Weiser, C. J., Van Huystee, R., *Plant Cell Physiol. (Tokyo)*, **7**, 475–84 (1966)

49. Lovelock, J. E., *Biochim. Biophys. Acta*, **10**, 414–26 (1953)

50. Lovelock, J. E., *ibid.*, **11**, 28–36

51. Lovelock, J. E., *Nature*, **173**, 659–61 (1954)

52. Lovelock, J. E., *Proc. Roy. Soc. (London), Ser. B*, **147**, 427–33 (1957)

53. Luyet, B. J., Anatomy of the freezing process in physical systems, *Cryobiology*, 115–38 (See Ref. 74)

54. Luyet, B. J., Gibbs, M. C., *Biodynamica*, **1**, No. 25, 1–18 (1937)

55. Luyet, B. J., Rapatz, G. L., Gehenio, P. M., *Biodynamica*, **9**, 95–124 (1963)

56. Marshall, D. C., *Australian J. Biol. Sci.*, **14**, 368–90 (1961)

57. Mazur, P., *Ann. N.Y. Acad. Sci.*, **85**, 610–29 (1960)

58. Mazur, P., *J. Bacteriol.*, **82**, 662–72 (1961)

59. Mazur, P., *ibid.*, 673–84

60. Mazur, P., *J. Gen. Physiol.*, **47**, 347–69 (1963)

61. Mazur, P., *Biophys. J.*, **3**, 323–53 (1963)

62. Mazur, P., *Ann. N.Y. Acad. Sci.*, **125**, 658–76 (1965)

63. Mazur, P., Physical and chemical basis of injury in single-celled microorganisms subjected to freezing and thawing, *Cryobiology*, 213–315 (See Ref. 74)

64. Mazur, P., *Cryobiology*, **2**, 181–92 (1966)

65. Mazur, P., Physical-chemical basis of injury from intracellular freezing in yeast, in *Cellular Injury and Resistance in Freezing Organisms*, 171–89 (See Ref. 16)

66. Mazur, P., Physical and chemical changes during freezing and thawing of cells, with special reference to blood cells, *Proc. XI Congr. Intern. Soc. Blood Transfusion* (S. Karger, AG, Basel, Switzerland, in press)

67. Mazur, P., Survival of fungi after freezing and desiccation, *The Fungi*, **III**, 325–94 (Ainsworth, G. C., Sussman, A. S., Eds., Academic Press, New York, 738 pp., 1968)

68. Mazur, P., Miller, R. H., *Cryobiology*, **3**, 365 (1967)

69. Mazur, P., Schmidt, J. J., *Cryobiology*, **5**, 1–17 (1968)

70. Mazur, P., Rhian, M. A., Mahlandt, B. G., *Arch. Biochem. Biophys.*, **71**, 31–51 (1957)

71. Mazur, P., Farrant, J., Leibo, S. P., Chu, E. H. Y. (In preparation)

72. Meryman, H. T., *Proc. Roy. Soc. (London), Ser. B*, **147**, 452–59 (1957)

73. Meryman, H. T., Review of biological freezing, *Cryobiology*, 1–114 (See Ref. 74)

74. Meryman, H. T., Ed., *Cryobiology* (Academic Press, London, New York, 775 pp., 1966)

75. Meryman, H. T., The relationship between dehydration and freezing injury in the human erythrocyte, in *Cellular Injury and Resistance in Freezing Organisms*, 231–44 (See Ref. 16)

76. Meryman, H. T., *Nature*, **218**, 333–36 (1968)

77. Meynell, G. G., *J. Gen. Microbiol.*, **19**, 380–89 (1958)

78. Modlibowska, I., Rogers, W. S., *J. Exptl. Botany*, **6**, 384–91 (1955)

79. Olien, C.-R., *Ann. Rev. Plant Physiol.*, **18**, 387–408 (1967)

80. Packer, L., Barnard, A. C., *Biochim. Biophys. Acta*, **126**, 443–48 (1966)

81. Parker, J., *Biol. Bull.*, **119**, 474–78 (1960)

82. Parker, J., *J. Forestry*, **59**, 108–11 (1961)

83. Parker, J., *Forest Sci.*, **8**, 255–62 (1962)

84. Parker, J., *Plant Physiol.*, **37**, 809–13 (1962)

85. Prosser, C. L., Ed., *Molecular Mechanisms of Temperature Adaptation*, AAAS Symp., Publ. No. 84 (AAAS, Washington, D.C., 390 pp., 1967)

86. Rapatz, G., Luyet, B., *Cryobiology*, **4**, 215–22 (1968)

87. Rapatz, G. L., Menz, L. J., Luyet, B. J., Anatomy of the freezing process in biological materials, *Cryobiology*, 139–62 (See Ref. 74)

88. Rapatz, G., Nath, J., Luyet, B. J., *Biodynamica,* **9,** 83–94 (1963)

89. Record, B. R., Taylor, R., Miller, D. S., *J. Gen. Microbiol.,* **28,** 585–98 (1962)

90. Rey, L. R., *Ann. N.Y. Acad. Sci.,* **85,** 510–34 (1960)

91. Sakai, A., *Low Temp. Sci., Ser. B (Sapporo),* **16,** 35–39 (1958)

92. Sakai, A., *Nature,* **185,** 393–94 (1960)

93. Sakai, A., *ibid.,* **193,** 89–90 (1962)

94. Sakai, A., *Plant Physiol.,* **40,** 882–87 (1965)

95. Sakai, A., *ibid.,* **41,** 353–59 (1966)

96. Sakai, A., Otsuka, K., *Plant Physiol.,* **42,** 1680–94 (1967)

97. Sakai, A., Yoshida, S., *Plant Physiol.,* 1695–1701 (1967)

98. Salcheva, G., Samygin, G., *Soviet Plant Physiol.,* **10,** 50–57 (1963)

99. Salt, R. W., *Can. Entomologist,* **95,** 1190–1202 (1963)

100. Salt, R. W., *Can. J. Zool.,* **44,** 655–59 (1966)

101. Samygin, G. A., Matveeva, N. M., *Soviet Plant Physiol.,* **12,** 446–52 (1965)

102. Schmutz, W., Sullivan, C. Y., Levitt, J., *Plant Physiol.,* **36,** 617–20 (1961)

103. Shikama, K., *Nature,* **207,** 529–30 (1965)

104. Siminovitch, D., Briggs, D. R., *Plant Physiol.,* **28,** 177–200 (1953)

105. Siminovitch, D., Gfeller, F., Rheaume, B., The multiple character of the biochemical mechanism of freezing resistance of plant cells, in *Cellular Injury and Resistance in Freezing Organisms,* 93–117 (See Ref. 16)

106. Siminovitch, D., Therrien, H., Wilner, J., Gfeller, F., *Can. J. Botany,* **40,** 1267–69 (1962)

107. Sømme, L., *J. Insect Physiol.,* **13,** 805–14 (1967)

108. Souzu, H., *Arch. Biochem. Biophys.,* **120,** 344–51 (1967)

109. Souzu, H., Nei, T., Bito, M., *Low Temp. Sci., Ser. B (Sapporo),* **19,** 49–57 (1961)

110. Steponkus, P. L., Lanphear, F. O., *Plant Physiol.,* **43,** 151–56 (1968)

111. Stowell, R. E., Ed., *Cryobiology* (Proc. Conf. sponsored by the Am. Cancer Soc., Oct. 9-11, 1964, Rye, New York; published in *Federation Proc.,* **24,** No. 2, Part III, Suppl. 15, 1965)

112. Terumoto, I., Frost resistance in algae cells, in *Cellular Injury and Resistance in Freezing Organisms,* 191–209 (See Ref. 16)

113. Tumanov, I. I., The frost-hardening process of plants, in *The Cell and Environmental Temperature,* 6–14 (Proc. Intern. Symp. Cytoecology, May 31-June 5, 1963, Leningrad, USSR; Troshin, A. S., Editor-in-Chief, Prosser, C. L., Ed., Engl. ed., Pergamon, Oxford, London, 463 pp., 1967)

114. Tumanov, I. I., Krasavtsev, O. A., *Soviet Plant Physiol.,* **9,** 474–82 (1962)

115. van den Berg, L., *Arch. Biochem. Biophys.,* **84,** 305–15 (1959)

116. van den Berg, L., Rose, D., *ibid.,* **81,** 319–29 (1959)

117. Waisel, Y., Kohn, H., Levitt, J., *Plant Physiol.,* **37,** 272–76 (1962)

118. Wood, T. H., Rosenberg, A. M., *Biochim. Biophys. Acta,* **25,** 78–87 (1957)

119. Young, R., Peynado, A., *Am. Soc. Hort. Sci.,* **86,** 244–52 (1965)

HORMONES AND NUCLEIC ACID METABOLISM[1]

By Joe L. Key[2]

Department of Botany and Plant Pathology and Department of Biology
Purdue University, Lafayette, Indiana

Plant and animal hormones affect nucleic acid metabolism in a wide variety of systems. There is a growing literature which relates hormonal regulation to nucleic acid metabolism. This review represents a summary of this work on plant hormones [see review by Tata (166) for a synopsis of the work on animal hormones]. This review does not deal specifically with the topic of hormone action, and, accordingly, much related literature pertinent to that subject is not covered. Although any one of the hormones may prove eventually to have a primary effect on some aspect of nucleic acid metabolism, there is no definitive evidence that this is the case. A more detailed consideration of some aspects of this review and valuable background information are found in reviews by Trewavas (170), Filner et al. (44), Loening (98), van Overbeek (174), Helgeson (63), Paleg (134), Osborne (133), and Galston & Purves (51).

The Influence of Hormones on Nucleic Acid Synthesis

Work from the laboratory of Skoog was the first to show an effect of plant hormones on nucleic acid metabolism. Silberger & Skoog (157) reported auxin to affect markedly both the RNA and DNA content of tobacco pith tissue cultured on a sucrose agar medium. The auxin-regulated increase in nucleic acids occurred prior to the increase in tissue fresh weight, with a proportional increase in RNA and fresh weight with time. Higher concentrations of auxin blocked both cell enlargement and nucleic acid accumulation. Concentrations of IAA which were optimal for cell enlargement and RNA synthesis caused few if any cell divisions in spite of increases in nuclear material (158). Lower concentrations of auxin favored DNA syn-

[1] Abbreviations used in this review are: mRNA (messenger RNA); rRNA (ribosomal RNA); tRNA (transfer RNA); sRNA (4 and 5S RNA including tRNA); D-RNA (DNA-like RNA); TB-RNA (a fraction of RNA which remains preferentially absorbed to an MAK column after completion of the salt gradient and which after purification contains above 40 mole per cent AMP); 2,4-D (2,4-dichlorophenoxyacetic acid); GA (gibberellin); IPA [isopentenyladenine or (6-(γ-γ-dimethylallylamino) purine)].

[2] Unpublished research from the author's laboratory was supported by NIH grant GM 10157.

thesis and cell division when compared to the optimum for cell enlargement and RNA synthesis. Skoog (158) proposed that the auxin level affects the DNA/RNA ratio and that this in turn influenced the relative rates of cell multiplication and cell enlargement. Thus, Skoog's was the first suggestion that the action of a plant hormone is intimately concerned with nucleic acid metabolism. Since this pioneering study, numerous investigations of the influence of auxins, gibberellins, cytokinins, ethylene, and abscisic acid on nucleic acid metabolism in intact plants, excised plant parts, and cell-free systems have been reported and will be considered here.

Intact seedlings.—Rebstock et al. (140) showed that lethal concentrations of the auxin, 2,4-dichlorophenoxyacetic acid (2,4-D), applied to cranberry bean plants resulted in massive accumulation of nucleic acids and protein. Similar observations have been made on a variety of plant tissues (25, 84, 138, 155, 184). Generally, intact plants respond to the auxin-type growth regulators by an inhibition of growth (both cell division and cell enlargement) and inhibition of nucleic acid synthesis in the normal growing points; the more mature stem tissues are 'activated' relative to nucleic acid synthesis and massive cell proliferation (87). These relationships have recently been reviewed (62), and the implications are that the lethal action of the 2,4-D-type regulators relates to their hormonal effects rather than to some direct inhibitory action. Treatment of seedlings with 2,4-D, or some other auxin, while causing an increase in DNA and protein as well as in RNA, causes an apparent "over-production" of RNA resulting in increased RNA/DNA and RNA/protein ratios. The RNA accumulates in the form of ribosomes (25, 87), with the increase in rRNA being greater than the increase in sRNA (87). As noted, the synthesis of RNA and DNA is associated with an onset of massive cell proliferation, but considerable accumulation of RNA precedes the initiation of cell division (87). In fact, recent results from Maclachlan's laboratory (40) show that auxin induces the normal increase in RNA for about 48 hr in decapitated pea seedlings in the presence of 5-fluorodeoxyuridine, and thus in the absence of DNA synthesis and cell division.

Holm & Abeles (68) added a new dimension to the biochemistry of 2,4-D action by showing that ethylene causes stem swelling and nucleic acid synthesis similar to the 2,4-D response in soybean seedlings. However, Holm's more recent results indicate that, even though ethylene enhances RNA accumulation, when used in combination with 2,4-D, ethylene impairs the accumulation of RNA in response to auxin. Ethylene production by plants in response to 2,4-D (68, 117) was suggested as a governing factor in the aberrant growth. In addition to ethylene, endogenous cytokinins have been implicated to be involved in the pattern of development following treatment of seedlings with 2,4-D (58, 87).

Kinetin has been shown to increase the level of nuclear RNA in onion bulbs (57) and to increase the labeling of nucleoloar RNA by ^{14}C-adenine within 1 hr (130). Cytoplasmic labeling was increased after longer incubation times. Jensen et al. (75) reported that kinetin treatment of young onion bulbs resulted in a marked increase in the RNA of cells in the elongating zone of the root. The benzyladenine treatment of *Lemna* (175) increased the ^{32}P-labeling of all nucleic acid species. Whereas benzyladenine enhanced nucleic acid synthesis and promoted *Lemna* growth, abscisic acid inhibited both nucleic acid synthesis and growth. Benzyladenine caused considerable growth in abscisic acid-treated *Lemna*. Additional results indicated that DNA synthesis may be inhibited prior to the inhibition of RNA synthesis by abscisic acid.

Gibberellins (GA) likewise influence nucleic acid synthesis in intact plants. GA increased the level of both DNA and RNA in etiolated dwarf pea seedlings (18, 52, 54), a response that increased when the plants were light-grown. The increase in RNA preceded enhanced DNA synthesis. A small increase in RNA in response to GA was observed in clover (131). Nitsan & Lang (122) found that GA increased both RNA and DNA in the epicotyl of lentil seedlings. These responses initially were thought to occur without cell division, but it seems that the increase in nucleic acids is associated, at least in part, with mitotic activity in the GA-treated tissue (Atsmon & Lang, personal communication).

Excised plant parts.—When plant tissues are excised and cultured for a few hours in solution, there is usually a decrease in the RNA (12, 47, 84, 148, 184). Even with this limitation, excised tissues are usually preferred to intact plants for studies of RNA metabolism because of greater manipulative ease in feeding radioactive nucleic acid precursors and in applying various hormones or inhibitors. Numerous studies, recently reviewed by Trewavas (170), have shown effects of plant hormones on nucleic acid metabolism in excised tissues.

The influence of auxin on RNA metabolism in corn mesocotyl and soybean hypocotyl will be discussed as examples of the diversity of responses which have been reported. In excised elongating corn mesocotyl there is a decrease in RNA content during incubation. Auxin, at optimum concentrations for growth, enhances the rate of RNA breakdown, while growth-inhibitory concentrations prevent this loss in RNA (80, 184). Results from experiments where the incorporation of ^{14}C-adenosine was used as a relative measure of RNA synthesis indicate that low concentrations of auxin enhance the rate of RNA loss by affecting the rate of RNA breakdown without appreciably affecting apparent RNA synthesis (^{14}C-incorporation) (80). On the other hand, high concentrations of auxin inhibit RNA synthesis (^{14}C-incorporation), and thus must impair also the mechanism of RNA degradation. The work of Shannon et al. (155) supports these conclusions since low concentrations of the auxin greatly enhanced ribonuclease activity during incubation of excised corn mesocotyl, whereas growth-inhibitory concentrations of auxin prevented the increase in ribonuclease activity which normally accompanies excised or intact cell elongation. However, the corn mesocotyl ribonucleases do not realize their potential to degrade RNA *in vivo,* since there is sufficient enzyme activity to degrade all cellular RNA in a few minutes under the conditions of assay.

In excised elongating soybean hypocotyl the RNA decreases during incubation (84, 88), but not nearly as much as in corn mesocotyl. Growth-enhancing concentrations of auxin cause the maintenance of RNA at or near the initial level. The enhanced incorporation of ^{14}C-precursor into RNA in response to auxin indicates that auxin maintains the higher RNA content by enhancing synthesis. Growth-inhibiting concentrations of auxin inhibit ^{14}C-precursor incorporation without appreciably affecting the RNA content relative to the control system. In contrast to corn mesocotyl, there is no increase in total ribonuclease activity in either control of auxin-treated tissue during excised elongation (88), and the total ribonuclease activity is much lower in soybean than in corn (185).

In contrast to the elongating section, auxin caused a large net synthesis of RNA in excised maturing soybean hypocotyl, while the RNA content of control tissue was not changing (88). IAA and 2,4-D were equally effective in causing net RNA synthesis in this tissue, although the optimum concentration for the two auxins was different. The net accumulation of RNA in response to auxin was associated with about a twofold enhancement of incorporation of [14]C- or ^{32}P-precursor (66, 88), and was linear after an initial lag of 2 to 3 hr. A definite but small enhancement of incorporation of ^{14}C-precursor occurred during this lag.

Auxin-enhanced incorporation of radioactive precursors into RNA of many plant tissues has been reported (11, 17, 56, 61, 66, 84, 88, 109, 123, 167, 169, 172), but there are some tissues which do not show this response (22, 80). Increases in RNA labeling in response to auxin have been reported to occur within 10 to 20 min (36, 123). Most auxin-responsive tissues show enhanced synthesis (precursor incorporation) within a few minutes up to 1 to 2 hr (88, 106, 109, 169, 172). Although auxin does enhance precursor uptake in some tissues (123), the levels of incorporation are usually such that enhanced uptake of the precursor in response to auxin cannot account for the effect of auxin on apparent RNA synthesis (170).

The net accumulation of RNA in response to auxin leaves little doubt about the capacity of auxin to enhance RNA synthesis (88). The work of Masuda et al. (109) indicates that the enhancement of RNA synthesis by auxin is not a result of the growth response. They showed that auxin enhanced RNA synthesis in *Avena* coleoptiles where growth (water uptake) was blocked by isotonic mannitol concentrations.

There are several reports on the characterization of the newly synthesized RNA in control and auxin-treated tissues. Analysis by differential centrifugation showed that the major increase in RNA in response to auxin occurred in the ribosome (microsome) fraction of the cell (88). Additional studies on the characterization of purified RNA by sucrose gradient or MAK column fractionation show that auxin brings about a general enhancement of the synthesis of all species of RNA including 18 and 25S [light and heavy plant cytoplasmic rRNA, respectively (97)] rRNA as well as sRNA (4 and 5S RNAs) and the polydisperse AMP-rich species of RNA (61, 66, 106, 167). A somewhat selective effect of auxin on RNA synthesis (accumulation) in some plant tissues has been noted. In the soybean hypocotyl there is a higher specific activity of rRNA than of sRNA after several hours of incubation in ^{32}P-orthophosphate (72). This effect becomes magnified when one considers that as much as 20 per cent of the label in sRNA can be accounted for by end-group exchange in the $_pC_pC_pA$ terminus of the sRNA (73). If this is true for other tissues (61, 106, 167), auxin may generally cause a greater accumulation of rRNA relative to sRNA.

Since the polydisperse, AMP-rich species of RNA (86) [D-RNA (73) TB-RNA (167)] have a much shorter mean life than rRNA and sRNA (73), it is to be expected that rRNA and sRNA are the only species of newly synthesized RNA which accumulate in response to auxin over long labeling periods. Auxin does, however, increase the incorporation of radioactive precursors into the AMP-rich species of RNA (86, 106, 109, 167). This is especially noticeable when the accumulation of rRNA is blocked by 5-fluorouracil (86). In *Avena* coleoptile (167), auxin increases the incorporation of ^{32}P-orthophosphate into TB-RNA more than into rRNA. Furthermore, the auxin treatment resulted in a change in the base composition of the TB-RNA, with the resultant composition being similar to *Avena* DNA (167). A similar change in the composition of TB-RNA was noted in soybean hypocotyl in response to auxin (Key, unpublished). In this case the change in composition apparently results from a change in the proportion of the two major species of AMP-rich RNA present in the TB-RNA fraction, one being similar in composition to soybean DNA (D-RNA) with the other containing much more AMP and less UMP than the DNA (TB-RNA). Masuda et al. (106, 109) reported that auxin causes the greatest enhancement of precursor incorporation into the mRNA region of MAK profiles [D-RNA region of (73)] of both *Avena* coleoptile and pea internode. Trewavas (171), on the other hand, showed the major effect of auxin on enhanced RNA synthesis to be on rRNA in pea internode.

Another indication of a possible effect of auxin on the availability or utilization of mRNA comes from studies on polyribosomes. In excised pea internode there is a loss in total ribosomes during incubation with this loss occurring in the polyribosome fraction (171). Auxin caused a slight increase in total ribosomes over zero time controls (about 30 per cent over incubated controls) and about a 60 per cent increase in the proportion of ribosomes present as polyribosomes during a 12-hr incubation. Sucrose caused changes similar to auxin in the ribosome distribution. Unfortunately, no data for tissue incubated in both auxin and sucrose were reported. In excised elongating soybean hypocotyl, there also is a decrease in the proportion of ribosomes present as polyribosomes, but auxin seems to have, at best, only a slight positive effect (Anderson & Key, unpublished). In maturing excised soybean hypocotyl there is little change in ribosome distribution during incubation. Auxin, after a lag of about 2 hr, causes a shift of monoribosomes to polyribosomes with the proportion of polyribosomes increasing from 30 to 35 per cent to 60 to 65 per cent between 6 and 9 hr of treatment. The auxin-induced shift in ribosome distribution is blocked by actinomycin D but not by 5-fluorouracil. These results show that the formation of new ribosomes [blocked by 5-fluorouracil (85, 86)] in response to auxin is not essential for polyribosome formation, but rather indicate that synthesis of the AMP-rich RNAs [(86) D-RNA and TB-RNA] is essential for the transition. The results to date are inconclusive as to whether the effect of auxin on polyribosome formation may relate to an effect of auxin on mRNA synthesis or on the utilization of mRNA whose synthesis must occur during the period of polyribosome formation.

Auxins, cytokinins, and gibberellins (15, 47, 48, 132, 149, 151, 162, 183, 186, 189) affect nucleic acid metabolism markedly while delaying senescence in excised plant parts. Much of this work was recently summarized by several investigators (165) and will be dealt with only briefly in this review. The work of Richmond & Lang (142), which showed that kinetin retarded protein loss in senescing leaves, stimulated considerable work on the effects of hormones on nucleic acid and protein metabolism in senescing tissues. Osborne's results showed that kinetin delayed or slowed the decrease in both RNA and DNA which normally accompanies senescence in excised *Xanthium* leaves (132). The kinetin-enhanced incorporation of ^{14}C precursors into protein and RNA caused Osborne (132, 133) to suggest that the effect of kinetin in retarding senescence was through its action in sustaining nucleic acid and protein synthesis. Burdett & Wareing (19) showed that kinetin increased the incorporation of ^{32}P-orthophosphate into nucleic acids of sterile senescing radish leaves. Carpenter & Cherry (21) and Wollgiehn (188) reported enhancements of RNA synthesis in response to benzyladenine and kinetin, respectively. Higher concentrations of benzyladenine (21) and kinetin (177) inhibit RNA synthesis, with a selective inhibition of rRNA synthesis being noted with kinetin. In segments of pods of *Phaseolus,* auxin enhanced the incorporation of precursors into both RNA and protein while causing a net increase in both RNA and protein (151). The effect of kinetin on RNA synthesis was variable in this system, possibly due to the stage of tissue senescence at the time of treatment. In *Rhoeo,* both kinetin and auxin enhanced nucleic acid synthesis in leaves which had just completed expansion, while only auxin was effective in enhancing synthesis in more mature leaves (150). Kinetin also augmented the enhancing effect of auxin on RNA synthesis in just-expanding leaves. Sacher showed that the enhancing effect of auxin on precursor incorporation into RNA and protein was over and above any effect on uptake (150, 151). From their studies on the influence of auxin and kinetin on RNA synthesis and senescence in detached leaves, von Abrams & Pratt (183) concluded that "failure of synchrony between changes in cholorophyll and RNA does not substantiate the proposal that kinetin regulates senescence by a direct effect upon DNA-dependent RNA synthesis."

The retardation of senescence by GA is associated with a maintenance of a higher level of RNA in leaves of *Taraxacum* (47, 48) and *Nasturtium* (15). GA treatment increased the incorporation of ^{14}C-adenine into RNA (48). Thus the maintenance of a high RNA content in GA-treated tissues correlates with an apparent higher synthetic rate.

The effects of hormones on nucleic acid and protein content of senescing tissue may be related to the nuclease and protease activity of the tissue. Srivastava & Ware (162) reported that the kinetin-treated barley leaves contained less RNase and DNase activities than control tissue. The RNase and DNase activities associated with chromatin isolated from excised barley leaves increased several fold during 4 days of senescence (163). Kinetin suppressed the increase in these activities. Balz (9) showed that kinetin suppressed almost completely the increase in activity of protease and RNase which was associated with senescence of excised tobacco leaves. These suppressing effects of kinetin on nuclease and protease activities during senescence may have a twofold influence on the observed enhancements of ^{14}C-precursor incorporation into RNA and protein. First, less of the newly synthesized ^{14}C-containing RNA and protein would be degraded in kinetin-treated tissues. Kuraishi (91) showed this to be the case for ^{14}C-protein in *B. rapa* leaf discs. Second, the precursor pools would be expected to be larger in control tissue than in kinetin-treated tissue because of the greater conversion of RNA and protein to nucleotides and amino acids, thus possibly causing more dilution of the absorbed ^{14}C-precursors in control than in kinetin-treated tissue. Again, this view is supported by measurements of total α-amino nitrogen (5) of senescing tobacco leaf discs. Anderson & Rowan (6) have pointed out, however, that senescence is clearly retarded by kinetin before any significant effect on nuclease or protease activity is observed. Thus, the effects of kinetin on hydrolytic enzyme activities and on ^{14}C-precursor incorporation may be secondary to the retardation of senescence by kinetin.

GA causes a very marked increase in the incorporation of ^{14}C-uridine, ^{14}C-adenine, or ^{32}P-orthophosphate into RNA of barley half seed and aleurone layers during the initial 24 hr treatment (23, 180). The increased precursor incorporation was apparent within 8 hr after initiation of imbibition. After about 24 hr there was net loss of label from RNA of GA-treated tissues, whereas RNA of control tissue continued to accumulate label. This may relate to the GA-regulated increase in RNase activity (27). Actinomycin D and bromouracil prevented the GA-enhanced incorporation into RNA without appreciably affecting control incorporation. The change in ^{32}P-distribution among the four nucleotides of newly synthesized RNA indicates that GA might affect the kinds as well as the amount of RNA being synthesized (23).

GA enhances RNA and DNA synthesis and mitotic activity in excised

plugs of resting potato tubes (139). These effects may relate to the breaking of dormancy of potato where a "derepression" of DNA templates may be
critical to the onset of growth (173).

Isolated nuclei and chromatin.—From the foregoing discussion, it seems
reasonable to conclude that plant hormones generally enhance RNA synthesis in hormone-responsive tissues. Yet from the studies reported one cannot always be certain whether the synthetic rate or the rate of destruction
was affected in different tissues by the hormones. To extend results from
studies with intact seedlings and tissue slices and to gain additional information on the significance of the hormone effects on RNA metabolism,
there have been several studies of the effects of hormones on RNA synthesis by isolated nuclei and chromatin.

Some reports indicate that hormones may enhance RNA synthesis by
isolated nuclei (24, 102, 127, 144–147). The reported effects of auxin on precursor incorporation into RNA of nuclei varies from no enhancement in
some experiments (24, 102) to one- or twofold increases in other experiments (24, 102, 145–147). In addition to the variable response, the interpretation of many of these experiments is complicated by the fact that the nuclei were incubated in radioactive RNA precursors for from 1 up to 12 hr
with no apparent attempts to control bacterial contamination (102, 144–147).
[See (170) for a more detailed discussion of some of this work.] However, in some experiments the enhancing effect of auxin, kinetin, and GA
on RNA synthesis occurred even in 15-min assays (144), under conditions
which may somewhat lessen the possibility of contributions to RNA synthesis by the bacteria. Data of Cherry (24) and O'Brien (127) indicate that
the label incorporated into RNA was in fact in the nuclei.

The variable response of isolated nuclei to plant hormones may relate to
the results reported recently by Johri & Varner (76) and Matthysse (113).
Johri & Varner (76) showed that nuclei from dwarf pea isolated and incubated in the presence of $10^{-8}M$ GA_3 incorporated up to 80 per cent more
^3H-nucleotide into RNA than control nuclei. The addition of GA_3 to purified nuclei isolated in the absence of GA_3 had no effect on subsequent RNA
synthesis. Intact cells were not required for the GA_3 response, but the
later GA_3 was added during the isolation, the smaller the response was.
Thus, the failure of purified nuclei to respond to GA_3 was apparently
caused by the loss during isolation of some essential hormone-sensitive
factor. The response to GA_3 was optimal at about $10^{-8}M$ and decreased
with increasing concentration. Furthermore, GA_8, which is ineffective in
promoting internode elongation in dwarf peas, was ineffective in enhancing
RNA synthesis by pea nuclei. Nearest neighbor analysis of the *in vitro*-
synthesized RNA along with sucrose gradient and MAK column fractionation showed that GA_3 affected the kind of RNA being made as well as the
rate of RNA synthesis.

Matthysse, in a preliminary study (113), found that isolated pea bud
nuclei, but not nuclei from tobacco or soybean culture cells, showed enhanced

RNA synthesis in response to added auxin. If the nuclei from tobacco and soybean were isolated in the presence of auxin, an auxin enhancement of RNA synthesis was obtained. In this study, Matthysse showed that in the absence of auxin a substance required for the hormone response was lost from the nucleus. The 'hormone-reactive' substance, probably a protein, was obtained from lysates of pea bud, tobacco, and soybean nuclei. In a pea chromatin system fortified with *E. coli* RNA polymerase, neither the factor nor auxin affected RNA synthesis when assayed separately. The addition of both auxin and the factor to the chromatin system resulted in as much as a twofold increase in RNA synthesis.

Isolated chromatin does not show enhanced nucleic acid synthesis in response to hormone *in vitro* (113, 127, 153). However, chromatin isolated from auxin-treated soybean seedling hypocotyls shows higher RNA synthetic activity *in vitro* than chromatin isolated from controls (127–129). (These auxin-treated hypocotyls normally accumulate RNA at a much greater rate than the controls). The increase in activity of isolated chromatin is apparent within 4 hr following treatment of seedlings with the auxin, 2,4-D, with the increase in chromatin activity being roughly proportional to the increase in RNA accumulation produced in the tissue after several hr of treatment. Saturation studies with *E. coli* RNA polymerase show that only a small proportion of the available templates of chromatin from control (7 per cent) and 2,4-D-treated (16 per cent) seedlings was transcribed *in vitro* by endogenous RNA polymerase (assuming an equal rate of transcription or read-out by endogenous and *E. coli* RNA polymerases). A greater than twofold increase in endogenous chromatin RNA synthetic activity resulted from auxin treatment; when fortified with *E. coli* RNA polymerase, a much smaller relative (about 12 per cent) increase in RNA synthesis was obtained. This result caused O'Brien *et al.* (129) to suggest that the major influence of auxin was to increase the endogenous RNA polymerase of the isolated chromatin. However, the actual amount of RNA synthesis ($\mu\mu$moles) occurring in response to auxin was as great in the presence of added *E. coli* RNA polymerase as with endogenous polymerase. This would indicate that some difference exists between chromatin from control and auxin-treated tissue in addition to (or instead of) an effect of auxin on RNA polymerase. This point can only be resolved with further study directed to an analysis of chromatin properties in addition to endogenous RNA synthetic activity. Additional evidence [O'Brien, personal communication; (69)] which shows a different nearest neighbor frequency of the polymerized nucleotides in the RNA product from chromatin isolated from control and auxin-treated tissue, indicates that there is some difference in the portion of the genome being read. This could, however, result from a change in the template available for transcription or from the association of RNA polymerase with templates previously available but not being transcribed because of 'deficiency' in RNA polymerase.

Ethylene, commensurate with its effect on RNA accumulation in the hypocotyl of soybean (68), causes as much as a twofold increase in the synthesis of RNA *in vitro* by chromatin isolated from treated seedlings (69). Again, nearest neighbor analysis of the products indicates differences in chromatin from control and ethylene-treated seedlings.

RNA AND PROTEIN BIOSYNTHESIS AND THE EXPRESSION OF HORMONE ACTION

In this discussion, an attempt will be made to relate the gibberellin regulation of hydrolase synthesis in barley aleurone, the auxin (and gibberellin) regulation of cell elongation, and the ethylene regulation of abscission to the requirement for RNA and protein biosynthesis for the expression of these responses. Since interpretation of most of the results assumes specificity of action of selected inhibitors of RNA and protein biosynthesis, a brief discussion of the action of some of the most used inhibitors is included.

Probably the most used inhibitor of RNA synthesis is actinomycin D [see review by Reich & Goldberg (141) for detailed discussion of this antibiotic]. The binding of actinomycin to DNA, requiring guanine in a helical structure, is responsible for the inhibition of DNA-dependent RNA synthesis. This effect is considered to account for the biological properties of actinomycin (141). Actinomycin causes as much as 90 to 95 per cent inhibition of RNA synthesis at concentrations of 1 to 10 μg/ml in some plant tissues (33, 81, 88), but smaller inhibitions occur at even higher concentrations in other plant tissues (28, 33, 110, 180). Actinomycin inhibits DNA-dependent RNA synthesis *in vitro* (129, 164) as well as in most plant tissues studied, but little is known in plant systems about possible effects of the antibiotic other than the inhibition of RNA synthesis. There are, however, several reasons for assuming specificity of action. Actinomycin inhibits normal RNA synthesis without affecting the multiplication and increase in infectivity of an RNA virus in soybean hypocotyl (10). Likewise, multiplication of TMV in infected host leaves was not affected by actinomycin (152). Protein synthesis continues in plant tissues for several hours after RNA synthesis is inhibited (83), with the decay in protein synthesis paralleling the decay in functional polyribosomes (96). Steady-state respiration of potato discs was not affected by actinomycin (32). Actinomycin does not appreciably affect high energy phosphate metabolism (ADP and ATP levels) except possibly to increase slightly the ATP/ADP ratio in excised soybean hypocotyl; this might be expected to occur following the inhibition of utilization of nucleoside triphosphates in RNA synthesis.

Cycloheximide (actidione) is an effective inhibitor of protein synthesis in plant tissues (83, 180). Its action appears to be relatively specific for 80S ribosomes compared to 70S ribosomes (29, 30). The mechanism of inhibition relates possibly to a direct inhibition of peptide bond formation and to some impairment of the termination or release mechanism (29, 55, 156). Cycloheximide may be the preferred inhibitor of protein synthesis in plants because of its effectiveness at low concentration and its rapidity of action. There are at this time no known side effects. For example, cycloheximide does not appear to be a respiratory poison, since the ATP/ADP ratio is maintained or increased in tissues treated for several hours.

Because of the high concentrations which are required to accomplish inhibition of RNA or protein synthesis or to inhibit some physiological event, reagents such as puromycin, chloramphenicol, 6-methylpurine, and 8-azaguanine should be used with extreme caution. One must be aware that even actinomycin and cycloheximide may prove to have side effects independent of their direct inhibition of RNA and protein synthesis, respectively. In the following discussion a specificity of action will be assumed. One must be aware also that the inhibition of a physiological process, such as cell elongation (or any other hormone-regulated event), by the compounds discussed above only shows a requirement for continued RNA and protein synthesis for accomplishment of the event. Other evidence, which is often lacking, is required to establish that the hormone response is mediated by an effect of the hormone on transcription (at the genome level) or on translation (at the unit level of proten synthesis).

The gibberellin regulation of hydrolase synthesis.—Work from several laboratories shows that GA is responsible for the development of hydrolase activities during germination of barley, and that the aleurone layer is the site of production of these activities [see (134) and (180) for details]. Varner (178) showed that inhibitors of protein synthesis, including respiratory inhibitors, prevented the appearance of α-amylase activity in response to GA. Further, there was marked incorporation of ^{14}C-phenylalanine into a protein band (obtained by DEAE-cellulose fractionation) containing the amylase activity in the presence of GA but not in its absence. Fingerprints of tryptic digests of purified α-amylase produced in the presence of GA showed that the entire amylase molecule was synthesized in response to GA (179, 180). Knowing that at least some of the α-amylase produced in response to GA was the result of *de novo* synthesis (180), Filner & Varner conducted density labeling experiments (43, 71) which allowed them to conclude (43) that essentially all of the amylase activity arose by *de novo* synthesis from free amino acids. Protease, another hydrolase produced in response to GA, is induced with the same kinetics and at the same GA concentrations as amylase (74). Again, Jacobson & Varner (74) showed by the density labeling technique that protease is synthesized *de novo* in response to GA.

There is a lag of about 8 hr in the appearance of GA-induced amylase (74, 179) in the barley half-seed or in isolated aleurone layers. This lag can be shortened by extending the period of imbibition prior to the addition of GA (192). The removal of GA in "mid-course" results in a rapidly diminishing rate of increase in amylase activity (27, 28). Clearly, GA does not serve as a trigger but is required throughout the period of enzyme synthesis. Furthermore, Chrispeels & Varner (28) showed that reintroduction

of GA into the barley aleurone system, in which the rate of amylase production was greatly diminished following removal of GA, results in an almost immediate increase in the apparent rate of amylase synthesis (i.e.,
equivalent to the rate under continuous GA treatment). A somewhat analogous situation was observed when aleurone layers were incubated with a
low concentration of GA, which resulted in a low rate of amylase synthesis;
addition of the optimum GA concentration to the aleurone layers resulted in
the higher rate of amylase synthesis with a lag of only 3 or 4 hr.

The addition of protein synthesis inhibitors such as cycloheximide,
before or after the addition of GA, rapidly and completely inhibits amylase
synthesis (28, 179, 180). Actinomycin and base analogues which inhibit
RNA synthesis prevent amylase formation if added before or at the same
time as the hormone (28, 179, 180). If added after 4 hr of GA treatment,
actinomycin has a reduced effect on amylase synthesis; it is essentially
without effect if added 8 hr (the lag period before appearance of GA-induced amylase) or more after GA (28). Yet, RNA synthesis is inhibited
about 65 per cent during the 4-hr interval following the addition of 100
μg/ml actinomycin at 8 hr. The base analogues, 6-methylpurine and
8-azaguanine, inhibit amylase production with a lag of 2 to 3 hr commensurate with a marked inhibition of RNA synthesis (28). Also the synthesis of
amylase, which depends upon a second addition of GA (i.e., adding GA
back following midcourse removal of the GA), is not very sensitive to actinomycin D but is inhibited markedly by 6-methylpurine and 8-azaguanine.
If continued synthesis of functional RNA is essential for continued GA-
regulated amylase synthesis, including the midcourse addition of GA, based
on the inhibition of both processes by 6-methylpurine and 8-azaguanine, the
failure of actinomycin to inhibit amylase synthesis when added at 8 or more
hr after GA may relate to a failure to inhibit specifically that RNA fraction
required for continued amylase synthesis. An alternative explanation might
be that the inhibition by the base analogues does not relate to their inhibition
of RNA synthesis. Data on the types of RNA being synthesized under these
conditions would be informative.

Another most interesting aspect of the hormonal regulation of amylase
synthesis in the barley aleurone relates to the effects of abscisic acid (26
28). Abscisic acid inhibits the GA induction of amylase without affecting
total amino acid incorporation into protein and only slightly depressing apparent RNA synthesis (26). The inhibition of GA-induced enzyme formation appears to be rather specific, since abscisic acid only inhibited the substrate induction of nitrate reductase activity in barley aleurone by about 20
per cent while amylase synthesis was inhibited by 80 to 90 per cent (42).
Although inhibition of amylase synthesis by abscisic acid can be partially
overcome by increasing the concentration of GA, the inhibition does not appear to be strictly competitive (26, 28). Chrispeels & Varner (26) suggested that the interaction of GA and abscisic acid may derive from their
action at similar or identical sites. The midcourse addition of abscisic acid

results in the inhibition of amylase synthesis with essentially the same kinetics as base analogues. The similar inhibition by abscisic acid and certain base analogues of amylase synthesis suggests that abscisic acid may control by inhibiting the synthesis of a specific RNA fraction required for amylase synthesis (28).

In summarizing the GA- and abscisic acid-regulated synthesis of hydrolases in barley aleurone, I quote from Chrispeels & Varner (28):

> It is not yet possible to decide whether these hormones work at the level of transcription or at the level of translation. The data . . . are consistent with the hypothesis that GA exerts its control at the level of the gene, to bring about the synthesis of an RNA fraction specific for the proteins being synthesized. (Abscisic acid would be assumed to repress this synthesis.) The data are equally consistent with a control mechanism at the level of translation with a requirement for continued RNA synthesis.

There is no evidence for an effect of GA or abscisic acid on these specific RNAs, nor are any data available dealing with a specific regulation at the translational level.

Auxin and gibberellin regulation of cell enlargement.—An accumulating body of evidence shows that continued synthesis of RNA and protein is essential for continued cell elongation. Masuda (103) showed that cell elongation in response to auxin was impaired by treatment of *Avena* coleoptiles with ribonuclease. Noodén & Thimann (124) and Key (83) showed that endogenous and auxin-induced growth of excised *Avena* coleoptile and soybean hypocotyl were inhibited by actinomycin D. Similar observations have now been made in many excised plant tissues (31, 33, 35, 110, 118, 123, 126, 136). In support of these observations, several base analogues such as 8-azaguanine, 6-methylpurine, and cordycepin (81, 82, 105, 123) have been shown to be effective inhibitors of cell elongation. Many pyrimidine base analogues, including 5-fluorouracil, are generally without effect on cell enlargement (82, 85, 107, 123). The essential observations on the requirement for RNA synthesis in excised cell elongation have been extended to cell elongation in the intact growing soybean root where actinomycin, but not 5-fluorouracil, effectively inhibits cell elongation (96).

The magnitude and timing of inhibition by actinomycin of cell elongation in excised tissues varies from species to species. The interpretation of the partial inhibitions is complicated because many studies on the effects of actinomycin on cell elongation have not included observations on the extent of inhibition of RNA synthesis. In addition, actinomycin at some concentrations selectively inhibits rRNA synthisis (137). Thus, without studies on the characterization of the newly synthesized RNA in tissues where only partial inhibition of RNA synthesis by actinomycin is realized, or of studies where the inhibition of RNA synthesis is essentially complete, a precise interpretation of the data is impossible. Generally, whether inhibition of RNA synthesis is essentially complete (over 90 per cent after a short lag)as in the soybean hypocotyl (83, 88) or corn mesocotyl or only partial as in the case of the pea epicotyl (33) and the *Avena* coleoptile (33, 110), the degree of inhibition of cell elongation correlates positively with the magnitude of inhibition of RNA synthesis. In soybean hypocotyl growing at a constant rate, actinomycin inhibits cell elongation after a lag of 1 to 2 hr, with the degree of inhibition depending upon the concentration of actinomycin (83). Following the lag, which occurs in many plant tissues (35, 110, 123, 124, 136), the newly established growth rate continues for many hours relative to the untreated controls. There is a shorter lag in the inhibition of RNA synthesis by actinomycin, but as with growth, after the short lag the new rate of RNA synthesis continues for long periods (83). Actinomycin clearly inhibits RNA synthesis prior to its inhibiton of cell elongation (81, 83, 123).

It is clear that continued RNA synthesis is essential for cell elongation and equally clear that considerable RNA synthesis can be inhibited without affecting this growth (82, 83, 85, 123). Actinomycin, at concentrations up to about 0.2 μg/ml, inhibited RNA synthesis by 30 to 40 per cent over 8 hr without affecting cell elongation in the soybean hypocotyl (85). Higher concentrations inhibited RNA synthesis and cell elongation in parallel. Further, 5-fluorouracil inhibited RNA synthesis by as much as 60 per cent without affecting cell elongation in soybean (85). Fluorouracil did not inhibit cell enlargement in excised artichoke tuber when added during the growth interval in the presence of auxin (123), while causing severe inhibition of RNA synthesis (123); when added during the "aging" interval prior to the addition of auxin, 5-fluorouracil did impair cell enlargement (154). The failure of 5-fluorouracil and low concentrations of actinomycin to inhibit cell enlargement relates to their selective inhibition of RNA synthesis (82, 85, 123, 137). The results are not so clear cut with actinomycin, but 5-fluorouracil causes almost complete inhibition of the accumulation of rRNA and a lesser inhibition of sRNA accumulation without affecting the synthesis of the AMP-rich species of RNA [D-RNA and TB-RNA discussed earlier in this review (86)]. It has thus been concluded that the synthesis of new ribosomes, and possibly sRNA as well, is not required during continued cell elongation of excised and intact plant tissues. Whether the synthesis of both species of the AMP-rich RNA (86) is required for cell enlargement is not known.

The requirement for RNA synthesis during cell elongation implies a requirement for protein synthesis. Indeed, a wide range of protein synthesis inhibitors (chloramphenicol, puromycin, and cycloheximide) inhibit cell elongation of both excised and intact plant tissues (35, 77, 81, 83, 96, 105, 124–126, 136). The ability of base analogues to inhibit cell elongation apparently depends upon their final inhibition of protein synthesis, independent of the observed effects on total RNA synthesis (82). There is a close parallel between the inhibition of cell elongation and protein synthesis by chloramphenicol in *Avena* coleoptile and pea stem sections (124) and by cycloheximide in soybean hypocotyl (83). Although not inhibiting protein synthesis directly, actinomycin leads to an inhibition of protein synthesis which increases with increasing times of treatment (83, 96).

The above discussion dealt with the general requirement for the continued synthesis of RNA and protein for continued cell enlargement. What is the relationship of this requirement to the regulation of cell enlargement by auxin? The data do not allow for a definitive conclusion, but several observations indicate that the ability of auxin to enhance the rate of cell elongation is dependent upon new RNA and protein synthesis, and that auxin cannot cause a growth response by utilizing pre-existing RNA or protein (83, 86, 123).

In soybean hypocotyl, corn mesocotyl, and corn coleoptile, actinomycin at 5 to 10 μg/ml causes a 60 to 70 per cent inhibition of RNA synthesis during the initial 2 hr of treatment (81, 83, 85, and unpublished data). During this same interval, endogenous growth, which is considerable in these tissues, is inhibited only 5 to 10 per cent, but auxin-induced growth is inhibited 60 to 70 per cent. After about 2 hr, RNA synthesis is inhibited 85 to 95 per cent, endogenous growth is slowed, but measurable, and the addition of auxin fails to increase the growth rate more than 5 to 10 per cent. Cycloheximide treatment of soybean hypocotyl causes similar responses (83). At 1 μg/ml, cycloheximide causes 85 to 90 per cent inhibition of protein synthesis without an appreciable lag. Endogenous growth is inhibited 35 to 40 per cent over the initial 2 hr followed by increasing inhibition. The simultaneous addition of auxin with cycloheximide results in only a 10 to 15 per cent increase in the growth rate over the control. Later additions of auxin result in a smaller growth increment, commensurate with the level of protein synthesis which persists. Conversely, if these tissues are pretreated with auxin to obtain the typical two- or threefold increase in growth rate prior to the addition of actinomycin or cycloheximide, the auxin-induced component of growth is maintained to about the same extent for the same time as the original endogenous growth (83, 86). Thus, in auxin-pretreated tissues there is about three times as much growth as in control tissue following inhibition of RNA or protein synthesis. Since the ability of auxin to enhance cell elongation is directly proportional to the level of AMP-rich RNA synthesis (83), this has been interpreted to mean that auxin-treated tissues contain about three times as much "growth essential" RNA (and/or protein) as control tissue (86). This, of course, assumes that auxin does not affect the stability of the "growth essential" RNA (and protein). Recently, Gayler & Glasziou (53) presented indirect evidence consistent with an auxin stabilization of mRNA. Auxin does not stabilize protein synthesis in excised soybean hypocotyl following actinomycin inhibition of RNA synthesis, thus apparently not stabilizing template RNA.

Some data related to the inhibition of auxin-induced growth in the pea internode indicate that auxin causes an initial enhancement in growth rate almost equal in control and actinomycin-pretreated tissue (136). This observation is not in agreement with most of the data presented above for other tissues and is not supported by other work on pea internode growth (35). In neither case were any data presented on the effects of actinomycin on RNA synthesis, but in the pea internode RNA synthesis is not completely inhibited by actinomycin (33).

A relaxation or loosening of the cell wall is a property long associated with the ability of auxin to induce growth of excised plant tissues (51). Although there are conflicting reports for the *Avena* coleoptile (31, 33, 110), actinomycin and cycloheximide generally inhibit the auxin-induced cell wall loosening as well as growth of excised tissues (33, 83, 110, 118). In soybean hypocotyl and corn mesocotyl (33), where the inhibition of RNA synthesis is essentially complete, actinomycin blocks the effects of auxin on cell wall relaxation. In tissues such as *Avena* and pea where inhibition of RNA synthesis by actinomycin is less, a corresponding partial inhibition of cell wall loosening, as well as growth, in response to auxin occurs (33, 110)

In most of the tissues discussed, auxin is required continuously to maintain the maximum growth rate, and inhibitors of RNA and protein synthesis inhibit growth after a lag when added with, or any time after, the auxin. Clearly the "growth essential" RNA and protein, which are associated with the rate limiting system for growth, turn over with a reasonably short halflife. Artichoke tuber discs respond differently (123). When aged discs are treated with 8-azaguanine or actinomycin simultaneously with auxin, auxin induced growth is prevented. If the inhibitors are added 24 hr after auxin, there is no effect on growth over the next 48 hr. Significantly, exogenous auxin is not required for growth during this 48-hr period. Noodén (123) thus concluded that "it appears that auxin-induction of cell enlargement, but not cell enlargement itself, requires RNA synthesis in the tuber discs." It should be pointed out that RNA synthesis during the aging period (105, 123, 154), as well as during the initial phases of auxin treatment (123), is required for subsequent auxin-induced growth. Evidently the "growth essential" RNA, once formed, is reasonably stable in this tissue because protein synthesis inhibitors, such as cycloheximide, inhibited auxin-induced growth of the discs when added 24 hr after IAA (123).

There is not much information on specific effects of auxin on protein synthesis, and the effects of auxin on protein synthesis in excised tissues (usually necessarily evaluated by ^{14}C-amino acid incorporation) are variable from small enhancements to no effect. [A more detailed consideration of effects of auxin on enzymic activities is in the review by Filner *et al.* (44)]. Some specific examples of effects of auxin on protein synthesis follow. Thimann & Loos (168) showed a large net synthesis of protein in potato and artichoke tuber discs in response to auxin which may in part relate to synthesis of respiratory enzymes (125). Maclachlan and co-workers (38, 39, 100) showed a very large specific enhancement of cellulase activity in pea in response to auxin, an effect which is blocked by the inhibition of

RNA synthesis or protein synthesis. Venis (181, 182) reported the induction by auxin of an enzyme which conjugates aspartate with aromatic acids such as IAA, NAA, and benzoic acid. Again this induction was blocked by inhibitors of RNA and protein biosynthesis. Patterson & Trewavas (135) and Morris (120) observed changes in protein bands on Sephadex gel filtration and polyacrylamide gels in response to auxin. Auxin causes a small enhancement of ^{14}C-leucine incorporation into soybean hypocotyl protein (81). This effect on protein synthesis (and growth in response to auxin) is blocked by actinomycin, while protein synthesis in control tissue is inhibited only slightly over the same interval. Unfortunately, at this time nothing is known about the type of protein(s), presumably enzymic, required to maintain cell elongation and responsiveness to auxin. The synthesis and utilization in growth of some structual protein, such as cell wall or cell membrane protein, serve as an attractive alternative to the protein synthesis being required to maintain sufficient activity of an unstable enzyme. Baker & Ray (8) showed that actinomycin inhibits cell wall synthesis in *Avena,* possibly suggestive of a requirement for continued synthesis of enzymes associated with cell wall formation or modification for continued cell enlargement. However, the inhibition of cell wall synthesis may be the result of a more direct inhibition of cell elongation.

Two aspects of GA-related cell elongation will be considered. Cell elongation (including GA-induced growth) in lettuce hypocotyl is inhibited by actinomycin and puromycin (121). The GA-enhanced growth of *Avena* internode and the GA-induced increase in invertase activity of this tissue also depend upon RNA and protein biosynthesis (77). In addition, the synthesis of DNA seems to be involved in the GA-regulated elongation (121, 122), but not auxin-regulated elongation [(86), (123); Groves, Lang & Nitsan, personal communication], based on the inhibition of both elongation and DNA synthesis by 5-fluorodeoxyuridine, mitomycin, and other inhibitors of DNA synthesis. Thymidine, but not uridine, reversed the fluorodeoxyuridine inhibition of GA-induced and endogenous elongation (122). Based on these experiments with lettuce and cucumber hypocotyl and lentil epicotyl elongation, Nitsan & Lang (122) and Groves, Lang & Nitsan (personal communication) concluded that DNA synthesis is essential for elongation of certain plant cells and their elongation in response to GA but not to auxin. More recent results of Atsmon & Lang (personal communication) indicate that a possible revision of these conclusions is necessary since it now appears that a certain amount of mitotic activity is present in the tissue. While apparently contributing little if anything to the growth response, the mitotic activity may be necessary for the GA-regulated cell elongation. Thus, while DNA synthesis appears necessary for the GA-regulated elongation, it may be an indirect relationship.

Yanagishima (190) and Masuda (104) have presented evidence consistent with the conclusion that GA makes yeast cells and artichoke tuber discs responsive to auxin in bringing about cell elongation. They also found that GA could be replaced, at least in part, by an RNA fraction isolated from either GA-treated yeast cells or artichoke tuber (111, 191). The GA-like activity was also found in an RNA fraction extracted from oat coleoptiles and a mutant strain of yeast. Both were fully responsive to auxin without added GA. Recent results indicate that the active material in the extracts is a low molecular weight RNA (108). These intriguing results deserve confirmation and need to be extended using other auxin-responsive tissues.

Ethylene-mediated abscission.—Ethylene enhances the rate of abscission of explants which have reached some appropriate state of senescence, but does not so affect juvenile explants (3, 67). It has not been possible to ascertain if endogenously produced ethylene normally regulates abscission because there is no known way of selectively preventing this endogenous synthesis (67), although this level of ethylene production appears sufficient eventually to cause abscission (67).

Ethylene enhances protein synthesis in senescent (stage II) explants (3, 4) but not in juvenile explants (3). This enhancement of protein synthesis is preceded by an enhancement of RNA synthesis (3), with both preceding noticeable evidence of an effect on abscission proper (i.e., within 2 to 3 hr after ethylene treatment). The ethylene-enhanced synthesis of RNA and protein (3) occurs primarily in the abscission zone of explants, but not in the regions of the pulvinus and petiole away from the abscission zone.

The ethylene enhancement of the rate of abscission is effectively blocked by treatment with either actinomycin D or cycloheximide (3). The addition of either cycloheximide or actinomycin at or before the addition of ethylene prevents any ethylene response. The inhibitors are without appreciable effect if added 4 hr after ethylene, with cycloheximide sensitivity persisting somewhat longer than that of actinomycin. X irradiation also blocks the effect of ethylene on abscission if the treatment is given before or at the time of ethylene addition (3). Data of Valdovinos & Ernest (176) on the effect of inhibitors of protein and RNA synthesis on abscission are not in complete agreement with the results presented above. They did not show, however, whether RNA and protein synthesis were inhibited [See Abeles (1) for further discussion of this problem.]

These results show a requirement for RNA and protein synthesis in the abscission process. The enhancement of both RNA and protein synthesis, only in the responsive tissue, commensurate with the enhanced rate of abscission, is consistent with the primary role of ethylene being to bring about specific RNA synthesis necessary for the synthesis of enzymes essential for cell wall digestion in the separation layer (4). Several enzymes are possible candidates (2, 119). A local rise in cellulase activity has been noted before cell separation occurs in *Phaseolus* (70). Abeles (2) found an enhanced production of cellulase in the abscission zone in response to ethylene. The greatest response occurred in the separation layer of bean, cotton, and *Co-*

leus. Actinomycin and cycloheximide blocked the ethylene-induced increase in cellulase activity. Abeles (2) thus concluded that one of the roles of ethylene in abssision is to regulate the production of cellulase which is required for cell separation.

The Occurrence of Cytokinins in the Primary Structure of tRNA

Since the discovery of kinetin, a wide array of 6-substituted amino purines, including (6-(γ-γ-dimethylallylamino) purine (IPA), has been shown to possess the same or similar biological activity (see review by Helgeson, (63). The free naturally occurring cytokinins which have been identified from higher plants are zeatin (94) [6-(4 hydroxy-3-methyl-trans-2-butenylamino) purine] and dihydrozeatin (90). Zeatin riboside (92, 114) and zeatin ribotides (95, 114, 115) occur naturally. Zeatin and zeatin riboside have also been isolated from a mycorrhizal fungus (116). IPA was isolated from cultures of *Corynebacterium fascians* (64, 89).

McCalla, Morré & Osborne (99) observed a conversion of benzyladenine to its riboside and ribotide in *Xanthium* leaves; no significant incorporation of benzyladenylic acid into RNA occurred. Using benzyladenine-8-^{14}C, Fox (49) found considerable incorporation into RNA of cytokinin-requiring soybean and tobacco callus with most of the incorporated label occurring in adenylic and guanylic acids. Similar observations have been made by others (161, 187). Fox (49, 50), however, observed a small but repeatable incorporation of benzyl-labeled ^{14}C-benzyladenine into RNA. About half of this incorporated label, after acid hydrolysis of the RNA, was in benzyladenine. After alkaline hydrolysis of the RNA, the ^{14}C incorporated from benzyladenine-methylene-^{14}C or benzene-^{14}C was in benzyladenylic acid. Thus there is little doubt that incorporation of benzyladenine (at least the side chain) into an RNA-like product occurs in soybean callus (50). The term RNA-like product is used because in Fox's experiments (49, 50) essentially all of the label from ^{14}C-side-chain benzyladenine is in a fraction which separates on the MAK column in the region of sRNA. Since this fraction represented severalfold more of the total RNA than the sRNA normally represents (about 15 per cent in most tissues including soybean callus), it is not clear if the ^{14}C-benzyladenine was incorporated into the sRNA. The ^{14}C-benzyladenylic acid-containing fraction separates on 0-benzoyl-0-DEAE cellulose columns in a discrete fraction separated from about 75 per cent of the total low-molecular weight RNA (50). Apparently, amino acid acceptor activity has yet to be demonstrated for this fraction of RNA. Kende & Tavares (79) also detected a small incorporation of radioactivity from benzyladenine (benzyl-7-^{14}C) into total nucleic acid of soybean callus. There was no measurable incorporation of 6-benzylamino-9-methylpurine (benzyl-7-^{14}C) into RNA of soybean callus (79). However, this compound was biologically active in promoting callus growth. [It has been suggested that high activity of 9-substituted purines may result from hydrolysis because of the lability of the 9-substituent (160)]. Hall (60) was also unable to detect the incorporation of IPA-8-^{14}C into the IPA of tRNA of several plant tissues.

Transfer RNA preparations from a wide range of organisms contain cytokinin activity. Recently, Zachau and associates (41, 193) identified IPA as a component base in two species of serine tRNA of yeast. The same base was found by Madison et al. (101) in tyrosine tRNA. In each case this base was present adjacent to the anticodon. This same base was found by Hall and associates (59, 143) in hydrolysates of RNA from yeast, liver, peas, and spinach. Skoog et al. (159) showed that hydrolysates of tRNA from yeast, liver, and *E. coli* contained cytokinin activity when used in the tobacco callus assay; rRNA had no activity. The *cis*-isomer of zeatin was found in hydrolysates of tRNA of pea, spinach, and corn (59). Hydrolysates of corn tRNA, but not rRNA, contained cytokinin activity (93). The presence of the riboside of IPA in sRNA of *Corynebacterium fascians* was indicated by the chromatographic and bioassay behavior of the cytokinin obtained by hydrolysis of the sRNA (112). One active cytokinin of *E. coli* tRNA was shown to be 6-(3-methyl-2-butenylamino)-2-methylthio-9-β-D-ribofuranosylpurine (20).

Direct estimates of the total amount of cytokinins in tRNA show that about 0.05 to 0.1 per cent of the bases may be cytokinins (143). If only a single cytokinin molecule were present in one molecule of tRNA, this would be from 0.75 to 1.5 cytokinin molecules per 20 molecules of tRNA. Based on cytokinin activity as measured in the tobacco callus assay, Skoog et al. (159) estimated about one cytokinin molecule per 20 molecules of tRNA. Purified preparations of glycine, valine, arginine, phenylalanine, and alanine tRNA do not contain a cytokinin, based on lack of activity in the tobacco callus assay (159). As shown by the base sequence of alanine tRNA (65), no cytokinin activity would be expected.

One approach to the possible importance of the isoprenoid side chain of the adenylate residue adjacent to the anticodon of serine tRNA was made by Fittler & Hall (45). These workers selectively modified the IPA residue of this tRNA by reaction with iodine in neutral aqueous solution. The modified tRNA accepted the serine residue as well as the untreated tRNA, but the modified seryl-tRNA did not bind effectively with the messenger-RNA-ribosome complex (45). Thus, the structural integrity of the region of the anticodon of this tRNA appears necessary for proper functioning of the charged tRNA.

The significance of the presence of cytokinins in tRNA relative to the action of cytokinins as a plant hormone remains to be determined. As attractive as this possibility is, one must be aware that the modification of bases in tRNA usually occurs after the primary structure is formed (16). Recent work by Fittler, Kline & Hall (46) indicates that isopentenyl pyrophosphate or mevalonate can be incorporated *in vitro* into the isopentenyl group of IPA of yeast and liver tRNA.

The Attachment of Auxin to RNA

A hypothesis concerning auxin action was put forward by Armstrong (7) which would involve the attachment of auxin to tRNA; there is no published evidence at this time to support or reject the proposal. Several reports from Galston's laboratory, however, indicated that auxin becomes attached to RNA during the process of growth induction in green pea stem sections (13, 14, 78). At least a part of the label was recovered from hydrolyzed, phenol-prepared RNA preparations as IAA (14). However, most of the label was detected in the cytidylate and adenylate regions following paper electrophoresis of the hydrolysates. It was concluded that IAA couples directly with sRNA, while some IAA is degraded with the products of degradation being utilized in RNA synthesis (14). The ^{14}C from IAA or 2,4-D was found rather evenly distributed in the nucleic acid fractions of soybean hypocotyl (86). Further, incorporation of ^{14}C from IAA into RNA was inhibited by actinomycin (86) to the same extent as incorporation of ^{14}C-RNA precursors (81). The incorporation of ^{14}C into soybean hypocotyl RNA clearly results from utilization of ^{14}C degradation products of IAA since ^{14}C was detected only in the four ribonucleotides of RNA hydrolysates from tissue treated with IAA-1-^{14}C. Davies & Galston (34) have now achieved separation of the IAA-^{14}-C-containing fraction of their nucleic acid extracts from the RNA. Thus, there is no specific attachment of auxin to tRNA of green pea stem tissue.

Concluding Remarks

The influence of plant hormones (growth regulators) on RNA synthesis and the role of RNA synthesis in the expression of hormone action were reviewed. Hormone responses such as GA-induced synthesis of hydrolases in barley aleurone, cell enlargement in response to auxin, and ethylene enhancement of abscission are usually associated with enhanced RNA synthesis. The hormone enhancement of RNA synthesis may be a rather direct effect in view of the fact that under appropriate conditions (usually including the presence of hormone during the isolation) isolated nuclei show enhanced RNA synthesis in response to the hormone. Further, chromatin isolated from auxin- and ethylene-treated soybean hypocotyl shows increased RNA synthesis relative to control chromatin. There is one preliminary report which shows that auxin in combination with some nuclear "factor" increases RNA synthesis by RNA polymerase-fortified pea chromatin, while auxin or "factor" alone has no effect. The hormones appear to affect the kind as well as the amount of RNA being synthesized by these systems. In addition, in order for the systems mentioned above to respond to the hormone, the tissues must be able to carry out DNA-dependent RNA synthesis.

Possibly the simplest interpretation of these observations when taken together is that the hormones are involved in the regulation of the synthesis of specific RNAs (transcriptional control). These RNAs would then serve as templates for the synthesis of the proteins required for the physiological response in question. The evidence for such a role for the hormones is at best indirect and fragmentary at present. There is no direct evidence for the production of these specific gene products, even though new enzymes are in some cases known to be produced *de novo* in response to the hormone. The detection of only a few new kinds of RNA molecules out of the total cellular population will be a difficult, perhaps impossible, task. Thus, an intensified study of the mechanism of hormone enhancement of RNA synthesis by nuclei and chromatin may prove to be a most fruitful effort. An integral part of this study is the search for hormone receptor molecules. The systems described by Johri & Varner (76), O'Brien et al. (128, 129), and Matthysse (113) may prove most valuable in these studies.

The topic of a mechanism of hormone action has been avoided in this review. As pointed out by van Overbeek (174), there may be several sites of primary hormone action. Thus, while some hormone responses which require the involvement of DNA-dependent RNA synthesis may prove to be mediated by a rather direct effect of the hormone at the level of transcription, other responses might result from the action of the hormone at the level of translation. Others might possibly result from an involvement of the hormone in the selective transfer of these required RNAs from the nucleus to the cytoplasmic sites of protein synthesis. In the latter case, the hormone would not be involved directly in either transcriptional or translational regulation of protein synthesis as intermediate steps in causing the physiological response. Other hormone effects probably are not mediated by any of the mechanisms which involve RNA or protein synthesis. Among these would be cytoplasmic streaming in response to auxin.

The occurrence of cytokinins in certain species of tRNA raises the intriguing possibility that cytokinin action may be intimately connected to translational regulation of protein synthesis. Certainly both the quantitative and qualitative effects of cytokinins on plant growth and development could be accommodated in a model involving cytokinin-containing "modulator" species of tRNA. However, there is no evidence that the presence of cytokinins in tRNA is associated with the action of cytokinins as growth regulators.

Addendum

After this review was written, a manuscript by Evans & Ray (37) was received which is relevant to the subject of the auxin regulation of cell elongation. Based on the timing of the auxin response in *Avena* and corn coleoptiles as measured by a sensitive optical method and the responses to actinomycin and cycloheximide, Evans & Ray concluded "that auxin probably does not act on the elongation of these tissues by promoting the synthesis of informational RNA or enzymatic protein."

LITERATURE CITED

1. Abeles, F. B., *Plant Physiol.*, **43**, 1577–86 (1968)
2. **Abeles, F. B., *ibid.*, 44 (In press)**
3. Abeles, F. B., Holm, R. E., *Plant Physiol.*, **41**, 1337–42 (1966)
4. Abeles, F. B., Holm, R. E., *Ann. N. Y. Acad. Sci.*, **144, 367–73** (1967)
5. Anderson, J. W., Rowan, K. S., *Biochem. J.*, **98**, 401–4 (1966)
6. Anderson, J. W., Rowan, K. S., *ibid.*, **101**, 15–18 (1966)
7. Armstrong, D. J., *Proc. Natl. Acad. Sci.*, **56**, 64–66 (1966)
8. Baker, D. B., Ray, P. M., *Plant Physiol.*, **40**, 360–68 (1965)
9. Balz, H. P., *Planta*, **70**, 207–36 (1966)
10. Bancroft, J. B., Key, J. L., *Nature*, **202**, 729–30 (1964)
11. Basler, E., Hansen, T. L., *Botan. Gaz.*, **125**, 50–55 (1964)
12. Basler, E., Nakazawa, K., *Botan. Gaz.*, **122**, 228–32 (1961)
13. Bendana, F. E., Galston, A. W., *Science*, **150**, 69–70 (1965)
14. Bendana, F. E., Galston, A. W., Kaur-Sawhney, R., Penny, P. J., *Plant Physiol.*, **40**, 977–83 (1965)
15. Beevers, L., *Plant Physiol.*, **41**, 1074–76 (1966)
16. Borek, E., Srinivasan, P. R., *Ann. Rev. Biochem.*, **35**, 275–98 (1966)
17. Briquet, M. V., Decallonne, J. R., Lambert, R. R., Wiaux, A. L., *Physiol. Plantarum*, **20**, 337–41 (1967)
18. Broughton, W. J., *Biochim. Biophys. Acta*, **155**, 308–10 (1968)
19. Burdett, A. N., Wareing, P. F., *Planta*, **81**, 88–96 (1968)
20. Burrows, W. J., Armstrong, D. J., Skoog, F., Hecht, S. M., Boyle, J. T. A., Leonard, N. J., Occolowitz, J., *Science*, **161**, 691–93 (1968)
21. Carpenter, W. J. G., Cherry, J. H., *Biochim. Biophys. Acta*, **114**, 640–42 (1966)
22. Carpenter, W. J. G., Cherry, J. H., *Plant Physiol.*, **41**, 919–22 (1966)
23. Chandra, G. R., Varner, J. E., *Biochim. Biophys. Acta*, **108**, 583–92 (1965)
24. Cherry, J. H., *Ann. N. Y. Acad. Sci.*, **144**, 154–68 (1967)
25. Chrispeels, M. J., Hanson, J. B., *Weeds*, **10**, 123–25 (1962)
26. Chrispeels, M. J., Varner, J. E., *Nature*, **212**, 1066–67 (1966)
27. Chrispeels, M. J., Varner, J. E., *Plant Physiol.*, **42**, 398–406 (1967)
28. Chrispeels, M. J., Varner, J. E., *ibid.*, 1008–16
29. Clark, J. M., Jr., Chang, A. Y., *J. Biol. Chem.*, **240**, 4734–39 (1965)
30. Clark-Walker, G. D., Linnane, A. W., *Biochem. Biophys. Res. Commun.*, **25**, 8–13 (1966)
31. Cleland, R., *Plant Physiol.*, **40**, 595–600 (1965)
32. Click, R. E., Hackett, D. P., *Proc. Natl. Acad. Sci.*, **50**, 243–50 (1963)
33. Coartney, J., Morré, D. J., Key, J. L., *Plant Physiol.*, **42**, 434–39 (1967)
34. Davies, P. J., Galston, A. W., *Abstr. N. E. Section of Amer. Soc. Plant Physiol.*, Boyce-Thompson Institute (1968)
35. De Hertogh, A. A., McCune, D. C., Brown, J., Antonie, D., *Contrib. Boyce Thompson Inst.*, **23**, 23–31 (1965)
36. Esnault, R., *Bull. Soc. Franc. Physiol. Vegetale*, **11**, 55 (1965)
37. Evans, M. L., Ray, P. M., *J. Gen. Physiol.* (In press)
38. Fan, D. F., Maclachlan, G. A., *Can. J. Botany*, **44**, 1025–34 (1966)
39. Fan, D. F., Maclachlan, G. A., *ibid.*, **45**, 1837–44 (1967)
40. Fan, D. F., Maclachlan, G. A., *Plant Physiol.*, **42**, 1114–22 (1967)
41. Feldmann, H., Dütting, D., Zachau, H. G., *Z. Physiol. Chem.*, **347**, 236–48 (1966)
42. Ferrari, L. E., Varner, J. E., *Plant Physiol.* (In press)
43. Filner, P., Varner, J. E., *Proc. Natl. Acad. Sci.*, **58**, 1520–26 (1967)
44. Filner, P., Wray, J., Varner, J. E., *Science* (In press)
45. Fittler, F., Hall, R. H., *Biochem. Biophys. Res. Commun.*, **25**, 441–46 (1966)
46. Fittler, F., Kline, L. K., Hall, R. H., *Biochem. Biophys. Res. Commun.*, **31**, 571–76 (1968)
47. Fletcher, R. A., Osborne, D. J., *Nature*, **207**, 1176–77 (1965)
48. Fletcher, R. A., Osborne, D. J., *Can. J. Botany*, **44**, 739–45 (1966)
49. Fox, J. E., *Plant Physiol.*, **41**, 75–82 (1966)

50. Fox, J. E., Chen, C.-M., *J. Biol. Chem.*, **242**, 4490–94 (1967)
51. Galston, A. W., Purves, W. K., *Ann. Rev. Plant Physiol.*, **11**, 239–76 (1960)
52. Gamburg, K. Z., Mal'tseva, V. N., Kohyl'skii, G. I., *Fiziol. Rast.*, **12**, 120–24 (1965)
53. Gayler, K. R., Glasziou, K. T., *Planta* (In press, 1968)
54. Giles, K. W., Myers, A., *Phytochemistry*, **5**, 193–96 (1966)
55. Godchaux, W. III, Adamson, S. D., Herbert, E., *J. Mol. Biol.*, **27**, 57–72 (1967)
56. Gupta, A. S., Sen, S. P., *Nature*, **192**, 1291–92 (1961)
57. Guttman, R., *J. Biophys. Biochem. Cytol.*, **3**, 129–31 (1957)
58. Haber, A. H., *Plant Physiol.*, **37**, 18–26 (1962)
59. Hall, R. H., Csonka, H. D., McLennan, B., *Science*, **156**, 69–71 (1967)
60. Hall, R. H., in *Biochemistry and Physiology of Plant Growth Substances*, Proc. VI Intern. Conf. Plant Growth Substances, Ottawa (In press, 1968)
61. Hamilton, T. H., Moore, R. J., Rumsey, A. F., Means, A. R., Schrank, A. R., *Nature*, **208**, 1180–83 (1965)
62. Hanson, J. B., Slife, F. W., *Residue Reviews* (In press)
63. Helgeson, J. P., *Science*, **161**, 974–81 (1968)
64. Helgeson, J. P., Leonard, N. J., *Proc. Natl. Acad. Sci.*, **56**, 60–63 (1966)
65. Holley, R. W., Apgar, J., Everett, G. A., Madison, J. T., Marquisse, M., Merrill, S. H., Penswick, J. R., Zamir, A., *Science*, **147**, 1462–65 (1965)
66. Holm, R. E., Characterization of RNA Formed Under Control and 2,4-Dichlorophenoxyacetic Acid-Induced Conditions in Excised Soybean Hypocotyl (Master's thesis, Purdue Univ., 1964)
67. Holm, R. E., Abeles, F. B., *Plant Physiol.*, **42**, 1094–1102 (1967)
68. Holm, R. E., Abeles, F. B., *Planta*, **78**, 293–304 (1968)
69. Holm, R. E., O'Brien, T. J., Cherry, J. H., Key, J. L., *Plant Physiol. Suppl.*, **43**, S-19 (1968)
70. Horton, R. F., Osborne, D. J., *Nature*, **214**, 1086–88 (1967)
71. Hu, A. S. L., Bock, R. M., Halvorson, H. O., *Anal. Biochem.*, **4**, 489–504 (1962)
72. Ingle, J., Key, J. L., *Plant Physiol.*, **40**, 1212–19 (1965)
73. Ingle, J., Key, J. L., Holm, R. E., *J. Mol. Biol.*, **11**, 730–46 (1965)
74. Jacobson, J. V., Varner, J. E., *Plant Physiol.*, **42**, 1596–1600 (1967)
75. Jensen, W. A., Pollock, E. G., Healey, P., Ashton, M., *Exptl. Cell Res.*, **33**, 523–30 (1964)
76. Johri, M. M., Varner, J. E., *Proc. Natl. Acad. Sci.*, **59**, 269–76 (1968)
77. Kaufman, P. B., Ghosheh, N., Ikuma, H., *Plant Physiol.*, **43**, 29–34 (1968)
78. Kaur-Sawhney, R., Bara, M., Galston, A. W., *Ann. N.Y. Acad. Sci.*, **144**, 63–67 (1967)
79. Kende, H., Tavares, J. E., *Plant Physiol.*, **43**, 1244–48 (1968)
80. Key, J. L., *Weeds*, **11**, 177–81 (1963)
81. Key, J. L., *Plant Physiol.*, **39**, 365–70 (1964)
82. Key, J. L., *ibid.*, **41**, 1257–64 (1966)
83. Key, J. L., Barnett, N. M., Lin, C. Y., *Ann. N.Y. Acad. Sci.*, **144**, 49–62 (1967)
84. Key, J. L., Hanson, J. B., *Plant Physiol.*, **36**, 145–52 (1961)
85. Key, J. L., Ingle, J., *Proc. Natl. Acad. Sci.*, **52**, 1382–88 (1964)
86. Key, J. L., Ingle, J., in *Biochemistry and Physiology of Plant Growth Substances* (See Ref. 60)
87. Key, J. L., Lin, C. Y., Gifford, E. M., Jr., Dengler, R., *Botan. Gaz.*, **127**, 87–94 (1966)
88. Key, J. L., Shannon, J. C., *Plant Physiol.*, **39**, 360–64 (1964)
89. Klämbt, D., Thies, G., Skoog, F., *Proc. Natl. Acad. Sci.*, **56**, 52–59 (1966)
90. Koshimizu, K., Kusaki, T., Mitsui, T., Matsubara, S., *Tetrahedron Letters* No. 14, 1317 (1967)
91. Kuraishi, S., *Physiol. Plantarum*, **21**, 78–83 (1968)
92. Letham, D. S., *Life Sci.*, **5**, 551–54 (1966)
93. Letham, D. S., Ralph, R. K., *Life Sci.*, **6**, 387–94 (1967)
94. Letham, D. S., Shannon, J. S., McDonald, I. R., *Proc. Chem. Soc.*, 230–31 (July 1964)
95. Letham, D. S., *Life Sci.*, **5**, 1999–2004 (1966)
96. Lin, C. Y., Key, J. L., *Plant Cell Physiol.*, **9**, 553–60 (1968)

97. Loening, U. E., Ingle, J., *Nature,*
 215, 363–67 (1967)
98. Loening, U. E., *Ann. Rev. Plant
 Physiol.,* **19,** 37–70 (1967)
99. McCalla, D. R., Morré, D. J., Osborne, D. J., *Biochim. Biophys.
 Acta,* **55,** 522–28 (1962)
100. Maclachlan, G. A., in *Biochemistry
 and Physiology of Plant Growth
 Substances* (See Ref. 60)
101. Madison, J. T., Everett, G. A., Kung,
 H., *J. Biol. Chem.,* **242,** 1318–23
 (1967)
102. Maheshwari, S. C., Guha, S., Gupta,
 S., *Biochim. Biophys. Acta,* **117,**
 470–72 (1966)
103. Masuda, Y., *Physiol. Plantarum,* **12,**
 324–35 (1959)
104. Masuda, Y., *ibid.,* **18,** 15–23 (1965)
105. Masuda, Y., *Plant Cell Physiol.,* **7,**
 75–91 (1966)
106. Masuda, Y., Tanimoto, E., *Plant Cell
 Physiol.,* **8,** 459–65 (1967)
107. Masuda, Y., Setterfield, G., Bayley,
 S. L., *Plant Cell Physiol.,* **7,** 243–
 62 (1966)
108. Masuda, Y., Tanimoto, E., Shimoda,
 C., Kamisaka, S., Yanagishima, N.,
 Plant Cell Physiol., **8,** 221–25
 (1967)
109. Masuda, Y., Tanimoto, E., Wada, S.,
 Physiol. Plantarum, **20,** 713–19
 (1967)
110. Masuda, Y., Wada, S., *ibid.,* **19,**
 1055–63 (1966)
111. Masuda, Y., Yanagishima, N., *Plant
 Cell Physiol.,* **5,** 365–68 (1964)
112. Matsubara, S., Armstrong, D. J.,
 Skoog, F., *Plant Physiol.,* **43,** 451–
 53 (1968)
113. Matthysse, A. G., *Plant Physiol.
 Suppl.,* **43,** S–42 (1968)
114. Miller, C. O., *Proc. Natl. Acad. Sci.,*
 54, 1052–58 (1965)
115. Miller, C. O., *Ann. N.Y. Acad. Sci.,*
 144, 251–57 (1967)
116. Miller, C. O., *Science,* **157,** 1055–57
 (1967)
117. Morgan, P. W., Hall, W. C.,
 Physiol. Plantarum, **15,** 420–27
 (1962)
118. Morré, D. J., *Plant Physiol.,* **40,**
 615–19 (1965)
119. Morré, D. J., *ibid.,* **43,** 1545–59
 (1968)
120. Morris, R. O., *Biochim. Biophys.
 Acta,* **127,** 273–76 (1966)
121. Nitsan, J., Lang, A., *Develop. Biol.,*
 12, 358–76 (1965)
122. Nitsan, J., Lang, A., *Plant Physiol.,*
 41, 965–70 (1966)

123. Noodén, L. D., *Plant Physiol.,* **43,**
 140–50 (1968)
124. Noodén, L. D., Thimann, K. V.,
 Proc. Natl. Acad. Sci., **50,** 194–
 200 (1963)
125. Noodén, L. D., Thimann, K. V.,
 Plant Physiol., **40,** 193–201
 (1965)
126. Noodén, L. D., Thimann, K. V.,
 ibid., **41,** 157–64 (1966)
127. O'Brien, T. J., *Induction of Ribo-
 nucleic Acid Polymerase Activity
 in Soybean Hypocotyls with 2,4-
 Dichlorophenoxyacetic Acid* (Doctoral thesis, Univ. Illinois, 1967)
128. O'Brien, T. J., Jarvis, B. C., Cherry,
 J. H., Hanson, J. B., in *Biochemistry and Physiology of Plant
 Growth Substances* (See Ref. 60)
129. O'Brien, T. J., Jarvis, B. C., Cherry,
 J. H., Hanson, J. B., *Biochim.
 Biophys. Acta,* **169,** 35–43 (1968)
130. Olszewka, M. J., *Exptl. Cell Res.,*
 16, 193–201 (1959)
131. Ormrod, O. P., Williams, W. A.,
 Plant Physiol., **35,** 81–87 (1960)
132. Osborne, D. J., *Plant Physiol.,* **37,**
 595–602 (1962)
133. Osborne, D. J., *J. Sci. Food Agr.,*
 16, 1–13 (1965)
134. Paleg, L. G., *Ann. Rev. Plant
 Physiol.,* **16,** 291–322 (1965)
135. Patterson, B. D., Trewavas, A. J.,
 Plant Physiol., **42,** 1081–86 (1967)
136. Penny, P., Galston, A. W., *Am. J.
 Botany,* **53,** 1–7 (1966)
137. Perry, R. P., *Proc. Natl. Acad. Sci.,*
 48, 2179–86 (1962)
138. Pilet, P. E., Braun, R., *Physiol.
 Plantarum,* **20,** 870–78 (1967)
139. Rappaport, L., Wolf, N., *Intern.
 Symp. Biochem. Reg. Viral and
 Other Diseases, Japan. J. Phytopath.* (In press)
140. Rebstock, T. L., Hammer, C. L.,
 Sell, H. M., *Plant Physiol.,* **29,**
 490–91 (1954)
141. Reich, E., Goldberg, I. H., *Progr.
 Nucleic Acid Res. Mol. Biol.,* **3,**
 184–230 (1964)
142. Richmond, A. E., Lang, A., *Science,*
 125, 650–51 (1957)
143. Robins, M. J., Hall, R. H., Thedford, R., *Biochemistry,* **6,** 1837–48
 (1967)
144. Roychoudhry, R., Datta, A., Sen, S.
 P., *Biochim. Biophys. Acta,* **107,**
 346–51 (1965)
145. Roychoudhry, R., Sen, S. P., *Biochem. Biophys. Res. Commun.,* **14,**
 7–11 (1964)

146. Roychoudhry, R., Sen, S. P., *Physiol. Plantarum,* **17,** 352–62 (1964)
147. Roychoudhry, R., Sen, S. P., *Plant Cell Physiol.,* **6,** 761–65 (1965)
148. Sacher, J. A., *Life Sci.,* **11,** 866–71 **(1963)**
149. Sacher, J. A., *Am. J. Botany,* **52,** 841–48 (1965)
150. Sacher, J. A., *Exptl. Gerontol.,* **2,** 261–78 **(1967)**
151. Sacher, J. A., *Plant Physiol.,* **42,** 1334–42 (1967)
152. Sänger, H. L., Knight, C. A., *Biochem. Biophys. Res. Commun.,* **13,** 455–61 (1963)
153. Schwimmer, S., *Plant Physiol.,* **43,** 1008–10 (1968)
154. Setterfield, G., *Symp. Soc. Exptl. Biol.,* **17,** 98–126 (1963)
155. Shannon, J. C., Hanson, J. B., Wilson, C. M., *Plant Physiol.,* **39,** 804–9 (1964)
156. Siegel, M. R., Sisler, H. D., *Biochim. Biophys. Acta,* **103,** 558–67 (1965)
157. Silberger, J., Skoog, F., *Science,* **118,** 443–44 (1953)
158. Skoog, F., *Brookhaven Symp. Biol. No. 6,* 1–21 (1954)
159. Skoog, F., Armstrong, D. J., Cherayil, J. D., Hampel, A. E., Bock, R. M., *Science,* **154,** 1354–56 (1966)
160. Skoog, F., Hamzi, H. Q., Szweykowska, M., Leonard, N. J., Carraway, K. L., Fujii, T., Helgeson, J. P., Loeppky, R. N., *Phytochemistry,* **6,** 1169–92 (1967)
161. Srivastava, B. I. S., *Plant Physiol.,* **41,** 5–62 (1966)
162. Srivastava, B. I. S., Ware, G., *Plant Physiol.,* **40,** 62–64 (1965)
163. Srivastava, B. I. S., *Biochem. Biophys. Res. Commun.,* **32,** 533–38 (1968)
164. Stout, E. R., Mans, R. J., *Biochim. Biophys. Acta,* **134,** 327–36 (1967)
165. *Symp. Soc. Exptl. Biol.,* **21** (1967)
166. Tata, J. R., *Nature,* **219,** 331–37 (1968)
167. Tester, C. F., Dure, L. S. III, *Biochemistry,* **6,** 2532–37 (1967)
168. Thimann, K. V., Loos, G. M., *Plant Physiol.,* **32,** 274–79 (1957)
169. Trewavas, A., Johnston, I. R., Crook, E. M., *Biochim. Biophys. Acta,*
136, 301–11 (1967)
170. Trewavas, A., in *Progress in Phytochem.,* **1,** 113–60 (1968)
171. Trewavas, A., *Phytochemistry,* **7,** 673–81 (1968)
172. Truelsen, T. A., Galston, A. W., *Physiol. Plantarum,* **19,** 167–76 (1966)
173. Tuan, D. Y. H., Bonner, J., *Plant Physiol.,* **39,** 368–72 (1964)
174. van Overbeek, J., *Science,* **152,** 721–31 (1966)
175. van Overbeek, J., Loeffler, J. E., Mason, M. I. R., *Science,* **156,** 1497–99 (1967)
176. Valdovinos, J. G., Ernest, L. C., *Physiol. Plantarum,* **20,** 1027–38 (1967)
177. Vanderhoef, L. N., Key, J. L., *Plant Cell Physiol.,* **9,** 343–51 (1968)
178. Varner, J. E., *Plant Physiol.,* **39,** 413–15 (1964)
179. Varner, J. E., Chandra, G. R., *Proc. Natl. Acad. Sci.,* **52,** 100–6 (1964)
180. Varner, J. E., Chandra, G. R., Chrispeels, M. J., *J. Cellular Comp. Physiol.,* **66,** 55–68 (1965)
181. Venis, M. A., *Nature,* **202,** 900–1 (1964)
182. Venis, M. A., *ibid.,* **210,** 534–35 (1966)
183. Von Abrams, G. J., Pratt, H. K., *Plant Physiol.,* **43,** 1271–78 (1968)
184. West, S. H., Hanson, J. B., Key, J. L., *Weeds,* **8,** 333–40 (1960)
185. Wilson, C. M., Shannon, J. C., *Biochim. Biophys. Acta,* **68,** 311–13 (1963)
186. Wollgiehn, R., *Flora,* **151,** 411–37 (1961)
187. Wollgiehn, R., *ibid.,* **156,** 291–302 (1965)
188. Wollgiehn, R., *Soc. Exptl. Biol.,* **21,** 231–46 (1967)
189. Wollgiehn, R., Parthier, B., *Phytochemistry,* **3,** 241–48 (1964)
190. Yanagishima, N., *Physiol. Plantarum,* **18,** 306–12 (1965)
191. Yanagishima, N., Masuda, Y., *Plant Cell Physiol.,* **5,** 369–72 (1964)
192. Yung, K.-H., Mann, J. D., *Plant Physiol.,* **42,** 195–200 (1967)
193. Zachau, H. G., Dütting, D., Feldmann, H., *Angew. Chem.,* **78,** 392–93 (1966)

ASPECTS OF SELENIUM METABOLISM IN HIGHER PLANTS

By Alex Shrift

Biology Department, State University of New York, Binghamton

Selenium in soils is available to a limited number of unique plants which accumulate this comparatively rare element to levels highly toxic for livestock. The earliest work with selenium was largely concerned with such fundamental studies as identification, location, and mapping of seleniferous vegetation (60, 74). Later, when it became apparent that certain plant species, notably the genus *Astragalus,* were invariably associated with seleniferous soils, interest shifted from considerations of economic hazard to very much broader scientific concerns.

The botanist finds in the genus *Astragalus* an unusual example of biochemical evolution. The latest taxonomic revision, based on morphological criteria, establishes approximately 500 North American species (8); of these, about 25 not only have evolved the ability to accumulate selenium but also the ability to assimilate the element in a distinctive way.

The biochemist finds here a novel type of assimilation in which the selenium atom becomes covalently bound to carbon to form analogues of many sulfur compounds (62, 63, 65). The close resemblance between the selenium and sulfur atoms has led many investigators to suspect that the two atoms or their compounds are metabolized by the same enzyme systems. Now unfolding is evidence that the selenium atom does not always penetrate every branch of the sulfur pathway, and that selenium at times seems to follow certain metabolic routes not open to sulfur.

To some plant physiologists, selenium accumulators represent evidence that selenium is a possible micronutrient. It has been accepted as a micronutrient for several animals (50, 61, 72), but it has not been widely accepted in such a role for plants (10). The most recent evidence may indeed sustain these doubts.

And to biologists, the widespread distribution of accumulators and their ability to assimilate selenium into a variety of organic compounds represents one phase of an extensive biological turnover of the element (48, 55), perhaps as part of a selenium cycle comparable to the cycles for sulfur, carbon, and nitrogen (64).

ASSOCIATION OF ACCUMULATOR SPECIES WITH SELENIFEROUS SOILS

After selenium had been implicated as the toxic component in a variety of range plants, many early surveys of the 1930's (60, 74) established the association of at least two dozen species of *Astragalus* with the seleniferous soils which extend over immense regions in the western part of the United States, Canada, and Mexico (Fig. 1). These regions are considered seleniferous, not because the selenium level is significantly higher than in other soils, but because the selenium is available to many of the native plants. Other soils have been discovered in the United States and in other parts of the world with equal or even higher concentrations of selenium, but plants growing on these soils rarely accumulate selenium to the levels known for accumulator species (24, 25, 37, 38).

The accumulators are unique because they can extract thousands of ppm of selenium from soils which contain only several ppm of selenium. Table I gives representative analyses of plants collected from a small plot of seleniferous soil which contained only two ppm of selenium (47). Species in the first three genera, as well as members of a fourth genus, *Machaeranthera* (*Xylorhiza*), not listed, are considered to be accumulators; these species have never been reported on nonseleniferous soils. *Gutierrezia* is an example of a small number of native genera which accumulate moderate amounts of selenium from seleniferous soils, but which can also be found on nonseleniferous soils. The other plants in Table 1 are typical of the majority of plants which do not accumulate the element and which may grow on both types of soil.

The high levels of selenium in accumulator species are of an order of magnitude 100 to 10,000 times greater than the levels in most other native and crop plants. Selenium contents do vary, however; not every specimen collected gives such a high selenium analysis. Figure 2 illustrates the distribution of selenium content in samplings of three *Astragalus* species. In each group are specimens which assay very low for selenium, in the range usually found for nonseleniferous plants. Such a distribution range is common for several other species (60, 74). In these early studies, low selenium levels in some samples were attributed to a volatilization of selenium during drying and storage of plant specimens (9, 49), and in more recent studies volatile components from some plants have been characterized (7, 12, 19, 23, 41). But whether volatilization caused such low values in the small number of specimens of *Astragalus* is certainly not established; local soil differences or a genetic variability within the species are equally plausible reasons. Because of the possible role of selenium as a micronutrient in these plants, it becomes important to determine the precise reason for this minimal accumulation. But whatever the reason, it remains clear that these species, in contrast to nonaccumulator species, have evolved a distinct ecological niche.

PHYSIOLOGICAL DIFFERENTIATION WITHIN THE GENUS *Astragalus*

Most Astragali are nonaccumulators. Of the 500 North American species listed by Barneby in his recent monograph (8), about 475 are nonaccumulators usually found growing in nonseleniferous soils. Though the distributions of selenium content among these specimens have not been recorded

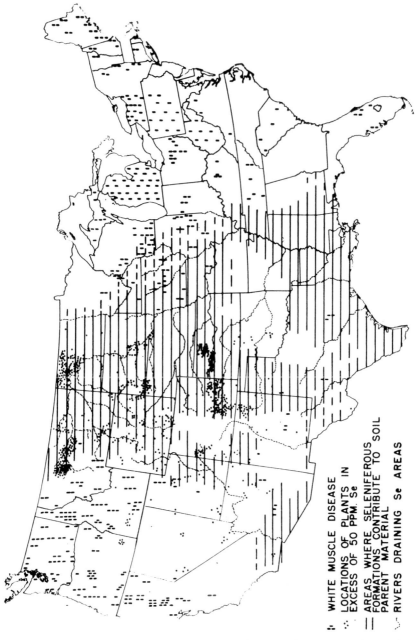

WHITE MUSCLE DISEASE

LOCATIONS OF PLANTS IN
EXCESS OF 50 PPM. Se

AREAS WHERE SELENIFEROUS
FORMATIONS CONTRIBUTE TO SOIL
PARENT MATERIAL

RIVERS DRAINING Se AREAS

FIG. 1. The geographical distribution of seleniferous soils with associated seleniferous vegetation, and non-seleniferous soils with associated white muscle disease
of sheep. From Muth & Allaway (51).

TABLE I

SELENIUM IN PLANTS COLLECTED FROM A CLAY LOAM CONTAINING
2 TO 4 PPM SE

	Ppm
Astragalus pectinatus (narrow-leaved milkvetch)	4000
Stanleya pinnata (prince's plume)	330
Haplopappus fremontii (goldenweed)	320
Gutierrezia sarothrae (turpentine or snake weed)	70
Zea mays (corn)	10
Euphorbia sp. (spurge)	10
Xanthium sp. (cocklebur)	6
Salsola pestifer (Russian thistle)	5
Munroa squarrosa (false buffalo grass)	4
Helianthus annuus (sunflower)	2
Bouteloua gracilis (blue grama)	2
Malvastrum coccineum (scarlet mallow)	1

From Miller & Byers (47).

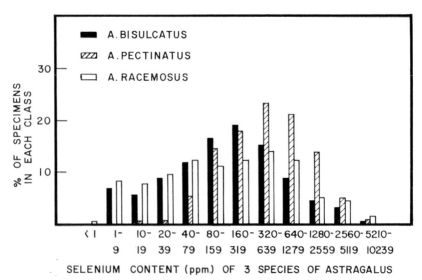

FIG. 2. Ranges of selenium content of three accumulator species of *Astragalus*.
From Rosenfeld & Beath (60, p. 92).

as thoroughly as for the accumulators, there is no evidence, in the published references, of appreciable absorption by any of these species. Even when found growing adjacent to accumulators, these species contain levels of selenium comparable to nonaccumulators from other genera (Table II). The genus *Astragalus,* apparently, has evolved in two distinct directions with respect to the accumulation of selenium.

The divergence noted in the field has been confirmed experimentally by Trelease & Trelease (77). They grew accumulators in liquid and sand cultures with levels of selenite that inhibited the growth of nonaccumulators. Figure 3 and Table III show that in liquid cultures the addition of concentrations of selenite starting as low as 0.33 ppm of selenium allowed progressive increases in the growth of *Astragalus racemosus,* whereas these same concentrations were highly inhibitory to the growth of *A. crassicarpus,* a nonaccumulator. The differences were even more marked in sand cultures. Table III shows that the yield of *A. racemosus* in the presence of selenium reached about 2.8 times the yield without selenium; *A. crassicarpus* with selenium yielded about one-eighth the yield without selenium. Why nonaccumulators can grow on seleniferous soils and escape symptoms of toxicity is not known.

A rapid germination test to differentiate between the two types of species was also devised by Trelease (73). Concentrations of sodium selenite as high as 20 ppm selenium allowed normal growth in 15 species of accumulator seedlings, whereas these same levels severely inhibited both root and hypocotyl growth of all 11 species of nonaccumulator seedlings.

TABLE II

SELENIUM CONTENTS OF ACCUMULATOR AND NONACCUMULATOR *Astragalus*
SPECIES GROWING SIDE BY SIDE ON SELENIFEROUS SOILS

Species	Se content (μg Se/g) Plant	Soil	Location	Reference
A. racemosus	450	2–14	Nebraska	16
A. missouriensis	5			
A. racemosus	5560	5	Nebraska	16
A. missouriensis	25			
A. racemosus	400	0.7	Nebraska	16
A. missouriensis	25			
A. bisulcatus	2620	1.6	North Dakota	36
A. caryocarpus	30			
A. bisulcatus	2050	2	Wyoming	15
A. missouriensis	5			
A. pectinatus	1980	—	Wyoming	15
A. crassicarpus	6			

FIG. 3. Opposite effects of selenium (as selenite) on two species of *Astragalus* grown in solution cultures. Above: *Astragalus racemosus;* Below: *Astragalus crassicarpus.* Concentrations of selenium (left to right): 0, 0.33, 1, 3, 9 ppm. From Trelease & Trelease (77).

In trying to further characterize the physiological divergence within the genus, Ulrich & Shrift investigated the accumulation of selenium by excised roots of these plants. Uptake of selenate and possibly of selenite was found to be metabolically linked in both types of species, but no consistent differences could be detected between them under the experimental conditions used (78).

BIOCHEMICAL DIFFERENTIATION BETWEEN *Astragalus* SPECIES

Accumulation of selenium and tolerance to high concentrations of selenium compounds are accompanied by assimilation patterns which differ distinctly in the accumulators from the patterns in nonaccumulators. Table IV summarizes these findings. The preponderant soluble selenium compound in accumulators is Se-methylselenocysteine (CH_3 · Se · CH_2 · $CHNH_2$ · COOH) first isolated from *A. bisulcatus* (75). The compound was later identified by tracer work in this and four other accumulator species of *Astragalus;* levels were significantly higher than in four nonaccumulators (66, 67). What distinguished the nonaccumulators was the presence of Se-methylselenomethionine [$(CH_3)_2$ · Se^+ · CH_2 · CH_2 · $CHNH_2$ · COOH]; in accumulators it occurred either in minute amounts or could not be detected at all (80).

A comparable distinction between the two types of species was uncovered by Dunnill & Fowden during an extensive survey of the soluble components in seeds of approximately 120 *Astragalus* species (22). In 10 North American accumulators, S-methylcysteine and glutamyl-S-methyl-

TABLE III

INFLUENCE OF Na_2SeO_3 ON YIELDS OF *Astragalus racemosus* AND
A. crassicarpus GROWN IN SOLUTION AND SAND CULTURES[a]

Selenium in medium (ppm)	A. racemosus	A. crassicarpus
Solution Cultures	Dry weight (grams) per culture of 5 plants	
0	2.33	1.06
1/3	3.14	0.68
1	3.85	0.37
3	3.78	0.25
9	3.81	0.20
Sand Cultures	Dry weight (grams) per culture of 10 plants	
0	9.4	8.44
9[b]	26.4	1.13

[a] From Trelease & Trelease (77).

[b] 9 ppm Se for *A. racemosus;* 1 ppm Se for *A. crassicarpus* (during first 12 days 9 ppm were used).

TABLE IV

SELENO-AMINO ACIDS IN SELENIUM ACCUMULATOR AND NONACCUMULATOR
PLANTS GIVEN SELENITE OR SELENATE[a]

	Se-methyl-selenocysteine	Se-methyl-selenomethionine
Accumulators		
Astragalus crotalariae	+++[b]	—[c]
Astragalus bisulcatus	+++	—
Astragalus sabulosus	+++	—
Astragalus racemosus	+++	+
Astragalus preussii	+++	+
Oonopsis condensata	+++	—
Stanleya pinnata	+++	—
Nonaccumulators		
Astragalus canadensis	++	+++
Astragalus vàsei	++	+++
Astragalus succulentus	+	+++
Astragalus lentiginosus	—	+++

[a] From Virupaksha & Shrift (80).

[b] The assignment of (+) signs is semiquantitative and is based on the distribution of
^{75}Se in Dowex-50 column eluates.

[c] Not found in detectable amounts.

cysteine were identified; they were absent in the remaining nonaccumulators. The paper chromatographic methods used did not allow resolution of selenium and sulfur analogues. However, both S-methylcysteine and Se-methylselenocysteine were present in seeds of three accumulators examined by Martin & Gerlach (43), and each could be identified in excised leaves of most accumulators supplied with ^{75}SeO$_3^{--}$ or ^{35}SO$_4^{--}$ (67). S-methylmethionine was not reported by Dunnill & Fowden, even though Se-methylseleno-methionine was consistently found in leaves of nonaccumulators after incubation with ^{75}Se-labeled selenite or selenate (80).

Other biochemical distinctions between the two types of species became apparent during metabolic studies with (^{75}Se, CH$_3$-^{14}C)-labeled seleno-methionine (81). These results are summarized in Table V and show that the products formed by the accumulator differed considerably from those formed by the nonaccumulator. Not only did the accumulator methylate the selenomethionine, as did the nonaccumulator, but it formed seleno-homocystine and Se-methylselenocysteine as well. In the latter compound, the ratio of ^{75}Se to ^{75}Se + ^{14}C had increased, indicating that the —SeCH$_3$ group had not been transferred intact to a three carbon residue, a reaction comparable to the sulfuration of O-acetylserine by methylmercaptan as described by Giovanelli & Mudd for spinach (28). It was suggested by Virupakasha, Shrift & Tarver that selenocysteine was first synthesized from the administered selenomethionine and then transmethylated (81); transmethylation is described by Thompson & Gering for the synthesis of S-methylcysteine in radish (71). A further difference reported by Virupaksha et al. between the two species of *Astragalus* was the occurrence of a selenopeptide in the nonaccumulator but not in the accumulator.

The gathering evidence shows that accumulators not only have a distinct ecological distribution but also distinct patterns of selenium metabolism. The functional significance of these patterns is not entirely clear. The two main suggested explanations involve a micronutrient role as opposed to a detoxification mechanism.

ASSIMILATION OF SELENIUM BY OTHER PLANTS

The ability to synthesize organic selenium compounds is not restricted to members of the genus *Astragalus* but is widespread among plants, bacteria, and fungi. Table VI is a compilation of selenium compounds reported in a variety of plants. Because many of these substances are labile, even more labile than their sulfur analogues, identification is sometimes difficult. Criteria to firmly establish the presence of a selenium compound have been discussed in a previous review (65). Of the compounds listed in Table VI, several have been authenticated by more than one investigator. It is now established that plants from many taxa biosynthesize organic selenium compounds.

SULFUR AND SELENIUM METABOLISM

Most of the selenium compounds in Table VI have their sulfur counterparts, already well known as metabolites in plants and microorganisms (63, 65). One can infer from such correlations that enzyme systems responsible

TABLE V

METABOLISM OF (^{75}SE, ME-^{14}C)SELENOMETHIONINE BY TWO SPECIES OF *Astragalus*[a]

Species	Ratio of ^{75}Se to ^{75}Se+^{14}C in selenomethionine administered	Compound isolated	$\dfrac{^{75}\text{Se}}{^{75}\text{Se} + {}^{14}\text{C}}$
A. crotalariae (accumulator)	0.60	Se-methylselenocysteine	1.1
		Se-methylselenomethionine	0.62
		selenohomocystine	—
A. lentiginosus (nonaccumulator)	0.55	Se-methylselenomethionine	0.60
		seleno-peptide	0.50

[a] From Virupaksha et al. (81).

TABLE VI

SELENIUM COMPOUNDS REPORTED IN HIGHER PLANTS

Selenium compound	Plant	References
Selenocystine	*Zea mays*	32
	Trifolium pratense, T. repens, Lolium perenne	59
	Allium cepa	68
	Spirodela oligorrhiza	14
Selenocysteine-seleninic acid	*Trifolium pratense, T. repens, Lolium perenne*	59
Se-methylselenocysteine	*Astragalus species*	43, 66, 67, 75, 80, 81
	Oonopsis condensata, Stanleya pinnata	66, 67
Se-propenyl-scleno-cysteine selenoxide	*Allium cepa*	68
Selenohomocystine	*Astragalus crotalariae*	81
Selenomethionine	*Allium cepa*	68
	Trifolium pratense, T. repens, Lolium perenne	59
	Spirodela oligorrhiza	14
Se-methylselenomethionine	*Astragalus* species	80
	Trifolium pratense, T. repens, Lolium perenne	59
Selenomethionine selenoxide	*Trifolium pratense, T. repens, Lolium perenne*	59
Selenocystathionine	*Astragalus* species	30, 43
	Stanleya pinnata	79
	Lecythis ollaria	5, 6, 33, 34, 54
	Neptunia amplexicaulis	58
Selenopeptides	*Astragalus* species	67, 80, 81
Seleno-wax	*Stanleya bipinnata*	44
Dimethyl diselenide	*Astragalus racemosus*	23

for assimilation of the sulfur atom will also handle the selenium atom which so resembles sulfur in its physical and chemical properties (62). This inference has been substantiated by several studies with microbial and animal systems (63, 65), but it has not been checked with enzymes from plant sources. The findings that certain enzymes handle sulfur and selenium analogues equally well as substrates reopens the question of selenium toxicity. It has been widely held that selenium compounds interfere with sulfur metabolism by a typical antimetabolite action. Other explanations must now be sought.

The many resemblances between sulfur and selenium assimilation should not be construed as universal, for there are indications that sulfur and selenium are not always metabolically equivalent (Table VII). The first four biosyntheses in Table VII, one from an animal system, have in common the intermediate PAPS (3′-phosphoadenosine 5′-phosphosulfate). In the fifth biosynthesis, PAPSe (3′-phosphoadenosine 5′-phosphoselenate) could not be demonstrated in a system which made PAPS. By analogy with the sulfur pathway, therefore, no compound could be made whose synthesis would require PAPSe. This may prove to be one branch in the sulfur pathway closed to selenium. However, the general nature of this block should be further examined.

Of special interest are reports in which certain organisms seem to assimilate selenium along pathways apparently closed to sulfur (Table VIII). When (^{35}S)methionine was given to *A. crotalariae*, a small amount was converted to S-methylmethionine and most was recovered unchanged. Homocystine and S-methylcysteine could not be detected even though their selenium analogues were readily formed from selenomethionine by this species (81).

A. vàsei is a nonaccumulator whose leaves convert selenite to Se-methylselenocysteine but apparently are unable to convert sulfate to S-methylcysteine. Though sulfate and selenate are the actual analogues, selenite and selenate are apparently interchangeable and can be assimilated into the same amino acids (80). Dunnill & Fowden, in their survey of non-protein

TABLE VII

METABOLIC REACTIONS INVOLVING SULFUR FOR WHICH COMPARABLE REACTIONS WITH SELENIUM HAVE BEEN SOUGHT BUT NOT DEMONSTRATED

Reaction	Organism	References
SO_4^- → choline sulfate	*Aspergillus niger*	52
	Zea mays	
	Hordeum vulgare	
	Triticum aestivum	
	Helianthus annuus	
SO_4^- → flavonoid sulfates	*Zostera marina*	52
SO_4^- → plant sulfolipid	*Euglena gracilis*	52
	Chlorella sp.	
	Brassica oleracea var. *acephala*	
	Phaseolus vulgaris	
	Triticum aestivum	
SO_4^- → chondroitin sulfate	*Bos tauros* (calf)	17
SO_4^- → PAPS	*Saccharomyces cerevisiae*	84
SO_4^- → glutathione	*Escherichia coli*	20
	Astragalus species	67, 80
SO_4^- → sulfur amino acids in proteins	*Neptunia amplexicaulis*	58, 59

TABLE VIII

METABOLIC REACTIONS INVOLVING SELENIUM FOR WHICH COMPARABLE
REACTIONS WITH SULFUR HAVE NOT BEEN DEMONSTRATED

Reaction	Plant	References
Selenomethionine → Se-methylselenocysteine + selenohomocystine	*Astragalus crotalariae*	81
SeO_3^- → Se-methylseleno-cysteine	*Astragalus vàsei*	80
SeO_4^- → selenocystathionine	*Stanleya pinnata*	79
SeO_3^- → selenocystathionine	*Neptunia amplexicaulis*	58
Se → selenocystine + selenomethionine	*Spirodela oligorrhiza*	14

amino acids in seeds of Astragali, failed to detect S-methylcysteine and substantiated this result with *A. vàsei* (22).

Selenocystathionine ($HOOC \cdot CHNH_2 \cdot CH_2 \cdot Se \cdot CH_2 \cdot CH_2 \cdot
CHNH_2 \cdot COOH$) is a selenium metabolite for which the comparable
sulfur analogue is poorly established. The existence of selenocystathionine
was first inferred by Horn & Jones (30), who isolated from *A. pectinatus*
a crystalline material which contained sulfur and selenium. From the ratio
of selenium to sulfur, the empirical formula, and group analysis, they deduced the presence of a mixture of two parts of selenocystathionine to one
part of cystathionine. Subsequently, the selenium compound was identified in
several other plants (Table VI).

What makes this compound so interesting is the absence of good evidence in higher plants for its sulfur analogue, cystathionine, which is well
known in microorganisms and animals. Millar reported a sulfur-containing
substance from mint leaves, with a paper chromatographic position close to
that of cystathionine, but further identification was not carried out (46);
and the material isolated by Horn & Jones, which they had deduced to be
an isomorphic mixture of the sulfur and selenium analogues, was never resolved (30). Furthermore, the results of Horn & Jones are at variance with
the recent work of Martin & Gerlach, whose column chromatographic techniques enable them to separate the following seleno-amino acids from each
other and from other amino acids: selenocystine, selenomethionine, selenocystathionine, Se-methylselenocysteine, and selenohomocystine (43). Martin
& Gerlach examined extracts prepared from seeds of three accumulator *Astragalus* species and found considerable amounts of selenocystathionine in
A. pectinatus and *A. osterhouti* but only traces in *A. racemosus*. Significant
was the absence of cystathionine in any of the three species, even though
other seleno-amino acids were accompanied by approximately equal

amounts of their sulfur analogues. Particularly significant was the absence of cystathionine from *A. pectinatus,* the plant from which Horn & Jones had isolated their crystals. Dunnill & Fowden, in their survey of seeds from Astragali, including *A. pectinatus,* also failed to detect cystathionine (22).

Other recent work also clearly establishes the existence of selenocystathionine; this work can also be interpreted to indicate the absence of cystathionine. Seeds of *Lecythis ollaria* yielded appreciable amounts of crystalline selenocystathionine; some sulfur, attributed to a co-crystallization of cystathionine, was found in the initial material isolated (6, 34). The authors report, however, that subsequent recrystallization gave a product essentially free of sulfur. Isomorphic mixtures of selenium and sulfur compounds, however, are difficult to resolve. Would a single recrystallization have given a product free of the sulfur analogue? The small amount of sulfur present after the first crystallization could very well have been another substance. That this interpretation is probably correct is seen from the ease with which selenocystathionine was isolated and purified, as reported later (54).

Is there any unequivocal evidence for cystathionine in plants? An enzymatic synthesis with crude extracts of spinach has been demonstrated by Giovanelli & Mudd (27). The compound was detected after incubation of the enzyme preparation with cysteine and either acetylhomoserine or O-succinylhomoserine in a reaction comparable to transsulfuration in bacteria. However, as the authors point out, the products could have arisen by an exchange reaction; there is no certainty, therefore, that the reaction represented an actual net synthesis.

Why then were Martin & Gerlach unable to find cystathionine in *A. pectinatus,* whereas Horn & Jones reported its presence? The selenocystathionine identified by Martin & Gerlach and by Kerdel-Vegas et al. (34) was derived from seeds; the material of Horn & Jones was isolated from leaf and stem material. Several possibilities can be suggested to explain the disparity: seeds may not be able to synthesize cystathionine; both cystathionine and selenocystathionine are synthesized in the plant, but only selenocystathionine is translocated to the seeds; selenocystathionine accumulates in seeds, but cystathionine, whether made or translocated there, is utilized at rates that prevent accumulation of detectable amounts. Any of these interpretations is supported by the results of Painter & Franke, who, during an examination of different parts of cereal plants and of proteins from the same part of the plant, found variations in S to Se ratios (56). Their data, though reported as quantitative differences, could be the result of qualitative differences.

What may prove to be another unusual dissimilarity between sulfur and selenium metabolism has been reported by Butler & Peterson (14). In their work with the duckweed, *Spirodela oligorrhiza,* carried out axenically, they found that ^{75}Se-labeled elemental selenium was appreciably converted into selenocystine and selenomethionine. Higher plants do not use elemental sulfur. The authors are careful to point out that an atmospheric oxidation of the elemental form to an assimilable form such as selenite must first be ruled out.

Selenium as a Micronutrient for *Astragalus*

The evidence that selenium serves as micronutrient for accumulator species of *Astragalus* may be summarized as follows: (*a*) In nature these plants always grow in seleniferous soils. (*b*) They accumulate selenium to the thousands of micrograms per gram of dry weight; nonaccumulators are reported to contain only a few micrograms of selenium per gram of dry weight. (*c*) Traces of selenite or selenate, added to the culture medium, stimulated the growth of accumulator species; even these trace levels severely inhibited nonaccumulators. The amount of growth of one accumulator species in the presence of selenium was remarkable (Fig. 4). (*d*) Accumulator species assimilate selenite, selenate, and selenomethionine differently than do nonaccumulators. (*e*) Higher plants, microorganisms, and animals (26, 45) assimilate selenium in ways that sometimes differ from the way in which they handle sulfur. (*f*) Selenium is now recognized to be a micronutrient for sheep and chickens. A wide variety of selenium-responsive disorders is known. (*g*) Though not proved to be necessary for growth, selenite is needed for the induction of formic dehydrogenase in several enteric microorganisms (59a).

When the evidence is weighed, the balance seems to favor selenium as a micronutrient for this group of plants. In at least one respect, however, it falls somewhat short of the criteria set forth by Arnon & Stout (3, 4). The experiments of Trelease & Trelease, though they show a marked difference in growth between plants grown with and those grown without selenium, were not carried through the reproductive stages of the life cycle. Nevertheless, there was growth stimulation, a criterion often used to study the essential nature of a nutrient. The effect obtained by the Treleases seems to have been specific for selenium, since their medium contained all micronutrients currently recognized in higher plants. Here too, it may be argued that the Treleases had failed to vary the proportions of the micronutrients to see if growth could be improved. The criterion of participation in the metabolism of the plant seems to be answered by the several cases in which selenium is assimilated differently from sulfur and by those cases in which the assimilation of selenium in accumulators differs from that in nonaccumulators.

But Broyer & Johnson (personal communication) offer another suggestion for the growth stimulation obtained by the Treleases .They examined the Treleases' photographs and found that the selenium-free controls, whose growth was relatively poor (Fig. 4), resembled legumes which show symptoms, presumably, of phosphate toxicity. The level of phosphate that had been used ranged from 0.001 to 0.002 *M;* Broyer & Johnson suggest that these levels may have been too high for these legumes. Rather

Fig. 4. Influence of selenium on the growth of *Astragalus beathii* in sand culture. Plants on the left received selenium in the culture solution; those on the right did not. From Trelease & Beath (74, p. 17).

than a direct growth stimulation from selenium, the data of the Treleases could reflect an indirect effect of ion antagonism between phosphate and selenate or selenite. The tolerance of these species to internally accumulated selenium would then reflect an assimilation of the selenium into non-toxic constituents. Nonaccumulators, sensitive to selenium, may simply lack this detoxification mechanism.

Antagonism between selenite and phosphate has been found in experiments on respiration (11) and ion uptake (42) by yeast. In the respiration studies, phosphate markedly reversed selenite but not selenate toxicity, and the slight inhibition caused by very high levels of phosphate could be partially reversed by selenite. It is instructive to compare the concentrations used in the yeast respiration experiments with those used by the Treleases. Concentrations of KH_2PO_4 ranging from 1×10^{-5} to 7.5×10^{-5} M caused approximately 15 to 20 percent inhibition of yeast respiration; as little as 6.25×10^{-5} M selenite almost completely restored respiration to normal. Trelease & Trelease grew their Astragali with 1×10^{-3} M phosphate and as little as 1.3×10^{-5} M selenite. Here the ratio between phosphate and selenite is of an order of magnitude 100 times the effective ratio in the yeast respiration experiments and would imply a very strong antagonism by the selenite ion. In the yeast uptake experiments, uptake of 6.25×10^{-4} M phosphate was inhibited 33 to 44 percent by 1.25×10^{-5} M selenite. Here the phosphate/selenite ratio was 50. These relationships require additional study, especially because phosphate is also known to enhance selenite toxicity in *Salmonella typhimurium* (53), and because antagonism between selenate and phosphate could not be demonstrated during kinetic uptake studies with barley roots (39).

Broyer & Johnson (personal communication), in testing their interpretation of the early work of Trelease & Trelease, have discovered that *Astragalus crotalariae*, an accumulator, grew successfully without selenium in Hoagland's medium in which the phosphate was decreased to 2.5×10^{-5} M.

A. crotalariae, however, was not included among the nine species studied by the Treleases (60, p. 86). Could there be, among the 25 accumulator species of *Astragalus*, several which are intermediate in some physiological characteristics between accumulators and nonaccumulators? A thorough survey of the accumulators in this genus is now needed.

The views of Broyer & Johnson are supported by the recent work of Peterson & Butler, who offer a possible explanation for the relatively large amounts of nonprotein seleno-amino acids in accumulator species (58). They hypothesize that selenium is shunted into these inocuous seleno-amino acids and thereby excluded from the proteins of these plants. The basis for this view is that no selenomethionine or selenocystine could be detected in the proteins of *Neptunia amplexicaulis*, an Australian selenium accumulator, whereas large amounts of selenocystathionine predominated in the soluble fraction. To back their argument, they point to the large amounts of Se-methylselenocysteine which predominate in the soluble fraction of *Astragalus* accumulators (67), and to the presence of selenomethionine in the proteins of nonaccumulating crop plants (59). According to Peterson & Butler, non-accumulating plants have not evolved this detoxification mechanism. These plants, therefore, will incorporate selenium as analogues of the usual sulfur amino acids into their proteins which become altered and inactive with a resultant poisoning of the plants.

If Broyer & Johnson and Peterson & Butler prove to be correct, it may become necessary to amplify the criteria of Arnon & Stout to take into account results which simulate essentiality due to ion antagonism within an unfavorable culture medium. This new interpretation raises two important questions. First, what is the physiological or biochemical basis for the invariable association of accumulators with seleniferous soils? Is it possible that there exists some soil factor other than selenium which favors such an association? Second, what is the mechanism for the accumulation of such large amounts of selenium? Do the nonprotein seleno-amino acids act as a "sink" into which selenium from the soil is continuously pulled and "deposited"?

Selenium as a Micronutrient for Other Plants

There is almost no evidence that selenium serves as a micronutrient for plants other than those in the genus *Astragalus*. Several references report small amounts of growth stimulation in plants after the addition of selenium compounds to the culture medium. The growth stimulation, however, was slight, and no attempts were made to meet criteria for essentiality (9, 31, 40, 57, 69, 70, 82).

Recently, a number of field trials have been carried out to raise the low selenium content of forage plants responsible for the selenium-deficiency condition of sheep known as white muscle disease (18, 21, 29, 83). But since it was not the purpose of these studies to test crop yield, only one report, by Cary et al., even mentions growth response (18). They found that alfalfa, with a selenium content of 0.07 ppm, could be raised to varying levels of selenium by altering the application rate of selenite to the soils, but there was no change in growth or yield.

Forages which cause white muscle disease in sheep contain less than 0.1 ppm selenium. This value is considered the approximate "critical level" below which the disease is induced (2). Crop yields in these low selenium regions seem to be normal, though they require the usual applications of fertilizers common to agricultural practice. Since plants from these white muscle disease regions sometimes assay for as little as 0.02 ppm selenium, it will be necessary to conduct experiments at even lower levels before any micronutrient status for selenium can be determined.

The one detailed investigation specifically designed to test selenium as a micronutrient was carried out by Broyer, Lee & Asher at Berkeley (13). Salts were meticulously freed of contaminating selenium until each salt contained less than 1×10^{-8} g atoms Se/mole (0.79 μg Se/mole). Addition of as little as 0.025 μg atoms/L (2 μg/L or 0.002 ppm) of selenium in the form of selenite failed to stimulate growth of either alfalfa or subterranean clover. Nor were deficiency symptoms observed in the selenium-free controls. Assays of the plants showed selenium contents in proportion to the amounts admitted to the culture medium.

Surprisingly, control plants contained more selenium than had been present in the medium. For example, the selenium-free medium that had been used during the course of one experiment contained a total of 0.0005

μg atoms Se/culture (0.0395 μg Se/culture), but the alfalfa plants which were harvested from this medium assayed for a total of 0.019 μg atoms Se (1.5 μg Se). This aberrant result was attributed to a foliar uptake of volatile selenium compounds from the greenhouse atmosphere.

The authors estimate that if alfalfa and subterranean clover require selenium, the level will probably be less than 0.001 μg atoms/g of dry weight (0.079 ppm). Their estimate comes in very close to the levels found in the natural forages responsible for white muscle disease. Unfortunately, research at even less than these low levels is hampered by the limited sensitivity of existing techniques for selenium analysis (1).

Biological Turnover of Selenium

Geological distributions of selenium point to an accumulation of the element by plants possibly as long ago as the Paleozoic era (9, 60, p. 28). It has even been suggested that during the Mesozoic, dinosaurs ate themselves into oblivion with massive ingestion of seleniferous vegetation (35). If seleniferous vegetation was at one time global, an intriguing question arises with regard to the evolutionary direction within the genus *Astragalus:* are accumulators recent invaders of seleniferous regions, or do they represent a few species which have retained what was an ancient ability, widespread among plants, to accumulate the element? Are we now witnessing a leaching into the oceans of an element at one time more widely utilized? Are the animal species which have a need for selenium in trace amounts and the few dozen plant species which accumulate the element only biological remnants?

Astragali and other accumulators still occupy vast regions of the Western Hemisphere. This geographic spread of itself gives convincing testimony that extensive biological turnover of selenium continues. It is unfortunate that full quantiative aspects of the turnover have yet to be adequately measured and analyzed.

Biochemical cycling, through the plants themselves, is receiving more attention than ever before; it is known that Astragali play a major role in the reduction of oxidized forms of selenium to reduced organic selenium compounds. But we still lack contemporary work concerning the reoxidation of selenium in these compounds, especially the contribution to the cycling process of soil microorganisms (64).

LITERATURE CITED

1. Allaway, W. H., Cary, E. E., *Anal. Chem.*, **36**, 1359–62 (1964)
2. Allaway, W. H., Hodgson, J. F., *J. Animal Sci.*, **23**, 271–77 (1964)
3. Arnon, D. I., in *Trace Elements in Plant Physiology*, 31–39 (Chronica Botanica, Waltham, Mass., 1950)
4. Arnon, D. I., Stout, P. R., *Plant Physiol.*, **14**, 371–75 (1939)
5. Aronow, L., Kerdel-Vegas, F., *Separata de la Revista Dermatologia Venezolana*, **IV**, 109–209 (1964)
6. Aronow, L., Kerdel-Vegas, F., *Nature*, **205**, 1185–86 (1965)
7. Asher, C. J., Evans, C. S., Johnson, C. M., *Australian J. Biol. Sci.*, **20**, 737–48 (1967)
8. Barneby, R. C., *Atlas of North American Astragalus* (Memoirs of the New York Botanical Garden, **13**, Part I and II, 1964)
9. Beath, O. A., Eppson, H. F., Gilbert, C. S., *J. Am. Pharm. Assoc.*, **26**, 394–405 (1937)
10. Beeson, K. C., in *Selenium in Agriculture*, 34–40 (Anderson, M. S., Lakin, H. W., Beeson, K. C., Smith, F. F., Thacker, E., Handbook No. 200, Agricultural Service, U. S. Dept. Agr. in cooperation with the Geol. Survey, U. S. Dept. Interior, 65 pp., 1961)
11. Bonhorst, C. W., *Agr. Food Chem.*, **3**, 700–3 (1955)
12. Broyer, T. C., *Proc. Symp. Use of Isotopes and Radiation in Soil Nutrition Studies*, Ankara, Turkey, 181–206 (Intern. Atomic Energy Agency, Vienna, Austria, 1965)
13. Broyer, T. C., Lee, D. C., Asher, C. J., *Plant Physiol.*, **41**, 1425–28 (1966)
14. Butler, G. W., Peterson, P. J., *Australian J. Biol. Sci.*, **20**, 77–86 (1967)
15. Byers, H. G., *U. S. Dept. Agr. Tech. Bull.* No. 482, 1–47 (1935)
16. Byers, H. G., *ibid.*, No. 530, 1–78 (1936)
17. Campo, R. D., Wengert, P. A., Jr., Tourtellotte, C. D., Kirsch, M. A., *Biochim. Biophys. Acta*, **124**, 101–8 (1966)
18. Cary, E. E., Wieczorek, G. A., Allaway, W. H., *Soil Sci. Soc. Am. Proc.*, **31**, 21–26 (1967)
19. Challenger, F., *Advan. Enzymol.*, **12**, 429–91 (1951)
20. Cowie, D. B., Cohen, G. N., *Biochim. Biophys. Acta*, **26**, 252–61 (1957)
21. Davies, E. B., Watkinson, J. H., *New Zealand J. Agr. Res.*, **9**, 317–27 (1966)
22. Dunnill, P. M., Fowden, L., *Phytochemistry*, **6**, 1659–63 (1967)
23. Evans, C. S., Asher, C. J., Johnson, C. M., *Australian J. Biol. Sci.*, **21**, 13–20 (1968)
24. Fleming, G. A., *Soil Sci.*, **94**, 28–35 (1962)
25. Fleming, G. A., Walsh, T., *Proc. Roy. Irish Acad.*, **58**, 151–66 (1957)
26. Ganther, H. E., *World Rev. Nutr. Dietet.*, **5**, 338–66 (1965)
27. Giovanelli, J., Mudd, S. H., *Biochem. Biophys. Res. Commun.*, **25**, 366–71 (1966)
28. Giovanelli, J., Mudd, S. H., *ibid.*, **31**, 275–80 (1968)
29. Grant, A. B., *New Zealand J. Agr. Res.*, **8**, 681–90 (1965)
30. Horn, M. J., Jones, D. B., *J. Biol. Chem.*, **139**, 645–60 (1941)
31. Hurd-Karrer, A. M., *Am. J. Botany*, **24**, 720–28 (1937)
32. Jacobs, A. L., *The Isolation and Identification of a Seleno-Amino Acid from Corn* (Doctoral thesis, Columbia Univ., 1963)
33. Kerdel-Vegas, F., *Separata de la Revista Dermatologia Venezolana*, **IV**, 109–209 (1964)
34. Kerdel-Vegas, F., Wagner, F., Russell, P. B., Grant, N. H., Alburn, H. E., Clark, D. E., Miller, J. A., *Nature*, **205**, 1186–87 (1965)
35. Koch, N. C., *J. Paleontol.*, **41**, 970–72 (1967)
36. Lakin, H. W., Byers, H. G., *U. S. Dept. Agr. Tech. Bull.* **950**, 1–36 (1948)
37. Lakin, H. W., Davidson, D. F., in *Selenium in Biomedicine*, 27–56 (Symposium, Oregon State Univ.; Muth, O. H., Oldfield, J. E., Weswig, P. H., Eds., Avi Publ. Co., Westport, Conn., 1967)
38. Lakin, H. W., Williams, K. T., Byers, H. G., *Ind. Eng. Chem.*, **30**, 599–600 (1938)
39. Leggett, J. E., Epstein, E., *Plant Physiol.*, **31**, 222–26 (1956)
40. Levine, V. E., *Am. J. Botany*, **12**, 82–90 (1925)
41. Lewis, B. G., Johnson, C. M., Delwiche, C. C., *Agr. Food Chem.*, **14**, 638–40 (1966)

42. Mahl, M. C., Whitehead, E. I., *Proc. S. Dakota Acad. Sci.*, **40**, 93–97 (1961)

43. Martin, J. L., Gerlach, M. L., *Anal. Biochem.* (In press, 1969)

44. McColloch, R. J., Hamilton, J. W., Brown, S. K., *Biochem. Biophys. Res. Commun.*, **11**, 7–13 (1963)

45. McConnell, K. P., Portman, O. W., *J. Biol. Chem.*, **195**, 277–82 (1952)

46. Millar, F. K., *Investigation upon the Growth, Salt Accumulation, and Related Metabolic Problems of Plant Tissues by the Use of Radioactive Isotopes* (Doctoral thesis, Univ. Rochester, 1953)

47. Miller, J. T., Byers, H. G., *J. Agr. Res.*, **55**, 59–68 (1937)

48. Moxon, A. L., Olson, O. E., Searight, W. V., *S. Dakota Agr. Exptl. Sta. Tech. Bull.*, **2**, 1–94 (1939)

49. Moxon, A. L., Rhian, M., *Proc. S. Dakota Acad. Sci.*, **18**, 20–22 (1938)

50. Muth, O. H., *J. Am. Vet. Med. Assoc.*, **142**, 272–77 (1963)

51. Muth, O. H., Allaway, W. H., *J. Am. Vet. Med. Assoc.*, **142**, 1379–84 (1963)

52. Nissen, P., Benson, A. A., *Biochim. Biophys. Acta*, **82**, 400–2 (1964)

53. North, W. R., Bartram, M. T., *Appl. Microbiol.*, **1**, 130–34 (1953)

54. Olivares, G. J., Aronow, L., Kerdel-Vegas, F., *Acta Cient. Venezolana*, **18**, 9–12 (1967)

55. Olson, O. E., in *Selenium in Biomedicine*, 297–311 (See Ref. 37)

56. Painter, E. P., Franke, K. W., *Am. J. Botany*, **274**, 336–39 (1940)

57. Perkins, A. T., King, H. H., *J. Am. Soc. Agron.*, **30**, 664–67 (1938)

58. Peterson, P. J., Butler, G. W., *Nature*, **213**, 599–600 (1967)

59. Peterson, P. J., Butler, G. W., *Australian J. Biol. Sci.*, **15**, 126–46 (1962)

59a. Pinsent, J., *Biochem. J.*, **57**, 10–16 (1954)

60. Rosenfeld, I., Beath, O. A., *Selenium—Geobotany, Biochemistry, Toxicity, and Nutrition* (Academic Press, N.Y., 411 pp., 1964)

61. Schwartz, K., *Federation Proc.*, **20**, 666–73 (1961)

62. Shrift, A., *Botan. Rev.*, **24**, 550–83 (1958)

63. Shrift, A., *Federation Proc.*, **20**, 695–702 (1961)

64. Shrift, A., *Nature*, **201**, 1304–5 (1964)

65. Shrift, A., in *Selenium in Biomedicine*, 241–71 (See Ref. 37)

66. Shrift, A., Virupaksha, T. K., *Biochim. Biophys. Acta*, **71**, 483–85 (1963)

67. Shrift, A., Virupaksha, T. K., *ibid.*, **100**, 65–75 (1965)

68. Spare, C. G., Virtanen, A. I., *Acta Chem. Scand.*, **18**, 280–82 (1964)

69. Stanford, G. W., Olson, O. E., *Proc. S. Dakota Acad. Sci.*, **19**, 25–31 (1939)

70. Stoklasa, J., *Biochem. Z.*, **130**, 604–43 (1922)

71. Thompson, J. F., Gering, R. K., *Plant Physiol.*, **41**, 1301–7 (1966)

72. Thompson, J. N., Scott, M. L., *Federation Proc.*, **27**, 417, Abstr. 1145 (1968)

73. Trelease, S. F., *Science*, **95**, 656–57 (1942)

74. Trelease, S. F., Beath, O. A., *Selenium* (Publ. by the authors, 292 pp., 1949)

75. Trelease, S. F., DiSomma, A. A., Jacobs, A. L., *Science*, **132**, 618 (1960)

76. Trelease, S. F., Trelease, H. M., *Am. J. Botany*, **25**, 372–80 (1938)

77. Trelease, S. F., Trelease, H. M., *ibid.*, **26**, 530–35 (1939)

78. Ulrich, J. M., Shrift, A., *Plant Physiol.*, **43**, 14–20 (1968)

79. Virupaksha, T. K., Shrift, A., *Biochim. Biophys. Acta*, **74**, 791–93 (1963)

80. Virupaksha, T. K., Shrift, A., *ibid.*, **107**, 69–80 (1965)

81. Virupaksha, T. K., Shrift, A., Tarver, H., *Biochim. Biophys. Acta*, **130**, 45–55 (1966)

82. von Scharrer, K., Schropp, W., *Z. Pflanzenernaehr. Dueng. Bodenk.*, **50**, 187–202 (1950)

83. Watkinson, J. H., Davies, E. B., *New Zealand J. Agr. Res.*, **10**, 116–21 (1967)

84. Wilson, L. G., Bandurski, R. S., *J. Biol. Chem.*, **233**, 975–81 (1958)

NITRATE REDUCTION IN HIGHER PLANTS

By Leonard Beevers and R. H. Hageman

Departments of Horticulture and Agronomy, respectively
University of Illinois, Urbana, Illinois

INTRODUCTION

Nitrogen constitutes approximately 2 per cent and carbon approximately 40 per cent of the dry weight of plants. On a world-wide scale it is estimated that 200 billion tons of carbon are fixed annually by photosynthetic processes (48), which on a basis of approximate analysis would require the incorporation of 10 billion tons of nitrogen. Apart from those species that have a symbiotic association with nitrogen fixing bacteria, the bulk of the plant nitrogen arises from the reduction of nitrate taken up from the soil. It is of interest to note that 6 million tons of nitrogen, in various fertilizer forms, are applied annually in the United States alone. Since the reduction of nitrate to the usable (ammoniacal) form requires the donation of 8 electrons, while carbon requires but 4 electrons, the reduction of nitrate to ammonia utilizes a massive amount of solar energy.

The sequence of reviews in the *Annual Review* series (7, 17, 22, 47, 60, 81, 88, 96, 144, 173, 176) chronicles the development of knowledge of the general aspects of nitrogen metabolism in plants. In addition, a large number of reviews (18, 64, 66, 91, 99, 100, 106) are more directly concerned with the metabolism of inorganic nitrogen.

The current review is directed primarily on the developments since 1962, and confined principally to the literature relating to higher plants.

ENZYMATIC CONVERSION OF NITRATE TO NITRITE

General characteristics.—Although the enzymatic reduction of nitrate to nitrite has been inferred for over half a century (77), and the existence of nitrate reductase conclusively established for 15 years (44), the enzyme has not, as yet, been fully purified or characterized from higher plants. From studies with partially purified preparations, the following characteristics have been reported: (*a*) a molecular weight of 500,000 to 600,000 (8); (*b*) the enzyme contains molybdenum (8, 43), Fe^{++} (8) and FAD (8, 43); (*c*) Michaelis constants (K_m) for NO_3^-, $FMNH_2$, and NADH are in the order of 2×10^{-4} M (12, 124, 132, 141), 3 to 6×10^{-4} M (32) and 2.5×10^{-6} M (12); (*d*) a pH optimum of 7.5 when NADH is the electron donor and 6.0 to 6.25 when NADPH is the electron donor (12, 44); (*e*) maximum activities of 700 and 600 mμ moles NO_2^- produced min^{-1}, mg protein^{-1} for the enzyme from corn (132) and spinach leaves (89, 114), respec-

tively; (*f*) the enzyme is adaptive in that the activity is inducible by nitrate
(52, 61, 124, 151) and by molybdenum (3) ; and (*g*) the enzyme is unstable
both *in vitro* (8) and *in vivo* (25, 52, 61) [the enzyme exhibits a half-life
of 4 hr in detached corn leaves at 35° (132) and a diurnal variation (53)].

   Electron donors.—There is a preponderance of evidence (12, 83, 97,
124) that nitrate reductase from leaves of most plant species has a specific
requirement for NADH as electron donor. The earlier and commonly held
belief that NADPH was the preferred cofactor had its origin in the initial
work on nitrate reductase obtained from the leaves from young soybean
seedlings (44). It is ironic that the enzyme from this tissue, when extracted
in the presence of cysteine, is twice as active with NADH as with NADPH
(12), and that the leaves from mature plants lose the capability of utilizing
NADPH. Recently, Sims et al. (137) reported that *Lemna minor* plants exhibited a 20-fold increase in NADPH-specific nitrate reductase when sucrose was added to the culture medium. They indicate that these plants contain two enzymes, each with specific cofactor requirement, and that the primary energy source determines the cofactor specificity of the nitrate reductases.

   It would appear that the enzyme from young soybeans is exceptional in
that it is capable of directly utilizing either cofactor (12). The enzyme
from young leaves of several other plant species show only traces of activity when NADPH is the added electron donor (12). It is not known
whether the traces of activity obtained with NADPH in these instances
represent direct utilization or transformation of NADPH to NADH by
phosphatase or transhydrogenase.

   In some instances, the addition of FMN or FAD to the nitrate reductase
assay mixture stimulated activity when pyridine nucleotides were the electron donor (44, 66). Furthermore, Stoy (147) demonstrated that photore-
duced riboflavin under anaerobic conditions was more effective than NADH
as an electron donor for nitrate reductase from wheat. This suggests that
the pyridine nucleotide may not be the primary electron donor to the
enzyme.

   Hageman et al. (51) found that partially reduced benzyl viologen could
also serve as an electron donor for nitrate reductase extracted from marrow leaves. Subsequently, Del Campo et al. (36) reported that illuminated
broken chloroplasts were able to reduce nitrate to nitrite in the presence of
benzyl viologen. Although ferredoxin or ferredoxin plus NADP would not
substitute for the dye (36), the physiological cofactors FMN or FAD could
(117). Since pyridine nucleotides were not required for nitrate reduction, it
was proposed (113) that the well-known pyridine nucleotide dependent nitrate reductase was, in fact, two separate enzymes, a NADP :reductase and
nitrate reductase. An extensively purified preparation of nitrate reductase
from spinach required only the addition of nitrate and reduced FMN or
FAD to effect reduction (113). The FAD could be reduced in the light by
grana or in the dark by NADPH and a NADP :reductase (92). Based on

this evidence, it was proposed that the enzyme be reclassified as $FMNH_2$ ($FADH_2$): nitrate oxidoreductase (113). However, apart from the nature of the electron donor, the properties of the enzyme described by Paneque et al. (113) are similar (K_m's for $FMNH_2 - 1.5 \times 10^{-5}\ M$, $NO_3 - 1.8 \times 10^{-4}\ M$, and pH optimum between 7.3 and 7.8) to the pyridine nucleotide dependent enzyme.

Several following lines of evidence suggest that there is no substantial basis for renaming the enzyme. In fact, these same investigators (114) later found that their highly (800- to 1000-fold) purified enzyme could utilize NADH as the electron donor for nitrate reduction. No additional enzyme or cofactor was required. In this respect the spinach enzyme is comparable to that present in most other plant species (12, 97, 124, 141). However, it was postulated (114) that the reduction of nitrate by NADH may require a separate NAD reductase and an unknown cofactor to transfer electrons to the proposed $FMNH_2$ ($FADH_2$): nitrate oxidoreductase. More recently, these workers (111) have shown the occurrence in chloroplasts of a NADH-specific diaphorase capable of supplying electrons to FMN for nitrate reduction.

Schrader et al. (132) investigated the possibility that nitrate reduction in plant leaves is achieved by: (a) two separate enzymes each with different cofactor requirements; (b) a single enzyme, possibly composed of subunits that can utilize both reduced NAD or flavins as electron donors; or (c) $FMNH_2$ ($FADH_2$): nitrate oxidoreductase that is capable of utilizing reduced pyridine nucleotides indirectly via separate pyridine nucleotide reductases and flavin. Based on the observations that the $FMNH_2$ requirement for optimal activity was 40- to 100-fold higher than for NADH and that all attempts to separate the NADH and $FMNH_2$ dependent activities by purification, differential induction, and differential decay failed, it was concluded that alternative (b) was most likely. This opinion is also supported by the recent crystallization of a pyridine nucleotide dependent nitrate reductase from *Neurospora* (49).

Thus it appears that nitrate reductase is versatile in its use of electron donors. However, all these observations can be accommodated in an electron transport scheme (see p. 498). A similar scheme described by Hewitt & Nicholas (66) is based on direct evidence obtained with microbial systems; however, it is equally applicable to higher plants.

Nitrate reductase most commonly found in plant leaves is depicted as a molybdoflavoprotein that is capable of accepting electrons directly from NADH, or $FMNH_2$ ($FADH_2$) but not from NADPH. An alteration in binding site for the pyridine nucleotide would explain the NADPH specific enzyme reported by Sims et al. (137) or for the enzyme from young soybean leaves. As stated in 1956 by Stoy (147), the *in vivo* role of reduced flavins as electron donors is unknown.

For the NAD-specific nitrate reductase from plants the electrons apparently can be accepted by the enzyme directly from NADH, free $FMNH_2$

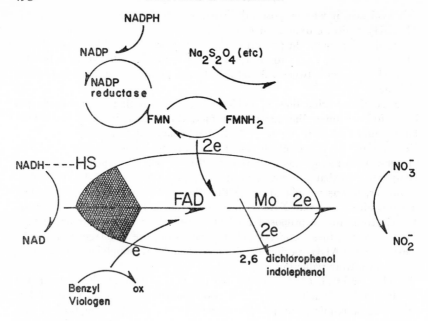

(FADH$_2$), or reduced dyes such as benzyl viologen. NADPH can serve as an electron donor only indirectly via NADP: reductase and FMN. It appears that the component (subunit) binding the NADH is more labile during purification and storage than that part of the enzyme binding FMNH$_2$ (132). A sulphydryl group is implicated in the binding of NADH in that the addition of sulphydryl reagents restores activity lost during purification and alleviates the inhibitory effects of p-chloromercuribenzoate (132). For the plant enzyme no clear delineation can be given as to electron entry sites. It has been shown that when oxidized 2,6-dichlorophenolindolephenol (DCPIP) was added to the plant enzyme (standard NADH nitrate reductase assay), the dye accepted the electrons and excluded the reduction of nitrate. It does not appear that DCPIP accepts electrons from the molybdenum as DCPIP can still be reduced when nitrate reduction is blocked by cyanide (132). The identification of molybdenum as the metal prosthetic group in nitrate reductase has been demonstrated only in the case of soybeans and wheat (44, 141). However, physiological observations (60) indicate that molybdenum is involved in nitrate metabolism in higher plants. Attempts to use reduced molybdenum as an electron donor for nitrate reductase from plants were unsuccessful (127), in contrast to its successful use with the enzyme from *Neurospora* (108). Garrett & Nason (49) have recently shown that the enzyme from *Neurospora* contains cytochrome *b*-557.

They have tentatively positioned the cytochrome between FAD and molybdenum in the electron flow pattern, depicted in the preceding diagram.

ENZYMATIC REDUCTION OF NITRITE

Characteristics of nitrite reductase.—The enzyme has not been purified or extensively studied; however, evidence is available to support the following statements: (*a*) the enzyme is probably not a flavoprotein, but receives electrons from ferredoxin when the latter has been reduced by illuminated chloroplasts or by NADPH and a diaphorase enzyme (31, 65, 76, 118, 135); (*b*) the Michaelis constant (K_m) for NO_2^- is between 10^{-4} M and 10^{-6} M (31, 76, 118, 125, 135), but the cause of this wide spread of values is not known; (*c*) the K_m value for ferredoxin is 0.01 mM (118); (*d*) the enzyme is located in the chloroplasts (118, 121); (*e*) it is induced by nitrite (74) and appears to be more stable *in vivo* than nitrate reductase (74, 132).

Electron donors.—Early reports of the reduction of hydroxylamine and nitrite by extracts from plants supplied with exogenous reduced pyridine nucleotides (107, 123, 155) were not conclusive and were not verified by subsequent work. Cresswell & Hewitt (32) found that the failure to detect ammonia in assay systems that showed loss of hydroxylamine and oxidation of reduced pyridine nucleotides reported by Roussos & Nason (123) could be explained by oxidation of the hydroxylamine. Both Cresswell (29)and Sanderson & Cocking (125) concluded that reduced pyridine nucleotides did not function as direct electron donors for nitrite reductase.

A new insight into nitrite metabolism was provided by the demonstration of a nitrite reductase in cell-free extracts of higher plants capable of reducing nitrite and hydroxylamine to ammonia (51). In the initial work, benzyl viologen reduced chemically by hydrogen or enzymatically by NADPH was used as the electron donor (30, 51) for the enzyme. Concurrently, Huzisige & Satoh (71) demonstrated that nitrite was reduced by illuminated spinach chloroplasts fortified with an additional soluble protein fraction. Sanderson & Cocking (125) identified a similar enzyme-grana system from tomatoes and suggested that the cofactor involved in nitrite reduction is present in the grana. Nason (106) suggested that the electron carrier in the photochemical system might be the photosynthetic pyridine nucleotide reductase described by San Pietro & Lang (126). Following the demonstration (150) that ferredoxin was the electron transporting component of photosynthetic pyridine nucleotide reductase (150), it was independently demonstrated by a number of groups (63, 72, 90, 112, 115) that ferredoxin could replace benzyl viologen as the electron carrier in nitrite metabolism and was apparently the physiological carrier for the reduction of nitrite to ammonia. Reduced ferredoxin for the enzymatic reduction of nitrite can be supplied by light and a chloroplast system or by NADPH via ferredoxin reductase (90) as shown in scheme on p. 500.

Subsequent studies (76, 118, 135) demonstrated that nitrite reductase partially purified from corn, spinach, and marrow leaves cannot accept elec-

(a) Ferredoxin - NADP: reductase
(b) Nitrite reductase

trons directly from NADPH in the dark, but requires ferredoxin or nonphys-
iological dyes as electron carriers for reduction of nitrite to ammonia. In
the light, ferredoxin is apparently the physiological cofactor and nitrite can
be a recipient of electrons from the noncyclic photophosphorylation process.
For each mole of nitrite reduced, 1 mole of ammonia, 1.5 moles of oxygen,
and 3 moles of ATP are formed (90, 115). Electrons, which would normally be transferred from ferredoxin to NADP via ferredoxin-NADP reductase, become rerouted in some circumstances to nitrite via the nitrite reductase enzyme. Addition of NADP to a chloroplast system which is reducing nitrite suppresses nitrite reduction in favor of the reduction of NADP
(65, 135). The mechanism of this adjustment is not yet clear. The initial
electron donor, water, can be replaced by ascorbate-dichlorophen-
olindolephenol couple after inhibition of photosystem II by treatment with
heat or p-chlorophenyldimethylurea (63).

The findings that ferredoxin, which could be reduced photochemically,
functions as the electron donor in nitrite reduction agrees with the physiological observation of accelerated nitrite utilization in the light (57, 80,
156). However, it has been reported that wavelengths of light other than
those which promote photosynthesis function in stimulating nitrite metabolism (148). Further physiological evidence of the function of ferredoxin in
nitrite assimilation is suggested by the experiments of Kessler & Czygan
(84) and Cresswell et al. (31) that iron-deficient plants exhibit a decreased
capacity to reduce nitrite. Presumably the iron deficiency would cause a
reduction in the level of ferredoxin. The fact that nongreen tissues can
metabolize nitrite suggests that electron donors other than ferredoxin might
function in these systems, since to date the presence of ferredoxin in plants
has been reported only in photosynthetic tissues. However, Sanderson &
Cocking (125) report that a factor required for nitrite reduction in extracts
from tomatoes is present in cellular particles from organs other than leaves.
If ferredoxin is present in nongreen tissues, then nitrite reduction could
proceed via NADPH and an appropriate diaphorase or enzyme system.
Such a system is consistent with the observation of Butt & Beevers (24) of
an increased respiratory metabolism of carbohydrate via the pentose phos-

phate pathway in maize roots in the presence of nitrite. It was proposed that nitrite reduction utilized the NADPH generated by the oxidation of glucose-6-phosphate, thus constituting a coupled enzyme system. However, it was not demonstrated that nitrite had been reduced. It is of interest that the addition of nitrate did not stimulate the oxidation of glucose-6-phosphate. Miflin (103) reports that nitrite reductase activity per unit of protein in barley roots is approximately equal to that of leaves, and the enzyme appeared to be associated with a mitochondrial fraction. Although viologen dyes could serve as electron donors, the physiological reducing system was not established.

In view of experimental data showing that nitrite reduction is inhibited by DNP, it has been proposed that this step of nitrite metabolism required the utilization of high energy phosphate (81). However, the demonstration by Wessels (166–168) that DNP could serve as a Hill oxidant, and the finding of Del Campo et al. (37) that ferredoxin was able to catalyze the reduction of DNP, indicate that such arguments may not be valid. It is possible that the decreased nitrite reduction in the presence of DNP is the result of a diversion of electrons for DNP reduction rather than associated with the uncoupling action of DNP.

Ahmed & Morris have subsequently indicated (6) that their earlier suggestion (5) that reduction of DNP might account for its inhibitory effect on nitrite metabolism may not be valid. Furthermore, such an explanation for the mode of action of DNP in inhibiting nitrite metabolism is difficult to reconcile with the observation that arsenate, another uncoupler, also inhibits nitrite metabolism (58, 82).

While the conversion of nitrite to ammonium by nitrite reductase in the presence of ferredoxin has been established, the intermediate reduction stages have not been determined. Ferredoxin is a single electron donor and thus reduction might proceed by a series of one-electron stages; such a scheme has been proposed by Fewson & Nicholas (45). If such intermediates do occur, it appears unlikely that they are released in the free form. Hageman et al. (31, 51) originally pointed out that the rate of conversion of nitrite to ammonia was more rapid than the reduction of hydroxylamine to ammonia, indicating that hydroxylamine was not a free intermediate. In a detailed survey on the comparative rates of nitrite and hydroxylamine reduction, Hewitt et al. (65) indicated that the nitrite reductase from marrow and spinach also reduced hydroxylamine, but the K_m values for hydroxylamine exceeded those for nitrite. Nitrite severely inhibited hydroxylamine reduction, whereas hydroxylamine had a negligible effect on nitrite reduction. It was concluded that free hydroxylamine is not an intermediate in nitrite reduction in higher plants. Thus the conversion of nitrite to ammonia requires a series of single electron steps with all the reactions occurring on a single enzyme. These findings are in agreement with the investigations of Lazzarini & Atkinson (94) and Kemp et al. (79), who earlier had concluded that in *E. coli* the reduction of nitrite to ammonia was carried out by a single enzyme without the production of free intermediates.

Hewitt et al. (65) showed two major hydroxylamine reductase activities in leaves of marrow (*Cucurbita pepo*) and spinach. One, which was associated with nitrite reductase activity, could accept electrons from ferredoxin. The other, which did not reduce nitrite, accepted electrons from reduced benzyl viologen but not from physiological donors. Neither of these hydroxylamine reductases seems to be obligate for the reduction of nitrite to ammonia, and their physiological role is obscure. Hydroxylamine produced endogenously or supplied in the culture solutions should be reduced and utilized by the plant. Bundel et al. (20, 21) have demonstrated that various plants have the capacity to incorporate N^{15} from N^{15}-labeled hydroxylamine, and this process is stimulated by light (57). This hydroxylamine could be reduced to ammonia by one of the reductases described by Hewitt et al. (65). Bundel (21) has reported that a hydroxylamine reductase can be obtained from a variety of plant tissues that utilizes NADH as the electron donor. It is difficult to reconcile this work with the other investigations reported (29, 65, 66).

GENERATION OF ELECTRON DONORS FOR NITRATE ASSIMILATION

The current biochemical evidence shows that the enzyme involved in the reduction of nitrate requires reduced pyridine nucleotides but that the reduction of nitrite in leaves in the light involves ferredoxin. In the dark, it would appear that reduced ferredoxin can also be generated by NADPH in leaf tissue. The nature of the cofactor for nitrite reduction in nonphotosynthetic tissue has not been established.

Nitrate reductase.—The question of the source of reduced pyridine nucleotides for nitrate reduction has been an enigma. In nonphotosynthetic tissue, the observations that nitrate influences oxygen consumption (172) and the existence of a NADH-dependent nitrate reductase (97, 103, 124, 158) suggest that respiratory metabolism supplies the electron donors for nitrate reduction. Although the commonly held view has been that light is rather closely linked to nitrate reduction in photosynthetic tissue, the same respiratory metabolism could be providing the reductant in both light and dark. Moreover, the fact that leaves will reduce nitrate in the dark indicates the involvement of respiration. Currently, it is not clear whether the influence of light on nitrate metabolism resides in its effect on nitrate reductase level per se (52), availability of nitrate (15), the generation of reductant, or a combination of all.

If the influence of light is mediated through the generation of reductant, the reductant could be produced directly by the photosynthetic system or derived indirectly from the carbon products. Since the chloroplast is the prime source of reduced pyridine nucleotide (primarily NADPH), and since nitrate reduction can be coupled to light via NADP and a chloroplast preparation (44), it has been accepted (22, 95, 100) that photosynthetically generated NADPH was the electron donor for nitrate reduction in leaves.

With time this pathway did not appear to satisfy all experimental observations, as nitrate reductase from green leaves was NADH- rather than NADPH-specific (12, 97, 124), and the enzyme appears to be localized in the cytoplasm rather than in the chloroplasts (121, 128).

There is evidence that chloroplasts can photoreduce NAD as well as NADP *in vitro* (93, 126, 134); however, the K_m is much larger (3.8 × 10⁻³ M versus 9.8 × 10⁻⁶ M) and the rate of reduction slower (25 to 60 per cent). It is obvious that if NADH is generated in the chloroplasts and supplied to the enzyme in adequate amounts, nitrate could be reduced (89). However, Ogren & Krogmann (110) have shown that illumination of leaves converts much of the NAD present in the chloroplasts to NADP and markedly increases the amount of NADPH. No increase in NADH was observed upon illumination.

In proposing the direct photosynthetic reduction of nitrate, Ramirez et al. (117) have shown that nitrate can serve as the terminal electron acceptor for a noncyclic photophosphorylation. If this is the case, it would be expected that nitrate would be reduced at an accelerated rate in the absence of CO_2. However, it has been shown that plants exposed to light but deprived of CO_2 reduce nitrate at a very slow rate (35, 81). The requirement of CO_2 for nitrate reduction may be explained by the observations of Walker et al. (162). These workers found that oxygen production by isolated intact chloroplasts is dependent upon an adequate supply of CO_2. Apparently, *in vivo* CO_2 is required for the continued flow of electrons in noncyclic photophosphorylation. Alternatively, the requirement of CO_2 for rapid nitrate reduction may indicate that the reductant utilized for nitrate reduction is generated in conjunction with or from the carbon products formed during CO_2 fixation.

In this context, Klepper (86), vacuum infiltrated leaf discs from morning-glory and corn with water, pyruvate, phosphyglycerate (PGA), 3-phosphoglyceraldehyde (3 PGAld), glucose-6-phosphate (G-6-P) and fructose-1-6-diphosphate (FDP), in the presence of nitrate. The tissue was then incubated in the dark in the infiltration medium and rate of nitrite production determined. The least and equal amounts of nitrite were found in the control, PGA and pyruvate treatments. The tissue infiltrated with the three sugar phosphates produced more (up to twofold) nitrite than the control. The amount of nitrite formed was related to the concentration of the sugar phosphates added to the medium.

When nitrite was substituted for nitrate in a comparable set of experiments, a slow but steady decrease in nitrite content was observed. There was no effect of the various substrates on nitrite utilization. However, if these experiments were conducted in the light (2,500 ft-c), nitrite was rapidly lost. This pronounced effect of light on nitrite utilization is consistent with previous observations (29, 57, 80, 156).

In confirming experiments, Klepper (86) found that clarified homogenates (30,000 × g for 15 min) when supplied with (PGA), ATP, NADPH, and NAD could reduce appreciable amounts of nitrate to nitrite. No nitrite was produced if any of the four metabolites were omitted. The addition of phosphoglyeraldehyde (3-PGAld) and NAD gave maximum reduction of nitrite and was as effective as NADH alone. The addition of NADPH alone was ineffective.

These processes per se constitute no more than the coupling of several enzymes that are present in the homogenates. However, they do permit the development of a basic concept of the influence of light on nitrate reduction.

It can be assumed that the chloroplast, when illuminated *in vivo* and supplied with CO_2 would be capable of producing the gamut of phosphorylated trioses, hexoses, sugars, and starches (11). As the phosphorylated intermediates or carbohydrates move into the cytoplasm, they are metabolized by the glycolytic enzymes and thus provide the energy source for nitrate reduction via the NAD-dependent phosphoglyceralde dehydrogenase (PGD). Heber et al. (59) have estimated that approximately 70 per cent of the total NAD-dependent PGD is localized in the cytoplasm. Further, the NADH-dependent nitrate reductase has been found to be exo-chloroplastically located (121, 128).

This hypothesis is attractive in that it: (*a*) explains the marked stimulation of light on nitrate reduction dependent upon CO_2 (23) by increasing the supply of 3-PGAld which in turn generates NADH; (*b*) concurs with Kessler's view (81) on the involvement of ATP, NAD, and carbon compounds; and (*c*) provides a means of recycling the NADH generated by the appreciable amounts of NAD-dependent PGD localized in the cytoplasm of leaf tissue (54, 55). This data permits the conclusion that 3-PGAld and the cytoplasmically located NAD-dependent PGD is the electron generating system for nitrate reductase in both light and dark.

In contrast, the work of Mendel & Visser (101), based only on the incorporation of $^{15}NO_3^-$ into reduced nitrogen, suggests a mitochondrial source of electrons in the dark and a photosynthetically produced reductant in the light. Their conclusions are based on enhanced nitrate assimilation obtained with substrates for mitochondrial respiration or with illumination and the inhibition of nitrate assimilation in the dark by addition of iodoacetate (10^{-4} M). In this vein, Klepper (86) found that 10^{-4} M iodoacetate did not suppress reduction of nitrate to nitrite, while 10^{-3} M gave a 70 per cent inhibition. Since Mendel & Visser (101) did not measure nitrite accumulated in the media or tissue, it can be argued that the enhanced incorporation which they observed in the light is more pertinent to nitrite assimilation than to the actual reduction of nitrate to nitrite.

Nitrite reductase.—It is significant that in studies of nitrate metabolism of leaf tissue in the dark that respiration is able to support the reduction of nitrate to nitrite, but further reduction of nitrite appears to be closely cou-

pled to light in leaf tissues. Such observations are consistent with a requirement for reduced ferredoxin for nitrite assimilation (65, 76, 118). In nonphotosynthetic tissues it has been demonstrated that the conversion of nitrate to nitrite, apparently supported by respiration, proceeds rapidly with
secretion of nitrite into the surrounding media (42, 81). However, the subsequent utilization of nitrite is dependent upon adequate aeration. Thus nitrate can be converted to nitrite under partially anaerobic conditions, but the
subsequent reduction of nitrite appears to depend on oxidative reactions. If
nitrite functions as a terminal electron acceptor, as respiratory studies indicate (172), it is difficult to envisage why nitrite utilization should be stimulated by oxygen. Currently, the electron donor for nitrite reduction in nonphotosynthetic tissue is not known.

LOCATION

The majority of recent studies on nitrate metabolism in higher plants
have been made with leaf tissue, because of the abundance of enzymes and
availability of material. There is adequate evidence, however, to show that
the capacity for nitrate metabolism is not solely associated with leaves. The
most convincing evidence that all living cells have the capability for assimilating nitrate are those studies in which tissues are grown in a medium in
which nitrate serves as the sole nitrogen source. The initial work indicated
that while nitrate supported growth of excised tomato roots (169, 170) ammonia failed to do so (122, 138). This was a surprising observation in view
of the predicted conversion of nitrate to ammonia prior to the incorporation
of ammonia into an organic form. However, it was indicated by Sheat et al.
(133) that ammonia was an effective nitrogen source for excised roots if
suitable precautions were taken to maintain pH. Growth on nitrate was optimal at acidic conditions, while neutral to slightly alkaline conditions were
optimal for ammonium nitrogen. Roots could also be cultured effectively
with nitrite serving as the sole nitrogen source; however, the concentration
of nitrite had to be maintained at a constant low level, or else toxicity
symptoms developed (133). It was further demonstrated (56) that growth
of roots in nitrate was dependent upon the presence of an adequate level of
molybdenum. In contrast, roots grown on nitrite are capable of growth in
the absence of molybdenum, although it stimulated growth.

In the absence of photosynthetically derived reductant to be utilized for
nitrate reduction in roots or nongreen tissues, it appears that the reducing
potential is furnished by the respiration of carbohydrates. Extensive surveys in this area have been performed by Yemm and co-workers (172, 177),
who demonstrated that incubation of excised barley roots with nitrate, nitrite, or ammonia resulted in a changed respiratory activity as indicated by
changes in CO_2 output or O_2 consumption. Characteristically, it was found
that incubation of the roots in nitrate or nitrite resulted in a stimulated
carbon dioxide production and a less marked increase in oxygen consumption. Thus the net effect of these treatments was to increase the respiratory

quotient (RQ) from 0.9 to 1.15 and 1.25 for nitrite and nitrate, respectively, clearly indicating that the respiratory mechanism had been modified. It was suggested that nitrate and nitrite might be replacing oxygen as the hydrogen acceptor. It is significant that the different forms of nitrogen supplied to the roots had distinctive effects on respiration. Thus the change in RQ produced by nitrate was slower than that caused by nitrite. Furthermore, although nitrate accumulated in roots incubated in nitrate, the same was not true with nitrite (177). It appeared that nitrite was taken up and metabolized immediately. The data could be taken to indicate an adaptive development of nitrate reductase, whereas nitrite reductase (or at least the capacity to metabolize nitrite) is constitutive. In this respect it is interesting that Czygan (34) reports a similar situation in the alga *Ankistrodesmus,* nitrate reductase being a soluble adaptive enzyme and nitrite reductase constitutive and particle bound. Detailed analyses by Yemm & Willis (177) indicated that in addition to altering the respiratory activity, the nitrogenous compounds were assimilated by the roots in a manner consistent with a conversion to ammonia prior to their incorporation into glutamine.

The mechanism by which nitrate is reduced to ammonia in nongreen tissues is not well established. Eckerson (39) described a scheme in which aqueous extracts of tissues of fresh plant organs were employed to measure the nitrate reducing ability of the structure involved. In this scheme it was demonstrated that the capacity of the extracts to convert nitrate to nitrite was dependent upon the maintenance of pH of 7.2 and an adequate supply of glucose and oxygen. Using these methods, it was consistently demonstrated that root extracts contained nitrate reducase (109). Eckerson (40) demonstrated that reducase activity (i.e., the capacity to convert nitrate to nitrite under defined conditions) varied with plant part, species, and age. Although investigations were thorough and detailed, it appears that the conversions being measured were nonenzymatic because it was shown (39) that boiled plant extracts were effective in converting nitrate to nitrite.

More convincing evidence for the enzymatic reduction of nitrate in root extracts is provided in the pioneer paper of Evans & Nason (44) ; however, nitrate reductase activity of the extracts was very low. Candela et al. (25), Hageman & Flesher (52), Maretzki & Dela Cruz (97), similarly reported only low levels of nitrate reductase in extracts of roots from cauliflower, corn, and sugar cane, respectively.

Sanderson & Cocking (124) demonstrated appreciable nitrate reductase in extracts from roots of several plant species; however, the activity of the root extracts was consistently lower than that in leaf extracts. The properties of nitrate reductase from the root extracts were very similar to those of the leaf enzyme, and it was concluded that they were identical. It was also demonstrated that the level of nitrate reductase activity in excised tomato roots grown in sterile nutrient culture was comparable to that found in intact roots, thus precluding the possibility that microbial enzymes were being measured. It was interesting that Sanderson & Cocking (124) were unable to detect nitrate reductase activity in leaves or roots of apples; it had been postulated (16) that since nitrate level was low in xylem sap, then the reduction of nitrate and amino acid assimilation occurred predominantly in roots. Grasmanis & Nicholas (50) reported that reduced benzyl viologen functioned as the electron donor for an apparently atypical nitrate reductase in apple roots. More recently, however, Klepper & Hageman (87) have demonstrated that by using adequate levels of polyvinylpyrrolidone in the extraction medium it is possible to extract a typical NADH-dependent nitrate reductase from apple leaves, stems, petioles, and roots. Thus it appears that, given adequate nitrate levels, all parts of the apple plant have the capacity to utilize nitrate in a seemingly conventional manner (NADH as electron donor). Using similar criteria to those of Bollard (16), Wallace & Pate (160) indicate that plants may be categorized as those which reduce nitrate in their roots (field pea) and those which do not (*Xanthium*). In support of this view, they report that all of the nitrate is metabolized in the roots of peas and only reduced nitrogen is found in the exuded sap, but only if the plants are cultured on low levels of nitrate. However, if the plants are supplied with nitrate levels higher than 10 ppm, nitrate is transported to the shoot and nitrate reductase induced. In contrast, *Xanthium* transports 95 per cent of the supplied nitrate to the shoots and negligible amounts are metabolized in the root.

Boutard (19) has reported that the distribution of nitrate reductase activity in etiolated barley seedlings cultured in the absence of nitrate is similar to that in field peas on minimal nitrate. When nitrate was supplied to illuminated barley, nitrate reductase activity was increased in the leaves and decreased in the roots. The nitrate reductase detected in pea roots was dependent on NADH and thus appeared characteristic of that found in most plants (12). The capacity for nitrate reduction in pea roots appears to be confined to the elongating zone, i.e., the region of most active respiration (26, 116). In contrast, no nitrate reductase was detected in the roots of *Xanthium* (160).

Boutard (19) and Coupé et al. (27) extracted nitrate reductase from barley roots and concluded that roots are more efficient than leaves in nitrate assimilation. Miflin (103) has reported on the occurrence of nitrate and nitrite reductase in extracts of roots of young barley seedlings, and the level of nitrate reductase activity on a per unit protein basis was comparable to that from leaf tissue. There appear to be two systems capable of metabolizing nitrate in barley root extracts, a soluble component utilizing NADH as electron donor (19, 27, 103) and a particulate fraction which can utilize succinate more efficiently than NADH (103). A similar succinate stimulated nitrate reduction by particulate fractions from different organs of tomatoes is reported by Sanderson & Cocking (125). Particulate fractions of barley roots were able to reduce nitrite in the presence of reduced benzyl viologen, but the physiological cofactor was not demonstrated (103).

Since the concept that roots play an important if not a major role in reducing nitrate is widely accepted, it is worthwhile to consider the relative abundance of nitrate reductase in roots and shoots (leaves). Miflin's work (103) shows that the specific activity of nitrate reductase is slightly higher in roots than in leaves. However, if activity is computed on the basis of fresh weight or plant part, the shoots have a much greater amount of the enzyme. This is illustrated by work with field peas (159) showing that shoots contain about the same amount of enzyme as the roots only when nitrate levels of the nutrient medium were maintained at 10 ppm. Even when the plants were grown on low (500 ppm) levels of nitrate, the shoots had from 3 to 12 times more enzyme than the root.

Roots from young corn seedlings contained but 20 per cent of the activity found in the shoots (52). The capacity of corn leaves to reduce nitrate (estimated by nitrate reductase levels found in composite samples of all leaves, sampled twice weekly over the growing season) exceeded by 3- to-4-fold the total reduced nitrogen found in the total shoot and ear at the end of the growing season (129). Leaves of corn and wheat maintain high (10 to 15 μmole NO_2^- $\times$ hr^{-1} $\times$ (grams fresh weight) average levels of nitrate reductase activity throughout the growing season (41, 180).

From an agronomic standpoint, and especially in view of current fertilizer practices, this work (41, 52, 129, 180) as well as that of Wallace & Pate (159, 160) would suggest that except for the early seedling stages, the bulk of the nitrate is reduced in the leaves of crop plants, excluding legumes and paddy rice.

The only report found on the occurrence of nitrite reductase in roots was that of Miflin (103). He showed that a particulate fraction from barley roots was able to reduce nitrite using reduced benzyl viologen as the electron donor. The presence of a physiological cofactor was not demonstrated. Klepper & Hageman (87), using the assay system of Joy & Hageman (76), were able to detect nitrite reductase activity in extracts from leaves but failed to detect nitrite reductase activity in extracts from roots, stem, or petiole tissue.

Other reports have been made of nitrate reductase activity in extracts from nongreen tissue. Spencer (141) was able to isolate and purify nitrate reductase from the embryos of germinating wheat seed; characteristically, the reduction of nitrate was coupled specifically to reduced NAD. Varner (157) has recently reported that nitrate reductase activity can be detected in extracts of barley aleurone cells which have been incubated with nitrate. Elsner & Hageman (42) have also demonstrated the enzyme in extracts of corn scutella preincubated with nitrate. Filner's studies with tobacco pith cultures clearly demonstrate the capacity of this tissue to utilize nitrate as principal nitrogen source (46).

Thus it appears that most plant cells and tissues have the capacity to utilize nitrate, and given an adequate supply of nitrate, the presence of nitrate reductase specific for reduced pyridine nucleotide can be demonstrated in these tissues.

Although it is obvious that nonphotosynthetic tissue can reduce and assimilate nitrate, more work is needed to establish the mechanism for reduction of nitrite to the ammonium ion.

Subcellular location.—The observations that nitrate metabolism in green tissues is intimately associated with photosynthesis, and in nongreen tissue appears to be related to respiratory metabolism, suggest that the enzymes required for nitrate metabolism might be directly associated with organelles responsible for photosynthesis and respiration. There is strong evidence for the association of at least part of the machinery for nitrate utilization being associated with the chloroplasts; however, it is debatable whether nitrate reductase is located within this organelle. Evans & Nason (44) originally demonstrated that illuminated chloroplast grana could provide the electrons for nitrate reduction, but the chloroplast grana themselves were unable to reduce nitrate unless fortified with a purified nitrate reductase. Del Campo et al. (36) reported that illuminated isolated chloroplasts had the capacity to reduce nitrate. However, the system had to be supplied with benzyl viologen as electron carrier, and it appeared that the reductase was present in a ferredoxin free-chloroplast extract. In a subsequent paper (117), purporting to show nitrate reduction in chloroplasts, it was demonstrated that nitrite was not formed by illuminated washed broken chloroplasts unless nitrate reductase (prepared from a 27,000 X g supernatant of a spinach leaf homogenate) was added. Thus, although it is clearly demonstrated that chloroplasts have the capacity to generate a reductant for nitrate reduction, it is not conclusively demonstrated that nitrate reductase is located in the chloroplast. On the contrary, the extraction techniques used for the preparation of nitrate reductase seem to indicate a cytoplasmic location. It is significant that the same workers (90) were able to demonstrate that nitrite reduction could proceed at an appreciable rate in a system consisting only of washed chloroplasts and ferredoxin. While the addition of a ferredoxin-free chloroplast extract increased nitrite reduction, it was not an absolute requirement, as in the case for nitrate reduction by the chloroplast system.

In a critical study aimed at establishing the intracellular location of enzymes of nitrate metabolism in leaf tissue, Ritenour et al. (121) compared nonaqueous and aqueous techniques and concluded that nitrite reductase is located within the chloroplast, but that nitrate reductase and glutamic acid dehydrogenase are not. Glutamic acid dehydrogenase was shown to be localized within the mitochondria. Nitrate reductase was stated to be an exo-chloroplastic enzyme, but the possibility was not eliminated that the enzyme might be associated with the external chloroplast membrane which is removed during aqueous and nonaqueous isolations.

Coupé et al. (27), also using nonaqueous techniques, but using density gradient centrifugation separation rather than stepwise fractionation, concluded that nitrate reductase of barley was a chloroplastic enzyme. The apparently conflicting results may be related to the method of interpretation of data. Ritenour et al. (121) based their conclusions on the distribution of marker enzymes, whereas Coupé et al. (27) determined activity in relation to distribution of chlorophyll and protein. In view of the possibility that nitrate reductase could be associated with the chloroplast membrane, it should be worthwhile to use the more functional chloroplasts isolated by the methods of Jensen & Bassham (75) and Walker (161) to re-evaluate the current views of localization of nitrate and nitrite reductase. In work of this type, recognition should be given to Stocking's warning (146) that enzymes can be adsorbed by, as well as lost from, the chloroplasts.

Further indirect evidence for the cytoplasmic as opposed to the chloroplastic location of nitrate reductase is provided by the observation of Schrader et al. (128), which demonstrated that chloramphenicol inhibited the synthesis of nitrite reductase but not of nitrate reductase. Anderson & Smillie (9) had previously shown that at appropriate levels chloramphenicol binds with chloroplast ribosomes and thus inhibits protein synthesis at that site, but is without effect on cytoplasmic ribosomes.

The distribution of enzymes involved in nitrate metabolism in roots and other nongreen tissues—e.g., barley aleurone layers, corn scutellum, wheat embryos—is similarly open to speculation. The observed influence of nitrate in root respiration might indicate an association of nitrate metabolism with the mitochondria. However, Spencer stated (141) that nitrate reductase from etiolated wheat embryos was soluble, and the extraction procedures utilized by other investigators (97, 124, 159) suggest a cytoplasmic location. In contrast, Sanderson & Cocking (125) and Miflin (103) reported that particulates from a range of nongreen tissue were able to produce nitrite from nitrate in the presence of succinate. Miflin's work (103) also indicates that nitrite reduction with reduced dyes as the electron donor occurred with particulate preparations. It is interesting that the crude homogenates of barley roots used NADH more effectively than succinate and that NAD activity was retained predominantly in the supernatant fraction, while the succinate mediated reduction was confined to the particulate fraction (103). It has been possible to demonstrate the alteration of respiration of mitochondrial preparations from corn roots (13) similar to those reported by Willis & Yemm (172) for intact barley roots. The utilization of nitrate and nitrite could not be estimated due to the fact that nitrite disappeared nonenzymatically when reaction mixes were acidified with trichloroacetic acid at the termination of the reaction (13). Caution is also needed in interpreting experiments supposedly demonstrating metabolism of nitrate by particulates because of the interference by microorganisms. In this respect, Dubinina (38) reports that nitrate and nitrite respiration of roots occurs readily under nonsterile conditions, but the induction of nitrate respiration in roots themselves after the beginning of anaerobiosis is slow (cf. 172).

REGULATION

A characteristic feature of the nitrate metabolism in higher plants is its susceptibility to a range of environmental conditions. It has been established that light, drought, mineral nutrition, hormonal treatment, plant age, and genetic composition all influence the capacity of nitrate reduction. In most of these cases it appears that the control of nitrate reduction is mediated through a regulation of the enzyme nitrate reductase.

Nitrate reductase is the logical point to effect regulation of the input of reduced nitrogen for the plant because it is (a) the first enzyme in the pathway; (b) the rate limiting step; (c) substrate inducible; and (d) relatively unstable (high turnover rate). Further, the toxic effects of excess levels of nitrite and ammonium ions also indicate the desirability of regulating their production.

Substrate induction. Nitrate.—Evidence that nitrate reductase is inducible by nitrate has been provided by several workers (2–4, 15, 25, 52, 62, 78, 145, 151). A feature of these observations is that different levels of nitrate are required for optimum induction in different species (15) and in some cases high concentrations of nitrate are needed. These differences probably indicate differences in rate of uptake between species because with a given species the level of enzyme is dependent, within limits, upon the concentration and rate of supply of nitrate to the tissue (15).

The induction of nitrate reductase in various tissue in response to inducers is related to maturation and age (1, 3, 74, 78, 164). In general, the ability to induce nitrate reductase is related to the capacity for protein synthesis, and increasing maturity is associated with a decreased nitrate reductase inducibility. It is not clear whether the change in inducibility with age is directly associated with a decreased capacity for protein synthesis or due to an accumulation of soluble nitrogenous products which specifically repress the synthesis of nitrate reductase. The reduced capacity for induction which occurs with increasing age is not an irreversible process. Wallace (158) and Carr & Pate (26) have shown that there is a resurgence of nitrate reductase activity in old leaves remaining on plants after partial defoliation or detopping. Such leaves frequently contain high nitrate before defoliation and thus the increased induction cannot be interpreted as being associated with an increased delivery of inducer following defoliation or detopping. It may be that the acceleration of synthesis of nitrate reductase is associated with an increased availability of soluble precursors which facilitates the synthesis of proteins. There is certainly a requirement for an adequate level of precursors for protein and nucleic acid synthesis before induction of nitrate reductase can occur. Schrader (127) has shown with corn seedlings that appreciable induction of nitrate reductase by nitrate, in short-term experiments, can only be shown if the seedlings have been grown in ammonia containing medium. The ammonia grown seedlings, although lacking nitrate reductase, had a higher nucleic acid, protein, soluble nucleotide, and amino acid content than the water controls and induced readily on transfer to nitrate. Boutard (19), using nitrogen deficient etiolated barley seedlings, indicated that nitrate reductase activity was present in seedlings cultured in distilled water and the activity was predominantly associated with roots. Addition of nitrate caused an increase in nitrate reductase activity in the leaves and a decline in the roots. The increase in nitrate reductase, which was much smaller than that observed in corn, was greater in illuminated barley seedlings than in those maintained in darkness. The data of Boutard (19) is analogous to that reported by Wallace & Pate (159) for pea seedlings receiving minimal nitrate.

Ammonium or nitrite ions did not induce nitrate reductase in cauliflower (3) or corn seedlings (15); however, these ions were reported to induce (directly or indirectly) the enzyme in radish cotyledons (74). Paradoxically, negligible levels of nitrate reductase were found in cotyledons from radish seedlings cultured on nitrite for 7 days.

Induction of nitrate reductase by nitrate is followed (3 hrs) by the appearance of nitrite reductase, whereas no lag period is noted if nitrite is used as the inducer (74). This work, in conjunction with the independent induction and regulation of nitrate and nitrite reductases in *Lemna* (137), suggests that synthesis of the two enzymes is not coordinate.

Molybdenum.—It has been demonstrated (1–4, 25, 62) that in molybdenum-deficient plants grown in the presence of nitrate, molybdenum can serve as an inducer for nitrate reductase. Since no increase in enzyme activity could be induced by adding molybdenum to cell-free extracts of deficient plants (3), it appears that the metal is involved in the induction process and is not merely activating pre-existing protein. Furthermore, the induction of nitrate reductase by molybdenum shows the same sensitivity to inhibitors of protein synthesis as does induction by nitrate (4).

Light.—The level of nitrate reductase in leaf tissue varies diurnally (53) and is influenced by intensity of illumination (15, 53, 124). The mode of operation of light in controlling nitrate reductase is complex. However, the data of Candela et al. (25) and Hageman & Flesher (52) clearly indicate that light influences the level of the enzyme per se. Thus, extracts from plants exposed to increasing periods of darkness show a progressive decrease in nitrate reducing ability (even though adequate electron donor is present in the assay medium) which is restored on subsequent illumination (25, 52). It is difficult to delineate the action of light in controlling the level of nitrate reductase. Beevers et al. (15) demonstrated that light was not an absolute requirement for induction of nitrate reductase in green leaf tissue as long as sufficient nitrate was present in the induction medium. Furthermore, the induction of nitrate reductase in nongreen tissue (42, 46, 141, 157) indicates that light is not a prerequisite for induction. Beevers et al. (15) indicated that illumination increased the uptake of nitrate into corn seedlings and suggested that this stimulated uptake could account for the effect of light on induction. A similar conclusion for the effect of light on nitrate utilization had been made by Warburg & Negelein (163). This conclusion is supported by the observations of Hope & Walker (69), MacRobbie & Dainty (98), and Nagai & Tazawa (105) of changed permeability of cell membranes following illumination. However, it is recognized that some of the stimulating effect of light on induction of nitrate reductase may be associated with the increased protein synthesis occurring after illumination (143). In contrast to the observations with corn and radish (15), Kannangara & Woolhouse (78) indicate that there is an absolute and direct requirement for photosynthetic CO_2 fixation for the induction of nitrate reductase in leaves of *Perilla*. It will be of interest to see if *Perilla* tissue can induce nitrate reductase in the dark in the presence of sufficient nitrate. Another possible function of light in induction may lie in its influence on redox potential in leaf tissue. Showe & DeMoss (136) have demonstrated that induction of nitrate reductase in *Escherichia coli* is dependent upon a reductive environment in the cell. A generally more reduced state of leaf cells following illumination (110) may account for the observed greater induction following illumination.

Regulation of nitrate reductase by endogenous metabolites.—The failure to demonstrate the occurrence of appreciable nitrate reductase in extracts from tissues containing nitrate—e.g., plants grown under shaded conditions (53) or mature leaves (26, 180)—can be attributed to a variety of causes. It is possible that the nitrate which is accumulated is maintained in the vacuoles and in this location cannot function as an inducer. A lowered capacity for protein synthesis in shaded or more mature tissue could also contribute to a failure of induction. Alternatively, under shaded conditions or in older tissue nitrate metabolism may be impaired due to a depletion of photosynthetically produced electron donors and ATP. Thus intermediate products of nitrate metabolism might accumulate and repress induction of nitrate reductase. End product repression of nitrate reductase has been demonstrated with *Neurospora* (85) and *Chlorella* (104). However, the primary metabolites of nitrate reduction, nitrite or ammonia, do not inhibit or suppress the induction of nitrate reductase in higher plants (3, 15, 25, 74).

Filner (46) demonstrated that casein hydrolysates and 11 amino acids, added individually, would repress the synthesis of nitrate reductase of cultured tobacco pith cells. Arginine or lysine would counteract the repressive action of any of the 11 amino acids, when tested in matched pairs. In like manner, cysteine and isoleucine were effective "derepressors" except when added with methionine or alanine. He also reported (46) that since the casein hydrolysate repressed induction in proportion to its ability to meet the nitrogen needs of the cells, the repression by the individual amino acids does not appear to be consequence of toxic growth effects. Smith & Thompson (139) recently reported that when 20 protein amino acids, orinithine, citrulline, urea, and ammonium ion were tested as regulators of nitrate reductase in *Chlorella,* only arginine, lysine, leucine, glutamate, and the compounds named above were effective in suppressing induction. While it is possible that the first five compounds were providing ammonium ions, which would effect repression (139), leucine and glutamate would appear to be unique. None of these compounds inhibited nitrate reductase activity.

In contrast, most of the compounds used by Filner (46) and Smith &

Thompson (139), as well as other compounds, were not effective in inhibiting nitrate reductase induction in excised corn seedlings or radish cotyledons (15, 130). Of several secondary (phenylpropanes and derivatives) metabolites of nitrogen metabolism tested, only coumarin, *trans*-cinnamate, and *trans*-o-hydroxycinnamate inhibited induction of nitrate reductase (130). Since these compounds inhibited protein synthesis in general, they cannot be considered as specific co-repressors of nitrate reductase activity. Carbamyl phosphate was shown to inhibit nitrate reductase in *Chlorella* (149). Other work demonstrated that carbamyl phosphate and its chemical derivative cyanate were shown to be competitive inhibitors of nitrate reductase and not co-repressors (130).

Induction, de novo *synthesis, and decay of nitrate reductase.*—The rapid fluctuations of nitrate reductase activity that occur daily (53) and seasonally (180), when plants are placed in the dark (25, 52), or exposed to heat or drought (178), indicate an effective *in vivo* regulatory mechanism. Obviously, fluctuations in activity could be brought about by changes in relative rates of synthesis or activation and breakdown or deactivation. Thus an increased activity could be due to a decreased breakdown or to an increased activation or synthesis; conversely, a decreased activity could be associated with an increased breakdown or deactivation or with decreased synthesis. The inhibition of induction of nitrate reductase by actinomycin D, cycloheximide (2, 4, 15, 145), L-azetidine-2-carboxylate (64), and a range of substituted amino acids and bases (15, 67, 68) constitutes the best evidence that increase in activity during induction is due to *de novo* synthesis of the enzyme rather than activation. These results should be interpreted with some caution. While these studies show that a prerequisite for induction of nitrate reductase is a normal RNA and protein synthesis, they do not demonstrate conclusively *de novo* synthesis of the enzyme. In fact, thus far all attempts to demonstrate *de novo* synthesis have been inconclusive (15, 73). These failures are attributable to (*a*) the inability to isolate the enzyme in pure form which precludes finger printing and demonstration of uniform incorporation of label; (*b*) the possibility that nitrate is not a specific inducer for nitrate reductase but rather stimulates a gamut of activities (73); and (*c*) the fact that during the normal course (3 to 5 hr) of induction, especially with chlorophyllous tissue, the newly synthesized amino acids dilute and mask incorporation of exogenously labeled amino acids.

It is not known whether the enzyme is only inactivated, completely destroyed, or both, with changes in environment that lead to a loss of nitrate reductase activity. For example, when plants or leaves containing nitrate are transferred to the dark, there is a rapid decline in nitrate reductase activity (15, 25, 52, 78). In contrast, nitrite reductase activity shows a much less rapid decline (74, 132). A similar decline in nitrate reductase activity occurs if nitrate grown seedlings are transferred to a nitrate free medium (15, 132). Schrader et al. (132) demonstrated that in the presence of nitrate and cycloheximide (to inhibit protein synthesis), nitrate reductase activity declined at a rate which permitted an estimated enzyme half-life of about 4 hr. A similar rate of enzyme depletion was observed when seedlings preinduced with nitrate were transferred to a nitrate free medium, but without cycloheximide. Kannangara & Woolhouse (78) found that the rate of decline in nitrate reductase activity in the light in the absence of CO_2 (a condition which they state prevents nitrate reductase induction) was similar to that observed when plants were transferred to darkness. Thus it appears (78, 132) that the enzyme is continuously declining in activity, but in the presence of light or sufficient nitrate or both, this decline is more than counterbalanced by the apparent synthesis of new enzyme. It is not known whether the decreased enzyme activity of extracts from plants placed in the dark or depleted of nitrate is due to enzyme degradation, or partial inactivation due to change in enzyme configuration in the absence of substrate, or loss of essential prosthetic groups.

Genetic regulation.—It has been shown that corn inbreds and hybrids differed widely (up to fivefold) in their seasonal level of nitrate reductase and that the level of activity was under genetic control (179). Commercial corn inbreds were used (131, 164, 165, 179) and all genotypes used had the capacity to produce nitrate reductase. Thus it should be emphasized that in corn the genetic control studied is over the level of activity and not concerned with the number of structural genes involved in the synthesis of the enzyme as reported by others (28, 140) for microorganisms. A subsequent study demonstrated that by proper combination of inbred lines, followed by selection based on enzyme assay, a hybrid could be developed with a high, medium, or low level of nitrate reductase activity (131). One other aspect of the corn studies was the finding that certain F_1 hybrids obtained by crossing inbreds with low (relative) levels possessed a heterotic level of nitrate reductase activity. This superiority in ability to reduce nitrate existed from seedling stage to maturity. Further investigations of this phenomenon with two corn inbreds and their progeny (F_1, F_2, F_3, F_4 generations) indicate that the level of activity of this material was under control of a two-gene system (164, 165). Whether this control of level of activity is due to different rates of synthesis or decay cannot be stated at this time. In these experiments, inducer (NO_3^-) levels in the tissue were not considered to be the causal factor in the regulation of the enzyme level. Inducer level could be a regulating factor since ap Griffith (10) has found that different grass strains possess different nitrate levels; unfortunately, nitrate reductase levels were not measured in these grasses.

Marked variations in levels of nitrate reductase have also been observed among several varieties of cauliflower (3) and with various wheat genotypes (33, 41). The work with wheat also indicates a relatively simple genetic control system.

That this genetic control is real and of practical significance was established with wheat by showing that the seasonal input of reduced nitrogen to the plant, computed on an acreage basis from the enzyme assay, was related in a linear manner to the protein accumulated in the vegetation and grain or grain alone (33, 41). This work with wheat and corn provides an initial step in the establishment of guidelines for breeding plants with genetically controlled potential for metabolic activities and their products.

Hormonal effects.—As early as 1950, studies revealed that several broad-leaf weed species (142) and sugar beets (171) accumulated nitrate when treated with herbicidal levels of 2,4-dichlorophenoxyacetate (2,4-D). In contrast, no record of nitrate accumulation has been reported for plants of the Gramineae family, similarly treated. An explanation for this divergence in response was reported by Beevers et al. (14). They found that nitrate reductase activity was decreased in cucumber plants sprayed with 2,4-D solutions, while the opposite effect was noted with corn seedlings. The changes in enzyme activity were positively correlated with changes in protein content for both species. Nitrate content varied inversely with enzyme activity. The results obtained with growth chamber plants were reproducible, while much greater variability was encountered when the plants were grown under field conditions.

Taylor (152, 153) was among the first to find that sub-herbicidal levels of 2,4-D would increase dry weight accumulation of plants. Subsequently, Wort (174, 175) applied mixtures of 2,4-D and micronutrients as foliar dusts and observed increases in growth rates and yields for several crop plants. These treatments have not been widely adopted commercially because of the variability of results obtained from season to season and with location.

Huffaker et al. (70) found that the isopropyl ester of 2,4-D, supplemented with iron salts or chelates, would increase grain yields of barley and wheat when applied at appropriate stages of plant development. With these treatments, the percentage of protein in the grain was increased in barley but not in wheat. However, if the isooctyl ester was used in conjunction with Fe-diethylenetriaminepentaacetate as the spray treatment for wheat, grain yields were depressed slightly, but protein content was significantly increased. Treatment of field beans with the isopropyl ester and micronutrients increased bean yields significantly. The major problem encountered in this work, especially with beans, was predicting the proper concentration, time of application, and the interaction with environment that would insure beneficial results. Similar problems have been encountered in effecting efficient weed control with herbicides (102).

Recently, Tweedy et al. (154) observed that simazin (2-chloro-4,6-bis-ethylamino-s-triazine) increased growth rates and nitrogen content of tolerant plants. They found the effects were more pronounced if the plants were cultured on suboptimal levels of nitrate or grown at low temperatures. These changes were associated with increased nitrate reductase activity, and plants cultured on ammonium salts did not respond in a similar manner with treatment. Further studies with peas and rye grown in growth chambers confirmed and extended these observations [Ries et al. (119)]. Field trials where six different plant species were treated with subherbicidal levels of simazin were reported to show that appropriate treatments increased total crude protein production per acre from 10 to 52 per cent (120). It was stated that the simazin treatment enhanced uptake of nitrate from the media. The data indicated that in some instances the nitrate content of treated tissue was higher. Since protein content was measured by a Kjeldahl procedure which could reduce a portion of the nitrate present in the tissue, some of the protein values, especially for the forages, are questionable. Again, as with 2,4-D treatments, the effects on growth, yield, and protein content were variable for a given crop and simazin level applied, depending on environment.

It is of interest that in induction studies with seedlings or mature corn leaves and radish cotyledons no enhancement has been observed by additions of indoleacetic acid, various cytokinins and gibberellins, or 2,4-D to the induction medium (unpublished work of this laboratory). Varner (157) reported that gibberellic acid did not stimulate the induction of nitrate reductase by nitrate in barley aleurone layers.

The major conclusions for this section are that (a) the enhancement of yields and protein content achieved with sub-lethal levels of herbicides emphasizes the role of nitrate reductase in maximizing grain yields with high protein content; (b) nitrate reductase activity is interwoven with metabolism as a whole; (c) hormonal and herbicidal effects on nitrate reductase are probably indirect through changes in overall metabolism; (d) the application of herbicides and related compounds to achieve enhanced yields and protein production offer promise but are developing slowly because of the complexity of the system.

Concluding Remarks

Since the appearance of Kessler's review in 1964 (81), additional information on the enzymes and mechanisms of nitrate assimilation has been published. Most interesting in this respect has been the demonstration of the existence of nitrite reductase and its physiological cofactor, ferredoxin, in leaf tissue. Thus, there is now evidence for the complete sequence of enzymes capable of converting nitrate to ammonia. The nature of the precise mechanism of reduction of nitrite remains to be elucidated. Current data suggest that nitrite reductase affects the transfer of six electrons at one enzyme surface in converting nitrite to ammonia, a disturbing phenomenon from the standpoint of thermodynamics and kinetics. In contrast, knowledge concerning nitrite metabolism in nonphotosynthetic tissues is meager, and future investigations into this area are warranted.

Although conflicting evidence has been presented as to the intracellular localization of nitrate reductase in leaf tissue, recent findings that link triosephosphate catabolism to nitrate reduction favors the cytoplasmic location. This work also offers an explanation for the enhanced reduction of nitrate in the light and the requirement for CO_2. Current evidence also suggests that the NADH-dependent nitrate reductase is the most prevalent form in *in vivo* leaf tissue. However, the induction of a NADPH-dependent enzyme achieved by exogenous carbohydrates suggests the need for additional work to determine if there are two separate enzymes or one enzyme with the ability to use both cofactors.

Nitrate assimilation in the roots appears to make only a limited contribution to the nitrogenous components of the mature plant. However, in early seedling growth, or under conditions of nitrogen deficiency, the capacity of the roots to reduce nitrate is probably of major importance. In the presence of adequate nitrate, it appears that the nitrate reduction occurs predominantly in the aerial portion of the plant.

The inducible nature of nitrate reductase, and the dependence of nitrate reductase level on substrate level, provides the plant with an efficient mechanism of controlling the input of reduced nitrogen and growth. In this context, field experiments have demonstrated that in wheat, each increment of fertilizer nitrogen applied over and above that usually considered optimal for cultural practices is associated with an increase in nitrate reductase level and protein content of the plant. Such results are encouraging in that they indicate an increased potential for food and protein production through improved management of fertilizers. The report of genetic control of nitrate reductase, and the association of high enzyme activities with increased grain protein production, indicates the possibilities of a biochemical approach to plant breeding. Such biochemically improved varieties should be able to utilize applied fertilizers with maximum efficiency. Furthermore, an understanding of the mechanism of nitrate utilization should allow for a more efficient use of nitrogenous fertilizers and minimize detrimental contamination of the environment.

LITERATURE CITED

1. Afridi, M. M. R. K., *Some Aspects of Induced Formation of Nitrate Reductase in Plants* (Doctoral thesis, Univ. Bristol, Bristol, England, 1960)
2. Afridi, M. M. R. K., Hewitt, E. J., *Life Sci.*, **1**, 287–95 (1962)
3. Afridi, M. M. R. K., Hewitt, E. J., *J. Exptl. Botany*, **15**, 251–71 (1964)
4. Afridi, M. M. R. K., Hewitt, E. J., *ibid.*, **16**, 628–45 (1965)
5. Ahmad, J., Morris, I., *Arch. Mikrobiol.*, **56**, 219–26 (1967)
6. Ahmad, J., Morris, I., *Biochim. Biophys. Acta*, **162**, 32–38 (1968)
7. Altschul, A. M., Yatsu, L. Y., Ory, R. L., Engleman, E. M., *Ann. Rev. Plant Physiol.*, **17**, 113–36 (1966)
8. Anacker, W. F., Stoy, V., *Biochem. Z.*, **330**, 141–59 (1958)
9. Anderson, L. A., Smillie, R. M., *Biochem. Biophys. Res. Commun.*, **23**, 535–39 (1966)
10. ap Griffith, G., *Nature*, **182**, 1099–1100 (1958)
11. Bassham, J. A., Calvin, M., *The Path of Carbon in Photosynthesis*, 104 (Prentice-Hall, Englewood Cliffs, New Jersey, 1957)
12. Beevers, L., Flesher, D., Hageman, R. H., *Biochim. Biophys. Acta*, **89**, 453–64 (1964)
13. Beevers, L., Flesher, D., Hageman, R. H. (Unpublished work)
14. Beevers, L., Peterson, D. M., Shannon, J. C., Hageman, R. H., *Plant Physiol.*, **38**, 675–79 (1963)
15. Beevers, L., Schrader, L. E., Flesher, D., Hageman, R. H., *Plant Physiol.*, **40**, 691–98 (1965)
16. Bollard, E. G., *Australian J. Biol. Sci.*, **10**, 279–87 (1957)
17. Bond, G., *Ann. Rev. Plant Physiol.*, **18**, 107–26 (1967)
18. Bonner, J., Varner, J. E., Eds., *Plant Biochemistry* (Academic Press, 1054 pp., 1965)
19. Boutard, J., *Physiol. Vegetale*, **6**, 105–23 (1966)
20. Bundel, A. A., Kretovich, W. L., Borovikova, N. V., *Plant Physiol. (USSR)*, **11**, 25–30 (1964) (Eng. transl.)
21. Bundel, A. A., Kretovich, V. L., Prokosheva, G. A., *ibid.*, **12**, 854–61 (1965) (Eng. transl.)
22. Burris, R. H., *Ann. Rev. Plant Physiol.*, **10**, 301–28 (1959)
23. Burström, H., *Ann. Agr. Coll. Sweden*, **11**, 1–50 (1943)
24. Butt, V., Beevers, H., *Biochem. J.*, **80**, 21–27 (1961)
25. Candela, M. C., Fisher, E. G., Hewitt, E. J., *Plant Physiol.*, **32**, 280–88 (1957)
26. Carr, D. J., Pate, J. S., *Aspects of the Biology of Aging*, SEB Symposium 21 (Cambridge University Press, 559–600, 1967)
27. Coupé, M., Champigny, M. L., Moyse, A., *Physiol. Vegetale*, **5**, 271–91 (1967)
28. Cove, D. J., Pateman, J. A., *Nature*, **198**, 262–63 (1963)
29. Cresswell, C. F., *An investigation into the Nitrate, Nitrite and Hydroxylomine Metabolism in Higher Plants* (Doctoral thesis, Univ. Bristol, Bristol, England, 1961)
30. Cresswell, C. F., Hageman, R. H., Hewitt, E. J., *Biochem. J.*, **83**, 38 (1962)
31. Cresswell, C. F., Hageman, R. H., Hewitt, E. J., Hucklesby, D. P., *Biochem. J.*, **94**, 40–53 (1965)
32. Cresswell, C. F., Hewitt, E. J., *Biochem. Biophys. Res. Commun.*, **3**, 544–48 (1960)
33. Croy, L. I., *Nitrate Reductase in Wheat and its Relationship to Grain Protein and Yield* (Doctoral thesis, Univ. Illinois, Urbana, Ill., 1967)
34. Czygan, F. C., *Planta*, **60**, 225–42 (1963)
35. Davis, E. A., *Plant Physiol.*, **28**, 539–44 (1953)
36. Del Campo, F. F., Paneque, A., Ramirez, J. M., Losada, M., *Biochim. Biophys. Acta*, **66**, 450–52 (1963)
37. Del Campo, F. F., Ramirez, J. M., Paneque, A., Losada, M., *Biochem. Biophys. Res. Commun.*, **22**, 547–53 (1966)
38. Dubinina, I. M., *Plant Physiol. (USSR)*, **12**, 862–70 (1965) (Eng. transl.)
39. Eckerson, S. H., *Botan. Gaz.*, **77**, 377–90 (1924)
40. Eckerson, S. H., *Contrib. Boyce Thompson Inst.*, **3**, 405–12 (1931)
41. Eilrich, G. L., *Nitrate Reductase in Wheat and its Relationship to Grain Protein Production as Affected by Genotype and Spring*

Application of Calcium Nitrate (Doctoral thesis, Univ. Illinois, Urbana, Ill., 1968)

42. Elsner, J. E., Hageman, R. H. (Unpublished work)

43. Evans, H. J., Hall, H. S., *Science*, **122**, 922–23 (1955)

44. Evans, H. J., Nason, A., *Plant Physiol.*, **28**, 233–54 (1953)

45. Fewson, C. A., Nicholas, D. J. D., *Nature*, **190**, 2–7 (1961)

46. Filner, P., *Biochim. Biophys. Acta*, **118**, 299–310 (1965)

47. Fowden, L., *Ann. Rev. Plant Physiol.*, **18**, 85–106 (1967)

48. Galston, A. W., in *The Life of the Green Plant* (Prentice Hall, Englewood Cliffs, New Jersey, 116, 1961)

49. Garrett, R. H., Nason, A., *Proc. Natl. Acad. Sci. U. S.*, **58**, 1603–10 (1967)

50. Grasmanis, V. O., Nicholas, D. J. D., *Phytochemistry*, **6**, 217–18 (1967)

51. Hageman, R. H., Cresswell, C. F., Hewitt, E. J., *Nature*, **193**, 247–50 (1962)

52. Hageman, R. H., Flesher, D., *Plant Physiol.*, **35**, 700–8 (1960)

53. Hageman, R. H., Flesher, D., Gitter, A., *Crop Sci.*, **1**, 201–4 (1961)

54. Hageman, R. H., Waygood, E. R., *Plant Physiol.*, **34**, 396–400 (1959)

55. Hall, D. O., Whatley, F. R., in *Enzyme Cytology* (Roodyn, D. B., Ed., Academic Press, N.Y., 181–237, 1967)

56. Hannay, J. W., Fletcher, B. H., Street, H. E., *New Phytologist*, **58**, 142–54 (1959)

57. Hattori, A., *Plant Cell Physiol.*, **3**, 355–69 (1962)

58. Hattori, A., Myers, J., *Plant Physiol.*, **41**, 1031–36 (1966)

59. Heber, U., Pon, N. G., Heber, M., *Plant Physiol.*, **38**, 355–60 (1963)

60. Hewitt, E. J., *Ann. Rev. Plant Physiol.*, **2**, 25–52 (1951)

61. Hewitt, E. J., *Nature*, **180**, 1020–22 (1957)

62. Hewitt, E. J., Afridi, M. M. R. K., *Nature*, **183**, 57–58 (1959)

63. Hewitt, E. J., Betts, G. F., *Biochem. J.*, **89**, 20 (1963)

64. Hewitt, E. J., Cutting, C. V., Eds., *Recent Aspects of Nitrogen Metabolism in Plants* (Academic Press, N.Y., 280 pp., 1968)

65. Hewitt, E. J., Hucklesby, D. P., Betts, G. F., in *Recent Aspects of Nitrogen Metabolism in Plants* (See Ref. 64)

66. Hewitt, E. J., Nicholas, D. J. D., *Modern Methods of Plant Analysis*, **VII** (Liskens, H. F., Sanwal, B. D., Tracey, M. V., Eds., Springer Verlag, Berlin, 67–172, 735, 1964)

67. Hewitt, E. J., Notton, B. A., *Biochem. J.*, **101**, 391 (1966)

68. Hewitt, E. J., Notton, B. A., Afridi, M. M. R. K., *Plant Cell Physiol.*, **8**, 385–97 (1967)

69. Hope, A. B., Walker, N. A., *Australian J. Biol. Sci.*, **13**, 277–91 (1960)

70. Huffaker, R. C., Miller, M. D., Baghott, K. G., Smith, F. L., Schaller, C. W., *Crop Sci.*, **7**, 17–19 (1967)

71. Huzisige, H., Satoh, K., *Botan. Mag. (Tokyo)*, **74**, 178–85 (1961)

72. Huzisige, H., Satoh, K., Tanaka, K., Hayasida, T., *Plant Cell Physiol. Tokyo*, **4**, 307–22 (1964)

73. Ingle, J., *Biochem. J.*, **108**, 715–24 (1968)

74. Ingle, J., Joy, K. W., Hageman, R. H., *Biochem. J.*, **100**, 577–88 (1966)

75. Jensen, R. G., Bassham, J. A., *Proc. Natl. Acad. Sci. U. S.*, **56**, 1095–1101 (1966)

76. Joy, K. W., Hageman, R. H., *Biochem. J.*, **100**, 263–73 (1966)

77. Kastle, A. T., Elvove, E., *Am. Chem. J.*, **31**, 606–14 (1904)

78. Kannangara, C. G., Woolhouse, H. W., *New Phytologist*, **66**, 553–61 (1967)

79. Kemp, J. D., Atkinson, D. E., Ehret, A., Lazzarini, R. A., *J. Biol. Chem.*, **238**, 3466–71 (1963)

80. Kessler, E., *Flora*, **140**, 1–38 (1953)

81. Kessler, E., *Ann. Rev. Plant Physiol.*, **15**, 57–72 (1964)

82. Kessler, E., Bucker, W., *Planta*, **55**, 512–24 (1960)

83. Kessler, E., Czygan, F. C., *Experientia*, **19**, 89–90 (1963)

84. Kessler, E., Czygan, F. C., *Arch. Mikrobiol.*, **60**, 282–91 (1968)

85. Kinsky, S. C., *J. Bacteriol.*, **82**, 898–904 (1961)

86. Klepper, L., *Generation of Reduced Nicotinamide Adenine Dinucleotide for Nitrate Reduction in Green Leaf Tissue* (Doctoral thesis, Univ. Illinois, Urbana, Ill., 1969)

87. Klepper, L., Hageman, R. H., *Plant Physiol.*, **44**, 110–14 (1969)

88. Kretovich, W. L., *Ann. Rev. Plant Physiol.*, **16**, 141–54 (1965)

89. Losada, M., Paneque, A., *Biochim.*

Biophys. Acta, **126,** 578–80 (1966)

90. Losada, M., Paneque, A., Ramirez, J. M., Del Campo, F. F., *Biochem. Biophys. Res. Commun.,* **10,** 298–303 (1963)

91. Losada, M., Paneque, A., Ramirez, J. M., Del Campo, F. F., in *Non-Haem Iron Proteins* (San Pietro, A., Ed., Antioch Press, Yellow Springs, Ohio, 211–220, 1965)

92. Losada, M., Paneque, A., Ramirez, T. M., Del Campo, F. F., *Biochim. Biophys. Acta,* **109,** 86–96 (1965)

93. Losada, M., Whatley, F. R., Arnon, D. I., *Nature,* **190,** 606–10 (1961)

94. Lazzarini, R. A., Atkinson, D. E., *J. Biol. Chem.,* **236,** 3330–35 (1961)

95. Machlis, L., Torrey, J. G., *Plants in Action* (Freeman, San Francisco, 119 pp., 1956)

96. Mans, R. J., *Ann. Rev. Plant Physiol.,* **18,** 127–46 (1967)

97. Maretzki, A., Dela Cruz, A., *Plant Cell Physiol.,* **8,** 605–11 (1967)

98. MacRobbie, E. A. C., Dainty, J., *Physiol. Plantarum,* **11,** 782–801 (1958)

99. McElroy, W. D., Glass, B., Eds., in *Inorganic Nitrogen Metabolism* (Johns Hopkins Press, Baltimore, 728 pp., 1956)

100. McKee, H. S., *Nitrogen Metabolism in Plants* (Oxford Univ. Press, Oxford, 728 pp., 1963)

101. Mendel, T. L., Visser, D. W., *Arch. Biochem. Biophys.,* **32,** 158–69 (1951)

102. Mitchell, J. W., *Proc. Northeast. Weed Control Conf., New York, 1948,* p. 207

103. Miflin, B. J., *Nature,* **214,** 1133–34 (1967)

104. Morris, I., Syrett, P. J., *Arch. Mikrobiol.,* **47,** 32–41 (1963)

105. Nagai, R., Tazawa, M., *Plant Cell Physiol.,* **3,** 323–29 (1962)

106. Nason, A., *Bacteriol. Rev.,* **26,** 16–41 (1962)

107. Nason, A., Abraham, R. G., Averbach, B. C., *Biochim. Biophys. Acta,* **15,** 159–61 (1954)

108. Nicholas, D. J. D., Nason, A., *J. Biol. Chem.,* **211,** 183–97 (1954)

109. Nightingale, G. T., *Botan. Rev.,* **3,** 85–174 (1937)

110. Ogren, W. L., Krogmann, D. W., *J. Biol. Chem.,* **240,** 4603–8 (1966)

111. Paneque, A., Aparicio, P. J., Catalina, L., Losada, M., *Biochim. Biophys. Acta,* **162,** 149–51 (1968)

112. Paneque, A., Del Campo, F. F., Losada, M., *Nature,* **198,** 90–91 (1963)

113. Paneque, A., Del Campo, F. F., Ramirez, J. M., Losada, M., *Biochim. Biophys. Acta,* **109,** 79–85 (1965)

114. Paneque, A., Losada, M., *Biochim. Biophys. Acta,* **128,** 202–4 (1966)

115. Paneque, A., Ramirez, J. M., Del Campo, F. F., Losada, M., *J. Biol. Chem.,* **239,** 1737–41 (1964)

116. Pate, J. S., in *Recent Aspects of Nitrogen Metabolism in Plants,* 219–40 (See Ref. 64)

117. Ramirez, J. M., Del Campo, F. F., Paneque, A., Losada, M., *Biochem. Biophys. Res. Commun.,* **15,** 297–302 (1964)

118. Ramirez, J. M., Del Campo, F. F., Paneque, A., Losada, M., *Biochim. Biophys. Acta,* **118,** 58–71 (1966)

119. Ries, S. K., Chmiel, H., Dilley, D. R., Filner, P., *Proc. Natl. Acad. Sci. U. S.,* **58,** 526–32 (1967)

120. Ries, S. K., Schweizer, C. J., Chmiel, H., *Biol. Sci.,* **18,** 205–8 (1968)

121. Ritenour, G. L., Joy, K. W., Bunning, J., Hageman, R. H., *Plant Physiol.,* **42,** 233–37 (1966)

122. Robbins, W. J., Schmidt, M. B., *Botan. Gaz.,* **99,** 671–728 (1938)

123. Roussos, G. G., Nason, A., *J. Biol. Chem.,* **235,** 2997–3007 (1960)

124. Sanderson, G. W., Cocking, E. C., *Plant Physiol.,* **39,** 416–22 (1964)

125. Sanderson, G. W., Cocking, E. C., *ibid.,* 423–31

126. San Pietro, A., Lang, H. M., *J. Biol. Chem.,* **231,** 211–9 (1958)

127. Schrader, L. E. (Unpublished work)

128. Schrader, L. E., Beevers, L., Hageman, R. H., *Biochem. Biophys. Res. Commun.,* **26,** 14–17 (1967)

129. Schrader, L. E., Hageman, R. H., *Agron. Abstr.,* 30 (1965)

130. Schrader, L. E., Hageman, R. H., *Plant Physiol.,* **42,** 1750–56 (1967)

131. Schrader, L. E., Peterson, D. M., Leng, E. R., Hageman, R. H., *Crop Sci.,* **6,** 169–73 (1966)

132. Schrader, L. E., Ritenour, G. L., Eilrich, G. L., Hageman, R. H., *Plant Physiol.,* **43,** 930–40 (1968)

133. Sheat, D. C. G., Fletcher, B. H., Street, H. E., *New Phytologist,* **58,** 128–41 (1959)

134. Shin, M., Arnon, D. I., *J. Biol. Chem.,* **240,** 1405–11 (1965)

135. Shin, M., Oda, Y., *Plant Cell Physiol.,* **7,** 643–50 (1966)

136. Showe, M. K., DeMoss, J. A., *J.*

Bacteriol., **95**, 1305–13 (1968)

137. Sims, A. P., Folkes, B. F., Bussey, A. H., in *Recent Aspects of Nitrogen Metabolism in Plants*, 91–114 (See Ref. 64)

138. Skinner, J. C., Street, H. E., *New Phytologist*, **53**, 44–67 (1964)

139. Smith, F. W., Thompson, J. F., *Plant Physiol.*, **43** (suppl.), 58 (1968)

140. Sorger, H. T., Giles, N. H., *Genetics*, **52**, 777–78 (1965)

141. Spencer, D., *Australian J. Biol. Sci.*, **12**, 181–91 (1959)

142. Stahler, L. M., Whitehead, E. I., *Science*, **112**, 749–51 (1950)

143. Stephenson, M. C., Thimann, K. V., Zamecnik, P. C., *Arch. Biochem. Biophys.*, **65**, 194–209 (1965)

144. Steward, F. C., Pollard, J. K., *Ann. Rev. Plant Physiol.*, **8**, 65–114 (1957)

145. Stewart, G. R., *Phytochemistry*, **7**, 1139–42 (1968)

146. Stocking, C. R., *Plant Physiol.*, **34**, 56–61 (1959)

147. Stoy, V., *Biochim. Biophys. Acta*, **21**, 395–97 (1956)

148. Strotmann, H., *Planta*, **73**, 376–80 (1967)

149. Syrett, P. J., Morris, I., *Biochim. Biophys. Acta*, **67**, 566–75 (1963)

150. Tagawa, K., Arnon, D. I., *Nature*, **195**, 537–43 (1962)

151. Tang, P. S., Wu, H. Y., *Nature*, **179**, 1355–56 (1957)

152. Taylor, D. L., *Botan. Gaz.*, **107**, 597–611 (1946)

153. Taylor, D. L., *ibid.*, 611–19

154. Tweedy, J. A., Ries, S. K., *Plant Physiol.*, **42**, 280–82 (1967)

155. Vaidyanathan, C. S., Street, H. E., *Nature*, **184**, 531–33 (1959)

156. Vanecko, S., Varner, J. E., *Plant Physiol.*, **30**, 388–90 (1955)

157. Varner, J. E., *Physiology and Biochemistry of Growth Regulators* (Runge Press, Ottawa, 1968)

158. Wallace, W. (Doctoral thesis, Univ. Belfast, Ireland, 1966)

159. Wallace, W., Pate, J. S., *Ann. Botany*, **29**, 655–67 (1965)

160. Wallace, W., Pate, J. S., *ibid.*, **31**, 213–28 (1967)

161. Walker, D. A., *Plant Physiol.*, **40**, 1157–61 (1965)

162. Walker, D. A., Hill, R., *Biochem. Biophys. Acta*, **131**, 330–38 (1967)

163. Warburg, O., Negelein, E., *Biochem. Z.*, **110**, 66–115 (1920)

164. Warner, R. L., *Inheritance of Nitrate Reductase Activity in Characterization of Nitrate Reductase in Zea mays L.* (Doctoral thesis, Univ. Illinois, Urbana, Ill., 1968)

165. Warner, R. L., Dudley, T. W., Lambert, R. J., Hageman, R. H., *Proc. Natl. Acad. Sci. U. S.* (In press)

166. Wessels, J. S. C., *Biochim. Biophys. Acta*, **36**, 264–65 (1959)

167. Wessels, J. S. C., *ibid.*, **38**, 195–96 (1960)

168. Wessels, J. S. C., *Proc. Intern. Congr. Biochem.*, *5th, Vol. VI*, 263–66, *Mechanism of Photosynthesis* (Tamiya, H., Ed., Pergamon, 1963)

169. White, P. R., *Plant Physiol.*, **8**, 489–508 (1933)

170. White, P. R., *A Handbook of Plant Tissue Culture* (Ronald Press, Lancaster, N.Y., 1943)

171. Willard, C. J., *Proc. N. Central Weed Control Conf., 1960*, 110–12

172. Willis, A. J., Yemm, E. W., *New Phytologist*, **54**, 163–81 (1955)

173. Wood, J. G., *Ann. Rev. Plant Physiol.*, **4**, 1–22 (1953)

174. Wort, D. J., *Proc. West Canada Weed Control Conf., 7th*, 93–101 (1953)

175. Wort, D. J., *Summaries of Papers, Intern. Congr. Crop Protection, 4th, Hamburg*, 70–71 (1957)

176. Yemm, E. W., Folkes, B. F., *Ann. Rev. Plant Physiol.*, **9**, 245–80 (1958)

177. Yemm, E. W., Willis, A. J., *New Phytologist*, **55**, 229–52 (1956)

178. Younis, M. A., Pauli, A. W., Mitchell, H. L., Stickler, F. C., *Crop Sci.*, **5**, 321–26 (1965)

179. Zieserl, J. F., Jr., Hageman, R. H., *Crop Sci.*, **2**, 512–15 (1962)

180. Zieserl, J. F., Jr., Rivenbark, W. L., Hageman, R. H., *Crop Sci.*, **3**, 27–32 (1963)

THE ANALYSIS OF PHOTOSYNTHESIS USING MUTANT STRAINS OF ALGAE AND HIGHER PLANTS[1]

By R. P. Levine

The Biological Laboratories, Harvard University, Cambridge, Massachusetts

Introduction

Major contributions to the understanding of biological processes have been made with the aid of mutant organisms in which the processes have been disrupted; the use of auxotrophic mutant strains of microorganisms to elucidate metabolic pathways is a classic example of this approach. Mutations that affect chloroplast structure, chlorophyll and carotenoid synthesis, synthesis of components of the photosynthetic electron transport chain, and synthesis of enzymes of the reductive pentose phosphate cycle are known to occur in higher plants and green algae, and it is the purpose of this review to describe how certain mutant strains have been used to study the mechanism of photosynthesis. This review will be particularly concerned with the nature and function of components of the photosynthetic electron transport chain as deduced from studies of mutant strains of green algae and higher plants having normal pigment content, and only secondarily will it consider mutant strains having gross abnormalities in either their chloroplast structure or amounts of pigment. Several excellent general reviews of photosynthesis have appeared recently (1, 2), and the material presented here should be considered as a special supplement to them rather than as an overall view of the subject.

In organisms in which genetic analysis is possible, it has been shown that mutations affecting photosynthesis are of both nuclear and extranuclear genes. Nuclear gene mutations show a classical Mendelian inheritance, whereas mutations of extranuclear genes usually show maternal inheritance. The plastom mutations of higher plants are examples that show maternal inheritance, and characteristically these mutations lead to marked changes in chloroplast structure and in the amount of chlorophyll.

The principal mutant strains to be considered in this review (Table I) have been obtained from the algae *Chlamydomonas reinhardi, Euglena gracilis,* and *Scenedesmus obliquus* and from the higher plants *Hordeum vulgare, Nicotiana tabacum,* and *Vicia faba.* The mutations in *C. reinhardi, H.*

[1] The literature survey for this review was completed in September 1968. Work in the author's laboratory was carried out with the support of research grants from the National Science Foundation and the National Institutes of Health.

vulgare, and *V. faba* are of nuclear genes. An extranuclear gene mutation of *N. tabacum* will be discussed. The genetics of the *Scenedesmus* mutations is unknown, and a knowledge of it depends upon further studies of the sexual phase in its life cycle (3). A sexual phase in the life cycle of *E. gracilis* has not been discovered. A discussion of the genetics of mutations affecting photosynthesis is beyond the scope of this review, and the reader is referred to the fine monograph by Kirk & Tilney-Bassett (4). In addition, a review concerned with the genetics of many of the mutations discussed below will appear elsewhere (5).

It must be pointed out that there are certain limitations to the study of photosynthesis with mutant organisms and that certain precautions must be taken in using mutant strains and in interpreting the data obtained from them. For example, several of the mutant strains of *C. reinhardi* and *S. obliquus* that cannot grow phototrophically are capable of carrying out some photosynthesis, as seen by their limited ability to fix carbon dioxide or to evolve oxygen (6, 7). The partial nature of these mutations can be attributed to one of several causes. First, the mutation may be "leaky," that is, a component or enzyme is synthesized which, although altered or perhaps changed in amount, can perform its function at something less than the

TABLE I

COMPONENTS AFFECTED IN MUTANT STRAINS OF ALGAE AND HIGHER PLANTS

Organism	Affected component	Reference
Chlamydomonas reinhardi		
ac-115	cytochrome 559 (Q?)	50, 51, 68
ac-141	cytochrome 559 (Q?)	50, 51, 68
ac-21	Unidentified	50, 51
ac-206	cytochrome 553	8
ac-208	plastocyanin	8
ac-80a	P-700	7
F-60	phosphoribulokinase	20
Euglena gracilis		
P$_4$	Q (?)	69
Scenedesmus obliquus		
No. 8	P-700	31, 32
No. 50	cytochrome 552	42
Hordeum vulgare		
strain without notation	chlorophyll *b*	108–112
Nicotiana tabacuum		
NC 95	?	16
Oenothera		
IIγ	Q (?)	70
Vicia faba		
strain without notation	ferredoxin or ferridoxin-NADP reductase (?)	27

wild-type rate; in this case, the possibility always exists that under certain environmental conditions the mutation will be fully expressed, whereas under other conditions its expression will be partial and thus resemble the wild-type strain. Second, in the absence of an active component of the normal photosynthetic pathway, the reaction may follow an alternative, yet less efficient, pathway—one that may be either repressed or inhibited in the wild-type organism. Third, the partial nature of the mutation may result from the presence of a suppressor mutation, a second, independently occurring, mutation whose effect is to restore at least part of the photosynthetic activity characteristic of the wild-type strain. Fortunately, the presence of suppressor mutations can be detected in organisms in which genetic analysis is feasible. Appropriate crosses will show a pattern of inheritance characteristic of the presence of two mutations: the mutation affecting photosynthesis and the suppressor mutation. Suppressor mutations that restore at least partial activity to several photosynthetically deficient mutant strains of *C. reinhardi* have been identified in this way (8, 9).

KINDS OF MUTATIONS AFFECTING PHOTOSYNTHESIS

Mutant organisms having abnormal pigment contents have been known for many years (4), but the first application of mutant strains to the study of the photosynthetic apparatus is probably Granick's (10) use of chlorophyll-deficient strains of *Chlorella* to study the biosynthesis of chlorophyll. Later, Davis (11) obtained normally-pigmented strains of *Chlorella* that were unable to grow phototrophically, and he showed that they had lost the ability to evolve oxygen by photosynthesis at the wild-type rate. His studies were not extended until 1960, when a technique was developed (12) to screen for normally pigmented mutant strains of unicellular algae that were unable to fix carbon dioxide by photosynthesis. This technique has been used successfully with *C. reinhardi* and *S. obliquus*. More recently, a detection procedure has been found for *C. reinhardi* that takes advantage of the high level of light-induced fluorescence found in colonies of mutant cells (13, 14).

Two classes of photosynthetic mutation can be recognized. In the first, the development of the chloroplast from the proplastid is arrested at some stage, and gross structural abnormalities—for example, the absence of a recognizable thylakoid system—are often evident with the electron microscope. Such grossly distorted chloroplasts are found, for example, in the plastom mutants of *Oenothera* (15) and *N. tabacum* (16) and in certain pigment-deficient higher plants (17). It is clearly difficult to investigate photosynthetic mechanisms in such organisms, since frequently large portions of the photosynthetic apparatus have either never been assembled or have been secondarily destroyed.

In the second class, the entire structural and biochemical apparatus of the chloroplast is present and intact, with the exception of, ideally, a single component which has been affected by the mutation of a single gene. This component could be an enzyme of the carbon reduction cycle of photosynthesis, a carrier molecule in the photosynthetic electron transport chain, or a factor required to couple photosynthetic phosphorylation to electron transport. Clearly, the ideal is often not met, for the presence of one molecule may be essential for the synthesis or the proper functional positioning of another. Moreover, the absence of certain molecular species may secondarily endow the chloroplast with a distinctive fine-structural phenotype. Hopefully, the use of mutant organisms will aid in revealing the nature of some of these intimate structural and functional relationships.

MUTATIONS AFFECTING ENZYMES OF PHOTOSYNTHETIC CARBON METABOLISM

Mutations affecting photosynthetic carbon metabolism are of interest in at least two respects. First, if a single gene mutation results in the loss of activity of a single enzyme of the pathway, and in turn there is a loss of the capacity to reduce carbon dioxide by photosynthesis, then it can be concluded that the enzyme in question is an essential one for photosynthesis. For example, the enzymes phosphoribulokinase and ribulose diphosphate carboxylase are unique components of the carbon reduction cycle of photosynthesis proposed by Calvin and his co-workers (18), and the correlation between mutation, loss of enzyme activity, and loss of carbon dioxide fixation would assure the role of these enzymes in photosynthesis. Second, enzymes of the cycle have been shown to occur in the chloroplast (19), and the location of their genetic determinants is of interest to the overall question of organelle heredity and autonomy.

To date, one mutant strain of *C. reinhardi* is known in which only photosynthetic carbon metabolism is affected. The mutant gene (F-60) segregates in a Mendelian fashion (20).

Cells of F-60 require sodium acetate for growth. They do not evolve oxygen or fix carbon dioxide by photosynthesis; however, reactions of the photosynthetic electron transport chain, such as the Hill reaction with DPIP (2,6-dichlorophenolindophenol) or NADP, the photoreduction of NADP with the ascorbate-DPIP couple, and the light-induced absorbance changes of cytochromes 553 and 559 and P700, occur as in the wild-type strain. There is no phosphoribulokinase activity, whereas the activities of other enzymes of photosynthetic carbon metabolism are comparable to those of the wild-type strain. The mutation probably lies in the structural gene for the enzyme, but proof for this depends in part upon the isolation and characterization of the mutant protein. Nevertheless, control of the synthesis of this chloroplast enzyme is vested in at least one nuclear gene.

MUTATIONS AFFECTING COMPONENTS OF THE PHOTOSYNTHETIC ELECTRON TRANSPORT CHAIN

Photosynthetic electron transport, defined in terms of the capacity of chloroplast fragments to photoreduce NADP in the presence of ferredoxin and ferredoxin-NADP reductase with water as the electron donor, has been shown to be blocked in mutant strains of *C. reinhardi* (7, 8, 21–23), *E. gra-*

cilis (24), *S. obliquus* (25, 26), and *V. faba* (27). Each mutant strain is characterized by having an insignificant rate of NADP reduction with water as the electron donor, indicating that there is a block in the photosynthetic electron transport chain, and it has been shown that transport is blocked in certain of the mutant strains because a component, present and active in the wild-type strain, is either missing or inactive.

P-700.—A form of chlorophyll showing a light-induced absorbance change having a maximum at 700 nm (28) and called P-700 is considered to be the reaction center of photochemical system I (PS I) (29). Its activity, detected by its light- and chemically-induced oxidation (29) and by its electron spin resonance signal (30), is missing from a mutant strain of *S. obliquus* known as No. 8 (31, 32) and from *ac-80a,* a mutant strain of *C. reinhardi* (7).

According to the series formulation for photosynthetic electron transport (33), mutant strains lacking an active P-700 should be capable of carrying out reactions sensitized by photochemical system II (PS II) but not those sensitized by photochemical system I (PS I) or those depending upon both systems. Mutant No. 8 of *S. obliquus* and *ac-80a* of *C. reinhardi* can carry out the Hill reaction with oxidants such as *p*-benzoquinone, DPIP, and potassium ferricyanide at rates that are significantly higher than for mutant strains in which electron flow is blocked close to PS II. However, they are incapable of carrying out the photoreduction of NADP with either water or the ascorbate-DPIP couple as the electron donor, and have lost the capacity to fix carbon dioxide by photoreduction when adapted to an atmosphere of hydrogen. The photoreduction of NADP with water as the electron donor depends upon the operation of both photochemical systems, whereas the photoreduction of NADP with the ascorbate-DPIP couple and the fixation of carbon dioxide by photoreduction depend upon PS I alone.

The series formulation also predicts that in the absence of an active P-700 the light-induced reduction of components lying between the systems will occur but that their light-induced oxidation will not. This prediction has been borne out in studies with *ac-80a* of *C. reinhardi* in which the light-induced reduction but not the light-induced oxidation of cytochromes 559 and 553 has been detected (7). These studies also show that the cytochromes must lie on the PS II side of P-700.

Cyclic photosynthetic phosphorylation is independent of PS II and, as expected, cyclic photosynthetic phosphorylation catalyzed by PMS (phenazine methosulfate) is missing from the mutant strains lacking an active P-700 (7, 26). It is of interest that the P-700-less mutant strain of *C. reinhardi* can carry out noncyclic photosynthetic phosphorylation coupled to the reduction of potassium ferricyanide (7). This observation reveals that there is at least one site for phosphorylation on the PS II side of P-700, as suggested by Hill & Bendall in the original statement of the series formulation (33). Further discussion of this observation will be found in the section of the review dealing with photosynthetic phosphorylation (see page 533).

The results obtained with both mutant No. 8 of *S. obliquus* and *ac-80a* of *C. reinhardi* support the contention that P-700 is essential in photosynthesis; it is required for reactions dependent upon the operation of PS I. Some of the observations made with mutant No. 8 of *S. obliquus* have been used in an effort to define the relationship between P-700 and C-705, a pigment associated with PS I (34, 35) and detected by absorption, derivative absorption, and fluorescence spectra at −196°C. In contrast to P-700, C-705 does not show light-induced bleaching at −196° C, and in terms of total chlorophyll its concentration is at least 10 times greater than that of P-700 (35, 36). Mutant No. 8 of *S. obliquus* lacks the C-705 absorption band seen at low temperature (37). Thus the absence of an active P-700, as described above, is correlated with the absence of C-705. Kok (32) has offered two hypotheses to explain the relationship between the two pigments. One hypothesis assumes that C-705, not P-700, is affected in the mutant strain. Kok estimates that there are 20 C-705 molecules for each P-700 molecule and suggests that the 20 C-705 molecules could act to collect light energy and to transfer it to one molecule of P-700. The absence of P-700 activity in mutant No. 8 (i.e., no light- or chemically induced oxidation and no rapid, light-induced electron spin resonance signal) can then be explained by assuming that in the absence of C-705 there is no energy transfer to P-700. This hypothesis does not exclude the possibility that P-700 is still present in the mutant strain. As a second hypothesis, Kok suggested (32) that the two pigments are identical. He assumed that C-705 was a species of oriented chlorophyll (38). Upon excitation, a molecule of C-705 would lose an electron to the primary acceptor of PS I and would regain it from an electron donor on the PS II side. This donor could be either cytochrome *f* or plastocyanin (see page 530), both of which are present at a concentration of about 1 per every 400 chlorophyll molecules or about 1 per every 20 C-705 molecules. Accordingly, if the electron donor and the electron acceptor are present at 1/20th of the concentration of C-705, then at any one time the activity of only one "P-700" molecule would be observed for every 400 chlorophyll molecules present.

A species of oriented chlorophyll has been demonstrated in mutant No. 8 of *S. obliquus* (39) even though there is no evidence for P-700 or C-705, but it is not clear how this oriented chlorophyll relates to either pigment, or how the two pigments related functionally to one another.

The organization of chlorophyll in a reaction center may be under complex genetic control, for in *C. reinhardi* there are at least four mutant strains that lack P-700 activity and each of them may represent mutation at genetically distinct loci (40).

Cytochromes.—Hill & Bendall (33) emphasized the important role of chloroplast cytochromes when they proposed the series formulation for photosynthetic electron transport, and they have recently reviewed (41) the distribution and function of hemeproteins in photosynthesis. Mutant strains in which cytochromes are affected have been obtained in *C. reinhardi* (8) and recently in *S. obliquus* (42).

Cytochrome 553, a c-type cytochrome, has been isolated and purified from cells of the wild-type strain of *C. reinhardi* (43). With respect to the position of the α, β, and γ absorption peaks (552.5 nm, 522.5 nm, and 416.5 nm, respectively) and the normal oxidation-reduction potential (E'_0 at pH 7.0 is $+0.37$v), the purified cytochrome 553 of *C. reinhardi* is similar to cytochrome f of other algae and higher plants (see Table I in ref. 41 and Table I in ref. 43). Its molecular weight of 12,000 (43) is similar to that of the cytochrome from the red alga, *Porphyra tenera* (44), and the green alga *Euglena gracilis* (45).

In wild-type *C. reinhardi,* the cytochrome can be detected in aqueous suspensions of acetone-extracted cells, both before and after washing with buffer to remove soluble proteins, and a soluble form is obtained in preparations that are purified by chromatography on DEAE cellulose (43, 46). When such preparations are made using the mutant strain, *ac-206,* no trace of either the insoluble or soluble form of cytochrome 553 is detected (8). Cytochrome c is, however, detected in the soluble fraction obtained from *ac-206,* indicating that the lack of cytochrome 553 does not extend to other c-type cytochromes.

There appear to be two b-type cytochromes that participate in the photosynthesis of green algae and higher plants: cytochrome b_6 (47, 48) and cytochrome 559 (49–54). The latter shares some of the properties of cytochrome b_3 (55): namely, the position of the α-band (559 nm), a reduction with ascorbate, and a sensitivity to extraction with organic solvents. However, it appears to differ from cytochrome b_3 in that it has not been obtained in aqueous extracts.

Cytochrome 559 has been detected in chloroplast fragments of *C. reinhardi* on the basis of both light-minus-dark and chemically reduced-minus oxidized difference spectra (50, 51). The difference spectra are particularly clear in *ac-206* because of the absence of cytochrome 553. At least two genetically distinct (56) mutant strains of *C. reinhardi* (*ac-115* and *ac-141*) lack an active cytochrome 559 (50, 51); their difference spectra reveal only cytochrome 553. Since photosynthetic electron transport is blocked in these mutant strains, cytochrome 559 would appear to play an essential role in photosynthesis (however, see discussions relating to Q, page 530).

The relative positions of cytochrome 553 and 559 in the electron transport chain of *C. reinhardi* have been deduced from the study of the light-induced absorbance changes exhibited by the wild-type and the mutant strains that lack one or the other cytochrome (50, 51). In chloroplast fragments of the wild-type strain, red light (650 nm) sensitizes the reduction of both cytochromes and far-red light (720 nm) sensitizes their oxidation. DCMU inhibits the light-induced reduction of the two cytochromes but not their oxidation. In the absence of cytochrome 553 (*ac-206*), light sensitizes the reduction of cytochrome 559 but not its oxidation, and in the absence of cytochrome 559 (*ac-115* and *ac-141*) light sensitizes the oxidation of cytochrome 553 but not its reduction. Therefore, according to the series formulation, cytochrome 559 is on the PS II side of cytochrome 553.

A mutant strain of *S. obliquus* having photosynthetic properties similar to those of *ac-206* of *C. reinhardi* apparently has defects in its chloroplast cytochrome 552 (42).

The tightly bound, insoluble cytochrome b_6 (41), or cytochrome 564 as it will be referred to here, has been detected in cells of *C. reinhardi* that have been extracted with acetone (57). Mutant strains have not been found in which this cytochrome has been affected. However, the study of its light-induced absorbance changes in the wild-type strain and in mutant strains lacking other components of the photosynthetic electron transport chain suggests (58) that it may play a role in or be a reflection of cyclic electron flow sensitized by PS I (see page 535).

Plastocyanin.—The copper protein plastocyanin (59) is an essential component for photosynthetic electron transport in *C. reinhardi,* for in its absence from the mutant strain *ac-208,* there is no photoreduction of NADP with either water or the ascorbate-DPIP couple as the electron donor (8, 23). Applying a modification (46) of the purification procedures for plastocyanin described by Katoh (59, 60), it was shown that the mutant strain has no detectable plastocyanin, but that its cytochrome 553 and 559 contents are comparable to those of the wild-type strain (8).

The relative position of plastocyanin with respect to the cytochromes in the photosynthetic electron transport chain has been the subject of much debate (8, 27, 61–66). The properties of *ac-208* suggest that for *C. reinhardi* the sequence is PS II→ cytochrome 559→ cytochrome 553→ plastocyanin→ PS I. This statement is based on two sorts of evidence. First, neither of the cytochromes is required for the photoreduction of NADP with the ascorbate-DPIP couple, for this reaction occurs in *ac-115, ac-141,* and *ac-206,* that lack one or other of the cytochromes. However, plastocyanin is required for this reaction, for the reaction does not occur in *ac-208,* the mutant strain lacking an active plastocyanin. However, when purified plastocyanin obtained from the wild-type strain (46) is added to preparations of *ac-208,* the photoreduction of NADP with either water or the ascorbate-DPIP couple is restored (8). These observations provide evidence that plastocyanin is on the PS I side of cytochrome 553. They also provide evidence that electrons from the ascorbate-DPIP couple enter the transport chain between cytochrome 553 and plastocyanin or at plastocyanin.

The second sort of evidence for the sequence given above is that in chloroplast fragments of *ac-208,* cytochrome 553 can not be oxidized by light unless plastocyanin, prepared from wild-type, is added. On the other hand, in the absence of plastocyanin, oxidized cytochrome 553 can be reduced by light (8).

Q.—The nature of Q, the quencher of fluorescence of PS II (67), is unknown. However, some information is being gained from mutant strains in which its activity is affected. PS II activity, defined as the Hill reaction with oxidants such as *p*-benzoquinone, DPIP, or ferricyanide, is impaired in these mutant strains, whereas PS I activity is normal as measured by the photoreduction of NADP with the ascorbate-DPIP couple. The mutant strains that have been studied are *ac-115* and *ac-141* of *C. reinhardi* (68), P_4 of *E. gracilis* (69), IIγ of *Oenothera* (70), and No. 11 of *S. obliquus* (37). Preparations of each strain have a high fluorescence yield that is unaffected by actinic light. The kinetics of fluorescence have been studied in *E. gracilis* (69), where the typical biphasic curve of fluorescence emission seen for the wild-type strain is missing from the mutant strain P_4.

The results show that in this group of mutant strains, Q is either missing or that its redox state is unaffected by light. There are a number of reasons why the second phenomenon might occur. First, Q may be present in an inactive form. Second, mutation may have brought about a change in chloroplast structure such that Q cannot be placed in the proper functional position to quench fluorescence. Third, Q may be fully reduced, as in the case of DCMU-treated preparations (71). At present, only the last reason seems unlikely, since reduced Q is autoxidizible (67).

Though Q appears to be a component affected in the mutant strains, it must be kept in mind that cytochrome 559 is either missing or inactive in the case of both *ac-115* and *ac-141* of *C. reinhardi*. Clearly cytochrome 559 cannot be identified with Q, for the oxidation of the former is not inhibited by DCMU (50) whereas that of the latter is (67). In addition to lacking a detectable cytochrome 559 and Q, *ac-115* and *ac-141* are also deficient in plastoquinone (57), and it is tempting to assume that the quinone deficiency is somehow related to the absence of or inactivity of Q. However, there is as yet no adequate simple explanation for the complex phenotype of these mutant strains, although hypotheses have been offered (68).

Unidentified components.—The components affected in several of the mutant strains of *C. reinhardi* (50) and *S. obliquus* (6, 26) and in the mutant strains of *V. faba* (27) have not yet been identified. A strain of *C. reinhardi, ac-21*, possesses cytochromes 553 and 559, plastocyanin, and P-700, but its electron transport is blocked between the two photochemical systems (21, 22). In this mutant strain, cytochrome 559 can be reduced by light but not oxidized, and cytochrome 553 can be oxidized by light but not reduced (50). These observations suggest that there is at least one component between cytochromes 559 and 553. This component has been given the notation M, and it is so positioned in the electron transport chain that it could have a low redox potential; hence, it could possibly be a quinone. However, a detailed investigation of the strain's quinone compounds has not yet been carried out.

The mutant strain of *V. faba* (27) apparently lacks a component that lies between PS I and NADP, for there is no NADP photoreduction with either water or with the ascorbate-DPIP couple as the electron donor. There is, however, PMS-catalyzed cyclic photosynthetic phosphorylation, suggesting that the mutant strain lacks a component that lies between PS I and NADP, a component not required for cyclic photosynthetic phosphory-

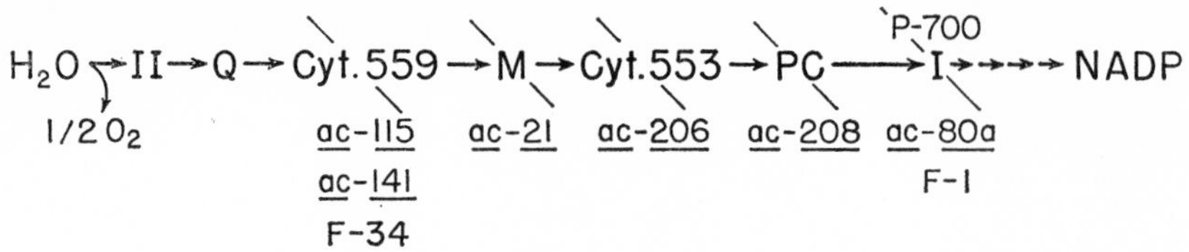

$$H_2O \underset{1/2\,O_2}{\overset{}{\gamma}} II \rightarrow Q \rightarrow Cyt.559 \rightarrow M \rightarrow Cyt.553 \rightarrow PC \xrightarrow{\quad} \overset{`P\text{-}700}{I} \dashrightarrow NADP$$

ac-115   ac-21   ac-206   ac-208   ac-80a

ac-141   F-1

F-34

Fig. 1. A scheme for photosynthetic electron transport in *Chlamydomonas reinhardi* based upon the properties of mutant strains. The dashed lines refer to the affected components of the transport chain, and the notations below the chain refer to different mutant strains.

lation. Ferredoxin or ferredoxin-NADP reductase which mediates electron transfer between ferredoxin and NADP could be missing or inactive in the mutant strain.

THE SEQUENCE OF PHOTOSYNTHETIC ELECTRON TRANSPORT

The series formulation of Hill & Bendall (33) for photosynthetic electron transport is now so strongly supported and so generally accepted that its expected "strait jacket-like effect on imagination and research in photosynthesis"[2] has been almost forgotten. There are other formulations, however, and some account of these must be given when attempting to deduce the sequence of photosynthetic electron transport from the properties of the mutant strains. Clearly, the results obtained with the mutant strains fit most simply into the series formulation, for it is only necessary to assume that each mutant strain is incapable of normal photosynthesis because it has lost the capacity to carry out one step in electron transport between water and NADP, and that this loss is the consequence of its inability to synthesize one specific component of the electron transport chain. With this assumption in mind, the photosynthetic electron transport chain as deduced principally from the study of the mutant strains of *C. reinhardi* appears as illustrated in Figure 1.

Three alternative hypotheses for the sequence of photosynthetic electron transport will be mentioned briefly. Frank & Rosenberg (72) proposed that the two photochemical reactions occur alternately within a single reaction center containing two pigment systems, and that both reactions can be sensitized by a short-wavelength form of chlorophyll. The theory predicts, therefore, that both reactions should proceed in the absence of an active P-700. However, as described earlier, the mutant strains of *C. reinhardi* and *S. obliquus* that lack P-700 activity retain reactions sensitized by red light only, whereas they lose those that can be sensitized by far-red. Moreover, they cannot fix carbon dioxide or evolve oxygen by photosynthesis. On these grounds, at least, the Frank-Rosenberg theory seems difficult to accept.

[2] From a statement made in an informal discussion during the Symposium on Photosynthetic Mechanisms in Green Plants held at Arlie House, Warrentown, Virginia, Oct. 1963.

Parallel formulations for photosynthetic electron transport have been proposed by several investigators (61, 62, 73, 74). Results obtained with mutant strains do not rule out the possibility suggested by Gaffron (73) of two parallel chains, each driven by a different light reaction and each producing a strong oxidant and strong reductant, but neither capable of bringing about photosynthesis by itself. The loss by mutation of a component from either chain would then result in a loss of photosynthetic capability. It seems, however, that this sort of formulation can be eliminated on the basis of the antagonistic effects of red and far-red light in sensitizing the reduction and oxidation of cytochromes that lie in the transport chain.

A partially parallel formulation, as proposed by Kok et al. (61, 62), involving plastocyanin in one branch and cytochrome f in another, is ruled out by the results obtained with the mutant strains of *C. reinhardi,* for, as explained earlier, electron flow, if blocked along one branch, should follow the other, unblocked branch.

The rather unique schemes proposed by Arnon (75) to explain noncyclic and cyclic electron flow can be excluded if one accepts the observation that red and far-red light have antagonistic effects on the redox state of cytochrome f and P-700. This alone tends to exclude a pathway for noncyclic electron flow that contains water, chlorophyll, ferredoxin, ferredoxin-NADP reductase, and NADP as its only components. Nevertheless, Arnon places cytochrome f only in a pathway of cyclic electron flow (75). The data obtained with the mutant strains described so far in this review also tend to exclude Arnon's hypothesis, for they show that the usual antagonistic effects of red and far-red light are lost when cytochrome 559, cytochrome 553, plastocyanin, or P-700 have been affected by mutation. Accordingly, Q, cytochrome 559, cytochrome 553, P-700, and other unidentified components appear to lie in the main chain of electron transport, and two light reactions must cooperate in electron transport from water to NADP.

THE APPLICATION OF MUTANT STRAINS TO THE STUDY OF SPECIFIC PHOTOSYNTHETIC PHENOMENA

Many phenomena of photosynthesis have been studied by examining the partial reactions carried out by mutant strains. The knowledge that photosynthesis is altered, often in a specific way, can be used to interpret certain of the phenomena or to determine the role played by the phenomena in the overall process of photosynthesis. For example, with the appropriate mutant strain, delayed light has been interpreted as arising from PS II (68, 76), and the 520 nm absorbance change has been shown to be associated with both photochemical systems and possibly with cyclic and noncyclic electron flow (77).

Photosynthetic phosphorylation.—A review of photosynthetic phosphorylation in algae and higher plants has appeared recently (78), and reference to it will provide general information. Mutant strains in which only photosynthetic phosphorylation has been affected have not been identified, but certain of the mutant strains in which photosynthetic electron transport is blocked provide some information regarding the components of the chain that appear to be required for phosphorylation and possible sites for its occurrence.

For example, noncyclic photosynthetic phosphorylation coupled to ferricyanide reduction has been detected in *ac-80a,* the mutant strain of *C. reinhardi* lacking P-700 activity (7). Since PS I is inactive in this mutant strain, at least one site for noncyclic phosphorylation must occur between the two photochemical systems. This observation supports the conclusion of Avron & Chance (*79*), based on kinetic studies of tightly coupled systems, that a limiting step in electron transport exists on the PS II side of cytochrome *f.*

Noncyclic photosynthetic phosphorylation has not been detected in *ac-21, ac-206,* and *ac-208,* mutant strains of *C. reinhardi* that can reduce ferricyanide in a Hill reaction (8, 80). Assuming the sequence of electron transport given in Figure 1, and accepting the fact that *ac-80a* reveals that there is at least one site for noncyclic photosynthetic phosphorylation between the two photochemical systems, the absence of phosphorylation in *ac-21, ac-206,* and *ac-208* could be explained if a site were between plastocyanin and P-700. However, according to conventional hypotheses for the coupling of phosphorylation to electron transport, the potential difference between plastocyanin [+0.37v (46)] and P-700 [+0.43v (81)] is not great enough. Another explanation could be that the rate of electron flow to fericyanide is insufficient in *ac-21, ac-206,* and *ac-208* to generate ATP. If one makes the admittedly artificial calculation of the rate of phosphorylation expected for each mutant strain on the basis of its rate of ferricyanide reduction and the highest coupling ratio found for wild-type [0.3 (8, 80)], the rates obtained for *ac-21, ac-206* and *ac-208* are, respectively, 13, 5, and 19 μmoles of ATP formed per hour per mg chlorphyll. These rates would be detectable by the methods used. There is, therefore, no adequate explanation for the absence of noncyclic photosynthetic phosphorylation coupled to ferricyanide reduction in these strains.

Studies with mutant strains of *C. reinhardi* have revealed that plastocyanin (8, 23) and P-700 (7) are required for cyclic photosynthetic phosphorylation catalyzed by PMS, whereas M, cytochrome 559, and cytochrome 553 (8, 23) are not. In agreement with these results, the mutant strain of *S. obliquus* lacking P-700 activity has recently been shown to lack cyclic photosynthetic phosphorylation, whereas it is present in a mutant strain (No. 50) that lacks cytochrome 552 (26, 42).

The lack of cyclic photosynthetic phosphorylation in mutant strains devoid of P-700 activity is in accord with the well-known PS I-dependence of the process. It is interesting that plastocyanin is also required, at least in *C. reinhardi.* The requirement of plastocyanin for cyclic photosynthetic phosphorylation can be explained by assuming that the cycle enters the electron transport chain at the level of plastocyanin, and that a site of phosphorylation lies between PS I and the site at which the cycle re-enters the chain.

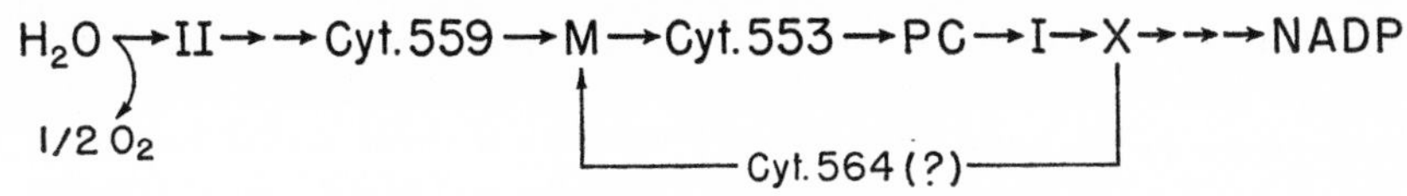

$$H_2O \xrightarrow{\hspace{0.3cm}} II \to \to Cyt.559 \to M \to Cyt.553 \to PC \to I \to X \to \to \to NADP$$

$$1/2\ O_2$$

$$\vdash\! Cyt.564\,(?) \!\dashv$$

FIG. 2. A scheme for cyclic electron flow in *Chlamydomonas reinhardi*. See text for details.

There is, however, evidence from the *in vivo* measurements of cyclic electron flow and carbon dioxide fixation by photoreduction under hydrogen that argues against this possibility, as discussed in the following section.

Cyclic electron flow and its relation to cyclic photosynthetic phosphorylation.—Several phenomena in algae that require ATP can be sensitized by PS I alone. They include the fixation of carbon dioxide by photoreduction under hydrogen (82), carbon dioxide fixation under nitrogen in the presence of DCMU and either PMS or DPIP (83), and the anaerobic assimilation of acetate (84) and of glucose (85) in the presence of DCMU. Each of these phenomena suggests the existence of an *in vivo* cyclic photosynthetic phosphorylation and thus an *in vivo* cyclic electron flow.

Mutant strains of *C. reinhardi* and *S. obliquus* fall into two classes with respect to their capacity to fix carbon dioxide by photoreduction. In the case of *C. reinhardi*, mutant strains lacking electron transport components that lie on the PS I side of cytochrome 559 (Fig. 1) cannot fix carbon dioxide by this process, whereas those lacking cytochrome 559 do so at the wild-type rate (86). Similar observations have been made for certain of the mutant strains of *S. obliquus*. Thus, mutant strains lacking either cytochrome 552 (42) or P-700 activity (6) do not fix carbon dioxide by photoreduction nor do they carry out the anaerobic assimilation of glucose in the presence of DCMU (26, 42, 87). On the other hand, mutant No. 11, which is blocked close to PS II, can carry out both processes (42, 87).

The ability of cells of *C. reinhardi* to fix carbon dioxide by photoreduction is correlated with their ability to show a light-induced absorbance change that has a maximum at 564 nm. This change, which has been attributed to the oxidation of cytochrome 564 (58, 88), is sensitized by either red or far-red light and is resistant to DCMU. Therefore, it appears to be sensitized by PS I alone. Mutant strains such as *ac-115* and *ac-141* display the absorbance change, whereas mutant strains *ac-21, ac-206, ac-208, ac-80a* and F-1 (a mutant strain phenotypically similar to *ac-80a*) do not. One interpretation (58) of this phenomenon is given in Figure 2. It assumes a cycle of electron flow sensitized by PS I that enters the main chain of electron transport at the level of M, the component affected in *ac-21*.

Evidence in support of cyclic electron flow of the sort depicted in Figure 2 for cells of *C. reinhardi* has come recently from measurements (89, 90) of the light-induced turnover or alternate oxidation and reduction of cytochrome 553 and P-700 in the presence of DCMU. The turnover is exhibited by cells of wild type, *ac-115,* and *ac-141,* but not by cells of *ac-206* and *ac-80a.* Since the rate of turnover is unaffected by DCMU and increased upon the addition of the uncoupler FCCP, it has been suggested (89, 90) that it reflects *in vivo* cyclic electron transport sensitized by PS I, to which a phosphorylation step is coupled.

The 520 nm light-induced absorbance change.—The 520 nm absorbance change has been described as being a "weird and wonderful phenomenon" (91), in part because of the differences of opinion regarding the nature of the component responsible for it and the uncertainty regarding its role in photosynthesis. The absorbance change, occurring in the 515 nm to 520 nm region of the spectrum, was first reported by Duysens (92), and it is found in higher plants and algae. It has been attributed to β-carotene (88, 93) and to chlorophyll *b* ((94–97), and is believed to be an indicator of the operation of PS II (94–96) or, on the other hand, to be sensitized by PS I (98, 99).

Rubinstein (100) clarified some of these contradictions when he found that responses at 520 nm depended on experimental conditions, and that they could be sensitized by either PS I or PS II. Fork & de Kouchkovsky confirmed his results (101) and went on to demonstrate the absence of antagonistic effects of red and far-red light, thus suggesting that there are two different absorption changes at 520 nm.

There appear to be two different 520 nm absorbance changes in cells of *C. reinhardi* (77). One is sensitized by PS I; it is detected in wild-type cells treated with DCMU and in cells of mutant strains lacking cytochrome 559. It is enhanced under anaerobic conditions and decreased with increasing oxygen tension. It seems, therefore, to be associated with a photo-oxidation upon the activation of PS I, a conclusion reached by Chance & Strehler (93), who showed that the change could be induced in the dark by the oxygenation of anaerobic cells of *C. reinhardi*. The second absorbance change, sensitized by PS II, is most easily studied in mutant strains lacking P-700 activity (77). This absorbance change is sensitive to DCMU and is absent under anaerobic conditions, suggesting that it is associated with a photoreduction, for under anaerobic conditions, electron carriers between PS II and PS I, including the electron acceptor of PS II, would be in the reduced state.

The confusion regarding the nature of the component or components responsible for the 520 nm absorbance changes remains. Fork, Amesz & Anderson (97) compared the spectral changes in the 450 nm to 550 nm region in several different organisms, including the chlorophyll *b*-less mutant strain of *H. vulgare,* and they concluded that at least two different pigments contribute to the absorbance changes. One pigment, having minima at 480 nm and 650 nm and a maximum at 515 nm, is believed to be chlorophyll *b,* and they show that the 480 nm band is missing in the chlorophyll *b*-less mutant strain of *H. vulgare.* The nature of the second pigment is unknown, but the difference spectrum for the initial absorbance change in leaves of the *Hordeum* mutant strain suggest a shift in the absorption of a carotenoid (102). Chance & Sager (88) and Hildreth, Avron & Chance (103) attribute the absorbance change to a carotenoid, since it is absent from the pale-green mutant strain of *C. reinhardi* in which the total carotenoids are some

500-fold less, and the β-carotene some 400-fold less, than in the comparably grown cells of the wild-type strain (104). However, it must be pointed out that this mutant strain also has a tenfold deficiency in total chlorophyll (104), and it thus may be premature to attribute its loss of the 520 nm absorbance change to the absence of carotenoid alone.

Both chlorophyll b and carotenoid, then, may be involved in the 520 nm absorbance changes, but the reactions responsible for the absorbance changes have yet to be identified. In this regard, it is of interest to note that an absorbance change at 520 nm attributed to carotenoid in the purple photosynthetic bacterium *Rhodopseudomonas speroides* (105, 106) is probably not due to a chemical reaction, for it has been shown (105) that the absorption of one quantum of light causes change in the absorbance of about three molecules of carotenoid. Consequently, it has been suggested that the 520 nm absorbance changes result not from a redox reaction but rather from some unspecified alteration in the environment of the pigment molecules responsible for the change (97).

CHLOROPLAST STRUCTURE AND PHOTOSYNTHESIS

The suggestion that the 520 nm absorbance changes arise through an alteration of the environment of chlorophyll and carotenoid pigments raises the general question of the role played by chloroplast structure in the operation of the photosynthetic process. It should be stated at the outset that structure-function correlations are generally difficult to make, for ambiguity usually arises as to which lesions are primary and which secondary. Nonetheless, it seems reasonable to assume that mutant strains would be profitable material to use in an approach to this question.

The suggestion (16, 107) that stacking of chloroplast lamellae is required for maximal activity of PS II can be examined in the light of studies of mutant organisms. The hypothesis is apparently not supported by the chlorophyll b-less mutant strain of *H. vulgare* (108–112). Compared to wild type, the chloroplasts of this mutant strain exhibit fewer lamellae and grana per chloroplast, a reduced number of lamellae per grana, and a significant increase in single, unstacked lamellae; nonetheless, their PS II activity, at high light intensities, is equal to or more active than that of the wild-type strain on a chlorophyll basis. It might be argued that a sufficient number of stacked lamellae remain in this mutant to account for the photosynthesis observed, and indeed, chloroplasts from yellow sections of the leaves of *Nicotiana tabacum*, NC 95 var, exhibit no stacked lamellae and show essentially no PS II activity as measured by the Hill reaction with ferricyanide (16). PS I activity, measured as NADP photoreduction with the ascorbate-DPIP couple, is unaffected in the tobacco mutant. Similarly, mutant strains of *C. reinhardi, ac-115* and *ac-141*, in which electron transport is blocked close to PS II at the level of cytochrome 559, show an unusually high percentage of unstacked lamellae (113). However, *ac-31*, a pigment-deficient mutant strain of *C. reinhardi*, has normal PS II activity and normal photosynthesis in spite of the fact that there is essentially no stacking of lamellae (113). It seems premature, therefore, to argue that the stacking of lamellae into discs or grana is a prerequisite for PS II activity. In fact, it would seem that a mutant strain such as *ac-31* lacks some factor essential for stacking, whereas mutant strains such as *ac-115* and *ac-141* of *C. reinhardi* and the mutant strain of *H. vulgare* have reduced amounts of stacking as a secondary consequence of their defects in cytochrome 559 and chlorophyll *b* respectively.

Another possible structure-function relationship is that alterations in chloroplast structure may affect a mutant strain's light-harvesting capacity. This is clearly seen in the case of the chlorophyll *b*-less mutant strain of barley (110, 111) and in certain of the mutant strains of *N. tabacum* (16), where higher intensities of light are required for saturating rates of photosynthesis. Limited stacking of lamallae is a general property of these mutant strains, suggesting that there is an optimal stack size for maximum light harvesting capability.

LITERATURE CITED

1. Hind, G., Olson, J. M., *Ann. Rev. Plant Physiol.*, **19**, 249–82 (1968)
2. Boardman, N. K., *Advan. Enzymol.*, **30**, 1–79 (1968)
3. Trainor, F. R., Burg, C. A., *Science*, **148**, 1094–95 (1965)
4. Kirk, J. T. O., Tilney-Bassett, R. A. E., *The Plastids* (Freeman, London, 608 pp., 1967)
5. Levine, R. P., *Ann. Rev. Genetics*, **4** (to appear in 1970)
6. Bishop, N. I., *Record Chem. Progr.*, **25**, 181–95 (1964)
7. Givan, A. L., Levine, R. P., *Plant Physiol.*, **42**, 1264–68 (1967)
8. Gorman, D. S., Levine, R. P., *Plant Physiol.*, **41**, 1648–56 (1966)
9. Cosbey, E., Hastings, P. J., Levine, R. P., *Microbial Gen. Bull.*, **23**, 20–21 (1965)
10. Granick, S., *Harvey Lectures*, **44**, 220–45 (1949)
11. Davis, E. A., *Am. J. Botany*, **39**, 535–39 (1952)
12. Levine, R. P., *Nature*, **188**, 339–40 (1960)
13. Bennoun, P., Levine, R. P., *Plant Physiol.*, **42**, 1284–87 (1967)
14. Garnier, J., *Compt. Rend. Acad. Sci. Paris*, **265**, 874–77 (1967)
15. Dolzmann, P., *Z. Pflanzenphysiol.*, **58**, 300–9 (1968)
16. Homann, P. H., Schmid, G. H., *Plant Physiol.*, **42**, 1619–32 (1967)
17. von Wettstein, D., *Brookhaven Symp. Biol.*, **11**, 138–59 (1959)
18. Bassham, J. A., Calvin, M., *The Path of Carbon in Photosynthesis* (Prentice-Hall, Englewood Cliffs, N.J., 104 pp., 1957)
19. Smillie, R. M., *Can. J. Botany*, **41**, 123–54 (1963)
20. Moll, B. (Unpublished observations)
21. Levine, R. P., Smillie, R. M., *Proc. Natl. Acad. Sci. U.S.*, **48**, 417–21 (1962)
22. Levine, R. P., Smillie, R. M., *J. Biol. Chem.*, **238**, 4052–57 (1962)
23. Gorman, D. S., Levine, R. P., *Proc. Natl. Acad. Sci. U.S.*, **54**, 1665–69 (1965)
24. Russell, G. K., Lyman, H., *Plant Physiol.*, **43**, 1284–90 (1968)
25. Kok, B., Datko, E. A., *Plant Physiol.*, **40**, 1171–77 (1965)
26. Pratt, L. H., Bishop, N. I., *Biochim. Biophys. Acta*, **153**, 664–74 (1968)
27. Heber, U., Gottschalk, W., *Z. Naturforsch.*, **18**, 36–43 (1963)
28. Kok, B., *Biochim. Biophys. Acta*, **22**, 399–401 (1956)
29. Kok, B., Hoch, G., in *Light and Life*, 397 (McElroy, W. D., Glass, B., Eds., Johns Hopkins Press, Baltimore, 1961)
30. Beinert, H., Kok, B., in *Photosynthetic Mechanisms in Green Plants*, 131 (Kok, B., Jagendorf, A., Eds., Natl. Acad. Sci.-Natl. Res. Council Publ. 1145, Washington, D.C., 1963)
31. Weaver, E. C., Bishop, N. I., *Science*, **140**, 1095–97 (1963)
32. Kok, B., in *Photosynthetic Mechanisms in Green Plants*, 45 (See Ref. 30)

33. Hill, R., Bendall, D. S., *Nature,* **186,** 136–37 (1960)
34. Butler, W. L., *Biochem. Biophys. Res. Commun.,* **3,** 685–88 (1960)
35. Butler, W. L., *Arch. Biochem. Biophys.,* **93,** 413–22 (1961)
36. Butler, W. L., Baker, J. E., *Biochim. Biophys. Acta,* **66,** 206–11 (1963)
37. Butler, W. L., Bishop, N. I., in *Photosynthetic Mechanisms in Green Plants,* 91 (See Ref. 30)
38. Olson, R. A., Butler, W. L., Jennings, W. H., *Biochim. Biophys. Acta,* **54,** 615–17 (1961)
39. Butler, W. L., Olson, R. A., Jennings, W. H., *Biochim. Biophys. Acta,* **88,** 651–53 (1964)
40. Cosbey, E., Levine, R. P. (Unpublished observations)
41. Bendall, D. S., Hill, R., *Ann. Rev. Plant Physiol.,* **19,** 167–86 (1968)
42. Powls, R., Bishop, N. I., *Abstr. Ann. Meeting Am. Soc. Plant Physiol.,* 1968 (Univ. Mass., Amherst, Mass., supplement to *Plant Physiol.,* **43,** S–20)
43. Gorman, D. S., Levine, R. P., *Plant Physiol.,* **41,** 1643–47 (1966)
44. Katoh, S., *Plant Cell Physiol.,* **1,** 91–98 (1960)
45. Perini, F., Schiff, J. A., Kamen, M. D., *Biochim. Biophys. Acta,* **88,** 74–90 (1964)
46. Gorman, D. S., Levine, R. P., *Plant Physiol.,* **41,** 1637–42 (1966)
47. Davenport, H. E., *Nature,* **170,** 1112–14 (1952)
48. Hill, R., *Nature,* **174,** 501–3 (1954)
49. Lundegårdh, H., *Proc. Natl. Acad. Sci. U.S.,* **52,** 1587–90 (1964)
50. Levine, R. P., Gorman, D. S., *Plant Physiol.,* **41,** 1293–1300 (1966)
51. Levine, R. P., Gorman, D. S., Avron, M., Butler, W. L., *Brookhaven Symp. Biol.,* **19,** 143–48 (1967)
52. Boardman, N. K., Anderson, J. M., *Biochim. Biophys. Acta,* **143,** 187–203 (1967)
53. Cramer, W. A., Butler, W. L., *Biochim. Biophys. Acta,* **143,** 332–39 (1967)
54. Hind, G., *Biochim. Biophys. Acta,* **153,** 235–40 (1968)
55. Hill, R., Scarisbrick, R., *New Phytologist,* **50,** 98–111 (1951)
56. Hastings, P. J., Levine, E. E., Cosbey, E. E., Hudock, M. O., Gillham, N. W., Surzycki, S. J., Loppes, R., Levine, R. P., *Microbial Gen. Bull.,* **23,** 17–20 (1965)
57. Smillie, R. M., Levine, R. P., *J. Biol. Chem.,* **238,** 4058–62 (1962)
58. Levine, R. P., *Proc. Intern. Congr. Photosyn. Res.,* 1968, Freudenstadt, Germany (In press)
59. Katoh, S., *Nature,* **186,** 533–34 (1960)
60. Katoh, S., Shiratori, I., Takamiya, A., *J. Biochem. (Tokyo),* **51,** 32–40 (1962)
61. Kok, B., Rurainski, H. J., Harmon, E. A., *Plant Physiol.,* **39,** 513–20 (1964)
62. Kok, B., Rurainski, H. J., *Biochim. Biophys. Acta,* **94,** 588–90 (1965)
63. Wessels, J. S. C., *Biochim. Biophys. Acta,* **126,** 581–83 (1966)
64. Fork, D. C., Urbach, W., *Proc. Natl. Acad. Sci. U.S.,* **53,** 1307–15 (1965)
65. Davenport, H. E., in *Non-heme Iron Proteins,* 115 (San Pietro, A., Ed., Antioch Press, Yellow Springs, Ohio, 1965)
66. Katoh, S., San Pietro, A., *Biochem. Biophys. Res. Commun.,* **24,** 903–8 (1966)
67. Duysens, L. N. M., Sweers, H. E., in *Studies on Microalgae and Photosynthetic Bacteria,* speeial issue of *Plant Cell Physiol.,* 353–72 (1963)
68. Lavorel, J., Levine, R. P., *Plant Physiol.,* **43,** 1049–55 (1968)
69. Russell, G. K. (Personal communication)
70. Fork, D. C., Heber, U., *Plant Physiol.,* **43,** 606–12 (1968)
71. Zweig, G., Tamas, I., Greenberg, E., *Biochim. Biophys. Acta,* **66,** 196–205 (1963)
72. Frank, J., Rosenberg, J. L., *J. Theoret. Biol.,* **7,** 276–301 (1964)
73. Gaffron, H., in *Horizons in Biochemistry,* 59 (Kasha, M., Pullman, B., Eds., Academic, N.Y., 1962)
74. Hind, G., Olson, J. M., *Brookhaven Symp. Biol.,* **19,** 188–94 (1966)
75. Arnon, D. I., *Physiol. Rev.,* **47,** 317–58 (1967)
76. Bertsch, W., Azzi, J. R., Davidson, J. B., *Biochim. Biophys. Acta,* **143,** 129–43 (1967)
77. Chua, N. H., Levine, R. P., *Plant Physiol.,* **43,** 1–6 (1969)
78. Avron, M., Neumann, J., *Ann. Rev. Plant Physiol.,* **19,** 137–66 (1968)
79. Avron, M., Chance, B., *Brookhaven Symp. Biol.,* **19,** 149–60 (1966)
80. Gorman, D. S., *Photosynthetic Electron Transport and Photosynthetic Phosphorylation in Chlamydomonas reinhardi* (Doctoral thesis,

Harvard Univ., Cambridge, Mass., 1966)

81. Givan, A. L., *Photosynthetic Properties of a Mutant Strain of Chlamydomonas reinhardi Lacking a Photochemical Reaction Center* (Doctoral thesis, Harvard Univ., Cambridge, Mass., 1968)

82. Gaffron, H., *Am. J. Botany*, **27**, 273–83 (1940)

83. Togasaki, R. K., Levine, R. P., *Abstr. Ann. Meeting Am. Soc. Plant Physiol.*, 1968, S–29 (See Ref. 42)

84. Weissner, W., *Nature*, **205**, 56–57 (1965)

85. Kandler, O., Tanner, W., *Ber. Deut. Botan. Ges.*, **79**, (48)–(57) (1966)

86. Togasaki, R. (Unpublished observations)

87. Tanner, W., Zinecker, O., Kandler, O., *Z. Naturforsch.*, **22**, 358–59 (1967)

88. Chance, B., Sager, R., *Plant Physiol.*, **32**, 548–61 (1957)

89. Teichler-Zallen, D., Hoch, G., *Arch. Biochem. Biophys.*, **120**, 227–30 (1967)

90. Teichler-Zallen, D., Bannister, T. T., Hoch, G. (Personal communication)

91. Chance, B., in discussion of paper by Fork, D. C., Amesz, J., Anderson, J. M., *Brookhaven Symp. Biol.*, **19**, 81–94 (1966)

92. Duysens, L. N. M., *Science*, **120**, 353–54 (1954)

93. Chance, B., Strehler, B., *Plant Physiol.*, **32**, 536–48 (1957)

94. Muller, A., Fork, D. C., Witt, H. T., *Z. Naturforsch.*, **18b**, 142–45 (1963)

95. Witt, H. T., Goring, G., Rumberg, B., Schmidt-Mende, P., Siggel, U., Stiehl, H. H., *Brookhaven Symp. Biol.*, **19**, 81–93 (1966)

96. Witt, H. T., Rumberg, B., Schmidt-Mende, P., Siggel, U., Skerre, B., Vater, J., Weikard, J., *Angew.*

Chem. Intern. Ed. Engl., **4**, 799–819 (1965)

97. Fork, D. C., Amesz, J., Anderson, J., *Brookhaven Symp. Biol.*, **19**, 81–94 (1966)

98. Rubinstein, D., Rabinowitch, E., *Biophys. J.*, **4**, 107–13 (1964)

99. Kok, B., Cooper, B., Yang, L., in *Studies on Microalgae and Photosynthetic Bacteria*, 373–96 (See Ref. 67)

100. Rubinstein, D., *Biochim. Biophys. Acta*, **109**, 41–44 (1965)

101. Fork, D. C., de Kouchkovsky, Y., *Photochem. Photobiol.*, **5**, 609–19 (1966)

102. Fork, D. C., Amesz, J., *Ann. Rept. Director, Dept. Plant Biol., Carnegie Inst. Yearbook No. 66*, 160–65 (1968)

103. Hildreth, W. W., Avron, M., Chance, B., *Plant Physiol.*, **41**, 983–91 (1966)

104. Sager, R., Zalokar, M., *Nature*, **182**, 98–100 (1958)

105. Amesz, J., Vredenberg, W. J., in *Currents in Photosynthesis*, 75 (Thomas, J., Goedheer, J. C., Eds., Ad. Donker, Rotterdam, 1966)

106. Vredenberg, W. J., Amesz, J., Duysens, L. N. M., *Biochem. Biophys. Res. Commun.*, **18**, 435–39 (1965)

107. Weier, T. E., Benson, A. W., *Am. J. Botany*, **54**, 389–402 (1967)

108. Highkin, H. R., *Plant Physiol.*, **25**, 294–306 (1950)

109. Highkin, H. R., Frenkel, A. W., *Plant Physiol.*, **37**, 814–20 (1962)

110. Boardman, N. K., Highkin, H. R., *Biochim. Biophys. Acta*, **126**, 189–99 (1966)

111. Boardman, N. K., Thorne, S. W., *Biochim. Biophys. Acta*, **153**, 448–58 (1967)

112. Goodchild, D. J., Highkin, H. R., Boardman, N. K., *Exptl. Cell Res.*, **43**, 684–88 (1966)

113. Goodenough, U. (Unpublished observations)

PHYSIOLOGICAL ROLES OF ETHYLENE
IN PLANTS

By Harlan K. Pratt[1]

Department of Vegetable Crops, University of California, Davis, California

and John D. Goeschl

Department of Biology, Texas A. & M. University, College Station, Texas

Introduction

Ethylene is the simplest organic compound which affects plants, it is a natural product of plant metabolism, it is active in trace amounts (41), and its effects are spectacular and commercially important (136). Burg & Burg (52) and Abeles & Gahagan (8) have restudied the relative activities of volatile compounds having ethylene-like action and have shown that ethylene is at least 60 to 100 times more active than its nearest competitor (propylene) in terms of concentration required for ethylene-like effects; much higher concentrations were required for all other compounds tested (135). Ethylene is the only such compound so far known to be produced by any plant tissue in significant amounts, and if one were to allege that another endogenous compound was exerting the effect attributed to ethylene, it would have to be rigorously proven that ethylene was absent.

For many years, ethylene physiology was the province of those concerned with fruit ripening and a few other aspects of postharvest physiology and those concerned with air pollution. Progress was slow and stepwise, each advance depending on a new analytical technique, but until the advent of gas chromatography it was not possible to measure the very low concentrations of ethylene which are present (and which may be physiologically effective) within plant organs and tissues. The most modern instruments for gas chromatography make it possible to detect and measure concentrations as low as a fraction of a part per thousand million in a small gas sample —concentrations below the level of any known physiological effect. With very sensitive instruments and very careful technique, it has become possible to show that ethylene is an endogenous growth regulator in plants, and that it is present in fruits from early stages of development. Recent studies have revealed that the concentration of ethylene in cells and tissues is related to the concentrations and effects of other growth regulators. As a re-

[1] Our own work, cited herein, was supported in part by a research grant (UI-00102) from the National Center for Urban and Industrial Health, United States Public Health Service.

541

sult of these observations, many laboratories have taken up work on ethylene physiology, and the number of publications related to some aspect of ethylene physiology has increased enormously.

The most important recent reviews are those of Burg (39, 41) and Hansen (131). Other earlier reviews can be traced through these, and work cited therein will not usually be covered here. In addition, one should mention the recent ones of Jansen (154) and Spencer (323) and some earlier reviews by Smock (320), Ulrich (337), and Pentzer & Heinze (257). One interested in historical aspects of this field should see Mack & Livingston (191) and Crocker (74) for accounts of ethylene as a growth regulator, and Thornton (333) and Von Loesecke (344) for accounts of ethylene as a treatment for or a product of ripening fruits; the semipopular account by Miller (222) is also of interest. Previous reviewers have tended to concentrate on the relations of ethylene to fruit ripening—the aspect of ethylene physiology which has received the most study because of its practical importance. We shall attempt to enlarge on the historical aspects of ethylene phenomena, especially those having to do with growth relations which were lightly touched on by Burg (39) and not covered by Hansen (131). We shall cover some papers ignored in the previous reviews and try to bring the subject of ethylene physiology up to the present date. We will not, however, list the numerous papers which have only a strictly applied horticultural purpose.

METHODOLOGY

All earlier chemical methods for measuring ethylene production (39) must be considered obsolete now that the flame-ionization gas chromatograph is available. No elaborate accessories are needed, but all components, especially the burner and electrometer, should be of the highest quality. A good instrument will be sensitive enough to record the amount of ethylene contained in a small gas sample drawn from the interior of a plant organ or from a small container containing modest amounts of tissue (56, 118, 262); it should not be necessary to accumulate ethylene from large volumes of air or over lengths of times too great for physiological interpretation. Discussions of gas chromatographic technique are readily found in the chemical literature.

If one only has available less sensitive instrumentation, an accumulation system may be useful, and several have been suggested. Gibson & Young (113), following a scheme first proposed by Stitt & Tomimatsu (328), absorbed ethylene on cold silica gel and then freed it by heating, and Galliard et al. (108) used a liquid oxygen trap. The mercuric perchlorate absorbent, originally proposed for manometric measurement of ethylene (363), has been adapted for accumulation of gas before its final analysis by more sensitive means. Phan (260) adsorbed the mercuric perchlorate on silica gel, allowing collection from very small samples, and adapted the method to gas chromatography (264). Gibson & Crane (110, 112) moved the adsorbed ethylene from mercuric perchlorate to mercuric acetate and then on to paper chromatograms for qualitative identification; the samples could then be run in a liquid scintillation counter if desired. Shimokawa & Kasai (309) and Yang el al. (360) have also proposed scintillation counting of ethylene in mercuric acetate, but Thompson & Spencer (330) counted the mercuric perchlorate-ethylene complex. Burg & Burg (45) pointed out that ethanol might be converted to ethylene in some circumstances by the mercuric perchlorate reagent. In counting radioethylene, one may attach a gas counting device directly to a thermal conductivity gas chromatograph. The proportional counter type is more sensitive, as it requires a smaller sample than does the ionization type.

On the other hand, if one has no apparatus at all, the triple response of etiolated peas gives a good approximation of the amount of ethylene in a system. The principal disadvantage of the method is the requirement for about 2 days exposure, since it is the new growth which responds. The amount of light to which the peas are exposed must be standardized because the peas will be much more sensitive if they are very strictly etiolated (116) than if they are exposed at any time during their preparation to even modest room lighting (273, 293). Allegations that the triple response is not specific for olefins (345) are in error; an experienced worker will not confuse the responses of etiolated peas to ethylene with those to ethanol (95).

Those trained with conventional gas analysis techniques are surprised to find how accurately gas samples can be handled in ordinary medical syringes lubricated with glycerol. Repeatable results can be obtained with these simple devices which are well within the sampling errors of any biological system. For preparation of traces of ethylene in closed systems, or for standardization, syringes may be used, perhaps with successive dilutions. If a flowing air stream is required, ethylene may be added continuously from a Mariotte bottle system (279), or mixtures of ethylene and other gases can be made up in pressure cylinders (362). Dunham & O'Connor (89) have patented a method for treating fruit in containers with ethylene-saturated zeolite molecular sieves in the package, and Burg & Burg (48) presented techniques for investigating diffusion of ethylene and other gases through fruit tissue. Burg (41) has useful comments on the relations between ethylene production rate, concentration of applied ethylene, and the ethylene content of tissues in experimental systems.

It appears now to be generally assumed that a gas chromatographic peak at the right place on a time scale denotes the presence of ethylene. While this assumption is generally correct, it should be approached with caution in examining any new system, as serious errors have been made (39). If one has a sufficiently sensitive instrument, allegedly fresh air may contain enough ethylene to require a blank correction; air supply intakes should be as far from automotive traffic as possible. We have found 0.1 ppm in cylinder oxygen. The presence of traces of ethylene and other light hydrocarbons as impurities can be an advantage, on the other hand, as they provide constant qualitative markers for the ethylene peak. For example, at Davis, California, one always finds traces of methane, ethane, ethylene, propane, propylene, and butane in "fresh" air. Ethylene has ranged from 0.003 to 0.005 ppm, fortunately still below the level of physiological interference.

ETHYLENE AS A PLANT GROWTH REGULATOR

EARLY HISTORICAL ASPECTS

The earliest history of ethylene as it relates to the growth of plants was rightly described by Burg (39) as ". . . hopelessly entangled in a literature describing the toxic action of illuminating gas and smoke on plant tissues." Much descriptive information covering the effects of ethylene on growth was accumulated during the first 30 years of this century, followed by the first proof of the endogenous production of ethylene by plant tissues. This led to the suggestion in 1935 (76) that ethylene should be considered a plant growth hormone. However, only in the last few years has any clear correlative evidence been obtained to support that suggestion in a limited number of cases. As a result of these recent findings, the older literature takes on new significance, not so much as a source of specific evidence, but as a source of interesting observations and ideas which may be re-examined, tested experimentally, and expanded upon.

That series of observations which led most directly to the concept of ethylene as a plant growth hormone can be traced back at least to the study in 1878 by Wiesner (350) of nutations or curvatures in the stems of growing seedlings. Wiesner observed that dark-grown seedlings would sometimes curve away from their normal vertical (negatively geotropic) habit to a nearly horizontal orientation, and he interpreted this condition as an "autonomous nutation" induced by darkness. In 1884, Rimmer (292) concluded that such curvatures resulted from high temperatures or low humidity or both. In the same year, Molisch (225) reported on the effects of gaseous contaminants, such as illuminating gas and smoke, on the geotropic behavior of roots. This report and its significance were apparently overlooked by his contemporaries and followers, for Neljubow (237) in 1901 demonstrated independently that the horizontal orientation observed by Wiesner was caused by traces of illuminating gas in the laboratory air. He identified ethylene and acetylene as the active fractions and went on in a series of papers (238–241) to describe in considerable detail the effects of these and other gases and vapors on plant growth. Of the various gases tested, he found ethylene to be by far the most potent in causing the characteristic reduction of elongation, increased radial expansion, and horizontal orientation which came to be known as the "triple response" of legume seedlings (163). These responses to as little as 0.06 ppm of ethylene were observed with seedlings of *Pisum, Vicia, Ervum, Lathyrus,* and *Tropaeolum.* Two responses of current interest which Neljubow apparently did not notice, but which can be seen in photographs that he and others published (163, 240), are an inhibition of leaf or terminal bud expansion and a tightening of the plumular hook.

Neljubow became somewhat preoccupied with the horizontal growth which he interpreted as transverse geotropism (237, 239–241). This was the basis of an extended polemic with Richter (287–290), Molisch (226, 227), von Guttenberg (121), and others who maintained that the curvatures were either an exaggeration of the automonous secondary recurvature just below the apical hook or an exaggerated phototropic curvature, either of which would result from a loss of geotropic sensitivity. Richter, especially, noted that pea seedlings treated with "laboratory air" would consistently curve in the direction of the secondary curvature (away from the plumular hook), and that a similar anatomically oriented curvature would occur in very young pea seedlings which were rotated around the horizontal axis of a clinostat. This, he argued, was evidence of autonomous control in the absence of gravitational responses in the plants. On the other hand, Neljubow had found that once the growing zone had reached the horizontal plane, it would continue to grow in that direction for at least 2 or 3 days. If the plant were reoriented during that time so that the growing zone were placed in an upright position, it would again curve until it reached the horizontal plane. If the ethylene were removed at any time, the stems would revert to negative geotropism and curve upward. In addition, he found that pea seedlings could be oriented to any angle of inclination, ranging from vertically upward through vertically downward, and in the presence of ethylene the stem would curve without regard to anatomical position until the stem tip reached the horizontal plane. The tendency of vertically oriented seedlings to curve away from the direction of the apical hook, as described by Richter, was explained by Neljubow as resulting from the slight inclination imparted by the secondary "autonomous nutation" just below and curving away from the apical hook. In several places, Neljubow (239–241) comments on the remarkable similarity in the behavior of ethylene treated pea seedlings and naturally transversely geotropic organs such as rhizomes and stolons. Thus, he came within a single logical step (he apparently did not suspect the endogenous production of ethylene by plants) of suggesting a possible role for ethylene in naturally occurring transverse geotropism. To our knowledge, this idea has not yet been tested, but Chadwick & Burg (68) have proposed a role for ethylene in the positive geotropism of roots.

Another currently significant observation by Neljubow was that ethylene would not induce transverse geotropism in the presence of strong light or would cause only a partial response in weak light, as from a laboratory window on bright or cloudy days (239). This confirmed and explained Wiesner's (350) original observation that the curvatures occurred primarily in the absence of light and anticipated our recent findings on the photoinduced decrease in sensitivity of plants to ethylene (116).

As noted earlier, during the three decades which followed Neljubow's initial publication (237), most of the research effort was devoted to symptomology of various air pollutants with special emphasis on the development of bioassays for "toxic" agents, especially ethylene. Eventually, however, the triple response of peas and potato sprouts and the epinastic bending of leaf petioles (87, 133) came to be used as bioassays to detect and estimate the production of ethylene by ripening fruit or by vegetative or floral tissue, which in most cases was either injured or senescent (39).

EARLY PROPOSALS FOR THE HORMONAL ROLE OF ETHYLENE

Drawing on previous evidence that both ethylene and auxins would cause root initiation and leaf epinasty in some plants, Zimmerman & Wilcoxon (365) tested the effects of several auxins and their inactive analogues on root initiation, leaf epinasty, and ethylene production. When administered systemically, the active auxins not only stimulated root initiation but caused a marked epinasty of the leaves, accompanied by a surge of ethylene production. These results, along with some additional ethylene-like effects of auxins on pea seedlings and *Mimosa*, were cited (365) to suggest that ". . . some of the effects attributed to the so-called 'growth substances' might be due indirectly to the unsaturated hydrocarbon gas produced in the tissue. . ." Later, Crocker, Hitchcock & Zimmerman (76) proposed the more general hypothesis that ethylene ". . . may act as a natural developmental regulator in a manner similar to the plant auxins." They noted the similarity in the minimum effective concentrations of ethylene and auxins, but failed to point out that, at these minimum levels, ethylene and auxin have generally opposite rather than similar effects. This point was not overlooked by Michener (216), who proposed that the tropistic effects of ethylene could all be explained by its effect on auxin transport or metabolism, and that under natural conditions auxin was necessary to regulate the types of growth induced by exogenous ethylene.

Denny found that an increased rate of ethylene production occurred when tomato stem segments were placed horizontally (while tied to a glass rod to prevent geotropic curvature) as compared to a vertical placement (81), and newly germinated seedlings of lima bean, onion, muskmelon, lettuce, and other plants produced easily detectable amounts of ethylene (82); lesser amounts were produced by germinating cereal grains such as oats, millet, corn, and wheat. Nevertheless, Michener (217) continued to doubt a hormonal role for ethylene, since he found that auxin was necessary in order for applied ethylene to induce swelling in pea stem sections, and that ethylene caused a reduction in the amount of auxin recoverable from pea stems owing to its increased destruction at the cut surface; on the other hand, he was unable to demonstrate any alteration of auxin transport. His suggestion that ethylene was not quantitative in its effects apparently resulted from his use of superoptimal concentrations of the gas ranging from 2.0 ppm to 1000 ppm. Between 1938 and 1962, only a few scattered papers appeared dealing with specific effects of ethylene on growth or with its mode of action, and none attempted to determine an endogenous role in the regulation of growth.

POSSIBLE ROLES OF ETHYLENE IN AUXIN-INDUCED GROWTH PHENOMENA

The earlier proposal that certain effects of auxins on growth and development were attributable to their stimulation of ethylene production (365) has been reiterated in several recent studies. For example, Morgan & Hall (128, 232) have found that 2,4-dichlorophenoxyacetic acid (2, 4-D) induces a sharp increase in ethylene production by cotton plants but has only a modest effect on ethylene production by grain sorghum. A close correlation was found between the production of ethylene and the epinastic bending of petioles caused by application of both 2,4-D and indoleacetic acid (IAA) (128, 232, 233). These observations were extended and supported by Abeles & Rubinstein (15), who found that naphthaleneacetic acid (NAA), IAA, and to a lesser extent indolepropionic acid and indolebutyric acid, would induce an increase in ethylene production by petiole explants of *Phaseolus* which correlated with the relative ability of these compounds to induce abscission in the explants (2). In relation to growth, they observed that more ethylene was produced by tissues which presumably had higher levels of endogenous auxin. For example, higher rates were found in the lower side of geotropically stimulated bean hypocotyls, on the shaded side of phototropically stimulated hypocotyls, and in intact hypocotyls as compared to those which were decapitated or treated with 2,3,5-triiodobenzoic acid. Gibberellin was also found to stimulate ethylene production to some extent, and Curtis (78) attributes the epinastic effects of malformin to the stimulation of ethylene production.

Burg & Burg (49) showed that the classic inhibitory effect of superoptimal concentrations of auxin was mediated (in the case of dicotyledonous stem segments) by the auxin-induced production of ethylene, and more recently they have described a similar function of ethylene in the auxin-induced inhibition of bud growth. The inhibitory effect of auxin on the elongation of monocotyledonous tissues could not be satisfactorily explained on the same basis. Root elongation has long been known to be inhibited by relatively low concentrations of auxin, and this has also been suggested as resulting from induced ethylene production (68). However, a careful study of the kinetics of the inhibition of elongation and the promotion of ethylene evolution by auxin in roots has revealed that the two may be independent effects of the auxin (21).

Another developmental response known to result from an application of either auxins or unsaturated hydrocarbons is the flowering of pineapples (39). Again the effect of auxin appears to be mediated by the ethylene produced by the treated plants (50). Ethylene production in the tissues may explain the flowering of horizontally placed pineapple plants (341), since it is known that this geotropic stimulus increases ethylene formation in stems

(81). It is apparently not known whether an autonomous increase in ethylene production is part of the natural sequence of events leading to the flowering of pineapple or other Bromeliads. Auxin tends to inhibit flowering in *Xanthium* plants which have been photoperiodically induced by short days, and here again the auxin-induced production of ethylene appears to intervene in this response (5).

Many of the formative effects and possible roles of endogenous ethylene have become evident as a result of horticultural applications of auxins. In a comprehensive review of abscission in agricultural crops, Cooper et al. (72) have pointed out the possible induction of ethylene to explain the action of numerous growth regulators and other chemicals. It has long been known that 2,4,5-trichlorophenoxyacetic acid (2,4,5-T) will accelerate growth during the normally quiescent portion (called phase II) of the double sigmoid growth pattern of fig fruits, *Ficus carica,* and it has been found recently that 2,4,5-T induces ethylene formation (202). Although application of 5 ppm ethylene has been shown to inhibit the early, rapid growth of the fig fruit (phase I), it will, like 2,4,5-T, almost completely eliminate the decelleration of growth which normally occurs during phase II (203). The ethylene-induced expansion is accompanied by most of the symptoms of ripening which are normally observed during the later part of the rapid phase III growth. Therefore, it was suggested that normal onset of rapid growth and eventual ripening of the fig fruit may be regulated by the endogenous production of ethylene. Galil (106) got similar results with *Ficus sycomorus* and attributed success of the ancient practice of ripening by wounding to the wound-induced production of ethylene.

REGULATORY EFFECTS OF ENDOGENOUS ETHYLENE

Although the evidence cited above confirms the proposal that ethylene intervenes in certain auxin-induced phenomena, it contributes only circumstantially to the proposal of a normal hormonal role for ethylene in plant growth. The production of ethylene by germinating seeds and seedlings (80, 82, 83, 211, 324) suggests that ethylene might be involved in the growth and development of the embryonic or seedling plants. The first proposal for such a role was suggested by the demonstration that low concentrations of applied ethylene would block the photoacceleration of apical bud expansion and hook opening in etiolated pea seedlings (114). It was then found that these apical tissues of the etiolated seedling were the major site of ethylene production, and that exposure of these tissues to light resulted in a sharp decrease in ethylene production which correlated with the acceleration of growth (115–117). Similar effects of red light on ethylene production and opening of the bean hypocotyl hook have been reported (13, 141, 158). Light has also been found to decrease the tendency of pea stem segments to produce ethylene in response to high concentrations of auxin (49, 57). On the other hand, red light apparently stimulates ethylene formation in dormant lettuce seeds, and application of ethylene will overcome the far-red-induced dormancy (13). Therefore, the production of ethylene in some plant tissues is regulated by the phytochrome system and indeed may be related to a number of photoperiodic or light-induced phenomena. The reduced ability of ethylene to cause transverse geotropism in light-grown plants reported by Neljubow (239) can be observed under red light, along with a reduced ability of ethylene to inhibit leaf expansion or to promote radial expansion of the stems (116). Light does not completely remove the response of the apical hook to ethylene, for the hook can be reclosed after it has been allowed to open following exposure to light (57). Hook closure may also be caused by substances such as auxin (158) and coumarin (234) which induce ethylene formation.

Another important role for the ethylene produced by etiolated seedlings is the regulation of radial expansion of the pea epicotyl in a region just below the apical hook (115, 116). Both the exposure of the plant to red light (which reduces ethylene production) or to CO_2 (a competitive inhibitor of ethylene action) will decrease the final diameter of the epicotyl (116). In fact, the first demonstration of a role of endogenous ethylene as a growth regulator in intact plants was the finding of Goeschl et al. (118) that a sharp increase in ethylene evolution and in radial expansion occurs when the elongation of the etiolated pea epicotyl is mechanically impeded as it would be while emerging from the soil. Both the increase in endogenous ethylene and the resulting increase in diameter appear to be proportional to the amount of mechanical resistance and would therefore adjust the emergence force and mechanical strength of the seedling to the prevailing soil conditions. This, along with the other ethylene-regulated features such as the inhibited expansion of the leaves and plumular hook, all appear to adapt the legume seedling to the conditions of subsurface germination (116). Similar mechanisms may occur in other plants; for example, etiolated potato sprouts have the same general features as pea epicotyls and the same responses to applied ethylene (94, 315). It is possible that the transverse geotropism which occurs when ethylene production is sufficiently stimulated can also contribute to the ability of these shoots to escape mechanical confinement.

The positive geotropism of roots has been attributed to a localized production of ethylene resulting from the asymmetric distribution of auxin (53, 68), as suggested earlier (15). Presumably, the increased production of ethylene on the lower side of a horizontally oriented root would inhibit elongation and cause the root to curve downward. In stems, which require higher concentrations of IAA to induce ethylene production, the accumulation of auxin on the lower side would not be of sufficient magnitude to cause the same response as in roots and would therefore result in an acceleration of growth and an upward curvature. This hypothesis is open to question at present because of evidence that auxin may act directly to inhibit root growth and that the induced ethylene production may be a secondary effect (21).

The possibilities that ethylene may promote or inhibit flowering can be inferred from existing evidence. In addition to mediating some of the effects of auxin on flowering, as noted above, the data of Hall et al. (129) show a higher rate of ethylene production in cotton plants which are flowering or fruiting than in those which are vegetative. Flowering of cotton can be stimulated by ethylene fumigation (129), and a similar induction of flowering in certain tissue cultures has been reported (245). Ethylene has also been reported to stimulate flower initiation in stored iris bulbs (329). In mango, smudging will induce flowering, and this is attributed to the heat rather than the smoke in Singh's review (316); one must wonder if the effect is actually caused by ethylene in the smoke. Minina has been cited (246) as showing that ethylene treatments increase the proportion of female to male flowers on cucumber vines.

Role of Ethylene in Rest

Potatoes.—The possible role of ethylene in potato sprouting has been studied off and on since the gas was first shown to have physiological effects; indeed, the abnormal sprouts observed by Elmer (93) opened the field of investigation of ethylene production by fruits. A comprehensive review of studies on potato dormancy has been presented by Burton (62). Huelin & Barker (144) studied effects of ethylene treatment on respiration rate and sugar content of stored potatoes. Unless the potatoes had a high sugar content because of low temperature storage, ethylene treatment caused a rise in respiration rate and an increase in sugar content. These changes appeared to represent normal senescent changes hastened by ethylene. Burton (61) reviewed earlier work on the effects of ethylene and carbon dioxide on sprouting; results of earlier workers were variable and seemed to depend on the duration of treatment. Brief treatments at intervals stimulated sprouting, while ethylene treatments of longer duration suppressed it. Since conditions leading to ethylene accumulation in storage would also lead to carbon dioxide accumulation, Burton suggests that sprout suppression attributed to high CO_2 was, in fact, caused by ethylene; his own work suggests that carbon dioxide stimulates sprouting when ethylene is removed. This may be another example of the competitive role of the two gases in a system. Poapst et al. (267) made the first rigorous chemical proof that potato tubers contain endogenous ethylene, and treatment with gibberellic acid (GA_3) increased the ethylene content. This result conflicts with Burton's hypothesis, since GA_3 stimulates potato sprouting. It may be that the influence of GA_3 is strong enough to overcome any ethylene produced as a result of its application.

Other plant materials.—Treatments with ethylene have been reported to accelerate or increase the sprouting of various corms and bulbs (79, 123, 338), roots (34), and of hardwood cuttings (338), as well as the germination of some species of seeds (25, 90, 123, 334, 338). As with potatoes, these accelerative effects occurred only when the ethylene was applied as a short pretreatment, such as during inbibition of seeds or for a few hours or days preceding the sprouting of the various buds. Continued treatment after germination or sprouting would inhibit growth of the shoots or leaves, and indeed reports of this effect have been incorrectly cited as evidence that ethylene reinforces rest (61). There is little evidence given in these papers that the organs tested were in a true state of rest, except possibly in the case of peanuts (334). In fact, Denny (79) noted that ethylene was not effective on freshly harvested corms but was effective after one month storage. It is also unfortunate that the concentrations of ethylene applied in these studies (100 ppm to 100 per cent) were far above the levels likely to result from endogenous production, so they contribute little to our knowledge of a normal function of ethylene. However, Ketring and Morgan have stimulated germination of peanut seeds with relatively low concentrations of ethylene and noted a sharp increase in ethylene production concurrent with the end of dormancy (personal communication).

If ethylene does not break rest per se in these tissues, then by what mechanism does it stimulate germination and sprouting? Elmer (93) felt that ethylene broke apical dominance in potato tubers and so led to increased, rather than accelerated, sprouting. A recent clue to the role which ethylene might play in the early stages of germination and the mechanism by which it might act has been provided in the work of Jones (156). He finds that application of ethylene to the isolated barley aleurone layer accelerates the release of the gibberellin-induced amylase enzyme from the aleurone cells. The synthesis of the enzyme was apparently not affected by the ethylene as had been suggested previously (304). The enhanced movement of such hydrolytic enzymes in storage tissues would surely contribute to the growth of sprouts, and could account for the observation by many of the authors cited above that the effects of ethylene treatments would persist for several days. It is quite possible that the production of ethylene by the awakening embryo or bud may constitute part of the hormonal mechanism by which the embryonic tissues control the mobilization of food reserves in the surrounding tissues. It is interesting that the pretreatment of oat coleoptile sections also increases their subsequent growth in response to auxin (197, 217); the effect has been interpreted as either an increased ability to utilize food materials within the tissue or as an undefined increase in sensitivity to auxin.

ETHYLENE AS A PLANT HORMONE

It is now evident that ethylene may be safely referred to as an endogenous plant growth regulator, at least in an increasing number of specific instances. Some may object to its inclusion in the list of plant growth hormones since, as noted by Burg (39), ". . . it would be unique in that it is a vapor at physiological temperatures so that its production, accumulation, transport, and function would involve special problems not encountered in other areas of hormone physiology . . ." Many of the doubts in the past have resulted from a lack of data regarding the concentrations of ethylene within the tissues in question (e.g., 76, 217). Even with the continued improvement of gas chromatographic methods (now capable of detecting less than 10^{-12} moles of ethylene) it has not been possible to determine directly the concentration of the gas in the tissues of a seedling, for example. Some progress toward circumventing this problem has been made, using the physical principles of diffusion (42, 48, 118). This, along with the constantly increasing amount of good correlative data, confirms that sufficient amounts of ethylene probably are produced, diffuse, and accumulate within the plant so that cells producing ethylene may influence the physiological behavior of neighboring cells and tissues. If ethylene were to be transported over the distance typical of other hormones, then its production in the apical zone of the etiolated pea seedling would inhibit the elongation of the entire epicotyl. The production of ethylene in or near meristematic tissues, for example in the pea apex and lateral buds (56, 116, 117) and in tissue cultures (327), suggests that its presence may be directly related to cell division. If so, it could serve in the apical region to coordinate the growth of all cells to a mode suitable to that of the dividing cells. Its ready escape from the tissue provides a control of ethylene effect that eliminates the need for an inactivating system, so the gaseous nature of this hormone may be of considerable adaptive value.

THE ROLE OF ETHYLENE IN ABSCISSION

In addition to its effects on plant growth, ethylene has long been noted for its ability to induce premature abscission of leaves and other organs. In fact, this ability may be horticulturally useful for planting stock before storage or transplanting (218, 270, 281); it can be a horticultural disaster in the case of holly (219, 220), and it assumes new importance in interpreting control of abscission for mechanical harvesting of crops (72). Correlations between increased ethylene production and the induction of abscission by pathogens or auxins provided the first evidence for a role of ethylene in the abscission of leaves and fruit (39). The subject of leaf abscission has been thoroughly reviewed in a recent symposium [*Plant Physiology,* 43:1471–1586 (1968)]; significant references to ethylene appear in each of this group of papers, and that of Burg (41) is specifically devoted to its role.

In recent years, additional evidence has appeared, mostly in relation to chemically induced abscission. For example, the selective herbicidal and defoliative effects of 2,4-D are related (possibly indirectly) to its tendency to induce ethylene production strongly in dicotyledons (cotton), but only slightly in monocots (grain sorghum) (232). The observed correlation between ethylene production induced by NAA and abscission of *Phaseolus* explants (15) has been supplemented by evidence that nearly all abscission accelerators act by inducing ethylene formation (5, 10, 12, 78, 202, 229, 256, 299). Some difficulties in the interpretation of these results have occurred because substances like auxins, cytokinins, and gibberellins can induce ethylene formation in tissues and at the same time apparently protect the treated tissue from the effects of the ethylene (12, 173). Such evidence has been used to explain the differential effects of distally applied auxin (inhibits abscission) and proximally applied auxin (promotes abscission). Both would tend to induce ethylene production in or near the abscission zone, but the proximally applied auxin would move by polar transport through the zone and thus protect it from the effects of the ethylene (6).

The use of explants to evaluate the role of ethylene and other regulators of abscission in the natural abscission of plant organs has resulted in considerable controversy. For example, the explants from *Phaseolus* (7, 12, 299), and possibly those of cotton (6), appear to be insensitive to the effects of abscission accelerators including ethylene for 24 to 48 hr following excision. On the other hand, application of ethylene (127) or of 2-chloroethanephosphonic acid (229) causes a rapid abscission of even the young leaves from intact cotton plants. It has been proposed (41) that the injury-induced production of ethylene in freshly cut explants masks the effects of applied ethylene in the first few hours. Other differences in the behavior of explants have resulted in questions regarding the role of senescence in abscission and hence in the mechanism by which ethylene might induce abscission (12, 14, 105, 143, 254, 255). As yet, it is not known whether ethylene is produced in or near the abscission zone under natural conditions, either preceding or during abscission, so the role of ethylene will not be understood until such evidence is obtained and until the physiology of abscission is further clarified (17, 152).

Although the "ethylene-auxin balance hypothesis" appears no longer to be considered seriously, at least in the form originally proposed, recent reviews (65, 349) are still perpetuating the erroneous assumption that Gawadi & Avery (109) studied the role of ethylene in abscission. All their experiments were conducted with ethylene chlorohydrin, which they and others have mistakenly assumed to be equivalent to ethylene. As Crocker & Barton (75) say in this connection, ". . . ethylene chlorohydrin is a saturated compound that produces none of the hormone-like effects of ethylene and must be used in relatively high concentrations compared with ethylene to produce any effects." Ethylene chlorohydrin is a very toxic chemical, and any ethylene-like effects which it might produce could be attributed to the injury it causes.

MECHANISM OF ETHYLENE ACTION IN GROWTH REGULATION

As in fruit ripening (below), considerable effort has been devoted toward determining the mechanism by which ethylene regulates growth and development, including abscission. There is a possibility, supported by some evidence, that all of these various phenomena may be affected through an identical mechanism. Many of the effects of ethylene on ripening (46), growth (52, 116, 158), and abscission (7, 8, 41) are competitively inhibited by CO_2. Based upon Lineweaver-Burk plots, the apparent kinetics of some of these ethylene responses are remarkably similar, having a half-maximum value (K_m) of about 0.1 to 0.2 ppm. Burg & Burg (52) have described this apparently common molecular site of action as being a metal-containing enzyme because of the known tendency of certain metals to complex with olefins and because of the likelihood that CO_2 might compete weakly for such a site. They have further proposed that the site is of relatively small dimensions, offering considerable hindrance to the entry of larger molecules of olefins and other ethylene analogues. They present evidence that the site may require activation by oxygen before ethylene can be effective (297), although this view has been contested, especially in the case of the acceleration of abscission (8). While little evidence has been presented to conflict with these proposals, by no means do all overt effects of ethylene have the same apparent kinetics as those mentioned. For example, dark-grown leaves are inhibited by considerably lower concentrations of ethylene than are light-grown leaves (116). We have also found that the respiratory and pigmentation changes of 'Honey Dew' melons have a higher (tenfold) minimum and maximum ethylene requirement than does the system which leads to softening of the tissue (Goeschl & Pratt, unpublished), so the possibility of multiple sites of action must be left open. The use of any overt physiological response as a means for kinetic study of the presumed primary site of ethylene action requires that the site be related to a process which is so rate-limiting that no other intermediate step can significantly affect the final result; this point needs further study.

Another proposed primary site of action is the lipid portion of the membranes where ethylene might dissolve and alter the lipophilic/hydrophilic balance. In nearly all studies purporting to show such effects, the tissues or cell components were treated with concentrations ranging from 20 ppm to pure ethylene (38, 190, 248–250, 307). Most growth responses are nearly saturated with applications of about 1 ppm or, in some cases, as little as 0.04 ppm (116), so it is difficult to ascribe these responses to a mechanism which can only be demonstrated with considerably higher concentrations. It is unfortunate, for example, that Nord (247, 249, 250) used pretreatments of pure ethylene in obtaining a persistent stimulatory effect on the activity of isolated "zymase" preparations, for this is the only report of an effect of ethylene on an isolated (albeit crude) enzyme system. It is of interest that Nord related the "protective" effect of ethylene to the presumed lipoid nature of the enzyme. He interpreted the mechanism as being what we would probably now refer to as an allosteric effect, in which ethylene protected the enzyme from the inactivating influence of the reaction products. It is possible, noting the extreme effectiveness of ethylene in some growth responses, that the site of action has an affinity for ethylene much higher than simple lipid solubility.

Growth, flowering, abscission, and fruit ripening (discussed later) may all be considered as developmental phenomena involving the currently accepted model of transcription and translation from DNA to RNA to protein (enzymes). The effects of ethylene on abscission (7, 11, 41, 140, 349) and on growth (141) may be mediated through this mechanism. In her review of the anatomical aspects of leaf abscission, Webster (349) has examined the localization of protein in *Phaseolus* petiole explants. In the ethylene-treated explants, nucleolar RNA and nuclear and cytoplasmic protein increased in the cortical cells proximal to the abscission zone, supporting the work of Abeles & Holm (10). There is indeed evidence of increased activity of various enzymes, especially peroxidases and other hydrolytic enzymes, in tissues treated with ethylene (128, 143, 151, 230, 235, and section on fruit ripening, below). It has not been conclusively proven that proteins (enzymes) are synthesized *de novo,* although some indirect evidence exists (7, 11, 235, 349). The relevance of this intervening mechanism to the primary site of ethylene action is in question, since some effects of ethylene can be seen before new proteins are believed to be synthesized (41, 55). In the case of abscission, there is disagreement whether protein synthesis is greater (11) or lesser (254, 255, 349) in the abscission zone, and whether the induction of enzyme synthesis is a result or a cause of senescence in the surrounding tissue (254, 255). The techniques of Abeles & Holm (10) would not resolve these questions as well as those of Osborne (255) or Webster (349). Evidence for relatively direct effects of ethylene on the transcription and translation processes can be inferred from the evidence that ethylene alters the activity of extracted chromatin (142).

There are two additional physiological effects of ethylene whose relationship to the primary site of action can only be guessed, but which evoke more speculation. The first of these is the hypothesis proposed by Michener (216, 217) that ethylene might be altering auxin transport or metabolism (230, 339). That hypothesis now has considerable (although somewhat qualified) support (3, 39, 49, 53, 54, 230, 231). The most recent interpretation has been given by Morgan et al. (230) to the effect that ethylene inhibits polar auxin transport (Burg refers to this as a decrease in transport capacity) in both intact stems or stem sections of some plant species. However, this requires an extended treatment, with the first symptoms requiring at least 3 to 4 hr, and at least 15 hr for a complete response. A more immediate effect on lateral auxin transport was reported by Burg & Burg (49, 53). There is a considerable range in the responsiveness of the various species reported (230), but in many of the experiments rather high concentrations of ethylene were used. It can be inferred from these reports that ethylene severely or even nearly completely curtails auxin transport. The continued transverse geotropism of the pea seedling described by Neljubow (see above) would preclude this, assuming that some form of auxin transport is necessary for geotropic behavior. The second physiological effect of ethylene, which bears on this problem, is that observed by Jones (156) wherein ethylene stimulates the excretion of alpha-amylase from the aleurone cells of barley. Like the active, directional transport of auxin, the ex·

cretion of enzymes must involve energy-driven enzyme or enzyme-like mechanisms, such as permeases associated with the cell membranes. This might be the identity of the metallo-enzyme suggested by Burg & Burg (52).

The final note on this subject must not overlook the recent observation that ethylene may be incorporated into RNA (313), a fate also suggested for other regulators. If this is of physiological significance, then the mechanisms discussed above may be of a secondary nature, or else may reflect the existence of two or more primary sites or modes of action. It is clear that our understanding of this problem is in its infancy.

ETHYLENE PRODUCTION BY FLOWERS

Burg (39) has cited much of the earlier work on production of ethylene by flowers and the effects of ambient ethylene thereon (186). It should be noted that flowers constitute a considerable portion of the list of plant organs producing enough ethylene to be detected by bioassays or chemical tests (39, and below). Akamine (19) gave chemical proof that fading orchid flowers evolve ethylene; their rate of production is exceedingly high. Phan (263) has added to the list of flowers known to produce the gas and presented quantitative data on rates of production by various flowers and flower parts; the reproductive organs produced more than the perianth. Hall & Forsyth (126) confirmed Phan's observation; in fact, excised floral parts, especially the stigma and style, produced more ethylene than did intact flowers. Most plant tissues produce ethylene when senescent, infected, or wounded, and flowers are no exception (84). Smith et al. (317) observed a surge of ethylene from carnations at the onset of fungal attack, and they were able to accelerate the production of ethylene by inoculating flowers with spores of *Botrytis,* a fungus which appeared not to produce ethylene in culture. Nichols (242) related ethylene production to senescent wilting in the absence of injury or infection; the results were temperature dependent.

Hall & Forsyth (126) found that pollination of blueberry and strawberry flowers increased their ethylene production significantly, and treatment of the flowers with IAA did likewise. They suggest that pollination increases the auxin content, leading to increased ethylene production (49), and it is interesting in this connection that ethylene recently has been reported to stimulate pollen tube growth (305). Using orchids, Burg & Dijkman (60) confirmed the effects of pollination; swelling of the column was attributed to endogenous ethylene formation. Ethylene evolution appeared to be autocatalytic, the fading spreading outward as each cell gassed its neighbor and triggered it to produce ethylene in turn.

FRUIT RIPENING

INTRODUCTION

Fruit ripening has often been presented as though it were a simple definable process, marked by the climacteric rise in respiration. Actually, ripening should be regarded as a collective term covering many changes in the fruit which are not necessarily causally related to each other but which occur more or less in parallel and in a time relation to the climacteric. Fruit ripening is a special case of organ senescence; the fleshy fruit is more complex in its senescence than other plant organs, and all of the changes which occur do not represent deterioration. Many or all of the following phenomena may occur during fruit ripening and final senescence: abscission of the fruit from the plant, change in rate of ethylene production, change in rate of respiration, change in tissue and organelle permeability, change in color (including destruction of chlorophyll, revelation of pigments previously masked, and synthesis of new pigments), change in carbohydrate composition (especially a shift from starch to sugar), changes in pectic composition leading to softening, changes in protein content and composition including enzyme changes, synthesis and release of flavor volatiles, development of wax on the skin, and changes in organic acid composition.

The climacteric.—All of the above changes can be related in time to the climacteric rise in respiration which is characteristic of ripening in most fleshy fruits, so this respiratory pattern provides an excellent framework with which to relate the various phenomena of ripening to one another. However, much effort has been expended in seeking to define and explain the climacteric per se (323), probably because this was historically the first event which was found to be of characteristic occurrence and to be readily measurable (35, 160, 161). It now seems reasonable to suspect that the respiratory pattern only reflects the integrated energy requirements of the various more or less simultaneous but separate processes listed above. Not enough is known in detail about most of these processes in most fruits, but it now appears clear that they are collectively initiated irreversibly by ethylene, and that ethylene is therefore a primary endogenous fruit ripening regulator or hormone. Although minimizing the importance of the climacteric per se, it is convenient and realistic to refer to the climacteric respiration pattern as though it represents the collective ripening process, and we shall do so henceforward. One should remember though that when we relate ethylene phenomena to the climacteric we mean to relate them to all the changes during fruit ripening.

Nonclimacteric fruits.—The concept of nonclimacteric fruits, which was introduced by Biale (29), remains puzzling. Several of the fruits he listed are, in fact, climacteric fruits when their life cycles and physiology are fully investigated. The citrus fruits (30) are the best example of nonclimacteric fruits, if the concept has validity, and whether they show a respiratory climacteric coordinated with ripening changes has been disputed. Aharoni (18) obtained climacteric patterns of respiration and ethylene production only with immature fruits, although he asserts that color changes and calyx abscission accompanied these patterns. The results of Trout et al. (335) were obtained at or below the threshold for chilling injury. Certainly horticulturally mature citrus fruits, especially lemons, can be held for prolonged periods in storage, and a climacteric can be induced at will over a period of several months by ethylene treatment (28). This climacteric is accompanied by many of the usual symptoms of ripening, including color change, pectic changes in the peel, onset of senescence, and stem abscission. These same changes occur over a longer period in the controls, and the fruit usually succumbs to decay, without a well-defined respiratory peak. Fidler (97) believes respiration in oranges is limited by availability of substrate, and it may be that the endogenous ethylene (42) is insufficient to stimulate all tissues of the fruit to pass through the stages of ripening in unison. Vines et al. (342) were able to find endogenous ethylene only in citrus fruits subjected to stress, but their instrument may have been insufficiently sensitive.

ETHYLENE AS A FRUIT RIPENING HORMONE

Because mature but unripe fruits could be ripened by applied ethylene, and self-ripening fruits produced ethylene during the ripening period, it was logical to suspect that endogenous ethylene controlled fruit ripening. However this could not be demonstrated conclusively until sufficiently sensitive methodology existed. Even then, a simple arithmetic plotting of data on ethylene production and respiration rate does not show clearly that increased ethylene precedes increased respiration. However, when the data are presented in log form (276), it is clear that a significant rise (50- to 100-fold) in the rate of ethylene production precedes the rise in respiration rate; in 'Honey Dew' melons the rise in ethylene begins at least 8 days before the preclimacteric minimum.

The role of ethylene as an endogenous fruit ripening agent has been previously reviewed from different points of view. Biale (31, 32) has been reluctant to accept the essentiality of ethylene for ripening, but newer evidence (46, 131) has given strength to the arguments in its favor, especially the experiments of Burg & Burg (51) showing that ripening is delayed by treatments which can actually remove ethylene from within the tissues of preclimacteric fruit, and those of Mapson & Robinson (194) in which ethylene synthesis was controlled when preclimacteric bananas were held at oxygen concentrations between 1 and 7.5 per cent. In this range there was no damage to the fruit, but the synthesis of ethylene was completely controlled, and the fruit did not ripen until restored to air. If ethylene were added to the system, the fruit proceeded to ripen even though still held in low oxygen. It is particularly interesting that the addition of ethylene in the low oxygen system catalyzed subsequent endogenous ethylene production.

Germane to this discussion is the work of Burg & Burg (48) on gas exchange through fruit tissues; they found that passage of ethylene and CO_2 occurred with equal facility, but the nature of any barrier to diffusion was a characteristic of the kind of fruit. Gas exchange was proved to be governed by Fick's law for diffusion. Bussel & Maxie (63) confirmed earlier studies showing that ethylene production was reduced by anaerobiosis; gas exchange between internal and external atmospheres was rapid.

Students of the role of ethylene in fruit ripening have tended to confuse two separate phenomena related to ethylene—ethylene as the trigger of ripening and the excess production of ethylene which accompanies ripening, the climacteric, and final senescence. The latter was the only component of ethylene production which could be measured before the advent of gas chromatography, and the role of this ethylene supply in fruit ripening is unknown. Because of the complexity of fruit ripening and the relation of respiration thereto, there is no reason to believe that there should be any direct relation between gross rate of respiration and rate of ethylene production (31, 33, 39); a lack of such a direct relation should not be taken as evidence against an active relation of ethylene to ripening.

It appears that fruits may fall into several classes in their ripening response to ethylene. In most fleshy fruits, the onset of ripening is preceded by an increase in ethylene production. In fact, the mechanism for ethylene production is present throughout the life of the fruit, although the concentration of ethylene may not rise to a physiologically effective level until just before the onset of the climacteric (39, 42, 46, 188, 189, 194). Earlier observations, with less sensitive methods, had led Kidd & West (162) to propose that ". . . throughout its growth the apple produces ethylene in very small quantities, but that a minimum threshold concentration in the tissues is necessary before respiratory activity is affected." Pratt & Goeschl (276) have shown that 'Honey Dew' melon belongs in this category with an absolute requirement for a minimum concentration (about 3 ppm) of ethylene in the tissues to induce ripening; the sensitivity of the fruit to ethylene does not change as it matures, and ripening is not controlled by attachment to the vine. In a few species, notably avocado (43) and mango (40, 44), significant concentrations of ethylene may be present some time before ripening, but the response to ethylene is inhibited until after the fruit is harvested. In apple, it appears that a step in ethylene synthesis may be inhibited by a product from the parent tree (215); when detached from the tree, the inhibitor presumably disappears and the rate of ethylene production rises (351). In another group of fruits, including certain kinds of banana (47), a presumably effective ethylene concentration may be present in the unripe fruit, but the fruit is insensitive to that concentration at that stage of its development; as the fruit matures, it becomes more sensitive, and ripening ensues when sensitivity matches the endogenous ethylene content. Ripening of apples can be delayed by application of succinic acid-2,2-dimethyl hydrazide (known commercially as "Alar," "B-995," or "B-9"), and this effect can be overcome by ethylene treatment (183). It is not known whether the chemical acts by inhibiting ethylene formation specifically or by reducing its effectiveness in the fruit. On the other hand, the effects of various growth regulators on fruit ripening are now believed to be attributable to induced ethylene production by the treated fruit (72).

In contrast to the tree fruits mentioned, it is interesting that ethylene production, ripening, and senescence occur at about the same age from anthesis, regardless of age at harvest, in several annual crops such as tomato (189) and melons (209, 276). It appears that the basic ethylene forming mechanism exists and operates at a low level, but it is not fully activated until the fruit reaches a critical physiological age. If the fruit is harvested too young, it is never capable of being fully activated, but if the fruit has reached the critical state of maturity with regard to this system, ethylene production will somehow be activated and will then trigger the ripening complex, including further ethylene production (276). Dostal & Leopold (86) showed that gibberellin would delay development of red color in tomato fruits while not significantly changing their respiratory pattern. This suggests that gibberellin may oppose ethylene action in some parts of the ripening process, as it does in some other phenomena (304), and it may participate in the control of ripening.

Use of Ethylene in Commercial Fruit Ripening

As Burg (39) has pointed out, ethylene accelerates the ripening of all fleshy fruits including the pericarp of pecans and walnuts, erroneously referred to as "dry fruits." Successful use of ethylene requires mature fruit, an adequate concentration and duration of treatment, favorable temperature, and an atmosphere neither too low in oxygen nor too high in carbon dioxide. If the fruit has started to ripen spontaneously, it will be producing adequate ethylene itself, and treatment will be without further effect. A large number of papers have appeared in horticultural trade journals around the world with recommendations for commercial practice; it would not be useful to list them here. Kaltenbach (157) has summarized the practical information to 1938, and Rakitin (280) has summarized much Russian work. Ethylene was early proposed for blanching celery (157), but this was never an important commercial practice, and blanching varieties are no longer popular.

Ethylene is now used commercially for very few crops, although it has been tested on many. Banana handlers are usually prepared to use ethylene although they prefer not to; Von Loesecke (344) has summarized the earlier work with this fruit and Simmonds (314) the more recent. Ethylene is frequently used in removing green color from citrus fruits before they are marketed; Miller (221, 223), Rose et al. (296), and Grierson & Newhall (119) have reviewed much of this literature. In the western United States, almost all 'Honey Dew' melons are treated with ethylene before shipment, and those that are not should be (271, 272, 274–276) in order to unify the ripeness of shipments and to initiate ripening in melons which are horticulturally mature but which will not produce enough ethylene for self-ripening.

Although most fleshy fruits which are mature but as yet unripe will respond to ethylene treatment before they start to produce their own ethylene, there is no commercial advantage in treating most fruits, as they will ripen soon enough under proper holding conditions. If anything, it is usually preferable to delay ripening, and some effort has been made to eliminate ethylene from commercial storages for fruits and flowers (see below). Nevertheless, the question arises frequently from the trade whether ethylene should be used, especially for tomatoes which are often picked mature-green for the market. Pratt & Workman (278) reviewed work on the effect of ethylene treatments on tomato ripening, and Lyons & Pratt (189) studied the treatment of fruits at various ages. Technological changes may make reconsideration of tomato treatments advisable (181).

Eaks (91) re-examined the old problem of persimmon ripening, finding that ethylene would hasten ripening of the fruit with normal mushy softening and removal of astringency. Alternatively, treatment of mature fruits with CO_2 would remove the astringency but the fruits remained firm; this treatment prevented subsequent soft ripening, even under ethylene treatment. Other fruits whose response has been investigated include apple (353), cantaloupe (209), Chinese gooseberry (356), cranberry (88), cucumber (23), fig (203), and olive (201). Fruits whose ripening mechanism has been damaged by chilling can not respond fully to ethylene (236).

EVOLUTION OF ETHYLENE BY FRUIT

So far as we know, the first observation of what we now recognize as the production of ethylene by plant tissue was made by an alert layman. Cousins (73) says: "Experiments on the emanations from oranges and bananas were carried out to test the contention of Captain Selfe, R.N.R., the Commander of the S.S. Port Antonio, that the gases from oranges packed in a hold were apt to cause premature ripening of bananas. This was found to be the case . . ." in confirming tests carried out in the laboratory of the Jamaica Department of Agriculture. Other early observations of the influence of emanations from one plant tissue on another were also published in obscure journals (66, 291), so it fell to Elmer (93) to attract widespread attention first. These and related early works have been reviewed by Thornton (333) and Von Loesecke (344). In addition to this historical material, much evidence for ethylene evolution by fruits and other plant tissues has been reviewed (39, 131). Some additional works on specific fruits include apple (37, 351), banana (199), cantaloupe (210), citrus fruits (18, 342), cranberry (99), fig (202), peach (130, 179), and pear (137, 139, 265, 294). Although a study of snap bean fruits revealed large changes in respiration rate as the fruit matured, no cycle of ethylene production was detected (348).

EFFECTS OF ETHYLENE TREATMENT OF FRUITS

When the possibility of hastening the ripening of fruits was first discovered, there was concern that this might cause delivery of an inferior or harmful product to consumers. This anxiety has been alleviated. It was discovered that immature fruits could not be ripened by ethylene treatment, and fruits ripened under the influence of ethylene proved to have the same nutritional value as those harvested at the same time and allowed to ripen without the treatment (39, 333).

Numerous workers have investigated the effects of ethylene on fruits, reporting changes in chemical composition or biochemical characteristics which were attributed to ethylene treatments. In retrospect, now that the complexity of ripening is better understood, it can be seen that most of these authors were actually comparing ripening fruits (stimulated to ripen early by ethylene treatment) with unripe fruits harvested at the same time. Alternatively, they treated fruits harvested before ripening was initiated, and compared them with those which were allowed to ripen on the plant. In either case, they have investigated the changes which normally occur in fruit tissues during ripening, and which were triggered by ethylene treatment; no direct effect of ethylene has been shown. For example, Regeimbal & Harvey (283) compared enzyme activity in pineapple fruits harvested at the same time. One lot was created with ethylene, the other was not. Obviously, they were comparing fruits of different ripeness states and could not say that this was an effect of ethylene directly on enzymes. Even in recent work (251), increased volatile production by ethylene-treated lemons is reported as an effect of the gas. Ethylene hastens all ripening and senescence phenomena of fruits, and to show a true chemical effect of ethylene treatment, one must compare fruits of the same physiological age.

ETHYLENE BIOCHEMISTRY

BIOCHEMICAL EFFECTS OF ETHYLENE

Since the earliest work on the biochemical effects of ethylene (134), it has been apparent that most work purporting to deal with this subject has not dealt with the direct biochemical action of ethylene but indirectly with biochemical changes which occur in tissues that have been treated with ethylene. The changes which have been examined in this way are almost certainly the changes which would take place in due course as fruits ripen or as other plant parts senesce, and it is not proven whether ethylene acts directly on an enzyme or, in an as yet undefined way, acts to affect the general condition of cells and tissues so that a particular reaction can take place sooner because of the treatment. For example, Jones (156) showed that ethylene enhanced the apparent activity of α-amylase by barley aleurone cells when gibberellic acid was present, but the effect of ethylene was only to enhance the release of the enzyme from the tissue; it had no effect on the total amount present, although Scott & Leopold (304) had proposed an effect of ethylene on enzyme synthesis. When Ramsey & Wang (282) examined the catabolism of ripening tomato fruits, they found that the metabolic pathways were the same, whether or not ripening was hastened with ethylene treatment.

Hansen (132) treated immature pears with ethylene, and the rate of respiration increased as did the concentration of protein nitrogen; these were accelerations of the normal pattern. Metabolism of malic and shikimic acids was affected also, but he had insufficient data to state whether they were in the normal trend. It appeared to Hansen that ethylene was exerting its effect on a mechanism or substance which controls the normal pattern of development rather than on individual reactions of the ripening complex. This concept was carried forward in greater detail by Frenkel et al. (102).

Herrero & Hall (138) treated young cotton plants with ethylene until the leaves were about to fall and then examined various enzyme activities in leaf extracts; controls were held in chambers without ethylene for the same length of time. A number of enzyme activities were greater in the extracts of treated leaves. When Turkova and co-workers (192, 336) sprayed tomato plants with ethylene-saturated water, they observed an increase in RNA content, a decrease in DNA content, and increased ATPase activity in the leaves and stems. In these and similar experiments, it cannot be determined whether ethylene actually affected the enzymes or whether instead it was accelerating general senescence responses of the tissue.

Potatoes and parsnips treated with ethylene are said by Stahmann et al. (326) to show an increase in polyphenol oxidase activity but not in peroxidase; carrot, turnip, and radish tissue showed neither effect, but sweet potato showed an increase in both. Imaseki et al. (151) studied effects of ethylene in sweet potato slices. In short-term experiments, there was a rapid increase in the rate of peroxidase synthesis when ethylene was added to a system and a rapid decrease in rate of synthesis when it was withdrawn; if ethylene binds to a cellular component to stimulate the reaction, the binding is reversible. Phenylalanine-ammonia lyase was also increased as was the content of chlorogenic acid. Less than 10 ppm were required for maximal effect. Shimokawa & Kasai (313) treated morning glory seedlings with ethylene-^{14}C and found incorporation of radioactivity into the lighter RNA fractions. They believe this resembles the binding of IAA to RNA and that it might induce a conformational change in the RNA. Ethylene treatment of green banana peel tissue increased the incorporation of ^{32}P into RNA (140). Some biochemical responses to ethylene in abscission have been mentioned above.

A response to ethylene treatment may help define the attainment of critical stages of fruit maturity. For example, Rowan et al. (298) treated immature cantaloupe fruits with ethylene, and although a respiratory increase could be induced in fruits as young as 9 days old, an increase in ATP with corresponding decrease in ADP was seen only in fruits harvested at 23 days or older. These are about the youngest melon fruits that will ripen after harvest.

MECHANISM OF ETHYLENE ACTION

How ethylene exerts its effect on the initiation of ripening is not yet clear. Ethylene has not been shown to be incorporated into any known sequence of biochemical events. One is forced to wonder if its effect is then on the physical state of the cells or membranes, so that reactions can go forward that were previously prevented, perhaps by compartmentation or by the masking of active sites. Burg & Burg (52) restudied the specificity of ethylene and related compounds for biological responses, and concluded that ethylene binds to a metallic receptor from which it can be competitively displaced by carbon dioxide.

On the other hand, it has long been thought that ethylene might affect cell permeability (122), and ethylene has been reported to alter the composition of lipids in stored peas (171) and to induce changes in the distribution of lipid materials and enzymes in plant tissues (340), phenomena which may relate to potential membrane effects.

Changes in tissue permeability are associated with the maturation and ripening of fruits; the evidence includes leakage of solutes, increase in free space, and liquid filling of intercellular spaces. Sacher (301) showed that leakage of solutes increased progressively with the climacteric rise in ripening banana and avocado fruits and noted that these results were consistent with the hypothesis that alteration in membrane properties may cause the climacteric—an hypothesis that can be traced back to the theory of change in "organization resistance" as the explanation of the climacteric proposed by Blackman & Parija (36).

Lyons & Pratt (190) showed that rather high concentrations of ethylene could cause reversible swelling of isolated mitochondria and postulated that this might explain the role of ethylene in enhanced respiration and other metabolic processes. Olson & Spencer (252, 253) prepared reasonably active mitochondria from bean cotyledons to test the mechanism of ethylene action, and found that ethylene concentrations as low as 20 ppm could affect mitochondrial permeability as revealed by volume changes. (They obtained similar results with mitochondria from rat liver and yeast.) Their results with inhibitors suggest that ethylene may increase the adenosine triphosphatase activity of the mitochondria and hence affect cellular metabolism, including respiration. They were not able to demonstrate an effect of ethylene on the purified enzyme.

Burg el al. (58) reported that ethylene did not alter the pattern of leakage from pea sections and argued that permeability of the tonoplast to sugar remained unaltered in banana fruits despite the presence of ethylene, so that Sacher's (301) relation of permeability changes to the respiratory climacteric was not valid. However, Sacher (302, 303) studied banana tissue further and showed that there was also a decline in the capacity of the tissue to take up and retain solutes and an acceleration in leakage of amino acids, so it was not necessary to base his contention on sugar leakage alone. Sacher's curve for permeability changes (as per cent free space) in the preclimacteric and early climacteric stages resembles closely curves for ethylene production by tissue.

Because Sacher's permeability change (302, 303) was observable 4 days before initiation of the respiratory climacteric, he assumed that it also preceded the initial rise in ethylene production. However, his assumption was based on an inadequate consideration of ethylene data presented by others (47). When ethylene production data are presented in log form (276), it can be seen that an increase in ethylene production actually starts much earlier and very likely precedes the permeability change.

Hulme et al. (149) hold that the initiation of the climacteric cannot be related to general changes in cell or tissue permeability (302), since they found that, in apple, the permeability changes observed were characteristic of the uptake of particular substrates. They admit, however, that small selective permeability changes could be mediated by enzymes and could lead to increased enzyme synthesis. Using water flux as an index of tissue slice permeability, Von Abrams & Pratt (343) showed that a brief treatment with ethylene could increase the permeability of young cantaloupe fruit tissue. They argued that, since this change in permeability could be induced by a treatment too brief to cause a typical respiratory response, then the permeability response must precede the respiratory response in fruit during a continuous exposure to ethylene, lending weight to the concept that fruit ripening may be initiated by permeability changes as an early response to the triggering action of ethylene. Burg (41) has again criticized permeability studies without referring to Sacher's most recent work (302, 303), and his arguments opposing permeability change as an explanation of the results of Von Abrams & Pratt (343) were recognized and refuted in their report. Neither induced changes in wall plasticity nor in solute content can account for the observed water efflux from ethylene-treated tissue which exceeds that from the control within a few hours. Further study of these phenomena is indicated.

Hansen (131) reviewed much information on active ripening changes in fruits and the relation of the climacteric to ripening. The work on changes in protein content is particularly important (145–148), as there seems to be no doubt that an important early event in ripening is synthesis of enzyme protein (107, 108, 149, 184, 285). In 1967, Hansen (132) showed that application of ethylene stimulated respiration and protein synthesis in immature pears and suggested that ethylene set in motion the train of biochemical events required for ripening. The same response had been shown earlier in apple (145).

Frenkel et al. (102) used inhibitors of protein synthesis to show that protein synthesis was essential for fruit ripening and for the large increase in ethylene production which accompanies the climacteric. They were led to conclude that ethylene is an effector for specific protein syntheses and is then a product of ripening metabolism involving some of the same proteins. Applied ethylene could not overcome the inhibitory effect of cycloheximide or actinomycin-D infiltration. Rhodes et al. (284, 286) also showed that ethylene could induce more rapidly an enzyme system for malate decarboxylation in apple peel slices, and inhibitors of ethylene production prevented development of the malate effect, because synthesis of new protein was required. In preclimacteric apple peel disks, Galliard et al. (108) showed that cycloheximide would inhibit development of the ethylene-producing system but would not inhibit ethylene production once the necessary system was present.

Perhaps ethylene production in maturing and ripening fruit can be considered in at least three stages. A system for making ethylene exists in the fruit, but it is operating at an ineffectively low level because of insufficiency of substrate, cofactor, or a critical enzyme. Meigh et al. (215) suggest that the first event of ripening might be production or activation of lipoxidase. This is confirmed by the work of Galliard et al. (108), showing that addition of linolenic acid and lipoxidase together (but not separately) initiated ethylene production in fresh preclimacteric apple peel slices. Influence on the cell membranes might then result in formation of lipid peroxides. These in turn might increase the formation of ethylene (196) to the critical level for induction of ripening (1 to 3 ppm in the tissue), perhaps by further changes in membrane permeability. In due course, the ethylene production autocatalytically increases still further (194), perhaps playing a part in the final senescence of the fruit.

The following sequence is envisaged by Hulme's group (108, 149) for the events during the climacteric in apple peel: increasing incorporation of acetate into lipid; second, enzyme synthesis and enzymic production of ethylene; third, increased capacity to incorporate labeled valine into protein; finally, increased capacity to decarboxylate added malate. Unfortunately, these studies are based on tissue slices with inevitable and undetermined wound effects (108). Final working out of the detailed sequence of events in intact fruit will require more effort with very sensitive methods and very careful sampling. If production or activation of lipoxidase controls the first triggering action of ethylene, what controls its production?

While it may be unlikely that increased membrane permeability is a direct cause of the initiation of fruit ripening, such changes may make possible the biochemical reactions collectively responsible for ripening. The ripening trigger, presumably ethylene, may act through induced permeability change to set off irreversibly the reactions of ripening and senescence. Whatever control the cell membranes may exert may be lost as their permeability control mechanism is upset. If ethylene cannot be accepted as directly acting on the membranes in this fashion, it is still conceivable that this gas acts on the system which does control membrane integrity. The metal-binding concept of Burg & Burg (52) helps explain the actions of high carbon dioxide or low oxygen concentrations in delaying fruit ripening. Carbon dioxide was shown to be a competitive inhibitor of ethylene, and oxygen insufficiency reduced the effect of ethylene at concentrations that did not seriously affect respiration. Young et al. (364) found some results that do not fit this concept; in lemons, the addition of both 10 ppm ethylene and 5 per cent CO_2 stimulates respiration more than either did separately.

BIOSYNTHESIS OF ETHYLENE BY *Penicillium digitatum*

Although other microbes have been shown to produce ethylene, none is known to equal *Penicillium digitatum* in the rate of production from a comparable medium. This copious production of ethylene led to its being the first such fungus discovered, as the ethylene was readily detected by bioassays and relatively crude chemical tests. Although Biale (27) and Miller et al. (224) independently showed ethylene production specifically by *P. digitatum*, Chace & Sorber (67) had reported that "in storing lemons, it has been known that the fruit in boxes adjacent to those containing decayed fruits would color sooner than that in boxes not so located," and *P. digitatum* was almost certainly among the molds present.

It was early thought that this fungus could be used to determine easily the biosynthetic mechanism for ethylene, but this has not proved to be the case. While the fungus grows readily on completely known media, ethylene production ceases when the mycelial mat is disturbed. It appears that ethylene is produced during active growth of the culture and will be produced while it is growing on a variety of carbon sources (39, 111, 259, 261, 322). From labeling experiments, Phan (259, 261) concluded that ethylene is derived from C-2 or C-3 of glucose and is formed easily from alanine, glycerol, and ethanol. The rapidity of appearance of radioactivity in the ethylene produced led him to suggest that ethanol was the closest precursor of ethylene; alanine and glucose were further away in a reaction chain.

Wang et al. (346) cultured the fungus on labeled glucose and four amino acids, each closely related to a member of the TCA cycle. All were active in ethylene production, and they propose that the conversion of glucose carbon atoms to ethylene followed the usual glycolytic and TCA cycle steps. They suggest that ethylene or its precursor may be derived from the middle carbon atoms of fumarate. Jacobsen & Wang (153) later suggested acrylic acid as an intermediate between fumaric acid and ethylene. Additional amino acids were tested by Sprayberry et al. (325), confirming the concept of ethylene formation via glycolysis and the TCA cycle.

Gibson (110) showed pyruvate-2- or -3-^{14}C gave labeled ethylene, but that labeled in the -1- position did not. Gibson & Young (113) found that *P. digitatum* produced ethylene most effectively from acetate-2-^{14}C or pyruvate -3-[14]C. They concluded that in the fungus only C-2 of acetate or C-3 of pyruvate are extensively incorporated in the ethylene molecule, and that the path to ethylene synthesis is not via the steps of the TCA cycle; rather TCA cycle intermediates go to pyruvate or glycolate and acetate, where C-2 or C-3 combines with another molecule leading in turn to ethylene synthesis. Ketring et al. (159) carried this line of investigation further and found that acetate-2-^{14}C and citrate-2,4-^{14}C were quite comparable as ethylene precursors in 30-min. incubations. When acetate 2-^{14}C condenses with oxalacetate, C-4 of citrate is labeled so it is most probable that C-4 of citrate is converted to ethylene. Monofluoracetate prevented incorporation of label from acetate or citrate into ethylene, but addition of isocitrate restored ethylene production, suggesting the following sequence of reactions:

$$\text{Acetate} \rightarrow \text{citrate} \rightarrow \text{isocitrate} \rightarrow \rightarrow \rightarrow \text{ethylene}$$

Uniformly labeled methionine was not metabolized to ethylene by *P. digitatum* in a 1-hr incubation. Any specifically labeled metabolite that can provide label to the methylene carbons of citrate could serve as an ethylene precursor, accounting for observations of other workers.

The fact that *P. digitatum* can metabolize many carbon sources into its entire organic complement, including ethylene, confuses attempts to trace the mechanism of ethylene production in this organism. Altering the carbon source alters its growth rate and so alters the rate of ethylene production indirectly. Even tracer experiments which yield radio-ethylene from labeled sources can only show that ethylene is made ultimately from such a source, but it cannot be claimed that it is made directly. Most of the metabolic steps which yield carbon dioxide and ethylene from glucose, for example, are readily reversible. Hence, feeding experiments of the sort so far carried out with *P. digitatum* cannot be as conclusive as experiments showing ethylene production by specific enzymes from specific substrates. It is, of course, very likely that the mechanisms for ethylene production by this and other fungi are quite different from the mechanisms operating in higher plant tissue such as fruits.

BIOSYNTHESIS OF ETHYLENE BY HIGHER PLANT TISSUES

In this section we will consider work relating to ethylene production in fruits and other tissues of higher plants. Work in this field has been very active since the review of Hansen (131). While many compounds have been shown to be precursors of ethylene, their low rate of conversion in a reasonable time in tracer experiments suggests that they are far back in any metabolic series (277). Direct proof of the path of ethylene synthesis requires a high rate of conversion of labeled carbon into ethylene and ultimately the isolation and characterization of the enzymes involved.

Nonenzymatic systems.—The formation of ethylene from peroxidized linolenate and methionine in a nonenzymatic model system consisting of Cu^{++} and ascorbate was first described by Lieberman & Mapson (178), and they suggested that linolenate and methionine might be precursors of ethylene *in vivo*. Subsequently, Abeles (4) found that the level of linolenate in plant tissues did not correlate with the rate of ethylene production and questioned whether linolenate could serve as a precursor, but Wooltorton et al. (352) had estimated that a rise in lipoxidase activity preceded the evolution of ethylene in apple and suggested that lipids may play an important role in ethylene formation (215). More recently, Lieberman & Kunishi (174) reported that propanal, which is a major breakdown product of peroxidized linolenate, forms ethylene efficiently in their model system and also stimulates ethylene formation in tomato tissue. However, Baur & Yang (26) have shown that carbons 2 and 3 of propanal give rise to ethylene in Lieberman's model system but are not converted into ethylene by apple tissue.

In a Cu^{++}-H_2O_2-ascorbate system, methionine was converted to ethylene more effectively than linolenate (176). Carbons 3 and 4 of methionine were shown to be converted to ethylene. Methional was a very effective producer of ethylene and was thought to be an intermediate in the reaction forming ethylene from methionine. Yang et al. (359, 360) developed a nonenzymatic photochemical system which also produced ethylene from carbons 3 and 4 of methionine (and accounted elegantly for the rest of that molecule) in the presence of flavin mononucleotide and light; the role of FMN had been observed by Abeles & Rubinstein (16), but their proposal for an enzymic reaction was not confirmed (359). The FMN-light system was much more efficient than the Cu^{++}-H_2O_2-ascorbate system (176). The analogues of methionine (ethionine and α-hydroxy-γ-methylmercaptobutyric acid) were equally effective, and α-keto-γ-methylmercaptobutyric acid and β-methylmercaptopropionaldehyde (methional) were three times as effective. The latter two derive from methionine by oxidative deamination and decarboxylation, again suggesting that they may be intermediates. Shimokawa & Kasai (311) report formation of ethylene from the ethyl moiety of ethionine in a similar system. The presence of components of one of these systems as "impurities" may account for ethylene production which has been attributed to various *in vitro* systems which have been unconfirmed or disputed.

Another nonenzymatic system has been proposed by Thompson et al. (332). The subtrate is β-alanine and the reaction required autoclaving with pyridoxal hydrochloride and Cu^{++}; conversion to ethylene was only 0.0028 per cent. While they propose this as a model for enzymatic production from β-alanine, the conditions seem too severe to be useful.

Enzymatic systems.—Enzymatic systems for ethylene production have been sought actively in several laboratories, and results have appeared almost simultaneously from each. Soluble enzymes were extracted from pea seedlings by Ku et al. (166) and from cauliflower florets by Mapson & Wardale (195). Both systems produced ethylene from methional but not from methionine, required enzyme and cofactor fractions (358), and resembled each other in many aspects. While the pea seedling enzyme system utilized oxygen, the cauliflower system required hydrogen peroxide.

Yang (357, 358) was first to demonstrate ethylene formation by peroxidase from either methional or α-keto-γ-methylmercaptobutyric acid. The system requires pure horseradish peroxidase, sulfite, monophenol, Mn^{++}, and oxygen; hydrogen peroxide can replace Mn^{++} and oxygen. Because of its resemblance, he speculated that the pea seedling and cauliflower floret enzymes were also peroxidases. Mapson & Wardale (196) agreed and suggested that their enzyme might be an iron-proteinate peroxidase rather than a copper enzyme. They also showed that their peroxide-generating system was probably a glucose oxidase. Cauliflower florets contained a lipoxidase which could supply the necessary peroxides if linolenic or other unsaturated acids were present. The latter finding is particularly interesting in view of the observations of Meigh et al. (215) that a rise in lipoxidase concentration precedes the increase in ethylene production associated with the climacteric; they suggest that production or activation of lipoxidase might be the first event in the biogenesis of ethylene.

The nature of the heat-stable cofactor required in the cauliflower peroxidase system was elucidated by Mapson & Mead (193). It consists of two components; one is phenolic in nature and appears to be an ester of *p-coumaric* acid, and the other was identified as methanesulfinic acid. In its action, methanesulfinic acid proved to be fully comparable to the sulfite of Yang's horseradish peroxidase system (357).

It has been believed that production of ethylene in fruits ceases when the cells are disintegrated (195). This problem has been clarified by Ku et al. (167, 168); attempts to demonstrate production of ethylene from α-keto-γ-methylmercaptobutyrate by a tomato fruit homogenate were unsuccessful until the homogenate was fractionated with ammonium sulfate and either dialyzed or treated with activated carbon or Sephadex. These treatments removed heat-stable inhibitors, probably *o*-dihydric phenols such as quercetin and caffeic acid derivatives. When the inhibitors were removed, the active enzyme appeared to be a peroxidase with characteristics similar to those reported above.

Yang (358) has incorporated the evidence for the methionine pathway into the following scheme:

Glucose → pyruvic acid → acetyl Co A → fumaric acid → aspartic acid → aspartic-β-semialdehyde → homoserine → homocysteine → methionine → α-keto-γ-methylmercaptobutyric acid → (methional) → ethylene.

That the methionine pathway may be the true *in vivo* situation is supported by Lieberman et al. (177) and Burg & Clagett (59). Both groups showed that carbons 3 and 4 of methionine were converted to ethylene when supplied to plant tissues. However, Galliard et al. (108) could not stimulate ethylene production by addition of methionine to peel disks from preclimacteric apples.

Frey-Wyssling (103, 104) speculated that ethylene might be formed from alanine via pyruvate and acetaldehyde, and Spencer and her co-workers (212–214, 330, 331) have proposed that β-alanine is the precursor of ethylene. They suggested a pathway of biosynthesis via propionate and acrylate (214), but the best conversion claimed for ethylene production from β-alanine is only 0.002 per cent (331). They suggest that methionine can go to ethylene via propionate, but Lieberman & Kunishi (175) report no incorporation of carbon from propionate into ethylene. The evidence seems much stronger that ethylene is derived from methionine via α-keto-γ-methylmercaptobutyrate and methional as possible intermediates. Most compounds that have been proposed, including β-alanine and all TCA cycle intermediates (308, 310), can be accommodated as distant precursors in Yang's proposal, as can the interesting suggestions of Moreno Calvo (228), which he based on chemical reasoning.

For some years it has been thought that plant mitochondria might play a part in ethylene biosynthesis (131, 312). However, there is now quite conclusive evidence that ethylene is formed by a soluble peroxidase (above), and Ku & Pratt (165) have shown that the only ethylene produced by a very high quality mitochondrial preparation from tomato fruit can be attributed to soluble enzyme as an impurity. It is also likely that the results of other workers may be attributed to the presence of a nonenzymatic system in their particular preparations.

MISCELLANEOUS ETHYLENE RELATIONS

Ethylene in Relation to Stresses

Radiation.—Radiation treatment as a means for extending the life of fruits in storage or marketing channels has been of world-wide interest since study of the peaceful use of atomic energy began to be encouraged. Because many fruits are stored for long periods or shipped over long distances, it was natural to hope that they might profit from radiation treatment. Naturally, this raised questions regarding the effects of radiation on the ripening process and, inevitably, on the role of ethylene in relation to both radiation and ripening. Maxie & Abdel-Kader (198) have recently written a very thorough general review of the subject.

Young (361) treated preclimacteric avocados with low doses of radiation and found that respiration and ethylene production were immediately stimulated, but subsequent rates were lower than in controls; ripening was delayed but normal. Higher doses injured the fruit; ripening was inhibited, but ethylene production remained relatively high. Once normal ethylene synthesis and the climacteric were initiated, no effect of radiation could be perceived. Because the amount of ethylene induced was relatively independent of radiation dose, it did not appear to be formed by direct radiation conversion. Young postulates that ethylene production follows a radiation-induced membrane lesion.

When preclimacteric pears were irradiated at several stages of the climacteric and with various doses of radiation (198, 208), there was an immediate small stimulation of ethylene production, but after doses large enough to inhibit ripening, the rate subsequently declined. Ripening was not affected by their noninhibiting treatments, but the treated fruits produced higher levels of ethylene at the climacteric peak than did the controls. Pears irradiated at the climacteric peak showed a decreased rate of ethylene production. Injurious doses of radiation could not be counteracted by ethylene treatment. On the other hand, treatment of peaches and nectarines (206) stimulated ethylene production and ripening with radiation doses that inhibited both in pears; the rate of ethylene production was higher than in the controls.

If preclimacteric bananas were treated with low doses of radiation (199), the production of ethylene, the climacteric, and ripening were delayed but normal. Treatments applied after initiation of the climacteric were without effect. A longer time was required to stimulate irradiated bananas with an ethylene treatment than was required for the controls, suggesting that the radiation doses reduced the sensitivity of the fruit to ethylene.

Lee et al. (172) studied the effect of gamma radiation on four stages of tomato fruit development. There was an immediate rise in respiration rate and ethylene production which soon diminished to near normal. Subsequent ripening was delayed and abnormal in the more mature fruits, but the younger fruits showed some recovery from the treatment. Mature and ripening tomatoes were studied by Adbel-Kader et al. (1) with generally similar results. Very high doses tended to depress ethylene evolution. Ripening was delayed or inhibited in proportion to radiation dosage and appeared not to be directly related to the change in rate of ethylene production.

When lemons, which do not normally show a well-defined climacteric, were treated with radiation, the respiration rate and content of ethylene were increased with increasing doses (204, 205). The respiratory and coloring responses resemble those caused by ethylene treatment. Similar results were obtained with oranges (120).

The production of ethylene by etiolated pea seedlings was greatly increased by γ-radiation for periods up to 3 hr; the rate declined below normal afterward (306). The amount of ethylene formed was not proportional to the dose and appears to result mainly from stimulation of the metabolic pathways rather than from direct radiolysis of pea seedling constituents. Luchko et al. (185) found that radiation increased ethylene production by maturing peas, attributing the increase to an increased amino acid content in accord with earlier hypotheses that ethylene was formed from alanine (103, 104). It is interesting that Molisch (227) shows a picture of etiolated pea seedlings growing horizontally toward a radium source; the seedlings show all signs of the triple response to ethylene.

Maxie and co-workers (207, 208) suggest that radiation induces ethylene formation either by a nonenzymatic radiolysis of fruit constituents or by an oxygen dependent metabolic system. Whether the latter is related to older observations (39) that ethylene production is stimulated by injury to plant tissue is not known.

Microbes and disease.—Ethylene is produced by many diseased plant tissues (39), and it appears in general to be produced by the sick host tissue rather than by the organism; this problem has been insufficiently investigated. In the cases where it is known to be produced by the pathogen, e.g., *Penicillium digitatum* and some other microbes, ethylene may hasten senescence of host cells and tissues, making spread of the infection easier. Free-bairn & Buddenhagen (101) have reported ethylene production by *Pseudomonas solanacearum,* believed to be the first report of production by a bacterial species. This organism infects bananas, and the diseased fruits produce more ethylene than healthy ones of the same age. The organism used peptone, glucuronic acid, glutamic acid, and fumaric acid, but not glucose as substrates for ethylene formation. Seven other bacteria of various genera were tested (including one which also infected banana fruits), but ethylene was not found. Ilag & Curtis (150) tested 228 species of fungi for ethylene production; qualitative gas chromatography suggested ethylene production in 58 of these, and ethylene was verified chemically from 22 species. The amount produced by *Aspergillus clavatus* was most noteworthy. They concluded that ethylene is probably a common metabolic product of fungi and should be considered in studies of growth disturbances of plants. The cultivated mushroom, *Agaricus bisporus,* produces ethylene (182).

A very interesting case of another sort is reported by Stahmann et al. (326) for sweet potato infected with *Ceratocystis fimbriata.* Some non-pathogenic strains of this fungus can induce resistance in the host by increasing the ethylene production of the host tissue, and resistance can be induced by treating susceptible tissues with ethylene. The fungus itself did not produce the gas. Ethylene acted on the sweet potato tissue to induce increased peroxidase and polyphenoloxidase, and these enzymes may participate in reactions making adjacent cells resistant to invasion. Chalutz & DeVay (69) found that all their isolates of this fungus did produce ethylene, although they varied greatly in amount produced. Ethylene production by various host-fungus combinations corresponded with the rate of growth of fungus on the host tissue, reflecting relative virulence of various strains, and did not correspond with ability of the same fungus strains to produce ethylene *in vitro;* they did not confirm Stahmann et al.

Wound and other stress effects.—Burg (39) reviewed studies on the ethylene responses of wounded tissue; some additional work has been done and should be noted. Cantaloupe tissue slices were studied by McGlasson & Pratt (210), and they report tenfold increases in ethylene production by flesh tissue slices compared to intact fruit; slices from nearly mature fruits showed a climacteric pattern, and a respiratory increase could be induced in slices treated with ethylene. Phan (266), on the other hand, found that respiration and ethylene production by apples were not stimulated by wounding per se but by exposure of new surface to the atmosphere. Hulme's group has made extensive metabolic studies with apple peel slices (cited above); they report (149) a sharp rise in ethylene production compared to whole fruit. Imaseki et al. (151) found a rapid production of ethylene by sweet potato root slices after slicing and considered the amount due to wounding sufficient to induce metabolic increases in their control slices. In the course of radiation experiments, Maxie et al. (199) studied the effect of various mechanical injuries on bananas. Crushing or scraping parts of preclimacteric fruits caused ethylene production to increase several days earlier, with corresponding earlier ripening than shown by the controls.

When Vines et al. (342) investigated the internal atmosphere of citrus fruits, they were unable to detect ethylene unless the fruits had been subjected to some stress such as chilling or dropping. They suggest that high oxygen, which has led to ethylene formation in other experiments with cittrus (33), is also a source of stress. Ethylene production accompanied the higher induced respiration rates, but they confirm the contention that citrus fruits are nonclimacteric. It has been mentioned earlier that such a simple stress as growing against an obstruction led to ethylene production by pea seedlings (118), and even changing the orientation toward gravity of tomato stem sections (81) and *Coleus* plants (9) increased their ethylene output, resulting in increased leaf abscission in the latter. We may well wonder if the stress of a clinostat experiment leads to production of enough ethylene to account for leaf epinasty (187). A number of the chemical treatments reviewed by Cooper et al. (72) must act by stress or injury.

As Burg says (39), almost all that has been accomplished so far is still descriptive. The relations of ethylene to disease, wound, and stress responses deserve further study.

Undesirable Effects of Ethylene on Stored Vegetables

Lettuce.—Russet spotting is a physiological disorder of unknown cause in head lettuce. The expression of the symptoms is markedly increased by ethylene (180, 295). It is likely that ethylene acts to hasten senescence, and hence symptom expression, in the cells which have been weakened by another cause, e.g., virus infection.

Carrot.—Ethylene appears to have a catalytic effect in stimulating formation of a bitter principle (isocoumarin) in stored carrot roots (64). Further studies by Chalutz et al. (70) showed that ethylene production in carrot root disks could be stimulated by fungus infection or growth regulators (IAA; 2,4-D; 2,4,5-T), and the disks then produced isocoumarin; the concentrations of isocoumarin produced depended on the concentrations of ethylene in the atmosphere. Formation of isocoumarin was inhibited by high carbon dioxide, even in the presence of exogenous ethylene, another example of CO_2 inhibition of ethylene action. Although Carlton et al. (64) could not show incorporation of ethylene-^{14}C into isocoumarin, ethylene is definitely required for its formation (70).

Air Purification

Production of ethylene by fruits has led many workers to be concerned about the practical implications in storages, and much effort has been spent on evaluation of the problem and of possible systems for air purification. Porritt (268) has reviewed some of this work. Methods of ethylene removal attempted have included use of activated charcoal (155), brominated charcoal, ozone (125), chlorine, alkaline potassium permanganate (354), paraffin oil (85), modified soda lime (243), and water spray (22, 155). The results have been confusing (200, 321). Fidler (96) has put the problem in perspective by pointing out that, at least for apples and pears, storage at a correctly low temperature allows tolerance of quite high ethylene concentrations because the fruit will not react at these temperatures. However, stored nursery stock has been injured even at low temperature (77). Air purification may be useful for cold-sensitive crops or varieties which must be stored warmer (314), or if volatile removal is required for other reasons (186). Ability to remove ethylene would be useful for orchid greenhouses in air pollution areas.

Accumulation of endogenous ethylene around packaged cut flowers is a commercially important problem (186), and brominated charcoal in the packages has been recommended (20, 98); modified soda lime (243) might be better. However, Smith et al. (318, 319) showed that the deleterious effect of ethylene could be completely counteracted by carbon dioxide, as little as 0.4 per cent being effective; they suggest that partial restriction of ventilation may be beneficial.

Curing

"Curing" of some crops represents a partial control of senescent processes to achieve a more desirable commercial product (100). Use of ethylene has been proposed in the curing of vanilla (24), peppermint (244), and tobacco (169, 258). Certain seed treatments may be considered in this category, since ethylene has been recommended to improve the quality of the oil of stored soybeans (355) and the baking quality of flour from treated wheat (124).

Seed Treatment

It has been alleged that treatment of seeds with ethylene before planting will affect subsequent crop growth and yield in alfalfa (164) and oats (170). Seed treatment with other compounds is said to affect the rate of ethylene production by cotton and pea plants (269).

Ethylene-Releasing Chemicals

A great deal of horticultural interest has recently been aroused by 2-chloroethanephosphonic acid which is available commercially ("Amchem 66-329", "Ethrel", "CEP"). Applications of this material by usual horticultural methods cause effects similar to ethylene on pineapple flowering (71), fruit ripening (92, 300), abscission (72, 229), and various growth phenomena (71, 347). The material apparently breaks down in plant tissue, releasing ethylene close to a site of action (71, 92) and so providing a method for convenient field treatments with ethylene. Betahydroxyethylhydrazine (BOH) appears to act in a similar way (256), but it is not applicable as an abscission agent (72).

CONCLUSIONS

Significant progress has been made in our knowledge of the role of ethylene in fruit ripening, and the concept of ethylene as an endogenous growth regulator has come forward in the last few years. As usual, great problems lie ahead. We must find out the mechanisms by which ethylene acts as a hormone for fruit ripening and growth regulation. In fruit ripening two interesting additional questions present themselves. What is the nature of maturation in fruits which makes them susceptible to the action of ethylene as a ripening trigger? What controls the rate of ethylene synthesis during fruit growth and development and then allows enough ethylene to be made to serve as the trigger? Finally, it is evident that much previous work on growth regulators must be re-examined to see if knowledge of the role of ethylene will explain old problems or create new ones. It seems likely that many growth regulator effects will be found to operate through an effect on ethylene production or will be controlled by endogenous ethylene; in any event, the possible presence of ethylene may be a source of confusion that must be taken into account.

LITERATURE CITED

1. Abdel-Kader, A. S., Morris, L. L., Maxie, E. C., *Proc. Am. Soc. Hort. Sci.,* **92,** 553–67 (1968)
2. Abeles, F. B., *Plant Physiol.,* **41,** 585–88 (1966)
3. Abeles, F. B., *ibid.,* 946–48
4. Abeles, F. B., *Nature,* **210,** 23–25 (1966)
5. Abeles, F. B., *Plant Physiol.,* **42,** 608–9 (1967)
6. Abeles, F. B., *Physiol. Plantarum,* **20,** 442–54 (1967)
7. Abeles, F. B., *Plant Physiol.,* **42,** 1577–86 (1968)
8. Abeles, F. B., Gahagan, H. E., *Plant Physiol.,* **43,** 1255–58 (1968)
9. Abeles, F. B., Gahagan, H. E., *Life Sci.,* **7,** 653–55 (1968)
10. Abeles, F. B., Holm, R. E., *Plant Physiol.,* **41,** 1337–42 (1966)
11. Abeles, F. B., Holm, R. E., *Ann. N. Y. Acad. Sci.,* **144,** 367–73 (1967)
12. Abeles, F. B., Holm, R. E., Gahagan, H. E., *Plant Physiol.,* **42,** 1351–56 (1967)
13. Abeles, F. B., Holm, R. E., Gahagan, H. E., *ibid.,* 5–9
14. Abeles, F. B., Holm, R. E., Gahagan, H. E., in *Biochemistry and Physiology of Plant Growth Substances* (Wightman, F., Setterfield, G., Eds., Runge Press, Ottawa, in press, 1968)
15. Abeles, F. B., Rubinstein, B., *Plant Physiol.,* **39,** 963–69 (1964)
16. Abeles, F. B., Rubinstein, B., *Biochim. Biophys. Acta,* **93,** 675–77 (1964)
17. Addicott, F. T., *Plant Physiol.,* **43,** 1471–79 (1968)
18. Aharoni, Y., *Plant Physiol.,* **43,** 99–102 (1968)
19. Akamine, E. K., *Science,* **140,** 1217–18 (1963)
20. Akamine, E. K., Sakamoto, H. I., *Am. Orchid Soc. Bull.,* **20,** 149–52 (1951)
21. Andreae, W. A., Venis, M. A., Jursic, F., Dumas, T., *Plant Physiol.,* **43,** 1375–79 (1968)
22. Antoniani, C., Monzini, A., Kaderavek, G. P., *Ann. Sper. Agrar. (Rome),* **13,** 945–48 (1959) (Chem. Abstr., **54,** 12416e)
23. Apeland, J., *Bull. Inst. Intern. Froid, Com. 4, Annexe 1961-1,* 45–58
24. Arana, F. E., *U. S. Dept. Agr. Fed. Expt. Sta., Puerto Rico, Bull.* **42,** 16 pp. (1944)
25. Balls, A. K., Hale, W. S., *Cereal Chem.,* **17,** 490–94 (1940)
26. Baur, A., Yang, S. F., *Plant Physiol.,* **44** (In press, 1969)
27. Biale, J. B., *Calif. Citrograph,* **25,** 186, 212 (1940)
28. Biale, J. B., *Proc. Am. Soc. Hort. Sci.,* **52,** 187–91 (1948)
29. Biale, J. B., *Handbuch Pflanzenphysiol.,* **12(2),** 536–92 (1960)
30. Biale, J. B., in *The Orange. Its Biochemistry and Physiology,* 96–130 (Sinclair, W. B., Ed., Div. Agr. Sci., Univ. Calif., Berkeley, 1961)
31. Biale, J. B.,, *Food Preserv. Quart.,* **22(3),** 57–62 (1962)
32. Biale, J. B., *Science,* **146,** 880–88 (1964)
33. Biale, J. B., Young, R. E., Olmstead, A. J., *Plant Physiol.,* **29,** 168–74 (1954)
34. Bjornseth, E. H., *Proc. Am. Soc. Hort. Sci.,* **48,** 369–73 (1946)
35. Blackman, F. F., *Analytic Studies in Plant Respiration* (Cambridge Univ. Press, Cambridge, 240 pp., 1954)
36. Blackman, F. F., Parija, P., *Proc. Roy Soc. (London), Ser. B,* **103,** 412–45 (1928)
37. Brown, D. S., Buchanan, J. R., Hicks, J. R., *Proc. Am. Soc. Hort. Sci.,* **88,** 98–104 (1966)
38. Brown, H. D., Jackson, R. T., Dupuy, H. J., *Nature,* **202,** 722–23 (1964)
39. Burg, S. P., *Ann. Rev. Plant Physiol.,* **13,** 265–302 (1962)
40. Burg, S. P., in *Régulateurs naturels de la croissance végétale,* 719–25 (Nitsch, J. P., Ed., Centre National de la Recherche Scientifique, Paris, 1964)
41. Burg, S. P., *Plant Physiol.,* **43,** 1503–11 (1968)
42. Burg, S. P., Burg, E. A., *Plant Physiol.,* **37,** 179–89 (1962)
43. Burg, S. P., Burg, E. A., *Nature,* **194,** 398–99 (1962)
44. Burg, S. P., Burg, E. A., *Plant Physiol.,* **39**(suppl.), x (1964)
45. Burg, S. P., Burg, E. A., *Nature,* **203,** 869–70 (1964)
46. Burg, S. P., Burg, E. A., *Science,* **148,** 1190–96 (1965)
47. Burg, S. P., Burg, E. A., *Botan. Gaz.,* **126,** 200–4 (1965)
48. Burg, S. P., Burg, E. A., *Physiol. Plantarum,* **18,** 870–84 (1965)
49. Burg, S. P., Burg, E. A., *Proc. Natl.*

Acad. Sci. U.S., **55**, 262–69 (1966)
50. Burg, S. P., Burg, E. A., *Science*, **152**, 1269 (1966)
51. Burg, S. P., Burg, E. A., *ibid.*, **153**, 314–15 (1966)
52. Burg, S. P., Burg, E. A., *Plant Physiol.*, **42**, 144–52 (1967)
53. Burg, S. P., Burg, E. A., *ibid.*, 891–93
54. Burg, S. P., Burg, E. A., *ibid.*, 1224–28
55. Burg, S. P., Burg, E. A., *ibid.*, S–31
56. **Burg, S. P., Burg, E. A.**, *ibid.*, **43**, 1069–74 (1968)
57. Burg, S. P., Burg, E. A., in *Biochemistry and Physiology of Plant Growth Substances* (See Ref. 14)
58. Burg, S. P., Burg, E. A., Marks, R., *Plant Physiol.*, **39**, 185–95 (1964)
59. Burg, S. P., Clagett, C. O., *Biochem. Biophys. Res. Commun.*, **29**, 125–30 (1967)
60. Burg, S. P., Dijkman, M. J., *Plant Physiol.*, **42**, 1648–50 (1967)
61. Burton, W. G., *New Phytologist*, **51**, 154–62 (1952)
62. Burton, W. G., *Food Sci. Abstr.*, **29**, 1–12 (1957)
63. Bussel, J., Maxie, E. C., *Proc. Am. Soc. Hort. Sci.*, **88**, 151–59 (1966)
64. Carlton, B. C., Peterson, C. E., Tolbert, N. E., *Plant Physiol.*, **36**, 550–52 (1961)
65. Carns, H. R., *Ann. Rev. Plant Physiol.*, **17**, 295–314 (1966)
66. Chace, E. M., Sorber, D. G., *Canning Age*, **11**, 391–92 (1930)
67. Chace, E. M., Sorber, D. G., *Food Ind.*, **8**, 292–94 (1936)
68. Chadwick, A. V., Burg, S. P., *Plant Physiol.*, **42**, 415–20 (1967)
69. Chalutz, E., DeVay, J. E., *Phytopathology* (In press, 1969)
70. Chalutz, E., DeVay, J. E., Maxie, E. C., *Plant Physiol.*, **44** (In press, 1969)
71. Cooke, A. R., Randall, D. I., *Nature*, **218**, 974–75 (1968)
72. Cooper, W. C., Rasmussen, G. K., Rogers, B. J., Reece, P. C., Henry, W. H., *Plant Physiol.*, **43**, 1560–76 (1968)
73. Cousins, H. H., *Jamaica Dept. Agr. Ann. Rept.*, **7**, 15 (1910)
74. Crocker, W., *Growth of plants* (Reinhold, N.Y., 459 pp., 1948)
75. Crocker, W., Barton, L. V., *Physiology of seeds* (Chronica Botanica, Waltham, Mass., 267 pp., 1953)
76. Crocker, W., Hitchcock, A. E., Zimmerman, P. W., *Contrib. Boyce Thompson Inst.*, **7**, 231–48 (1935)
77. Curtis, O. F., Jr., Rodney, D. R., *Proc. Am. Soc. Hort. Sci.*, **60**, 104–8 (1952)
78. Curtis, R. W., *Plant Physiol.*, **43**, 76–80 (1968)
79. Denny, F. E., *Am. J. Botany*, **17**, 602–13 (1930)
80. Denny, F. E., *Contrib. Boyce Thompson Inst.*, **7**, 341–47 (1935)
81. Denny, F. E., *ibid.*, **8**, 99–104 (1936)
82. Denny, F. E., *ibid.*, **9**, 431–38 (1938)
83. Denny, F. E., Miller, L. P., *ibid.*, **7**, 97–102 (1935)
84. Dimock, A. W., Baker, K. F., *Florists Review*, **106** (2754), 27–29 (1950)
85. Dostal, H. C., Hoff, J. E., *HortScience*, **3**, 46–48 (1968)
86. Dostal, H. C., Leopold, A. C., *Science*, **158**, 1579–80 (1967)
87. Doubt, S. L., *Botan. Gaz.*, **63**, 209–24 (1917)
88. Doughty, C. C., Patterson, M. E., Shawa, A. Y., *Proc. Am. Soc. Hort. Sci.*, **91**, 192–204 (1967)
89. Dunham, M. L., Jr., O'Connor, F. M., *U. S. Pat. 3,234,028* (Cl. 99–103), Feb. 8, 1966 (*Chem. Abstr.*, **64**, 20534a)
90. Dykyj-Sajfertova, D., Dykyj, J., *Z. Zuckerind. Böhmen Mähren*, **66**, 193–97 (1943) (*Chem. Abstr.*, **38**, 5880²)
91. Eaks, I. L., *Proc. Am. Soc. Hort. Sci.*, **91**, 868–75 (1967)
92. Edgerton, L. J., Blanpied, G. D., *Nature*, **219**, 1064–65 (1968)
93. Elmer, O. H., *Science*, **75**, 193 (1932)
94. Elmer, O. H., *J. Agr. Res.*, **52**, 609–26 (1936)
95. Fergus, C. L., *Mycologia*, **46**, 543–55 (1954)
96. Fidler, J. C., *Handbuch Pflanzenphysiol.*, **12**(2), 347–59 (1960)
97. Fidler, J. C., *J. Exptl. Botany*, **19**, 41–51 (1968)
98. Fischer, C. W., Jr., *Proc. Am. Soc. Hort. Sci.*, **55**, 447–54 (1950)
99. Forsyth, F. R., Hall, I. V., *Can. J. Plant Sci.*, **47**, 153–56 (1967)
100. Forsyth, W. G. C., *Ann. Rev. Plant Physiol.*, **15**, 443–50 (1964)
101. Freebairn, H. T., Buddenhagen, I. W., *Nature*, **202**, 313–14 (1964)
102. Frenkel, C., Klein, I., Dilley, D. R., *Plant Physiol.*, **43**, 1146–53 (1968)
103. Frey-Wyssling, A., *Naturwissenschaften*, **26**, 624–28 (1938)
104. Frey-Wyssling, A., *Ernährung und Stoffwechsel der Pflanzen*, 244–45 (Büchergilde Gutenberg, Zürich, 1945)

105. dela Fuente, R. K., Leopold, A. C., *Plant Physiol.*, **43**, 1496–1502 (1968)
106. Galil, J., *Econ. Botany*, **22**, 178–90 (1968)
107. Galliard, T., Rhodes, M. J. C., Wooltorton, L. S. C., Hulme, A. C., *Phytochemistry*, **7**, 1453–63 (1968)
108. Galliard, T., Rhodes, M. J. C., Wooltorton, L. S. C., Hulme, A. C., *ibid.*, 1465–70
109. Gawadi, A. G., Avery, G. S., Jr., *Am. J. Botany*, **37**, 172–80 (1950)
110. Gibson, M. S., *Arch. Biochem. Biophys.*, **106**, 312–16 (1964)
111. Gibson, M. S., *Nature*, **202**, 902–3 (1964)
112. Gibson, M. S., Crane, F. L., *Plant Physiol.*, **38**, 729–30 (1963)
113. Gibson, M. S., Young, R. E., *Nature*, **210**, 529–30 (1966)
114. Goeschl, J. D., Pratt, H. K., *Plant Physiol.*, **40**(suppl.), lii–liii (1965)
115. Goeschl, J. D., Pratt, H. K., *ibid.*, **41**(suppl.), lii (1966)
116. Goeschl, J. D., Pratt, H. K., in *Biochemistry and Physiology of Plant Growth Substances* (See Ref. 14)
117. Goeschl, J. D., Pratt, H. K., Bonner, B. A., *Plant Physiol.*, **42**, 1077–80 (1967)
118. Goeschl, J. D., Rappaport, L., Pratt, H. K., *Plant Physiol.*, **41**, 877–85 (1966)
119. Grierson, W., Newhall, W. F., *Florida Agr. Expt. Sta. Bull. 620*, 80 pp. (1960)
120. Guerrero, F. P., Maxie, E. C., Johnson, C. F., Eaks, I. L., Sommer, N. F., *Proc. Am. Soc. Hort. Sci.*, **90**, 515–28 (1967)
121. von Guttenberg, H. R., *Jahrb. wiss. Botan.*, **47**, 462–92 (1910)
122. von Guttenberg, H., Beythien, A., *Planta*, **40**, 36–69 (1951)
123. Haber, E. S., *Proc. Am. Soc. Hort. Sci.*, **23**, 201–3 (1927)
124. Hale, W. S., Schwimmer, S., Bayfield, E. G., *Cereal Chem.*, **20**, 224–35 (1943)
125. Hall, E. G., *Food Preserv. Quart.*, **15**, 66–68 (1955)
126. Hall, I. V., Forsyth, F. R., *Can. J. Botany*, **45**, 1163–66 (1967)
127. Hall, W. C., *Botan. Gaz.*, **113**, 310–22 (1952)
128. Hall, W. C., Morgan, P. W., in *Régulateurs naturels de la croissance végétale*, 727–45 (See Ref. 40)
129. Hall, W. C., Truchelut, G. B., Leinweber, C. L., Herrero, F. A., *Physiol. Plantarum*, **10**, 306–17 (1957)
130. Haller, M. H., *U. S. Dept. Agr. Biblio. Bull. 21*, 105 pp. (1952)
131. Hansen, E., *Ann. Rev. Plant Physiol.*, **17**, 459–80 (1966)
132. Hansen, E., *Proc. Am. Soc. Hort. Sci.*, **91**, 863–67 (1967)
133. Harvey, E. M., *Botan. Gaz.*, **56**, 439–42 (1913)
134. Harvey, E. M., *ibid.*, **60**, 193–214 (1915)
135. Heck, W. W., Pires, E. G., *Texas Agr. Expt. Sta. MP–603*, 12 pp. (1962)
136. Heck, W. W., Pires, E. G., *ibid.*, *MP–613*, 12 pp. (1962)
137. Heinz, D. E., Creveling, R. K., Jennings, W. G., *J. Food Sci.*, **30**, 641–43 (1965)
138. Herrero, F. A., Hall, W. C., *Physiol. Plantarum*, **13**, 736–50 (1960)
139. Hewitt, A. A., *Proc. Am. Soc. Hort. Sci.*, **91**, 90–95 (1967)
140. Holm, R. E., Abeles, F. B., *Plant Physiol.*, **42**, 1094–1102 (1967)
141. Holm, R. E., Abeles, F. B., *Planta*, **78**, 293–304 (1968)
142. Holm, R. E., O'Brien, T. J., Cherry, J. H., Key, J. L., *Plant Physiol.*, **43**, S–19 (1968)
143. Horton, R. F., Osborne, D. J., *Nature*, **214**, 1086–88 (1967)
144. Huelin, F. E., Barker, J., *New Phytologist*, **38**, 85–104 (1939)
145. Hulme, A. C., *Advan. Food Res.*, **8**, 297–413 (1958)
146. Hulme, A. C., *Advan. Hort. Sci. Appl.* (Proc. Intern. Hort. Congr., 15th, 1958), **1**, 77–95 (1961)
147. Hulme, A. C., *Proc. Intern. Congr. Biochem., 5th*, **8**, 143–53 (1963)
148. Hulme, A. C., Jones, J. D., Wooltorton, L. S. C., *Proc. Roy. Soc. (London), Ser. B*, **158**, 514–35 (1963)
149. Hulme, A. C., Rhodes, M. J. C., Galliard, T., Wooltorton, L. S. C., *Plant Physiol.*, **43**, 1154–61 (1968)
150. Ilag, L., Curtis, R. W., *Science*, **159**, 1357–58 (1968)
151. Imaseki, H., Uchiyama, M., Uritani, I., *Agr. Biol. Chem.*, **32**, 387–89 (1968)
152. Jacobs, W. P., *Plant Physiol.*, **43**, 1480–95 (1968)
153. Jacobsen, D. W., Wang, C. H., *Plant Physiol.*, **40**(suppl.), xix (1965)
154. Jansen, E. F., in *Plant Biochemistry*, 641–64 (Bonner, J., Varner, J.

E., Eds., Academic Press, N.Y., 1965)

155. Johansson, J., *Proc. Am. Soc. Hort. Sci.*, **80**, 137–45 (1962)

156. Jones, R. L., *Plant Physiol.*, **43**, 442–44 (1968)

157. Kaltenbach, D., *Intern. Rev. Agr., Monthly Bull. Agr. Sci. Pract.*, **29**, 81T–116T (1938)

158. Kang, B. G., Yocum, C. S., Burg, S. P., Ray, P. M., *Science*, **156**, 958–59 (1967)

159. Ketring, D. L., Young, R. E., Biale, J. B., *Plant Cell Physiol.*, **9**, 617–31 (1968)

160. Kidd, F., West, C., *Gt. Brit. Dept. Sci. Ind. Res., Food Invest. Bd. Rept. (1924)*, 27–33 (1925)

161. Kidd, F., West, C., *Proc. Roy. Soc. (London), Ser. B*, **106**, 93–109 (1930)

162. Kidd, F., West, C., *Plant Physiol.*, **20**, 467–504 (1945)

163. Knight, L. I., Crocker, W., *Botan. Gaz.*, **55**, 337–71 (1913)

164. Koperzhinskii, V. V., *Dokl. Vses. Akad. Sel'sko-khoz. Nauk*, 57–59 (1939) (*Herbage Abstr.*, **10**, 455)

165. Ku, H. S., Pratt, H. K., *Plant Physiol.*, **43**, 999–1001 (1968)

166. Ku, H. S., Yang, S. F., Pratt, H. K., *Arch. Biochem. Biophys.*, **118**, 756–58 (1967)

167. Ku, H. S., Yang, S. F., Pratt, H. K., *Plant Physiol.*, **43**, S–45 (1968)

168. Ku, H. S., Yang, S. F., Pratt, H. K., *Phytochemistry*, **8** (In press, 1969)

169. La Rotonda, C., Rossi, U., Petrosini, G., *Z. Untersuch. Lebensm.*, **85**, 64–69 (1943)

170. Lazanyi, A., Căbulea, I., *Acad. rep. populare Romîne, Filiala Cluj, Studii cercetări agron.*, **8**, 117–28 (1957) (*Chem. Abstr.*, **53**, 13287c)

171. Lee, F. A., *Nature*, **184**, 462 (1959)

172. Lee, T. H., McGlasson, W. B., Edwards, R. A., *Radiation Botany*, **8**, 259–67 (1968)

173. Lewis, L. N., Palmer, R. L., Hield, H. Z., in *Biochemistry and Physiology of Plant Growth Substances* (See Ref. 14)

174. Lieberman, M., Kunishi, A. T., *Science*, **158**, 938 (1967)

175. Lieberman, M., Kunishi, A. T., *Plant Physiol.*, **43**, S–45 (1968)

176. Lieberman, M., Kunishi, A. T., Mapson, L. W., Wardale, D. A., *Biochem. J.*, **97**, 449–59 (1965)

177. Lieberman, M., Kunishi, A., Mapson, L. W., Wardale, D. A., *Plant Physiol.*, **41**, 376–82 (1966)

178. Lieberman, M., Mapson, L. W., *Nature*, **204**, 343–45 (1964)

179. Lim, L., Romani, R. J., *J. Food Sci.*, **29**, 246–53 (1964)

180. Lipton, W. J., *Proc. Am. Soc. Hort. Sci.*, **78**, 367–74 (1961)

181. Lipton, W. J., Uota, M., *U. S. Dept. Agr. ARS 51–22*, 8 pp. (1968)

182. Lockard, J. D., Kneebone, L. R., *Proc. Intern. Conf. Sci. Aspects Mushroom Growing, 5th (Philadelphia)*, 1962, 281–99

183. Looney, N. E., *Plant Physiol.*, **43**, 1133–37 (1968)

184. Looney, N. E., Patterson, M. E., *Nature*, **214**, 1245–46 (1967)

185. Luchko, A. S., Porutskii, G. V., Yavorskii, A. G., *Soviet Plant Physiol.*, **11**, 46–50 (1964)

186. Lutz, J. M., Hardenburg, R. E., *U. S. Dept. Agr. Handbook 66*, 94 pp. (1968)

187. Lyon, C. J., *Plant Physiol.*, **38**, 567–74 (1963)

188. Lyons, J. M., McGlasson, W. B., Pratt, H. K., *Plant Physiol.*, **37**, 31–36 1962)

189. Lyons, J. M., Pratt, H. K., *Proc. Am. Soc. Hort. Sci.*, **84**, 491–500 (1964)

190. Lyons, J. M., Pratt, H. K., *Arch. Biochem. Biophys.*, **104**, 318–24 (1964)

191. Mack, W. B., Livingston, B. E., *Botan. Gaz.*, **94**, 625–87 (1933)

192. Madeikyte, E., Turkova, N. S., *Lietuvos TSR Mokslu Akad. Darbai, Ser. C*, 37–45 (1965) (*Chem. Abstr.*, **64**, 13303d)

193. Mapson, L. W., Mead, A., *Biochem. J.*, **108**, 875–81 (1968)

194. Mapson, L. W., Robinson, J. E., *J. Food Technol.*, **1**, 215–25 (1966)

195. Mapson, L. W., Wardale, D. A., *Biochem. J.*, **102**, 574–85 (1967)

196. Mapson, L. W., Wardale, D. A., *ibid.*, **107**, 433–42 (1968)

197. Marinos, N. G., *J. Exptl. Botany*, **11**, 227–35 (1960)

198. Maxie, E. C., Abdel-Kader, A., *Advan. Food Res.*, **15**, 105–45 (1966)

199. Maxie, E. C., Amezquita, R., Hassan, B. M., Johnson, C. F., *Proc. Am. Soc. Hort. Sci.*, 235–54 (1968)

200. Maxie, E. C., Baker, C. E., *Proc. Am. Soc. Hort. Sci.*, **64**, 235–47 (1954)

201. Maxie, E. C., Catlin, P. B., Hartmann, H. T., *Proc. Am. Soc. Hort. Sci.*, **75**, 275–91 (1960)

202. Maxie, E. C., Crane, J. C., *Science*, **155**, 1548–50 (1967)
203. Maxie, E. C., Crane, J. C., *Proc. Am. Soc. Hort. Sci.*, **92**, 255–67 (1968)
204. Maxie, E. C., Eaks, I. L., Sommer, N. F., *Radiation Botany*, **4**, 405–411 (1964)
205. Maxie, E. C., Eaks, I. L., Sommer, N. F., Rae, H. L., El-Batal, S., *Plant Physiol.*, **40**, 407–9 (1965)
206. Maxie, E. C., Johnson, C. F., Boyd, C., Rae, H. L., Sommer, N. F., *Proc. Am. Soc. Hort. Sci.*, **89**, 91–99 (1966)
207. Maxie, E. C., Rae, H. L., Eaks, I. L., Sommer, N. F., *Radiation Botany*, **6**, 445–455 (1966)
208. Maxie, E. C., Sommer, N. F., Muller, C. J., Rae, H. L., *Plant Physiol.*, **41**, 437–42 (1966)
209. McGlasson, W. B., Pratt, H. K., *Plant Physiol.*, **39**, 120–27 (1964)
210. McGlasson, W. B., Pratt, H. K., *ibid.*, 128–32
211. Meheriuk, M., Spencer, M., *Can. J. Botany*, **42**, 337–40 (1964)
212. Meheriuk, M., Spencer, M., *Phytochemistry*, **6**, 535–43 (1967)
213. Meheriuk, M., Spencer, M., *ibid.*, 545–49
214. Meheriuk, M., Spencer, M., *ibid.*, 551–58
215. Meigh, D. F., Jones, J. D., Hulme, A. C., *Phytochemistry*, **6**, 1507–15 (1967)
216. Michener, H. D., *Science*, **82**, 551–52 (1935)
217. Michener, H. D., *Am. J. Botany*, **25**, 711–20 (1938)
218. Milbrath, J. A., Hansen, E., Hartman, H., *Science*, **91**, 100 (1940)
219. Milbrath, J. A., Hartman, H., *Science*, **92**, 401 (1940)
220. Milbrath, J. A., Hartman, H., *Oregon Agr. Exptl. Sta. Bull. 413*, 11 pp. (1942)
221. Miller, E. V., *Botan. Rev.*, **12**, 393–423 (1946)
222. Miller, E. V., *Sci. Monthly*, **65**, 335–42 (1947)
223. Miller, E. V., *Botan. Rev.*, **24**, 43–59 (1958)
224. Miller, E. V., Winston, J. R., Fisher, D. F., *J. Agr. Res.*, **60**, 269–78 (1940)
225. Molisch, H., *Sitzber. kais. Akad. Wiss. (Wien)*, **90**, 111–96 (1884)
226. Molisch, H., *ibid.*, **111**, 141–48 (1902)
227. Molisch, H., *Ber. Deut. Botan. Ges.*, **23**, 1–8 (1905)

228. Moreno Calvo, J., *Ion*, **21**, 561–67 (1961)
229. Morgan, P. W., *Proc. Beltwide Cotton Prod. Res. Conf., Jan. 1968 (Natl. Cotton Council, Memphis, Tenn.)* (In press, 1968)
230. Morgan, P. W., Beyer, E., Gausman, H. E., in *Biochemistry and Physiology of Plant Growth Substances* (See Ref. 14)
231. Morgan, P. W., Gausman, H. W., *Plant Physiol.*, **41**, 45–52 (1966)
232. Morgan, P. W., Hall, W. C., *Physiol. Plantarum*, **15**, 420–27 (1962)
233. Morgan, P. W., Hall, W. C., *Nature*, **201**, 99 (1964)
234. Morgan, P. W., Powell, R. D., *Plant Physiol.*, **43**, S-45 (1968)
235. Morre, D. J., *Plant Physiol.*, **43**, 1545–59 (1968)
236. Murata, T., Ogata, K., *Nippon Shokuhin Kogyo Gakkaishi*, **13**, 367–70 (1966) (*Chem. Abstr.*, **66**, 104155h)
237. Neljubow, D., *Beih. Botan. Centralbl.*, **10**, 128–38 (1901)
238. Neljubow, D. N., *Imp. Acad. Sci. (St. Petersburg) Bull.*, **4**, 1443–58 (1910)
239. Neljubow, D., *Ber. Deut. Botan. Ges.*, **29**, 97–112 (1911)
240. Neljubow, D., *J. Imp. Acad. Sci. (St. Petersburg), Ser. VIII*, **31**, 1–163 (1913)
241. Neljubow, D., *ibid.*, **32**, 1–177 (1914)
242. Nichols, R., *J. Hort. Sci.*, **41**, 279–90 (1966)
243. Nichols, R., Topping, A., *Nature*, **211**, 217 (1966)
244. Nilov, V. I., Ponta, D. D., *Trudy Vsesoyuz. Nauch.-Issledovatel. Inst. Efirno Masl. Prom., Sbornik Rabot Perechnoi Myate*, 1939(5), 104–30 (*Chem. Abstr.*, **36**, 1981⁹)
245. Nitsch, C., in *Biochemistry and Physiology of Plant Growth Substances* (See Ref. 14)
246. Nitsch, J. P., *Handbuch Pflanzenphysiol.*, **15(1)**, 1552–53 (1965)
247. Nord, F. F., *Trans. Faraday Soc.*, **26**, 760–68 (1930)
248. Nord, F. F., *Australian J. Exptl. Biol. Med. Sci.*, **14**, 131–34 (1936)
249. Nord, F. F., Franke, K. W., *Protoplasma*, **4**, 547–95 (1928)
250. Nord, F. F., Franke, K. W., *J. Biol. Chem.*, **79**, 27–51 (1928)
251. Norman, S., Craft, C. C., *HortScience*, **3**, 66–68 (1968)
252. Olson, A. O., Spencer, M., *Can. J. Biochem.*, **46**, 277–82 (1968)

253. Olson, A. O., Spencer, M., *ibid.*, 283–88
254. Osborne, D. J., *Nature*, **219**, 564–67 (1968)
255. Osborne, D. J., in *Biochemistry and Physiology of Plant Growth Substances* (See Ref. 14)
256. Palmer, R. L., Lewis, L. N., Hield, H. Z., Kumamoto, J., *Nature*, **216**, 1216–17 (1967)
257. Pentzer, W. T., Heinze, P. H., *Ann. Rev. Plant Physiol.*, **5**, 205–24 (1954)
258. Pfützer, G., Losch, H., *Umschau*, **39**, 202–6 (1935)
259. Phan, C. T., *Compt. Rend. Acad. Sci. (Paris)*, **251**, 122–24 (1960)
260. Phan, C. T., *Rev. Gen. Froid*, **38**, 867–71 (1961)
261. Phan, C. T., *Rev. Gen. Botan.*, **69**, 505–43 (1962)
262. Phan, C. T., *ibid.*, **70**, 679–90 (1963)
263. Phan, C. T., *Compt. Rend. Acad. Agr. France*, **49**, 53–59 (1963)
264. Phan, C. T., *Phytochemistry*, **4**, 353–55 (1965)
265. Phan, C. T., *Fruits*, **20**, 383–90 (1965)
266. Phan, C. T., *Compt. Rend. Acad. Sci. (Paris)*, **260**, 5089–92 (1965)
267. Poapst, P. A., Durkee, A. B., McGugan, W. A., Johnston, F. B., *J. Sci. Food Agr.*, **19**, 325–27 (1968)
268. Porritt, S. W., *Sci. Agr.*, **31**, 99–112 (1951)
269. Porutskii, G. V., Matkovskii, K. I., *Izv. Inst. po Biol. "Metodii Popov", Bulgar. Akad. Nauk.*, **13**, 147–58 (1963) (*Chem. Abstr.*, **61**, 1184h)
270. Post, K., *N.Y. State Flower Growers Bull.*, **25**, 1–3 (1947)
271. Pratt, H. K., *Proc. Conf. Transport. Perishables, Univ. Calif., Davis, Feb. 5-7, 1953*, 104–10 (Assoc. Am. Railroads, Chicago, 1953)
272. (Pratt, H. K.), *Western Grower & Shipper*, **32**(12), 15, 20 (1961)
273. Pratt, H. K., Biale, J. B., *Plant Physiol.*, **19**, 519–28 (1944)
274. Pratt, H. K., Goeschl, J. D., *Plant Physiol.*, **37**(suppl.), xix (1962)
275. Pratt, H. K., Goeschl, J. D., *ibid.*, **39**(suppl.), ix (1964)
276. Pratt, H. K., Goeschl, J. D., in *Biochemistry and Physiology of Plant Growth Substances* (See Ref. 14)
277. Pratt, H. K., Meigh, D. F., *Plant Physiol.*, **41**(suppl.), lii (1966)
278. Pratt, H. K., Workman, M., *Proc. Am. Soc. Hort. Sci.*, **81**, 467–78 (1962)
279. Pratt, H. K., Workman, M., Martin, F. W., Lyons, J. M., *Plant Physiol.*, **35**, 609–11 (1960)
280. Rakitin, Yu. V., *Izd. Akad. Nauk SSSR (Moscow)*, 168 pp. (1955)
281. Rakitin, Yu. V., *Soviet Plant Physiol.*, **14**, 789–99 (1967)
282. Ramsey, J. C., Wang, C. H., *Nature*, **193**, 800–1 (1962)
283. Regeimbal, L. O., Harvey, R. B., *J. Am. Chem. Soc.*, **49**, 1117–18 (1927)
284. Rhodes, M. J. C., Galliard, T., Wooltorton, L. S. C., Hulme, A. C., *Phytochemistry*, **7**, 405–8 (1968)
285. Rhodes, M. J. C., Wooltorton, L. S. C., *ibid.*, **6**, 1–12 (1967)
286. Rhodes, M. J. C., Wooltorton, L. S. C., Galliard, T., Hulme, A. C., *ibid.*, **7**, 1439–51 (1968)
287. Richter, O., *Ber. Deut. Botan. Ges.*, **21**, 180–94 (1903)
288. Richter, O., *Jahrb. wiss. Botan.*, **46**, 481–502 (1909)
289. Richter, O., *Verhandl. Ges. Deut. Naturforsch. Ärzte*, **85** (II, 1), 649–50 (1913)
290. Richter, O., *Sitzber. kais. Akad. Wiss. (Wien)*, **123**, 967–97 (1914)
291. Ridley, V. W., *Fruit Dispatch*, **8**, 523–25 (1923)
292. Rimmer, F., *Sitzber. kais. Akad. Wiss. (Wien), Math.-naturw. Kl.*, **89**, 393–422 (1884)
293. Rohrbaugh, P. W., *Plant Physiol.*, **18**, 79–89 (1943)
294. Romani, R. J., Ku, L., *J. Food Sci.*, **31**, 558–60 (1966)
295. Rood, P., *Proc. Am. Soc. Hort. Sci.*, **68**, 296–302 (1956)
296. Rose, D. H., Cook, H. T., Redit, W. H., *U. S. Dept. Agr. Biblio. Bull.* **13**, 178 pp. (1951)
297. Rosen, L. A., Siegel, S. M., *Plant Physiol.*, **38**, 189–91 (1963)
298. Rowan, K. S., McGlasson, W. B., Pratt, H. K., *J. Exptl. Botany* (In press, 1969)
299. Rubinstein, B., Abeles, F. B., *Botan. Gaz.*, **126**, 255–59 (1965)
300. Russo, L., Jr., Dostal, H. C., Leopold, A. C., *BioScience*, **18**, 109 (1968)
301. Sacher, J. A., *Nature*, **195**, 577–78 (1962)
302. Sacher, J. A., *Plant Physiol.*, **41**, 701–8 (1966)
303. Sacher, J. A., *Soc. Exptl. Biol. Symp.*, **21**, 269–304 (1967)
304. Scott, P. C., Leopold, A. C., *Plant Physiol.*, **42**, 1021–22 (1967)

305. Search, R. W., Stanley, R. G., *Plant Physiol.*, **43**, S–52 (1968)
306. Shah, J., Maxie, E. C., *Physiol. Plantarum*, **18**, 1115–20 (1965)
307. Shaw, F. H., *Australian J. Exptl. Biol. Med. Sci.*, **13**, 95–102 (1935)
308. Shimokawa, K., Kasai, Z., *Mem. Res. Inst. Food Sci., Kyoto Univ.*, **26**, 24–26 (1965)
309. Shimokawa, K., Kasai, Z., *Radioisotopes (Tokyo)*, **14**, 137–41 (1965)
310. Shimokawa, K., Kasai, Z., *Plant Cell Physiol.*, **7**, 1–9 (1966)
311. Shimokawa, K., Kasai, Z., *Science*, **156**, 1362–63 (1967)
312. Shimokawa, K., Kasai, Z., *Plant Cell Physiol.*, **8**, 227–30 (1967)
313. Shimokawa, K., Kasai, Z., *Agr. Biol. Chem.*, **32**, 680–82 (1968)
314. Simmonds, N. W., *Bananas* (Longmans, Green, London, 512 pp., 1966)
315. Singer, M., *Ber. Deut. Botan. Ges.*, **21**, 175–80 (1903)
316. Singh, L. B., *The Mango* (Interscience, N.Y., 438 pp., 1960)
317. Smith, W. H., Meigh, D. F., Parker, J. C., *Nature*, **204**, 92–93 (1964)
318. Smith, W. H., Parker, J. C., *Nature*, **211**, 100–1 (1966)
319. Smith, W. H., Parker, J. C., Freeman, W. W., *Nature*, **211**, 99–100 (1966)
320. Smock, R. M., *Botan. Rev.*, **10**, 560–98 (1944)
321. Smock, R. M., *Proc. Am. Soc. Hort. Sci.*, **66**, 111–17 (1955)
322. Spalding, D. H., Lieberman, M., *Plant Physiol.*, **40**, 645–48 (1965)
323. Spencer, M., in *Plant Biochemistry*, 793–825 (See Ref. 154)
324. Spencer, M., Olson, A. O., *Nature*, **205**, 699–700 (1965)
325. Sprayberry, B. A., Hall, W. C., Miller, C. S., *Nature*, **208**, 1322–23 (1965)
326. Stahmann, M. A., Clare, B. G., Woodbury, W., *Plant Physiol.*, **41**, 1505–12 (1966)
327. Stewart, E. R., Freebairn, H. T., *Plant Physiol.*, **42**, S–30 (1967)
328. Stitt, F., Tomimatsu, Y., *Anal. Chem.*, **25**, 181–83 (1953)
329. Stuart, N. W., Asen, S., Gould, C. J., *HortScience*, **1**, 19–20 (1966)
330. Thompson, J. E., Spencer, M., *Nature*, **210**, 595–97 (1966)
331. Thompson, J. E., Spencer, M., *Can. J. Biochem.*, **45**, 563–72 (1967)
332. Thompson, J. E., Tribe, T. A., Spencer, M., *Can. J. Biochem.*, **44**, 389–91 (1966)
333. Thornton, N. C., *Food Ind.*, **12(7)**, 48–50, 80; **(8)** 51–52 (1940)
334. Toole, V. K., Bailey, W. K., Toole, E. H., *Plant Physiol.*, **39**, 822–32 (1964)
335. Trout, S. A., Huelin, F. E., Tindale, G. B., *C.S.I.R.O., Div. Food Pres. Trans. Tech. Paper 14*, 11 pp. (1960)
336. Turkova, N. S., Vasil'eva, L. N., Cheremukhina, L. F., *Soviet Plant Physiol.*, **12**, 721–26 (1965)
337. Ulrich, R., *Fruits d'Outre-Mer*, **5**, 359–64 (1950)
338. Vacha, G. A., Harvey, R. B., *Plant Physiol.*, **2**, 187–93 (1927)
339. Valdovinos, J. G., Ernest, L. C., Henry, E. W., *Plant Physiol.*, **42**, 1803–6 (1967)
340. Van Fleet, D. S., *Nature*, **200**, 889 (1963)
341. Van Overbeek, J., Cruzado, H. J., *Am. J. Botany*, **35**, 410–12 (1948)
342. Vines, H. M., Grierson, W., Edwards, G. J., *Proc. Am. Soc. Hort. Sci.*, **92**, 227–34 (1968)
343. Von Abrams, G. J., Pratt, H. K., *Plant Physiol.*, **42**, 299–301 (1967)
344. Von Loesecke, H. W., *Bananas—Chemistry, Physiology, Technology* (Interscience, N.Y., 189 pp., 1950)
345. Waggoner, P. E., Dimond, A. E., *Science*, **119**, 123–24 (1954)
346. Wang, C. H., Persyn, A., Krackov, J., *Nature*, **195**, 1306–8 (1962)
347. Warner, H. L., Leopold, A. C., *BioScience*, **17**, 722 (1967)
348. Watada, A. E., Morris, L. L., *Plant Physiol.*, **42**, 757–61 (1967)
349. Webster, B. D., *Plant Physiol.*, **43**, 1512–44 (1968)
350. Wiesner, J., *Sitzber. kais. Akad. Wiss. (Wien), Math.-naturw. Kl.*, **77**, 15–54 (1878)
351. Wilkinson, B. G., *Nature*, **199**, 715–16 (1963)
352. Wooltorton, L. S. C., Jones, J. D., Hulme, A. C., *Nature*, **207**, 999–1000 (1965)
353. Workman, M., *Proc. Am. Soc. Hort. Sci.*, **83**, 149–61 (1963)
354. Workman, M., Patterson, M. E., *Proc. Am. Soc. Hort. Sci.*, **74**, 106–12 (1959)
355. Worsham, C. H., Waddell, C. C., Vilbrandt, F. C., *Bull. Va. Polytech. Inst., Eng. Expt. Sta. Ser. Bull. 36*, 34 pp. (1939)
356. Wright, H. B., Heatherbell, D. A., *New Zealand J. Agr. Res.*, **10**, 405–14 (1967)

357. Yang, S. F., *Arch. Biochem. Biophys.*, **122,** 481–87 (1967)
358. Yang, S. F., in *Biochemistry and Physiology of Plant Growth Substances* (See Ref. 14)
359. Yang, S. F., Ku, H. S., Pratt, H. K., *Biochem. Biophys. Res. Commun.*, **24,** 739–43 (1966)
360. Yang, S. F., Ku, H. S., Pratt, H. K., *J. Biol. Chem.*, **242,** 5274–80 (1967)
361. Young, R. E., *Nature,* **205,** 1113–14 (1965)
362. Young, R. E., Biale, J. B., *Plant Physiol.*, **37,** 409–15 (1962)
363. Young, R. E., Pratt, H. K., Biale, J. B., *Anal. Chem.*, **24,** 551–55 (1952)
364. Young, R. E., Romani, R. J., Biale, J. B., *Plant Physiol.*, **37,** 416–22 (1962)
365. Zimmerman, P. W., Wilcoxon, F., *Contrib. Boyce Thompson Inst.*, **7,** 209–29 (1935)

PERMEABILITY OF THE PLANT CELL[1]

By Ed. J. Stadelmann

Department of Horticultural Science, University of Minnesota
St. Paul, Minnesota

Introduction

The term permeability is used in the physiological literature to describe two different but related concepts: (*a*) capacity of cells or tissue to take up or exchange material with their environment (18, p. 12; 57, p. 236); (*b*) permeability of membranes to gases, liquids, dissolved substances (cf. 85, p. 358).

This review is almost exclusively limited to the discussion of permeability in the latter sense, and of such membranes as the plasmalemma, tonoplast, and protoplasmic layer of a vacuolated cell. For discussion of cuticular permeability the articles by Darlington & Cirulis (31), Yamada, Bukovac & Wittwer (151), and Yamada, Wittwer & Bukovac (152, 153) should be consulted. Active permeability in plants seems to be adequately covered in the literature in papers on mineral nutrition and salt uptake (cf. 90). Lack of space permits consideration of only selected articles. Hence some important contributions may not be mentioned.

No section on vital staining is included here, since main interest in this method is upon the adsorption and accumulation of the dye. No new data on passive permeability for vital stains have been collected. However, advanced instrumentation may help to obtain such information by this very useful method in protoplasmic research. A most comprehensive presentation of methods and results of vital staining of plant cells has been published (35). An earlier summary (80) emphasizes the use of vital staining as a cyto-chemical tool in living cells. Other contributions are found in the recent volumes of *Protoplasma.*

Monographs.—Since the survey of this subject by Collander (17), a number of monographs, symposia, and summarizing articles have reflected the active interest in this important field. In Ruhland's monumental *Encyclopedia of Plant Physiology* (114), several contributions are devoted to exchange of material between the plant cell and its milieu and the influence of external and internal factors upon this exchange.

An excellent state-of-the-art survey composed with mastery and compe-

[1] Supported by the Minnesota Agricultural Experiment Station. Scientific Journal Series, Paper No. 6695. The author wishes to thank Mrs. A. V. Pedeliski, University of Minnesota, and Professor T. T. Kozlowski, University of Wisconsin, for their help in revising this article.

tence was given by Collander (18), who is widely considered to be the grand master of permeability. He traced the historical development of permeability studies and summarized the wealth of knowledge on passive permeability of plant cells.

Wartiovaara & Collander (144; cf. 63) presented a balanced survey on theories of permeability and emphasized that it is not permeability, but rather the inverse quality, the permeation resistance, which is of primary biological importance for isolating the cell selectively from its environment. Stein (126) surveyed various problems of permeability and membrane structure, with emphasis on the molecular aspects and primary reference to characteristics of membranes in animal and human tissues. Monographs devoted to recent research on membrane structure and membrane components (13) and the membrane in general (30) were not yet available before the completion of this manuscript.

Schoffeniels (114a) described the permeability characteristics of animal and human tissues and cells primarily for substances occurring in their natural environment and also discussed the electrical properties and structures of these membranes.

Symposia, conferences, or special issues were devoted to particular aspects of passive permeability (61, 101, 121, 140, 145); to the plasma membrane [(37) with an excellent contribution on the history of the plasma membrane concept (74a, 96, 116)]; to biophysics and physiology of biological transport and cell membranes (5, 113); to colloid chemistry, ultrastructure of membranes, and active uptake (150); and to membrane structure and function (3a, 107, 141a). Biophysics of permeability (74) and transport and distribution of material in cells of higher plants (105) were discussed in meetings scheduled for 1968. Some data on permeability of algae were compiled by Stadelmann (118).

To a limited extent, topics related to passive permeability were discussed in several monographs and treatises [ion and water transport in animal cells (45, 81); water relations (84)] and symposia [water movement (38); intracellular transport (142)].

Sorption theory.—A theory that the interior of the protoplasm alone determines the exchange of material with cell surroundings and that in plant cells the tonoplast alone acts as semipermeable membrane (133, pp. 26/27) was advanced by Troshin (132–134). Similarly, Ling (93) in his "association-induction hypothesis" denied any control function of the cell membrane for material exchange. However, he later (94) assumed that K-ion exchange was controlled by the outer cell surface. Both authors were mainly concerned with animal cells and apparently were unaware of the wealth of evidence supporting the membrane theory which was obtained with plant cells. Also some important cellular functions are in disagreement with the sorption theory (6, p. 9f). However, it is possible that, depending upon the substance entering the cell, membrane permeability or sorption capacity of protoplasm combined control uptake (cf. 47, p. 643).

Active uptake of nonelectrolytes.—Active ("nonosmotic") uptake of nonelectrolytes which are used in experiments on passive permeability (e.g., urea, malonamide, methylurea) and water into plant cells, especially during plasmolysis, was again inferred by Follmann (39) and Follmann-Schrag (40) from differences in plasmolysis and cell content concentration on diatoms and *Cladophora* with and without treatment with metabolic inhibitors. Höfler & Url (62, 137) found similar experimental results working with sodium azide and dinitrophenol applied to cells of *Blechnum spicant* and *Gentiana sturmiana*. These authors and Höfler (56) discussed in detail the data from which the hypothesis of nonosmotic uptake in plasmolysis experiments was developed. Höfler & Url (62, pp. 466, 468) suggested that recovery in hypertonic sugar solutions or irregularities of the protoplast volume in stepwise increased sugar concentrations can be interpreted without difficulty by changes of passive permeability and exosmosis. Effects of sodium azide on plasmolysis and deplasmolysis of *Rhoeo* epidermal cells are best explained by changes of passive permeability (12). Urea uptake by petiole segments of *Nymphaea alba* and of the peduncle of *Taraxacum officinale* was tested and found to occur only as long as concentration equilibrium with the external solution was reached. Accumulation never was recorded (104). In all these experiments, evidence for support of the hypothesis of active uptake of these nonelectrolytes was lacking. Therefore, Bogen's criticism of earlier results seemed to be unfounded (144, p. 29f).

Permeability formulas.—Kusel (87, p. 151) presented a formula for an absolute permeability constant for solutes for filamentous algae like *Oscillatoria,* where contraction and expansion of the whole cell thread without plasmolysis was observed after perfusion of the preparation with a solution of the permeator. The formula gives a good approximation for the permeability constant. However, the factor 2.5 introduced at the end of the derivation must be omitted, since the permeability constant as derived up to this point is already reduced to unit concentration difference.

Much effort has been devoted to application of irreversible thermodynamics to the passive permeation process (22, 76). The classical kinetic approach resulted in a permeability constant from a modified Fick's law of diffusion, referring to the relationship of a specific substance (permeator) to a given membrane. The irreversible thermodynamics of permeation starts from more general premises which allow for inclusion of the important case of simultaneous passage of solvent and solute through a membrane under pressure and/or concentration difference. Three phenomenological coefficients result:

(*a*) The coefficient of the volume flow of water through a membrane under a pressure gradient, when no permeator is present, L_p. Dimension: length^2 × mass^{-1} × time; unit: cm × sec^{-1} × atm^{-1}.

(*b*) The solute permeability coefficient at zero volume flow, ω, which is a magnitude expressing the permeation of a solute. Dimension:

length^{-1} × mass^{-1} × time × mole; unit: cm × sec^{-1} × atm^{-1} × mole × cm^{-3}.

(c) The reflection coefficient σ, a measure of the degree of semipermeability of a membrane. Sigma indicates a ratio and is dimensionless.

These three coefficients are related to the usual permeability constants for water K_w and solute K_s: when K_w is expressed in a unit (e.g., cm/sec) with the same dimension as L_p, it is $K_w = L_p$. The permeability constant for solutes is $K_s = \omega \cdot R \cdot T$. This formula is strictly correct only when no simultaneous water flow through the membrane occurs, i.e., when K_s is measured by chemical or isotopic analysis. For osmotic and plasmolytic measurements the formula $K_{so} = \omega \cdot R \cdot T / \sigma^2$ is derived (126, p. 48), where K_{so} is the permeability constant determined by osmotic or plasmolytic measurements. The importance of σ in this formula, however, may be questioned since in experiments on *Chara australis* and *Nitella translucens* K_s and K_{so} values were found to be the same (27, p. 124).

The phenomenological coefficients are considered to contribute little information about the kinetics of permeation or the structure of the membrane (36, p. 967; 129, p. 336). Also the derivation of a set of three implicit functions which relate phenomenological coefficients to frictional coefficients (77; 126, p. 49) does not significantly advance the understanding of the membrane phenomena involved. The concept of the reflection coefficient (125, pp. 344/345) seems to be an important contribution to the theory of membrane permeability, since it is a new parameter for quantitative measurement of a membrane quality.

Some investigators have calculated a number of mathematical formulas and models based on the phenomenological approach (cf. 24, 78, 79). These theoretical results frequently exceed any possibility of experimental proof and applicability. They, therefore, often contribute very little to the understanding of permeability problems. It seems to me much more urgent to expand accurate experimental data concerning permeability for an increased number of cell types, substances, and conditions.

Mathematical treatments were applied by Hall (44) to analyze the permeation process through a spherical membrane of a haemolyzing erythrocyte. A formula was established for the absolute water permeability constant for cylindrical cells when deplasmolyzing in a nonpermeating and hypertonic solution (119, p. 682; 120).

Advancements in methods.—Substances with high specific activity of radioactive tracers are now available. Use of these substances will expand the application of compartmental analysis (117, p. 119f) for ions (33) or nonelectrolytes (26), where it is now possible to determine the permeability of the tonoplast membrane and plasmalemma separately. The application of the plasmometric method for permeability measurements and the possible errors involved are discussed by Höfler (56, p. 241). Microphotographic time-lapse techniques have provided detailed analyses of the time course of deplasmolysis in plasmometric experiments (121, p. 58f; 122). The numerical value of the degree of plasmolysis [as introduced by Höfler (53, p. 712)] for irregularly shaped cells or cells with concave plasmolysis forms can be determined by using an integrating eyepiece (46). This procedure may be considered an important improvement since it overcomes the limits of the plasmometric method and makes irregularly shaped cells accessible for quantitative evaluation of osmotic and permeability measurements.

The time course of changes in volume or weight of tissue disks (e.g., parenchyma cells of the hypocotyl tuber of *Beta vulgaris*), when transferred into a solution with different osmotic pressure, was found not to reflect cell permeability but rather extracellular (or extraprotoplast) diffusion of the solute (82, p. 819), so that this method is not available for determinating cellular permeability constants.

The reliability of plasmolytic water permeability determinations is occasionally questioned on the grounds of the uptake of saccharose and mannitol in leaf disks or entire plants after they are exposed for several hours or longer to a solution of these chemicals [Literature: (115, pp. 193/194)]. However, these authors overlook that it is routine in plasmolytic work to check for any sugar permeability or change in degree of plasmolysis after the osmotic equilibrium is reached. A great number of observations on plasmolysis with sugars and mannitol accumulated over the last decades. The results prove that with very few exceptions (e.g., some diatoms) these substances do not (or only negligibly) penetrate into the vacuole during the time of a plasmolytic experiment for determination of the water permeability.

NONELECTROLYTES

The relation between partition coefficient and permeability constant was further investigated for special classes of molecules. Substances with similar partition coefficients permeate more slowly when molecules are higher branched than when they are not (19, p. 143). Relatively large molecules (polypropylene glycols with mean mol wt of 425 and 1025) do not permeate as expected from their lipid solubility. Their size is a more important factor than their partition coefficients for permeation (20).

Permeability constants of 2.06 to 4.82 μ/sec for rapidly permeating substances, such as alcohols, were found with *Chara* and *Nitella* (27, p. 128). Radioactive tracer and washing techniques were used. The results were comparable to those found microchemically by Collander (15). The authors considered the effect of the "unstirred layer" which gives appreciable corrections for the permeability constant of rapidly permeating substances (27, p. 125).

Permeation rates of urea and formamide, expressed as ΔG (change of the degree of plasmolysis in cylindrical cells per time unit), of different cell types of six species of liverworts and five species of higher plants were determined to compare the degree of "porosity" of plasma membranes. A variation of the $\triangle G$ ratio for formamide/urea from 7.7 to 57.3 for liver-worts and of 2.0 to 6.3 for higher plants was found. The ratio of the distribution coefficients for formamide/urea is about 5.0 (100, p. 512). The $\triangle G$ values for formamide are among the few accurate data about its permeation into plant cells. Unfortunately these results are of limited value only, since urea was chosen as reference substance. An appreciable portion of urea is generally thought to penetrate through the "pores." Also, absolute permeability constants were not calculated, this omission rendering invalid any comparisons with results of other investigators.

Oscillatoria margaritifera and *O. lloydiana* have permeability series with the same sequence as that for *Chara* and *Majanthemum,* but the permeability values are about 100 times higher. The water permeability seems to be extremely high also. Permeation of substances of small molecular size is very little enhanced, thus a low "pore" permeability of the plasma membranes of these organisms is indicated (87).

Permeability series were recently established for *Blechnum spicant* (56, p. 276), *Gentiana germanica,* and *G. ciliata* (139, pp. 279 and 280; see also Fig. 2 in 139).

Relative values of saccharose permeability of some diatoms were measured by Übeleis (135, p. 416). An exception to the generally high sugar permeability of diatom cells is *Caloneis obtusa,* which showed no appreciable permeability for glucose, while the other nonelectrolytes used in permeability experiments permeated at about the rate found for other plant cells (58).

Protoplasmic permeability for methyl and ethyl alcohol has been reinvestigated by using a perfusion chamber in an improved plasmolytic technique (148). Longitudinal cuttings of the stem base from eight different species of flowering plants and two species of algae were used. The cuttings were plasmolyzed in specific concentrations of glucose, and transferred to a mixture which contains glucose in a concentration equimolar to that used for plasmolysis plus 5 to 20 per cent alcohol (total concentration). The protoplasts underwent a temporary (of a few minutes duration) length change prior to the equilibrium size. When alcohol permeated faster into the vacuole than water could leave it, the protoplast expanded. If alcohol permeated more slowly than water could leave, the protoplast contrated. Examples of each of these types and of intermediates were found in the experimental material. However, the situation appeared to be more complex since the protoplast size for most cell types tested at equilibrium is smaller in the mixture, and yet regains its original equilibrium size when transferred back into pure glucose solution. There also are changes from contraction type to expansion type, depending upon the concentration of alcohol applied, which supposedly are not caused by pathological alterations. For all mixture concentrations the subepidermal cells of *Impatiens sultani* exhibit the concentration type, while *Cladophora utriculosa* and *C. fracta* belong to the expansion type.

Values for the reflection coefficient [first mentioned by De Vries (32, p. 333) as "isotonic coefficient"], most of them calculated for artificial and animal cell membranes, were recently compiled by Stein (126, p. 56). For methanol, ethanol, and DHO with *Nitella* and *Chara* cells, σ is 0.25, 0.29, and 0.0033 to 0.0061, the last value depending upon the DHO concentration applied (28, p. 133). The value for σ for urea and *Allium cepa* epidermis cells determined from plasmometric evaluations was 0.87 to 0.93 (121, p. 25).However, it seems that in most of this experimental work the differences in water activity in equimolar concentrations of different substances were not taken into account.

A list of relative and absolute permeability constants for various substances with lower plants was compiled by Stadelmann (123).

Ions and Acids

The complex problem of active ion uptake in plant cells and its involvement with metabolism has been treated thoroughly in recent monographs (e.g., 11, 73, 128, and survey articles 23, 88, 102).

Passive permeability of the plasmalemma and the entire protoplasm layer for ions has been reviewed briefly by Sutcliffe (127, p. 197). Different mechanisms such as diffusion, ion exchange, adsorption, and mass flow may be involved in passive ion permeation. In addition, permeabilities of the plasma membranes (plasmalemma and tonoplast) for anions and cations and their species may vary considerably.

The giant Characean cells are especially suited for studies of passive permeation of ions at the cellular level with microchemical and tracer techniques. The ion concentration in the cell wall, the protoplasm layer, and the central vacuole can be determined. It is also possible, under certain assumptions, to calculate fluxes and permeability constants for an individual ion species (see Table I).

In *Vallisneria* leaves the plasmalemma shows no passive permeability for the Cl ion (leakage) during the process of active Cl uptake. However, by internal and external factors (antagonistic effects of other ions in the external solution), the structure of the plasma membrane can be changed so that leakage and passive uptake occurs (1, p. 23; 2, p. 55). Under optimum conditions no passive permeability for ions can be demonstrated for the cell membranes of *Vallisneria* leaves (1, p. 41).

Fatty acids with straight carbon chain permeate into *Saccharomyces cerevisiae* cells corresponding to their relative ether solubility. Acids possessing branched carbon chains, however, have a smaller permeability constant than expected from ether solubility (107a).

Water

Absolute permeability constants for water have been recalculated for a variety of plant cells from relative water permeability constants (119)

TABLE I

PASSIVE ION FLUXES (pmoles·cm⁻²·sec⁻¹) AND PERMEABILITY CONSTANTS (nm/sec)[a] UNDER STEADY STATE CONDITIONS[b]

Species	Fluxes Plasmalemma Na	Fluxes Plasmalemma K	Fluxes Tonoplast Na	Fluxes Tonoplast K	Permeability constants Plasmalemma Na	Permeability constants Plasmalemma K	Permeability constants Tonoplast Na	Permeability constants Tonoplast K	Reference
Chara globularis	0.7[d] 6.2[e]	2.8[d] 6.7[e]	—	—	0.1[e]	3[c]	—	—	(41, p. 516)
Nitellopsis obtusa	8[f]	4[f]	0.4[d] 0.6[e]	0.25[f]	0.5[e]	10[e]	0.64[e]	11[d] 0.025[e]	(99, pp. 342, 343, 345, 350, 351)
Nitella axillaris	—	0.47[f]	—	0.72[f]	—	13[e]	—	—	(33, p. 1118)
Nitella translucens	0.55[d]	0.3[d]	—	—	0.9[d]	5[d]	—	—	(98, pp. 875, 877)
Chara australis	0.1[e]	0.8[e]	—	—	10[c]	100[c]	—	—	(66, p. 42)

[a] 1 nm (=nanometer) = 10⁻⁹ m = 10⁻⁷ cm.
[b] After (66, p. 43); with additions.
[c] From (66, p. 43); influx or efflux not specified.
[d] Influx.
[e] Efflux.
[f] Influx and Efflux.

derived earlier, mostly with the osmotic method. To increase accuracy the re-calculations should use differences of water activities rather than concentration differences (10, p. 68).

One previously overlooked cause of the discrepancy between absolute water permeability constants obtained from osmotic experiments and those based on diffusion experiments may be "back diffusion." This occurs in such experiments in which permeation resistance is doubled because volume of the vacuole did not change. Hence, for each molecule of heavy water penetrating into the vacuole a molecule of H_2O has to leave the vacuole (119, p. 670). When considering "back diffusion" most of the values of the absolute water permeability constant are between 1.0 and 15 μ/sec (119, p. 696). This agrees well with a list of water permeability values for animal cells (34), which lie within the same limits, in most cases.

Artificial bimolecular phospholipid membranes have a water permeability constant of about 2.8 to 4.4 μ/sec (130, p. 92; 67, p. 546) in diffusion experiments. Constants calculated from osmotic experiments for the same kind of membrane are 17.3 to 104 μ/sec (67, p. 547). However, this range of latter values might be too low because of experimental conditions under which they were obtained. It is still difficult to explain the discrepancies between the permeability constants obtained by these two methods (67, p. 553).

Dainty & Hope (29) and Dainty & Ginzburg (25) found extremely high values for water permeability (up to 142 μ/sec) in transcellular osmosis experiments on *Nitella translucens*. They assumed that diffusion experiments gave values that were too low because cell diameter is rate limiting. Initial stages of transcellular osmosis are complicated by the additional action of cell wall shrinkage (25, p. 109). The permeability constants derived are concentration dependent. Further evaluation of transcellular osmosis experiments might be necessary to explain existing discrepancies.

The half-time value for water withdrawal in secondary roots of *Vicia faba* in hypertonic solutions (80 to 100 sec) was almost the same as for exchange of DHO (80 sec). Hence the same mechanism apparently determined the rate in both cases (69, p. 421). The H_2O/DHO exchange is only about 12 times slower than for free diffusion and the endodermis does not increase diffusion resistance for water (68, p. 589). When preplasmolyzed roots are tested for their H_2O/DHO exchange, at first a rapid exchange occurs with water in the "Vorraum" (the space between the plasmolyzed protoplast and the cell wall) and in cell walls. The half-time value for exchange of water with the protoplast is higher than in nonplasmolyzed tissue, probably because the volume of the vacuole and the total protoplasm surface is smaller (69).

Comparison of the diffusion rate of DHO and H_2O^{18} indicates that undissociated water molecules permeate into the cells (72, p. 256). For *Tolypella nidifica* the half-time value for the entrance of H_2O_2 is about 50 sec (71). Experiments with heavy water show that an equilibrium of the DHO concentration is reached between the cell water and the milieu when measured after 30 min (70).

The accuracy of the low values of the water permeability constant (0.3 μ/sec) reported by Myers (106, p. 141) for unplasmolyzed parenchyma cells of the hypocotyl tuber of *Beta vulgaris* has been questioned (91, p. 242; 119, p. 696; 82, p. 810). Occasionally investigators have overlooked these later references (e.g., 42, p. 1043) and have referred to Myer's data as providing proof of an effect of plasmolysis on water permeability.

Changes in Permeability

Interpretation of quantitatively determined permeability changes may contribute significantly to further understanding of membrane structure and function if a sufficiently large body of coherent data can be analyzed. At present such information is very scarce. A few examples of recently reported permeability changes caused by a variety of factors will be mentioned here and will hopefully stimulate more detailed studies in this area [for earlier observations see (56, p. 286, and 18, p. 65f)].

Permeability changes may be caused by endogenous conditions within cells or by natural or artificial changes in their environment. Reversibility of changes indicates the harmlessness of the causal factor. An increase in permeability often reflects pathological or premortal conditions. Little is known about the site of action of any factor, as to whether it influences the sieve effect of membranes or changes the capacity of membranes to act as a lipid solvent. The latter factor seems to be more easily restored after cells have been damaged, while the principle of the sieve effect is assumed to be more sensitive (86, p. 29), more unstable, and less easily restored when changed by external factors (59, p. 148).

A change in permeability of cell membranes does not just increase with strength of the causing factor. Occasionally, application of the same factor at a low intensity results in a permeability decrease, which changes to permeability increase with increasing strength of the causing factor. This reversal of the effect is one of the causes for contradictory reports on the action of external factors on permeability (cf. 146, p. 491). A number of explanations for the observed permeability changes exist but none is based on adequate experimental evidence.

Reversal of permeability changes could be explained by postulating micelle leaflet transitions in the lipid membrane (123a). Any altering factor would first cause the transition micelles into the more stable leaflet structure (this would decrease the water permeability by diminishing the number of "pores" between the micelles). When the intensity of the altering factor increases further, breakdown of the lipid membrane structure begins, with a subsequent increase of water permeability.

Internal factors.—Failure to consider changes in these factors may account for apparent discrepancies in results obtained by different investigators (cf., 95). The effect of various cations (e.g., calcium ions and potassium ions) on water permeability was different at different seasons of the year. This can be explained on the basis of their action on the membrane coacervates and seems to indicate seasonal changes in water permeability (95, p. 416).

External physical factors.—Alpha-irradiation with about 75 krad decreased urea permeability of onion epidermal cells, whereas dosages greater than about 1 Mrad increased permeability for urea (146, p. 490). A 50 per cent increase in water permeability was found after about 2 to 5 krad beta-radiation. Only 250 to 500 rad from this source were needed to cause a decrease in water permeability when tested about 20 to 72 hr after exposure (124).

External chemical factors.—Most of the permeability changes reported concern the action of solutes on permeability. While inorganic substances (inorganic ions) were intensively investigated earlier, present interest concerns organic substances.

Solute permeability.—Urea permeability of the tonoplast of one end of a *Nitella translucens* cell was reduced by a factor of 3 after the same end of the cell was placed in a molal solution of saccharose (26, p. 119).

Humic acid with pH 7.0 increased urea permeability of epidermal cells of *Gentiana rochelii* and subepidermal cells of the stem base of *Majanthemum bifolium* with a maximum at 0.1 mM humic acid (50, p. 405).

Water permeability.—Fusaric acid increased water permeability of subepidermal cells of the stem base of *Majanthemum bifolium* and other test plants from concentrations of 1 nM to 1 μM. At higher concentrations the water permeability decreased again and at 100 mM the value of the control was reached (49).

Concentrations of 10 nM to 10 μM of humic acid increased water permeability of cells of the outer epidermis of *Allium cepa* but higher concentrations had no effect (50, p. 418).

Indolylacetic acid buffered to pH 7.5 caused a decrease of water permeability of *Majanthemum* cells in concentrations down to 100 μM, but 0.1 to 10 μM caused an increase, while 10 nM produced no effect (49, p. 348). Further work on permeability changes induced by indolylacetic acid was reviewed by Pohl (111, p. 731).

Gibberellic acid at concentrations of 100 μM caused a maximum increase of water permeability in cells of the outer epidermis of *Allium cepa*. The effectiveness decreased with lower concentrations and 10 nM caused almost no change. Concentrations of 1 mM decreased the water permeability and still higher concentrations were toxic under the experimental conditions applied (50, p. 418).

2,4-Dinitrophenol and sodium-iodine acetate decreased water permeability of epidermal cells of the lower leaf side of *Rhoeo discolor* at 0.1 mM and 10 mM, respectively. Higher concentrations were toxic while threshold concentrations for any effect on water permeability were found to be 0.1 μM and 0.1 mM, respectively (43, p. 519).

Breakdown of protoplasmic semipermeability in parenchyma cells of the hypocotyl tuber of *Beta vulgaris* can easily be detected by leakage of anthocyanin-containing cell sap. This criterion was used by Van Overbeek & Blondeau (141) to determine toxicity of organic acids. These substances were found to be increasingly toxic (i.e.,effective in altering protoplasmic permeability) with increasing concentrations of the undissociated molecule (i.e., the lipid-soluble portion). Acids of lower molecular weight were more effective than those of high ones.

Similar experiments in which isolated sections of *Zea mays* coleoptiles were treated with hydrocarbons of different chain length show that the smallest hydrocarbon molecules were the most effective in producing permeability changes. Aromatics were more effective than paraffines and olefines. Van Overbeek & Blondeau (141) suggested that incorporation of the toxic molecules in the plasmalemma is the cause for the permeability breakdown. However, the passage of these toxic molecules inside the plasma and their action on centers important for maintenance of the membrane should also be considered.

Toxic increase of water permeability was found when 1 mM decenyl succinic acid was applied for 30 min at pH 4 to cells of the inner epidermis of *Allium cepa*. Here too the undissociated molecule is damaging (while the anion is not harmful) but decreases the water permeability when the substance is applied above about 1mM $\times$ min. Under these conditions decenyl succinic acid seems also to enter the mesoplasm, since occasional cap plasmolysis was observed (89).

To distinguish effects of certain chemical treatments on the hydraulic permeability constant from those on the reflection coefficient, Glinka & Reinhold (42) introduced criteria based on measurements of influx and efflux in tissue disks. Their approach seems to be incomplete as provision was not made to include the possibility of differences in the L_p values caused by the direction of water flow (cf, 25, p. 109f). The authors also overlooked that any interfering permeation of the solute during plasmolysis experiments for water permeability determination can easily be detected by observation of changes in the degree of protoplasmic contraction after osmotic equilibrium is reached.

MEMBRANE STRUCTURE AND PERMEATION

One of the most active areas of cell membrane research involves interpretation of the constantly increasing amount of information on membrane structure. The situation is presently characterized by a multitude of new concepts, yet these often lack general applicability since they often were developed hastily and were based on results from a few isolated experiments without considering and synthesizing data from other research areas of investigation on cell membranes (cf. 6, p. 5; 14). Since some aspects of cell membranes seem to be basically alike for plant, animal, and human cells, references on the latter also are included. A comprehensive review on membrane structure is given in this volume by Branton (9).

A great need exists for an updated and rational concept on structure and dynamics of cell membranes which will explain the large amount of recently obtained data on membrane characteristics. This concept must also synthesize the observations leading to the membrane concept of Overton, Collander, and Danielli. It must allow for the diversity found in individual membranes of cells of different species, and must treat the plasmalemma and the tonoplast as surface layers of the living protoplasm.

Basic information for theories of cell membrane structure and permeability are derived primarily from three sources: (a) studies of passage of solutes and water through the more or less intact or altered membranes of living cells and of electrical qualities of membranes; (b) other biophysical and biochemical analyses of cell membranes and their components, or of artificial membranes, as well as mathematical evaluations at the molecular level; (c) electron microscopy.

Membrane structure.—While most recent concepts of membrane structure are still based on the lipid nature of membrane [as developed by Overton (108, p. 109), and Collander & Bärlund (21, p. 99)], they differ widely with respect to membrane architecture. Danielli's bimolecular leaflet model was further developed and an organization of locked hexagonal subunits was suggested for the two layers of protein coats. Also proposed was a hexagonal icelike water structure between the protein and bimolecular lipid layer (48) as well as a membrane model containing globular proteins with an aqueous phase (147).

Lucy (97) mentioned a micellar model of membrane organization with globular micelles of lipids (diameter about 50 Å). Between the globular micelles, globular protein molecules might be located. This micellar structure was thought to be in a dynamic equilibrium with the bimolecular leaflet structure, so that certain areas of the membrane temporarily were in one phase or the other.

Rectangular micelles ("pillars") in membranes and their reversible transition to the leaflet structure were assumed by Kavenau (75). However, it is questionable if Kavenau's concept can be applied to a structure as thin as the plasma membranes (7).

The welcomed unit membrane hypothesis (cf. 112, p. 1) is in need of major revision since an increasing number of investigations on cell membranes show a diversity of membrane thickness and composition, which hardly can be brought into agreement with the original concept (83, p. 1493; 149, p. 102).

Surface views of the plasmalemma of *Saccharomyces cerevisiae* cells, made possible by the freeze-etching technique, show more or less regular patterns of different elements (103, p. 570). Branton (8) interprets the oblique fractions of membranes seen in the electron microscope pictures to explain details of the interior structure of the membrane.

Permeability series.—The differences in the permeability series at least partially reflect variations in membrane composition or structure. Causal analysis of these differences may become an important tool for investigating intact cell membranes.

Previous observations of differences in the ratio of permeability con-

stants for urea and glycerol in different series led to a concept of amidophilic and amidophobic types of protoplasm (cf. 57, p. 241). A new arrangement of 38 permeability series is based on relative permeability constants (glycerol arbitrarily set at 1) and the ratio of glycerol to malonamide. The resulting sequence shown in Figure 1 indicates the amidophilia of
the protoplasm and, for the first time, shows some consistency (139). Permeability for urea and methyl urea somewhat parallels malonamide, while erythritol more or less follows the line for glycerol. As might be expected,
marked oscillations in these values occur. These are caused by errors in
measurement and in variations among cells. The permeability series and
their width vary much more in those plants listed in the middle part of the
diagram (the width is the ratio of the permeability constants for the two
extremes of the permeators tested). The cell types with unusually high urea
permeability also are located in the same part of this diagram. To the far left
the diagram contains the permeability series for leaf epidermis cells of
Rhoeo discolor. On the extreme right is *Oedogonium itzigsohnii,* which has
the most amidophilic protoplasm.

Cells with the same width of the permeability series may have similar
membrane composition but different degrees of sieve effect. Variation in
width may be caused by chemical or structural differences between membranes. However, recalculation of many of these permeability constants
seems to be necessary before well-founded conclusions about membrane
structure can be made from comparing permeability series.

Plasmalemma.—The outer plasma membrane is known to protect the
cell against an unfavorable environment (110, p. 217; 60, p. 236). Qualitative differences in the resistance of cells to harmful Na_2CO_3 solutions are
interpreted as differences in the qualities of the plasmalemma. In cells of
higher plants the plasmalemma usually is rather delicate and plasmolysis
with Na_2CO_3 solutions damages the cell. In desmids of bogs, however, the
plasmalemma often is resistant to damage and the cells show normal plasmolysis with Na_2CO_3 solutions. Hypertonic solutions of $MnSO_4$ (136, p. 209)
and even aluminum salts (4, p. 133f) cause normal plasmolysis which persists for many hours without causing pathological changes in protoplasm.
Desmids also do not need Ca^{++} for restitution of the plasmalemma as do
higher land plants (51, 54, 138; see also 52, p. 51).

Membrane formation.—The dynamics of plasmalemma and tonoplast
formation and absorption involve basically a change in area of a surface
layer. There exists an immediately accessible reservoir (probably the entire
ground plasma) of plasmalemma and tonoplast material in the protoplasm.
This is strikingly demonstrated by the ease with which new (secondary)
plasmalemma and tonoplast are formed when the protoplast increases its
surface area (e.g., experimentally during plasmolysis; plasmalemma formation alone occurs when Hecht's strands are formed). An increase in surface
area at a rate of 23 μ^2/sec was measured for the plasmalemma and the tonoplast during deplasmolysis (121, p. 41). Little attention has been given recently to the surface quality of the plasmalemma and tonoplast, and most

new models of membrane structure do not consider the mesoplasm or its intimate connection with the membranes.

The secondary plasmalemma is very similar if not equal in characteristics to the primary plasmalemma (52, p. 47). With certain chemical treatments (EDTA followed by plasmolysis with urea), the plasmalemma is destroyed and the uncovered cytoplasm, in direct contact with the external solutions, immediately swells (52, p. 31). The breakdown of the plasmalemma started at a specific point on the plasmalemma surface. Breakdown then progressed gradually over the entire surface (52, p. 33).

Site of permeation resistance.—It generally is assumed that plasma membranes exhibit the major permeation resistance; for some electrolytes the plasmalemma may be the main barrier, whereas passive uptake of non-electrolytes from external solution into the vacuole may be controlled by the tonoplast as well as the plasmalemma (cf. 16, p. 218f; 26, p. 117). Recently Höfler (56, p. 287; 60) postulated that a continuous lipid phase existed in the ground plasm. This phase, which extends from the plasmalemma to the tonoplast, acts as a solvent for lipophilic permeators. The continuity of this lipid phase (protein-lipid complex) through the entire plasma layer is inferred from vital staining experiments as well as previous evidence (57, p. 239; 3, p. 47). There might also be a continuous aqueous phase in the mesoplasm (55, p. 393).

The "pores" (or the sievelike action) of the plasmalemma control passage of that portion of the total amount of a penetrating small molecular substance, which does not enter by lipid solution through the plasmalemma and the lipid phase of the plasma into the vacuole [two-pathway theory (60, p. 240)].

Levitt's criticism of the two-pathway theory is based on the hypothesis that all lipids of the cytoplasm are located in the cell membrane (92), and is not correct for all cell types. Formation of new plasmalemma may involve considerable surface increase. Also, naked protoplasts show high expansion capacity (131).

While Höfler's concept of a continuous lipid phase in the mesoplasm deserves some consideration, it is unlikely that the main portion of the permeator continues to move inside the lipid phase after it has passed through the membrane itself. The distribution coefficient definitely favors migration inside the mesoplasm in the aqueous phase.

For the "lipid phase," factors, such as membrane thickness, the number of solute molecules present in the lipid phase, and the decrease of their migratory speed while passing through the membrane may be important in the permeation process (144, p. 66).

The water phase of the ground plasma contributes significantly to permeation resistance of the entire protoplasm layer for passage of water into or out of the vacuole from or to the external solutions. This may be inferred from the much higher speed of plasmolysis of tonoplasts when compared wth plasmolysis of protoplasts in cells of the same tissue (57, p. 241). Hofmeister (64, p. 419f) compared the permeability constants for water

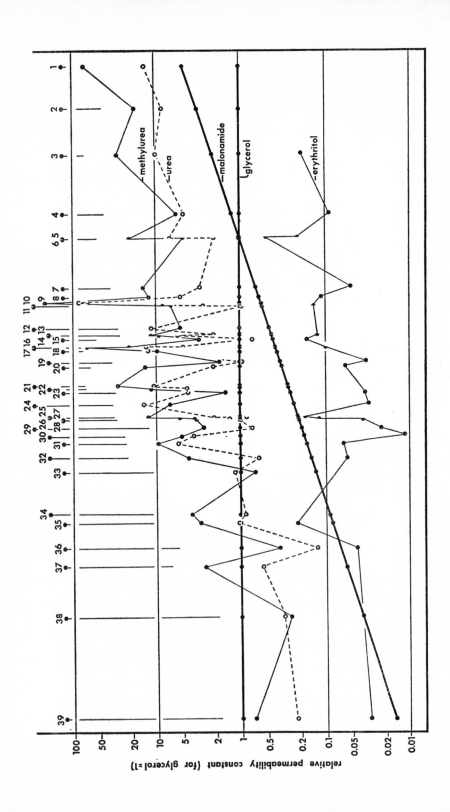

relative permeability constant (for glycerol = 1)

methylurea
urea
malonamide
glycerol
erythritol

and urea for 25 different kinds of plant cells: Cells with high urea permeability still exhibited average values for water permeability. This may indicate that at least partially different pathways are involved in urea and water permeation. Also Dainty & Hope (29, p. 143) emphasized that resistance to water movement was not confined to the tonoplast. Plasmalemma and tonoplast resistance to water permeation still reach an appreciable magnitude since microinjection of water into protoplasm of plasmolyzed cells results in a temporary swelling of the protoplasm (65). Microinjection of water-soluble sulfonic acid dyes was followed by rapid distribution of the dye inside the mesoplasm. Because these dyes have low lipid solubility, they

----

←◀◀◀

Fig. 1. Permeability series for 39 different cell species. Abscissa: ratio permeability constant (malonamide) / permeability constant (glycerol). All permeability constants are relative values for the glycerol permeability constant $=1$. Ordinate: Relative permeability constants (logarithmic presentation). After Url (139, p. 278f).

Numbers indicating the cell species:

1 *Oedogonium itzigsohnii*
2 *Oedogonium* sp.
3 *Plagiothecium denticulatum* (leaf cells)
4 *Ceramium diaphanum*
5 *Zygnema cyanosporum*
6 *Blechnum spicant* (parenchyma of the leaf midrib)
7 *Pylaiella litoralis*
8 *Elodea densa* (cells of the leaf upper side) "Hauptreihe"
9 *Oedogonium echinosporum*
10 *Majanthemum bifolium* (subepidermis cells of the stem)
11 *Cladophora glomerata*
12 *Elodea densa* (cells of the leaf upper side, leaves from below the top region of the stem)
13 *Mougeotia scalaris*
14 *Spirogyra* sp.
15 *Oscillatoria lloydiana*
16 *Spirogyra* cf. *dubia*
17 *Pleurotaenium ehrenbergii*
18 *Oedogonium pringsheimii* (vegetative cells)
19 *Gentiana germanica* (epidermis cells of the stem)
20 *Hippuris vulgaris* (water leaf, cells of the mesophyll)
21 *Taraxacum pectinatiforme* (epidermis cells of the upper side of the midrib; "leaf No. 1")
22 *Oedogonium* sp.
23 *Gentiana sturmiana* (epidermis cells of the stem)
24 *Lemna minor* (epidermis cells of root)
25 *Elodea densa* (cells of the leaf upper side, leaves from the top region of the stem)
26 *Curcuma rubescens* (subepidermis cells of the leaf sheath)
27 *Hippuris vulgaris* (air leaf, cells of the mesophyll)
28 *Oscillatoria princeps*
29 *Zygnema* sp.
30 *Solanum tuberosum* (epidermis cells of the stem)
31 *Chara ceratophylla*
32 *Taraxacum pectinatiforme* (epidermis cells of the upper side of the leaf midrib; "Hauptreihe")
33 *Lamium maculatum* (epidermis cells of the stem; watered plants)
34 *Tradescantia elongata* (stem parenchyma cells)
35 *Gentiana ciliata* (stem epidermis cells)
36 *Gentiana sturmiana* (corolla cells)
37 *Muscari racemosum* (subepidermis cells of the stem)
38 *Lamium maculatum* (epidermis cells of the stem; plants grown under drought conditions)
39 *Rhoeo discolor* (epidermis cells of the lower side of the leaf midrib)

cannot diffuse out through the plasmalemma or the tonoplast into either the external solution or the vacuole (92, p. 161).

The question of whether protein layers of plasma membranes contribute to the resistance against water permeation is still open. Huang & Thompson (67, p. 553) suggested from comparison with values for the artificial lipid bilayer membrane that the protein layer can play only a minor role as permeation resistance against water. However, the water permeability values for the different cell species vary too much to make such comparisons meaningful.

Permeation process.—Very little is known about the permeation process itself. Although pores or porelike structures have been assumed to exist, and thereby to account for passage of small molecules (cf. 109, p. 133f), they have never been seen in electron microscope pictures, although their supposed size is within resolution of the electron microscope (cf. 6, p. 16; 109, p. 130). Also the equality of the half-time values for water exchange by DHO and for osmotic water withdrawal [see p. 593; 69, p. 407)] does not support the assumption of pores. Only transient rather than permanent pores could be assumed for the artificial liquid lipid bilayer membrane (67, p. 553).

Two theories were promoted to explain the pore effect by molecular kinetics rather than by the assumption of pores. Wartiovaara (143) compared the permeability constants of homologue series of permeators (e.g., alcohols: methanol, ethanol, propanol, butanol) and concluded that two parallel and alternative pathways for permeation of molecules through the protoplasm membranes did not exist. It seems that the sieve effect can be explained by a sievelike plate covering the membrane. The effect of such sievelike plates depends on the molecular size of the permeator molecule.

The lipid layer of the plasmalemma is assumed to consist of vertically oriented lipid molecules which form temporary holes by thermal motion. A sieve effect results when thermal motion causes the permeator molecule to come into contact with the surface of the lipid layer: The permeator molecule can penetrate only when it is or can be oriented fast enough parallel to the orientation of the lipid molecules of the membrane surface. The speed of molecular orientation depends on the moment of inertia. A close parallelism exists between the inverse moment of inertia of the permeator molecule and the sieve effect calculated from the permeability constant.

A lattice model for the cell membrane was suggested by Stein (126). The breaking of hydrogen bonds between permeator molecule and water during the passage of the permeator through the membrane is considered to be the important feature. The product $P \cdot M^{1/2}$ (P = permeability constant, M = mole weight) can be related to the number of hydrogen bonds of the permeator by using an assigned value for the number of bonds formed for individual atom groups. Thermodynamic parameters for the cell can be calculated from these data and from the temperature dependency of the permeability constant.

Wartiovaara's model attracts by its simplicity and because it can be used to explain, in addition to the permeability constants of other permeators, the experimentally determined value of the water permeability constant. However, the model has not yet been elaborated so that hidden shortcomings may not as yet be apparent.

Many quantitative data are available for the lattice model, but a correction factor for CH_2 groups must be introduced and the value of $P \cdot M^{1/2}$ for water still lies far from the other points when they are plotted against the number of hydrogen bonds. It also is difficult to explain the marked differences in the permeability constant for the same substance with different types of cells on the basis of the amount of energy needed to disrupt a hydrogen bond with the permeator molecule. This energy depends upon the structure of the permeator molecule only. Therefore it would be expected that different membranes would have the same permeability constant for the same substance, if the rupture of hydrogen bonds alone determines passage of the molecule through the membrane.

LITERATURE CITED

1. Arisz, W. H., *Protoplasma*, **57**, 5–26 (1963)
2. Arisz, W. H., *Acta Botan. Neerl.*, **13**, 1–58 (1964)
3. Bancher, E., Hölzl, J., *Protoplasma*, **57**, 33–50 (1963)
3a. Bell, J. D., Grant, J. K., Eds., *The Structure and Function of the Membranes and Surfaces of Cells* (Biochem. Soc. Symp., 22, University Press, Cambridge, 172 pp., 1963)
4. Böhm-Tüchy, E., *Protoplasma*, **52**, 108–42 (1960)
5. Bolis, L., Ed., *Symp. Biophys. Physiol. Biol. Transport, Frascati (Italy), June 15–18, 1965, Protoplasma*, **63** (1967)
6. Booij, H. L., in *Permeability*, 5–35 (See Ref. 150)
7. Booij, H. L. (Private communication, 1968)
8. Branton, D., *Proc. Natl. Acad. Sci. U.S.*, **55**, 1048–56 (1966)
9. Branton, D., *Ann. Rev. Plant Physiol.*, **20**, 209–38 (1969)
10. Briggs, G. E., *Movement of water in plants* (F. A. Davis Co., Philadelphia, 142 pp., 1967)
11. Briggs, G. E., Hope, A. B., Robertson, R. N., *Electrolytes in Plant Cells* (Blackwell, Oxford, 217 pp., 1961)
12. Burström, H. G., *Indian J. Plant Physiol.*, **5**, 88–96 (1962)
13. Chapman, D., *Biological Membranes* (Academic Press, New York, ca. 480 pp., 1968)
14. Cole, K. S., *Ann. N.Y. Acad. Sci.*, **137**, Art. 2, 405–8 (1966)
15. Collander, R., *Physiol. Plantarum*, **7**, 420–45 (1954)
16. Collander, R., in *Encyclopedia of Plant Physiology*, **2**, 218–29 (See Ref. 114)
17. Collander, R., *Ann. Rev. Plant Physiol.*, **8**, 335–48 (1957)
18. Collander, R., in *Plant Physiology*, **2**, 3–102 (Steward, F. C., Ed., Academic Press, New York, 758 pp., 1959a)
19. Collander, R., *Physiol. Plantarum*, **12**, 139–44 (1959b)
20. Collander, R., *ibid.*, **13**, 179–85 (1960)
21. Collander, R., Bärlund, H., *Acta Botan. Fennica*, **11**, 1–114 (1933)
22. Dainty, J., *Advan. Botan. Res.*, **1**, 279–362 (1963)
23. Dainty, J., in *The Cellular Functions of Membrane Transport*, 41–52 (Symp. Soc. Gen. Physiologists, Woods Hole, 1963, Prentice-Hall, Englewood Cliffs, N.J., 291 pp., 1964)
24. Dainty, J., Ginzburg, B. Z., *J. Theoret. Biol.*, **5**, 256–65 (1963)
25. Dainty, J., Ginzburg, B. Z., *Biochim. Biophys. Acta*, **79**, 102–11 (1964)
26. Dainty, J., Ginzburg, B. Z., *ibid.*, 112–21 (1964)
27. Dainty, J., Ginzburg, B. Z., *ibid.*, 122–28 (1964)
28. Dainty, J., Ginzburg, B. Z., *ibid.*, 129–37 (1964)
29. Dainty, J., Hope, A. B., *Australian J. Biol. Sci.*, **12**, 136–45 (1959)
30. Dalton, A. J., Haguenau, F., *The*

Membranes (Academic Press, New York, 223 pp., 1968)
31. Darlington, W. A., Cirulis, N., *Plant Physiol.*, **38**, 462–67 (1963)
32. De Vries, H., *Botan. Ztg.*, 309–33 (1889)
33. Diamond, J. M., Solomon, A. K., *J. Gen. Physiol.*, **42**, 1105–21 (1959)
34. Dick, D. A., *Intern. Rev. Cytol.*, **8**, 388–448 (1959)
35. Drawert, H., Vitalfärbung und Vital-flourochromierung pflanzlicher Zellen und Gewebe, in *Protoplasmatologia*, **II**/D/3 (Heilbrunn, L. V., Weber, F., Eds., Springer, Wien, 780 pp., 1968)
36. Eisenman, G., Sandblom, J. P., Walker, J. L., Jr., *Science,* **155**, 965–74 (1967)
37. Fishman, A. P., Ed., Symp. Plasma Membrane, Dec. 8–9, New York City, *Circulation*, **26**, 987–1232 (1962)
38. Fogg, G. E. Ed., *Symp. Soc. Exptl. Biol.*, **19** (1965)
39. Follmann, G., *Planta*, **50**, 671–700 (1958)
40. Follmann, G., Follmann-Schrag, I.-A., *Z. Naturforsch.*, **14b**, 181–87 (1959)
41. Gaffey, C. T., Mullins, L. J., *J. Physiol. (London)*, **144**, 505–24 (1958)
42. Glinka, Z., Reinhold, L., *Plant Physiol.*, **39**, 1043–50 (1964)
43. Guttenberg, H. v., Reiff, B., *Protoplasma*, **48**, 499–521 (1957)
44. Hall, G. G., *J. Theoret. Biol.*, **1**, 18–26 (1961)
45. Harris, E. J., *Transport and Accumulation in Biological Systems* (Butterworths, London, 291 pp., 1956)
46. Härtel, O., *Protoplasma*, **57**, 354–70 (1963)
47. Hechter, O., *Ann. N.Y. Acad. Sci.*, **125**, 625–46 (1965a)
48. Hechter, O., *Federation Proc.*, **24**, Suppl. 15, S–91—S–102 (1965b)
49. Heinrich, G., *Protoplasma*, **55**, 320–56 (1962)
50. Heinrich, G., *ibid.*, **58**, 402–25 (1964)
51. Herrmann, R., *Protoplasma*, **58**, 172–89 (1964)
52. Herrmann, R., *ibid.*, **61**, 12–59 (1966)
53. Höfler, K., *Ber. Deut. Botan. Ges.*, **35**, 706–27 (1917)
54. Höfler, K., *Protoplasma*, **40**, 426–60 (1951)
55. Höfler, K., *Ber. Deut. Botan. Ges.*, **65**, 391–99 (1953)
56. Höfler, K., *Österr. Akad. Wiss. Mathem.-Naturwiss. Kl. Sitzber. Abt. I*, **167**, 237–95 (1958)
57. Höfler, K., *Ber. Deut. Botan. Ges.*, **72**, 236–45 (1959)
58. Höfler, K., *Protoplasma*, **52**, 5–25 (1960)
59. Höfler, K., *ibid.*, 145–56 (1960)
60. Höfler, K., *Ber. Deut. Botan. Ges.*, **76**, 233–42 (1961)
61. Höfler, K., *Protoplasma*, **60**, 150–58 (1965)
62. Höfler, K., Url, W., *Ber. Deut. Botan. Ges.*, **70**, 462–76 (1958)
63. Hofmeister, L., *Protoplasma*, **54**, 317–22 (1962)
64. Hofmeister, L., *ibid.*, **57**, 410–28 (1963)
65. Hofmeister, L. (Personal communication, 1968)
66. Hope, A. B., Walker, N. A., *Australian J. Biol. Sci.*, **14**, 26–44 (1961)
67. Huang, C., Thompson, T. E., *J. Mol. Biol.*, **15**, 539–54 (1966)
68. Hübner, G., *Flora (Jena)*, **148**, 549–94 (1960)
69. Hübner, G., *Protoplasma*, **60**, 401–25 (1965a)
70. Hübner, G., *Naturwissenschaften*, **52**, 619 (1965b)
71. Hübner, G., Ludewig, R., *Z. Naturforsch.*, **19b**, 383–86 (1964)
72. Hübner, G., Wetzel, K., *Ber. Deut. Botan. Ges.*, **74**, 255–56 (1961)
73. Jennings, D. H., *The Absorption of Solutes by Plant Cells* (Oliver & Boyd, Edinburgh, 204 pp., 1963)
74. Katchalsky, A., *Symp. Biophys. Aspects Permeability* (Polymer Dept. Weizmann Inst. Sci., Rehovot, Israel, 1968)
74a. Kates, M., *Bioscience*, **17**, 485–86 (1967)
75. Kavanau, J. L., *Structure and Function in Biological Membranes* (Holden-Day, Inc., San Francisco, 760 pp., 1965)
76. Kedem, O., Katchalsky, A., *Biochim. Biophys. Acta*, **27**, 229–46 (1958)
77. Kedem, O., Katchalsky, A., *J. Gen. Physiol.*, **45**, 143–79 (1962)
78. Kedem, O., Katchalsky, A., *Trans. Faraday Soc.*, **59**, 1941–53 (1963)
79. Kimizuka, H., Koketsu, K., *J. Theoret. Biol.*, **6**, 290–305 (1964)
80. Kinzel, H., *Österr. Apotheker-Ztg.*, **16**, 573–78 (1962)
81. Kleinzeller, A., Kotyk, A., Eds., *Membrane Transport and Metabo-*

lism (Proc. Symp. Prague, 1960; Academic Press, London, 608 pp., 1961)

82. Kohn, P. G., Dainty, J., *J. Exptl. Botany,* **17,** 809–21 (1966)

83. Korn, E. D., *Science,* **153,** 1491–98 (1966)

84. Kozlowski, T. T., *Water deficits and plant growth,* **I:** *Development, Control, and Measurement* (Academic Press, New York, 390 pp., 1968)

85. Kramer, P. J., in *Encyclopedia of Plant Physiology,* 358–68 (See Ref. 114)

86. Kreuz, J., *Österr. Botan. Z.,* **90,** 1–30 (1941)

87. Kusel, H., *Protoplasma,* **56,** 141–77 (1963)

88. Laties, G. G., *Ann. Rev. Plant Physiol.,* **20,** 89–116 (1969)

89. Lee, O. Y., *The influence of decenyl succinic acid on permeability of plant cells to water and its possible effect on frost hardiness* (M.S. thesis, Univ. Minnesota, St. Paul, Minn., 1967)

90. Leggett, J. E., *Ann. Rev. Plant Physiol.,* **19,** 333–46 (1968)

91. Levitt, J., *Physiol. Plantarum,* **6,** 240–52 (1953)

92. Levitt, J., *Protoplasma,* **52,** 161–63 (1960)

93. Ling, G. N., *A Physical Theory of the Living State. The association-induction hypothesis* (Blaisdell Publ. Co., New York, 680 pp., 1962)

94. Ling, G. N., *Ann. N.Y. Acad. Sci.,* **137,** Art. 2, 837–59 (1966)

95. Loeven, W. A., *Koninkl. Ned. Akad. Wentenschap., Proc. Ser. C,* **54,** 411–20 (1951)

96. Loewenstein, W. R., Ed., Biological Membranes: Recent Progress, *Ann. N.Y. Acad. Sci.,* **137,** Art. 2, 403–1048 (1966)

97. Lucy, J. A., *Brit. Med. Bull.,* **24,** 127–29 (1968)

98. MacRobbie, E. A. C., *J. Gen. Physiol.,* **45,** 861–78 (1962)

99. MacRobbie, E. A. C., Dainty, J., *J. Gen. Physiol.,* **42,** 335–53 (1958)

100. Mayer, E., *Protoplasma,* **58,** 497–550 (1964)

101. Mayer, E., *ibid.,* **60,** 159–61 (1965)

102. Mengel, K., Marschner, H., *Z. Pflanzenernähr., Düng., Bodenk.,* **100,** 193–208 (1963)

103. Moor, H., *Z. Zellforsch. Mikroskop. Anat.,* **62,** 546–80 (1964)

104. Müller, E., *Flora (Jena),* **148,** 529–48 (1960)

105. Müller, E., *Intern. Symp. Transport and Distribution of Matter in Cells of Higher Plants, Reinhardsbrunn Castle* (Inst. Biochem. Pflanzen, Halle (Saale), Germany, 1968)

106. Myers, G. M. P., *J. Exptl. Botany,* **2,** 129–44 (1951)

107. Northcote, D. H., Ed., *Brit. Med. Bull.,* **24,** 101–6 (1968)

107a. Oura, E., Suomaleinen, H., Collander, R., *Physiol. Plantarum,* **12,** 534–44 (1959)

108. Overton, E., *Vierteljahresschr. Naturforsch. Ges. Zürich,* **44,** 88–135 (1899)

109. Passow, H., *Klin. Wochschr.,* **41,** 130–38 (1963)

110. Plowe, J. Q., *Protoplasma,* **12,** 196–220 (1931)

111. Pohl, R., in *Encyclopedia of Plant Physiology,* **14,** 729–42 (Ruhland, W., Ed., Springer, Berlin, 1357 pp., 1961)

112. Robertson, J. D., in *Cellular Membranes in Development,* 1–81 (Locke, M., Ed., 22nd Symp. Soc. Development and Growth, Academic Press, New York, 382 pp., 1964)

113. Roche, M., Ed., Physiology of the Cell Membrane, Symp. Inst. Venezolano Invest. cient., Caracas, Venezuela, July 31–Aug. 3, 1959, *J. Gen. Physiol.,* **43,** 1–189 (1960)

114. Ruhland, W., Ed., *Encyclopedia of Plant Physiology,* **2** (Springer, Berlin, 1072 pp., 1956)

114a. Schoffeniels, E., *Cellular Aspects of Membrane Permeability* (Pergamon, Oxford, 266 pp., 1967)

115. Slayter, R. O., *Plant-Water Relationship* (Academic Press, New York, 366 pp., 1967)

116. Smith, H., *Circulation,* **26,** 897–1012 (1962)

117. Solomon, A. K., in *Mineral Metabolism* **1** A, 119–67 (Comar, C. L., Bronner, F., Eds., Academic Press, New York, 386+30 pp., 1960)

118. Stadelmann, E. J., in *Physiology and Biochemistry of Algae,* 493–528 (Lewin, R. A., Ed., Academic Press, New York, 929 pp., 1962)

119. Stadelmann, E. J., *Protoplasma,* **57,** 660–718 (1963)

120. Stadelmann, E. J., *ibid.,* **58,** 220–26 (1963)

121. Stadelmann, E. J., *ibid.,* **59,** 14–68 (1964)

122. Stadelmann, E. J., *Mikroskopie, 19,* 135–48 (1965)
123. Stadelmann, E. J., in *Environmental Biology,* 552–64 (Altman, P. L., Dittmer, D. S., Eds., Federation Am. Soc. Exptl. Biol., Bethesda, Md., 634 pp., 1966)
123a. Stadelmann, E. J., *Protoplasma* (In preparation, 1969)
124. Stadelmann, E. J., Pedeliski, A. (Unpublished, 1968)
125. Staverman, A. J., *Rec. Trav. Chim.,* **70,** 344–52 (1951)
126. Stein, W. D., *The Movement of Molecules Across Cell Membranes* (Academic Press, New York, 369 pp., 1967)
127. Sutcliffe, J. F., *Biol. Rev. Cambridge Phil. Soc.,* **34,** 159–220 (1959)
128. Sutcliffe, J. F., *Mineral Salt Absorption in Plants* (Pergamon, Oxford-London, 194 pp., 1962)
129. Teorell, T., *Protoplasma, 63,* 336–41 (1967)
130. Thompson, T. E., in *Cellular Membranes in Development,* 83–96 (Locke, M., Ed., 22nd Symp. Soc. Development and Growth, Academic Press, New York, 382 pp., 1964)
131. Törnävä, S. R., *Protoplasma,* **32,** 329–41 (1939)
132. Troshin, A. S., *Problema Kletočnoj Pronicaemosti* (Izdt. Akad. Nauk SSSR, Moskva, 474 pp., 1956)
133. Troshin, A. S., *Das Problem der Zellpermeabilität* (G. Fischer, Jena, 396 pp., 1958)
134. Troshin, A. S., *Problems of Cell Permeability* (Pergamon, London, 549 pp., 1966)
135. Übeleis, I., *Österr. Akad. Wiss., Mathem.-Naturwiss. Kl., Sitzber. Abt. I,* **166,** 395–433 (1957)
136. Url, , W., *Österr. Akad. Wiss. Mathem.-Naturwiss. Kl., Sitzber. Abt. I,* **164,** 207–30 (1955)
137. Url, W., *ibid.,* **167,** 297–319 (1958)
138. Url, W., *Protoplasma, 51,* 338–70 (1959)
139. Url, W., *Österr. Akad. Wiss., Mathem.-Naturwiss. Kl., Sitzber. Abt. I,* **171,** 259–87 (1962)
140. Url, W., Amidophilia—amidophobia and pore permeability (Engl. version of Url, 1962; Symp. permeability, Edinburgh, 1964, Intern. Assoc. Plant Physiol., 1964)
141. Van Overbeek, J., Blondeau, R., *Weeds, 3,* 55–65 (1954)
141a. Warner, D. T., *Science,* **153,** 324–26 (1966)
142. Warren, K. B., Intracellular transport, *5th Symp. Intern. Soc. Cell Biol.* (Academic Press, New York, 325 pp., 1966)
143. Wartiovaara, V., *Physiol. Plantarum,* **3,** 462–78 (1950)
144. Wartiovaara, V., Collander, R., Permeabilitätstheorien, in *Protoplasmatologia,* **II**/C8d (See Ref. 35)
145. Wattendorff, J., *Protoplasma,* **60,** 162–68 (1965)
146. Wattendorff, J., *Biol. Zentr.,* **85,** 455–95 (1966)
147. Weigl, J., *Z. Naturforsch.,* **22b,** 885–90 (1967)
148. Werth, W., *Protoplasma, 53,* 457–503 (1961)
149. Whittaker, V. P., *Brit. Med. Bull.,* **24,** 101–6 (1968)
150. Wilde, J. de, Ed., *Permeability,* Lectures held at the conference on permeability, Wageningen, May 1–4, 1962 (N. V. Uitgevers-Maatschappij W. E. J. Tjeenk Willink, Zwolle, Netherlands, 131 pp., 1963)
151. Yamada, Y., Bukovac, M. J., Wittwer, S. H., *Plant Physiol.,* **39,** 978–82 (1964)
152. Yamada, Y., Wittwer, S. H., Bukovac, M. J., *ibid.,* 28–32
153. Yamada, Y., Wittwer, S. H., Bukovac, M. J., *ibid.,* **40,** 170–75 (1965)

METABOLISM OF ORGANIC PESTICIDE CHEMICALS IN HIGHER PLANTS[1]

By John E. Casida and Louis Lykken

Division of Entomology, University of California, Berkeley, California

Pesticide chemicals continue to play a major role in the production and storage of our food, feed, and fiber supply, being important agents for the control of the large number and variety of pests that attack the crops and agricultural commodities involved. The benefits derived from the use of such chemicals in modern agriculture include increased crop yields, better crop quality, and less loss of the stored crop. There is a great variety of pesticide chemicals being applied to crops, weeds, soil, and stored commodities as insecticides, fungicides, and herbicides, most of them being synthetic organic compounds developed in the past quarter of a century. Their nature is such that, for the most part, they must be applied as formulated products such as dusts, emulsions, and granules instead of dilute water solutions. Since most organic pesticide chemicals are, by their very nature, toxic, and since many of them degrade to toxic materials, it is important to know their transitory and ultimate fate, both in amount and composition, in or on plants, not only to elucidate their mode of action and to increase the efficiency of their use, but also to provide a basis for residue tolerance and regulatory considerations.

Much information now exists in regard to the metabolic fate of organic pesticide chemicals in plants. Such data do not always concern chemicals that pose a hazard or are the major ones used; rather, much of it pertains to those that are peculiarly amenable to fate-of-chemical studies because analytical capabilities exist for them. In the case of herbicide and systemic insecticide chemicals, much of the metabolism data available have their origin in mode-of-action studies. Fortunately, appropriate tools, concepts, and methodology are now available for systematic work on metabolism of pesticide chemicals in plants and other organisms and, as a result, the knowledge in this field is increasing at a rapid pace. The important advancements in this field include: (*a*) increased capabilities for synthesizing radioactive chemicals for use as tracers and for counting radiolabeled compounds; (*b*) a variety of chromatographic and other means for resolution and isolation

[1] Preparation of this review was supported in part by grants from the U. S. Atomic Energy Commission [Contract AT(11-1)-34, Project Agreement No. 113] and the U. S. Public Health Service, National Institutes of Health (Grants GM-12248 and ESGM 00049).

of metabolic products; (c) refined ultraviolet, infrared, nuclear magnetic resonance, and mass spectroscopy instrumentation for identifying and characterizing very small amounts of such products; (d) improved synthesis procedures for authentic reference compounds; and (e) a vast accumulation of literature on metabolic and other degradation pathways for pesticide chemicals.

Plants have mechanisms for the degradation of almost every organic pesticide chemical even though such chemicals are, for all practical purposes, foreign to plants. Usually, these biotransformation mechanisms are independent of and bear no relation to the mode of action and physiological lesion(s) involved in the pesticidal activity of a chemical; instead they relate to the functional or reactive groups or linkages in the chemical which are susceptible to enzymatic or chemical attack. Thus, certain complex pesticide chemicals are readily metabolized while some relatively simple ones are surprisingly resistant to biodegradation. The types of transformations of pesticide chemicals that occur in plants are limited; they include oxidation, hydroxylation, epoxidation, hydrolysis, reduction, N-dealkylation, O-dealkylation, desulfuration, dehalogenation, dehydrohalogenation, dehydrogenation, and conjugation (mainly with sugars and amino acids). A large number of products sometimes form because the attack frequently takes place at more than one site on the molecule, either simultaneously or sequentially, some products being transitory. These chemical changes are not all enzymatically mediated, some resulting from reaction with normal plant constituents by nonenzymatic mechanisms and others arising from photochemical mechanisms. The pathway followed depends on the balance of enzymes of various capabilities, present in the species or system of interest, and of the chemical reactions possible.

The manner and rate of metabolic attack on a pesticide chemical also vary with the species and characteristics of the organism involved, the time of residence in or on the organism and the degree of entry into it being important factors. With some significant exceptions, plants, microorganisms, insects, and mammals metabolize foreign organic compounds by the same major pathways. There is much extrapolation from animals or microorganisms to higher plants, frequently without direct proof that this is justified. The processes in plants are, in most cases, slower than in animals, if similar mechanisms are involved; most mammals and insects have better degrading, circulating, and excreting systems than plants (which tend to store pesticide chemicals and their metabolic products for longer periods).

Differences in metabolic pathways in desirable and undesirable species (such as crops versus weeds, plant pathogens, or insects) contribute to the specificity and selectivity of pesticide chemical action; also, differences in rate of pesticide chemical absorption or translocation or both are contributing factors. Such differences sometimes lead to unanticipated and untoward effects as a result of interaction when one pesticide chemical (such as an insecticide) inhibits the enzyme which metabolizes a second pesticide chemical (such as a herbicide). Pesticide chemical metabolism generally results in detoxification but, at times, the biotransformation products have equal or greater toxicity than the respective parent compounds; this factor sometimes contributes to selective toxicity.

The literature pertaining to this general subject is very large, especially if one includes that dealing with photodecomposition and microbial factors in pesticide chemical metabolism. Certain studies are not designed to clearly differentiate between the chemical changes that occur before entry into the plant as a result of photoinstability or soil microorganisms and those that are the result of biotransformation in the plant. Since this review is of necessity brief, it does not reflect all of the literature that exists. Rather, it reflects a survey of the literature that deals with metabolism or biotransformation of major organic pesticide chemicals in higher plants, with emphasis on biochemical mechanisms and agents involved and on their importance to the subject. Thus, this review concerns only data that pertain to the chemistry of organic pesticide chemicals in higher plants and does not deal with data on pesticide chemical residue levels in crops or on the transfer and translocation of those chemicals which do not suffer chemical changes or transformation. A number of general and specific reviews exist on the subject (1–15).

Unless otherwise stated, the chemistry discussed is that involved in pesticide chemical breakdown in higher plants. The plant species involved in the studies usually are not mentioned because of space limitations; therefore, this omission in no way implies that the reactions mentioned are common to all plant species. Most compounds are referred to by their common or trade names and, for the sake of brevity, are not fully defined as to their chemical name or structure. Information on the nomenclature, structure, and chemistry of these pesticide chemicals is given in the article(s) referred to or in a number of compilations (16–19).

INSECTICIDE CHEMICALS

Botanicals.—Nicotine alkaloid is biosynthesized in the roots of the tobacco plant from two universal plant metabolites: nicotinic acid, the precursor for the pyridyl ring, and ornithine, the source of the pyrollidine ring (20). Anabasine probably arises in a similar manner, with lysine as the precursor for the piperidine ring (20), but it is not formed from nicotine (21–23). Nicotine undergoes partial N-demethylation in the leaves to yield nornicotine (21–28) and, on a similar basis, N^1-methyl- and N^1-ethylanabasine are N-dealkylated to form anabasine (28). Nicotine also metabolizes or converts by oxidative mechanisms that result in formation of cotinine (29) and nicotinic acid (30). In time, nicotine metabolizes completely, the products entering the plant's metabolic pool as ammonia, amino acids, and proteins (31–35). The biosynthesis of rotenone has a close connection with isoflavanoid biogenesis (36–38). Tracer studies with phenylalanine establish that the aryl ring provides ring A, and that the C-1, C-2, and C-3 carbons appear in the C-12, C-12a, and C-6a positions, respectively, of rotenone; thus, there is an aryl migration from the former C-3 of phenylalanine to the former C-2 (38, 39). The methyl group of methionine provides the methoxyl groups and the extra methylene group, C-6, of ring B (39). The biosynthesis of 8′-hydroxyrotenone (amorphigenin), which occurs naturally as a glycoside (amorphin) (40), from phenylalanine follows the same pathway noted for rotenone (38, 39). A comprehensive review considers other steps and possible intermediates in rotenoid biosynthesis (37). 11-Hydroxyrotenone (sumatrol) also occurs in plants (37), but it is not known whether this derivative is a metabolic product of rotenone or whether it forms via other intermediates. In fact, the literature does not contain any information on the metabolism of rotenone in plants; however, it is known that 8′-hydroxyrotenone is one of several rotenone metabolites in animals (41). The chrysanthemumate moiety of pyrethrins arises, in studies on the isolated ovules of the source plant, from two molecules of mevalonic acid with the fusion of the isoprenoid units involving a "middle to tail" arrangement (42–44). The pyrethrate moiety of pyrethrins forms from two molecules of mevalonic acid, as above, with methionine as the methyl donor for the carbomethoxy group (45). The biosynthesis scheme for the alcohol moiety of the pyrethrins is not known except that it partially arises from acetate but not from mevalonic acid (42, 44). The metabolic fate of pyrethrins and related insecticide chemicals in plants is not known; however, in house flies, pyrethrin I and related compounds enzymatically oxidize at the *trans*-methyl group in the isobutenyl portion of the acid moiety, to a carboxylic acid derivative which, on methylation, gives compounds in the pyrethrin II series (46). While these observations were not made with plants, it is reasonable to assume that plants, too, form pyrethrin II by oxidation of pyrethrin I and methylation of the oxidation product. An informational void exists on the metabolism in plants of methylenedioxyphenyl synergiests, mainly used to enhance the insecticidal activity of pyrethroids; the reason for this is that there is very little, if any, use of pyrethroid formulations on agricultural crops.

Chlorinated hydrocarbons.—The metabolic fate, in plants, of the insecticide chemicals grouped as chlorinated hydrocarbons is known only to a limited degree. This is true even though the availability of data on their fate in insects and mammals varies from abundant to meager (5) and even though a vast amount of data exist on the residue content of these chemicals in or on a variety of agricultural crops. The reason for this is that the chlorinated hydrocarbons are quite insoluble in water and that they do not enter the plant to an important degree. Thus, the attack on them by microorganisms and by photochemical processes overshadows the attack by plant metabolic processes.

Information on the fate of DDT and methoxychlor in plants is wanting, but in animals the metabolic attack is varied and complex (5). However, certain bacteria associated with plants reductively dechlorinate DDT to DDD and other metabolites (47), and the barley plant absorbs, but does not metabolize, DDT (48). DDT applied to foliage is converted in trace amounts to DDD and 4,4'-dichlorobenzophenone (49). Lindane (gamma-BHC) is more readily absorbed than DDT and a number of plants convert it to 2,3,4,5,6-pentachlorocyclohex-1-ene and, possibly, water-soluble metabolites (50–53). Among the chlorinated methano-bridged cyclodienes, aldrin, isodrin, and heptachlor readily epoxidize to dieldrin, endrin, and heptachlor epoxide, respectively, all products being as toxic or more toxic than the parent compounds (49, 54–60). Dieldrin and heptachlor epoxide are relatively stable in all organisms (6, 59); however, on the surface of growing plants (in sunlight), dieldrin converts to several oxidation products and an isomerization product having a partial "cage" structure (49, 59, 61, 62). In cabbage plants and wheat germ buds, endrin forms an isomeric bridged ketone analogue and a water-soluble metabolite(s) (60, 63, 64), products which are not the result of photodecomposition (60). In the manner of dieldrin—aldrin, isodrin, and endrin slowly transform under sunlight to compounds having "bird-cage" structures (59, 61, 65). Endosulfan (thiodan), a sulfite, converts in or on plants to the corresponding sulfate (endosulfan sulfate) and to several other products which result from ring cleavage and removal of the sulfur, with or without subsequent recyclization to a 5-membered ring (49, 66–68).

There are some acaricides that contain halogenated-phenyl groups, but they vary greatly in chemical type. Chlorbenzide, a sulfide, oxidizes to yield the sulfoxide and sulfone derivatives (69). One of the metabolities of ovex, a sulfonate ester, is the hydrolysis product, 4-chlorobenzenesulfonic acid (70). Isopropyl 4,4'-dibromobenzilate hydrolyzes to the corresponding benzylic acid (71). Chlorphenamidine undergoes N-demethylation and hydrolysis, probably yielding the formanilide and aniline derivatives (72). 5,6-Dichloro-1-phenoxycarbonyl-2-trifluoromethylbenzimidazole hydrolyzes, hydroxylates at the 4-position, and conjugates as N- and O-glycosides, probably the glucoside derivatives (73).

Ethylene dibromide, a stored-grain fumigant, is stable on treated wheat at normal temperatures but, upon heating, it breaks down to ethylene glycol- and hydrogen bromide (74). In wheat, the fumigant, methyl bromide, decomposes with the formation of inorganic bromide and methanol; it also reacts with wheat proteins to yield dimethylsulfonium derivatives, methoxyl- and thiomethoxyl derivatives, and N-methyl derivatives; the latter can be hydrolyzed to epsilon-N-methyl lysine, and a series of N-methyl- and N,N-dimethylhistidine derivatives (75, 76).

Organophosphorus compounds.—The metabolic fate of organophosphorus insecticide chemicals in plants and other organisms is discussed in a number of reviews and books (1–6, 77–83).

The dimethylphosphoramidates hydrolyze in plants but the dimethylamido group first oxidizes to yield dimethylphosphoramide-N-oxide or N-methyl-N-hydroxymethylphosphoramide intermediates or both which, subsequently, N-demethylate. Some of the intermediates are potent anticholinesterase agents, and the detoxification reaction with schradan and dimefox involves hydrolysis of the phosphoric anhydride bond (84–93).

Substituted-vinyl phosphates hydrolyze in plants at the P-O-vinyl and P-O-alkyl bonds to yield mono- and dialkylphosphoric acids, and the corresponding aldehyde or ketone, little if any attack occurring at the vinyl double bond. Also, when present, carboxylic esters and carboxylic amide groups hydrolyze and N-alkylamide substituents undergo N-dealkylation (5). Dichlorvos (94) and mevinphos hydrolyze, the cis-crotonate group in mevinphos being more rapidly cleaved than the trans-crotonate to dimethylphosphoric acid (95–97). Also, mevinphos undergoes cleavage of the carbomethoxy group followed by P-O-methyl and P-O-vinyl cleavage (97). Chlorfenvinphos metabolizes by O-deethylation, to a small extent, but mostly by vinylphosphate cleavage to dichloroacetophenone which is reduced and conjugated with a sugar; also, there is some evidence of the conversion of the trans- to the cis-isomer (98–100). Phosphamidon, Bidrin, and Azodrin contain N-alkylamide groups which are important in their metabolic pathways. Phosphamidon N-deethylates to the N-ethyl- and, possibly, the N-hydroxyethylamides; hydrolysis converts it to O-desmethylphosphamidon, dimethylphosphoric acid, and N-ethyl- and N,N-diethylchloroacetoacetamides (101–104). The metabolic pathways for Bidrin, a dimethylamide, and Azodrin, a methylamide, are similar because Azodrin is a primary intermediate in the N-demethylation of Bidrin. It is known that the N-demethylation of Bidrin forms the corresponding N-methyl-N-hydroxymethylamide, as an intermediate; that, similarly, Azodrin forms the N-hydroxymethylamide; and that, in the process, the corresponding N-methylamide and the respective unsubstituted amide also form. It is probable that the N-hydroxymethylamide intermediates appear, in part, as conjugates in plants. The hydrolysis products formed from these two chemicals include the phosphorus compounds that arise from amide hydrolysis and from P-O-methyl and P-O-vinyl cleavage; phosphoric acid is an ultimate product (105–107).

Although trichloro-alpha-hydroxyethyl phosphonates (such as trichlorfon) readily dehydrochlorinate to give dichlorovinyl phosphates (such as dichlorvos), their metabolism in plants does not appear to involve this pathway; actually, trichlorfon and its acetyloxy derivative hydrolyze quickly in plants (94), the products from trichlorfon being dimethylphosphate, methylphosphate, and inorganic phosphate (108). The butyryloxy derivative of trichlorfon, butonate, partially hydrolyzes in plants to trichlorfon (109). Naled reacts with sulfhydryls to yield dichlorvos; also formed are certain aldehydes and complex amino acid conjugates of its degradation products (110).

Phosphorothiolates, which arise from isomerization of phosphorothionates or from direct synthesis, hydrolyze in plants and, if groupings susceptible to oxidation are present, they also convert to oxidized derivatives. Amiton slowly hydrolyzes but does not form other toxicants (111, 112), although N-deethylation is a reasonable possibility. The methosulfate derivative of the demeton thiol isomer yields an unidentified metabolite (113). The phosphorothiolate isomer of methyl demeton oxidizes to the sulfoxide and the sulfone, and also hydrolyzes (114); in addition, it undergoes a nonenzymatic self-alkylation (115), but this probably does not occur after absorption by plants. A phosphorothiolate which contains a sulfoxide group and is closely related to methyl demeton converts to its respective sulfone as well as to dimethylphosphoric and phosphoric acids (116). Endothion undergoes cleavage of the P-O-methyl bond (117).

Phosphorothionates and phosphorodithioates oxidize to their phosphate and phosphorothiolate derivatives, which usually do not accumulate in plants; rather, the oxygen analogues, with some exceptions, hydrolyze with relative ease. Thionophosphorus compounds photodecompose to their oxygen analogues and to S-alkyl phosphorothiolates and, therefore, it is difficult to determine which of the products found in plants arise from metabolism and which come from photodecomposition. Parathion (118–122), methyl parathion (118, 123–127), fenitrothion (128, 129), bromophos (130, 131), diazinon (132–135), dursban (136, 137), colep (138), and Bayer 22,408 (139) hydrolyze, the thiono sulfur oxidizing before or after hydrolysis. Peroxidases in plants may play a role in the metabolism of parathion and related phosphorothionates (122). The hydrolytic cleavage takes place at the P-O-alkyl or the P-O-aryl or both bonds or at the P-O-enol bond. Phenol released from colep conjugates as glycosides and, probably, as sulfates (138); the pyrimidinol released from diazinon either conjugates or cleaves to free the carbon fragments which, in turn, oxidize to CO_2, but acetoacetic acid and its amide are not intermediates (132–134); the chloropyridinol from dursban partially dechlorinates and incorporates into the plant (136, 137). When a thioether group is present, the oxidation occurs on both the phosphorothionate and thioether sulfur, and hydrolysis takes place as shown with fenthion (127, 140–143), Bayer 30,237 (144), fensulfothion (145, 146), Abate (147), and Tinox (148–150). The phosphorothionate isomer of demeton undergoes oxidation at the thionophosphorus and thioether groupings and, also, undergoes isomerization to the phosphorothiolate which, in turn, oxidizes to the corresponding sulfoxide and sulfone (113, 151–160).

Phosphorodithioates oxidize to phosphorothiolates and hydrolyze before or after this oxidation; however, in other respects, their metabolism is similar to the phosphorothionates and phosphorothiolates (see above). Oxidation of the phosphorothionate group and hydrolysis of the phosphorus ester are the only reactions known for dioxathion (Delnav) (161) and Cidial (162). Of the compounds with a thiomethylene bridge between the phosphorus and various heterocyclic rings, azinophosmethyl (Gusathion) gives little if any oxygen analogue but does give other unidentified metabolites (163); GS-13005 gives the oxygen analogue and all anticipated hydrolysis products, including major amounts of the compound from P-O-methyl hydrolysis along with cleaved ring fragments and CO_2 (164, 165); menazon gives a number of metabolites containing the triazine ring (166); and Imidan gives phthalic acid or phthalamic acid or both, benzoic acid, and related compounds (167). Phosphorodithioates containing an additional thioether grouping undergo oxidation to the phosphorothiolate and to the sulfoxide and sulfone, all five of the possible oxidation products frequently being detected; examples of such compounds are phorate (Thimet) (168–170), disulfoton (Di-Syston) (168, 171, 172), thiometon (173), and carbophenothion (Trithion) (174). Additional metabolizable groups are present in the carboxylic amide, dimethoate, and the bis-carboxylic ester, malathion; these groups hydrolyze, but also there is oxidation of the phosphorothionate position and hydrolysis of the various groups attached to the phosphorus. Malathion hydrolyzes to give the mono- and dicarboxylic acid analogues, and other esters of phosphoric and phosphorothioic acids (121, 127, 131, 175–181); hydrolysis of the carboethoxy groups results from an enzyme which is sensitive to inhibition by organophosphates, such as paraoxon, so that the residual persistence is increased by combining malathion with an inhibitor for the enzyme involved in its detoxification (179, 180). The succinyl portion of malathion gives rise to several metabolites which are not identified (181). Dimethoate oxidizes to the oxygen analogue and cleaves, as the phosphorodithioate or phosphorothiolate, to the carboxylic acid derivatives and to the various phosphorus acids which result from splitting off the P-O-methyl group and from hydrolysis at either side of the sulfur in the phosphorothiolate grouping (131, 182–190).

   Methyl- and dimethylcarbamates.—Esters of *N*-methyl- and *N,N*-dimethylcarbamic acids with phenols, heterocyclic enols, and aliphatic aldoximes are not rapidly hydrolyzed in plants but metabolic reactions occur at other sites on the molecule including oxidation or hydroxylation with subsequent conjugation of the products which contain hydroxyl groupings. The nature of these reactions is known largely as the result of studies with carbaryl (191–197). Incorporation of metabolites into unextractable residues, both as carbamates and hydrolysis products, is a common finding with these insecticide chemicals. In plants, many *N*-methyl- and *N,N*-dimethylcarbamates, including isolan and dimetilan, convert to carbamate metabolites which are potent anticholinesterase agents, some of which are present as conjugates cleavable with beta-glucosidase (196). These glycosides, which probably involve conjugates of disaccharides as well as monosaccharides, persist in the plant for long periods, and possibly serve as precursors for potential toxic materials, their aglycones, which possibly are liberated, by glucosidase action, in an animal ingesting the treated plant material (196).

Hydroxylation of the *N*-methyl group to yield *N*-hydroxymethyl carbamates occurs with carbaryl, Banol, Baygon, the two Landrin constituents, and UC 10854 (196, 198); such hydroxylation possibly occurs also with a metabolite of Furadan (199). It is likely that *N*-methylhydroxylation is a common pathway for each of the methyl- and dimethylcarbamates, but the resulting *N*-hydroxymethyl- and *N*-methyl-*N*-hydroxymethylcarbamates probably do not always have sufficient stability for isolation. Hydroxylation of the tertiary carbon of the isopropyl group of UC 10854 yields a hydroxypropyl derivative, and *O*-depropylation of Baygon gives 2-hydroxyphenyl methylcarbamate (196). Hydroxylation of the ring-methyl substituents occurs with Landrin constituents (198) and either a ring-methyl group or the ring itself of Banol hydroxylates (196, 200). The benzylic carbon of Furadan hydroxylates to give 3-hydroxy-Furadan which conjugates as such or oxidizes to 3-keto-Furadan; each intermediate metabolite, before or after hydrolysis of the methylcarbamate group, conjugates if a free hydroxyl group is present (199, 201). Ring hydroxylation occurs with carbaryl at the 4- and 5-positions, and a 5,6-dihydro-5,6-dihydroxy derivative also forms (196); in addition, ring hydroxylation takes place with Baygon (196) and probably with Banol (200). Mesurol, containing a 4-methylthio group, oxidizes to the corresponding sulfoxide and sulfone (195). Temik, an aliphatic aldoxime with a methylthio group, not only oxidizes to the sulfoxide and sulfone but each of these methylcarbamates hydrolyze to the respective oximes, with some dehydration of the latter compounds to the corresponding nitrile (202, 203). Zectran and Matacil undergo attack at the dimethylaminophenyl moiety to give 4-methylformamido, 4-methylamino, 4-formamido, and 4-amino derivatives (195), these reactions being reproducible, in part, with horseradish peroxidase but not with tyrosinase (196). Zectran also undergoes hydrolysis and oxidation, before or after hydrolysis, to give the corresponding substituted-phenol, 2,6-dimethylhydroquinone, 2,6-dimethyl-*p*-benzoquinone, 4-dimethylamino-3,5-dimethyl-*o*-benzoquinone, and conjugates of certain of these materials, along with some incorporation of ring fragments into lignin (204).

Eserine or physostigmine is a very toxic *N*-methylcarbamate occurring naturally in Calabar beans but its biosynthetic pathway is not known, the mechanism of formation of the methylcarbamate group being of particular interest.

Fungicide Chemicals

Compounds with a great variety of functional groups are active as fungicide chemicals but, except for a few of them, the chemistry of their metabolism is not known (1, 7). The chemical transformations that take place in plant tissues are varied, because the compounds used as fungicides represent such diverse types and involve both enzymatic and nonenzymatic attack (7).

Cycloheximide appears to be relatively stable in plants, not yielding any identified metabolites (205–207). Preparations of cycloheximide containing protective groups, such as acetate, oxime, and semicarbazone, appear to be cleaved to liberate the actual fungitoxic agent, cycloheximide (7, 208, 209). The antibiotic griseofulvin rapidly metabolizes, certain of its metabolites and those of its derivatives possibly being demethylation products (210–213). Captan decomposes rapidly in plants but it does not lose its fungicidal activity at a parallel rate, suggesting that a metabolite may be a fungicidal agent (7, 214); it reacts readily with thiols, such as cysteine, to yield a great variety of products (215, 216). A related compound, Difolatan, hydrolyzes rapidly to the corresponding dicarboximide (together with the acid amide and dibasic acid) and dichloroacetic acid (217). Procaine probably metabolizes by pathways other than hydrolysis (218, 219). Dodine converts to several metabolites, probably by cleaving the guanidine group, and one or more of the metabolites yields creatine on hydrolysis (220), suggesting that methylation accompanies decomposition. Dexon rapidly metabolizes but the products, which probably arise in part from demethylation, are unidentified (221). In addition, Dexon transforms in the presence of a plant mitochondrial system and NADH to undetermined products (222). 6-Azauracil converts to its riboside, 6-azauridine, and probably to azauridine monophosphate which is assumed to be the actual fungitoxic agent (223). Sulfanilamide acetylates in the roots at each of the N^4 and N^1 positions but the products formed deacetylate in the stems and leaves (224–226). N^4-Acetylsulphanilamide is a precursor for sulphanilamide (227) but the N^1-acetyl derivative probably acts directly (7). N-Hydroxy-2-pyridine thione quickly metabolizes to fungitoxic products other than the original compound (228), the products possible being conjugates with amino acids (7). Pentachlorobenzyl alcohol oxidizes to pentachlorobenzaldehyde (229, 230) and, possibly, to pentachlorobenzoic acid and pentachlorophenol (229). Dichloran converts to more polar metabolites by mechanisms which involve, among others, ring opening and incorporation of ring fragments into carbohydrates (231). The major of two metabolites of dichloran in soybeans is 4'-amino-3',5'-dichloro-malonanilic acid, an unusual complex because it involves malonic acid (232). Phenylmercuric acetate (PMA) decomposes rapidly in the presence of a factor in wheat roots (233). Triphenyl tin acetate (fentin acetate) is not absorbed by plants; thus, its metabolic fate is not known (234).

Sodium dimethyldithiocarbamate (DDC) converts to the beta-glucoside, the L-alanine conjugate, an unidentified conjugate of dimethyldithiocarbamic acid which retains fungicidal activity, and the nonfungitoxic thiazolidine-2-thione-4-carboxylic acid, the latter compound being formed by nonenzymatic ring closure of the alanine conjugate with the elimination of dimethylamine (235–239); also, DDC suffers unspecific decomposition accompanied with the formation of carbon disulfide and dimethylamine (7). Possible mechanisms for the formation and cleavage of the DDC-conjugates are given in a recent review (7). Heavy metallic salts of dimethyldithiocarbamic acid (such as ferbam) probably yield the same metabolites as DDC. Tetramethylthiuram disulfide, the oxidation product of dimethyldithiocarbamic acid, gives rise to essentially the same metabolites as the acid itself (239, 240). The DL-alanine- and glucoside conjugates of dimethyldithiocarbamic acid serve as precursors for dimethyldithiocarbamic acid; so they yield the same metabolites produced by DDC (see above), the equilibrium in the plant favoring the conjugates (7, 239). Carboxymethyldimethyldithiocarbamate is another precursor in plants for dimethyldithiocarbamic acid and for each of the products mentioned above, but it is not known whether or not the initial cleavage to DDC is an enzymatic process (239, 241, 242). The carboxymethyl derivative also gives rise to the nonfungitoxic N-methylrhodanine (243), resulting from N-demethylation and spontaneous ring closure. On the basis of the N-alkylrhodanine formed, the N-dealkylation involves the removal of the N-methyl group from S-carboxymethyl-N-methyl-N-ethyldithiocarbamate (243). The carboxyethyl homologue undergoes N-demethylation without ring closure (243). Higher homologues, such as the butyric acid homologue, yield carboxymethyldimethyldithiocarbamate by beta-oxidation, and N-demethylation also occurs in these derivatives (243, 244). The systemic activity of carboxymethyldimethyldithiocarbamate possibly results from some reaction other than conversion to dimethyldithiocarbamic acid because the alpha, alpha-dimethyl derivative and the two isomers (+ and −) of the alpha-methyl derivative of carboxymethyldimethyldithiocarbamate convert to the alanine conjugate of dimethyldithiocarbamic acid but the fungitoxic activity does not correlate with formation of this conjugate; rather, it appears related to the antiauxin activity of the compounds (7, 239, 242, 245, 246). Zineb degrades to ethylenethiourea and other products (247), possibly including ethylenethiuram disulfide and an isothiocyanate which reacts with sulfhydryl groupings (216).

Certain plant species owe their resistance to—or tolerance for—certain parasites to their capacity for producing a fungicide from a natural precursor, but this occurs only at the site of attack of the parasite and, sometimes, from enzymes in the invading organism rather than in the plant. Examples of this phenomenon are the conversion of avenacin to nonfungitoxic products by glucosidase action (248, 249), and the conversion to fungitoxic products of a phenolic compound from leaves of sugar beet (250), trichocarpin (251, 252), arbutine (253, 254), phloretin (255, 256), and other glucosides. The action seems, in general, to involve beta-glucosidase cleavage of the glucoside and polyphenoloxidase oxidation of the aglycone to yield the actual fungitoxic agent.

Chlorinated phenoxyalkanecarboxylic acids and derivatives.—More studies have been carried out on the metabolism of 2,4-dichlorophenoxyacetic
acid (2,4-D) than any other herbicide, yet its metabolic fate in plants is not
fully clarified and there is not agreement on the extent, rate, and pathways
of degradation. It is known that 2,4-D metabolism is relatively rapid in non-
dormant plant tissues and that it suffers cleavage or modification or both of
the aliphatic side chain, ring hydroxylation, and conjugate or complex formation, the ratio of the attack varying with the species used, age of plant,
mode of administration, and other factors (8–15).

The first example of decarboxylation of 2,4-D relates to bean plants
(257), but there is conflicting evidence in regard to the effect of species
and varietal differences on the rate and extent of decarboxylation in plants
(257–274). The decarboxylation is more rapid in the root than in the shoot
(260). It is more extensive in tolerant than in susceptible varieties of apples, currants, and strawberries, each variety decarboxylating to some extent (261, 262, 266); however, there is no general correlation in this regard
for all species (267, 271). The substitution of fluorine in the 4-position of
2,4-D inhibits decarboxylation by leaves of tolerant apple varieties (262)
but, in leaves of woody plants, this substitution accelerates the decarboxylation (275). Meta-substituents in the ring and an alpha-alkyl substituent in
the side chain greatly reduce the rate of decarboxylation of 2,4-D (264, 265,
268, 275). There is good evidence that, in the loss of the aliphatic side
chain, true decarboxylation is not involved but that the 2-carbon side chain
is split off and subsequently oxidized to CO_2 (260, 264, 265, 269). This phenomenon explains, to some extent, the finding that in beans and red currants the carboxyl group gives more CO_2 than does the methylene carbon,
while in black currants and tick beans this is not true (260, 266, 269).

There are a number of metabolites of 2,4-D, 2,4,5-trichlorophenoxyacetic
acid (2,4,5-T), and related phenoxyacetic acids that persist in plants; the
identity of some of these products is known but many remain uncharacter-
ized (257, 260, 266, 268, 272, 273, 276–305). Although loss of the side chain
occurs, as mentioned above, with possible formation of phenolic compounds
and other degradation products derived from them, chlorinated phenoxyalkanecarboxylic acids metabolize by other pathways also. Unsubstituted
phenoxyacetic acid and the 2-chloro- and 2,6-dichloro-derivatives hydroxy-
late at the 4-position in the roots and stems of some plants (276–279);
2,4,6-T hydroxylates at the 3-position (279); 2,4-D converts in beans and
in some other organisms (but not in barley) to 4-hydroxy-2,5-D and
4-hydroxy-2,3-D (280–284). Ring hydroxylation of 2,4-D possibly is the
first in a series of reactions leading to chloroaliphatic acids. It is postulated,
without experimental evidence, that 2,4-D oxidizes to a quinone which

cleaves to chloromaleic acid (285). Chloroacetic acid appears to be a product of 2,4-D metabolism (286); this finding, coupled with structure-activity considerations, suggests that the actual herbicidal agent is chloroacetic acid released on 2,4-D metabolism (287). The chlorinated phenoxyacetic acids complex or bind with cytoplasmic proteins or lipoproteins in a variety of plants (259, 260, 288–292) but there is some disagreement on the importance of such binding (264, 265). The protein complexes appear to be intermediates in metabolism of 2,4-D in some plants (259, 260) but not in others (293). 2,4-D and 2-methyl-4-chlorophenoxyacetic acid (MCPA) form a number of amino acid conjugates but the significance of these products is not certain (258, 264, 265, 294–297); one minor 2,4-D metabolite appears to be 2,4-D aspartic acid (294). Sugars, such as glucose, form conjugates or complexes with 2,4-D (279, 296, 298–300), with some of its metabolites, and with metabolites of related compounds which contain ring-hydroxyl groupings (279, 281, 282).

Among the findings on herbicide chemical metabolism, there is no doubt that the discovery of beta-oxidation of omega-phenoxyalkanecarboxylic acids and related compounds will remain as one of the classical breakthroughs. As a result of beta-oxidation in plants, omega-(2,4-dichlorophenoxy)alkanecarboxylic acids, having an odd number of methylene groups in the side chain, convert to the active acetic acid analogues, whereas those having an even number of such groups yield 2,4-dichlorophenol (306–313). There is evidence of long standing that susceptible plants, including certain weeds, contain enzyme systems that beta-oxidize omega-substituted- phenoxyalkanecarboxylic acids with the odd number of methylene groups to the acetic acid derivative but tolerant ones, including certain crops, do not (308, 310, 312). With the omega-(2,4,5-trichlorophenoxy)alkanecarboxylic acid series, a species effect is also apparent (308, 314). Thus, the potential for beta-oxidation to the active acetic acid derivatives probably depends on the nature and position of the ring substituents, and on the source of the enzyme (308, 310, 312). A suitable acetone powder preparation of peas contains an enzyme system active in beta-oxidation of 4-(2,4-dichlorophenoxy)butyric acid [4-(2,4-DB)] yielding a number of unknown metabolites (315). Excised roots also are species-specific in their activity for beta-oxidation of phenoxyalkanecarboxylic acids; in such roots, hydroxylation of the 4-position seems to occur only after beta-oxidation to phenoxyacetic acid (277). Environmental factors have an important affect on the breakdown of 4-(2,4-DB) to form 2,4-D (316–318) but microorganisms are not necessary for the conversion (316). In addition to other factors, resistance is conferred in alfalfa by a synthetic mechanism involving addition of 2-carbon units, probably from incorporation of malonate, to convert 4-(2,4-DB) to the corresponding caproic and decanoic acids (319). In the same species, 4-(2,4-DB) dehydrogenates to the crotonic analogue and the latter saturates to 4-(2,4-DB); the saturation reaction occurs on the methyl ester without de-esterification taking place (319). The sodium salt of 4-(2,4-DB) metabolizes more rapidly than its butyl ester (320).

In normal practice, the phenoxyalkanecarboxylic acids are used in the form of esters, N-alkylamides, organic amine salts, or other salts (9). Enzymes present in various plant tissues hydrolyze esters and amides of 2,4-D and 2,4,5-T to the respective free acid (320–325); when purified enzymes from a variety of plants are used, the rate of ester hydrolysis decreases with chlorination of the phenoxyacetic acid derivatives (326). Sesone and related chlorophenoxyethyl sulfate herbicides hydrolyze to the ethanol analogue which, in turn, oxidizes to the 2,4-D analogue, soil microorganisms being important in the conversion steps (13, 327–329). Similarly, 2,4-DEP hydrolyzes and oxidizes, forming 2,4-D (330).

Symmetrical triazines.—The compounds in this group include the following s-triazines: 2-chloro series with 4,6-bis(ethylamino)-(simazine), 4-ethylamino-6-isopropylamino- (atrazine), 4-diethylamino-6-isopropylamino- (ipazine), and 4,6-bis(isopropylamino)- (propazine substituents; the 2-methoxy series with 4,6-bis-(isopropylamino)- (prometone) substituents; the 2-methylmercapto series with 4,6-bis(isopropylamino)- (prometryne) substituents.

Simazine degrades more quickly in the resistant corn plant, or in juice from corn plants, than in corresponding preparations of wheat plants, which are sensitive to simazine toxicity (331, 332). In corn, the metabolism is more rapid in roots than in shoots (333, 334). Both simazine and atrazine undergo extensive metabolism in corn because some ring carbons readily convert to CO_2 (335), and the rate of conversion of simazine to chloroform-insoluble materials increases in the order of cucumber, cotton, and corn, the order of decreasing susceptibility to the herbicidal action of simazine (336). The ability of plants grown in atrazine-treated soils to degrade the herbicide generally correlates with the degree of resistance of the species to atrazine (337). Absorption factors probably are as important or more important than metabolism rates in the mechanism of selective toxicity of simazine, based on the more rapid conversion of ring carbons to CO_2 in susceptible plants compared to resistant ones (338). The ipazine ring does not degrade in cotton, a tolerant species, but it converts, in part, to 2-hydroxyipazine and other unidentified metabolites, one of which possibly is a hydroxyipazine conjugate (339). The propazine ring degrades, in part, to CO_2 when sorghum plants are held in air but not when they are held in CO_2-free air (340), the mechanism of this effect being unknown.

Simazine degrades on incubation with various tissues or parts of the corn plant and with particle-free extracts of corn (340–343). Corn converts simazine to 2-hydroxysimazine by dechlorination (344), a reaction which takes place in incubated corn juice (332, 341, 345), the reactive constituent being 2,4-dihydroxy-7-methoxy-1,4-benzoxazine-3-one (346), a normal constituent of etiolated corn seedlings (347). A corn mutant low in this active constituent exhibits less tolerance to atrazine than one with a normal benzoxazinone content but this relationship does not extend to wheat and, therefore, is not a general phenomenon (348). Excised roots of six grass species convert simazine to hydroxysimazine in relation to their benzoxazinone content but not in relation to the degree of resistance to this herbicide, a low yield of hydroxysimazine being accompanied by a higher yield of other water-soluble metabolites (349). Benzoxazinone compounds are not unique with corn; they also occur in plants that do not readily destroy simazine (346), suggesting that the selective herbicidal action involves other factors as well. Sorghum, which is resistant to triazines, does not appear to contain an active resistance factor, but it is possible that it contains such a factor in the form of a glycoside which does not extract (340). Pyridine, hydroxylamine, and other compounds, as well as the benzoxazinone mentioned above, catalyze the nucleophilic attack on carbon-2 of simazine, probably producing an unstable intermediate that reacts with water to produce hydroxysimazine; however, their potency is much less than that of the benzoxazinone (345, 350). Hydroxysimazine undergoes further decomposition, possibly by oxidation to the keto form and cleavage to CO_2, basic amines, and other compounds, some of which are incorporated into plant products (315, 345, 351). There is evidence of other metabolites of the 2-chloro-s-triazines (315, 338, 339, 352–354) but, in most cases, dechlorination appears to be the first step. However, peas definitely metabolize atrazine by an alternate pathway that does not involve dechlorination but that involves N-deethylation at the 4-position to yield a persistent product (355, 356).

Prometone is less selective as a herbicide, probably because the methoxycarbon bond is more stable than the chlorine-carbon bond (340, 342). The prometryne ring appears to be stable in plants, but sometimes prometryne yields small amounts of hydroxypropazine and other metabolities (351, 357). While there is not any experimental basis as yet, it is reasonable to believe that prometryne converts to its sulfoxide and sulfone in plants.

N–Heterocyclic compounds.—Amitrole rapidly metabolizes in plants, but despite extensive studies, there is not complete agreement on the identity of even the two major metabolites (358–366). One metabolite probably is the amine glucoside of amitrole (360, 365, 367–372), which possibly phosphorylates and becomes incorporated into normal plant constituents (371). Other metabolites probably involve complex formation or conjugation with proteins or amino acids (360, 361, 365, 373–380) and include formation of beta-(3-amino-1,2,4-triazolyl-1-)-alpha-alanine (371, 377, 381), the amino acid portion arising from serine or phosphoserine (382). There is some evidence that flavin-mediated systems are involved in amitrole degradation (383) and that the multitude of metabolites formed result from the activation of amitrole by such free-radical generating systems to form a reactive species which, acting as an electrophile, attacks alanine or protein-bound amino acids (384, 385). One unidentified metabolite appears to be more herbicidal than amitrole itself (386). The ring of amitrol cleaves, particularly in young reproductive organs of plants, and the carbon fragments oxidize to CO_2 (315, 384) or incorporate into common biochemical compounds (387).

The plant growth regulator, maleic hydrazide, only slowly degrades in plants forming, among other products, a beta-glucoside of maleic hydrazide, possibly involving the disaccharide of glucose (388–390); complexes with proteins also form (391). N-benzyl- and N-methyl derivatives of maleic hydrazide convert in plants to maleic hydrazide (392). Pyrazon metabolizes in the shoots of plants tolerant to this herbicide but not in the shoots of susceptible plants (393). A chloropicolinic acid derivative, picloram (Tordon), undergoes decarboxylation, hydroxyl replacement of chlorine in the 6-position, cleavage to oxalic acid, and formation of protein and lipoidal conjugates of these acids (394, 395). The dipyridinium compounds, diquat and paraquat, are highly resistant to metabolism in plants (396–398) although they rapidly photodecompose.

Ureas.—3-(Substituted-phenyl)-1,1-dimethylureas suffer extensive N-demethylation along with other types of metabolic degradation. Monuron is not split by urease (399) but converts in plants to at least two metabolites (400–403). There is evidence that in *Chlorella* monuron complexes with flavin mononucleotide (FMN), and the complex undergoes photoinactivation involving products with the riboflavin moiety and several monuron molecules (404); however, this mechanism of breakdown possibly is not applicable to higher plants. The metabolic pathways of the substituted-phenyl dimethylureas generally involve progressive N-demethylation to the methyl urea and urea, and, finally, cleavage to the aniline derivative, which possibly converts to the nitro derivative (405); these reactions occur with chloroxuron (406, 407), monuron (408), diuron (405, 408), and Fluometuron (409). Phenylthiourea herbicide chemicals probably oxidize in plants to phenylureas, the actual herbicidal agent (410).

Carbamates.—The carbamate herbicides of interest are alkyl N-phenyl carbamates, N,N-dialkyl alkylthiolcarbamates, and N,N-dialkyl alkyldithiocarbamates. IPC undergoes hydrolysis to aniline (411) or, possibly, oxidation to N-hydroxy IPC (412), the rate of metabolism being rapid and species-dependent (411, 413). CIPC cleaves into a water-soluble product containing an aniline structure, as well as conjugates and other degradation products (414). Barban also rapidly metabolizes to yield an unidentified, water-soluble, nonherbicidal, carbamate ester (415, 416) which is not the

N-hydroxy derivative (417) but which contains the 3-chloroaniline moiety and probably is a complex containing some naturally occurring plant component (417). Swep apparently forms an immobile lignin complex (418). EPTC metabolizes (419, 420) more rapidly in species resistant to it than in susceptible ones (421); a portion of the ethyl group converts to CO_2 (422) and, after oxidation to the sulfate form, the sulfur possibly incorporates into sulfur-containing amino acids (421). The propyl group of pebulate (Tillam) oxidizes to CO_2 and forms other labeled products in plants, resistant mung beans degrading the compound faster than susceptible wheat (423). Vernolate also rapidly metabolizes (424). CDEC extensively degrades by reactions which include, among others, conversion of the 2-chloroallyl moiety to lactic acid, CO_2, and a number of amino acids (425).

Amides and anilides.—CDAA rapidly converts in plants to glycolic acid and, possibly, to diallylamine, the reaction starting either with hydrolysis of the amide or with dechlorination to form the hydroxy derivative and continuing with dechlorination or hydrolysis, respectively (332, 425). A stable intermediate does not appear to be involved because hydroxylated CDAA and chloroacetic acid are not among the metabolites detected (425). Also, the allyl group extensively degrades, the 2-position liberating an appreciable amount of CO_2 (425). Susceptible plants degrade CDAA less rapidly than resistant plants (10). Ramrod rapidly metabolizes, mainly to form a water-soluble metabolite containing a carboxy group and a N-isopropylaniline moiety (426). Diphenamid N-demethylates to the N-methylacetamide and acetamide derivatives, hydrolyzes to the acetic acid derivative, and forms some hydroxylated derivatives of diphenamid (427, 428). Propanil converts, in rice plants, to propionic acid, which metabolizes to normal plant products, and to dichloroaniline which, in turn, converts to three complexes, one of which is the N-glucosylamine. Propanil and the glucosylamine each give two other metabolites, but there is no evidence of the formation of azobenzene derivatives (429). Organophosphate and carbamate insecticide chemicals inhibit the *in vivo* and *in vitro* hydrolysis of propanil by rice plants, paraoxon being more effective than parathion; so, spraying of such insecticides on rice plants treated with propanil results in injury due to the inhibition of the propanil-detoxifying enzyme (13, 430, 431). The factor responsible for this hydrolysis is an aryl acylamidase which has been obtained, in purified form, from rice and barnyard grass, and which has been tested for substrate specificity and the inhibitory action of insecticidal organophosphates and carbamates (13, 432–434); it appears that the selectivity of the herbicide results from differences in the substrate-specificity of the enzyme from different plants rather than from the presence or absence of the enzyme (432). Alar, a growth retardant, is not rapidly metabolized (435).

Miscellaneous herbicide chemicals.—Amiben quickly metabolizes, particularly in the roots, by formation of complexes (436) consisting of the *N*-glucosylamine, in soybeans (only), and, in other plants, of at least two additional conjugates (437–439) ; amiben also suffers decarboxylation to some degree (315). Dicamba converts mostly to 5-hydroxy-2-methoxy-3,6-dichlorobenzoic acid along with small amounts of 3,6-dichlorosalicylic acid and a dicamba conjugate, possibly a glucoside (440). Dacthal hydrolyzes at each of the ester groupings, but this possibly occurs in the soil and not in the plant (441). Endothall metabolizes and certain of the fragments become a part of the plant carbohydrates (315). Dichlobenil oxidizes to 2,6-dichlorobenzoic acid (442). Trifluralin is relatively stable in plants but it suffers some *N*-dealkylation, yielding the *N*-monopropylaniline derivative (443). Diphenylether herbicides containing an *ortho*-substituent in one phenyl ring, but not those lacking such a substituent, are activated in plants by a photobiochemical process which is not fully understood (13). Chlorinated aliphatic acids do not readily metabolize in plants (444), TCA being a noteworthy example (445, 446). Dalapon metabolizes to a small extent only (447–451), although there is some evidence that it dechlorinates to a limited degree (451). Calcium cyanamide converts quickly in cotton plants to urea, CO_2, alanine or a closely related compound, and other products (452).

OTHER COMPOUNDS

Plants are exposed or potentially exposed to a variety of pesticide chemicals other than those mentioned above, including rodenticides and molluscicides. There is almost no information on the fate of rodenticides, other than tetramine, in plants (453). The molluscicide, *N*-tritylmorpholine, metabolizes mainly to triphenylcarbinol along with smaller amounts of *o*-, *m*-, and *p*-hydroxytriphenylcarbinols, the latter appearing in free and conjugated form (454). 2-Chloro-6-(trichloromethyl)pyridine, a chemical useful in extending the efficiency of nitrogen utilization from treated soils, hydrolyzes in plants to 6-chloropicolinic acid (455).

CONCLUDING REMARKS

It is clear from the material discussed in this review that a new area of specialization has arisen involving the biochemistry of foreign compounds in plants or the field of plant detoxication mechanisms. The related field of animal detoxication mechanisms arose from the need for information on the fate of drugs in mammals. The intensive and extensive use of—and search for—pesticide chemicals in crop production initiated a concerted effort to understand their fate in plants; the need for such information in residue determination and for tolerance considerations has been a factor, also. Future investigations in this area should consider: (*a*) model compounds, as well as the pesticide chemicals themselves; (*b*) the comparative biochemistry of plant detoxication mechanisms in a systematic survey of plant orders and families; and (c) active *in vitro* systems capable of at least qualitatively reproducing the reactions which occur in living plants, particularly those involving oxidative reactions dependent on enzymes from higher plants. It is the hope of the authors that this review will serve as a basis and guide for the work needed on the fate of foreign organic compounds in plants and that it will stimulate new investigators to enter into studies in this important, emerging field of endeavor.

LITERATURE CITED[2]

1. Menzie, C. M., *Metabolism of Pesticides* (U. S. Fish Wildlife Serv., Spec. Sci. Rept.: Wildlife, No. **96,** 274 pp., 1966)
2. Metcalf, R. L. Metabolism and fate of pesticides in plants and animals. In *Scientific Aspects of Pest Control,* 230–50 (NAS-NRC, Washington, Publ. **1402,** 470 pp., 1966)
3. Casida, J. E. Problems posed by plant and animal metabolism of pesticides. In *New Developments and Problems in the Use of Pesticides,* 39–53 (NAS-NRC, Washington, Publ. **1082,** 82 pp., 1963)
4. Spencer, E. Y., *Residue Rev.,* **9,** 153–68 (1965)
5. Lykken, L., Casida, J. E., *Can. Med. Assoc. J.,* **100,** 145–54 (1969)
6. O'Brien, R. D., *Insecticides—Action and Metabolism* (Academic, N.Y., 332 pp., 1967)
7. Sijpesteijn, A. K., van der Kerk, G. J. M., *Ann. Rev. Phytopathol.,* **3,** 127–52 (1965)
8. Swanson, C. R., *Metabolic Fate of Herbicides in Plants* (USDA-ARS, **34–66,** 36 pp., 1965)
9. Hilton, J. L., Jansen, L. L., Hull, H. M., *Ann. Rev. Plant Physiol.,* **14,** 353–84 (1963)
10. Shaw, W. C., Hilton, J. L., Moreland, D. E., Jansen, L. L. Herbicides in plants. In *The Nature and Fate of Chemicals Applied to Soils, Plants, and Animals,* 119–33 (USDA-ARS, Beltsville, Md., Publ. **20–9,** 221 pp., 1960)
11. Moreland, D. E., *Ann. Rev. Plant Physiol.,* **18,** 365–86 (1967)
12. Loeffler, J. E., van Overbeek, J. Metabolism of herbicides. In *Treatise on Pesticides,* **1** (White-Stevens, R., Ed., Marcel-Dekker, N.Y., submitted for publication, 1968)
13. Matsunaka, S., *Residue Rev.,* **25** (In press, 1968)
14. Brian, R. C., *Weed Res.,* **4,** 105–17 (1964)
15. Ennis, W. B., Jr., *Weed Res.,* **4,** 93–104 (1964)
16. Frear, D. E. H., *Pesticide Index* (College Sci. Publ., State College, Pa., 3rd Ed., 295 pp., 1965)
17. Spencer, E. Y., *Guide to the Chemicals Used in Crop Protection* (Canada Dept. Agr., Ottawa, Publ. **1093,** 5th Ed., 483 pp., 1968)
18. Stecher, P. G., Ed., *The Merck Index* (Merck & Co., Inc., Rahway, 8th ed., **1713** pp., 1968)
19. Kenaga, E. E., *Bull. Entomol. Soc. Am.,* **12,** 161–217 (1966)
20. Dawson, R. F., *Am. Scientist,* **48,** 321–40 (1960)
21. Schroter, H. B., *Z. Naturforsch,* **12b,** 334–36 (1957)
22. Schroter, H. B., *Actes Congr. Sci. Intern. Tabac, 2ᵉ, Brussels, 1958,* 426–33
23. Tso, T. C., Jeffrey, R. N., *Arch. Biochem. Biophys.,* **80,** 46–50 (1959)
24. Dawson, R. F., *Ind. Eng. Chem.,* **44,** 266–70 (1952)
25. Dawson, R. F., *Am. J. Botany,* **39,** 250–53 (1952)
26. Binopoulos, X., *Actes. Congr. Sci. Intern. Tabac, 2ᵉ, Brussels, 1958,* 270–76
27. Olin, G. S., *Biokhimiya,* **13,** 193–96 (1964)
28. Dawson, R. F., *J. Am. Chem. Soc.,* **73,** 4218–21 (1951)
29. Gunther, F. A., Blinn, R. C., Benjamini, E., Kinkade, W. R., Anderson, L. D., *J. Agr. Food Chem.,* **7,** 330–35 (1959)
30. Griffith, G. D., Griffith, T., Byerrum, R. U., *J. Biol. Chem.,* **235,** 3536–38 (1960)
31. Mashkovtsev, M. F., Sirotenko, A. A., *Fiziol. Rast.,* **3,** 79–86 (1956)
32. Tso, T. C., Jeffrey, R. N., *Arch. Biochem. Biophys.,* **92,** 253–56 (1961)
33. Yoshida, D., *Plant Cell Physiol. (Tokyo),* **3,** 391–95 (1962)
34. Franz, G., *Z. Pflanzenernaechr. Dueng. Bodenk.,* **96,** 218–30 (1962)
35. Lookova, M. Y., *Acta Biol. Acad. Sci. Hung.,* **14,** 273–79 (1964)
36. Grisebach, H., Ollis, W. D., *Experi-*

[2] The following abbreviations are used in this bibliography: AAAS (American Association for the Advancement of Science); ARS (Agricultural Research Service-USDA); IUPAC (International Union of Pure and Applied Chemistry); NAS-NRC (National Academy of Sciences—National Research Council); USDA (U. S. Department of Agriculture).

entia, **17,** 4–12 (1961)

37. Crombie, L., Chemistry of the natural rotenoids, *Fortschr. Chem. Org. Naturstoffe,* **21,** 275–325 (1963)

38. Crombie, L., Thomas, M. B., *J. Chem. Soc. C,* **1967,** 1796–1801

39. Crombie, L., Green, C. L., Whiting, D. A., *Chem. Commun.,* **1968,** 234–35

40. Crombie, L., Peace, R., *Proc. Chem. Soc.,* 246–47 (1963)

41. Fukami, J-I., Yamamoto, I., Casida, J. E., *Science,* **155,** 713–16 (1967)

42. Crowley, M. P., Inglis, H. S., Snarey, M., Thain, E. M., *Nature,* **191,** 281–82 (1961)

43. Godin, P. J., Thain, E. M., *Proc. Chem. Soc.,* 452 (1961)

44. Crowley, M. P., Godin, P. J., Inglis, H. S., Snarey, M., Thain, E. M., *Biochem. Biophys. Acta,* **60,** 312–19 (1962)

45. Godin, P. J., Inglis, H. S., Snarey, M., Thain, E. M., *J. Chem. Soc.,* 5878–80 (1963)

46. Yamamoto, I., Casida, J. E., *J. Econ. Entomol.,* **59,** 1542–43 (1966)

47. Johnson, B. T., Goodman, R. N., Goldberg, H. S., *Science,* **157,** 560–61 (1967)

48. Upshall, D. G., Goodwin, T. W., *J. Sci. Food Agr.,* **15,** 846–55 (1964)

49. Harrison, R. B., Holmes, D. C., Roburn, J., Tatton, J. O'G., *J. Sci. Food Agr.,* **18,** 10–15 (1967)

50. Bradbury, F. R., Whittaker, W. O., *J. Sci. Food Agr.,* **7,** 248–53 (1956)

51. Bogdarina, A. A., *Fiziol. Rast.,* **4,** 254–58 (1957)

52. San Antonio, J. P., *J. Agr. Food Chem.,* **7,** 322–25 (1959)

53. Van Tiel, N. The nature of terminal products arising from the use of gamma-BHC. In *Proceedings of the Commission on Terminal Residues and of the Commission on Residue Analysis,* 14–21 (IUPAC, Pesticide Sec., Vienna, 76 pp., 1967)

54. Gannon, N., Decker, G. C., *J. Econ. Entomol.,* **51,** 3–7 (1958)

55. Gannon, N., Decker, G. C., *ibid.,* 8–11

56. Glasser, R. F., Blenk, R. G., Dewey, J. E., Hilton, B. D., Weiden, M. H. J., *J. Econ. Entomol.,* **51,** 337–41 (1958)

57. Lichtenstein, E. P., *J. Agr. Food Chem.,* **7,** 430–33 (1959)

58. Lichtenstein, E. P., Schulz, K. R.,

J. Agr. Food Chem., **8,** 452–56 (1960)

59. Porter, P. E. A summary of metabolism and decomposition of cyclodiene insecticides in plants and animals. In *Proceedings of the Commission on Terminal Residues and the Commission on Residue Analysis,* 28–38 (See Ref. 53)

60. Korte, F. Metabolism of aldrin, dieldrin, and endrin. In *Symposium on the Science and Technology of Residual Insecticides in Food Production with Special Reference to Aldrin and Dieldrin,* 102–17 (Shell Chem. Co., N.Y., 241 pp., 1968)

61. Rosen, J. D., Sutherland, D. J., Lipton, G. R., *Bull. Environ. Contam. Toxicol.,* **1,** 133–40 (1966)

62. Robinson, J., Richardson, A., Bush, B., Elgar, K. E., *Bull. Environ. Contam. Toxicol.,* **1,** 127–32 (1966)

63. Weisgerber, I., Klein, W., Djirsarai, A., Korte, F., *Ann. Chem.,* **713,** 175–79 (1968)

64. Klein, W., Korte, F., Weisgerber, I., Karl, R., Muller, W., Djirsarai, A., *Qualitas Plant. Mater. Vegetabiles,* **15,** 225–38 (1968)

65. Rosen, J. D., *Chem. Commun.,* 189–90 (1967)

66. Maier-Bode, H., *Residue Rev.,* **22,** 1–44 (1968)

67. Terranova, A. C., Ware, G. W., *J. Econ. Entomol.,* **56,** 596–99 (1963)

68. Cassil, C. C., Drummond, P. E., *J. Econ. Entomol.,* **58,** 356–57 (1965)

69. Gunther, F. A., Blinn, R. C., Barnes, M. M., *J. Agr. Food Chem.,* **5,** 198–200 (1957)

70. Tomizawa, C., *Botyu-Kagaku,* **25,** 47–51 (1960)

71. Cassidy, J. E., Kocvara, H. M., Murphy, R. T. Fate of radioactive acarol (isopropyl 4,4'-dibromobenzilate) on apples. *Abstr. 156th Am. Chem. Soc. Meeting, A62, Atlantic City, Sept. 1968*

72. Kossman, K., Geissbühler, H., Boyd, F. (Personal communication, 1968)

73. Bowker, D. M., Casida, J. E. (Unpublished results, 1968)

74. Bridges, R. G., *J. Sci. Food Agr.,* **7,** 305–13 (1956)

75. Winteringham, F. P. W., Harrison, A., Bridges, R. G., Bridges, P. M., *J. Sci. Food Agr.,* **6,** 251–61 (1955)

76. Bridges, R. G., *J. Sci. Food Agr.*, **6**, 261–68 (1955)
77. Casida, J. E., *J. Agr. Food Chem.*, **4**, 772–85 (1956)
78. Casida, J. E. Organophosphorus systemic insecticides. In *Biological and Chemical Control of Plant and Animal Pests*, 85–92 (Reitz, L. P., Ed., AAAS, Washington, Publ. **61**, 273 pp., 1960)
79. O'Brien, R. D., *Toxic Phosphorus Esters* (Academic, N.Y., 434 pp., 1960)
80. Heath, D. F., *Organophosphorus Poisons—Anticholinesterases and Related Compounds* (Pergamon, N.Y., 403 pp., 1961)
81. Casida, J. E. Metabolism of organophosphate insecticides by plants: a review. In *Radioisotopes and Radiation in Entomology*, 49–64 (Intern. Atomic Energy Agency, Vienna, 304 pp., 1962)
82. Schrader, G., *Die Entwicklung Neuer Insektizider Phosphorsäure-ester* (Verlag Chemie, Weinheim/Bergstr., Germany, 444 pp., 1963)
83. Casida, J. E., *Science*, **146**, 1011–17 (1964)
84. DuBois, K. P., Doull, J., Coon, J. M., *J. Pharmacol. Exptl. Therap.*, **99**, 376–93 (1950)
85. Hartley, G. S., Heath, D. F., *Nature*, **167**, 816 (1951)
86. Wedding, R. T., Metcalf, R. L., *Botan. Gaz.*, **114**, 180–89 (1952)
87. Heath, D. F., Lane, D. W. J., Llewellyn, M., *J. Sci. Food Agr.*, **3**, 60–69, 69–73 (1952)
88. Casida, J. E., Chapman, R. K., Allen, T. C., *J. Econ. Entomol.*, **45**, 568–78 (1952)
89. Casida, J. E., Stahmann, M. A., *J. Agr. Food Chem.*, **1**, 883–88 (1953)
90. Hartley, G. S., *Chem. Ind. (London)*, 529–32 (1954)
91. Heath, D. F., Lane, D. W. J., Park, P. O., *Phil. Trans. Roy. Soc. London, Ser. B*, **239**, 191–214 (1955)
92. Heath, D. F., Cleugh, J., Otter, I. K. H., Park, P. O., *J. Agr. Food Chem.*, **4**, 230–33 (1956)
93. Arthur, B. W., Casida, J. E., *J. Econ. Entomol.*, **51**, 49–56 (1958)
94. Arthur, B. W., Casida, J. E., *J. Agr. Food Chem.*, **5**, 186–92 (1957)
95. Casida, J. E., *Science*, **122**, 597–98 (1955)
96. Casida, J. E., Gatterdam, P. E., Getzin, L. W., Jr., Chapman, R.

K., *J. Agr. Food Chem.*, **4**, 236–43 (1956)
97. Spencer, E. Y., Robinson, J. R., *J. Agr. Food Chem.*, **8**, 293–95 (1960)
98. Beynon, K. I., Wright, A. N., *J. Sci. Food Agr.*, **18**, 143–50 (1967)
99. Beynon, K. I., Wright, A. N., *ibid.*, **19**, 146–53 (1968)
100. Beynon, K. I., Edwards, M. J., Elgar, K., Wright, A. N., *ibid.*, 302–7
101. Jaques, R., Bein, H. J., *Arch. Toxikol.*, **18**, 316–30 (1960)
102. Anliker, R., Beriger, E., Geiger, M., Schmid, K., *Helv. Chim. Acta*, **44**, 1622–45 (1961)
103. Menzer, R. E., Ditman, L. P., *J. Agr. Food Chem.*, **11**, 170–73 (1963)
104. Bull, D. L., Lindquist, D. A., Grabbe, R. R., *J. Econ. Entomol.*, **60**, 332–41 (1967)
105. Bull, D. L., Lindquist, D. A., *J. Agr. Food Chem.*, **12**, 310–17 (1964)
106. Menzer, R. E., Casida, J. E., *J. Agr. Food Chem.*, **13**, 102–12 (1965)
107. Lindquist, D. A., Bull, D. L., *J. Agr. Food Chem.*, **15**, 267–72 (1967)
108. Mostafa, I. Y., Hassan, A., Zayed, S. M. A. D., *Z. Naturforsch. (B)*, **20**, 67–70 (1965)
109. Dedek, W., *Z. Naturforsch. (B)*, **23**, 504–6 (1968)
110. Kohn, G. K., Pack, D. E., Ospenson, J. N. The degradation paths and the metabolic fate of dibrom (dimethyl 1,2-dibromo-2,2-dichloroethyl phosphate) in plant and animal tissue. *Abstr. Am. Chem. Soc. Meeting, N.Y., 138th, Sept., 1960*
111. Metcalf, R. L., Stafford, E. M., Fukuto, T. R., March, R. B., *J. Econ. Entomol.*, **50**, 205–10 (1957)
112. Bowman, J. S., Casida, J. E., *J. Econ. Entomol.*, **51**, 773–80 (1958)
113. Metcalf, R. L., Fukuto, T. R., March, R. B., Stafford, E. M., *J. Econ. Entomol.*, **49**, 738–41 (1956)
114. Mühlmann, R., Tietz, H., *Höefchen Briefe*, **9**, 116–40 (1956)
115. Niessen, H., Tietz, H., Hecht, G., Kimmerle, G., *Arch. Toxikol.*, **20**, 44–60 (1963)
116. Tomizawa, C., *Nippon Oyo Dobutsu Konchu-Gaku Zasshi*, **7**, 140–49 (1963)
117. Schuppon, R., *Chim. Ind.*, **85**, 421–36 (1961)
118. Gar, K. A., Kiffiani, R. Y., *Proc. Intern. Conf. Peaceful Uses Atomic Energy* (Geneva, 1955), **12**, 185–99 (1956)

119. David, W. A. L., Aldridge, W. N., *Ann. Appl. Biol.*, **45**, 332–45 (1957)

120. El-Refai, A., Hopkins, T. L., *J. Agr. Food Chem.*, **14**, 588–92 (1966)

121. Coffin, D. E., *J. Assoc. Offic. Agr. Chemists*, **49**, 1018–21 (1966)

122. Knaak, J. B., Stahmann, M. A., Casida, J. E., *J. Agr. Food Chem.*, **10**, 154–58 (1962)

123. Shipp, O. E., Lindquist, D. A., Brazzel, J. R., *J. Econ. Entomol.*, **56**, 793–98 (1963)

124. Engst, R., Seidler, H., Haertig, M., *Nahrung*, **10**, 419–25 (1966)

125. Miyamoto, J., Sato, Y., Kadota, T., Fujinami, A., Endo, M., *Agr. Biol. Chem. (Tokyo)*, **27**, 381–89 (1963)

126. Miyamoto, J., Sato, Y., Kadota, T., Fujinami, A., *ibid.*, 669–76

127. Tomizawa, C., Sato, T., Yamashita, H., Fukuda, H., *Shokuhin Eiseigaku Zasshi*, **3**, 72–76 (1962)

128. Miyamoto, J., Sato, Y., *Botyu-Kagaku*, **30**, 45–49 (1965)

129. Miyamoto, J., Sato, Y., *ibid.*, 49–51

130. Rowlands, D. G. *J. Stored Prod. Res.*, **2**, 1–12 (1966)

131. Rowlands, D. G., *ibid.*, 105–16

132. Margot, A., Gysin, H., *Helv. Chim. Acta*, **40**, 1562–73 (1957)

133. Ralls, J. W., Gilmore, D. R., Cortes, A., *J. Agr. Food Chem.*, **14**, 387–92 (1966)

134. Ralls, J. W., Gilmore, D. R., Cortes, A., Schutt, S. M., Mercer, W. A., *Food Technol.*, **21**(7), 92–94 (1967)

135. Kansouh, A. S. H., Hopkins, T. L., *J. Agr. Food Chem.*, **16**, 446–50 (1968)

136. Smith, G. N., Watson, B. S., Fischer, F. S., *J. Agr. Food Chem.*, **15**, 870–77 (1967)

137. Smith, G. N., Watson, B. S., Fischer, F. S., *ibid.*, 127–31

138. Marco, G. J., Jaworski, E. G., *J. Agr. Food Chem.*, **12**, 305–10 (1964)

139. Boyd, N. R., Jr., Arthur, B. W., *J. Econ. Entomol.*, **53**, 848–53 (1960)

140. Niessen, H., Tietz, H., Frehse, H., *Pflanzenschutz-Nachrichten, Bayer*, **15**, 125–47 (1962)

141. Tomizawa, C., *J. Appl. Entomol. Zool. (Japan)*, **6**, 237–41 (1962)

142. Fikudo, H., Masuda, T., Miyahara, Y., *J. Appl. Entomol. Zool. (Japan)*, **6**, 230–36 (1962)

143. Bowman, M. C., Beroza, M., *J. Agr. Food Chem.*, **16**, 399–402 (1968)

144. Reynolds, H. T., Metcalf, R. L., Fukuto, T. R., *J. Econ. Entomol.*, **59**, 293–99 (1966)

145. Benjamini, E., Metcalf, R. L., Fukuto, T. R., *J. Econ. Entomol.*, **52**, 99–102 (1959)

146. Katague, D. B., Anderson, C. A., *Bull. Environ. Contam. Toxicol.*, **2**, 228–35 (1967)

147. Blinn, R. C., *J. Agr. Food Chem.*, **16**, 441–45 (1968)

148. Dedek, W., Grimmer, F., Koch, H., *Isotopen Tech.*, **2**, 150–57 (1962)

149. Woggon, H., Spranger, D., Ackermann, H., *Nahrung*, **7**, 612–18 (1963)

150. Dedek, W., Kisro, J., *Atompraxis*, **12**, 100–4 (1966)

151. Hartley, G. S., *World Crops*, **4**, 397 (1952)

152. Metcalf, R. L., March, R. B., Fukuto, T. R., Maxon, M. G., *J. Econ. Entomol.*, **47**, 1045–55 (1954)

153. Metcalf, R. L., March, R. B., Fukuto, T. R., Maxon, M. G., *ibid.*, **48**, 364–69 (1955)

154. Henglein, A., Schrader, G., *Z. Naturforsch. (B)*, **10**, 12–19 (1955)

155. Fukuto, T. R., Wolf, J. P. III, Metcalf, R. L., March, R. B., *J. Econ. Entomol.*, **49**, 147–51 (1956)

156. Thomas, W. D. E., Bennett, S. H., Lloyd-Jones, C. P., *Ann. Appl. Biol.*, **43**, 569–93 (1955)

157. Thomas, W. D. E., Glynne-Jones, G. D., *ibid.*, 182–91

158. Fukuto, T. R., Metcalf, R. L., March, R. B., Maxon, M. G., *J. Econ. Entomol.*, **48**, 347–54 (1955)

159. Fukuto, T. R., Wolf, J. P. III, Metcalf, R. L., March, R. B., *ibid.*, **50**, 399–401 (1957)

160. Coffin, D. E., McKinley, W. P., *J. Assoc. Offic. Agr. Chemists*, **47**, 632–40 (1964)

161. Casida, J. E., Ahmed, M. K., *J. Econ. Entomol.*, **52**, 111–16 (1959)

162. Santi, R., Radice, M., Martinotti, P., *Chim. Ind.*, **50**, 221–24 (1968)

163. Tietz, H., Metcalf, R. L., Fukuto, T. R., *Hoefchen-Briefe*, **10**, 279–89 (1957)

164. Bull, D. L., *J. Agr. Food Chem.*, **16**, 610–16 (1968)

165. Esser, H. O., Müller, P. W., *Experientia*, **22**, 36–42 (1966)

166. Calderbank, A., *J. Chem. Soc., C*, **1966**, 56–60

167. Menn, J. J., McBain, J. B., *J. Agr. Food Chem.*, **12**, 162–66 (1964)

168. Metcalf, R. L., Fukuto, T. R., March,

R. B., *J. Econ. Entomol.*, **50**, 338–45 (1957)

169. Bowman, J. S., Casida, J. E., *J. Agr. Food Chem.*, **5**, 192–97 (1957)

170. Bowman, J. S., Casida, J. E., *J. Econ. Entomol.*, **51**, 838–43 (1958)

171. Metcalf, R. L., Reynolds, H. T., Winton, M., Fukuto, T. R., *J. Econ. Entomol.*, **52**, 435–39 (1959)

172. Bull, D. L., *J. Econ. Entomol.*, **58**, 249–54 (1965)

173. Jucker, O., *Mitt. Gebiete Lebensm. Hyg.*, **49**, 299–322 (1958)

174. Coffin, D. E., *J. Assoc. Offic. Agr. Chemists*, **47**, 662–67 (1964)

175. Tomizawa, C., Sato, T., *Botyu-Kagaku*, **25**, 99–105 (1960)

176. Rowlands, D. G., *J. Sci. Food Agr.*, **15**, 824–29 (1964)

177. Rowlands, D. G., Clements, J. E., *J. Stored Prod. Res.*, **1**, 101–3 (1965)

178. Rowlands, D. G., *J. Sci. Food Agr.*, **16**, 325–30 (1965)

179. Koivistoinen, P., *Ann. Acad. Sci. Fennicae Ser. (A)* **IV**, No. 51, 91 pp. (1961)

180. Koivistoinen, P., Karinpaa, A., Kononen, M., *J. Agr. Food Chem.*, **12**, 555–57 (1964)

181. Bourke, J. B., Broderick, E. J., Hackler, L. R., Lippold, P. C., *J. Agr. Food Chem.*, **16**, 585–89 (1968)

182. Dauterman, W. C., Viado, G. B., Casida, J. E., O'Brien, R. D., *J. Agr. Food Chem.*, **8**, 115–19 (1960)

183. Chilwell, E. D., Beecham, P. T., *J. Sci. Food Agr.*, **11**, 400–7 (1960)

184. Santi, R., *Istit. Ric. Agrar. Contrib.* (Montecatini, Italy), **5**, 47–63 (1961)

185. Santi, R., Giacomelli, R., *J. Agr. Food Chem.*, **10**, 257–61 (1962)

186. Santi, R., Radice, M., Giacomelli, R., Bazzi, B., *Istit. Ric. Agrar. Contrib.* (Montecatini, Italy), **6**, 1–20 (1964)

187. Santi, R., Giacomelli, R., *ibid.*, 81–90

188. Sanderson, D. M., Edson, E. F., *Brit. J. Ind. Med.*, **21**, 52–64 (1964)

189. Hacskaylo, J., Bull, D. L., *J. Agr. Food Chem.*, **11**, 464–66 (1963)

190. Rowlands, D. G., *J. Sci. Food Agr.*, **17**, 90–93 (1966)

191. Dorough, H. W., Leeling, N. C., Casida, J. E., *Science*, **140**, 170–71 (1963)

192. Casida, J. E., *Ann. Rev. Entomol.*, **8**, 39–58 (1963)

193. Casida, J. E. Radiotracer approaches to carbamate insecticide toxicology. In *Radiation and Radioisotopes Applied to Insects of Agricultural Importance*, 223–39 (Intern. Atomic Energy Agency, Vienna. 508 pp., 1963)

194. Dorough, H. W., Casida, J. E., *J. Agr. Food Chem.*, **12**, 294–304 (1964)

195. Abdel-Wahab, A. M., Kuhr, R. J., Casida, J. E., *J. Agr. Food Chem.*, **14**, 290–98 (1966)

196. Kuhr, R. J., Casida, J. E., *J. Agr. Food Chem.*, **15**, 814–24 (1967)

197. Mostafa, I. Y., Hassan, A., Zayed, S. M. A. D., *Z. Naturforsch. (B)*, **21**, 1060–62 (1966)

198. Slade, M., Casida, J. E. (Unpublished results, 1968)

199. Dorough, H. W., *Bull. Environ. Contam. Toxicol.*, **3**, 164–73 (1968)

200. Friedman, A. R., Lemin, A. J., *J. Agr. Food Chem.*, **15**, 642–47 (1967)

201. Metcalf, R. L., Fukuto, T. R., Collins, C., Borck, K., Abd El-Aziz, S., Munoz, R., Cassil, C. C., *J. Agr. Food Chem.*, **16**, 300–11 (1968)

202. Metcalf, R. L., Fukuto, T. R., Collins, C., Borck, K., Burk, J., Reynolds, H. T., Osman, M. F., *ibid.*, **14**, 579–84 (1966)

203. Coppedge, J. R., Lindquist, D. A., Bull, D. L., Dorough, H. W., *J. Agr. Food Chem.*, **15**, 902–10 (1967)

204. Williams, E., Meikle, R. W., Redemann, C. T., *J. Agr. Food Chem.*, **12**, 453–57 (1964)

205. Lemin, A. J., Thomas, R. C., *J. Agr. Food Chem.*, **9**, 254–56 (1961)

206. Wallen, V. R., Millar, R. L., *Phytopathology*, **47**, 291–94 (1957)

207. Starzyk, M. J., Mitchell, J. E., *Phytopathology*, **53**, 309–12 (1963)

208. Hamilton, J. M., Szkolnik, M., Sondheimer, E., *Science*, **123**, 1175–76 (1956)

209. Lemin, A. J., Magee, W. E., *Plant Disease Reptr.*, **41**, 447–48 (1957)

210. Crowdy, S. H., Gardner, D., Grove, J. F., Pramer, D., *J. Exptl. Botany*, **6**, 371–83 (1955)

211. Crowdy, S. H., Grove, J. F., Hemming, H. G., Robinson, K. C., *J. Exptl. Botany*, **7**, 42–64 (1956)

212. Crowdy, S. H., Grove, J. F., Mc-

Closkey, P., *Biochem. J.*, **72,** 230–41 (1959)

213. Rhodes, A. Status of griseofulvin in crop protection. In *Antibiotics in Agriculture*, 101–24 (Woodline, M., Ed., Butterworths, London, 439 pp., 1962)

214. Wallen, V. R., Hoffman, I., *Phytopathology*, **49,** 680–83 (1959)

215. Owens, R. G., Blaak, G., *Contrib. Boyce Thompson Inst.*, **20,** 475–97 (1960)

216. Sisler, H. D., *Conn. Agr. Expt. Stat. Bull.*, No. **663,** 116–36 (1963)

217. Berteau, P. E., Pack, D. E., Ospenson, J. N., Crossley, J., *Vortex*, **27,** Insert p. 37 (1966)

218. Dekker, J., *Mededel. Landbouwhogeschool Gent*, **26,** 1378–84 (1961)

219. Niemann, G. J., *Investigations on the chemical control of powdery mildew* (Doctoral thesis, Univ. Utrecht, The Netherlands, 1964)

220. Curry, A. N., *J. Agr. Food Chem.*, **10,** 13–18 (1962)

221. Hills, F. J., *Phytopathology*, **52,** 389–92 (1962)

222. Tolmsoff, W. J., *Phytopathology*, **52,** 755 (1962)

223. Dekker, J., Oort, A. J. P., *Phytopathology*, **54,** 815–18 (1964)

224. Jones, D. R., Wignall, J., *Nature*, **175,** 207–8 (1955)

225. Jones, D. R., *Outlook Agr.*, **1,** 111–15 (1956)

226. Crowdy, S. H., Jones, D. R., *J. Exptl. Botany*, **9,** 220–28 (1958)

227. Crowdy, S. H., Elias, R. S., Jones, D. R., *Ann. Appl. Biol.*, **46,** 149–58 (1958)

228. Sijpesteijn, A. K., Kaslander, J., *Outlook Agr.*, **4,** 119–25 (1964)

229. Kakigi, K., Misato, T., *Ann. Phytopathol. Soc. Japan*, **33,** 319 (1967)

230. Ishida, M., Sumi, H., Oku, H., *Residue Rev.*, **25** (In press, 1968)

231. Lemin, A. J., *J. Agr. Food Chem.*, **13,** 557–60 (1965)

232. New metabolite of DCNA in soybeans. In *1967 Progress Report on Pesticides and Related Activities*, 194 (USDA, Feb., 1968)

233. Isobe, K., Takeda, M., Tanabe, H., Kawashiro, I., *Shokuhin Eiseigaku Zasshi*, **8,** 259–60 (1967)

234. Herok, J., Goette, H., *Intern. J. Appl. Radiation Isotopes*, **14,** 461–79 (1963)

235. Dekhuijzen, H. M., *Nature*, **191,** 198–99 (1961)

236. Dekhuijzen, H. M., *Mededel. Land-*

bouwhogeschool Gent, **26,** 1542–47 (1961)

237. Kaslander, J., Sijpesteijn, A. K., van der Kerk, G. J. M., *Biochim. Biophys. Acta*, **52,** 396–97 (1961)

238. Kaslander, J., Sijpesteijn, A. K., van der Kerk, G. J. M., *ibid.*, **60,** 417–19 (1962)

239. Dekhuijzen, H. M., *J. Plant Pathol. (Netherlands)*, **70,** 1–75 (1964)

240. Massaux, F., *Mededel. Landbouwhogeschool Gent*, **28,** 590–96 (1963)

241. Pluijgers, C. W., van der Kerk, G. J. M., *Rec. Trav. Chim.*, **80,** 1089–1100 (1961)

242. Pluijgers, C. W., *Direct and Systemic Antifungal Action of Dithiocarbamic Acid Derivatives* (Doctoral thesis, Univ. Utrecht, The Netherlands, 1959)

243. van der Kerk, G. J. M. New developments in organic fungicides. In *Fungicides in Agriculture and Horticulture*, 67–91 (SCI Monographs **15**, Soc. Chem. Ind., London, 145 pp., 1961)

244. Garraway, J. L., Wain, R. L., *Ann. Appl. Biol.*, **50,** 11–20 (1962)

245. van der Kerk, G. J. M., *Mededel. Landbouwhogeschool Gent*, **21,** 305–39 (1956)

246. Van Andel, O. M., *Phytopathol. Z.*, **45,** 66–80 (1962)

247. Sato, T., Tomizawa, C., *Bull. Natl. Inst. Agr. Sci.*, Ser. C, **12,** 181–87 (1960)

248. Turner, E. M. C., *J. Exptl. Botany*, **12,** 169–75 (1961)

249. Turner, E. M. C., *Nature*, **186,** 325–26 (1960)

250. Harrison, M., Payne, M. G., Gaskill, J. O., *J. Am. Soc. Sugar Beet Technologists*, **11,** 457–68 (1961)

251. Loeschcke, V., Butin, H., *Mededel. Landbouwhogeschool Gent*, **26,** 1548–52 (1961)

252. Loeschcke, V., Francksen, H., *Naturwissenschaften*, **51,** 140 (1964)

253. Hildebrand, D. C., Schroth, M. N., *Phytopathology*, **54,** 59–63 (1964)

254. Hildebrand, D. C., Schroth, M. N.. *ibid.*, 640–45

255. Noveroske, R. L., Kuć, J., Williams, E. B., *Phytopathology*, **54,** 92–97 (1964)

256. Noveroske, R. L., Williams, E. B., Kuć, J., *ibid.*, 98–103

257. Holley, R. W., Boyle, F. P., Hand, D. B., *Arch. Biochem. Biophys.*, **27,** 143–51 (1950)

258. Bach, M. K., Fellig, J., *Nature*, **189,** 763 (1961)

259. Butts, J. S., Fang, S. C. Tracer studies on the mechanism of action of hormonal herbicides. In *A Conference of Radioactive Isotopes in Agriculture*, 209–14 (U. S. At. Energy Comm. Rept. **TID–7512**, 1956)

260. Canny, M. J., Markus, K., *Australian J. Biol. Sci.*, **13**, 486–500 (1960)

261. Edgerton, L. J., *Proc. Am. Soc. Hort. Sci.*, **77**, 22–28 (1961)

262. Edgerton, L. J., Hoffman, M. B., *Science*, **134**, 341–42 (1961)

263. Fang, S. C., Jaworski, E. G., Logan, A. V., Freed, V. H., Butts, J. S., *Arch. Biochem. Biophys.*, **32**, 249–55 (1951)

264. Leafe, E. L., *Nature*, **193**, 485–86 (1962)

265. Leafe, E. L., *Brit. Weed Control Conf.*, **6**, 1–3 (1962)

266. Luckwill, L. C., Lloyd-Jones, C. P., *Ann. Appl. Biol.*, **48**, 613–25, 626–36 (1960)

267. Morgan, P. W., Hall, W. C., *Weeds*, **11**, 130–35 (1963)

268. Slife, F. W., Key, J. L., Yamaguchi, S., Crafts, A. S., *Weeds*, **10**, 29–35 (1962)

269. Weintraub, R. L., Brown, J. W., Fields, M., Rohan, J., *Am. J. Botany*, **37**, 682 (1950)

270. Weintraub, R. L., Brown, J. W., Fields, M., Rohan, J., *Plant Physiol.*, **27**, 293–301 (1952)

271. Weintraub, R. L., Reinhart, J. H., Scherff, R. A. Role of entry, translocation, and metabolism in specificity of 2,4-D and related compounds. In *A Conference on Radioactive Isotopes in Agriculture*, 203–8 (U.S. At. Energy Comm. Rept. **TID–7512**, 1956)

272. Weintraub, R. L., Reinhart, J. H., Scherff, R. A., Schisler, L. C., *Plant Physiol.*, **29**, 303–4 (1954)

273. Weintraub, R. L., Yeatman, J. N., Lockhart, J. A., Reinhart, J. H., Fields, M., *Arch. Biochem. Biophys.*, **40**, 277–85 (1952)

274. Winston, A. W., Ritty, P. M., *Proc. Northeastern Weed Control Conf., 15th*, 396–400 (New York, 1961)

275. Basler, E., *Weeds*, **12**, 14–16 (1964)

276. Wilcox, M., *The Metabolism of Phenoxyaliphatic Acids in Higher Plants* (Doctoral thesis, N.C. State College, Raleigh, 67 pp., 1961)

277. Wilcox, M., Moreland, D. E., Klingman, G. C., *Physiol. Plantarum*, **16**, 565–71 (1963)

278. Thomas, E. W., Loughman, B. C., Powell, R. G., *Nature*, **199**, 73–74 (1963)

279. Thomas, E. W., Loughman, B. C., Powell, R. G., *ibid.*, **204**, 286 (1964)

280. Holley, R. W., *Arch. Biochem. Biophys.*, **35**, 171–75 (1952)

281. Thomas, E. W., Loughman, B. C., Powell, R. G., *Nature*, **204**, 884–85 (1964)

282. Lemin, A. J., *J. Agr. Food Chem.*, **13**, 557–60 (1965)

283. Faulkner, J. K., Woodcock, D., *Nature*, **203**, 865 (1964)

284. Faulkner, J. K., Woodcock, D., *J. Chem. Soc.*, **1965**, 1187–91

285. Leaper, J. M. F., Bishop, J. R., *Botan. Gaz.*, **112**, 250–58 (1951)

286. Tutass, H. O., *Relationships Among Molecular Structure, Metabolism, and Biological Activity of Halogen-Substituted Phenoxyacetic Acids* (Doctoral thesis, Univ. California, Davis, 1968)

287. Tutass, H. O., Crosby, D. G. Relationships among molecular structure, metabolism, and biological activity of halogen-substituted phenoxyacetic acids, *Am. Abstr. Chem. Soc. Meeting, 155th, San Francisco, March-April, 1968*

288. Fang, S. C., *Weeds*, **6**, 179–86 (1958)

289. Brian, R. C., *Plant Physiol.*, **35**, 773–82 (1960)

290. Galston, A. W., Kaur, R., *Proc. Intern. Botan. Congr., 9th, 1959*, p. 129

291. Khubatiya, R. A., *Soobshch. Akad. Nauk Gruz.*, **21**, 313–18 (1960)

292. Brian, R. C., *Plant Physiol.*, **33**, 431–39 (1958)

293. Zemskaya, V. A., Rakitin, Y. V., *Agrokhimiya*, **7**, 101–12 (1964)

294. Andreae, W. A., Good, N. E., *Plant Physiol.*, **32**, 566–72 (1957)

295. Bach, M. K., *Plant Physiol.*, **36**, 558–65 (1961)

296. Klämbt, H. D., *Planta*, **57**, 339–53 (1961)

297. Zenk, M. H., *Naturforschung*, **15b**, 436–41 (1960)

298. Crosby, D. G., *J. Agr. Food Chem.*, **12**, 3–6 (1964)

299. Jaworski, E. G., Butts, J. S., *Arch. Biochem. Biophys.*, **38**, 207–18 (1952)

300. Bach, M. K., Fellig, J. The uptake and fate of C^{14}-labeled 2,4-D in bean stem sections. In *Plant Growth Regulation, Intern. Conf. Plant Growth Regulation, Yonkers,*

N.Y. (Iowa State Univ. Press, Ames, 1959)

301. Fang, S. C., Butts, J. S., *Plant Physiol.*, **29**, 56–60 (1954)

302. Jaworski, E. G., Fang, S. C., Freed, V. H., *Plant Physiol.*, **30**, 272–75 (1955)

303. Bach, M. K., Fellig, J., *Plant Physiol.*, **36**, 89–91 (1961)

304. Linscott, D. L., McCarty, M. K., *Weeds*, **10**, 65–68 (1962)

305. Morton, H. L., Meyer, R. E., *Plant Physiol.* (Suppl.), **37**, xxiv–xxv (1962)

306. Grace, N. H., *Can. J. Research*, **17**, 247–55 (1939)

307. Synerholm, M. E., Zimmerman, P. W., *Contrib. Boyce Thompson Inst.*, **14**, 369 (1947)

308. Wain, R. L., Wightman, F., *Proc. Roy. Soc. (London), Ser. B*, **142**, 525–36 (1954)

309. Fawcett, C. H., Ingram, J. M. A., Wain, R. L., *Proc. Roy. Soc. (London), Ser. B*, **142**, 60–72 (1954)

310. Wain, R. L., *Ann. Appl. Biol.*, **42**, 151–57 (1955)

311. Fawcett, C. H., Taylor, H. F., Wain, R. L., Wightman, F., The degradation of certain phenoxy acids, amides, and nitriles within plant tissues. In *The Chemistry and Mode of Action of Plant Growth Substances*, 187–94 (Wain, R. L., Wightman, F., Eds., Butterworth's, London, 1956)

312. Wain, R. L., *Advan. Pest Control Res.*, **2**, 263–305 (1958)

313. Wain, R. L., The oxidative metabolism of certain auxins and their derivatives within plant tissues. In *Recent Advances in Botany, The Growth Substances and Their Action*, 1083–88 (Univ. Toronto Press, Toronto, 1961)

314. Balayannis, P. G., Smith, M. S., Wain, R. L., *Ann. Appl. Biol.*, **55**, 261–65 (1965)

315. Freed, V. H., Montgomery, M., Kief, M., *Proc. Northeastern Weed Control Conf., 15th*, 6–16 (New York, 1961)

316. Fertig, S. N., Loos, M. A., Gutenmann, W. H., Lisk, D. J., *Weeds*, **12**, 147–48 (1964)

317. Gutenmann, W. H., Lisk, D. J., *J. Agr. Food Chem.*, **11**, 304–6 (1963)

318. Linscott, D. L., *J. Agr. Food Chem.*, **12**, 7–10 (1964)

319. Linscott, D. L., Hagin, R. D., Dawson, J. E., *J. Agr. Food Chem.*, **16**, 844–48 (1968)

320. Glastonbury, H. A., Stevenson, M. D., Ball, R. W. E., *Proc. Brit. Weed Conf., Brighton, England, 4th*, 33–38 (1958)

321. Bokarev, K. S., Shidlovskaia, I. L., *Fiziol. Rast.*, **5**, 373–76 (1958)

322. Sudi, J., Josepovits, G., Matolcsy, G., *J. Exptl. Botany*, **12**, 390–400 (1961)

323. Crafts, A. S., *Weeds*, **8**, 19–25 (1960)

324. Morré, D. J., Rogers, B. J., *Weeds*, **8**, 436–47 (1960)

325. Szabo, S. S., *Weeds*, **11**, 292–94 (1963)

326. Jooste, J. van der W., Moreland, D. E., *Phytochemistry*, **2**, 263–71 (1963)

327. Audus, L. J., *Nature*, **170**, 886–87 (1952)

328. Carroll, R. B., *Contrib. Boyce Thompson Inst.*, **16**, 409–17 (1952)

329. Vlitos, A. J., *Contrib. Boyce Thompson Inst.*, **17**, 127–49 (1953)

330. Sheets, T. J., Danielson, L. L., Herbicides in soils. In *The Nature and Fate of Chemicals Applied to Soils, Plants, and Animals*, 170–81 (USDA-ARS, publ. **20–9**, 221 pp., 1960)

331. Roth, W., *Compt. Rend.*, **245**, 942–44 (1957)

332. Gysin, H., Knüsli, E., *Advan. Pest Control Res.*, **3**, 289–358 (1960)

333. Sheets, T. J., *Weeds*, **9**, 1–13 (1961)

334. Plaisted, P. H., Ryskiewich, D. P., *Plant. Physiol.* (Suppl.) **37**, xxv–xxvi (1962)

335. Montgomery, M. L., Freed, V. H., *Western Weed Control Conf. Res. Prog. Rept.*, 93–94 (1959)

336. Davis, D. E., Funderburk, H. H., Jr., Sansing, N. G., *Weeds*, **7**, 300–9 (1959)

337. Negi, N. S., Funderburk, H. H., Jr., Davis, D. E., *Weeds*, **12**, 53–57 (1964)

338. Ragab, M. T. H., McCollum, J. P., *Weeds*, **9**, 72–84 (1961)

339. Hamilton, R. H., Moreland, D. E., *Weeds*, **11**, 213–17 (1963)

340. Foy, C. L., *Calif. Weed Conf. Proc.*, **14**, 82–86 (1962)

341. Foy, C. L., *Plant Physiol. (Suppl.)*, **36**, xl–xli (1961)

342. Foy, C. L., *West. Weed Control Conf. Res. Prog. Rept.*, 88–89 (1962)

343. Foy, C. L., Castelfranco, P., *Plant Physiol. (Suppl.)*, **35**, xxviii (1960)

344. Hamilton, R. H., Moreland, D. E., *Science*, **135**, 373–74 (1962)
345. Castelfranco, P., Foy, C. L., Deutsch, D. B., *Weeds*, **9**, 580–91 (1961)
346. Roth, W., Knüsli, E., *Experientia*, **17**, 312–13 (1961)
347. Hamilton, R. H., Bandurski, R. S., Reusch, W. H., *Cereal Chem.*, **39**, 107–13 (1962)
348. Hamilton, R. H., *Weeds*, **12**, 27–30 (1964)
349. Hamilton, R. H., *J. Agr. Food Chem.*, **12**, 14–17 (1964)
350. Castelfranco, P., Brown, M. S., *Weeds*, **10**, 131–36 (1962)
351. Montgomery, M. L., Freed, V. H., *J. Agr. Food Chem.*, **12**, 11–14 (1964)
352. Montgomery, M. L., Freed, V. H., *Weeds*, **9**, 231–37 (1961)
353. Funderburk, H. H., Jr., Davis, D. E., *Weeds*, **11**, 101–4 (1963)
354. Plaisted, P. H., Thornton, M. L., *Contrib. Boyce Thompson Inst.*, **22**, 399–404 (1964)
355. Shimabukuro, R. H., Kadunce, R. E., Frear, D. S., *J. Agr. Food Chem.*, **14**, 392–95 (1966)
356. Shimabukuro, R. H., *J. Agr. Food Chem.*, **15**, 557–62 (1967)
357. Whitenberg, D. C., *Weeds*, **13**, 68–71 (1965)
358. Riden, J. R., *North Central Weed Control Conf. Proc.*, **12**, 3–4 (1955)
359. Riden, J. R., *Weeds*, **5**, 5–11 (1957)
360. Riden, J. R., *Hormolog*, 10–12 (1957)
361. Racusen, D., *Arch. Biochem. Biophys.*, **74**, 106–13 (1958)
362. Palmer, L. E., Williams, E. F., Studies on the metabolism of 3-amino-1,2,4-triazole (triazole). *Am. Chem. Soc. Meeting, Agr. Food Chem. Div., Sept. 1958*
363. Yost, J. F., Williams, E. F., *Northeastern Weed Control Conf. Proc., 12th*, 9–15 (New York, 1958)
364. Herrett, R. A., *Dissertation Abstr.*, **20**, 2002 (1959)
365. Herrett, R. A., Linck, A. J., *Physiol. Plantarum*, **14**, 767–76 (1961)
366. Miller, C. S., Hall, W. C., *J. Agr. Food Chem.*, **9**, 210–12 (1961)
367. Fredrick, J. F., *Physiol. Plantarum*, **14**, 734–40 (1961)
368. Fredrick, J. F., Gentile, A. C., *Physiol. Plantarum*, **13**, 761–65 (1960)
369. Fredrick, J. F., Gentile, A. C., *Phyton (Buenos Aires)*, **15**, 1–6 (1960)
370. Fredrick, J. F., Gentile, A. C., *Arch. Biochem. Biophys.*, **92**, 356–59 (1961)
371. Fredrick, J. F., Gentile, A. C., *Physiol. Plantarum*, **15**, 186–93 (1962)
372. Gentile, A. C., Fredrick, J. F., *Physiol. Plantarum*, **12**, 862–67 (1959)
373. Aldrich, F. D., McLane, S. R., Jr., *Plant Physiol.* **32**, 153–54 (1957)
374. Carter, M. C., *Dissertation Abstr.*, **20**, 3483 (1960)
375. Carter, M. C., Naylor, A. W., *Plant Physiol. (Suppl.)*, **34**, vi (1959)
376. Carter, M. C., Naylor, A. W., *Physiol. Plantarum*, **14**, 62–71 (1961)
377. Massini, P., *Biochem. Biophys. Acta*, **36**, 548–49 (1959)
378. Naylor, A. W., Carter, M. C., Deamer, D., *Elisha Mitchell Sci. Soc. J.*, **76** (1960)
379. Naylor, A. W., *J. Agr. Food Chem.*, **12**, 21–25 (1964)
380. Carter, M. C., Naylor, A. W., *Physiol. Plantarum*, **14**, 20–27 (1961)
381. Massini, P., *Acta Botan. Neerl.*, **12**, 64–72 (1963)
382. Carter, M. C., *Physiol. Plantarum*, **18**, 1054–58 (1965)
383. Hilton, J. L., *Plant Physiol.*, **37**, 238–44 (1962)
384. Castelfranco, P., Brown, M. S., *Weeds*, **11**, 116–24 (1963)
385. Castelfranco, P., Oppenheim, A., Yamaguchi, S., *Weeds*, **11**, 111–15 (1963)
386. Herrett, R. A., Bagley, W. P., *J. Agr. Food Chem.*, **12**, 17–20 (1964)
387. Shimabukuro, R. H., Linck, A. J., *Physiol. Plantarum*, **18**, 516–32 (1965)
388. Weller, L. E., Ball, C. D., Sell, H. M., *Plant Physiol.*, **32**, 146–48 (1957)
389. Smith, A. E., Zukel, J. W., Stone, G. M., Riddell, J. A., *J. Agr. Food Chem.*, **7**, 341–44 (1959)
390. Towers, G. H. N., Hutchinson, A., Andreae, W. A., *Nature*, **181**, 1535–36 (1958)
391. Baker, J. E., *An Investigation of the Mechanism of Maleic Hydrazide in Tobacco and Other Plants* (Doctoral thesis, N. C. State College, Raleigh, 1958)
392. Parups, E. V., Hoffman, I., Morley, H. V., *Can. J. Biochem. Physiol.*, **40**, 1159–65 (1962)

393. Stephenson, G. R., Ries, S. K., *Weed Res.*, **7**, 51–60 (1967)

394. Meikle, R. W., Williams, E. A., Redemann, C. T., The synthesis of 4-amino-3,5,6-trichloropicolinic-carboxy-C^{14} acid and its use in a study of the metabolism of tordon herbicide in carbon dioxide evolution from treated soil. *Abstr. 149th Am. Chem. Soc. Meeting, Detroit, April, 1965*, p. 19A.

395. Redemann, C. T., Hamilton, P. M., Younger, C. R. The fate of 4-amino-3,5,6-trichloropyridine-2,3,4,-5,6-C_5^{14}-2-carboxy-C^{14} acid in spring wheat. *Ibid.*, p. 20A

396. Funderburk, H. H., Jr., Lawrence, J. M., *Weeds*, **12**, 259–64 (1964)

397. Slade, P., *Chem. Ind. (London)*, 2101–2 (1965)

398. Funderburk, H. H., Jr., Bozarth, G. A., *J. Agr. Food Chem.*, **15**, 563–67 (1967)

399. Crafts, A. S., *Plant Physiol.*, **34**, 613–20 (1959)

400. Welker, W., Holm, L., *16th North Central and 10th Western Canad. Weed Control Conf. (Joint Meeting), Proc.*, **1959**, p. 17

401. Fang, S. C., Freed, V. H., Johnson, R. H., Coffee, D. R., *J. Agr. Food Chem.*, **3**, 400–2 (1955)

402. Muzik, T. J., Cruzado, H. J., Morris, M. P., *Weeds*, **5**, 133–34 (1957)

403. Muzik, T. J., Morris, M. P., Cruzado, H. J., *Plant Physiol. (Suppl.)*, **31**, 42 (1956)

404. Sweetser, P. B., *Biochim. Biophys. Acta*, **66**, 78–85 (1963)

405. Onley, J. H., Yip, G., Aldridge, M. H., *J. Agr. Food Chem.*, **16**, 426–33 (1968)

406. Geissbühler, H., Haselbach, C., Aebi, H., Ebner, L., *Weed Res.*, **3**, 277–97 (1963)

407. Geissbühler, H., Haselbach, C., Aebi, H., *ibid.*, 140–53

408. Smith, J. W., Sheets, T. J., *J. Agr. Food Chem.*, **15**, 577–81 (1967)

409. Rogers, R. L., Funderburk, H. H., Jr., *J. Agr. Food Chem.*, **16**, 434–40 (1968)

410. Good, N. E., *Plant Physiol.*, **36**, 788–803 (1961)

411. Baskakov, Y. A., *Zashchita Rast. ot Vreditelei i Boleznei*, **6**, 34–35 (1961) (Chem. Abstr. **56**, 1796e, 1962)

412. Baskakov, Y. A., Zemskaya, V. A., *Fiziol. Rast. (Transl.)*, **6**, 63–68 (1959)

413. Zemskaya, V. A., Rakitin, Y. V., *Fiziol. Rast. (Transl.)*, **8**, 164–67 (1961)

414. Metabolic fate of CIPC. *1967 Progress Report on Pesticide and Related Activities*, 195 (USDA, 256 pp., Feb., 1968)

415. Foy, C. L., *Res. Prog. Rept. Western Weed Control Conf.*, 96–97 (1961)

416. Hopkins, T. R., The fate of barban in soils and in plants. *Am. Chem. Soc. Meeting, 139th, St. Louis, March, 1961*

417. Riden, J. R., Hopkins, T. R., *J. Agr. Food Chem.*, **10**, 455–58 (1962)

418. Chin, W. T., Stanovick, R. P., Cullen, T. E., Holsing, G. C., *Weeds*, **12**, 201–5 (1964)

419. Fang, S. C., Thiesen, P., *J. Agr. Food Chem.*, **7**, 770–71 (1959)

420. Fang, S. C., Thiesen, P., *ibid.*, **8**, 295–98 (1960)

421. Fang, S. C., Yu, T. C., *Res. Progr. Rept., Western Weed Control Conf.*, 91–92 (1959)

422. Nalewaja, J. D., Behrens, R., Schmid, A. R., *Weeds*, **12**, 269–72 (1964)

423. Fang, S. C., George, M., *Plant Physiol. (Suppl.)*, **37**, 26 (1962)

424. Bourke, J. B., Fang, S. C., *J. Agr. Food Chem.*, **13**, 340–43 (1965)

425. Jaworski, E. G., *J. Agr. Food Chem.*, **12**, 33–37 (1964)

426. Jaworski, E. G., Porter, C. A., Uptake and metabolism of 2-chloro-N-isopropyl-acetanilide in plants. *Abstr. Am. Chem. Soc. Meeting, 149th, Detroit, April 1965*, p. 20A.

427. Lemin, A. J., *J. Agr. Food Chem.*, **14**, 109–11 (1966)

428. Golab, T., Herberg, R., Tepe, J. B., *J. Agr. Food Chem.*, **14**, 592–98 (1966)

429. Still, G. G., *Science*, **159**, 992–93 (1968)

430. Matsunaka, S., *Science*, **160**, 1360–61 (1968)

431. Bowling, C. C., Hudgins, H. R., *Weeds*, **14**, 94–96 (1966)

432. Ishizuka, K., Mitsui, S., Activation or inactivation mechanisms of biological active compounds in higher plants. II. On anilide degrading enzyme. *Abstr. Ann. Meeting Agr. Chem. Soc. Japan, 1966*, p. 62

433. Still, C. C., Kuzirian, O., *Nature*, **216**, 799–800 (1967)

434. Frear, D. S., Still, G. G., *Phytochemistry*, **7**, 913–20 (1968)

435. Martin, G. C., *Proc. Am. Soc. Hort. Sci.*, **89**, 1–9 (1966)

436. Colby, S. R., Warren, G. F., Baker,

R. S., *J. Agr. Food Chem.*, **12**, 320–21 (1964)

437. Colby, S. R., *Science*, **150**, 619–20 (1965)

438. Colby, S. R., *Weeds*, **14**, 197–201 (1966)

439. Swanson, C. R., Kadunce, R. E., Hodgson, R. H., Frear, D. S., *Weeds*, **14**, 319–23 (1966)

440. Broadhurst, N. A., Montgomery, M. L., Freed, V. H., *J. Agr. Food Chem.*, **14**, 585–88 (1966)

441. Skinner, W. A., Stallard, D. E., Priddle, W. E., The isolation and identification of the metabolites of dacthal herbicide. *Abstr. Am. Chem. Soc. Meeting, Philadelphia, April 1964*

442. Pate, D. A., Funderburk, H. H., Jr., *Proc. 18th Annual Meeting Southern Weed Conf., 1965*, 605–6

443. Probst, G. W., Golab, T., Herberg, R. J., Holzer, F. J., Parka, S. J., Van der Schans, C., Tepe, J. B., *J. Agr. Food Chem.*, **15**, 592–99 (1967)

444. Leasure, J. K., *J. Agr. Food Chem.*,

12, 40–43 (1964)

445. Tibbitts, T. W., Holm, L. G., *Weeds*, **3**, 146–51 (1954)

446. Blanchard, F. A., *Weeds*, **3**, 274–78 (1954)

447. Blanchard, F. A., Muelder, W. W., Smith, G. N., *J. Agr. Food Chem.*, **8**, 124–28 (1960)

448. Smith, G. N., Dyer, D. L., *J. Agr. Food Chem.*, **9**, 155–60 (1961)

449. Foy, C. L., *Plant Physiol.*, **36**, 698–709 (1961)

450. Andersen, R. N., Linck, A. J., Behrens, R., *Weeds*, **10**, 1–3 (1962)

451. Foy, C. L., *9th Intern. Botan. Congress Proc.*, **2**, 121 (1959)

452. Miller, C. S., Hall, W. C., *J. Agr. Food Chem.*, **11**, 222–25 (1963)

453. Radwan, M. A., *Forest Sci.*, **13**, 265–73 (1967)

454. Beynon, K. I., Wright, A. N., *Bull. World Health Organ.*, **37**, 65–72 (1967)

455. Redemann, C. T., Martin, T., Wien, J. D., Widofsky, J. G., *J. Agr. Food Chem.*, **13**, 518–21 (1965)

AUTHOR INDEX

SUBJECT INDEX

A

Abate
    metabolism of, 613
Abscisic acid, 139-64
    in aphid honeydew, 128
    chemistry of, 141-46
        assays, 142-43
        bioassays, 143, 145
        isolation, 141-42
        naturally occurring relatives of, 144-45
        stereoisomers, 145
        synthetic relatives of, 145-46
        yields, 142
    on enzyme activity, 73
    on enzyme synthesis, 82
    general physiology of, 157-59
        biosynthesis, 157
        inactivation, 158
        as plant hormone, 158-59
        transport, 157
    history of discovery of, 139
    introduction to, 139-40
    isomers of, 141
    nomenclature, 140-41
    on nucleic acid synthesis, 155, 451, 460-61
    occurrence of, 147-50
        chemical isolation of, 147
        correlative occurrence, 148-50
        distribution among species, 147
        evidence from co-chromatography and bioassay, 147
        evidence of related substances, 147-48
        identification by ORD or GLC, 147

in phloem, 119
physiological roles of, 159-61
    biochemical, 160-61
    hormonal, 160
    responses to, 150-57
        agricultural uses, 156-57
        biochemical responses, 154-56
        growth retardation and inhibition, 151-53
        interactions and other plant hormones, 153-54
        miscellaneous, 153
        morphological responses, 156
        senescence and abscission, 150-51
    structure of, 140
(R)-Abscisic acid
    structure and activity of, 146
2-trans-Abscisic acid
    structure and activity of, 144
2,4-trans,cis-Abscisic acid
    structure and activity of, 146
Abscisin II
    see Abscisic acid
Abscission
    abscisic acid role in, 150-51
    ethylene-mediated, 552-53, 575
    RNA role in, 466-67
(+)-Abscisyl-β-D-glucopyranoside
    structure and activity of, 144
Absorbance change (520 nm)
    explanation of, 536-37
Absorption
    kinetics of, 101-5
        salt absorption, 103-5

time factor in, 101-2
Acaricides
    metabolism of, 611
Acer
    abscisic acid in, 140, 142, 147, 150, 153
Acer pseudoplatanus
    microtubules of, 278
Acetomonas oxydans
    amino acid metabolism in, 49
Acids
    cell permeability of, 591
Actidione
    see Cycloheximide
Actinomycin D
    on enzyme synthesis, 65, 68, 70-72, 77-78, 81, 83
    on ethylene activity, 565
    on nitrate reduction, 514
    on nucleic acid synthesis, 454, 458, 460-67, 470
Action potential
    and plant movement, 169-75
    table of, 172
Action spectra
    measurement of, 305-7
    in photosynthesis, 305-28
Acytostelium
    microtubules of, 281
Adenosine triphosphatase
    in rapid plant movement, 180-82
Adenosine triphosphate (ATP)
    in amino acid synthesis, 46
    photosynthetic action spectra of, 316
    in rapid plant movement, 180-82
    and stomatal control, 333
    structural protein binding

ance, 599-602
of nonelectrolytes, 589-91
series for 39 cell species, 600-1
of water, 591-94
Cells, apical
origin of elongating surface from, 375
Cells, motor
in plant movement, 177-79
Cellulase
specific enhancement of, 464
Cellulose
in microfibrils, 372
oriented synthesis of
control of, 373-74
Cell wall
primary growth of, 274-78
structure of
reviews of, 369
Centriole
and microtubules, 260-64
Ceramium diaphanum
permeability of, 601
Ceratocystis fimbriata
on ethylene production, 573
Cesium
competitive interference with other cations, 90
Chaetomorpha
cell morphogenesis in, 371-72, 374-75
salt uptake in, 95, 102
Chara
cell morphogenesis in, 380-81
membrane structure of, 210
microtubules in, 259, 265, 272, 274, 281
permeability of, 589-92, 601
Chara australis
permeability studies of, 588, 592
Chenopodium rubrum
abscisic acid effect on, 152
Cherry
effects of freezing on, 433
Chitin
in cell morphogenesis, 372, 385
Chlamydomonas
effects of freezing on, 428
Chlamydomonas reinhardi
microtubules of, 262, 271
mutant strains of
photosynthetic analysis of, 523-38

scheme for cyclic electron flow in, 535
Chloramphenicol
biosynthesis of, 53
on enzyme synthesis, 65-66, 68, 74-75
on nitrite reduction, 510
on protein synthesis, 459, 462
Chlorbenzide
metabolism of, 611
Chlorella
cell morphogenesis in, 373
effects of freezing on, 428
membrane structure of, 227
mutant strains of
to study photosynthesis, 525
nitrate reduction in, 513-14
silicon in, 298
stomatal control in, 342
Chlorella pyrenoidosa
action spectra of, 313, 315, 317, 319-20, 322
Chlorfenvinphos
metabolism of, 612
Chloride
transport of, 120, 122
uptake mechanisms for, 103, 105, 108, 111-13
Chlorobium
photosynthetic action spectra in, 308
2-Chloroethanephosphonic acid
on abscission, 553
ethylene release by, 575
2-Chloroethyltrimethylammonium chloride
on transport, 127
Chlorogenic acid
ethylene effects on, 563
p-Chloromercuribenzoate
on nitrate reduction, 498
3-(Chlorophenyl)-1,1-dimethylurea (CMU)
to study photosynthetic action spectra and energy transfer, 319-20, 322
to study stomatal opening, 339
Chlorophyll
action spectra of, 311, 316-17
biosynthesis of, 525
Chlorophyll b
and 520 nm absorbance change, 536
Chloroplast
action spectra and energy transfer in, 312-15, 319

control of enzyme formation in, 74-75
effects of freezing on, 435, 440-43
lamellar stacking, 537-38
membrane structure in, 214-15, 217-18, 227-32
mutations of, 525
and photosynthesis, 537-38
nitrate reduction in, 509-10
photosynthetic role of, 193
and stomatal control, 347
structural proteins of, 239, 241-42, 244, 247, 250
molecular weight of, 242
Chloropseudomonas ethylicum
action spectra of, 308, 319
2-Chloro-6-(trichloromethyl) pyridine
metabolism of, 624
Chloroxuron
metabolism of, 622
Chromatin
ethylene effects on, 555
nucleic acids in, 457-58
Chromatium
photosynthetic action spectra in, 309-10, 319
Chromatium strain D
amino acid biosynthesis in, 44
Chromomycin A
on RNA synthesis, 65
Chrysophyceae
silicon in, 290
Cicer arietinum
amino acids in, 47
Cidial
metabolism of, 613
Cilia
reviews of, 254
Cinerubin
on RNA synthesis, 65
Citrus fruit
abscisic acid in, 151, 154
ethylene effects on, 557-58, 561, 574
Cladophora
cell morphogenesis in, 375
cell permeability of, 587, 590, 601
Clematis zeylanica
action potentials of, 172
Climacteric
definition of, 557
Clover (Melilotus alba)
microtubules of, 275
Colchicine
on cell morphogenesis, 372-73, 378
to study microtubules, 256-

CUMULATIVE INDEXES

VOLUMES 11-20

INDEX OF CONTRIBUTING AUTHORS

INDEX OF CHAPTER TITLES

VOLUMES 11-20